≫ 华章统计学原版精品系列 ≪

数理统计学导论

Introduction to Mathematical Statistics (Seventh Edition)

—— （英文版·第7版）——

（美）　**Robert V. Hogg**　　**Joseph W. McKean**　　**Allen T. Craig**　　著
　　　艾奥瓦大学　　　　西密歇根大学　　　　艾奥瓦大学

机械工业出版社
China Machine Press

本书版权登记号：图字：01-2012-2648

图书在版编目（CIP）数据

数理统计学导论（英文版・第 7 版）/（美）霍格（Hogg, R. V.）等著 . —北京：机械工业出版社，2012.6

（华章统计学原版精品系列）

书名原文：Introduction to Mathematical Statistics, Seventh Edition

ISBN 978-7-111-38580-6

I. 数⋯　II. 霍⋯　III. 数理统计 – 英文　IV. O212

中国版本图书馆 CIP 数据核字（2012）第 111993 号

机械工业出版社（北京市西城区百万庄大街 22 号　邮政编码　100037）
责任编辑：迟振春
北京京北印刷有限公司印刷
2012 年 6 月第 1 版第 1 次印刷
170mm×242mm・44 印张
标准书号：ISBN 978-7-111-38580-6
定价：99.00 元

凡购本书，如有缺页、倒页、脱页，由本社发行部调换
客服热线：（010）88378991；88361066
购书热线：（010）68326294；88379649；68995259
投稿热线：（010）88379604
读者信箱：hzjsj@hzbook.com

Preface

Changes for Seventh Edition

In the preparation of this seventh edition, our goal has remained steadfast: to produce an outstanding text in mathematical statistics. In this new edition, we have added examples and exercises to help clarify the exposition. For the same reason, we have moved some material forward. For example, we moved the discussion on some properties of linear combinations of random variables from Chapter 4 to Chapter 2. This helps in the discussion of statistical properties in Chapter 3 as well as in the new Chapter 4.

One of the major changes was moving the chapter on "Some Elementary Statistical Inferences," from Chapter 5 to Chapter 4. This chapter on inference covers confidence intervals and statistical tests of hypotheses, two of the most important concepts in statistical inference. We begin Chapter 4 with a discussion of a random sample and point estimation. We introduce point estimation via a brief discussion of maximum likelihood estimation (the theory of maximum likelihood inference is still fullly discussed in Chapter 6). In Chapter 4, though, the discussion is illustrated with examples. After discussing point estimation in Chapter 4, we proceed onto confidence intervals and hypotheses testing. Inference for the basic one- and two-sample problems (large and small samples) is presented. We illustrate this discussion with plenty of examples, several of which are concerned with real data. We have also added exercises dealing with real data. The discussion has also been updated; for example, exact confidence intervals for the parameters of discrete distributions and bootstrap confidence intervals and tests of hypotheses are discussed, both of which are being used more and more in practice. These changes enable a one-semester course to cover basic statistical theory with applications. Such a course would cover Chapters 1–4 and, depending on time, parts of Chapter 5. For two-semester courses, this basic understanding of statistical inference will prove quite helpful to students in the later chapters (6–8) on the statistical theory of inference.

Another major change is moving the discussion of robustness concepts (influence function and breakdown) of Chapter 12 to the end of Chapter 10. To reflect this move, the title of Chapter 10 has been changed to "Nonparametric and Robust Statistics." This additional material in the new Chapter 10 is essentially the important robustness concepts found in the old Chapter 12. Further, the simple linear model is discussed in Chapters 9 and 10. Hence, with this move we have eliminated

Chapter 12.

Additional examples of R functions are in Appendix B to help readers who want to use R for statistical computation and simulation. We have also added a listing of discrete and continuous distributions in Appendix D. This will serve as a quick and helpful reference to the reader.

Content and Course Planning

Chapters 1 and 2 give the reader the necessary background material on probability and distribution theory for the remainder of the book. Chapter 3 discusses the most widely used discrete and continuous probability distributions. Chapter 4 contains topics in basic inference as described above. Chapter 5 presents large sample theory on convergence in probability and distribution and ends with the Central Limit Theorem. Chapter 6 provides a complete inference (estimation and testing) based on maximum likelihood theory. This chapter also contains a discussion of the EM algorithm and its application to several maximum likelihood situations. Chapters 7–8 contain material on sufficient statistics and optimal tests of hypotheses. The final three chapters provide theory for three important topics in statistics. Chapter 9 contains inference for normal theory methods for basic analysis of variance, univariate regression, and correlation models. Chapter 10 presents nonparametric methods (estimation and testing) for location and univariate regression models. It also includes discussion on the robust concepts of efficiency, influence, and breakdown. Chapter 11 offers an introduction to Bayesian methods. This includes traditional Bayesian procedures as well as Markov Chain Monte Carlo techniques.

Our text can be used in several different courses in mathematical statistics. A one-semester course would include most of the sections in Chapters 1–4. The second semester would usually consist of Chapters 5–8, although some instructors might prefer to use topics from Chapters 9–11. For example, a Bayesian advocate might want to teach Chapter 11 after Chapter 5, a nonparametrician could insert Chapter 10 earlier, or a traditional statistician would include topics from Chapter 9.

Acknowledgements

We have many readers to thank. Their suggestions and comments proved invaluable in the preparation of this edition. A special thanks goes to Jun Yan of the University of Iowa, who made his web page on the sixth edition available to all, and also to Thomas Hettmansperger of Penn State University, Ash Abebe of Auburn University, and Bradford Crain of Portland State University for their helpful comments. We thank our accuracy checkers Kimberly F. Sellers (Georgetown University), Brian Newquist, Bill Josephson, and Joan Saniuk for their careful review. We would also like to thank the following reviewers for their comments and suggestions: Ralph Russo (University of Iowa), Kanapathi Thiru (University of Alaska), Lifang Hsu (Le Moyne College), and Xiao Wang (University of Maryland–Baltimore). Last, but not least, we must thank our wives, Ann and Marge, who provided great support for our efforts.

Bob Hogg & Joe McKean

Contents

Chapter 1

Probability and Distributions

1.1 Introduction

Many kinds of investigations may be characterized in part by the fact that repeated experimentation, under essentially the same conditions, is more or less standard procedure. For instance, in medical research, interest may center on the effect of a drug that is to be administered; or an economist may be concerned with the prices of three specified commodities at various time intervals; or the agronomist may wish to study the effect that a chemical fertilizer has on the yield of a cereal grain. The only way in which an investigator can elicit information about any such phenomenon is to perform the experiment. Each experiment terminates with an *outcome*. But it is characteristic of these experiments that the outcome cannot be predicted with certainty prior to the performance of the experiment.

Suppose that we have such an experiment, but the experiment is of such a nature that a collection of every possible outcome can be described prior to its performance. If this kind of experiment can be repeated under the same conditions, it is called a **random experiment**, and the collection of every possible outcome is called the experimental space or the **sample space**.

Example 1.1.1. In the toss of a coin, let the outcome tails be denoted by T and let the outcome heads be denoted by H. If we assume that the coin may be repeatedly tossed under the same conditions, then the toss of this coin is an example of a random experiment in which the outcome is one of the two symbols T and H; that is, the sample space is the collection of these two symbols. ■

Example 1.1.2. In the cast of one red die and one white die, let the outcome be the ordered pair (number of spots up on the red die, number of spots up on the white die). If we assume that these two dice may be repeatedly cast under the same conditions, then the cast of this pair of dice is a random experiment. The sample space consists of the 36 ordered pairs: $(1,1),\ldots,(1,6),(2,1),\ldots,(2,6),\ldots,(6,6)$. ■

Let $\mathcal{C}$ denote a sample space, let c denote an element of $\mathcal{C}$, and let C represent a collection of elements of $\mathcal{C}$. If, upon the performance of the experiment, the outcome

1

is in C, we shall say that the *event C has* occurred. Now conceive of our having made N repeated performances of the random experiment. Then we can count the number f of times (the **frequency**) that the event C actually occurred throughout the N performances. The ratio f/N is called the **relative frequency** of the event C in these N experiments. A relative frequency is usually quite erratic for small values of N, as you can discover by tossing a coin. But as N increases, experience indicates that we associate with the event C a number, say p, that is equal or approximately equal to that number about which the relative frequency seems to stabilize. If we do this, then the number p can be interpreted as that number which, in future performances of the experiment, the relative frequency of the event C will either equal or approximate. Thus, although we *cannot* predict the outcome of a random experiment, we *can*, for a large value of N, predict approximately the relative frequency with which the outcome will be in C. The number p associated with the event C is given various names. Sometimes it is called the *probability* that the outcome of the random experiment is in C; sometimes it is called the *probability* of the event C; and sometimes it is called the *probability measure* of C. The context usually suggests an appropriate choice of terminology.

Example 1.1.3. Let C denote the sample space of Example 1.1.2 and let C be the collection of every ordered pair of C for which the sum of the pair is equal to seven. Thus C is the collection $(1, 6), (2, 5), (3, 4), (4, 3), (5, 2)$, and $(6, 1)$. Suppose that the dice are cast $N = 400$ times and let f, the frequency of a sum of seven, be $f = 60$. Then the relative frequency with which the outcome was in C is $f/N = \frac{60}{400} = 0.15$. Thus we might associate with C a number p that is close to 0.15, and p would be called the probability of the event C. ∎

Remark 1.1.1. The preceding interpretation of probability is sometimes referred to as the *relative frequency approach*, and it obviously depends upon the fact that an experiment can be repeated under essentially identical conditions. However, many persons extend probability to other situations by treating it as a rational measure of belief. For example, the statement $p = \frac{2}{5}$ would mean to them that their *personal* or *subjective* probability of the event C is equal to $\frac{2}{5}$. Hence, if they are not opposed to gambling, this could be interpreted as a willingness on their part to bet on the outcome of C so that the two possible payoffs are in the ratio $p/(1-p) = \frac{2}{5}/\frac{3}{5} = \frac{2}{3}$. Moreover, if they truly believe that $p = \frac{2}{5}$ is correct, they would be willing to accept either side of the bet: (a) win 3 units if C occurs and lose 2 if it does not occur, or (b) win 2 units if C does not occur and lose 3 if it does. However, since the mathematical properties of probability given in Section 1.3 are consistent with either of these interpretations, the subsequent mathematical development does not depend upon which approach is used. ∎

The primary purpose of having a mathematical theory of statistics is to provide mathematical models for random experiments. Once a model for such an experiment has been provided and the theory worked out in detail, the statistician may, within this framework, make inferences (that is, draw conclusions) about the random experiment. The construction of such a model requires a theory of probability. One of the more logically satisfying theories of probability is that based on the concepts of sets and functions of sets. These concepts are introduced in Section 1.2.

1.2 Set Theory

The concept of a *set* or a *collection* of objects is usually left undefined. However, a particular set can be described so that there is no misunderstanding as to what collection of objects is under consideration. For example, the set of the first 10 positive integers is sufficiently well described to make clear that the numbers $\frac{3}{4}$ and 14 are not in the set, while the number 3 is in the set. If an object belongs to a set, it is said to be an *element* of the set. For example, if C denotes the set of real numbers x for which $0 \leq x \leq 1$, then $\frac{3}{4}$ is an element of the set C. The fact that $\frac{3}{4}$ is an element of the set C is indicated by writing $\frac{3}{4} \in C$. More generally, $c \in C$ means that c is an element of the set C.

The sets that concern us are frequently *sets of numbers*. However, the language of sets of *points* proves somewhat more convenient than that of sets of numbers. Accordingly, we briefly indicate how we use this terminology. In analytic geometry considerable emphasis is placed on the fact that to each point on a line (on which an origin and a unit point have been selected) there corresponds one and only one number, say x; and that to each number x there corresponds one and only one point on the line. This one-to-one correspondence between the numbers and points on a line enables us to speak, without misunderstanding, of the "point x" instead of the "number x." Furthermore, with a plane rectangular coordinate system and with x and y numbers, to each symbol (x, y) there corresponds one and only one point in the plane; and to each point in the plane there corresponds but one such symbol. Here again, we may speak of the "point (x, y)," meaning the "ordered number pair x and y." This convenient language can be used when we have a rectangular coordinate system in a space of three or more dimensions. Thus the "point $(x_1, x_2, \ldots, x_n)$" means the numbers $x_1, x_2, \ldots, x_n$ in the order stated. Accordingly, in describing our sets, we frequently speak of a set of points (a set whose elements are points), being careful, of course, to describe the set so as to avoid any ambiguity. The notation $C = \{x : 0 \leq x \leq 1\}$ is read "C is the one-dimensional set of points x for which $0 \leq x \leq 1$." Similarly, $C = \{(x, y) : 0 \leq x \leq 1, 0 \leq y \leq 1\}$ can be read "C is the two-dimensional set of points (x, y) that are interior to, or on the boundary of, a square with opposite vertices at $(0, 0)$ and $(1, 1)$."

We say a set C is **countable** if C is finite or has as many elements as there are positive integers. For example, the sets $C_1 = \{1, 2, \ldots, 100\}$ and $C_2 = \{1, 3, 5, 7, \ldots\}$ are countable sets. The interval of real numbers $(0, 1]$, though, is not countable.

We now give some definitions (together with illustrative examples) that lead to an elementary algebra of sets adequate for our purposes.

Definition 1.2.1. *If each element of a set C_1 is also an element of set C_2, the set C_1 is called a **subset** of the set C_2. This is indicated by writing $C_1 \subset C_2$. If $C_1 \subset C_2$ and also $C_2 \subset C_1$, the two sets have the same elements, and this is indicated by writing $C_1 = C_2$.*

Example 1.2.1. Let $C_1 = \{x : 0 \leq x \leq 1\}$ and $C_2 = \{x : -1 \leq x \leq 2\}$. Here the one-dimensional set C_1 is seen to be a subset of the one-dimensional set C_2; that is, $C_1 \subset C_2$. Subsequently, when the dimensionality of the set is clear, we do not make specific reference to it. ∎

Example 1.2.2. Define the two sets $C_1 = \{(x,y) : 0 \le x = y \le 1\}$ and $C_2 = \{(x,y) : 0 \le x \le 1, 0 \le y \le 1\}$. Because the elements of C_1 are the points on one diagonal of the square, then $C_1 \subset C_2$. ∎

Definition 1.2.2. *If a set C has no elements, C is called the **null set**. This is indicated by writing $C = \phi$.*

Definition 1.2.3. *The set of all elements that belong to at least one of the sets C_1 and C_2 is called the **union** of C_1 and C_2. The union of C_1 and C_2 is indicated by writing $C_1 \cup C_2$. The union of several sets $C_1, C_2, C_3, \ldots$ is the set of all elements that belong to at least one of the several sets, denoted by $C_1 \cup C_2 \cup C_3 \cup \cdots = \cup_{j=1}^{\infty} C_j$ or by $C_1 \cup C_2 \cup \cdots \cup C_k = \cup_{j=1}^{k} C_j$ if a finite number k of sets is involved.*

*We refer to a union of the form $\cup_{j=1}^{\infty} C_j$ as a **countable union**.*

Example 1.2.3. Define the sets $C_1 = \{x : x = 8, 9, 10, 11, \text{ or } 11 < x \le 12\}$ and $C_2 = \{x : x = 0, 1, \ldots, 10\}$. Then

$$
\begin{aligned}
C_1 \cup C_2 &= \{x : x = 0, 1, \ldots, 8, 9, 10, 11, \text{ or } 11 < x \le 12\} \\
&= \{x : x = 0, 1, \ldots, 8, 9, 10 \text{ or } 11 \le x \le 12\}. \ \blacksquare
\end{aligned}
$$

Example 1.2.4. Define C_1 and C_2 as in Example 1.2.1. Then $C_1 \cup C_2 = C_2$. ∎

Example 1.2.5. Let $C_2 = \phi$. Then $C_1 \cup C_2 = C_1$, for every set C_1. ∎

Example 1.2.6. For every set C, $C \cup C = C$. ∎

Example 1.2.7. Let

$$
C_k = \left\{ x : \tfrac{1}{k+1} \le x \le 1 \right\}, \quad k = 1, 2, 3, \ldots.
$$

Then $\cup_{k=1}^{\infty} C_k = \{x : 0 < x \le 1\}$. Note that the number zero is not in this set, since it is not in one of the sets $C_1, C_2, C_3, \ldots$. ∎

Definition 1.2.4. *The set of all elements that belong to each of the sets C_1 and C_2 is called the **intersection** of C_1 and C_2. The intersection of C_1 and C_2 is indicated by writing $C_1 \cap C_2$. The intersection of several sets $C_1, C_2, C_3, \ldots$ is the set of all elements that belong to each of the sets $C_1, C_2, C_3, \ldots$. This intersection is denoted by $C_1 \cap C_2 \cap C_3 \cap \cdots = \cap_{j=1}^{\infty} C_j$ or by $C_1 \cap C_2 \cap \cdots \cap C_k = \cap_{j=1}^{k} C_j$ if a finite number k of sets is involved.*

*We refer to an intersection of the form $\cap_{j=1}^{\infty} C_j$ as a **countable intersection**.*

Example 1.2.8. Let $C_1 = \{(0,0), (0,1), (1,1)\}$ and $C_2 = \{(1,1), (1,2), (2,1)\}$. Then $C_1 \cap C_2 = \{(1,1)\}$. ∎

Example 1.2.9. Let $C_1 = \{(x,y) : 0 \le x + y \le 1\}$ and $C_2 = \{(x,y) : 1 < x + y\}$. Then C_1 and C_2 have no points in common and $C_1 \cap C_2 = \phi$. ∎

Example 1.2.10. For every set C, $C \cap C = C$ and $C \cap \phi = \phi$. ∎

單射 one-to-one 或 injective.
滿射 onto.
雙射 bijective.

Figure 1.2.1: (a) $C_1 \cup C_2$ and (b) $C_1 \cap C_2$.

Example 1.2.11. Let

$$C_k = \left\{x : 0 < x < \tfrac{1}{k}\right\}, \quad k = 1, 2, 3, \ldots$$

Then $\cap_{k=1}^{\infty} C_k = \phi$, because there is no point that belongs to each of the sets $C_1, C_2, C_3, \ldots$. ∎

Example 1.2.12. Let C_1 and C_2 represent the sets of points enclosed, respectively, by two intersecting ellipses. Then the sets $C_1 \cup C_2$ and $C_1 \cap C_2$ are represented, respectively, by the shaded regions in the **Venn diagrams** in Figure 1.2.1. ∎

Definition 1.2.5. *In certain discussions or considerations, the totality of all elements that pertain to the discussion can be described. This set of all elements under consideration is given a special name. It is called the* **space**. *We often denote spaces by letters such as C and $\mathcal{D}$.*

Example 1.2.13. Let the number of heads, in tossing a coin four times, be denoted by x. Of necessity, the number of heads is of the numbers $0, 1, 2, 3, 4$. Here, then, the space is the set $C = \{0, 1, 2, 3, 4\}$. ∎

Example 1.2.14. Consider all nondegenerate rectangles of base x and height y. To be meaningful, both x and y must be positive. Then the space is given by the set $C = \{(x, y) : x > 0, y > 0\}$. ∎

Definition 1.2.6. *Let C denote a space and let C be a subset of the set C. The set that consists of all elements of C that are not elements of C is called the* **complement** *of C (actually, with respect to C). The complement of C is denoted by C^c. In particular, $C^c = \phi$.*

Example 1.2.15. Let $\mathcal{C}$ be defined as in Example 1.2.13, and let the set $C = \{0,1\}$. The complement of C (with respect to $\mathcal{C}$) is $C^c = \{2,3,4\}$. ∎

Example 1.2.16. Given $C \subset \mathcal{C}$. Then $C \cup C^c = \mathcal{C}$, $C \cap C^c = \phi$, $C \cup C = C$, $C \cap C = C$, and $(C^c)^c = C$. ∎

Example 1.2.17 (DeMorgan's Laws). A set of useful rules is known as DeMorgan's Laws. Let $\mathcal{C}$ denote a space and let $C_i \subset \mathcal{C}$, $i = 1, 2$. Then

$$\begin{cases} (C_1 \cap C_2)^c &= C_1^c \cup C_2^c \qquad\qquad (1.2.1)\\ (C_1 \cup C_2)^c &= C_1^c \cap C_2^c. \qquad\qquad (1.2.2) \end{cases}$$

The reader is asked to prove these in Exercise 1.2.4 and to extend them to countable unions and intersections. ∎

Many of the functions used in calculus and in this book are functions which map real numbers into real numbers. We are often, however, concerned with functions that map sets into real numbers. Such functions are naturally called functions of a set or, more simply, **set functions**. Next we give some examples of set functions and evaluate them for certain simple sets.

Example 1.2.18. Let C be a set in one-dimensional space and let $Q(C)$ be equal to the number of points in C which correspond to positive integers. Then $Q(C)$ is a function of the set C. Thus, if $C = \{x : 0 < x < 5\}$, then $Q(C) = 4$; if $C = \{-2,-1\}$, then $Q(C) = 0$; if $C = \{x : -\infty < x < 6\}$, then $Q(C) = 5$. ∎

Example 1.2.19. Let C be a set in two-dimensional space and let $Q(C)$ be the area of C if C has a finite area; otherwise, let $Q(C)$ be undefined. Thus, if $C = \{(x,y) : x^2 + y^2 \leq 1\}$, then $Q(C) = \pi$; if $C = \{(0,0),(1,1),(0,1)\}$, then $Q(C) = 0$; if $C = \{(x,y) : 0 \leq x, 0 \leq y, x + y \leq 1\}$, then $Q(C) = \frac{1}{2}$. ∎

Example 1.2.20. Let C be a set in three-dimensional space and let $Q(C)$ be the volume of C if C has a finite volume; otherwise, let $Q(C)$ be undefined. Thus, if $C = \{(x,y,z) : 0 \leq x \leq 2, 0 \leq y \leq 1, 0 \leq z \leq 3\}$, then $Q(C) = 6$; if $C = \{(x,y,z) : x^2 + y^2 + z^2 \geq 1\}$, then $Q(C)$ is undefined. ∎

At this point we introduce the following notations. The symbol

$$\int_C f(x)\,dx$$

means the ordinary (Riemann) integral of $f(x)$ over a prescribed one-dimensional set C; the symbol

$$\int\int_C g(x,y)\,dxdy$$

means the Riemann integral of $g(x,y)$ over a prescribed two-dimensional set C; and so on. To be sure, unless these sets C and these functions $f(x)$ and $g(x,y)$ are chosen with care, the integrals frequently fail to exist. Similarly, the symbol

$$\sum_C f(x)$$

means the sum extended over all $x \in C$; the symbol

$$\sum_C \sum g(x, y)$$

means the sum extended over all $(x, y) \in C$; and so on.

Example 1.2.21. Let C be a set in one-dimensional space and let $Q(C) = \sum_C f(x)$, where

$$f(x) = \begin{cases} (\frac{1}{2})^x & x = 1, 2, 3, \ldots \\ 0 & \text{elsewhere.} \end{cases}$$

If $C = \{x : 0 \le x \le 3\}$, then

$$Q(C) = \tfrac{1}{2} + (\tfrac{1}{2})^2 + (\tfrac{1}{2})^3 = \tfrac{7}{8}. \blacksquare$$

Example 1.2.22. Let $Q(C) = \sum_C f(x)$, where

$$f(x) = \begin{cases} p^x (1-p)^{1-x} & x = 0, 1 \\ 0 & \text{elsewhere.} \end{cases}$$

If $C = \{0\}$, then

$$Q(C) = \sum_{x=0}^{0} p^x (1-p)^{1-x} = 1 - p;$$

if $C = \{x : 1 \le x \le 2\}$, then $Q(C) = f(1) = p$. $\blacksquare$

Example 1.2.23. Let C be a one-dimensional set and let

$$Q(C) = \int_C e^{-x} dx.$$

Thus, if $C = \{x : 0 \le x < \infty\}$, then

$$Q(C) = \int_0^\infty e^{-x} dx = 1;$$

if $C = \{x : 1 \le x \le 2\}$, then

$$Q(C) = \int_1^2 e^{-x} dx = e^{-1} - e^{-2};$$

if $C_1 = \{x : 0 \le x \le 1\}$ and $C_2 = \{x : 1 < x \le 3\}$, then

$$
\begin{aligned}
Q(C_1 \cup C_2) &= \int_0^3 e^{-x} dx \\
&= \int_0^1 e^{-x} dx + \int_1^3 e^{-x} dx \\
&= Q(C_1) + Q(C_2). \blacksquare
\end{aligned}
$$

规律小结：

若 $0 \leq x_1 \leq x_2 \leq x_3$，则 $= \int_0^{x_3} dx_2 \int_0^{x_2} dx_1$.

$\underbrace{\quad}_{\therefore 0 \leq x_2 \leq x_3}$ $\underbrace{\quad}_{\therefore 0 \leq x_1 \leq x_2}$

类似于，若 $0 \leq x_1 \leq x_2 \leq 1$，则 $= \int_0^1 dx_2 \int_0^{x_2} dx_1$.

Example 1.2.24. Let C be a set in n-dimensional space and let

若 $0 \leq x_1 \leq x_2 \leq \cdots \leq x_n \leq 1$,

则 $= \int_0^1 dx_n \int_0^{x_n} dx_{n-1} \cdots \int_0^{x_2} dx_1$. $Q(C) = \int \cdots \int_C dx_1 dx_2 \cdots dx_n$.

$\underbrace{\quad}_{\therefore 0 \leq x_n \leq 1}$ $\underbrace{\quad}_{\therefore 0 \leq \cdots x_{n-1} \leq x_n}$ $\underbrace{\quad}_{\therefore 0 \leq x_1 \leq x_2}$

If $C = \{(x_1, x_2, \ldots, x_n) : 0 \leq x_1 \leq x_2 \leq \cdots \leq x_n \leq 1\}$, then

$= \int_0^1 dx_n \int_0^{x_n} dx_{n-1} \int_0^{x_{n-1}} dx_{n-2} \cdots \int_0^{x_2} dx_1$.

$$Q(C) = \int_0^1 \int_0^{x_n} \cdots \int_0^{x_3} \int_0^{x_2} dx_1 dx_2 \cdots dx_{n-1} dx_n$$

$$= \frac{1}{n!},$$

或 $\rightarrow \int_0^1 dx_1 \int_{x_1}^1 dx_2 \int_{x_2}^1 dx_3 \cdots$

where $n! = n(n-1) \cdots 3 \cdot 2 \cdot 1$. ■

EXERCISES

1.2.1. Find the union $C_1 \cup C_2$ and the intersection $C_1 \cap C_2$ of the two sets C_1 and C_2, where

(a) $C_1 = \{0, 1, 2, \}$, $C_2 = \{2, 3, 4\}$.

(b) $C_1 = \{x : 0 < x < 2\}$, $C_2 = \{x : 1 \leq x < 3\}$.

(c) $C_1 = \{(x, y) : 0 < x < 2, 1 < y < 2\}$, $C_2 = \{(x, y) : 1 < x < 3, 1 < y < 3\}$.

1.2.2. Find the complement C^c of the set C with respect to the space $\mathcal{C}$ if

(a) $\mathcal{C} = \{x : 0 < x < 1\}$, $C = \{x : \frac{5}{8} < x < 1\}$.

(b) $\mathcal{C} = \{(x, y, z) : x^2 + y^2 + z^2 \leq 1\}$, $C = \{(x, y, z) : x^2 + y^2 + z^2 = 1\}$.

(c) $\mathcal{C} = \{(x, y) : |x| + |y| \leq 2\}$, $C = \{(x, y) : x^2 + y^2 < 2\}$.

1.2.3. List all possible arrangements of the four letters m, a, r, and y. Let C_1 be the collection of the arrangements in which y is in the last position. Let C_2 be the collection of the arrangements in which m is in the first position. Find the union and the intersection of C_1 and C_2.

1.2.4. Referring to Example 1.2.17, verify DeMorgan's Laws (1.2.1) and (1.2.2) by using Venn diagrams and then prove that the laws are true. Generalize the laws to countable unions and intersections.

1.2.5. By the use of Venn diagrams, in which the space $\mathcal{C}$ is the set of points enclosed by a rectangle containing the circles C_1, C_2, and C_3, compare the following sets. These laws are called the **distributive laws**.

(a) $C_1 \cap (C_2 \cup C_3)$ and $(C_1 \cap C_2) \cup (C_1 \cap C_3)$.

(b) $C_1 \cup (C_2 \cap C_3)$ and $(C_1 \cup C_2) \cap (C_1 \cup C_3)$.

1.2.6. If a sequence of sets $C_1, C_2, C_3, \ldots$ is such that $C_k \subset C_{k+1}$, $k = 1, 2, 3, \ldots$, the sequence is said to be a *nondecreasing sequence*. Give an example of this kind of sequence of sets.

1.2.7. If a sequence of sets $C_1, C_2, C_3, \ldots$ is such that $C_k \supset C_{k+1}$, $k = 1, 2, 3, \ldots$, the sequence is said to be a *nonincreasing sequence*. Give an example of this kind of sequence of sets.

1.2.8. Suppose $C_1, C_2, C_3, \ldots$ is a *nondecreasing sequence* of sets, i.e., $C_k \subset C_{k+1}$, for $k = 1, 2, 3, \ldots$. Then $\lim_{k \to \infty} C_k$ is defined as the union $C_1 \cup C_2 \cup C_3 \cup \cdots$. Find $\lim_{k \to \infty} C_k$ if

(a) $C_k = \{x : 1/k \le x \le 3 - 1/k\}$, $k = 1, 2, 3, \ldots$.

(b) $C_k = \{(x, y) : 1/k \le x^2 + y^2 \le 4 - 1/k\}$, $k = 1, 2, 3, \ldots$.

1.2.9. If $C_1, C_2, C_3, \ldots$ are sets such that $C_k \supset C_{k+1}$, $k = 1, 2, 3, \ldots$, $\lim_{k \to \infty} C_k$ is defined as the intersection $C_1 \cap C_2 \cap C_3 \cap \cdots$. Find $\lim_{k \to \infty} C_k$ if

(a) $C_k = \{x : 2 - 1/k < x \le 2\}$, $k = 1, 2, 3, \ldots$.

(b) $C_k = \{x : 2 < x \le 2 + 1/k\}$, $k = 1, 2, 3, \ldots$.

(c) $C_k = \{(x, y) : 0 \le x^2 + y^2 \le 1/k\}$, $k = 1, 2, 3, \ldots$.

1.2.10. For every one-dimensional set C, define the function $Q(C) = \sum_C f(x)$, where $f(x) = (\frac{2}{3})(\frac{1}{3})^x$, $x = 0, 1, 2, \ldots$, zero elsewhere. If $C_1 = \{x : x = 0, 1, 2, 3\}$ and $C_2 = \{x : x = 0, 1, 2, \ldots\}$, find $Q(C_1)$ and $Q(C_2)$.
Hint: Recall that $S_n = a + ar + \cdots + ar^{n-1} = a(1 - r^n)/(1 - r)$ and, hence, it follows that $\lim_{n \to \infty} S_n = a/(1 - r)$ provided that $|r| < 1$.

1.2.11. For every one-dimensional set C for which the integral exists, let $Q(C) = \int_C f(x) \, dx$, where $f(x) = 6x(1 - x)$, $0 < x < 1$, zero elsewhere; otherwise, let $Q(C)$ be undefined. If $C_1 = \{x : \frac{1}{4} < x < \frac{3}{4}\}$, $C_2 = \{\frac{1}{2}\}$, and $C_3 = \{x : 0 < x < 10\}$, find $Q(C_1), Q(C_2)$, and $Q(C_3)$.

1.2.12. For every two-dimensional set C contained in R^2 for which the integral exists, let $Q(C) = \int \int_C (x^2 + y^2) \, dx dy$. If $C_1 = \{(x, y) : -1 \le x \le 1, -1 \le y \le 1\}$, $C_2 = \{(x, y) : -1 \le x = y \le 1\}$, and $C_3 = \{(x, y) : x^2 + y^2 \le 1\}$, find $Q(C_1), Q(C_2)$, and $Q(C_3)$.

1.2.13. Let $\mathcal{C}$ denote the set of points that are interior to, or on the boundary of, a square with opposite vertices at the points $(0, 0)$ and $(1, 1)$. Let $Q(C) = \int \int_C dy \, dx$.

(a) If $C \subset \mathcal{C}$ is the set $\{(x, y) : 0 < x < y < 1\}$, compute $Q(C)$.

(b) If $C \subset \mathcal{C}$ is the set $\{(x, y) : 0 < x = y < 1\}$, compute $Q(C)$.

(c) If $C \subset \mathcal{C}$ is the set $\{(x, y) : 0 < x/2 \le y \le 3x/2 < 1\}$, compute $Q(C)$.

1.2.14. Let $\mathcal{C}$ be the set of points interior to or on the boundary of a cube with edge of length 1. Moreover, say that the cube is in the first octant with one vertex at the point $(0, 0, 0)$ and an opposite vertex at the point $(1, 1, 1)$. Let $Q(C) = \int \int \int_C dx dy dz$.

(a) If $C \subset \mathcal{C}$ is the set $\{(x, y, z) : 0 < x < y < z < 1\}$, compute $Q(C)$.

(b) If C is the subset $\{(x, y, z) : 0 < x = y = z < 1\}$, compute $Q(C)$.

1.2.15. Let C denote the set $\{(x, y, z) : x^2 + y^2 + z^2 \leq 1\}$. Using spherical coordinates, evaluate

$$Q(C) = \int \int \int_C \sqrt{x^2 + y^2 + z^2} \, dx dy dz.$$

1.2.16. To join a certain club, a person must be either a statistician or a mathematician or both. Of the 25 members in this club, 19 are statisticians and 16 are mathematicians. How many persons in the club are both a statistician and a mathematician?

1.2.17. After a hard-fought football game, it was reported that, of the 11 starting players, 8 hurt a hip, 6 hurt an arm, 5 hurt a knee, 3 hurt both a hip and an arm, 2 hurt both a hip and a knee, 1 hurt both an arm and a knee, and no one hurt all three. Comment on the accuracy of the report.

1.3   The Probability Set Function

Given an experiment, let C denote the sample space of all possible outcomes. As discussed in Section 1.1, we are interested in assigning probabilities to events, i.e., subsets of C. What should be our collection of events? If C is a finite set, then we could take the set of all subsets as this collection. For infinite sample spaces, though, with assignment of probabilities in mind, this poses mathematical technicalities which are better left to a course in probability theory. We assume that in all cases, the collection of events is sufficiently rich to include all possible events of interest and is closed under complements and countable unions of these events. Using DeMorgan's Laws, Example 1.2.17, the collection is then also closed under countable intersections. We denote this collection of events by $\mathcal{B}$. Technically, such a collection of events is called a **σ-field** of subsets.

Now that we have a sample space, C, and our collection of events, $\mathcal{B}$, we can define the third component in our probability space, namely a probability set function. In order to motivate its definition, we consider the relative frequency approach to probability.

Remark 1.3.1. The definition of probability consists of three axioms which we motivate by the following three intuitive properties of relative frequency. Let C be a sample space and let $C \subset \mathcal{C}$. Suppose we repeat the experiment N times. Then the relative frequency of C is $f_C = \#\{C\}/N$, where $\#\{C\}$ denotes the number of times C occurred in the N repetitions. Note that $f_C \geq 0$ and $f_C = 1$. These are the first two properties. For the third, suppose that C_1 and C_2 are disjoint events. Then $f_{C_1 \cup C_2} = f_{C_1} + f_{C_2}$. These three properties of relative frequencies form the axioms of a probability, except that the third axiom is in terms of countable unions. As with the axioms of probability, the readers should check that the theorems we prove below about probabilities agree with their intuition of relative frequency. ∎

Definition 1.3.1 (Probability). *Let $\mathcal{C}$ be a sample space and let $\mathcal{B}$ be the set of events. Let P be a real-valued function defined on $\mathcal{B}$. Then P is a* **probability set function** *if P satisfies the following three conditions:*

1. $P(C) \geq 0$, *for all $C \in \mathcal{B}$.*   [handwritten: subset of the sample space]
2. $P(\mathcal{C}) = 1$.   [handwritten: sample space]
3. *If $\{C_n\}$ is a sequence of events in $\mathcal{B}$ and $C_m \cap C_n = \phi$ for all $m \neq n$, then*

$$P\left(\bigcup_{n=1}^{\infty} C_n\right) = \sum_{n=1}^{\infty} P(C_n).$$

A collection of events whose members are pairwise disjoint, as in (3), is said to be a **mutually exclusive** collection. The collection is further said to be **exhaustive** if the union of its events is the sample space, in which case $\sum_{n=1}^{\infty} P(C_n) = 1$. We often say that a mutually exclusive and exhaustive collection of events forms a **partition** of $\mathcal{C}$.

A probability set function tells us how the probability is distributed over the set of events, $\mathcal{B}$. In this sense we speak of a distribution of probability. We often drop the word "set" and refer to P as a probability function.

The following theorems give us some other properties of a probability set function. In the statement of each of these theorems, $P(C)$ is taken, tacitly, to be a probability set function defined on the collection of events $\mathcal{B}$ of a sample space $\mathcal{C}$.

Theorem 1.3.1. *For each event $C \in \mathcal{B}$, $P(C) = 1 - P(C^c)$.*

Proof: We have $\mathcal{C} = C \cup C^c$ and $C \cap C^c = \phi$. Thus, from (2) and (3) of Definition 1.3.1, it follows that
$$1 = P(C) + P(C^c),$$
which is the desired result. ∎

Theorem 1.3.2. *The probability of the null set is zero; that is, $P(\phi) = 0$.*

Proof: In Theorem 1.3.1, take $C = \phi$ so that $C^c = \mathcal{C}$. Accordingly, we have
$$P(\phi) = 1 - P(\mathcal{C}) = 1 - 1 = 0$$
and the theorem is proved. ∎

Theorem 1.3.3. *If C_1 and C_2 are events such that $C_1 \subset C_2$, then $P(C_1) \leq P(C_2)$.*

Proof: Now $C_2 = C_1 \cup (C_1^c \cap C_2)$ and $C_1 \cap (C_1^c \cap C_2) = \phi$. Hence, from (3) of Definition 1.3.1,
$$P(C_2) = P(C_1) + P(C_1^c \cap C_2).$$
From (1) of Definition 1.3.1, $P(C_1^c \cap C_2) \geq 0$. Hence, $P(C_2) \geq P(C_1)$. ∎

Theorem 1.3.4. *For each $C \in \mathcal{B}$, $0 \leq P(C) \leq 1$.*

Proof: Since $\phi \subset C \subset \mathcal{C}$, we have by Theorem 1.3.3 that

$$P(\phi) \leq P(C) \leq P(\mathcal{C}) \quad \text{or} \quad 0 \leq P(C) \leq 1,$$

the desired result. ■

Part (3) of the definition of probability says that $P(C_1 \cup C_2) = P(C_1) + P(C_2)$ if C_1 and C_2 are disjoint, i.e., $C_1 \cap C_2 = \phi$. The next theorem gives the rule for any two events.

Theorem 1.3.5. *If C_1 and C_2 are events in $\mathcal{C}$, then*

$$P(C_1 \cup C_2) = P(C_1) + P(C_2) - P(C_1 \cap C_2).$$

Proof: Each of the sets $C_1 \cup C_2$ and C_2 can be represented, respectively, as a union of nonintersecting sets as follows:

$$C_1 \cup C_2 = C_1 \cup (C_1^c \cap C_2) \quad \text{and} \quad C_2 = (C_1 \cap C_2) \cup (C_1^c \cap C_2).$$

Thus, from (3) of Definition 1.3.1,

$$P(C_1 \cup C_2) = P(C_1) + P(C_1^c \cap C_2)$$

and

$$P(C_2) = P(C_1 \cap C_2) + P(C_1^c \cap C_2).$$

If the second of these equations is solved for $P(C_1^c \cap C_2)$ and this result substituted in the first equation, we obtain

$$P(C_1 \cup C_2) = P(C_1) + P(C_2) - P(C_1 \cap C_2).$$

This completes the proof. ■

Remark 1.3.2 (Inclusion Exclusion Formula). It is easy to show (Exercise 1.3.9) that

$$P(C_1 \cup C_2 \cup C_3) = p_1 - p_2 + p_3,$$

where

$$
\begin{aligned}
p_1 &= P(C_1) + P(C_2) + P(C_3) \\
p_2 &= P(C_1 \cap C_2) + P(C_1 \cap C_3) + P(C_2 \cap C_3) \\
p_3 &= P(C_1 \cap C_2 \cap C_3).
\end{aligned}
\tag{1.3.1}
$$

This can be generalized to the **inclusion exclusion formula**:

$$P(C_1 \cup C_2 \cup \cdots \cup C_k) = p_1 - p_2 + p_3 - \cdots + (-1)^{k+1} p_k, \tag{1.3.2}$$

$\ulcorner C_1 \supset C_1 \cap C_2 \quad ; P(C_1) \geq P(C_1 \cap C_2)$
$\wedge \ C_2 \supset C_1 \cap C_3 \Rightarrow P(C_2) \geq P(C_2 \cap C_3) \Rightarrow P_1 = P(C_1) + P(C_2) + P(C_3)$
$\quad C_3 \supset C_1 \cap C_3 \quad (P(C_3) \geq P(C_1 \cap C_3)) \quad \geq P_2 = P(C_1 \cap C_2) + P(C_1 \cap C_3) + P(C_2 \cap C_3)$

1.3. The Probability Set Function

where p_i equals the sum of the probabilities of all possible intersections involving i sets. It is clear in the case $k = 3$ that $p_1 \geq p_2 \geq p_3$, but more generally $p_1 \geq p_2 \geq \cdots \geq p_k$. As shown in Theorem 1.3.7,

$$p_1 = P(C_1) + P(C_2) + \cdots + P(C_k) \geq P(C_1 \cup C_2 \cup \cdots \cup C_k).$$

This is known as **Boole's inequality**. For $k = 2$, we have

$$1 \geq P(C_1 \cup C_2) = P(C_1) + P(C_2) - P(C_1 \cap C_2),$$

which gives **Bonferroni's inequality**,

$(1.3.3)$ 式
$\{\Rightarrow 1 \geq P(C_1) + P(C_2) - P(C_1 \cap C_2) \Rightarrow P(C_1 \cap C_2) \geq P(C_1) + P(C_2) - 1$
$\{\Rightarrow P(C_1) + P(C_2) \geq P(C_1 \cup C_2) + P(C_1 \cap C_2) \Rightarrow P(C_1) + P(C_2) \geq P(C_1 \cup C_2)$

$$P(C_1 \cap C_2) \geq P(C_1) + P(C_2) - 1, \qquad (1.3.3)$$

that is only useful when $P(C_1)$ and $P(C_2)$ are large. The inclusion exclusion formula provides other inequalities that are useful, such as

$$p_1 \geq P(C_1 \cup C_2 \cup \cdots \cup C_k) \geq p_1 - p_2$$

and

$$p_1 - p_2 + p_3 \geq P(C_1 \cup C_2 \cup \cdots \cup C_k) \geq p_1 - p_2 + p_3 - p_4. \quad \blacksquare$$

Example 1.3.1. Let $\mathcal{C}$ denote the sample space of Example 1.1.2. Let the probability set function assign a probability of $\frac{1}{36}$ to each of the 36 points in $\mathcal{C}$; that is, the dice are fair. If $C_1 = \{(1,1),(2,1),(3,1),(4,1),(5,1)\}$ and $C_2 = \{(1,2),(2,2),(3,2)\}$, then $P(C_1) = \frac{5}{36}$, $P(C_2) = \frac{3}{36}$, $P(C_1 \cup C_2) = \frac{8}{36}$, and $P(C_1 \cap C_2) = 0$. $\blacksquare$

Example 1.3.2. Two coins are to be tossed and the outcome is the ordered pair (face on the first coin, face on the second coin). Thus the sample space may be represented as $\mathcal{C} = \{(H,H),(H,T),(T,H),(T,T)\}$. Let the probability set function assign a probability of $\frac{1}{4}$ to each element of $\mathcal{C}$. Let $C_1 = \{(H,H),(H,T)\}$ and $C_2 = \{(H,H),(T,H)\}$. Then $P(C_1) = P(C_2) = \frac{1}{2}$, $P(C_1 \cap C_2) = \frac{1}{4}$, and, in accordance with Theorem 1.3.5, $P(C_1 \cup C_2) = \frac{1}{2} + \frac{1}{2} - \frac{1}{4} = \frac{3}{4}$. $\blacksquare$

Example 1.3.3 (Equilikely Case). Let $\mathcal{C}$ be partitioned into k mutually disjoint subsets $C_1, C_2, \ldots, C_k$ in such a way that the union of these k mutually disjoint subsets is the sample space $\mathcal{C}$. Thus the events $C_1, C_2, \ldots, C_k$ are **mutually exclusive and exhaustive**. Suppose that the random experiment is of such a character that it is reasonable to *assume* that each of the mutually exclusive and exhaustive events $C_i, i = 1, 2, \ldots, k$, has the same probability. It is necessary then that $P(C_i) = 1/k$, $i = 1, 2, \ldots, k$; and we often say that the events $C_1, C_2, \ldots, C_k$ are *equally likely*. Let the event E be the union of r of these mutually exclusive events, say

$$E = C_1 \cup C_2 \cup \cdots \cup C_r, \quad r \leq k.$$

Then

$$P(E) = P(C_1) + P(C_2) + \cdots + P(C_r) = \frac{r}{k}.$$

Frequently, the integer k is called the total number of ways (for this particular partition of $\mathcal{C}$) in which the random experiment can terminate and the integer r is called the number of ways that are favorable to the event E. So, in this terminology, $P(E)$ is equal to the number of ways favorable to the event E divided by the total number of ways in which the experiment can terminate. It should be emphasized that in order to assign, *in this manner*, the probability r/k to the event E, we must assume that each of the mutually exclusive and exhaustive events $C_1, C_2, \ldots, C_k$ has the same probability $1/k$. This assumption of equally likely events then becomes a *part* of our probability model. Obviously, if this assumption is not realistic in an application, the probability of the event E cannot be computed in this way. ■

In order to illustrate the equilikely case, it is helpful to use some elementary counting rules. These are usually discussed in an elementary algebra course. In the next remark, we offer a brief review of these rules.

Remark 1.3.3 (Counting Rules). Suppose we have two experiments. The first experiment results in m outcomes, while the second experiment results in n outcomes. The composite experiment, first experiment followed by second experiment, has mn outcomes, which can be represented as mn ordered pairs. This is called the **multiplication rule** or the mn-**rule**. This is easily extended to more than two experiments.

Let A be a set with n elements. Suppose we are interested in k-tuples whose components are elements of A. Then by the extended multiplication rule, there are $n \cdot n \cdots n = n^k$ such a k-tuples whose components are elements of A. Next, suppose $k \leq n$ and we are interested in k-tuples whose components are distinct (no repeats) elements of A. There are n elements from which to choose for the first component, $n - 1$ for the second component, $\ldots$, $n - (k - 1)$ for the kth. Hence, by the multiplication rule, there are $n(n - 1) \cdots (n - (k - 1))$ such k-tuples with distinct elements. We call each such k-tuple a **permutation** and use the symbol P_k^n to denote the number of k permutations taken from a set of n elements. Hence, we have the formula

$$P_k^n = n(n-1)\cdots(n-(k-1)) = \frac{n!}{(n-k)!}. \qquad (1.3.4)$$

Next, suppose order is not important, so instead of counting the number of permutations we want to count the number of subsets of k elements taken from A. We use the symbol $\binom{n}{k}$ to denote the total number of these subsets. Consider a subset of k elements from A. By the permutation rule it generates $P_k^k = k(k-1)\cdots 1$ permutations. Furthermore, all these permutations are distinct from permutations generated by other subsets of k elements from A. Finally, each permutation of k distinct elements drawn from A must be generated by one of these subsets. Hence, we have just shown that $P_k^n = \binom{n}{k}k!$; that is,

$$\binom{n}{k} = \frac{n!}{k!(n-k)!}. \qquad (1.3.5)$$

We often use the terminology combinations instead of subsets. So we say that there are $\binom{n}{k}$ **combinations** of k things taken from a set of n things. Another common symbol for $\binom{n}{k}$ is C_k^n.

It is interesting to note that if we expand the binomial,

$$(a+b)^n = (a+b)(a+b)\cdots(a+b),$$

we get

$$(a+b)^n = \sum_{k=0}^{n} \binom{n}{k} a^k b^{n-k} \qquad (1.3.6)$$

because we can select the k factors from which to take a in $\binom{n}{k}$ ways. So $\binom{n}{k}$ is also referred to as a **binomial coefficient**. ∎

Example 1.3.4 (Poker Hands). Let a card be drawn at random from an ordinary deck of 52 playing cards which has been well shuffled. The sample space $\mathcal{C}$ is the union of $k = 52$ outcomes, and it is reasonable to assume that each of these outcomes has the same probability $\frac{1}{52}$. Accordingly, if E_1 is the set of outcomes that are spades, $P(E_1) = \frac{13}{52} = \frac{1}{4}$ because there are $r_1 = 13$ spades in the deck; that is, $\frac{1}{4}$ is the probability of drawing a card that is a spade. If E_2 is the set of outcomes that are kings, $P(E_2) = \frac{4}{52} = \frac{1}{13}$ because there are $r_2 = 4$ kings in the deck; that is, $\frac{1}{13}$ is the probability of drawing a card that is a king. These computations are very easy because there are no difficulties in the determination of the appropriate values of r and k.

However, instead of drawing only one card, suppose that five cards are taken, at random and without replacement, from this deck; i.e, a five card poker hand. In this instance, order is not important. So a hand is a subset of five elements drawn from a set of 52 elements. Hence, by (1.3.5) there are $\binom{52}{5}$ poker hands. If the deck is well shuffled, each hand should be equilikely; i.e., each hand has probability $1/\binom{52}{5}$. We can now compute the probabilities of some interesting poker hands. Let E_1 be the event of a flush, all five cards of the same suit. There are $\binom{4}{1} = 4$ suits to choose for the flush and in each suit there are $\binom{13}{5}$ possible hands; hence, using the multiplication rule, the probability of getting a flush is

$$P(E_1) = \frac{\binom{4}{1}\binom{13}{5}}{\binom{52}{5}} = \frac{4 \cdot 1287}{2598960} = 0.00198.$$

Real poker players note that this includes the probability of obtaining a straight flush.

Next, consider the probability of the event E_2 of getting exactly three of a kind, (the other two cards are distinct and are of different kinds). Choose the kind for the three, in $\binom{13}{1}$ ways; choose the three, in $\binom{4}{3}$ ways; choose the other two kinds, in $\binom{12}{2}$ ways; and choose one card from each of these last two kinds, in $\binom{4}{1}\binom{4}{1}$ ways. Hence the probability of exactly three of a kind is

$$P(E_2) = \frac{\binom{13}{1}\binom{4}{3}\binom{12}{2}\binom{4}{1}^2}{\binom{52}{5}} = 0.0211.$$

Now suppose that E_3 is the set of outcomes in which exactly three cards are kings and exactly two cards are queens. Select the kings, in $\binom{4}{3}$ ways, and select the queens, in $\binom{4}{2}$ ways. Hence, the probability of E_3 is

$$P(E_3) = \binom{4}{3}\binom{4}{2} \bigg/ \binom{52}{5} = 0.0000093.$$

The event E_3 is an example of a full house: three of one kind and two of another kind. Exercise 1.3.18 asks for the determination of the probability of a full house. ∎

Example 1.3.4 and the previous discussion allow us to see one way in which we can define a probability set function, that is, a set function that satisfies the requirements of Definition 1.3.1. Suppose that our space $\mathcal{C}$ consists of k distinct points, which, for this discussion, we take to be in a one-dimensional space. If the random experiment that ends in one of those k points is such that it is reasonable to assume that these points are equally likely, we could assign $1/k$ to each point and let, for $C \subset \mathcal{C}$,

$$
\begin{aligned}
P(C) &= \frac{\text{number of points in } C}{k} \\
&= \sum_{x \in C} f(x), \quad \text{where} \quad f(x) = \frac{1}{k}, \quad x \in \mathcal{C}.
\end{aligned}
$$

For illustration, in the cast of a die, we could take $\mathcal{C} = \{1, 2, 3, 4, 5, 6\}$ and $f(x) = \frac{1}{6}$, $x \in \mathcal{C}$, if we believe the die to be unbiased. Clearly, such a set function satisfies Definition 1.3.1.

The word *unbiased* in this illustration suggests the possibility that all six points might *not*, in all such cases, be equally likely. As a matter of fact, *loaded* dice do exist. In the case of a loaded die, some numbers occur more frequently than others in a sequence of casts of that die. For example, suppose that a die has been loaded so that the relative frequencies of the numbers in $\mathcal{C}$ *seem to stabilize* proportional to the number of spots that are on the *up* side. Thus we might assign $f(x) = x/21$, $x \in \mathcal{C}$, and the corresponding

$$P(C) = \sum_{x \in C} f(x)$$

would satisfy Definition 1.3.1. For illustration, this means that if $C = \{1, 2, 3\}$, then

$$P(C) = \sum_{x=1}^{3} f(x) = \frac{1}{21} + \frac{2}{21} + \frac{3}{21} = \frac{6}{21} = \frac{2}{7}.$$

Whether this probability set function is realistic can only be checked by performing the random experiment a large number of times.

We end this section with an additional property of probability which proves useful in the sequel. Recall in Exercise ·1.2.8 we said that a sequence of events

$\{C_n\}$ is a nondecreasing sequence if $C_n \subset C_{n+1}$, for all n, in which case we wrote $\lim_{n \to \infty} C_n = \cup_{n=1}^{\infty} C_n$. Consider $\lim_{n \to \infty} P(C_n)$. The question is: can we interchange the limit and P? As the following theorem shows, the answer is yes. The result also holds for a decreasing sequence of events. Because of this interchange, this theorem is sometimes referred to as the continuity theorem of probability.

Theorem 1.3.6. *Let $\{C_n\}$ be a nondecreasing sequence of events. Then*

$$\lim_{n \to \infty} P(C_n) = P(\lim_{n \to \infty} C_n) = P\left(\bigcup_{n=1}^{\infty} C_n \right). \tag{1.3.7}$$

Let $\{C_n\}$ be a decreasing sequence of events. Then

$$\lim_{n \to \infty} P(C_n) = P(\lim_{n \to \infty} C_n) = P\left(\bigcap_{n=1}^{\infty} C_n \right). \tag{1.3.8}$$

Proof. We prove the result (1.3.7) and leave the second result as Exercise 1.3.19. Define the sets, called rings, as $R_1 = C_1$ and for $n > 1$, $R_n = C_n \cap C_{n-1}^c$. It follows that $\bigcup_{n=1}^{\infty} C_n = \bigcup_{n=1}^{\infty} R_n$ and that $R_m \cap R_n = \phi$, for $m \neq n$. Also, $P(R_n) = P(C_n) - P(C_{n-1})$. Applying the third axiom of probability yields the following string of equalities:

$$P\left[\lim_{n \to \infty} C_n \right] = P\left(\bigcup_{n=1}^{\infty} C_n \right) = P\left(\bigcup_{n=1}^{\infty} R_n \right) = \sum_{n=1}^{\infty} P(R_n) = \lim_{n \to \infty} \sum_{j=1}^{n} P(R_j)$$

$$= \lim_{n \to \infty} \left\{ P(C_1) + \sum_{j=2}^{n} [P(C_j) - P(C_{j-1})] \right\} = \lim_{n \to \infty} P(C_n). \tag{1.3.9}$$

This is the desired result. ∎

Another useful result for arbitrary unions is given by

Theorem 1.3.7 (Boole's Inequality). *Let $\{C_n\}$ be an arbitrary sequence of events. Then*

$$P\left(\bigcup_{n=1}^{\infty} C_n \right) \leq \sum_{n=1}^{\infty} P(C_n). \tag{1.3.10}$$

Proof: Let $D_n = \bigcup_{i=1}^{n} C_i$. Then $\{D_n\}$ is an increasing sequence of events which go up to $\bigcup_{n=1}^{\infty} C_n$. Also, for all j, $D_j = D_{j-1} \cup C_j$. Hence, by Theorem 1.3.5,

$$P(D_j) \leq P(D_{j-1}) + P(C_j),$$

that is,

$$P(D_j) - P(D_{j-1}) \leq P(C_j).$$

In this case, the C_is are replaced by the D_is in expression (1.3.9). Hence, using the above inequality in this expression and the fact that $P(C_1) = P(D_1)$, we have

$$P\left(\bigcup_{n=1}^{\infty} C_n\right) = P\left(\bigcup_{n=1}^{\infty} D_n\right) = \lim_{n \to \infty} \left\{ P(D_1) + \sum_{j=2}^{n} [P(D_j) - P(D_{j-1})] \right\}$$

$$\leq \lim_{n \to \infty} \sum_{j=1}^{n} P(C_j) = \sum_{n=1}^{\infty} P(C_n). \quad \blacksquare$$

EXERCISES

1.3.1. A positive integer from one to six is to be chosen by casting a die. Thus the elements c of the sample space $\mathcal{C}$ are $1, 2, 3, 4, 5, 6$. Suppose $C_1 = \{1, 2, 3, 4\}$ and $C_2 = \{3, 4, 5, 6\}$. If the probability set function P assigns a probability of $\frac{1}{6}$ to each of the elements of $\mathcal{C}$, compute $P(C_1)$, $P(C_2)$, $P(C_1 \cap C_2)$, and $P(C_1 \cup C_2)$.

1.3.2. A random experiment consists of drawing a card from an ordinary deck of 52 playing cards. Let the probability set function P assign a probability of $\frac{1}{52}$ to each of the 52 possible outcomes. Let C_1 denote the collection of the 13 hearts and let C_2 denote the collection of the 4 kings. Compute $P(C_1)$, $P(C_2)$, $P(C_1 \cap C_2)$, and $P(C_1 \cup C_2)$.

1.3.3. A coin is to be tossed as many times as necessary to turn up one head. Thus the elements c of the sample space $\mathcal{C}$ are H, TH, TTH, $TTTH$, and so forth. Let the probability set function P assign to these elements the respective probabilities $\frac{1}{2}, \frac{1}{4}, \frac{1}{8}, \frac{1}{16}$, and so forth. Show that $P(\mathcal{C}) = 1$. Let $C_1 = \{c : c$ is $H, TH, TTH, TTTH,$ or $TTTTH\}$. Compute $P(C_1)$. Next, suppose that $C_2 = \{c : c$ is $TTTH$ or $TTTTH\}$. Compute $P(C_2)$, $P(C_1 \cap C_2)$, and $P(C_1 \cup C_2)$.

1.3.4. If the sample space is $\mathcal{C} = C_1 \cup C_2$ and if $P(C_1) = 0.8$ and $P(C_2) = 0.5$, find $P(C_1 \cap C_2)$.

1.3.5. Let the sample space be $\mathcal{C} = \{c : 0 < c < \infty\}$. Let $C \subset \mathcal{C}$ be defined by $C = \{c : 4 < c < \infty\}$ and take $P(C) = \int_C e^{-x} \, dx$. Show that $P(\mathcal{C}) = 1$. Evaluate $P(C)$, $P(C^c)$, and $P(C \cup C^c)$.

1.3.6. If the sample space is $\mathcal{C} = \{c : -\infty < c < \infty\}$ and if $C \subset \mathcal{C}$ is a set for which the integral $\int_C e^{-|x|} \, dx$ exists, show that this set function is not a probability set function. What constant do we multiply the integrand by to make it a probability set function?

1.3.7. If C_1 and C_2 are subsets of the sample space $\mathcal{C}$, show that

$$P(C_1 \cap C_2) \leq P(C_1) \leq P(C_1 \cup C_2) \leq P(C_1) + P(C_2).$$

1.3.8. Let C_1, C_2, and C_3 be three mutually disjoint subsets of the sample space $\mathcal{C}$. Find $P[(C_1 \cup C_2) \cap C_3]$ and $P(C_1^c \cup C_2^c)$.

1.3.9. Consider Remark 1.3.2.

(a) If C_1, C_2, and C_3 are subsets of $\mathcal{C}$, show that

$$\begin{aligned}
P(C_1 \cup C_2 \cup C_3) &= P(C_1) + P(C_2) + P(C_3) - P(C_1 \cap C_2) \\
&\quad - P(C_1 \cap C_3) - P(C_2 \cap C_3) + P(C_1 \cap C_2 \cap C_3).
\end{aligned}$$

(b) Now prove the general inclusion exclusion formula given by the expression (1.3.2).

Remark 1.3.4. In order to solve Exercises (1.3.10)-(1.3.18), certain reasonable assumptions must be made. ■

1.3.10. A bowl contains 16 chips, of which 6 are red, 7 are white, and 3 are blue. If four chips are taken at random and without replacement, find the probability that: (a) each of the four chips is red; (b) none of the four chips is red; (c) there is at least one chip of each color.

1.3.11. A person has purchased 10 of 1000 tickets sold in a certain raffle. To determine the five prize winners, five tickets are to be drawn at random and without replacement. Compute the probability that this person wins at least one prize. *Hint:* First compute the probability that the person does not win a prize.

1.3.12. Compute the probability of being dealt at random and without replacement a 13-card bridge hand consisting of: (a) 6 spades, 4 hearts, 2 diamonds, and 1 club; (b) 13 cards of the same suit.

1.3.13. Three distinct integers are chosen at random from the first 20 positive integers. Compute the probability that: (a) their sum is even; (b) their product is even.

1.3.14. There are five red chips and three blue chips in a bowl. The red chips are numbered 1, 2, 3, 4, 5, respectively, and the blue chips are numbered 1, 2, 3, respectively. If two chips are to be drawn at random and without replacement, find the probability that these chips have either the same number or the same color.

1.3.15. In a lot of 50 light bulbs, there are 2 bad bulbs. An inspector examines five bulbs, which are selected at random and without replacement.

(a) Find the probability of at least one defective bulb among the five.

(b) How many bulbs should be examined so that the probability of finding at least one bad bulb exceeds $\frac{1}{2}$?

1.3.16. If $C_1, \ldots, C_k$ are k events in the sample space $\mathcal{C}$, show that the probability that at least one of the events occurs is one minus the probability that none of them occur; i.e.,

$$P(C_1 \cup \cdots \cup C_k) = 1 - P(C_1^c \cap \cdots \cap C_k^c). \tag{1.3.11}$$

1.3.17. A secretary types three letters and the three corresponding envelopes. In a hurry, he places at random one letter in each envelope. What is the probability that at least one letter is in the correct envelope? *Hint:* Let C_i be the event that the ith letter is in the correct envelope. Expand $P(C_1 \cup C_2 \cup C_3)$ to determine the probability.

1.3.18. Consider poker hands drawn from a well-shuffled deck as described in Example 1.3.4. Determine the probability of a full house, i.e, three of one kind and two of another.

1.3.19. Prove expression (1.3.8).

1.3.20. Suppose the experiment is to choose a real number at random in the interval $(0,1)$. For any subinterval $(a,b) \subset (0,1)$, it seems reasonable to assign the probability $P[(a,b)] = b - a$; i.e., the probability of selecting the point from a subinterval is directly proportional to the length of the subinterval. If this is the case, choose an appropriate sequence of subintervals and use expression (1.3.8) to show that $P[\{a\}] = 0$, for all $a \in (0,1)$.

1.3.21. Consider the events C_1, C_2, C_3.

   (a) Suppose C_1, C_2, C_3 are mutually exclusive events. If $P(C_i) = p_i$, $i = 1,2,3$, what is the restriction on the sum $p_1 + p_2 + p_3$?

   (b) In the notation of part (a), if $p_1 = 4/10$, $p_2 = 3/10$, and $p_3 = 5/10$, are C_1, C_2, C_3 mutually exclusive?

For the last two exercises it is assumed that the reader is familar with σ-fields.

1.3.22. Suppose $\mathcal{D}$ is a nonempty collection of subsets of $\mathcal{C}$. Consider the collection of events

$$\mathcal{B} = \cap \{\mathcal{E} : \mathcal{D} \subset \mathcal{E} \text{ and } \mathcal{E} \text{ is a } \sigma\text{-field}\}.$$

Note that $\phi \in \mathcal{B}$ because it is in each σ-field, and, hence, in particular, it is in each σ-field $\mathcal{E} \supset \mathcal{D}$. Continue in this way to show that $\mathcal{B}$ is a σ-field.

1.3.23. Let $\mathcal{C} = R$, where R is the set of all real numbers. Let $\mathcal{I}$ be the set of all open intervals in R. The Borel σ-field on the real line is given by

$$\mathcal{B}_0 = \cap \{\mathcal{E} : \mathcal{I} \subset \mathcal{E} \text{ and } \mathcal{E} \text{ is a } \sigma\text{-field}\}.$$

By definition, $\mathcal{B}_0$ contains the open intervals. Because $[a, \infty) = (-\infty, a)^c$ and $\mathcal{B}_0$ is closed under complements, it contains all intervals of the form $[a, \infty)$, for $a \in R$. Continue in this way and show that $\mathcal{B}_0$ contains all the closed and half-open intervals of real numbers.

1.4 Conditional Probability and Independence

In some random experiments, we are interested only in those outcomes that are elements of a subset C_1 of the sample space C. This means, for our purposes, that the sample space is effectively the subset C_1. We are now confronted with the problem of defining a probability set function with C_1 as the "new" sample space.

Let the probability set function $P(C)$ be defined on the sample space C and let C_1 be a subset of C such that $P(C_1) > 0$. We agree to consider only those outcomes of the random experiment that are elements of C_1; in essence, then, we take C_1 to be a sample space. Let C_2 be another subset of C. How, relative to the new sample space C_1, do we want to define the probability of the event C_2? Once defined, this probability is called the *conditional probability* of the event C_2, relative to the hypothesis of the event C_1, or, more briefly, the conditional probability of C_2, given C_1. Such a conditional probability is denoted by the symbol $P(C_2|C_1)$. We now return to the question that was raised about the definition of this symbol. Since C_1 is now the sample space, the only elements of C_2 that concern us are those, if any, that are also elements of C_1, that is, the elements of $C_1 \cap C_2$. It seems desirable, then, to define the symbol $P(C_2|C_1)$ in such a way that

$$P(C_1|C_1) = 1 \quad \text{and} \quad P(C_2|C_1) = P(C_1 \cap C_2|C_1).$$

Moreover, from a relative frequency point of view, it would seem logically inconsistent if we did not require that the ratio of the probabilities of the events $C_1 \cap C_2$ and C_1, relative to the space C_1, be the same as the ratio of the probabilities of these events relative to the space C; that is, we should have

$$\frac{P(C_1 \cap C_2|C_1)}{P(C_1|C_1)} = \frac{P(C_1 \cap C_2)}{P(C_1)}.$$

These three desirable conditions imply that the relation

$$P(C_2|C_1) = \frac{P(C_1 \cap C_2)}{P(C_1)}$$

is a suitable definition of the **conditional probability** of the event C_2, given the event C_1, provided that $P(C_1) > 0$. Moreover, we have

1. $P(C_2|C_1) \geq 0$.

2. $P\left(\cup_{j=2}^{\infty} C_j|C_1\right) = \sum_{j=2}^{\infty} P(C_j|C_1)$, provided that $C_2, C_3, \ldots$ are mutually exclusive events.

3. $P(C_1|C_1) = 1$.

Properties (1) and (3) are evident and the proof of property (2) is left as Exercise 1.4.1. But these are precisely the conditions that a probability set function must satisfy. Accordingly, $P(C_2|C_1)$ is a probability set function, defined for subsets of C_1. It may be called the conditional probability set function, relative to the hypothesis C_1, or the conditional probability set function, given C_1. It should be noted that this conditional probability set function, given C_1, is defined at this time only when $P(C_1) > 0$.

Example 1.4.1. A hand of five cards is to be dealt at random without replacement from an ordinary deck of 52 playing cards. The conditional probability of an all-spade hand (C_2), relative to the hypothesis that there are at least four spades in the hand (C_1), is, since $C_1 \cap C_2 = C_2$,

$$P(C_2|C_1) = \frac{P(C_2)}{P(C_1)} = \frac{\binom{13}{5}/\binom{52}{5}}{\left[\binom{13}{4}\binom{39}{1} + \binom{13}{5}\right]/\binom{52}{5}}$$

$$= \frac{\binom{13}{5}}{\binom{13}{4}\binom{39}{1} + \binom{13}{5}} = 0.0441.$$

Note that this is not the same as drawing for a spade to complete a flush in draw poker; see Exercise 1.4.3. ∎

From the definition of the conditional probability set function, we observe that

$$P(C_1 \cap C_2) = P(C_1)P(C_2|C_1).$$

This relation is frequently called the **multiplication rule** for probabilities. Sometimes, after considering the nature of the random experiment, it is possible to make reasonable assumptions so that both $P(C_1)$ and $P(C_2|C_1)$ can be assigned. Then $P(C_1 \cap C_2)$ can be computed under these assumptions. This is illustrated in Examples 1.4.2 and 1.4.3.

Example 1.4.2. A bowl contains eight chips. Three of the chips are red and the remaining five are blue. Two chips are to be drawn successively, at random and without replacement. We want to compute the probability that the first draw results in a red chip (C_1) and that the second draw results in a blue chip (C_2). It is reasonable to assign the following probabilities:

$$P(C_1) = \tfrac{3}{8} \quad \text{and} \quad P(C_2|C_1) = \tfrac{5}{7}.$$

Thus, under these assignments, we have $P(C_1 \cap C_2) = (\tfrac{3}{8})(\tfrac{5}{7}) = \tfrac{15}{56} = 0.2679.$ ∎

Example 1.4.3. From an ordinary deck of playing cards, cards are to be drawn successively, at random and without replacement. The probability that the third spade appears on the sixth draw is computed as follows. Let C_1 be the event of two spades in the first five draws and let C_2 be the event of a spade on the sixth draw. Thus the probability that we wish to compute is $P(C_1 \cap C_2)$. It is reasonable to take

$$P(C_1) = \frac{\binom{13}{2}\binom{39}{3}}{\binom{52}{5}} = 0.2743 \quad \text{and} \quad P(C_2|C_1) = \frac{11}{47} = 0.2340.$$

The desired probability $P(C_1 \cap C_2)$ is then the product of these two numbers, which to four places is 0.0642. ∎

The multiplication rule can be extended to three or more events. In the case of three events, we have, by using the multiplication rule for two events,

$$P(C_1 \cap C_2 \cap C_3) = P[(C_1 \cap C_2) \cap C_3]$$
$$= P(C_1 \cap C_2)P(C_3|C_1 \cap C_2).$$

But $P(C_1 \cap C_2) = P(C_1)P(C_2|C_1)$. Hence, provided $P(C_1 \cap C_2) > 0$,

$$P(C_1 \cap C_2 \cap C_3) = P(C_1)P(C_2|C_1)P(C_3|C_1 \cap C_2).$$

This procedure can be used to extend the multiplication rule to four or more events. The general formula for k events can be proved by mathematical induction.

Example 1.4.4. Four cards are to be dealt successively, at random and without replacement, from an ordinary deck of playing cards. The probability of receiving a spade, a heart, a diamond, and a club, in that order, is $(\frac{13}{52})(\frac{13}{51})(\frac{13}{50})(\frac{13}{49}) = 0.0044$. This follows from the extension of the multiplication rule. ∎

Consider k mutually exclusive and exhaustive events $C_1, C_2, \ldots, C_k$ such that $P(C_i) > 0$, $i = 1, 2, \ldots, k$; i.e., $C_1, C_2, \ldots, C_k$ form a partition of $\mathcal{C}$. Here the events $C_1, C_2, \ldots, C_k$ do *not* need to be equally likely. Let C be another event such that $P(C) > 0$. Thus C occurs with one and only one of the events $C_1, C_2, \ldots, C_k$; that is,

$$\begin{aligned} C &= C \cap (C_1 \cup C_2 \cup \cdots C_k) \\ &= (C \cap C_1) \cup (C \cap C_2) \cup \cdots \cup (C \cap C_k). \end{aligned}$$

Since $C \cap C_i$, $i = 1, 2, \ldots, k$, are mutually exclusive, we have

$$P(C) = P(C \cap C_1) + P(C \cap C_2) + \cdots + P(C \cap C_k).$$

However, $P(C \cap C_i) = P(C_i)P(C|C_i)$, $i = 1, 2, \ldots, k$; so

$$\begin{aligned} P(C) &= P(C_1)P(C|C_1) + P(C_2)P(C|C_2) + \cdots + P(C_k)P(C|C_k) \\ &= \sum_{i=1}^{k} P(C_i)P(C|C_i). \end{aligned}$$

This result is sometimes called the **law of total probability**.

From the definition of conditional probability, we have, using the law of total probability, that

$$P(C_j|C) = \frac{P(C \cap C_j)}{P(C)} = \frac{P(C_j)P(C|C_j)}{\sum_{i=1}^{k} P(C_i)P(C|C_i)}, \tag{1.4.1}$$

which is the well-known **Bayes' Theorem**. This permits us to calculate the conditional probability of C_j, given C, from the probabilities of $C_1, C_2, \ldots, C_k$ and the conditional probabilities of C, given C_i, $i = 1, 2, \ldots, k$.

Example 1.4.5. Say it is known that bowl C_1 contains three red and seven blue chips and bowl C_2 contains eight red and two blue chips. All chips are identical in size and shape. A die is cast and bowl C_1 is selected if five or six spots show on the side that is up; otherwise, bowl C_2 is selected. In a notation that is fairly obvious, it seems reasonable to assign $P(C_1) = \frac{2}{6}$ and $P(C_2) = \frac{4}{6}$. The selected bowl is handed to another person and one chip is taken at random. Say that this chip is red, an event which we denote by C. By considering the contents of the bowls, it is reasonable to assign the conditional probabilities $P(C|C_1) = \frac{3}{10}$ and $P(C|C_2) = \frac{8}{10}$. Thus the conditional probability of bowl C_1, given that a red chip is drawn, is

$$P(C_1|C) = \frac{P(C_1)P(C|C_1)}{P(C_1)P(C|C_1) + P(C_2)P(C|C_2)}$$

$$= \frac{(\frac{2}{6})(\frac{3}{10})}{(\frac{2}{6})(\frac{3}{10}) + (\frac{4}{6})(\frac{8}{10})} = \frac{3}{19}.$$

In a similar manner, we have $P(C_2|C) = \frac{16}{19}$. ∎

In Example 1.4.5, the probabilities $P(C_1) = \frac{2}{6}$ and $P(C_2) = \frac{4}{6}$ are called **prior probabilities** of C_1 and C_2, respectively, because they are known to be due to the random mechanism used to select the bowls. After the chip is taken and observed to be red, the conditional probabilities $P(C_1|C) = \frac{3}{19}$ and $P(C_2|C) = \frac{16}{19}$ are called **posterior probabilities**. Since C_2 has a larger proportion of red chips than does C_1, it appeals to one's intuition that $P(C_2|C)$ should be larger than $P(C_2)$ and, of course, $P(C_1|C)$ should be smaller than $P(C_1)$. That is, intuitively the chances of having bowl C_2 are better once that a red chip is observed than before a chip is taken. Bayes' theorem provides a method of determining exactly what those probabilities are.

Example 1.4.6. Three plants, C_1, C_2, and C_3, produce respectively, 10%, 50%, and 40% of a company's output. Although plant C_1 is a small plant, its manager believes in high quality and only 1% of its products are defective. The other two, C_2 and C_3, are worse and produce items that are 3% and 4% defective, respectively. All products are sent to a central warehouse. One item is selected at random and observed to be defective, say event C. The conditional probability that it comes from plant C_1 is found as follows. It is natural to assign the respective prior probabilities of getting an item from the plants as $P(C_1) = 0.1$, $P(C_2) = 0.5$, and $P(C_3) = 0.4$, while the conditional probabilities of defective items are $P(C|C_1) = 0.01$, $P(C|C_2) = 0.03$, and $P(C|C_3) = 0.04$. Thus the posterior probability of C_1, given a defective, is

$$P(C_1|C) = \frac{P(C_1 \cap C)}{P(C)} = \frac{(0.10)(0.01)}{(0.1)(0.01) + (0.5)(0.03) + (0.4)(0.04)},$$

which equals $\frac{1}{32}$; this is much smaller than the prior probability $P(C_1) = \frac{1}{10}$. This is as it should be because the fact that the item is defective decreases the chances that it comes from the high-quality plant C_1. ∎

Example 1.4.7. Suppose we want to investigate the percentage of abused children in a certain population. The events of interest are: a child is abused (A) and its complement a child is not abused ($N = A^c$). For the purposes of this example, we assume that $P(A) = 0.01$ and, hence, $P(N) = 0.99$. The classification as to whether a child is abused or not is based upon a doctor's examination. Because doctors are not perfect, they sometimes classify an abused child (A) as one that is not abused

(N_D, where N_D means classified as not abused by a doctor). On the other hand, doctors sometimes classify a nonabused child (N) as abused (A_D). Suppose these error rates of misclassification are $P(N_D \mid A) = 0.04$ and $P(A_D \mid N) = 0.05$; thus the probabilities of correct decisions are $P(A_D \mid A) = 0.96$ and $P(N_D \mid N) = 0.95$. Let us compute the probability that a child taken at random is classified as abused by a doctor. Because this can happen in two ways, $A \cap A_D$ or $N \cap A_D$, we have

$$P(A_D) = P(A_D \mid A)P(A) + P(A_D \mid N)P(N) = (0.96)(0.01) + (0.05)(0.99) = 0.0591,$$

which is quite high relative to the probability of an abused child, 0.01. Further, the probability that a child is abused when the doctor classified the child as abused is

$$P(A \mid A_D) = \frac{P(A \cap A_D)}{P(A_D)} = \frac{(0.96)(0.01)}{0.0591} = 0.1624,$$

which is quite low. In the same way, the probability that a child is not abused when the doctor classified the child as abused is 0.8376, which is quite high. The reason that these probabilities are so poor at recording the true situation is that the doctors' error rates are so high relative to the fraction 0.01 of the population that is abused. An investigation such as this would, hopefully, lead to better training of doctors for classifying abused children. See also Exercise 1.4.17. ∎

Sometimes it happens that the occurrence of event C_1 does not change the probability of event C_2; that is, when $P(C_1) > 0$,

$$P(C_2 \mid C_1) = P(C_2).$$

In this case, we say that the events C_1 and C_2 are *independent*. Moreover, the multiplication rule becomes

$$P(C_1 \cap C_2) = P(C_1)P(C_2 \mid C_1) = P(C_1)P(C_2). \tag{1.4.2}$$

This, in turn, implies, when $P(C_2) > 0$, that

$$P(C_1 \mid C_2) = \frac{P(C_1 \cap C_2)}{P(C_2)} = \frac{P(C_1)P(C_2)}{P(C_2)} = P(C_1).$$

Note that if $P(C_1) > 0$ and $P(C_2) > 0$, then by the above discussion, independence is equivalent to

$$P(C_1 \cap C_2) = P(C_1)P(C_2). \tag{1.4.3}$$

What if either $P(C_1) = 0$ or $P(C_2) = 0$? In either case, the right side of (1.4.3) is 0. However, the left side is 0 also because $C_1 \cap C_2 \subset C_1$ and $C_1 \cap C_2 \subset C_2$. Hence, we take Equation (1.4.3) as our formal definition of independence; that is,

Definition 1.4.1. *Let C_1 and C_2 be two events. We say that C_1 and C_2 are* **independent** *if Equation (1.4.3) holds.*

Suppose C_1 and C_2 are independent events. Then the following three pairs of events are independent: C_1 and C_2^c, C_1^c and C_2, and C_1^c and C_2^c (see Exercise 1.4.11).

Remark 1.4.1. Events that are *independent* are sometimes called *statistically independent, stochastically independent,* or *independent in a probability sense.* In most instances, we use *independent* without a modifier if there is no possibility of misunderstanding. ∎

Example 1.4.8. A red die and a white die are cast in such a way that the numbers of spots on the two sides that are up are independent events. If C_1 represents a four on the red die and C_2 represents a three on the white die, with an equally likely assumption for each side, we assign $P(C_1) = \frac{1}{6}$ and $P(C_2) = \frac{1}{6}$. Thus, from independence, the probability of the ordered pair (red = 4, white = 3) is

$$P[(4,3)] = (\tfrac{1}{6})(\tfrac{1}{6}) = \tfrac{1}{36}.$$

The probability that the sum of the up spots of the two dice equals seven is

$$P[(1,6),(2,5),(3,4),(4,3),(5,2),(6,1)]$$
$$= \left(\tfrac{1}{6}\right)\left(\tfrac{1}{6}\right) + \left(\tfrac{1}{6}\right)\left(\tfrac{1}{6}\right) + \left(\tfrac{1}{6}\right)\left(\tfrac{1}{6}\right) + \left(\tfrac{1}{6}\right)\left(\tfrac{1}{6}\right) + \left(\tfrac{1}{6}\right)\left(\tfrac{1}{6}\right) + \left(\tfrac{1}{6}\right)\left(\tfrac{1}{6}\right) = \tfrac{6}{36}.$$

In a similar manner, it is easy to show that the probabilities of the sums of $2, 3, 4, 5, 6, 7, 8, 9, 10, 11, 12$ are, respectively,

$$\tfrac{1}{36}, \tfrac{2}{36}, \tfrac{3}{36}, \tfrac{4}{36}, \tfrac{5}{36}, \tfrac{6}{36}, \tfrac{5}{36}, \tfrac{4}{36}, \tfrac{3}{36}, \tfrac{2}{36}, \tfrac{1}{36}. \quad ∎$$

Suppose now that we have three events, C_1, C_2, and C_3. We say that they are **mutually independent** if and only if they are *pairwise independent*:

$$P(C_1 \cap C_3) = P(C_1)P(C_3), \quad P(C_1 \cap C_2) = P(C_1)P(C_2),$$
$$P(C_2 \cap C_3) = P(C_2)P(C_3),$$

and

$$P(C_1 \cap C_2 \cap C_3) = P(C_1)P(C_2)P(C_3).$$

More generally, the n events $C_1, C_2, \ldots, C_n$ are **mutually independent** if and only if for every collection of k of these events, $2 \leq k \leq n$, the following is true:

Say that $d_1, d_2, \ldots, d_k$ are k distinct integers from $1, 2, \ldots, n$; then

$$P(C_{d_1} \cap C_{d_2} \cap \cdots \cap C_{d_k}) = P(C_{d_1})P(C_{d_2}) \cdots P(C_{d_k}).$$

In particular, if $C_1, C_2, \ldots, C_n$ are mutually independent, then

$$P(C_1 \cap C_2 \cap \cdots \cap C_n) = P(C_1)P(C_2) \cdots P(C_n).$$

Also, as with two sets, many combinations of these events and their complements are independent, such as

1. The events C_1^c and $C_2 \cup C_3^c \cup C_4$ are independent,

2. The events $C_1 \cup C_2^c$, C_3^c and $C_4 \cap C_5^c$ are mutually independent.

If there is no possibility of misunderstanding, *independent* is often used without the modifier *mutually* when considering more than two events.

Example 1.4.9. Pairwise independence does not imply mutual independence. As an example, suppose we twice spin a fair spinner with the numbers 1, 2, 3, and 4. Let C_1 be the event that the sum of the numbers spun is 5, let C_2 be the event that the first number spun is a 1, and let C_3 be the event that the second number spun is a 4. Then $P(C_i) = 1/4$, $i = 1, 2, 3$, and for $i \neq j$, $P(C_i \cap C_j) = 1/16$. So the three events are pairwise independent. But $C_1 \cap C_2 \cap C_3$ is the event that $(1,4)$ is spun, which has probability $1/16 \neq 1/64 = P(C_1)P(C_2)P(C_3)$. Hence the events C_1, C_2, and C_3 are not mutually independent. ■

We often perform a sequence of random experiments in such a way that the events associated with one of them are independent of the events associated with the others. For convenience, we refer to these events as as outcomes of *independent experiments*, meaning that the respective events are independent. Thus we often refer to independent flips of a coin or independent casts of a die or, more generally, independent trials of some given random experiment.

Example 1.4.10. A coin is flipped independently several times. Let the event C_i represent a head (H) on the ith toss; thus C_i^c represents a tail (T). Assume that C_i and C_i^c are equally likely; that is, $P(C_i) = P(C_i^c) = \frac{1}{2}$. Thus the probability of an ordered sequence like HHTH is, from independence,

$$P(C_1 \cap C_2 \cap C_3^c \cap C_4) = P(C_1)P(C_2)P(C_3^c)P(C_4) = (\tfrac{1}{2})^4 = \tfrac{1}{16}.$$

Similarly, the probability of observing the first head on the third flip is

$$P(C_1^c \cap C_2^c \cap C_3) = P(C_1^c)P(C_2^c)P(C_3) = (\tfrac{1}{2})^3 = \tfrac{1}{8}.$$

Also, the probability of getting at least one head on four flips is

$$
\begin{aligned}
P(C_1 \cup C_2 \cup C_3 \cup C_4) &= 1 - P[(C_1 \cup C_2 \cup C_3 \cup C_4)^c] \\
&= 1 - P(C_1^c \cap C_2^c \cap C_3^c \cap C_4^c) \\
&= 1 - (\tfrac{1}{2})^4 = \tfrac{15}{16}.
\end{aligned}
$$

See Exercise 1.4.13 to justify this last probability. ■

Example 1.4.11. A computer system is built so that if component K_1 fails, it is bypassed and K_2 is used. If K_2 fails, then K_3 is used. Suppose that the probability that K_1 fails is 0.01, that K_2 fails is 0.03, and that K_3 fails is 0.08. Moreover, we can assume that the failures are mutually independent events. Then the probability of failure of the system is

$$(0.01)(0.03)(0.08) = 0.000024,$$

as all three components would have to fail. Hence, the probability that the system does not fail is $1 - 0.000024 = 0.999976$. ■

EXERCISES

1.4.1. If $P(C_1) > 0$ and if $C_2, C_3, C_4, \ldots$ are mutually disjoint sets, show that

$$P(C_2 \cup C_3 \cup \cdots | C_1) = P(C_2|C_1) + P(C_3|C_1) + \cdots.$$

1.4.2. Assume that $P(C_1 \cap C_2 \cap C_3) > 0$. Prove that

$$P(C_1 \cap C_2 \cap C_3 \cap C_4) = P(C_1)P(C_2|C_1)P(C_3|C_1 \cap C_2)P(C_4|C_1 \cap C_2 \cap C_3).$$

1.4.3. Suppose we are playing draw poker. We are dealt (from a well-shuffled deck) five cards, which contain four spades and another card of a different suit. We decide to discard the card of a different suit and draw one card from the remaining cards to complete a flush in spades (all five cards spades). Determine the probability of completing the flush.

1.4.4. From a well-shuffled deck of ordinary playing cards, four cards arc turned over one at a time without replacement. What is the probability that the spades and red cards alternate?

1.4.5. A hand of 13 cards is to be dealt at random and without replacement from an ordinary deck of playing cards. Find the conditional probability that there are at least three kings in the hand given that the hand contains at least two kings.

1.4.6. A drawer contains eight different pairs of socks. If six socks are taken at random and without replacement, compute the probability that there is at least one matching pair among these six socks. *Hint:* Compute the probability that there is not a matching pair.

1.4.7. A pair of dice is cast until either the sum of seven or eight appears.

(a) Show that the probability of a seven before an eight is 6/11.

(b) Next, this pair of dice is cast until a seven appears twice or until each of a six and eight has appeared at least once. Show that the probability of the six and eight occurring before two sevens is 0.546.

1.4.8. In a certain factory, machines I, II, and III are all producing springs of the same length. Machines I, II, and III produce 1%, 4%, and 2% defective springs, respectively. Of the total production of springs in the factory, Machine I produces 30%, Machine II produces 25%, and Machine III produces 45%.

(a) If one spring is selected at random from the total springs produced in a given day, determine the probability that it is defective.

(b) Given that the selected spring is defective, find the conditional probability that it was produced by Machine II.

1.4.9. Bowl I contains six red chips and four blue chips. Five of these 10 chips are selected at random and without replacement and put in bowl II, which was originally empty. One chip is then drawn at random from bowl II. Given that this chip is blue, find the conditional probability that two red chips and three blue chips are transferred from bowl I to bowl II.

1.4.10. In an office there are two boxes of computer disks: Box C_1 contains seven Verbatim disks and three Control Data disks, and box C_2 contains two Verbatim

$$\bullet \quad P(C_2^c | C_1) = 1 - P(C_2 | C_1)$$

disks and eight Control Data disks. A person is handed a box at random with prior probabilities $P(C_1) = \frac{2}{3}$ and $P(C_2) = \frac{1}{3}$, possibly due to the boxes' respective locations. A disk is then selected at random and the event C occurs if it is from Control Data. Using an equally likely assumption for each disk in the selected box, compute $P(C_1|C)$ and $P(C_2|C)$.

1.4.11. If C_1 and C_2 are independent events, show that the following pairs of events are also independent: (a) C_1 and C_2^c, (b) C_1^c and C_2, and (c) C_1^c and C_2^c. *Hint:* In (a), write $P(C_1 \cap C_2^c) = P(C_1)P(C_2^c|C_1) = P(C_1)[1 - P(C_2|C_1)]$. From the independence of C_1 and C_2, $P(C_2|C_1) = P(C_2)$.

1.4.12. Let C_1 and C_2 be independent events with $P(C_1) = 0.6$ and $P(C_2) = 0.3$. Compute (a) $P(C_1 \cap C_2)$, (b) $P(C_1 \cup C_2)$, and (c) $P(C_1 \cup C_2^c)$.

1.4.13. Generalize Exercise 1.2.5 to obtain

$$(C_1 \cup C_2 \cup \cdots \cup C_k)^c = C_1^c \cap C_2^c \cap \cdots \cap C_k^c.$$

Say that $C_1, C_2, \ldots, C_k$ are independent events that have respective probabilities $p_1, p_2, \ldots, p_k$. Argue that the probability of at least one of $C_1, C_2, \ldots, C_k$ is equal to

$$1 - (1 - p_1)(1 - p_2) \cdots (1 - p_k).$$

1.4.14. Each of four persons fires one shot at a target. Let C_k denote the event that the target is hit by person k, $k = 1, 2, 3, 4$. If C_1, C_2, C_3, C_4 are independent and if $P(C_1) = P(C_2) = 0.7$, $P(C_3) = 0.9$, and $P(C_4) = 0.4$, compute the probability that (a) all of them hit the target; (b) exactly one hits the target; (c) no one hits the target; (d) at least one hits the target.

1.4.15. A bowl contains three red (R) balls and seven white (W) balls of exactly the same size and shape. Select balls successively at random and with replacement so that the events of white on the first trial, white on the second, and so on, can be assumed to be independent. In four trials, make certain assumptions and compute the probabilities of the following ordered sequences: (a) WWRW; (b) RWWW; (c) WWWR; and (d) WRWW. Compute the probability of exactly one red ball in the four trials.

1.4.16. A coin is tossed two independent times, each resulting in a tail (T) or a head (H). The sample space consists of four ordered pairs: TT, TH, HT, HH. Making certain assumptions, compute the probability of each of these ordered pairs. What is the probability of at least one head?

1.4.17. For Example 1.4.7, obtain the following probabilities. Explain what they mean in terms of the problem.

(a) $P(N_D)$.

(b) $P(N | A_D)$.

(c) $P(A | N_D)$.

(d) $P(N \mid N_D)$.

1.4.18. A die is cast independently until the first 6 appears. If the casting stops on an odd number of times, Bob wins; otherwise, Joe wins.

(a) Assuming the die is fair, what is the probability that Bob wins?

(b) Let p denote the probability of a 6. Show that the game favors Bob, for all p, $0 < p < 1$.

1.4.19. Cards are drawn at random and with replacement from an ordinary deck of 52 cards until a spade appears.

(a) What is the probability that at least four draws are necessary?

(b) Same as part (a), except the cards are drawn without replacement.

1.4.20. A person answers each of two multiple choice questions at random. If there are four possible choices on each question, what is the conditional probability that both answers are correct given that at least one is correct?

1.4.21. Suppose a fair 6-sided die is rolled six independent times. A match occurs if side i is observed on the ith trial, $i = 1, \ldots, 6$.

(a) What is the probability of at least one match on the six rolls? *Hint:* Let C_i be the event of a match on the ith trial and use Exercise 1.4.13 to determine the desired probability.

(b) Extend part (a) to a fair n-sided die with n independent rolls. Then determine the limit of the probability as $n \to \infty$.

1.4.22. Players A and B play a sequence of independent games. Player A throws a die first and wins on a "six." If he fails, B throws and wins on a "five" or "six." If he fails, A throws and wins on a "four," "five," or "six." And so on. Find the probability of each player winning the sequence.

1.4.23. Let C_1, C_2, C_3 be independent events with probabilities $\frac{1}{2}$, $\frac{1}{3}$, $\frac{1}{4}$, respectively. Compute $P(C_1 \cup C_2 \cup C_3)$.

1.4.24. From a bowl containing five red, three white, and seven blue chips, select four at random and without replacement. Compute the conditional probability of one red, zero white, and three blue chips, given that there are at least three blue chips in this sample of four chips.

1.4.25. Let the three mutually independent events C_1, C_2, and C_3 be such that $P(C_1) = P(C_2) = P(C_3) = \frac{1}{4}$. Find $P[(C_1^c \cap C_2^c) \cup C_3]$.

1.4.26. Person A tosses a coin and then person B rolls a die. This is repeated independently until a head or one of the numbers $1, 2, 3, 4$ appears, at which time the game is stopped. Person A wins with the head and B wins with one of the numbers $1, 2, 3, 4$. Compute the probability that A wins the game.

1.4.27. Each bag in a large box contains 25 tulip bulbs. It is known that 60% of the bags contain bulbs for 5 red and 20 yellow tulips, while the remaining 40% of the bags contain bulbs for 15 red and 10 yellow tulips. A bag is selected at random and a bulb taken at random from this bag is planted.

   (a) What is the probability that it will be a yellow tulip?

   (b) Given that it is yellow, what is the conditional probability it comes from a bag that contained 5 red and 20 yellow bulbs?

1.4.28. A bowl contains 10 chips numbered $1, 2, \ldots, 10$, respectively. Five chips are drawn at random, one at a time, and without replacement. What is the probability that two even-numbered chips are drawn and they occur on even-numbered draws?

1.4.29. A person bets 1 dollar to b dollars that he can draw two cards from an ordinary deck of cards without replacement and that they will be of the same suit. Find b so that the bet is fair.

1.4.30 (Monte Hall Problem). Suppose there are three curtains. Behind one curtain there is a nice prize, while behind the other two there are worthless prizes. A contestant selects one curtain at random, and then Monte Hall opens one of the other two curtains to reveal a worthless prize. Hall then expresses the willingness to trade the curtain that the contestant has chosen for the other curtain that has not been opened. Should the contestant switch curtains or stick with the one that she has? To answer the question, determine the probability that she wins the prize if she switches.

1.4.31. A French nobleman, Chevalier de Méré, had asked a famous mathematician, Pascal, to explain why the following two probabilities were different (the difference had been noted from playing the game many times): (1) at least one six in four independent casts of a six-sided die; (2) at least a pair of sixes in 24 independent casts of a pair of dice. From proportions it seemed to de Méré that the probabilities should be the same. Compute the probabilities of (1) and (2).

1.4.32. Hunters A and B shoot at a target; the probabilities of hitting the target are p_1 and p_2, respectively. Assuming independence, can p_1 and p_2 be selected so that

$$P(\text{zero hits}) = P(\text{one hit}) = P(\text{two hits})?$$

1.4.33. At the beginning of a study of individuals, 15% were classified as heavy smokers, 30% were classified as light smokers, and 55% were classified as nonsmokers. In the five-year study, it was determined that the death rates of the heavy and light smokers were five and three times that of the nonsmokers, respectively. A randomly selected participant died over the five-year period: calculate the probability that the participant was a nonsmoker.

1.4.34. A chemist wishes to detect an impurity in a certain compound that she is making. There is a test that detects an impurity with probability 0.90; however, this test indicates that an impurity is there when it is not about 5% of the time.

The chemist produces compounds with the impurity about 20% of the time. A compound is selected at random from the chemist's output. The test indicates that an impurity is present. What is the conditional probability that the compound actually has the impurity?

$\mathcal{C} \xrightarrow{\ X(x)\ } \mathcal{D} \longrightarrow$ the dist.

sample space   the sample space of interest.   of X.

1.5   Random Variables

(the space/range of X.)

The reader perceives that a sample space $\mathcal{C}$ may be tedious to describe if the elements of $\mathcal{C}$ are not numbers. We now discuss how we may formulate a rule, or a set of rules, by which the elements c of $\mathcal{C}$ may be represented by numbers. We begin the discussion with a very simple example. Let the random experiment be the toss of a coin and let the sample space associated with the experiment be $\mathcal{C} = \{H, T\}$, where H and T represent heads and tails, respectively. Let X be a function such that $X(T) = 0$ and $X(H) = 1$. Thus X is a real-valued function defined on the sample space $\mathcal{C}$ which takes us from the sample space $\mathcal{C}$ to a space of real numbers $\mathcal{D} = \{0, 1\}$. We now formulate the definition of a random variable and its space.

$\{H,T\} \xrightarrow{\ X(x)\ } \{0,1\}$

Definition 1.5.1. *Consider a random experiment with a sample space $\mathcal{C}$. A function X, which assigns to each element $c \in \mathcal{C}$ one and only one number $X(c) = x$, is called a* **random variable.** *The* **space** *or* **range** *of X is the set of real numbers $\mathcal{D} = \{x : x = X(c), c \in \mathcal{C}\}$.*

In this text, $\mathcal{D}$ generally is a countable set or an interval of real numbers. We call random variables of the first type **discrete** random variables, while we call those of the second type **continuous** random variables. In this section, we present examples of discrete and continuous random variables and then in the next two sections we discuss them separately.

Given a random variable X, its range $\mathcal{D}$ becomes the sample space of interest. Besides inducing the sample space $\mathcal{D}$, X also induces a probability which we call the **distribution** of X.

Consider first the case where X is a discrete random variable with a finite space $\mathcal{D} = \{d_1, \ldots, d_m\}$. The only events of interest in the new sample space $\mathcal{D}$ are subsets of $\mathcal{D}$. The induced probability distribution of X is also clear. Define the function $p_X(d_i)$ on $\mathcal{D}$ by

$$p_X(d_i) = P[\{c : X(c) = d_i\}], \quad \text{for } i = 1, \ldots, m. \tag{1.5.1}$$

In the next section, we formally define $p_X(d_i)$ as the **probability mass function** (**pmf**) of X. Then the induced probability distribution, $P_X(\cdot)$, of X is

$$P_X(D) = \sum_{d_i \in D} p_X(d_i), \quad D \subset \mathcal{D}.$$

As Exercise 1.5.11 shows, $P_X(D)$ is a probability on $\mathcal{D}$. An example is helpful here.

Example 1.5.1 (First Roll in the Game of Craps). Let X be the sum of the upfaces on a roll of a pair of fair 6-sided dice, each with the numbers 1 through 6 on it. The sample space is $\mathcal{C} = \{(i,j) : 1 \le i, j \le 6\}$. Because the dice are fair, $P[\{(i,j)\}] = 1/36$. The random variable X is $X(i,j) = i + j$. The space of X is $\mathcal{D} = \{2, \ldots, 12\}$. By enumeration, the pmf of X is given by

Range value x	2	3	4	5	6	7	8	9	10	11	12
Probability $p_X(x)$	$\frac{1}{36}$	$\frac{2}{36}$	$\frac{3}{36}$	$\frac{4}{36}$	$\frac{5}{36}$	$\frac{6}{36}$	$\frac{5}{36}$	$\frac{4}{36}$	$\frac{3}{36}$	$\frac{2}{36}$	$\frac{1}{36}$

To illustrate the computation of probabilities concerning X, suppose $B_1 = \{x : x = 7, 11\}$ and $B_2 = \{x : x = 2, 3, 12\}$. Then, using the values of $p_X(x)$ given in the table,

$$P_X(B_1) = \sum_{x \in B_1} p_X(x) = \frac{6}{36} + \frac{2}{36} = \frac{8}{36}$$

$$P_X(B_2) = \sum_{x \in B_2} p_X(x) = \frac{1}{36} + \frac{2}{36} + \frac{1}{36} = \frac{4}{36}. \quad \blacksquare$$

The second case is when X is a continuous random variable. In this case, $\mathcal{D}$ is an interval of real numbers. In practice, continuous random variables are often measurements. For example, the weight of an adult is modeled by a continuous random variable. Here we would not be interested in the probability that a person weighs exactly 200 pounds, but we may be interested in the probability that a person weighs over 200 pounds. Generally, for the continuous random variables, the simple events of interest are intervals. We can usually determine a nonnegative function $f_X(x)$ such that for any interval of real numbers $(a, b) \in \mathcal{D}$, the induced probability distribution of X, $P_X(\cdot)$, is defined as

$$P_X[(a, b)] = P[\{c \in \mathcal{C} : a < X(c) < b\}] = \int_a^b f_X(x)\, dx; \quad (1.5.2)$$

that is, the probability that X falls between a and b is the area under the curve $y = f_X(x)$ between a and b. Besides $f_X(x) \ge 0$, we also require that $P_X(\mathcal{D}) = \int_{\mathcal{D}} f_X(x)\, dx = 1$ (total area under the curve over the sample space of X is 1). There are some technical issues in defining events in general for the space $\mathcal{D}$; however, it can be shown that $P_X(D)$ is a probability on $\mathcal{D}$; see Exercise 1.5.11. The function f_X is formally defined as the **probability density function (pdf)** of X in Section 1.7. An example is in order.

Example 1.5.2. For an example of a continuous random variable, consider the following simple experiment: choose a real number at random from the interval $(0, 1)$. Let X be the number chosen. In this case the space of X is $\mathcal{D} = (0, 1)$. It is not obvious as it was in the last example what the induced probability P_X is. But there are some intuitive probabilities. For instance, because the number is chosen at random, it is reasonable to assign

$$P_X[(a, b)] = b - a, \text{ for } 0 < a < b < 1. \quad (1.5.3)$$

It follows that the pdf of X is

$$f_X(x) = \begin{cases} 1 & 0 < x < 1 \\ 0 & \text{elsewhere.} \end{cases} \qquad (1.5.4)$$

For example, the probability that X is less than an eighth or greater than seven eighths is

$$P\left[\left\{X < \frac{1}{8}\right\} \cup \left\{X > \frac{7}{8}\right\}\right] = \int_0^{\frac{1}{8}} dx + \int_{\frac{7}{8}}^1 dx = \frac{1}{4}. \quad \blacksquare$$

Remark 1.5.1. In equations (1.5.1) and (1.5.2), the subscript X on p_X and f_X identifies the pmf and pdf, respectively, with the random variable. We often use this notation, especially when there are several random variables in the discussion. On the other hand, if the identity of the random variable is clear, then we often suppress the subscripts. ∎

The pmf of a discrete random variable and the pdf of a continuous random variable are quite different entities. The distribution function, though, uniquely determines the probability distribution of a random variable. It is defined by:

Definition 1.5.2 (Cumulative Distribution Function). *Let X be a random variable. Then its* **cumulative distribution function** *(cdf) is defined by $F_X(x)$, where*

$$F_X(x) = P_X((-\infty, x]) = P(\{c \in \mathcal{C} : X(c) \le x\}). \qquad (1.5.5)$$

As above, we shorten $P(\{c \in \mathcal{C} : X(c) \le x\})$ to $P(X \le x)$. Also, $F_X(x)$ is often called simply the distribution function (df). However, in this text, we use the modifier *cumulative* as $F_X(x)$ accumulates the probabilities less than or equal to x.

The next example discusses a cdf for a discrete random variable.

Example 1.5.3. Suppose we roll a fair die with the numbers 1 through 6 on it. Let X be the upface of the roll. Then the space of X is $\{1, 2, \ldots, 6\}$ and its pmf is $p_X(i) = 1/6$, for $i = 1, 2, \ldots, 6$. If $x < 1$, then $F_X(x) = 0$. If $1 \le x < 2$, then $F_X(x) = 1/6$. Continuing this way, we see that the cdf of X is an increasing step function which steps up by $p_X(i)$ at each i in the space of X. The graph of F_X is given by Figure 1.5.1. Note that if we are given the cdf, then we can determine the pmf of X. ∎

The following example discusses the cdf for the continuous random variable discussed in Example 1.5.2.

Example 1.5.4 (Continuation of Example 1.5.2). Recall that X denotes a real number chosen at random between 0 and 1. We now obtain the cdf of X. First, if $x < 0$, then $P(X \le x) = 0$. Next, if $x \ge 1$, then $P(X \le x) = 1$. Finally, if $0 < x < 1$, it follows from expression (1.5.3) that $P(X \le x) = P(0 < X \le x) = x - 0 = x$. Hence the cdf of X is

$$F_X(x) = \begin{cases} 0 & \text{if } x < 0 \\ x & \text{if } 0 \le x < 1 \\ 1 & \text{if } x \ge 1. \end{cases} \qquad (1.5.6)$$

Figure 1.5.1: Distribution function for Example 1.5.3.

A sketch of the cdf of X is given in Figure 1.5.2. Note, however, the connection between $F_X(x)$ and the pdf for this experiment $f_X(x)$, given in Example 1.5.2, is

$$F_X(x) = \int_{-\infty}^{x} f_X(t)\, dt, \quad \text{for all } x \in R,$$

and $\frac{d}{dx} F_X(x) = f_X(x)$, for all $x \in R$, except for $x = 0$ and $x = 1$. ■

Let X and Y be two random variables. We say that X and Y are equal in distribution and write $X \overset{D}{=} Y$ if and only if $F_X(x) = F_Y(x)$, for all $x \in R$. It is important to note while X and Y may be equal in distribution, they may be quite different. For instance, in the last example define the random variable Y as $Y = 1 - X$. Then $Y \neq X$. But the space of Y is the interval $(0,1)$, the same as X. Further, the cdf of Y is 0 for $y < 0$; 1 for $y \geq 1$; and for $0 \leq y < 1$, it is

$$F_Y(y) = P(Y \leq y) = P(1 - X \leq y) = P(X \geq 1 - y) = 1 - (1 - y) = y.$$

Hence, Y has the same cdf as X, i.e., $Y \overset{D}{=} X$, but $Y \neq X$.

The cdfs displayed in Figures 1.5.1 and 1.5.2 show increasing functions with lower limits 0 and upper limits 1. In both figures, the cdfs are at least right continuous. As the next theorem proves, these properties are true in general for cdfs.

Theorem 1.5.1. *Let X be a random variable with cumulative distribution function $F(x)$. Then*

(a) *For all a and b, if $a < b$, then $F(a) \leq F(b)$ (F is nondecreasing).*

(b) $\lim_{x \to -\infty} F(x) = 0$ *(the lower limit of F is 0).*

(c) $\lim_{x \to \infty} F(x) = 1$ *(the upper limit of F is 1).*

(d) $\lim_{x \downarrow x_0} F(x) = F(x_0)$ *(F is right continuous).*

Figure 1.5.2: Distribution function for Example 1.5.4.

Proof: We prove parts (a) and (d) and leave parts (b) and (c) for Exercise 1.5.10.
Part (a): Because $a < b$, we have $\{X \le a\} \subset \{X \le b\}$. The result then follows from the monotonicity of P; see Theorem 1.3.3.
Part (d): Let $\{x_n\}$ be any sequence of real numbers such that $x_n \downarrow x_0$. Let $C_n = \{X \le x_n\}$. Then the sequence of sets $\{C_n\}$ is decreasing and $\cap_{n=1}^{\infty} C_n = \{X \le x_0\}$. Hence, by Theorem 1.3.6,

$$\lim_{n \to \infty} F(x_n) = P\left(\bigcap_{n=1}^{\infty} C_n\right) = F(x_0),$$

which is the desired result. ∎

The next theorem is helpful in evaluating probabilities using cdfs.

Theorem 1.5.2. *Let X be a random variable with the cdf F_X. Then for $a < b$,*
$P[a < X \le b] = F_X(b) - F_X(a)$.

Proof: Note that

$$\{-\infty < X \le b\} = \{-\infty < X \le a\} \cup \{a < X \le b\}.$$

The proof of the result follows immediately because the union on the right side of this equation is a disjoint union. ∎

Example 1.5.5. Let X be the lifetime in years of a mechanical part. Assume that X has the cdf

$$F_X(x) = \begin{cases} 0 & x < 0 \\ 1 - e^{-x} & 0 \le x. \end{cases}$$

The pdf of X, $\frac{d}{dx}F_X(x)$, is

$$f_X(x) = \begin{cases} e^{-x} & 0 < x < \infty \\ 0 & \text{elsewhere.} \end{cases}$$

Actually the derivative does not exist at $x = 0$, but in the continuous case the next theorem (1.5.3) shows that $P(X = 0) = 0$ and we can assign $f_X(0) = 0$ without changing the probabilities concerning X. The probability that a part has a lifetime between one and three years is given by

$$P(1 < X \le 3) = F_X(3) - F_X(1) = \int_1^3 e^{-x}\, dx.$$

That is, the probability can be found by $F_X(3) - F_X(1)$ or evaluating the integral. In either case, it equals $e^{-1} - e^{-3} = 0.318$. ■

Theorem 1.5.1 shows that cdfs are right continuous and monotone. Such functions can be shown to have only a countable number of discontinuities. As the next theorem shows, the discontinuities of a cdf have mass; that is, if x is a point of discontinuity of F_X, then we have $P(X = x) > 0$.

Theorem 1.5.3. *For any random variable,*   (对比参照 P44.)

$$P[X = x] = F_X(x) - F_X(x-),\tag{1.5.7}$$

for all $x \in R$, where $F_X(x-) = \lim_{z \uparrow x} F_X(z)$. — 退化的 $F_X(x)$ 不是 a continuous function.

Proof: For any $x \in R$, we have

$$\{x\} = \bigcap_{n=1}^{\infty}\left(x - \frac{1}{n}, x\right];$$

that is, $\{x\}$ is the limit of a decreasing sequence of sets. Hence, by Theorem 1.3.6,

$$\begin{aligned}
P[X = x] &= P\left[\bigcap_{n=1}^{\infty}\left\{x - \frac{1}{n} < X \le x\right\}\right] \\
&= \lim_{n \to \infty} P\left[x - \frac{1}{n} < X \le x\right] \\
&= \lim_{n \to \infty}\left[F_X(x) - F_X(x - (1/n))\right] \\
&= F_X(x) - F_X(x-),
\end{aligned}$$

which is the desired result. ■

Example 1.5.6. Let X have the discontinuous cdf

$$F_X(x) = \begin{cases} 0 & x < 0 \\ x/2 & 0 \le x < 1 \\ 1 & 1 \le x. \end{cases}$$

∴ $F_X(1) = ($用当 $x\ge 1$ 时候 $F_X(x)$ 的值$) = 1$

$F_X(1-) = ($用当 $0\le x<1$ 时候的值$) = \left.\frac{x}{2}\right|_{x=1} = \frac{1}{2}$

Then

$$P(-1 < X \le 1/2) \overset{\text{IP}_0\ Theorem\ 1.5.2.}{=} F_X(1/2) - F_X(-1) = \frac{1}{4} - 0 = \frac{1}{4}$$

and

$$P(X = 1) = F_X(1) - F_X(1-) = 1 - \frac{1}{2} = \frac{1}{2}.$$

The value $1/2$ equals the value of the step of F_X at $x = 1$. ∎

Since the total probability associated with a random variable X of the discrete type with pmf $p_X(x)$ or of the continuous type with pdf $f_X(x)$ is 1, then it must be true that

$$\sum_{x \in D} p_X(x) = 1 \text{ and } \int_D f_X(x)\,dx = 1,$$

where D is the space of X. As the next two examples show, we can use this property to determine the pmf or pdf if we know the pmf or pdf down to a constant of proportionality.

Example 1.5.7. Suppose X has the pmf

$$p_X(x) = \begin{cases} cx & x = 1, 2, \ldots, 10 \\ 0 & \text{elsewhere,} \end{cases}$$

for an appropriate constant c. Then

$$1 = \sum_{x=1}^{10} p_X(x) = \sum_{x=1}^{10} cx = c(1 + 2 + \cdots + 10) = 55c,$$

and, hence, $c = 1/55$. ∎

Example 1.5.8. Suppose X has the pdf

$$f_X(x) = \begin{cases} cx^3 & 0 < x < 2 \\ 0 & \text{elsewhere,} \end{cases}$$

for a constant c. Then

$$1 = \int_0^2 cx^3\,dx = c\left[\frac{x^4}{4}\right]_0^2 = 4c,$$

and, hence, $c = 1/4$. For illustration of the computation of a probability involving X, we have

$$P\left(\frac{1}{4} < X < 1\right) = \int_{1/4}^1 \frac{x^3}{4}\,dx = \frac{255}{4096} = 0.06226. \quad \blacksquare$$

EXERCISES

1.5.1. Let a card be selected from an ordinary deck of playing cards. The outcome c is one of these 52 cards. Let $X(c) = 4$ if c is an ace, let $X(c) = 3$ if c is a king, let $X(c) = 2$ if c is a queen, let $X(c) = 1$ if c is a jack, and let $X(c) = 0$ otherwise. Suppose that P assigns a probability of $\frac{1}{52}$ to each outcome c. Describe the induced probability $P_X(D)$ on the space $D = \{0, 1, 2, 3, 4\}$ of the random variable X.

1.5.2. For each of the following, find the constant c so that $p(x)$ satisfies the condition of being a pmf of one random variable X.

(a) $p(x) = c(\frac{2}{3})^x$, $x = 1, 2, 3, \ldots$, zero elsewhere.

(b) $p(x) = cx$, $x = 1, 2, 3, 4, 5, 6$, zero elsewhere.

1.5.3. Let $p_X(x) = x/15$, $x = 1, 2, 3, 4, 5$, zero elsewhere, be the pmf of X. Find $P(X = 1 \text{ or } 2)$, $P(\frac{1}{2} < X < \frac{5}{2})$, and $P(1 \leq X \leq 2)$.

✓ **1.5.4.** Let $p_X(x)$ be the pmf of a random variable X. Find the cdf $F(x)$ of X and sketch its graph along with that of $p_X(x)$ if:

(a) $p_X(x) = 1$, $x = 0$, zero elsewhere.

(b) $p_X(x) = \frac{1}{3}$, $x = -1, 0, 1$, zero elsewhere.

(c) $p_X(x) = x/15$, $x = 1, 2, 3, 4, 5$, zero elsewhere.

1.5.5. Let us select five cards at random and without replacement from an ordinary deck of playing cards.

(a) Find the pmf of X, the number of hearts in the five cards.

(b) Determine $P(X \leq 1)$.

1.5.6. Let the probability set function of the random variable X be $P_X(D) = \int_D f(x)\,dx$, where $f(x) = 2x/9$, for $x \in D = \{x : 0 < x < 3\}$. Define the events $D_1 = \{x : 0 < x < 1\}$ and $D_2 = \{x : 2 < x < 3\}$. Compute $P_X(D_1)$, $P_X(D_2)$, and $P_X(D_1 \cup D_2)$.

1.5.7. Let the space of the random variable X be $D = \{x : 0 < x < 1\}$. If $D_1 = \{x : 0 < x < \frac{1}{2}\}$ and $D_2 = \{x : \frac{1}{2} \leq x < 1\}$, find $P_X(D_2)$ if $P_X(D_1) = \frac{1}{4}$.

1.5.8. Given the cdf

$$F(x) = \begin{cases} 0 & x < -1 \\ \frac{x+2}{4} & -1 \leq x < 1 \\ 1 & 1 \leq x, \end{cases}$$

sketch the graph of $F(x)$ and then compute: (a) $P(-\frac{1}{2} < X \leq \frac{1}{2})$; (b) $P(X = 0)$; (c) $P(X = 1)$; (d) $P(2 < X \leq 3)$.

✓ **1.5.9.** Consider an urn which contains slips of paper each with one of the numbers $1, 2, \ldots, 100$ on it. Suppose there are i slips with the number i on it for $i = 1, 2, \ldots, 100$. For example, there are 25 slips of paper with the number 25. Assume that the slips are identical except for the numbers. Suppose one slip is drawn at random. Let X be the number on the slip.

(a) Show that X has the pmf $p(x) = x/5050$, $x = 1, 2, 3, \ldots, 100$, zero elsewhere.

(b) Compute $P(X \leq 50)$.

(c) Show that the cdf of X is $F(x) = [x]([x] + 1)/10100$, for $1 \leq x \leq 100$, where $[x]$ is the greatest integer in x.

1.5.10. Prove parts (b) and (c) of Theorem 1.5.1.

1.5.11. Let X be a random variable with space $\mathcal{D}$. For $D \subset \mathcal{D}$, recall that the probability induced by X is $P_X(D) = P[\{c : X(c) \in D\}]$. Show that $P_X(D)$ is a probability by showing the following:

(a) $P_X(\mathcal{D}) = 1$.

(b) $P_X(D) \geq 0$.

(c) For a sequence of sets $\{D_n\}$ in $\mathcal{D}$, show that

$$\{c : X(c) \in \cup_n D_n\} = \cup_n \{c : X(c) \in D_n\}.$$

(d) Use part (c) to show that if $\{D_n\}$ is sequence of mutually exclusive events, then

$$P_X\left(\cup_{n=1}^{\infty} D_n\right) = \sum_{n=1}^{\infty} P(D_n).$$

Remark 1.5.2. In a probability theory course, we would show that the σ-field (collection of events) for $\mathcal{D}$ is the smallest σ-field which contains all the open intervals of real numbers; see Exercise 1.3.23. Such a collection of events is sufficiently rich for discrete and continuous random variables. ∎

1.6   Discrete Random Variables

The first example of a random variable encountered in the last section was an example of a discrete random variable, which is defined next.

Definition 1.6.1 (Discrete Random Variable). *We say a random variable is a* **discrete random variable** *if its space is either finite or countable.*

Example 1.6.1. Consider a sequence of independent flips of a coin, each resulting in a head (H) or a tail (T). Moreover, on each flip, we assume that H and T are equally likely; that is, $P(H) = P(T) = \frac{1}{2}$. The sample space $\mathcal{C}$ consists of sequences like TTHTHHT$\cdots$. Let the random variable X equal the number of flips needed to obtain the first head. Hence, $X(\text{TTHTHHT}\cdots) = 3$. Clearly, the space of X is $\mathcal{D} = \{1, 2, 3, 4, \ldots\}$. We see that $X = 1$ when the sequence begins with an H and thus $P(X = 1) = \frac{1}{2}$. Likewise, $X = 2$ when the sequence begins with TH, which has probability $P(X = 2) = (\frac{1}{2})(\frac{1}{2}) = \frac{1}{4}$ from the independence. More generally, if $X = x$, where $x = 1, 2, 3, 4, \ldots$, there must be a string of $x - 1$ tails followed by a head; that is, TT$\cdots$TH, where there are $x - 1$ tails in TT$\cdots$T. Thus, from independence, we have a geometric sequence of probabilities, namely,

$$P(X = x) = \left(\frac{1}{2}\right)^{x-1} \left(\frac{1}{2}\right) = \left(\frac{1}{2}\right)^{x}, \quad x = 1, 2, 3, \ldots, \quad (1.6.1)$$

the space of which is countable. An interesting event is that the first head appears on an odd number of flips; i.e., $X \in \{1, 3, 5, \ldots\}$. The probability of this event is

$$P[X \in \{1, 3, 5, \ldots\}] = \sum_{x=1}^{\infty} \left(\frac{1}{2}\right)^{2x-1} = \frac{1/2}{1 - (1/4)} = \frac{2}{3}. \quad \blacksquare$$

As the last example suggests, probabilities concerning a discrete random variable can be obtained in terms of the probabilities $P(X = x)$, for $x \in \mathcal{D}$. These probabilities determine an important function, which we define as

Definition 1.6.2 (Probability Mass Function (pmf)). *Let X be a discrete random variable with space $\mathcal{D}$. The **probability mass function** (pmf) of X is given by*

$$p_X(x) = P[X = x], \quad for \; x \in \mathcal{D}. \tag{1.6.2}$$

Note that pmfs satisfy the following two properties:

$$\text{(i)} \; 0 \le p_X(x) \le 1 \;, x \in \mathcal{D}, \text{ and (ii) } \textstyle\sum_{x \in \mathcal{D}} p_X(x) = 1. \tag{1.6.3}$$

In a more advanced class it can be shown that if a function satisfies properties (i) and (ii) for a discrete set $\mathcal{D}$, then this function uniquely determines the distribution of a random variable.

Let X be a discrete random variable with space $\mathcal{D}$. As Theorem 1.5.3 shows, discontinuities of $F_X(x)$ define a mass; that is, if x is a point of discontinuity of F_X, then $P(X = x) > 0$. We now make a distinction between the space of a discrete random variable and these points of positive probability. We define the **support** of a discrete random variable X to be the points in the space of X which have positive probability. We often use $\mathcal{S}$ to denote the support of X. Note that $\mathcal{S} \subset \mathcal{D}$, but it may be that $\mathcal{S} = \mathcal{D}$.

Also, we can use Theorem 1.5.3 to obtain a relationship between the pmf and cdf of a discrete random variable. If $x \in \mathcal{S}$, then $p_X(x)$ is equal to the size of the discontinuity of F_X at x. If $x \notin \mathcal{S}$ then $P[X = x] = 0$ and, hence, F_X is continuous at this x.

Example 1.6.2. A lot, consisting of 100 fuses, is inspected by the following procedure. Five of these fuses are chosen at random and tested; if all five "blow" at the correct amperage, the lot is accepted. If, in fact, there are 20 defective fuses in the lot, the probability of accepting the lot is, under appropriate assumptions,

$$\frac{\binom{80}{5}}{\binom{100}{5}} = 0.31931.$$

More generally, let the random variable X be the number of defective fuses among the five that are inspected. The pmf of X is given by

$$p_X(x) = \begin{cases} \dfrac{\binom{20}{x}\binom{80}{5-x}}{\binom{100}{5}} & \text{for } x = 0, 1, 2, 3, 4, 5 \\ 0 & \text{elsewhere.} \end{cases} \tag{1.6.4}$$

Clearly, the space of X is $\mathcal{D} = \{0, 1, 2, 3, 4, 5\}$, which is also its support. Thus this is an example of a random variable of the discrete type whose distribution is an illustration of a **hypergeometric distribution**. Based on the above discussion, it is easy to graph the cdf of X; see Exercise 1.6.5. ∎

1.6.1 Transformations

A problem often encountered in statistics is the following. We have a random variable X and we know its distribution. We are interested, though, in a random variable Y which is some **transformation** of X, say, $Y = g(X)$. In particular, we want to determine the distribution of Y. Assume X is discrete with space $\mathcal{D}_X$. Then the space of Y is $\mathcal{D}_Y = \{g(x) : x \in \mathcal{D}_X\}$. We consider two cases.

In the first case, g is one-to-one. Then, clearly, the pmf of Y is obtained as

$$p_Y(y) = P[Y = y] = P[g(X) = y] = P[X = g^{-1}(y)] = \underbrace{p_X(g^{-1}(y))}. \qquad (1.6.5)$$

Example 1.6.3. Consider the random variable X of Example 1.6.1. Recall that X was the flip number on which the first head appeared. Let Y be the number of flips before the first head. Then $Y = X - 1$. In this case, the function g is $g(x) = x - 1$, whose inverse is given by $g^{-1}(y) = y + 1$. The space of Y is $\mathcal{D}_Y = \{0, 1, 2, \ldots\}$. The pmf of X is given by (1.6.1); hence, based on expression (1.6.5), the pmf of Y is

$$p_Y(y) = p_X(y + 1) = \left(\frac{1}{2}\right)^{y+1}, \quad \text{for } y = 0, 1, 2, \ldots. \quad \blacksquare$$

Example 1.6.4. Let X have the pmf

$$p_X(x) = \begin{cases} \frac{3!}{x!(3-x)!} \left(\frac{2}{3}\right)^x \left(\frac{1}{3}\right)^{3-x} & x = 0, 1, 2, 3 \\ 0 & \text{elsewhere.} \end{cases}$$

We seek the pmf $p_Y(y)$ of the random variable $Y = X^2$. The transformation $y = g(x) = x^2$ maps $\mathcal{D}_X = \{x : x = 0, 1, 2, 3\}$ onto $\mathcal{D}_Y = \{y : y = 0, 1, 4, 9\}$. In general, $y = x^2$ does not define a one-to-one transformation; here, however, it does, for there are no negative values of x in $\mathcal{D}_X = \{x : x = 0, 1, 2, 3\}$. That is, we have the single-valued inverse function $x = g^{-1}(y) = \sqrt{y}$ (not $-\sqrt{y}$), and so

$$p_Y(y) = p_X(\sqrt{y}) = \frac{3!}{(\sqrt{y})!(3 - \sqrt{y})!} \left(\frac{2}{3}\right)^{\sqrt{y}} \left(\frac{1}{3}\right)^{3-\sqrt{y}}, \quad y = 0, 1, 4, 9. \quad \blacksquare$$

The second case is where the transformation, $g(x)$, is not one-to-one. Instead of developing an overall rule, for most applications involving discrete random variables the pmf of Y can be obtained in a straightforward manner. We offer two examples as illustrations.

Consider the geometric random variable in Example 1.6.3. Suppose we are playing a game against the "house" (say, a gambling casino). If the first head appears on an odd number of flips, we pay the house one dollar, while if it appears on an even number of flips, we win one dollar from the house. Let Y denote our net gain. Then the space of Y is $\{-1, 1\}$. In Example 1.6.1, we showed that the probability that X is odd is $\frac{2}{3}$. Hence, the distribution of Y is given by $p_Y(-1) = 2/3$ and $p_Y(1) = 1/3$.

As a second illustration, let $Z = (X - 2)^2$, where X is the geometric random variable of Example 1.6.1. Then the space of Z is $\mathcal{D}_Z = \{0, 1, 4, 9, 16, \ldots\}$. Note that $Z = 0$ if and only if $X = 2$; $Z = 1$ if and only if $X = 1$ or $X = 3$; while for the other values of the space there is a one-to-one correspondence given by $x = \sqrt{z} + 2$, for $z \in \{4, 9, 16, \ldots\}$. Hence, the pmf of Z is

$$p_Z(z) = \begin{cases} p_X(2) = \frac{1}{4} & \text{for } z = 0 \\ p_X(1) + p_X(3) = \frac{5}{8} & \text{for } z = 1 \\ p_X(\sqrt{z} + 2) = \frac{1}{4}\left(\frac{1}{2}\right)^{\sqrt{z}} & \text{for } z = 4, 9, 16, \ldots. \end{cases} \tag{1.6.6}$$

For verification, the reader is asked to show in Exercise 1.6.11 that the pmf of Z sums to 1 over its space.

EXERCISES

1.6.1. Let X equal the number of heads in four independent flips of a coin. Using certain assumptions, determine the pmf of X and compute the probability that X is equal to an odd number.

1.6.2. Let a bowl contain 10 chips of the same size and shape. One and only one of these chips is red. Continue to draw chips from the bowl, one at a time and at random and without replacement, until the red chip is drawn.

 (a) Find the pmf of X, the number of trials needed to draw the red chip.

 (b) Compute $P(X \leq 4)$.

1.6.3. Cast a die a number of independent times until a six appears on the up side of the die.

 (a) Find the pmf $p(x)$ of X, the number of casts needed to obtain that first six.

 (b) Show that $\sum_{x=1}^{\infty} p(x) = 1$.

 (c) Determine $P(X = 1, 3, 5, 7, \ldots)$.

 (d) Find the cdf $F(x) = P(X \leq x)$.

1.6.4. Cast a die two independent times and let X equal the absolute value of the difference of the two resulting values (the numbers on the up sides). Find the pmf of X. *Hint:* It is not necessary to find a formula for the pmf.

1.6.5. For the random variable X defined in Example 1.6.2, graph the cdf of X.

1.6.6. For the random variable X defined in Example 1.6.1, graph the cdf of X.

1.6.7. Let X have a pmf $p(x) = \frac{1}{3}$, $x = 1, 2, 3$, zero elsewhere. Find the pmf of $Y = 2X + 1$.

1.6.8. Let X have the pmf $p(x) = (\frac{1}{2})^x$, $x = 1, 2, 3, \ldots$, zero elsewhere. Find the pmf of $Y = X^3$.

1.6.9. Let X have the pmf $p(x) = 1/3$, $x = -1, 0, 1$. Find the pmf of $Y = X^2$.

1.6.10. Let X have the pmf

$$p(x) = \left(\frac{1}{2}\right)^{|x|}, \quad x = -1, -2, -3, \ldots.$$

Find the pmf of $Y = X^4$.

1.6.11. Show that the function given in expression (1.6.6) is a pmf.

1.7 Continuous Random Variables

In the last section, we discussed discrete random variables. Another class of random variables important in statistical applications is the class of continuous random variables, which we define next.

Definition 1.7.1 (Continuous Random Variables). *We say a random variable is a* **continuous random variable** *if its cumulative distribution function $F_X(x)$ is a continuous function for all $x \in R$.*

Recall from Theorem 1.5.3 that $P(X = x) = F_X(x) - F_X(x-)$, for any random variable X. Hence, for a continuous random variable X, there are no points of discrete mass; i.e., if X is continuous, then $P(X = x) = 0$ for all $x \in R$. Most continuous random variables are **absolutely continuous**; that is,

$$F_X(x) = \int_{-\infty}^{x} f_X(t)\, dt, \tag{1.7.1}$$

for some function $f_X(t)$. The function $f_X(t)$ is called a **probability density function** (pdf) of X. If $f_X(x)$ is also continuous, then the Fundamental Theorem of Calculus implies that

$$\frac{d}{dx} F_X(x) = f_X(x). \tag{1.7.2}$$

The **support** of a continuous random variable X consists of all points x such that $f_X(x) > 0$. As in the discrete case, we often denote the support of X by $\mathcal{S}$.

If X is a continuous random variable, then probabilities can be obtained by integration; i.e.,

$$P(a < X \le b) = F_X(b) - F_X(a) = \int_{a}^{b} f_X(t)\, dt.$$

Also, for continuous random variables,

$$P(a < X \le b) = P(a \le X \le b) = P(a \le X < b) = P(a < X < b).$$

From the definition (1.7.2), note that pdfs satisfy the two properties

$$\text{(i) } f_X(x) \geq 0 \text{ and (ii) } \int_{-\infty}^{\infty} f_X(t)\, dt = 1. \tag{1.7.3}$$

The second property, of course, follows from $F_X(\infty) = 1$. In an advanced course in probability, it is shown that if a function satisfies the above two properties, then it is a pdf for a continuous random variable; see, for example, Tucker (1967).

Recall in Example 1.5.2 the simple experiment where a number was chosen at random from the interval $(0,1)$. The number chosen, X, is an example of a continuous random variable. Recall that the cdf of X is $F_X(x) = x$, for $0 < x < 1$. Hence, the pdf of X is given by

$$f_X(x) = \begin{cases} 1 & 0 < x < 1 \\ 0 & \text{elsewhere.} \end{cases} \tag{1.7.4}$$

Any continuous or discrete random variable X whose pdf or pmf is constant on the support of X is said to have a **uniform** distribution.

Example 1.7.1 (Point Chosen at Random Within the Unit Circle). Suppose we select a point at random in the interior of a circle of radius 1. Let X be the distance of the selected point from the origin. The sample space for the experiment is $\mathcal{C} = \{(w,y) : w^2 + y^2 < 1\}$. Because the point is chosen at random, it seems that subsets of $\mathcal{C}$ which have equal area are equilikely. Hence, the probability of the selected point lying in a set $C \subset \mathcal{C}$ is proportional to the area of C; i.e.,

$$P(C) = \frac{\text{area of } C}{\pi}.$$

For $0 < x < 1$, the event $\{X \leq x\}$ is equivalent to the point lying in a circle of radius x. By this probability rule, $P(X < x) = \pi x^2 / \pi = x^2$; hence, the cdf of X is

$$F_X(x) = \begin{cases} 0 & x < 0 \\ x^2 & 0 \leq x < 1 \\ 1 & 1 \leq x. \end{cases} \tag{1.7.5}$$

The pdf X is given by

$$f_X(x) = \begin{cases} 2x & 0 \leq x < 1 \\ 0 & \text{elsewhere.} \end{cases} \tag{1.7.6}$$

For illustration, the probability that the selected point falls in the ring with radii $1/4$ and $1/2$ is given by

$$P\left(\frac{1}{4} < X \leq \frac{1}{2}\right) = \int_{\frac{1}{4}}^{\frac{1}{2}} 2w\, dw = [w^2]_{\frac{1}{4}}^{\frac{1}{2}} = \frac{3}{16}. \quad \blacksquare$$

Example 1.7.2. Let the random variable be the time in seconds between incoming telephone calls at a busy switchboard. Suppose that a reasonable probability model for X is given by the pdf

$$f_X(x) = \begin{cases} \frac{1}{4} e^{-x/4} & 0 < x < \infty \\ 0 & \text{elsewhere.} \end{cases}$$

Note that f_X satisfies the two properties of a pdf, namely, (i) $f(x) \geq 0$ and (ii)

$$\int_0^\infty \frac{1}{4} e^{-x/4}\, dx = \left[-e^{-x/4} \right]_0^\infty = 1.$$

For illustration, the probability that the time between successive phone calls exceeds 4 seconds is given by

$$P(X > 4) = \int_4^\infty \frac{1}{4} e^{-x/4}\, dx = e^{-1} = 0.3679.$$

The pdf and the probability of interest are depicted in Figure 1.7.1. ∎

Figure 1.7.1: In Example 1.7.2, the area under the pdf to the right of 4 is $P(X > 4)$.

1.7.1   Transformations

Let X be a continuous random variable with a known pdf f_X. As in the discrete case, we are often interested in the distribution of a random variable Y which is some **transformation** of X, say, $Y = g(X)$. Often we can obtain the pdf of Y by first obtaining its cdf. We illustrate this with two examples.

Example 1.7.3. Let X be the random variable in Example 1.7.1. Recall that X was the distance from the origin to the random point selected in the unit circle. Suppose instead that we are interested in the square of the distance; that is, let $Y = X^2$. The support of Y is the same as that of X, namely, $\mathcal{S}_Y = (0,1)$. What is the cdf of Y? By expression (1.7.5), the cdf of X is

$$F_X(x) = \begin{cases} 0 & x < 0 \\ x^2 & 0 \leq x < 1 \\ 1 & 1 \leq x. \end{cases} \tag{1.7.7}$$

Let y be in the support of Y; i.e., $0 < y < 1$. Then, using expression (1.7.7) and the fact that the support of X contains only positive numbers, the cdf of Y is

$$F_Y(y) = P(Y \leq y) = P(X^2 \leq y) = P(X \leq \sqrt{y}) = F_X(\sqrt{y}) = \sqrt{y}^2 = y.$$

It follows that the pdf of Y is $= F_y'(y) = (y)' = 1. \quad (0 < y < 1).$

$$f_Y(y) = \begin{cases} 1 & 0 < y < 1 \\ 0 & \text{elsewhere.} \end{cases} \quad \blacksquare$$

Example 1.7.4. Let $f_X(x) = \frac{1}{2}$, $-1 < x < 1$, zero elsewhere, be the pdf of a random variable X. Define the random variable Y by $Y = X^2$. We wish to find the pdf of Y. If $y \geq 0$, the probability $P(Y \leq y)$ is equivalent to

$$P(X^2 \leq y) = P(-\sqrt{y} \leq X \leq \sqrt{y}).$$

Accordingly, the cdf of Y, $F_Y(y) = P(Y \leq y)$, is given by

$$F_Y(y) = \begin{cases} 0 & y < 0 \\ \int_{-\sqrt{y}}^{\sqrt{y}} \frac{1}{2}\, dx = \sqrt{y} & 0 \leq y < 1 \\ 1 & 1 \leq y. \end{cases}$$

Hence, the pdf of Y is given by

$$f_Y(y) = \begin{cases} \frac{1}{2\sqrt{y}} & 0 < y < 1 \\ 0 & \text{elsewhere.} \end{cases} \quad \blacksquare$$

These examples illustrate the **cumulative distribution function technique**. The transformation in the first example is one-to-one, and in such cases we can obtain a simple formula for the pdf of Y in terms of the pdf of X, which we record in the next theorem.

Theorem 1.7.1. *Let X be a continuous random variable with pdf $f_X(x)$ and support S_X. Let $Y = g(X)$, where $g(x)$ is a one-to-one differentiable function, on the support of X, S_X. Denote the inverse of g by $x = g^{-1}(y)$ and let $dx/dy = d[g^{-1}(y)]/dy$. Then the pdf of Y is given by*

$$f_Y(y) = f_X(g^{-1}(y)) \left| \frac{dx}{dy} \right|, \quad \text{for } y \in S_Y, \tag{1.7.8}$$

where the support of Y is the set $S_Y = \{y = g(x) : x \in S_X\}$.

Proof: Since $g(x)$ is one-to-one and continuous, it is either strictly monotonically increasing or decreasing. Assume that it is strictly monotonically increasing, for now. The cdf of Y is given by

$$F_Y(y) = P[Y \leq y] = P[g(X) \leq y] = P[X \leq g^{-1}(y)] = F_X(g^{-1}(y)). \tag{1.7.9}$$

Hence, the pdf of Y is

$$f_Y(y) = \frac{d}{dy} F_Y(y) = f_X(g^{-1}(y)) \frac{dx}{dy}, \tag{1.7.10}$$

where dx/dy is the derivative of the function $x = g^{-1}(y)$. In this case, because g is increasing, $dx/dy > 0$. Hence, we can write $dx/dy = |dx/dy|$.

Suppose $g(x)$ is strictly monotonically decreasing. Then (1.7.9) becomes $F_Y(y) = 1 - F_X(g^{-1}(y))$. Hence, the pdf of Y is $f_Y(y) = f_X(g^{-1}(y))(-dx/dy)$. But since g is decreasing, $dx/dy < 0$ and, hence, $-dx/dy = |dx/dy|$. Thus Equation (1.7.8) is true in both cases. ∎

Henceforth, we refer to $dx/dy = (d/dy)g^{-1}(y)$ as the **Jacobian** (denoted by J) of the transformation. In most mathematical areas, $J = dx/dy$ is referred to as the Jacobian of the inverse transformation $x = g^{-1}(y)$, but in this book it is called the Jacobian of the transformation, simply for convenience.

Example 1.7.5. Let X have the pdf

$$f(x) = \begin{cases} 1 & 0 < x < 1 \\ 0 & \text{elsewhere.} \end{cases}$$

Consider the random variable $Y = -2\log X$. The support sets of X and Y are given by $(0, 1)$ and $(0, \infty)$, respectively. The transformation $g(x) = -2\log x$ is one-to-one between these sets. The inverse of the transformation is $x = g^{-1}(y) = e^{-y/2}$. The Jacobian of the transformation is

$$J = \frac{de^{-y/2}}{dy} = -\frac{1}{2}e^{-y/2}.$$

Accordingly, the pdf of $Y = -2\log X$ is

$$f_Y(y) = \begin{cases} f_X(e^{-y/2})|J| = \frac{1}{2}e^{-y/2} & 0 < y < \infty \\ 0 & \text{elsewhere.} \end{cases} \qquad ∎$$

We close this section by two examples of distributions that are neither of the discrete nor the continuous type.

Example 1.7.6. Let a distribution function be given by

$$F(x) = \begin{cases} 0 & x < 0 \\ \frac{x+1}{2} & 0 \le x < 1 \\ 1 & 1 \le x. \end{cases}$$

Then, for instance,

$$P\left(-3 < X \le \frac{1}{2}\right) = F\left(\frac{1}{2}\right) - F(-3) = \frac{3}{4} - 0 = \frac{3}{4}$$

and

$$P(X = 0) = F(0) - F(0-) = \frac{1}{2} - 0 = \frac{1}{2}.$$

The graph of $F(x)$ is shown in Figure 1.7.2. We see that $F(x)$ is not always continuous, nor is it a step function. Accordingly, the corresponding distribution is neither of the continuous type nor of the discrete type. It may be described as a mixture of those types. ∎

Figure 1.7.2: Graph of the cdf of Example 1.7.6.

Distributions that are mixtures of the continuous and discrete type do, in fact, occur frequently in practice. For illustration, in life testing, suppose we know that the length of life, say X, exceeds the number b, but the exact value of X is unknown. This is called *censoring*. For instance, this can happen when a subject in a cancer study simply disappears; the investigator knows that the subject has lived a certain number of months, but the exact length of life is unknown. Or it might happen when an investigator does not have enough time in an investigation to observe the moments of deaths of all the animals, say rats, in some study. Censoring can also occur in the insurance industry; in particular, consider a loss with a limited-pay policy in which the top amount is exceeded but it is not known by how much.

Example 1.7.7. Reinsurance companies are concerned with large losses because they might agree, for illustration, to cover losses due to wind damages that are between $2,000,000 and $10,000,000. Say that X equals the size of a wind loss in millions of dollars, and suppose it has the cdf

$$F_X(x) = \begin{cases} 0 & -\infty < x < 0 \\ 1 - \left(\frac{10}{10+x}\right)^3 & 0 \le x < \infty. \end{cases}$$

If losses beyond $10,000,000 are reported only as 10, then the cdf of this censored distribution is

$$F_Y(y) = \begin{cases} 0 & -\infty < y < 0 \\ 1 - \left(\frac{10}{10+y}\right)^3 & 0 \le y < 10, \\ 1 & 10 \le y < \infty, \end{cases}$$

which has a jump of $[10/(10+10)]^3 = \frac{1}{8}$ at $y = 10$. ∎

EXERCISES

1.7.1. Let a point be selected from the sample space $\mathcal{C} = \{c : 0 < c < 10\}$. Let $C \subset \mathcal{C}$ and let the probability set function be $P(C) = \int_C \frac{1}{10} \, dz$. Define the random variable X to be $X(c) = c^2$. Find the cdf and the pdf of X.

1.7.2. Let the space of the random variable X be $\mathcal{C} = \{x : 0 < x < 10\}$ and let $P_X(C_1) = \frac{3}{8}$, where $C_1 = \{x : 1 < x < 5\}$. Show that $P_X(C_2) \leq \frac{5}{8}$, where $C_2 = \{x : 5 \leq x < 10\}$.

1.7.3. Let the subsets $C_1 = \{\frac{1}{4} < x < \frac{1}{2}\}$ and $C_2 = \{\frac{1}{2} \leq x < 1\}$ of the space $\mathcal{C} = \{x : 0 < x < 1\}$ of the random variable X be such that $P_X(C_1) = \frac{1}{8}$ and $P_X(C_2) = \frac{1}{2}$. Find $P_X(C_1 \cup C_2)$, $P_X(C_1^c)$, and $P_X(C_1^c \cap C_2^c)$.

1.7.4. Given $\int_C [1/\pi(1+x^2)] \, dx$, where $C \subset \mathcal{C} = \{x : -\infty < x < \infty\}$. Show that the integral could serve as a probability set function of a random variable X whose space is $\mathcal{C}$.

1.7.5. Let the probability set function of the random variable X be

$$P_X(C) = \int_C e^{-x} \, dx, \quad \text{where } \mathcal{C} = \{x : 0 < x < \infty\}.$$

Let $C_k = \{x : 2 - 1/k < x \leq 3\}$, $k = 1, 2, 3, \ldots$. Find the limits $\lim_{k \to \infty} C_k$ and $P_X(\lim_{k \to \infty} C_k)$. Find $P_X(C_k)$ and show that $\lim_{k \to \infty} P_X(C_k) = P_X(\lim_{k \to \infty} C_k)$.

1.7.6. For each of the following pdfs of X, find $P(|X| < 1)$ and $P(X^2 < 9)$

(a) $f(x) = x^2/18$, $-3 < x < 3$, zero elsewhere.

(b) $f(x) = (x+2)/18$, $-2 < x < 4$, zero elsewhere.

1.7.7. Let $f(x) = 1/x^2$, $1 < x < \infty$, zero elsewhere, be the pdf of X. If $C_1 = \{x : 1 < x < 2\}$ and $C_2 = \{x : 4 < x < 5\}$, find $P_X(C_1 \cup C_2)$ and $P_X(C_1 \cap C_2)$.

1.7.8. A **mode** of the distribution of a random variable X is a value of x that maximizes the pdf or pmf. If there is only one such x, it is called the *mode of the distribution*. Find the mode of each of the following distributions:

(a) $p(x) = (\frac{1}{2})^x$, $x = 1, 2, 3, \ldots$, zero elsewhere.

(b) $f(x) = 12x^2(1-x)$, $0 < x < 1$, zero elsewhere.

(c) $f(x) = (\frac{1}{2})x^2 e^{-x}$, $0 < x < \infty$, zero elsewhere.

1.7.9. A **median** of a distribution of one random variable X of the discrete or continuous type is a value of x such that $P(X < x) \leq \frac{1}{2}$ and $P(X \leq x) \geq \frac{1}{2}$. If there is only one such x, it is called the *median of the distribution*. Find the median of each of the following distributions:

(a) $p(x) = \frac{4!}{x!(4-x)!} (\frac{1}{4})^x (\frac{3}{4})^{4-x}$, $x = 0, 1, 2, 3, 4$, zero elsewhere.

(b) $f(x) = 3x^2$, $0 < x < 1$, zero elsewhere.

(c) $f(x) = \frac{1}{\pi(1+x^2)}$, $-\infty < x < \infty$.

Hint: In parts (b) and (c), $P(X < x) = P(X \leq x)$ and thus that common value must equal $\frac{1}{2}$ if x is to be the median of the distribution.

1.7.10. Let $0 < p < 1$. A $(100p)$th **percentile** (**quantile** of order p) of the distribution of a random variable X is a value ξ_p such that $P(X < \xi_p) \leq p$ and $P(X \leq \xi_p) \geq p$. Find the 20th percentile of the distribution that has pdf $f(x) = 4x^3$, $0 < x < 1$, zero elsewhere.
Hint: With a continuous-type random variable X, $P(X < \xi_p) = P(X \leq \xi_p)$ and hence that common value must equal p.

1.7.11. For each of the following cdfs $F(x)$, find the pdf $f(x)$ [pmf in part (**d**)], the 25th percentile, and the 60th percentile. Also, sketch the graphs of $f(x)$ and $F(x)$.

(a) $F(x) = (1 + e^{-x})^{-1}$, $-\infty < x < \infty$.

(b) $F(x) = \exp\{-e^{-x}\}$, $-\infty < x < \infty$.

(c) $F(x) = \frac{1}{2} + \frac{1}{\pi}\tan^{-1}(x)$, $-\infty < x < \infty$.

(d) $F(x) = \sum_{j=1}^{x} \left(\frac{1}{2}\right)^j$.

1.7.12. Find the cdf $F(x)$ associated with each of the following probability density functions. Sketch the graphs of $f(x)$ and $F(x)$.

(a) $f(x) = 3(1-x)^2$, $0 < x < 1$, zero elsewhere.

(b) $f(x) = 1/x^2$, $1 < x < \infty$, zero elsewhere.

(c) $f(x) = \frac{1}{3}$, $0 < x < 1$ or $2 < x < 4$, zero elsewhere.

Also, find the median and the 25th percentile of each of these distributions.

1.7.13. Consider the cdf $F(x) = 1 - e^{-x} - xe^{-x}$, $0 \leq x < \infty$, zero elsewhere. Find the pdf, the mode, and the median (by numerical methods) of this distribution.

1.7.14. Let X have the pdf $f(x) = 2x$, $0 < x < 1$, zero elsewhere. Compute the probability that X is at least $\frac{3}{4}$ given that X is at least $\frac{1}{2}$.

1.7.15. The random variable X is said to be **stochastically larger** than the random variable Y if

$$P(X > z) \geq P(Y > z), \qquad (1.7.11)$$

for all real z, with strict inequality holding for at least one z value. Show that this requires that the cdfs enjoy the following property:

$$F_X(z) \leq F_Y(z),$$

for all real z, with strict inequality holding for at least one z value.

1.7.16. Let X be a continuous random variable with support $(-\infty, \infty)$. Consider the random variable $Y = X + \Delta$, where $\Delta > 0$. Using the definition in Exercise 1.7.15, show that Y is stochastically larger than X.

1.7.17. Divide a line segment into two parts by selecting a point at random. Find the probability that the larger segment is at least three times the shorter. Assume a uniform distribution.

1.7.18. Let X be the number of gallons of ice cream that is requested at a certain store on a hot summer day. Assume that $f(x) = 12x(1000-x)^2/10^{12}$, $0 < x < 1000$, zero elsewhere, is the pdf of X. How many gallons of ice cream should the store have on hand each of these days, so that the probability of exhausting its supply on a particular day is 0.05?

1.7.19. Find the 25th percentile of the distribution having pdf $f(x) = |x|/4$, where $-2 < x < 2$ and zero elsewhere.

1.7.20. Let X have the pdf $f(x) = x^2/9$, $0 < x < 3$, zero elsewhere. Find the pdf of $Y = X^3$.

1.7.21. If the pdf of X is $f(x) = 2xe^{-x^2}$, $0 < x < \infty$, zero elsewhere, determine the pdf of $Y = X^2$.

1.7.22. Let X have the uniform pdf $f_X(x) = \frac{1}{\pi}$, for $-\frac{\pi}{2} < x < \frac{\pi}{2}$. Find the pdf of $Y = \tan X$. This is the pdf of a **Cauchy distribution**.

1.7.23. Let X have the pdf $f(x) = 4x^3$, $0 < x < 1$, zero elsewhere. Find the cdf and the pdf of $Y = -\ln X^4$.

1.7.24. Let $f(x) = \frac{1}{3}$, $-1 < x < 2$, zero elsewhere, be the pdf of X. Find the cdf and the pdf of $Y = X^2$.
Hint: Consider $P(X^2 \le y)$ for two cases: $0 \le y < 1$ and $1 \le y < 4$.

1.8 Expectation of a Random Variable

In this section we introduce the expectation operator, which we use throughout the remainder of the text.

Definition 1.8.1 (Expectation). *Let X be a random variable. If X is a continuous random variable with pdf $f(x)$ and*

$$\int_{-\infty}^{\infty} |x| f(x)\, dx < \infty,$$

then the **expectation** *of X is*

$$E(X) = \int_{-\infty}^{\infty} x f(x)\, dx.$$

If X is a discrete random variable with pmf $p(x)$ and

$$\sum_x |x|\, p(x) < \infty,$$

then the **expectation** *of X is*

$$E(X) = \sum_x x\, p(x).$$

Sometimes the expectation $E(X)$ is called the **mathematical expectation** of X, the **expected value** of X, or the **mean** of X. When the mean designation is used, we often denote the $E(X)$ by μ; i.e, $\mu = E(X)$.

Example 1.8.1 (Expectation of a Constant). Consider a constant random variable, that is, a random variable with all its mass at a constant k. This is a discrete random variable with pmf $p(k) = 1$. Because $|k|$ is finite, we have by definition that

$$E(k) = kp(k) = k. \quad \blacksquare \tag{1.8.1}$$

Remark 1.8.1. The terminology of expectation or expected value has its origin in games of chance. This can be illustrated as follows: Four small similar chips, numbered 1, 1, 1, and 2, respectively, are placed in a bowl and are mixed. A player is blindfolded and is to draw a chip from the bowl. If she draws one of the three chips numbered 1, she will receive one dollar. If she draws the chip numbered 2, she will receive two dollars. It seems reasonable to assume that the player has a "$\frac{3}{4}$ claim" on the \$1 and a "$\frac{1}{4}$ claim" on the \$2. Her "total claim" is $(1)(\frac{3}{4}) + 2(\frac{1}{4}) = \frac{5}{4}$, that is, \$1.25. Thus the expectation of X is precisely the player's claim in this game. $\blacksquare$

Example 1.8.2. Let the random variable X of the discrete type have the pmf given by the table

x	1	2	3	4
$p(x)$	$\frac{4}{10}$	$\frac{1}{10}$	$\frac{3}{10}$	$\frac{2}{10}$

Here $p(x) = 0$ if x is not equal to one of the first four positive integers. This illustrates the fact that there is no need to have a formula to describe a pmf. We have

$$E(X) = (1)\left(\frac{4}{10}\right) + (2)\left(\frac{1}{10}\right) + (3)\left(\frac{3}{10}\right) + (4)\left(\frac{2}{10}\right) = \frac{23}{10} = 2.3. \quad \blacksquare$$

Example 1.8.3. Let X have the pdf

$$f(x) = \begin{cases} 4x^3 & 0 < x < 1 \\ 0 & \text{elsewhere.} \end{cases}$$

Then

$$E(X) = \int_0^1 x(4x^3)\, dx = \int_0^1 4x^4\, dx = \left[\frac{4x^5}{5}\right]_0^1 = \frac{4}{5}. \quad \blacksquare$$

Let us consider a function of a random variable X. Call this function $Y = g(X)$. Because Y is a random variable, we could obtain its expectation by first finding the distribution of Y. However, as the following theorem states, we can use the distribution of X to determine the expectation of Y.

Theorem 1.8.1. *Let X be a random variable and let $Y = g(X)$ for some function g.*

(a) *Suppose X is continuous with pdf $f_X(x)$. If $\int_{-\infty}^{\infty} |g(x)| f_X(x)\, dx < \infty$, then the expectation of Y exists and it is given by*

$$E(Y) = \int_{-\infty}^{\infty} g(x) f_X(x)\, dx. \qquad (1.8.2)$$

(b) *Suppose X is discrete with pmf $p_X(x)$. Suppose the support of X is denoted by $\mathcal{S}_X$. If $\sum_{x \in \mathcal{S}_X} |g(x)| p_X(x) < \infty$, then the expectation of Y exists and it is given by*

$$E(Y) = \sum_{x \in \mathcal{S}_X} g(x) p_X(x). \qquad (1.8.3)$$

Proof: We give the proof in the discrete case. The proof for the continuous case requires some advanced results in analysis; see, also, Exercise 1.8.1. The assumption of absolute convergence,

$$\sum_{x \in \mathcal{S}_X} |g(x)| p_X(x) < \infty, \qquad (1.8.4)$$

implies that the following results are true:

(c) The series $\sum_{x \in \mathcal{S}_X} g(x) p_X(x)$ converges.

(d) Any rearrangement of either series (1.8.4) or (c) converges to the same value as the original series.

The rearrangement we need is through the support set $\mathcal{S}_Y$ of Y. Result (d) implies

$$\sum_{x \in \mathcal{S}_X} |g(x)| p_X(x) = \sum_{y \in \mathcal{S}_Y} \sum_{\{x \in \mathcal{S}_X : g(x) = y\}} |g(x)| p_X(x) \qquad (1.8.5)$$

$$= \sum_{y \in \mathcal{S}_Y} |y| \sum_{\{x \in \mathcal{S}_X : g(x) = y\}} p_X(x) \qquad (1.8.6)$$

$$= \sum_{y \in \mathcal{S}_Y} |y| p_Y(y). \qquad (1.8.7)$$

By (1.8.4), the left side of (1.8.5) is finite; hence, the last term (1.8.7) is also finite. Thus $E(Y)$ exists. Using (d) we can then obtain another set of equations, which are the same as (1.8.5)–(1.8.7) but without the absolute values. Hence,

$$\sum_{x \in \mathcal{S}_X} g(x) p_X(x) = \sum_{y \in \mathcal{S}_Y} y p_Y(y) = E(Y),$$

which is the desired result. ∎

Theorem 1.8.2 shows that the expectation operator E is a linear operator.

Theorem 1.8.2. *Let $g_1(X)$ and $g_2(X)$ be functions of a random variable X. Suppose the expectations of $g_1(X)$ and $g_2(X)$ exist. Then for any constants k_1 and k_2, the expectation of $k_1g_1(X) + k_2g_2(X)$ exists and it is given by*

$$E[k_1g_1(X) + k_2g_2(X)] = k_1E[g_1(X)] + k_2E[g_2(X)]. \qquad (1.8.8)$$

Proof: For the continuous case, existence follows from the hypothesis, the triangle inequality, and the linearity of the integral; i.e.,

$$\int_{-\infty}^{\infty} |k_1g_1(x) + k_2g_2(x)|f_X(x)\,dx \leq |k_1| \int_{-\infty}^{\infty} |g_1(x)|f_X(x)\,dx$$
$$+ |k_2| \int_{-\infty}^{\infty} |g_2(x)|f_X(x)\,dx < \infty.$$

The result (1.8.8) follows similarly using the linearity of the integral. The proof for the discrete case follows likewise using the linearity of sums. ∎

The following examples illustrate these theorems.

Example 1.8.4. Let X have the pdf

$$f(x) = \begin{cases} 2(1-x) & 0 < x < 1 \\ 0 & \text{elsewhere.} \end{cases}$$

Then

$$E(X) = \int_{-\infty}^{\infty} xf(x)\,dx = \int_0^1 (x)2(1-x)\,dx = \frac{1}{3},$$

$$E(X^2) = \int_{-\infty}^{\infty} x^2 f(x)\,dx = \int_0^1 (x^2)2(1-x)\,dx = \frac{1}{6},$$

and, of course,

$$E(6X + 3X^2) = 6\left(\frac{1}{3}\right) + 3\left(\frac{1}{6}\right) = \frac{5}{2}. \quad \blacksquare$$

Example 1.8.5. Let X have the pmf

$$p(x) = \begin{cases} \frac{x}{6} & x = 1, 2, 3 \\ 0 & \text{elsewhere.} \end{cases}$$

Then

$$E(X^3) = \sum_x x^3 p(x) = \sum_{x=1}^3 x^3 \frac{x}{6}$$
$$= \frac{1}{6} + \frac{16}{6} + \frac{81}{6} = \frac{98}{6}. \quad \blacksquare$$

Example 1.8.6. Let us divide, at random, a horizontal line segment of length 5 into two parts. If X is the length of the left-hand part, it is reasonable to assume that X has the pdf

$$f(x) = \begin{cases} \frac{1}{5} & 0 < x < 5 \\ 0 & \text{elsewhere.} \end{cases}$$

The expected value of the length of X is $E(X) = \frac{5}{2}$ and the expected value of the length $5 - x$ is $E(5 - x) = \frac{5}{2}$. But the expected value of the product of the two lengths is equal to

$$E[X(5 - X)] = \int_0^5 x(5 - x)(\tfrac{1}{5})\,dx = \tfrac{25}{6} \neq (\tfrac{5}{2})^2.$$

That is, in general, the expected value of a product is not equal to the product of the expected values. ∎

Example 1.8.7. A bowl contains five chips, which cannot be distinguished by a sense of touch alone. Three of the chips are marked \$1 each and the remaining two are marked \$4 each. A player is blindfolded and draws, at random and without replacement, two chips from the bowl. The player is paid an amount equal to the sum of the values of the two chips that he draws and the game is over. If it costs \$4.75 to play the game, would we care to participate for any protracted period of time? Because we are unable to distinguish the chips by sense of touch, we assume that each of the 10 pairs that can be drawn has the same probability of being drawn. Let the random variable X be the number of chips, of the two to be chosen, that are marked \$1. Then, under our assumptions, X has the hypergeometric pmf

$$p(x) = \begin{cases} \dfrac{\binom{3}{x}\binom{2}{2-x}}{\binom{5}{2}} & x = 0, 1, 2 \\ 0 & \text{elsewhere.} \end{cases}$$

If $X = x$, the player receives $u(x) = x + 4(2 - x) = 8 - 3x$ dollars. Hence, his mathematical expectation is equal to

$$E[8 - 3X] = \sum_{x=0}^{2}(8 - 3x)p(x) = \frac{44}{10},$$

or \$4.40. Because \$4.40 < \$4.75, we probably should not play at all and certainly not for a long period of time as, on the average, we would lose 35 cents per play. ∎

EXERCISES

1.8.1. Our proof of Theorem 1.8.1 was for the discrete case. The proof for the continuous case requires some advanced results in in analysis. If, in addition, though, the function $g(x)$ is one-to-one, show that the result is true for the continuous case. *Hint:* First assume that $y = g(x)$ is strictly increasing. Then use the change-of-variable technique with Jacobian dx/dy on the integral $\int_{x \in S_X} g(x) f_X(x)\,dx$.

1.8.2. Let X have the pdf $f(x) = (x + 2)/18$, $-2 < x < 4$, zero elsewhere. Find $E(X)$, $E[(X + 2)^3]$, and $E[6X - 2(X + 2)^3]$.

1.8.3. Suppose that $p(x) = \frac{1}{5}$, $x = 1, 2, 3, 4, 5$, zero elsewhere, is the pmf of the discrete-type random variable X. Compute $E(X)$ and $E(X^2)$. Use these two results to find $E[(X + 2)^2]$ by writing $(X + 2)^2 = X^2 + 4X + 4$.

1.8.4. Let X be a number selected at random from a set of numbers $\{51, 52, \ldots, 100\}$. Approximate $E(1/X)$.
Hint: Find reasonable upper and lower bounds by finding integrals bounding $E(1/X)$.

1.8.5. Let the pmf $p(x)$ be positive at $x = -1, 0, 1$ and zero elsewhere.

(a) If $p(0) = \frac{1}{4}$, find $E(X^2)$.

(b) If $p(0) = \frac{1}{4}$ and if $E(X) = \frac{1}{4}$, determine $p(-1)$ and $p(1)$.

1.8.6. Let X have the pdf $f(x) = 3x^2$, $0 < x < 1$, zero elsewhere. Consider a random rectangle whose sides are X and $(1 - X)$. Determine the expected value of the area of the rectangle.

1.8.7. A bowl contains 10 chips, of which 8 are marked \$2 each and 2 are marked \$5 each. Let a person choose, at random and without replacement, three chips from this bowl. If the person is to receive the sum of the resulting amounts, find his expectation.

1.8.8. Let $f(x) = 2x$, $0 < x < 1$, zero elsewhere, be the pdf of X.

(a) Compute $E(1/X)$.

(b) Find the cdf and the pdf of $Y = 1/X$.

(c) Compute $E(Y)$ and compare this result with the answer obtained in part (a).

1.8.9. Two distinct integers are chosen at random and without replacement from the first six positive integers. Compute the expected value of the absolute value of the difference of these two numbers.

1.8.10. Let X have a Cauchy distribution which has the pdf

$$f(x) = \frac{1}{\pi}\frac{1}{x^2 + 1}, \quad -\infty < x < \infty.$$

Then X is symmetrically distributed about 0 (why?). Why isn't $E(X) = 0$?

1.8.11. Let X have the pdf $f(x) = 3x^2$, $0 < x < 1$, zero elsewhere.

(a) Compute $E(X^3)$.

(b) Show that $Y = X^3$ has a uniform$(0, 1)$ distribution.

(c) Compute $E(Y)$ and compare this result with the answer obtained in part (a).

1.9 Some Special Expectations

Certain expectations, if they exist, have special names and symbols to represent them. First, let X be a random variable of the discrete type with pmf $p(x)$. Then

$$E(X) = \sum_x x p(x).$$

If the support of X is $\{a_1, a_2, a_3, \ldots\}$, it follows that

$$E(X) = a_1 p(a_1) + a_2 p(a_2) + a_3 p(a_3) + \cdots.$$

This sum of products is seen to be a "weighted average" of the values of $a_1, a_2, a_3, \ldots,$ the "weight" associated with each a_i being $p(a_i)$. This suggests that we call $E(X)$ the arithmetic mean of the values of X, or, more simply, the *mean value* of X (or the mean value of the distribution).

Definition 1.9.1 (Mean). *Let X be a random variable whose expectation exists. The* **mean value** μ *of X is defined to be* $\mu = E(X)$.

The mean is the first moment (about 0) of a random variable. Another special expectation involves the second moment. Let X be a discrete random variable with support $\{a_1, a_2, \ldots\}$ and with pmf $p(x)$, then

$$\begin{aligned}
E[(X - \mu)^2] &= \sum_x (x - \mu)^2 p(x) \\
&= (a_1 - \mu)^2 p(a_1) + (a_2 - \mu)^2 p(a_2) + \cdots.
\end{aligned}$$

This sum of products may be interpreted as a "weighted average" of the squares of the deviations of the numbers $a_1, a_2, \ldots$ from the mean value μ of those numbers where the "weight" associated with each $(a_i - \mu)^2$ is $p(a_i)$. It can also be thought of as the second moment of X about μ. This is an important expectation for all types of random variables, and we usually refer to it as the variance.

Definition 1.9.2 (Variance). *Let X be a random variable with finite mean μ and such that $E[(X - \mu)^2]$ is finite. Then the* **variance** *of X is defined to be $E[(X - \mu)^2]$. It is usually denoted by σ^2 or by $Var(X)$.*

It is worthwhile to observe that $Var(X)$ equals

$$\sigma^2 = E[(X - \mu)^2] = E(X^2 - 2\mu X + \mu^2);$$

and since E is a linear operator,

$$\begin{aligned}
\sigma^2 &= E(X^2) - 2\mu E(X) + \mu^2 \\
&= E(X^2) - 2\mu^2 + \mu^2 \\
&= E(X^2) - \mu^2.
\end{aligned}$$

This frequently affords an easier way of computing the variance of X.

It is customary to call σ (the positive square root of the variance) the **standard deviation** of X (or the standard deviation of the distribution). The number σ is sometimes interpreted as a measure of the dispersion of the points of the space relative to the mean value μ. If the space contains only one point k for which $p(k) > 0$, then $p(k) = 1$, $\mu = k$, and $\sigma = 0$.

Remark 1.9.1. Let the random variable X of the continuous type have the pdf $f_X(x) = 1/(2a)$, $-a < x < a$, zero elsewhere, so that $\sigma_X = a/\sqrt{3}$ is the standard deviation of the distribution of X. Next, let the random variable Y of the continuous type have the pdf $f_Y(y) = 1/4a$, $-2a < y < 2a$, zero elsewhere, so that $\sigma_Y = 2a/\sqrt{3}$ is the standard deviation of the distribution of Y. Here the standard deviation of Y is twice that of X; this reflects the fact that the probability for Y is spread out twice as much (relative to the mean zero) as is the probability for X. ∎

Example 1.9.1. Let X have the pdf

$$f(x) = \begin{cases} \frac{1}{2}(x+1) & -1 < x < 1 \\ 0 & \text{elsewhere.} \end{cases}$$

Then the mean value of X is

$$\mu = \int_{-\infty}^{\infty} x f(x)\, dx = \int_{-1}^{1} x\frac{x+1}{2}\, dx = \frac{1}{3},$$

while the variance of X is

$$\sigma^2 = \int_{-\infty}^{\infty} x^2 f(x)\, dx - \mu^2 = \int_{-1}^{1} x^2\frac{x+1}{2}\, dx - \left(\frac{1}{3}\right)^2 = \frac{2}{9}. \quad ∎$$

Example 1.9.2. If X has the pdf

$$f(x) = \begin{cases} \frac{1}{x^2} & 1 < x < \infty \\ 0 & \text{elsewhere,} \end{cases}$$

then the mean value of X does not exist, because

$$\int_{1}^{\infty} |x|\frac{1}{x^2}\, dx = \lim_{b \to \infty} \int_{1}^{b} \frac{1}{x}\, dx$$
$$= \lim_{b \to \infty} (\log b - \log 1)$$

does not exist. ∎

We next define a third special expectation.

Definition 1.9.3 (Moment Generating Function). *Let X be a random variable such that for some $h > 0$, the expectation of e^{tX} exists for $-h < t < h$. The* **moment generating function** *of X is defined to be the function $M(t) = E(e^{tX})$, for $-h < t < h$. We use the abbreviation* **mgf** *to denote the moment generating function of a random variable.*

Actually, all that is needed is that the mgf exists in an open neighborhood of 0. Such an interval, of course, includes an interval of the form $(-h, h)$ for some $h > 0$. Further, it is evident that if we set $t = 0$, we have $M(0) = 1$. But note that for an mgf to exist, it must exist in an open interval about 0.

Example 1.9.3. Suppose we have a fair spinner with the numbers $1, 2$, and 3 on it. Let X be the number of spins until the first 3 occurs. Assuming that the spins are independent, the pmf of X is

$$p(x) = \frac{1}{3}\left(\frac{2}{3}\right)^{x-1}, \quad x = 1, 2, 3, \ldots.$$

Then, using the geometric series, the mgf of X is

$$M(t) = E(e^{tX}) = \sum_{x=1}^{\infty} e^{tx} \frac{1}{3} \left(\frac{2}{3}\right)^{x-1}$$

$$= \frac{1}{3} e^t \sum_{x=1}^{\infty} \left(e^t \frac{2}{3}\right)^{x-1}$$

$$= \frac{1}{3} e^t \left(1 - e^t \frac{2}{3}\right)^{-1},$$

provided that $e^t(2/3) < 1$; i.e., $t < \log(3/2)$. This last interval is an open interval of 0; hence, the mgf of X exists and is given in the final line of the above derivation. ∎

If we are discussing several random variables, it is often useful to subscript M as M_X to denote that this is the mgf of X.

Let X and Y be two random variables with mgfs. If X and Y have the same distribution, i.e, $F_X(z) = F_Y(z)$ for all z, then certainly $M_X(t) = M_Y(t)$ in a neighborhood of 0. But one of the most important properties of mgfs is that the converse of this statement is true too. That is, mgfs uniquely identify distributions. We state this as a theorem. The proof of this converse, though, is beyond the scope of this text; see Chung (1974). We verify it for a discrete situation.

Theorem 1.9.1. *Let X and Y be random variables with moment generating functions M_X and M_Y, respectively, existing in open intervals about 0. Then $F_X(z) = F_Y(z)$ for all $z \in R$ if and only if $M_X(t) = M_Y(t)$ for all $t \in (-h, h)$ for some $h > 0$.*

Because of the importance of this theorem, it does seem desirable to try to make the assertion plausible. This can be done if the random variable is of the discrete type. For example, let it be given that

$$M(t) = \frac{1}{10} e^t + \frac{2}{10} e^{2t} + \frac{3}{10} e^{3t} + \frac{4}{10} e^{4t}$$

is, for all real values of t, the mgf of a random variable X of the discrete type. If we let $p(x)$ be the pmf of X with support $\{a_1, a_2, a_3, \ldots\}$, then because

$$M(t) = \sum_x e^{tx} p(x),$$

we have

$$\frac{1}{10} e^t + \frac{2}{10} e^{2t} + \frac{3}{10} e^{3t} + \frac{4}{10} e^{4t} = p(a_1) e^{a_1 t} + p(a_2) e^{a_2 t} + \cdots.$$

Because this is an identity for all real values of t, it seems that the right-hand member should consist of but four terms and that each of the four should be equal, respectively, to one of those in the left-hand member; hence we may take $a_1 = 1$,

$p(a_1) = \frac{1}{10}$; $a_2 = 2$, $p(a_2) = \frac{2}{10}$; $a_3 = 3$, $p(a_3) = \frac{3}{10}$; $a_4 = 4$, $p(a_4) = \frac{4}{10}$. Or, more simply, the pmf of X is

$$p(x) = \begin{cases} \frac{x}{10} & x = 1, 2, 3, 4 \\ 0 & \text{elsewhere.} \end{cases}$$

On the other hand, suppose X is a random variable of the continuous type. Let it be given that

$$M(t) = \frac{1}{1-t}, \quad t < 1,$$

is the mgf of X. That is, we are given

$$\frac{1}{1-t} = \int_{-\infty}^{\infty} e^{tx} f(x)\, dx, \quad t < 1.$$

It is not at all obvious how $f(x)$ is found. However, it is easy to see that a distribution with pdf

$$f(x) = \begin{cases} e^{-x} & 0 < x < \infty \\ 0 & \text{elsewhere} \end{cases}$$

has the mgf $M(t) = (1-t)^{-1}$, $t < 1$. Thus the random variable X has a distribution with this pdf in accordance with the assertion of the uniqueness of the mgf.

Since a distribution that has an mgf $M(t)$ is completely determined by $M(t)$, it would not be surprising if we could obtain some properties of the distribution directly from $M(t)$. For example, the existence of $M(t)$ for $-h < t < h$ implies that derivatives of $M(t)$ of all orders exist at $t = 0$. Also, a theorem in analysis allows us to interchange the order of differentiation and integration (or summation in the discrete case). That is, if X is continuous,

$$M'(t) = \frac{dM(t)}{dt} = \frac{d}{dt} \int_{-\infty}^{\infty} e^{tx} f(x)\, dx = \int_{-\infty}^{\infty} \frac{d}{dt} e^{tx} f(x)\, dx = \int_{-\infty}^{\infty} x e^{tx} f(x)\, dx.$$

Likewise, if X is a discrete random variable,

$$M'(t) = \frac{dM(t)}{dt} = \sum_x x e^{tx} p(x).$$

Upon setting $t = 0$, we have in either case

$$M'(0) = E(X) = \mu.$$

The second derivative of $M(t)$ is

$$M''(t) = \int_{-\infty}^{\infty} x^2 e^{tx} f(x)\, dx \quad \text{or} \quad \sum_x x^2 e^{tx} p(x),$$

so that $M''(0) = E(X^2)$. Accordingly, $\text{Var}(X)$ equals

$$\sigma^2 = E(X^2) - \mu^2 = M''(0) - [M'(0)]^2.$$

For example, if $M(t) = (1 - t)^{-1}$, $t < 1$, as in the illustration above, then

$$M'(t) = (1 - t)^{-2} \quad \text{and} \quad M''(t) = 2(1 - t)^{-3}.$$

Hence

$$\mu = M'(0) = 1$$

and

$$\sigma^2 = M''(0) - \mu^2 = 2 - 1 = 1.$$

Of course, we could have computed μ and σ^2 from the pdf by

$$\mu = \int_{-\infty}^{\infty} x f(x)\, dx \quad \text{and} \quad \sigma^2 = \int_{-\infty}^{\infty} x^2 f(x)\, dx - \mu^2,$$

respectively. Sometimes one way is easier than the other.

In general, if m is a positive integer and if $M^{(m)}(t)$ means the mth derivative of $M(t)$, we have, by repeated differentiation with respect to t,

$$M^{(m)}(0) = E(X^m).$$

Now

$$E(X^m) = \int_{-\infty}^{\infty} x^m f(x)\, dx \quad \text{or} \quad \sum_x x^m p(x),$$

and the integrals (or sums) of this sort are, in mechanics, called *moments*. Since $M(t)$ generates the values of $E(X^m)$, $m = 1, 2, 3, \ldots$, it is called the moment-generating function (mgf). In fact, we sometimes call $E(X^m)$ the **mth moment** of the distribution, or the mth moment of X.

The next two examples concern random variables whose distributions do not have mgfs.

Example 1.9.4. It is known that the series

$$\frac{1}{1^2} + \frac{1}{2^2} + \frac{1}{3^2} + \cdots$$

converges to $\pi^2/6$. Then

$$p(x) = \begin{cases} \frac{6}{\pi^2 x^2} & x = 1, 2, 3, \ldots \\ 0 & \text{elsewhere} \end{cases}$$

is the pmf of a discrete type of random variable X. The mgf of this distribution, if it exists, is given by

$$\begin{aligned} M(t) &= E(e^{tX}) = \sum_x e^{tx} p(x) \\ &= \sum_{x=1}^{\infty} \frac{6 e^{tx}}{\pi^2 x^2}. \end{aligned}$$

The ratio test may be used to show that this series diverges if $t > 0$. Thus there does not exist a positive number h such that $M(t)$ exists for $-h < t < h$. Accordingly, the distribution has the pmf $p(x)$ of this example and does not have an mgf. ∎

Example 1.9.5. Let X be a continuous random variable with pdf

$$f(x) = \frac{1}{\pi} \frac{1}{x^2 + 1}, \quad -\infty < x < \infty. \tag{1.9.1}$$

This is of course the Cauchy pdf which was introduced in Exercise 1.7.22. Let $t > 0$ be given. If $x > 0$, then by the mean value theorem, for some $0 < \xi_0 < tx$,

$$\frac{e^{tx} - 1}{tx} = e^{\xi_0} \geq 1.$$

Hence, $e^{tx} \geq 1 + tx \geq tx$. This leads to the second inequality in the following derivation:

$$\int_{-\infty}^{\infty} e^{tx} \frac{1}{\pi} \frac{1}{x^2 + 1} \, dx \geq \int_{0}^{\infty} e^{tx} \frac{1}{\pi} \frac{1}{x^2 + 1} \, dx$$

$$\geq \int_{0}^{\infty} \frac{1}{\pi} \frac{tx}{x^2 + 1} \, dx = \infty.$$

Because t was arbitrary, the integral does not exist in an open interval of 0. Hence, the mgf of the Cauchy distribution does not exist. ∎

Example 1.9.6. Let X have the mgf $M(t) = e^{t^2/2}$, $-\infty < t < \infty$. We can differentiate $M(t)$ any number of times to find the moments of X. However, it is instructive to consider this alternative method. The function $M(t)$ is represented by the following Maclaurin's series:

$$e^{t^2/2} = 1 + \frac{1}{1!}\left(\frac{t^2}{2}\right) + \frac{1}{2!}\left(\frac{t^2}{2}\right)^2 + \cdots + \frac{1}{k!}\left(\frac{t^2}{2}\right)^k + \cdots$$

$$= 1 + \frac{1}{2!}t^2 + \frac{(3)(1)}{4!}t^4 + \cdots + \frac{(2k-1)\cdots(3)(1)}{(2k)!}t^{2k} + \cdots.$$

In general, the Maclaurin's series for $M(t)$ is

$$M(t) = M(0) + \frac{M'(0)}{1!}t + \frac{M''(0)}{2!}t^2 + \cdots + \frac{M^{(m)}(0)}{m!}t^m + \cdots$$

$$= 1 + \frac{E(X)}{1!}t + \frac{E(X^2)}{2!}t^2 + \cdots + \frac{E(X^m)}{m!}t^m + \cdots.$$

Thus the coefficient of $(t^m/m!)$ in the Maclaurin's series representation of $M(t)$ is $E(X^m)$. So, for our particular $M(t)$, we have

$$E(X^{2k}) = (2k-1)(2k-3)\cdots(3)(1) = \frac{(2k)!}{2^k k!}, \quad k = 1, 2, 3, \ldots \tag{1.9.2}$$

$$E(X^{2k-1}) = 0, \quad k = 1, 2, 3, \ldots. \tag{1.9.3}$$

We make use of this result in Section 3.4. ∎

Remark 1.9.2. As Example 1.9.5 shows, distributions may not have moment-generating functions. In a more advanced course, we would let i denote the imaginary unit, t an arbitrary real, and we would define $\varphi(t) = E(e^{itX})$. This expectation exists for *every* distribution and it is called the *characteristic function* of the distribution. To see why $\varphi(t)$ exists for all real t, we note, in the continuous case, that its absolute value

$$|\varphi(t)| = \left| \int_{-\infty}^{\infty} e^{itx} f(x)\, dx \right| \leq \int_{-\infty}^{\infty} |e^{itx} f(x)|\, dx.$$

However, $|f(x)| = f(x)$ since $f(x)$ is nonnegative and

$$|e^{itx}| = |\cos tx + i \sin tx| = \sqrt{\cos^2 tx + \sin^2 tx} = 1.$$

Thus

$$|\varphi(t)| \leq \int_{-\infty}^{\infty} f(x)\, dx = 1.$$

Accordingly, the integral for $\varphi(t)$ exists for all real values of t. In the discrete case, a summation would replace the integral. In reference to Example 1.9.5, it can be shown that the characteristic function of the Cauchy distribution is given by $\varphi(t) = \exp\{-|t|\}$, $-\infty < t < \infty$.

Every distribution has a unique characteristic function; and to each characteristic function there corresponds a unique distribution of probability. If X has a distribution with characteristic function $\varphi(t)$, then, for instance, if $E(X)$ and $E(X^2)$ exist, they are given, respectively, by $iE(X) = \varphi'(0)$ and $i^2 E(X^2) = \varphi''(0)$. Readers who are familiar with complex-valued functions may write $\varphi(t) = M(it)$ and, throughout this book, may prove certain theorems in complete generality.

Those who have studied Laplace and Fourier transforms note a similarity between these transforms and $M(t)$ and $\varphi(t)$; it is the uniqueness of these transforms that allows us to assert the uniqueness of each of the moment-generating and characteristic functions. ∎

EXERCISES

1.9.1. Find the mean and variance, if they exist, of each of the following distributions.

(a) $p(x) = \frac{3!}{x!(3-x)!}\left(\frac{1}{2}\right)^3$, $x = 0, 1, 2, 3$, zero elsewhere.

(b) $f(x) = 6x(1-x)$, $0 < x < 1$, zero elsewhere.

(c) $f(x) = 2/x^3$, $1 < x < \infty$, zero elsewhere.

1.9.2. Let $p(x) = \left(\frac{1}{2}\right)^x$, $x = 1, 2, 3, \ldots$, zero elsewhere, be the pmf of the random variable X. Find the mgf, the mean, and the variance of X.

1.9.3. For each of the following distributions, compute $P(\mu - 2\sigma < X < \mu + 2\sigma)$.

(a) $f(x) = 6x(1-x)$, $0 < x < 1$, zero elsewhere.

(b) $p(x) = (\frac{1}{2})^x$, $x = 1, 2, 3, \ldots$, zero elsewhere.

1.9.4. If the variance of the random variable X exists, show that

$$E(X^2) \geq [E(X)]^2.$$

1.9.5. Let a random variable X of the continuous type have a pdf $f(x)$ whose graph is symmetric with respect to $x = c$. If the mean value of X exists, show that $E(X) = c$.
Hint: Show that $E(X - c)$ equals zero by writing $E(X - c)$ as the sum of two integrals: one from $-\infty$ to c and the other from c to ∞. In the first, let $y = c - x$; and, in the second, $z = x - c$. Finally, use the symmetry condition $f(c-y) = f(c+y)$ in the first.

1.9.6. Let the random variable X have mean μ, standard deviation σ, and mgf $M(t)$, $-h < t < h$. Show that

$$E\left(\frac{X - \mu}{\sigma}\right) = 0, \quad E\left[\left(\frac{X - \mu}{\sigma}\right)^2\right] = 1,$$

and

$$E\left\{\exp\left[t\left(\frac{X - \mu}{\sigma}\right)\right]\right\} = e^{-\mu t/\sigma} M\left(\frac{t}{\sigma}\right), \quad -h\sigma < t < h\sigma.$$

✓ **1.9.7.** Show that the moment generating function of the random variable X having the pdf $f(x) = \frac{1}{3}$, $-1 < x < 2$, zero elsewhere, is

$$M(t) = \begin{cases} \frac{e^{2t} - e^{-t}}{3t} & t \neq 0 \\ 1 & t = 0. \end{cases}$$

1.9.8. Let X be a random variable such that $E[(X - b)^2]$ exists for all real b. Show that $E[(X - b)^2]$ is a minimum when $b = E(X)$.

1.9.9. Let X be a random variable of the continuous type that has pdf $f(x)$. If m is the unique median of the distribution of X and b is a real constant, show that

$$E(|X - b|) = E(|X - m|) + 2\int_m^b (b - x)f(x)\,dx,$$

provided that the expectations exist. For what value of b is $E(|X - b|)$ a minimum?

1.9.10. Let X denote a random variable for which $E[(X - a)^2]$ exists. Give an example of a distribution of a discrete type such that this expectation is zero. Such a distribution is called a *degenerate distribution*.

1.9.11. Let X denote a random variable such that $K(t) = E(t^X)$ exists for all real values of t in a certain open interval that includes the point $t = 1$. Show that $K^{(m)}(1)$ is equal to the mth *factorial moment* $E[X(X-1)\cdots(X-m+1)]$.

1.9.12. Let X be a random variable. If m is a positive integer, the expectation $E[(X-b)^m]$, if it exists, is called the mth moment of the distribution about the point b. Let the first, second, and third moments of the distribution about the point 7 be 3, 11, and 15, respectively. Determine the mean μ of X, and then find the first, second, and third moments of the distribution about the point μ.

1.9.13. Let X be a random variable such that $R(t) = E(e^{t(X-b)})$ exists for t such that $-h < t < h$. If m is a positive integer, show that $R^{(m)}(0)$ is equal to the mth moment of the distribution about the point b.

1.9.14. Let X be a random variable with mean μ and variance σ^2 such that the third moment $E[(X-\mu)^3]$ about the vertical line through μ exists. The value of the ratio $E[(X-\mu)^3]/\sigma^3$ is often used as a measure of *skewness*. Graph each of the following probability density functions and show that this measure is negative, zero, and positive for these respective distributions (which are said to be skewed to the left, not skewed, and skewed to the right, respectively).

(a) $f(x) = (x+1)/2$, $-1 < x < 1$, zero elsewhere.

(b) $f(x) = \frac{1}{2}$, $-1 < x < 1$, zero elsewhere.

(c) $f(x) = (1-x)/2$, $-1 < x < 1$, zero elsewhere.

1.9.15. Let X be a random variable with mean μ and variance σ^2 such that the fourth moment $E[(X-\mu)^4]$ exists. The value of the ratio $E[(X-\mu)^4]/\sigma^4$ is often used as a measure of *kurtosis*. Graph each of the following probability density functions and show that this measure is smaller for the first distribution.

(a) $f(x) = \frac{1}{2}$, $-1 < x < 1$, zero elsewhere.

(b) $f(x) = 3(1-x^2)/4$, $-1 < x < 1$, zero elsewhere.

1.9.16. Let the random variable X have pmf

$$p(x) = \begin{cases} p & x = -1, 1 \\ 1 - 2p & x = 0 \\ 0 & \text{elsewhere,} \end{cases}$$

where $0 < p < \frac{1}{2}$. Find the measure of kurtosis as a function of p. Determine its value when $p = \frac{1}{3}$, $p = \frac{1}{5}$, $p = \frac{1}{10}$, and $p = \frac{1}{100}$. Note that the kurtosis increases as p decreases.

1.9.17. Let $\psi(t) = \log M(t)$, where $M(t)$ is the mgf of a distribution. Prove that $\psi'(0) = \mu$ and $\psi''(0) = \sigma^2$. The function $\psi(t)$ is called the **cumulant generating function**.

1.9.18. Find the mean and the variance of the distribution that has the cdf

$$F(x) = \begin{cases} 0 & x < 0 \\ \frac{x}{8} & 0 \le x < 2 \\ \frac{x^2}{16} & 2 \le x < 4 \\ 1 & 4 \le x. \end{cases}$$

1.9.19. Find the moments of the distribution that has mgf $M(t) = (1-t)^{-3}$, $t < 1$. *Hint:* Find the Maclaurin series for $M(t)$.

1.9.20. Let X be a random variable of the continuous type with pdf $f(x)$, which is positive provided $0 < x < b < \infty$, and is equal to zero elsewhere. Show that

$$E(X) = \int_0^b [1 - F(x)] \, dx,$$

where $F(x)$ is the cdf of X.

1.9.21. Let X be a random variable of the discrete type with pmf $p(x)$ that is positive on the nonnegative integers and is equal to zero elsewhere. Show that

$$E(X) = \sum_{x=0}^{\infty} [1 - F(x)],$$

where $F(x)$ is the cdf of X.

1.9.22. Let X have the pmf $p(x) = 1/k$, $x = 1, 2, 3, \ldots, k$, zero elsewhere. Show that the mgf is

$$M(t) = \begin{cases} \frac{e^t(1-e^{kt})}{k(1-e^t)} & t \neq 0 \\ 1 & t = 0. \end{cases}$$

1.9.23. Let X have the cdf $F(x)$ that is a mixture of the continuous and discrete types, namely

$$F(x) = \begin{cases} 0 & x < 0 \\ \frac{x+1}{4} & 0 \leq x < 1 \\ 1 & 1 \leq x. \end{cases}$$

Determine reasonable definitions of $\mu = E(X)$ and $\sigma^2 = \text{var}(X)$ and compute each. *Hint:* Determine the parts of the pmf and the pdf associated with each of the discrete and continuous parts, and then sum for the discrete part and integrate for the continuous part.

1.9.24. Consider k continuous-type distributions with the following characteristics: pdf $f_i(x)$, mean μ_i, and variance σ_i^2, $i = 1, 2, \ldots, k$. If $c_i \geq 0$, $i = 1, 2, \ldots, k$, and $c_1 + c_2 + \cdots + c_k = 1$, show that the mean and the variance of the distribution having pdf $c_1 f_1(x) + \cdots + c_k f_k(x)$ are $\mu = \sum_{i=1}^k c_i \mu_i$ and $\sigma^2 = \sum_{i=1}^k c_i [\sigma_i^2 + (\mu_i - \mu)^2]$, respectively.

1.9.25. Let X be a random variable with a pdf $f(x)$ and mgf $M(t)$. Suppose f is symmetric about 0; i.e., $f(-x) = f(x)$. Show that $M(-t) = M(t)$.

1.9.26. Let X have the exponential pdf, $f(x) = \beta^{-1} \exp\{-x/\beta\}$, $0 < x < \infty$, zero elsewhere. Find the mgf, the mean, and the variance of X.

1.10   Important Inequalities

In this section, we discuss some famous inequalities involving expectations. We make use of these inequalities in the remainder of the text. We begin with a useful result.

Theorem 1.10.1. *Let X be a random variable and let m be a positive integer. Suppose $E[X^m]$ exists. If k is a positive integer and $k \leq m$, then $E[X^k]$ exists.*

Proof: We prove it for the continuous case; but the proof is similar for the discrete case if we replace integrals by sums. Let $f(x)$ be the pdf of X. Then

$$
\begin{aligned}
\int_{-\infty}^{\infty} |x|^k f(x)\, dx &= \int_{|x| \leq 1} |x|^k f(x)\, dx + \int_{|x| > 1} |x|^k f(x)\, dx \\
&\leq \int_{|x| \leq 1} f(x)\, dx + \int_{|x| > 1} |x|^m f(x)\, dx \\
&\leq \int_{-\infty}^{\infty} f(x)\, dx + \int_{-\infty}^{\infty} |x|^m f(x)\, dx \\
&\leq 1 + E[|X|^m] < \infty,
\end{aligned}
\tag{1.10.1}
$$

which is the the desired result. ∎

Theorem 1.10.2 (Markov's Inequality). *Let $u(X)$ be a nonnegative function of the random variable X. If $E[u(X)]$ exists, then for every positive constant c,*

$$
P[u(X) \geq c] \leq \frac{E[u(X)]}{c}.
$$

Proof. The proof is given when the random variable X is of the continuous type; but the proof can be adapted to the discrete case if we replace integrals by sums. Let $A = \{x : u(x) \geq c\}$ and let $f(x)$ denote the pdf of X. Then

$$
E[u(X)] = \int_{-\infty}^{\infty} u(x) f(x)\, dx = \int_A u(x) f(x)\, dx + \int_{A^c} u(x) f(x)\, dx.
$$

Since each of the integrals in the extreme right-hand member of the preceding equation is nonnegative, the left-hand member is greater than or equal to either of them. In particular,

$$
E[u(X)] \geq \int_A u(x) f(x)\, dx.
$$

However, if $x \in A$, then $u(x) \geq c$; accordingly, the right-hand member of the preceding inequality is not increased if we replace $u(x)$ by c. Thus

$$
E[u(X)] \geq c \int_A f(x)\, dx.
$$

Since

$$
\int_A f(x)\, dx = P(X \in A) = P[u(X) \geq c],
$$

it follows that

$$E[u(X)] \geq cP[u(X) \geq c],$$

which is the desired result. ∎

The preceding theorem is a generalization of an inequality that is often called *Chebyshev's Inequality*. This inequality we now establish.

Theorem 1.10.3 (Chebyshev's Inequality). *Let the random variable X have a distribution of probability about which we assume only that there is a finite variance σ^2 [by Theorem 1.10.1, this implies the mean $\mu = E(X)$ exists]. Then for every $k > 0$,*

$$P(|X - \mu| \geq k\sigma) \leq \frac{1}{k^2}, \tag{1.10.2}$$

or, equivalently,

$$P(|X - \mu| < k\sigma) \geq 1 - \frac{1}{k^2}.$$

Proof. In Theorem 1.10.2 take $u(X) = (X - \mu)^2$ and $c = k^2\sigma^2$. Then we have

$$P[(X - \mu)^2 \geq k^2\sigma^2] \leq \frac{E[(X - \mu)^2]}{k^2\sigma^2}.$$

Since the numerator of the right-hand member of the preceding inequality is σ^2, the inequality may be written

$$P(|X - \mu| \geq k\sigma) \leq \frac{1}{k^2},$$

which is the desired result. Naturally, we would take the positive number k to be greater than 1 to have an inequality of interest. ∎

Hence, the number $1/k^2$ is an upper bound for the probability $P(|X - \mu| \geq k\sigma)$. In the following example this upper bound and the exact value of the probability are compared in special instances.

Example 1.10.1. Let X have the pdf

$$f(x) = \begin{cases} \frac{1}{2\sqrt{3}} & -\sqrt{3} < x < \sqrt{3} \\ 0 & \text{elsewhere.} \end{cases}$$

Here $\mu = 0$ and $\sigma^2 = 1$. If $k = \frac{3}{2}$, we have the exact probability

$$P(|X - \mu| \geq k\sigma) = P\left(|X| \geq \frac{3}{2}\right) = 1 - \int_{-3/2}^{3/2} \frac{1}{2\sqrt{3}} \, dx = 1 - \frac{\sqrt{3}}{2}.$$

By Chebyshev's inequality, this probability has the upper bound $1/k^2 = \frac{4}{9}$. Since $1 - \sqrt{3}/2 = 0.134$, approximately, the exact probability in this case is considerably less than the upper bound $\frac{4}{9}$. If we take $k = 2$, we have the exact probability $P(|X - \mu| \geq 2\sigma) = P(|X| \geq 2) = 0$. This again is considerably less than the upper bound $1/k^2 = \frac{1}{4}$ provided by Chebyshev's inequality. ∎

In each of the instances in Example 1.10.1, the probability $P(|X - \mu| \geq k\sigma)$ and its upper bound $1/k^2$ differ considerably. This suggests that this inequality might be made sharper. However, if we want an inequality that holds for every $k > 0$ and holds for all random variables having a finite variance, such an improvement is impossible, as is shown by the following example.

Example 1.10.2. Let the random variable X of the discrete type have probabilities $\frac{1}{8}, \frac{6}{8}, \frac{1}{8}$ at the points $x = -1, 0, 1$, respectively. Here $\mu = 0$ and $\sigma^2 = \frac{1}{4}$. If $k = 2$, then $1/k^2 = \frac{1}{4}$ and $P(|X - \mu| \geq k\sigma) = P(|X| \geq 1) = \frac{1}{4}$. That is, the probability $P(|X - \mu| \geq k\sigma)$ here attains the upper bound $1/k^2 = \frac{1}{4}$. Hence the inequality cannot be improved without further assumptions about the distribution of X. ∎

A convenient form of Chebyshev's Inequality is found by taking $k\sigma = \epsilon$ for $\epsilon > 0$. Then Equation (1.10.2) becomes

$$P(|X - \mu| \geq \epsilon) \leq \frac{\sigma^2}{\epsilon^2}, \quad \text{for all } \epsilon > 0 . \tag{1.10.3}$$

The second inequality of this section involves convex functions.

Definition 1.10.1. *A function ϕ defined on an interval (a, b), $-\infty \leq a < b \leq \infty$, is said to be a* **convex** *function if for all x, y in (a, b) and for all $0 < \gamma < 1$,*

$$\phi[\gamma x + (1 - \gamma)y] \leq \gamma \phi(x) + (1 - \gamma)\phi(y). \tag{1.10.4}$$

We say ϕ is **strictly convex** *if the above inequality is strict.*

Depending on the existence of first or second derivatives of ϕ, the following theorem can be proved.

Theorem 1.10.4. *If ϕ is differentiable on (a, b), then*

(a) *ϕ is convex if and only if $\phi'(x) \leq \phi'(y)$, for all $a < x < y < b$,*

(b) *ϕ is strictly convex if and only if $\phi'(x) < \phi'(y)$, for all $a < x < y < b$.*

If ϕ is twice differentiable on (a, b), then

(a) *ϕ is convex if and only if $\phi''(x) \geq 0$, for all $a < x < b$,*

(b) *ϕ is strictly convex if $\phi''(x) > 0$, for all $a < x < b$.*

Of course, the second part of this theorem follows immediately from the first part. While the first part appeals to one's intuition, the proof of it can be found in most analysis books; see, for instance, Hewitt and Stromberg (1965). A very useful probability inequality follows from convexity.

Theorem 1.10.5 (Jensen's Inequality). *If ϕ is convex on an open interval I and X is a random variable whose support is contained in I and has finite expectation, then*

$$\phi[E(X)] \leq E[\phi(X)]. \tag{1.10.5}$$

If ϕ is strictly convex, then the inequality is strict unless X is a constant random variable.

Proof: For our proof we assume that ϕ has a second derivative, but in general only convexity is required. Expand $\phi(x)$ into a Taylor series about $\mu = E[X]$ of order 2:

$$\phi(x) = \phi(\mu) + \phi'(\mu)(x - \mu) + \frac{\phi''(\zeta)(x - \mu)^2}{2},$$

where ζ is between x and μ. Because the last term on the right side of the above equation is nonnegative, we have

$$\phi(x) \geq \phi(\mu) + \phi'(\mu)(x - \mu).$$

Taking expectations of both sides leads to the result. The inequality is strict if $\phi''(x) > 0$, for all $x \in (a, b)$, provided X is not a constant. ∎

Example 1.10.3. Let X be a nondegenerate random variable with mean μ and a finite second moment. Then $\mu^2 < E(X^2)$. This is obtained by Jensen's inequality using the strictly convex function $\phi(t) = t^2$. ∎

The last inequality concerns different means of finite sets of positive numbers.

Example 1.10.4 (Harmonic and Geometric Means). Let $\{a_1, \ldots, a_n\}$ be a set of positive numbers. Create a distribution for a random variable X by placing weight $1/n$ on each of the numbers $a_1, \ldots, a_n$. Then the mean of X is the *arithmetic mean*, (AM), $E(X) = n^{-1} \sum_{i=1}^n a_i$. Then, since $-\log x$ is a convex function, we have by Jensen's inequality that

$$-\log\left(\frac{1}{n} \sum_{i=1}^n a_i\right) \leq E(-\log X) = -\frac{1}{n} \sum_{i=1}^n \log a_i = -\log(a_1 a_2 \cdots a_n)^{1/n}$$

or, equivalently,

$$\log\left(\frac{1}{n} \sum_{i=1}^n a_i\right) \geq \log(a_1 a_2 \cdots a_n)^{1/n},$$

and, hence,

$$(a_1 a_2 \cdots a_n)^{1/n} \leq \frac{1}{n} \sum_{i=1}^n a_i. \tag{1.10.6}$$

The quantity on the left side of this inequality is called the *geometric mean* (GM). So (1.10.6) is equivalent to saying that GM $\leq$ AM for any finite set of positive numbers.

Now in (1.10.6) replace a_i by $1/a_i$ (which is also positive). We then obtain

$$\frac{1}{n} \sum_{i=1}^n \frac{1}{a_i} \geq \left(\frac{1}{a_1} \frac{1}{a_2} \cdots \frac{1}{a_n}\right)^{1/n}$$

or, equivalently,

$$\frac{1}{\frac{1}{n} \sum_{i=1}^n \frac{1}{a_i}} \leq (a_1 a_2 \cdots a_n)^{1/n}. \tag{1.10.7}$$

The left member of this inequality is called the *harmonic mean* (HM). Putting (1.10.6) and (1.10.7) together, we have shown the relationship

$$HM \leq GM \leq AM, \tag{1.10.8}$$

for any finite set of positive numbers. ∎

EXERCISES

1.10.1. Let X be a random variable with mean μ and let $E[(X - \mu)^{2k}]$ exist. Show, with $d > 0$, that $P(|X - \mu| \geq d) \leq E[(X - \mu)^{2k}]/d^{2k}$. This is essentially Chebyshev's inequality when $k = 1$. The fact that this holds for all $k = 1, 2, 3, \ldots$, when those $(2k)$th moments exist, usually provides a much smaller upper bound for $P(|X - \mu| \geq d)$ than does Chebyshev's result.

1.10.2. Let X be a random variable such that $P(X \leq 0) = 0$ and let $\mu = E(X)$ exist. Show that $P(X \geq 2\mu) \leq \frac{1}{2}$.

1.10.3. If X is a random variable such that $E(X) = 3$ and $E(X^2) = 13$, use Chebyshev's inequality to determine a lower bound for the probability $P(-2 < X < 8)$.

1.10.4. Let X be a random variable with mgf $M(t)$, $-h < t < h$. Prove that

$$P(X \geq a) \leq e^{-at}M(t), \quad 0 < t < h,$$

and that

$$P(X \leq a) \leq e^{-at}M(t), \quad -h < t < 0.$$

Hint: Let $u(x) = e^{tx}$ and $c = e^{ta}$ in Theorem 1.10.2. *Note:* These results imply that $P(X \geq a)$ and $P(X \leq a)$ are less than or equal to their respective least upper bounds for $e^{-at}M(t)$ when $0 < t < h$ and when $-h < t < 0$.

1.10.5. The mgf of X exists for all real values of t and is given by

$$M(t) = \frac{e^t - e^{-t}}{2t}, \quad t \neq 0, \quad M(0) = 1.$$

Use the results of the preceding exercise to show that $P(X \geq 1) = 0$ and $P(X \leq -1) = 0$. Note that here h is infinite.

1.10.6. Let X be a positive random variable; i.e., $P(X \leq 0) = 0$. Argue that

(a) $E(1/X) \geq 1/E(X)$

(b) $E[-\log X] \geq -\log[E(X)]$

(c) $E[\log(1/X)] \geq \log[1/E(X)]$

(d) $E[X^3] \geq [E(X)]^3$.

Chapter 2

Multivariate Distributions

2.1 Distributions of Two Random Variables

We begin the discussion of a pair of random variables with the following example. A coin is tossed three times and our interest is in the ordered number pair (number of H's on first two tosses, number of H's on all three tosses), where H and T represent, respectively, heads and tails. Let $\mathcal{C} = \{TTT, TTH, THT, HTT, THH, HTH, HHT, HHH\}$ denote the sample space. Let X_1 denote the number of H's on the first two tosses and X_2 denote the number of H's on all three flips. Then our interest can be represented by the pair of random variables (X_1, X_2). For example, $(X_1(HTH), X_2(HTH))$ represents the outcome $(1, 2)$. Continuing in this way, X_1 and X_2 are real-valued functions defined on the sample space $\mathcal{C}$, which take us from the sample space to the space of ordered number pairs.

$$\mathcal{D} = \{(0, 0), (0, 1), (1, 1), (1, 2), (2, 2), (2, 3)\}.$$

Thus X_1 and X_2 are two random variables defined on the space $\mathcal{C}$, and, in this example, the space of these random variables is the two-dimensional set $\mathcal{D}$, which is a subset of two-dimensional Euclidean space R^2. Hence (X_1, X_2) is a vector function from $\mathcal{C}$ to $\mathcal{D}$. We now formulate the definition of a random vector.

Definition 2.1.1 (Random Vector). *Given a random experiment with a sample space $\mathcal{C}$, consider two random variables X_1 and X_2, which assign to each element c of $\mathcal{C}$ one and only one ordered pair of numbers $X_1(c) = x_1$, $X_2(c) = x_2$. Then we say that (X_1, X_2) is a* **random vector**. *The* **space** *of (X_1, X_2) is the set of ordered pairs $\mathcal{D} = \{(x_1, x_2) : x_1 = X_1(c), x_2 = X_2(c), c \in \mathcal{C}\}$.*

We often denote random vectors using vector notation $\mathbf{X} = (X_1, X_2)'$, where the $'$ denotes the transpose of the row vector (X_1, X_2).

Let $\mathcal{D}$ be the space associated with the random vector (X_1, X_2). Let A be a subset of $\mathcal{D}$. As in the case of one random variable, we speak of the event A. We wish to define the probability of the event A, which we denote by $P_{X_1, X_2}[A]$. As with random variables in Section 1.5 we can uniquely define P_{X_1,X_2} in terms of the **cumulative distribution function** (cdf), which is given by

$$F_{X_1,X_2}(x_1,x_2) = P[\{X_1 \le x_1\} \cap \{X_2 \le x_2\}], \tag{2.1.1}$$

for all $(x_1,x_2) \in R^2$. Because X_1 and X_2 are random variables, each of the events in the above intersection and the intersection of the events are events in the original sample space $\mathcal{C}$. Thus the expression is well defined. As with random variables, we write $P[\{X_1 \le x_1\} \cap \{X_2 \le x_2\}]$ as $P[X_1 \le x_1, X_2 \le x_2]$. As Exercise 2.1.3 shows,

$$\begin{aligned} P[a_1 < X_1 \le b_1, a_2 < X_2 \le b_2] &= F_{X_1,X_2}(b_1,b_2) - F_{X_1,X_2}(a_1,b_2) \\ &\quad -F_{X_1,X_2}(b_1,a_2) + F_{X_1,X_2}(a_1,a_2). \end{aligned} \tag{2.1.2}$$

Hence, all induced probabilities of sets of the form $(a_1,b_1] \times (a_2,b_2]$ can be formulated in terms of the cdf. We often call this cdf the **joint cumulative distribution function** of (X_1, X_2).

As with random variables, we are mainly concerned with two types of random vectors, namely discrete and continuous. We first discuss the discrete type.

A random vector (X_1, X_2) is a **discrete random vector** if its space $\mathcal{D}$ is finite or countable. Hence, X_1 and X_2 are both discrete also. The **joint probability mass function** (pmf) of (X_1, X_2) is defined by

$$p_{X_1,X_2}(x_1,x_2) = P[X_1 = x_1, X_2 = x_2], \tag{2.1.3}$$

for all $(x_1,x_2) \in \mathcal{D}$. As with random variables, the pmf uniquely defines the cdf. It also is characterized by the two properties

$$\text{(i) } 0 \le p_{X_1,X_2}(x_1,x_2) \le 1 \text{ and (ii) } \sum_{\mathcal{D}}\sum p_{X_1,X_2}(x_1,x_2) = 1. \tag{2.1.4}$$

For an event $B \in \mathcal{D}$, we have

$$P[(X_1,X_2) \in B] = \sum_{B}\sum p_{X_1,X_2}(x_1,x_2).$$

Example 2.1.1. Consider the discrete random vector (X_1, X_2) defined in the example at the beginning of this section. We can conveniently table its pmf as

	Support of X_2			
	0	1	2	3
Support of X_1 0	$\frac{1}{8}$	$\frac{1}{8}$	0	0
1	0	$\frac{2}{8}$	$\frac{2}{8}$	0
2	0	0	$\frac{1}{8}$	$\frac{1}{8}$

At times it is convenient to speak of the **support** of a discrete random vector (X_1, X_2). These are all the points (x_1,x_2) in the space of (X_1, X_2) such that $p(x_1, x_2) > 0$. In the last example the support consists of the six points $\{(0,0), (0,1), (1,1), (1,2), (2,2), (2,3)\}$.

We say a random vector (X_1, X_2) with space $\mathcal{D}$ is of the **continuous** type if its cdf $F_{X_1, X_2}(x_1, x_2)$ is continuous. For the most part, the continuous random vectors in this book have cdfs which can be represented as integrals of nonnegative functions. That is, $F_{X_1, X_2}(x_1, x_2)$ can be expressed as

$$F_{X_1, X_2}(x_1, x_2) = \int_{-\infty}^{x_1} \int_{-\infty}^{x_2} f_{X_1, X_2}(w_1, w_2)\, dw_1 dw_2, \tag{2.1.5}$$

for all $(x_1, x_2) \in R^2$. We call the integrand the **joint probability density function** (pdf) of (X_1, X_2). Then

$$\frac{\partial^2 F_{X_1, X_2}(x_1, x_2)}{\partial x_1\, \partial x_2} = f_{X_1, X_2}(x_1, x_2),$$

except possibly on events which have probability zero. A pdf is essentially characterized by the two properties

(i) $f_{X_1, X_2}(x_1, x_2) \geq 0$ and (ii) $\int \int_{\mathcal{D}} f_{X_1, X_2}(x_1, x_2)\, dx_1 dx_2 = 1.$ \qquad (2.1.6)

For an event $A \in \mathcal{D}$, we have

$$P[(X_1, X_2) \in A] = \int \int_A f_{X_1, X_2}(x_1, x_2)\, dx_1 dx_2.$$

Note that the $P[(X_1, X_2) \in A]$ is just the volume under the surface $z = f_{X_1, X_2}(x_1, x_2)$ over the set A.

Remark 2.1.1. As with univariate random variables, we often drop the subscript (X_1, X_2) from joint cdfs, pdfs, and pmfs, when it is clear from the context. We also use notation such as f_{12} instead of f_{X_1, X_2}. Besides (X_1, X_2), we often use (X, Y) to express random vectors. ∎

Example 2.1.2. Let

$$f(x_1, x_2) = \begin{cases} 6x_1^2 x_2 & 0 < x_1 < 1, \ 0 < x_2 < 1 \\ 0 & \text{elsewhere} \end{cases}$$

be the pdf of two random variables X_1 and X_2 of the continuous type. We have, for instance,

$$\begin{aligned} P(0 < X_1 < \tfrac{3}{4}, \tfrac{1}{3} < X_2 < 2) &= \int_{1/3}^{2} \int_{0}^{3/4} f(x_1, x_2)\, dx_1 dx_2 \\ &= \int_{1/3}^{1} \int_{0}^{3/4} 6x_1^2 x_2\, dx_1 dx_2 + \int_{1}^{2} \int_{0}^{3/4} 0\, dx_1 dx_2 \\ &= \tfrac{3}{8} + 0 = \tfrac{3}{8}. \end{aligned}$$

Note that this probability is the volume under the surface $f(x_1, x_2) = 6x_1^2 x_2$ above the rectangular set $\{(x_1, x_2) : 0 < x_1 < \tfrac{3}{4}, \tfrac{1}{3} < x_2 < 1\} \in R^2$. ∎

For a continuous random vector (X_1, X_2), the **support** of (X_1, X_2) contains all points (x_1, x_2) for which $f(x_1, x_2) > 0$. We denote the support of a random vector by $\mathcal{S}$. As in the univariate case, $\mathcal{S} \subset \mathcal{D}$.

We may extend the definition of a pdf $f_{X_1, X_2}(x_1, x_2)$ over R^2 by using zero elsewhere. We do this consistently so that tedious, repetitious references to the space $\mathcal{D}$ can be avoided. Once this is done, we replace

$$\iint_{\mathcal{D}} f_{X_1, X_2}(x_1, x_2) \, dx_1 dx_2 \quad \text{by} \quad \int_{-\infty}^{\infty} \int_{-\infty}^{\infty} f(x_1, x_2) \, dx_1 \, dx_2.$$

Likewise we may extend the pmf $p_{X_1, X_2}(x_1, x_2)$ over a convenient set by using zero elsewhere. Hence, we replace

$$\sum_{\mathcal{D}} \sum p_{X_1, X_2}(x_1, x_2) \quad \text{by} \quad \sum_{x_2} \sum_{x_1} p(x_1, x_2).$$

Finally, if a pmf or a pdf in one or more variables is explicitly defined, we can see by inspection whether the random variables are of the continuous or discrete type. For example, it seems obvious that

$$p(x, y) = \begin{cases} \frac{9}{4^{x+y}} & x = 1, 2, 3, \ldots, \quad y = 1, 2, 3, \ldots \\ 0 & \text{elsewhere} \end{cases}$$

is a pmf of two discrete-type random variables X and Y, whereas

$$f(x, y) = \begin{cases} 4xy e^{-x^2 - y^2} & 0 < x < \infty, \ 0 < y < \infty \\ 0 & \text{elsewhere} \end{cases}$$

is clearly a pdf of two continuous-type random variables X and Y. In such cases it seems unnecessary to specify which of the two simpler types of random variables is under consideration.

Let (X_1, X_2) be a random vector. Then both X_1 and X_2 are random variables. We can obtain their distributions in terms of the joint distribution of (X_1, X_2) as follows. Recall that the event which defined the cdf of X_1 at x_1 is $\{X_1 \leq x_1\}$. However,

$$\{X_1 \leq x_1\} = \{X_1 \leq x_1\} \cap \{-\infty < X_2 < \infty\} = \{X_1 \leq x_1, -\infty < X_2 < \infty\}.$$

Taking probabilities, we have

$$F_{X_1}(x_1) = P[X_1 \leq x_1, -\infty < X_2 < \infty], \tag{2.1.7}$$

for all $x_1 \in R$. By Theorem 1.3.6 we can write this equation as $F_{X_1}(x_1) = \lim_{x_2 \uparrow \infty} F(x_1, x_2)$. Thus we have a relationship between the cdfs, which we can extend to either the pmf or pdf depending on whether (X_1, X_2) is discrete or continuous.

First consider the discrete case. Let $\mathcal{D}_{X_1}$ be the support of X_1. For $x_1 \in \mathcal{D}_{X_1}$, Equation (2.1.7) is equivalent to

$$F_{X_1}(x_1) = \sum_{w_1 \leq x_1, -\infty < x_2 < \infty} \sum p_{X_1, X_2}(w_1, x_2) = \sum_{w_1 \leq x_1} \left\{ \sum_{x_2 < \infty} p_{X_1, X_2}(w_1, x_2) \right\}.$$

$\searrow p_{X_1}(x_1)$

By the uniqueness of cdfs, the quantity in braces must be the pmf of X_1 evaluated at w_1; that is,

$$p_{X_1}(x_1) = \sum_{x_2 < \infty} p_{X_1, X_2}(x_1, x_2), \tag{2.1.8}$$

for all $x_1 \in \mathcal{D}_{X_1}$.

Note what this says. To find the probability that X_1 is x_1, keep x_1 fixed and sum p_{X_1, X_2} over all of x_2. In terms of a tabled joint pmf with rows comprised of X_1 support values and columns comprised of X_2 support values, this says that the distribution of X_1 can be obtained by the marginal sums of the rows. Likewise, the pmf of X_2 can be obtained by marginal sums of the columns. For example, consider the joint distribution discussed in Example 2.1.1. We have added these marginal sums to the table:

		\multicolumn{4}{c}{Support of X_2}	
		0	1	2	3	$p_{X_1}(x_1)$
Support of X_1	0	$\frac{1}{8}$	$\frac{1}{8}$	0	0	$\frac{2}{8}$
	1	0	$\frac{2}{8}$	$\frac{2}{8}$	0	$\frac{4}{8}$
	2	0	0	$\frac{1}{8}$	$\frac{1}{8}$	$\frac{2}{8}$
	$p_{X_2}(x_2)$	$\frac{1}{8}$	$\frac{3}{8}$	$\frac{3}{8}$	$\frac{1}{8}$	

Hence, the final row of this table is the pmf of X_2, while the final column is the pmf of X_1. In general, because these distributions are recorded in the margins of the table, we often refer to them as **marginal** pmfs.

Example 2.1.3. Consider a random experiment that consists of drawing at random one chip from a bowl containing 10 chips of the same shape and size. Each chip has an ordered pair of numbers on it: one with $(1, 1)$, one with $(2, 1)$, two with $(3, 1)$, one with $(1, 2)$, two with $(2, 2)$, and three with $(3, 2)$. Let the random variables X_1 and X_2 be defined as the respective first and second values of the ordered pair. Thus the joint pmf $p(x_1, x_2)$ of X_1 and X_2 can be given by the following table, with $p(x_1, x_2)$ equal to zero elsewhere.

x_1	\multicolumn{2}{c}{x_2}		
	1	2	$p_1(x_1)$
1	$\frac{1}{10}$	$\frac{1}{10}$	$\frac{2}{10}$
2	$\frac{1}{10}$	$\frac{2}{10}$	$\frac{3}{10}$
3	$\frac{2}{10}$	$\frac{3}{10}$	$\frac{5}{10}$
$p_2(x_2)$	$\frac{4}{10}$	$\frac{6}{10}$	

The joint probabilities have been summed in each row and each column and these sums recorded in the margins to give the marginal probability mass functions of X_1

and X_2, respectively. Note that it is not necessary to have a formula for $p(x_1, x_2)$ to do this. ∎

We next consider the continuous case. Let $\mathcal{D}_{X_1}$ be the support of X_1. For $x_1 \in \mathcal{D}_{X_1}$, Equation (2.1.7) is equivalent to

$$F_{X_1}(x_1) = \int_{-\infty}^{x_1} \int_{-\infty}^{\infty} f_{X_1,X_2}(w_1, x_2)\, dx_2 dw_1 = \int_{-\infty}^{x_1} \left\{ \int_{-\infty}^{\infty} f_{X_1,X_2}(w_1, x_2)\, dx_2 \right\} dw_1.$$

By the uniqueness of cdfs, the quantity in braces must be the pdf of X_1, evaluated at w_1; that is,

$$f_{X_1}(x_1) = \int_{-\infty}^{\infty} f_{X_1,X_2}(x_1, x_2)\, dx_2 \tag{2.1.9}$$

for all $x_1 \in \mathcal{D}_{X_1}$. Hence, in the continuous case the marginal pdf of X_1 is found by integrating out x_2. Similarly, the marginal pdf of X_2 is found by integrating out x_1.

Example 2.1.4. Let X_1 and X_2 have the joint pdf

$$f(x_1, x_2) = \begin{cases} x_1 + x_2 & 0 < x_1 < 1, \ 0 < x_2 < 1 \\ 0 & \text{elsewhere.} \end{cases}$$

The marginal pdf of X_1 is

$$f_1(x_1) = \int_0^1 (x_1 + x_2)\, dx_2 = x_1 + \tfrac{1}{2}, \quad 0 < x_1 < 1,$$

zero elsewhere, and the marginal pdf of X_2 is

$$f_2(x_2) = \int_0^1 (x_1 + x_2)\, dx_1 = \tfrac{1}{2} + x_2, \quad 0 < x_2 < 1,$$

zero elsewhere. A probability like $P(X_1 \leq \tfrac{1}{2})$ can be computed from either $f_1(x_1)$ or $f(x_1, x_2)$ because

$$\int_0^{1/2} \int_0^1 f(x_1, x_2)\, dx_2 dx_1 = \int_0^{1/2} f_1(x_1)\, dx_1 = \tfrac{3}{8}.$$

However, to find a probability like $P(X_1 + X_2 \leq 1)$, we must use the joint pdf $f(x_1, x_2)$ as follows:

$$\int_0^1 \int_0^{1-x_1} (x_1 + x_2)\, dx_2 dx_1 = \int_0^1 \left[x_1(1 - x_1) + \frac{(1 - x_1)^2}{2} \right] dx_1$$

$$= \int_0^1 \left(\frac{1}{2} - \frac{1}{2} x_1^2 \right) dx_1 = \frac{1}{3}.$$

This latter probability is the volume under the surface $f(x_1, x_2) = x_1 + x_2$ above the set $\{(x_1, x_2) : 0 < x_1, \ x_1 + x_2 \leq 1\}$. ∎

2.1.1 Expectation

The concept of expectation extends in a straightforward manner. Let (X_1, X_2) be a random vector and let $Y = g(X_1, X_2)$ for some real-valued function; i.e., $g : R^2 \to R$. Then Y is a random variable and we could determine its expectation by obtaining the distribution of Y. But Theorem 1.8.1 is true for random vectors also. Note the proof we gave for this theorem involved the discrete case, and Exercise 2.1.11 shows its extension to the random vector case.

Suppose (X_1, X_2) is of the continuous type. Then $E(Y)$ exists if

$$\int_{-\infty}^{\infty} \int_{-\infty}^{\infty} |g(x_1, x_2)| f_{X_1, X_2}(x_1, x_2)\, dx_1 dx_2 < \infty.$$

Then

$$E(Y) = \int_{-\infty}^{\infty} \int_{-\infty}^{\infty} g(x_1, x_2) f_{X_1, X_2}(x_1, x_2)\, dx_1 dx_2. \qquad (2.1.10)$$

Likewise if (X_1, X_2) is discrete, then $E(Y)$ exists if

$$\sum_{x_1} \sum_{x_2} |g(x_1, x_2)| p_{X_1, X_2}(x_1, x_2) < \infty.$$

Then

$$E(Y) = \sum_{x_1} \sum_{x_2} g(x_1, x_2) p_{X_1, X_2}(x_1, x_2). \qquad (2.1.11)$$

We can now show that E is a linear operator.

Theorem 2.1.1. *Let (X_1, X_2) be a random vector. Let $Y_1 = g_1(X_1, X_2)$ and $Y_2 = g_2(X_1, X_2)$ be random variables whose expectations exist. Then for all real numbers k_1 and k_2,*

$$E(k_1 Y_1 + k_2 Y_2) = k_1 E(Y_1) + k_2 E(Y_2). \qquad (2.1.12)$$

Proof: We prove it for the continuous case. The existence of the expected value of $k_1 Y_1 + k_2 Y_2$ follows directly from the triangle inequality and linearity of integrals; i.e.,

$$\int_{-\infty}^{\infty} \int_{-\infty}^{\infty} |k_1 g_1(x_1, x_2) + k_2 g_1(x_1, x_2)| f_{X_1, X_2}(x_1, x_2)\, dx_1 dx_2$$

$$\leq |k_1| \int_{-\infty}^{\infty} \int_{-\infty}^{\infty} |g_1(x_1, x_2)| f_{X_1, X_2}(x_1, x_2)\, dx_1 dx_2$$

$$+ |k_2| \int_{-\infty}^{\infty} \int_{-\infty}^{\infty} |g_2(x_1, x_2)| f_{X_1, X_2}(x_1, x_2)\, dx_1 dx_2 < \infty.$$

By once again using linearity of the integral, we have

$$
\begin{aligned}
E(k_1 Y_1 + k_2 Y_2) &= \int_{-\infty}^{\infty} \int_{-\infty}^{\infty} [k_1 g_1(x_1, x_2) + k_2 g_2(x_1, x_2)] f_{X_1, X_2}(x_1, x_2) \, dx_1 dx_2 \\
&= k_1 \int_{-\infty}^{\infty} \int_{-\infty}^{\infty} g_1(x_1, x_2) f_{X_1, X_2}(x_1, x_2) \, dx_1 dx_2 \\
&\quad + k_2 \int_{-\infty}^{\infty} \int_{-\infty}^{\infty} g_2(x_1, x_2) f_{X_1, X_2}(x_1, x_2) \, dx_1 dx_2 \\
&= k_1 E(Y_1) + k_2 E(Y_2),
\end{aligned}
$$

i.e., the desired result. ∎

We also note that the expected value of any function $g(X_2)$ of X_2 can be found in two ways:

$$
E(g(X_2)) = \int_{-\infty}^{\infty} \int_{-\infty}^{\infty} g(x_2) f(x_1, x_2) \, dx_1 dx_2 = \int_{-\infty}^{\infty} g(x_2) f_{X_2}(x_2) \, dx_2,
$$

the latter single integral being obtained from the double integral by integrating on x_1 first. The following example illustrates these ideas.

Example 2.1.5. Let X_1 and X_2 have the pdf

$$
f(x_1, x_2) = \begin{cases} 8x_1 x_2 & 0 < x_1 < x_2 < 1 \\ 0 & \text{elsewhere.} \end{cases}
$$

Then

$$
\begin{aligned}
E(X_1 X_2^2) &= \int_{-\infty}^{\infty} \int_{-\infty}^{\infty} x_1 x_2^2 f(x_1, x_2) \, dx_1 dx_2 \\
&= \int_0^1 \int_0^{x_2} 8x_1^2 x_2^3 \, dx_1 dx_2 \\
&= \int_0^1 \tfrac{8}{3} x_2^6 \, dx_2 = \tfrac{8}{21}.
\end{aligned}
$$

In addition,

$$
E(X_2) = \int_0^1 \int_0^{x_2} x_2(8x_1 x_2) \, dx_1 dx_2 = \tfrac{4}{5}.
$$

Since X_2 has the pdf $f_2(x_2) = 4x_2^3$, $0 < x_2 < 1$, zero elsewhere, the latter expectation can be found by

$$
E(X_2) = \int_0^1 x_2(4x_2^3) \, dx_2 = \tfrac{4}{5}.
$$

Thus

$$
\begin{aligned}
E(7X_1 X_2^2 + 5X_2) &= 7E(X_1 X_2^2) + 5E(X_2) \\
&= (7)(\tfrac{8}{21}) + (5)(\tfrac{4}{5}) = \tfrac{20}{3}. \quad \blacksquare
\end{aligned}
$$

(Handwritten annotations)

X_2取值方向 值方向

$\diamondsuit\ Y = g_1(x_1, x_2) = x_1 x_2^2 \Rightarrow E(y) = E(g_1(x_1,x_2)) = \iint g_1(x_1,x_2) f(x_1,x_2)\, dx_1 dx_2.$

$X_2 > X_1$ $X_2 = X_1$ $X_2 < X_1$

$E(X_1 X_2^2)$
$= \int_0^1 dx_1 \int_{x_1} g_1 \cdot f\, dx_2$
$\overset{\text{或}}{=} \int_0^1 dx_2 \int_0^{x_2} g_1 \cdot f\, dx_1$

X_1的取值 方向 $= (0 \to x_2)$

计算 $E(X_2)$ 有两法,

法一: 令 $y = g_2(x_1, x_2) = x_2$
$\Rightarrow E(x_2) = E(g_2) = \iint g_2 \cdot f\, dx_1 dx_2$
$= \iint x_2 \cdot f\, dx_1 dx_2.$

法二: 先计算 $f_2(x_2) = \int_{-\infty}^{+\infty} f(x_1, x_2)\, dx_1.$
再利用公式 $E(x_2) = \int x_2 \cdot f_2(x_2)\, dx_2$

$f_2(x_2) = \int_{-\infty}^{+\infty} f_{12}\, dx_1 = \int_0^{x_2} 8x_1 x_2\, dx_1 = 4x_2 \cdot x_1^2 \big|_0^{x_2} = 4x_2^3.$

X_1的取值方向 为从0到 x_2.

另一种方法求 $E(7X_1 X_2^2 + 5X_2)$:

令 $y = 7x_1 x_2^2 + 5x_2 = g_3(x_1, x_2)$

则 $E(y) = \iint g_3 \cdot f_{12}\, dx_1 dx_2 = \int_0^1 dx_2 \int_0^{x_2} (7x_1 x_2^2 + 5x_2) \cdot 8x_1 x_2\, dx_1$
$= \int_0^1 8 \cdot (\tfrac{7}{3} x_2^6 + \tfrac{5}{2} x_2^4)\, dx_2$
$= \tfrac{20}{3}$

Example 2.1.6. Continuing with Example 2.1.5, suppose the random variable Y is defined by $Y = X_1/X_2$. We determine $E(Y)$ in two ways. The first way is by definition; i.e., find the distribution of Y and then determine its expectation. The cdf of Y, for $0 < y \le 1$, is

$$F_Y(y) = P(Y \le y) = P(X_1 \le yX_2) = \int_0^1 \int_0^{yx_2} 8x_1 x_2 \, dx_1 dx_2$$

$$= \int_0^1 4y^2 x_2^3 \, dx_2 = y^2.$$

Hence, the pdf of Y is

$$f_Y(y) = F_Y'(y) = \begin{cases} 2y & 0 < y < 1 \\ 0 & \text{elsewhere,} \end{cases}$$

which leads to

$$E(Y) = \int_0^1 y(2y) \, dy = \frac{2}{3}.$$

For the second way, we make use of expression (2.1.10) and find $E(Y)$ directly by

$$E(Y) = E\left(\frac{X_1}{X_2}\right) = \int_0^1 \left\{ \int_0^{x_2} \left(\frac{x_1}{x_2}\right) 8x_1 x_2 \, dx_1 \right\} dx_2$$

$$= \int_0^1 \frac{8}{3} x_2^3 \, dx_2 = \frac{2}{3}. \quad \blacksquare$$

We next define the moment generating function of a random vector.

Definition 2.1.2 (Moment Generating Function of a Random Vector). *Let* $\mathbf{X} = (X_1, X_2)'$ *be a random vector. If* $E(e^{t_1 X_1 + t_2 X_2})$ *exists for* $|t_1| < h_1$ *and* $|t_2| < h_2$, *where* h_1 *and* h_2 *are positive, it is denoted by* $M_{X_1, X_2}(t_1, t_2)$ *and is called the* **moment generating function** *(mgf) of* $\mathbf{X}$.

As in the one-variable case, if it exists, the mgf of a random vector uniquely determines the distribution of the random vector.

Let $\mathbf{t} = (t_1, t_2)'$. Then we can write the mgf of $\mathbf{X}$ as

$$M_{X_1, X_2}(\mathbf{t}) = E\left[e^{\mathbf{t}'\mathbf{X}}\right], \tag{2.1.13}$$

so it is quite similar to the mgf of a random variable. Also, the mgfs of X_1 and X_2 are immediately seen to be $M_{X_1, X_2}(t_1, 0)$ and $M_{X_1, X_2}(0, t_2)$, respectively. If there is no confusion, we often drop the subscripts on M.

Example 2.1.7. Let the continuous-type random variables X and Y have the joint pdf

$$f(x, y) = \begin{cases} e^{-y} & 0 < x < y < \infty \\ 0 & \text{elsewhere.} \end{cases}$$

The mgf of this joint distribution is

$$M(t_1, t_2) = \int_0^\infty \int_x^\infty \exp(t_1 x + t_2 y - y)\,dy\,dx$$
$$= \frac{1}{(1 - t_1 - t_2)(1 - t_2)},$$

provided that $t_1 + t_2 < 1$ and $t_2 < 1$. Furthermore, the moment-generating functions of the marginal distributions of X and Y are, respectively,

$$M(t_1, 0) = \frac{1}{1 - t_1}, \quad t_1 < 1$$

$$M(0, t_2) = \frac{1}{(1 - t_2)^2}, \quad t_2 < 1.$$

These moment-generating functions are, of course, respectively, those of the marginal probability density functions,

$$f_1(x) = \int_x^\infty e^{-y}\,dy = e^{-x}, \quad 0 < x < \infty,$$

zero elsewhere, and

$$f_2(y) = e^{-y} \int_0^y dx = y e^{-y}, \quad 0 < y < \infty,$$

zero elsewhere. ■

We also need to define the expected value of the random vector itself, but this is not a new concept because it is defined in terms of componentwise expectation:

Definition 2.1.3 (Expected Value of a Random Vector). *Let $\mathbf{X} = (X_1, X_2)'$ be a random vector. Then the **expected value** of $\mathbf{X}$ exists if the expectations of X_1 and X_2 exist. If it exists, then the **expected value** is given by*

$$E[\mathbf{X}] = \begin{bmatrix} E(X_1) \\ E(X_2) \end{bmatrix}. \tag{2.1.14}$$

EXERCISES

2.1.1. Let $f(x_1, x_2) = 4x_1 x_2$, $0 < x_1 < 1$, $0 < x_2 < 1$, zero elsewhere, be the pdf of X_1 and X_2. Find $P(0 < X_1 < \frac{1}{2}, \frac{1}{4} < X_2 < 1)$, $P(X_1 = X_2)$, $P(X_1 < X_2)$, and $P(X_1 \leq X_2)$.
Hint: Recall that $P(X_1 = X_2)$ would be the volume under the surface $f(x_1, x_2) = 4x_1 x_2$ and above the line segment $0 < x_1 = x_2 < 1$ in the $x_1 x_2$-plane.

2.1.2. Let $A_1 = \{(x, y) : x \leq 2, y \leq 4\}$, $A_2 = \{(x, y) : x \leq 2, y \leq 1\}$, $A_3 = \{(x, y) : x \leq 0, y \leq 4\}$, and $A_4 = \{(x, y) : x \leq 0 \; y \leq 1\}$ be subsets of the space $\mathcal{A}$ of two random variables X and Y, which is the entire two-dimensional plane. If $P(A_1) = \frac{7}{8}$, $P(A_2) = \frac{4}{8}$, $P(A_3) = \frac{3}{8}$, and $P(A_4) = \frac{2}{8}$, find $P(A_5)$, where $A_5 = \{(x, y) : 0 < x \leq 2, 1 < y \leq 4\}$.

2.1.3. Let $F(x, y)$ be the ~~Cumulative~~ distribution function of X and Y. For all real constants $a < b$, $c < d$, show that $P(a < X \leq b, \ c < Y \leq d) = F(b, d) - F(b, c) - F(a, d) + F(a, c)$.

2.1.4. Show that the function $F(x, y)$ that is equal to 1 provided that $x + 2y \geq 1$, and that is equal to zero provided that $x + 2y < 1$, cannot be a distribution function of two random variables.
Hint: Find four numbers $a < b$, $c < d$, so that

$$F(b, d) - F(a, d) - F(b, c) + F(a, c)$$

is less than zero.

$\sqrt{}$**2.1.5.** Given that the nonnegative function $g(x)$ has the property that

$$\int_0^\infty g(x)\, dx = 1,$$

show that

$$f(x_1, x_2) = \frac{2g(\sqrt{x_1^2 + x_2^2})}{\pi \sqrt{x_1^2 + x_2^2}}, \ 0 < x_1 < \infty, 0 < x_2 < \infty,$$

zero elsewhere, satisfies the conditions for a pdf of two continuous-type random variables X_1 and X_2.
Hint: Use polar coordinates.

2.1.6. Let $f(x, y) = e^{-x-y}$, $0 < x < \infty$, $0 < y < \infty$, zero elsewhere, be the pdf of X and Y. Then if $Z = X + Y$, compute $P(Z < 0)$, $P(Z \leq 6)$, and, more generally, $P(Z \leq z)$, for $0 < z < \infty$. What is the pdf of Z?

2.1.7. Let X and Y have the pdf $f(x, y) = 1$, $0 < x < 1$, $0 < y < 1$, zero elsewhere. Find the cdf and pdf of the product $Z = XY$.

2.1.8. Let 13 cards be taken, at random and without replacement, from an ordinary deck of playing cards. If X is the number of spades in these 13 cards, find the pmf of X. If, in addition, Y is the number of hearts in these 13 cards, find the probability $P(X = 2, Y = 5)$. What is the joint pmf of X and Y?

$\sqrt{}$**2.1.9.** Let the random variables X_1 and X_2 have the joint pmf described as follows:

(x_1, x_2)	$(0, 0)$	$(0, 1)$	$(0, 2)$	$(1, 0)$	$(1, 1)$	$(1, 2)$
$p(x_1, x_2)$	$\frac{2}{12}$	$\frac{3}{12}$	$\frac{2}{12}$	$\frac{2}{12}$	$\frac{2}{12}$	$\frac{1}{12}$

and $p(x_1, x_2)$ is equal to zero elsewhere.

(a) Write these probabilities in a rectangular array as in Example 2.1.3, recording each marginal pdf in the "margins."

(b) What is $P(X_1 + X_2 = 1)$?

2.1.10. Let X_1 and X_2 have the joint pdf $f(x_1, x_2) = 15x_1^2 x_2$, $0 < x_1 < x_2 < 1$, zero elsewhere. Find the marginal pdfs and compute $P(X_1 + X_2 \leq 1)$.
Hint: Graph the space X_1 and X_2 and carefully choose the limits of integration in determining each marginal pdf.

2.1.11. Let X_1, X_2 be two random variables with the joint pmf $p(x_1, x_2)$, $(x_1, x_2) \in \mathcal{S}$, where $\mathcal{S}$ is the support of X_1, X_2. Let $Y = g(X_1, X_2)$ be a function such that

$$\sum \sum_{(x_1, x_2) \in \mathcal{S}} |g(x_1, x_2)| p(x_1, x_2) < \infty.$$

By following the proof of Theorem 1.8.1, show that

$$E(Y) = \sum \sum_{(x_1, x_2) \in \mathcal{S}} g(x_1, x_2) p(x_1, x_2) < \infty.$$

2.1.12. Let X_1, X_2 be two random variables with the joint pmf $p(x_1, x_2) = (x_1 + x_2)/12$, for $x_1 = 1, 2$, $x_2 = 1, 2$, zero elsewhere. Compute $E(X_1)$, $E(X_1^2)$, $E(X_2)$, $E(X_2^2)$, and $E(X_1 X_2)$. Is $E(X_1 X_2) = E(X_1)E(X_2)$? Find $E(2X_1 - 6X_2^2 + 7X_1 X_2)$.

2.1.13. Let X_1, X_2 be two random variables with joint pdf $f(x_1, x_2) = 4x_1 x_2$, $0 < x_1 < 1$, $0 < x_2 < 1$, zero elsewhere. Compute $E(X_1)$, $E(X_1^2)$, $E(X_2)$, $E(X_2^2)$, and $E(X_1 X_2)$. Is $E(X_1 X_2) = E(X_1)E(X_2)$? Find $E(3X_2 - 2X_1^2 + 6X_1 X_2)$.

2.1.14. Let X_1, X_2 be two random variables with joint pmf $p(x_1, x_2) = (1/2)^{x_1 + x_2}$, for $1 \leq x_i < \infty, i = 1, 2$, where x_1 and x_2 are integers, zero elsewhere. Determine the joint mgf of X_1, X_2. Show that $M(t_1, t_2) = M(t_1, 0)M(0, t_2)$.

2.1.15. Let X_1, X_2 be two random variables with joint pdf $f(x_1, x_2) = x_1 \exp\{-x_2\}$, for $0 < x_1 < x_2 < \infty$, zero elsewhere. Determine the joint mgf of X_1, X_2. Does $M(t_1, t_2) = M(t_1, 0)M(0, t_2)$?

2.1.16. Let X and Y have the joint pdf $f(x, y) = 6(1 - x - y)$, $x + y < 1$, $0 < x$, $0 < y$, zero elsewhere. Compute $P(2X + 3Y < 1)$ and $E(XY + 2X^2)$.

2.2 Transformations: Bivariate Random Variables

Let (X_1, X_2) be a random vector. Suppose we know the joint distribution of (X_1, X_2) and we seek the distribution of a transformation of (X_1, X_2), say, $Y = g(X_1, X_2)$. We may be able to obtain the cdf of Y. Another way is to use a transformation. We considered transformation theory for random variables in Sections 1.6 and 1.7. In this section, we extend this theory to random vectors. It is best to discuss the discrete and continuous cases separately. We begin with the discrete case.

There are no essential difficulties involved in a problem like the following. Let $p_{X_1, X_2}(x_1, x_2)$ be the joint pmf of two discrete-type random variables X_1 and X_2 with $\mathcal{S}$ the (two-dimensional) set of points at which $p_{X_1, X_2}(x_1, x_2) > 0$; i.e., $\mathcal{S}$ is the support of (X_1, X_2). Let $y_1 = u_1(x_1, x_2)$ and $y_2 = u_2(x_1, x_2)$ define a one-to-one

$$S(\subset \mathbb{R}^2) \to T(\subset \mathbb{R}^2), \quad \begin{pmatrix} x_1 \\ x_2 \end{pmatrix} \longrightarrow \begin{pmatrix} y_1 = u_1(x_1, x_2) \\ y_1 = u_2(x_1, x_2) \end{pmatrix}$$

transformation that maps S onto T. The joint pmf of the two new random variables $Y_1 = u_1(X_1, X_2)$ and $Y_2 = u_2(X_1, X_2)$ is given by

当事件对 (X_1, X_2) 发生时，(Y_1, Y_2) 事件也必

发生. $\Rightarrow P_{Y_1, Y_2}(y_1, y_2) \equiv P_{X_1, X_2}(x_1, x_2)$.

$$p_{Y_1, Y_2}(y_1, y_2) = \begin{cases} p_{X_1, X_2}[\underbrace{w_1(y_1, y_2)}_{=x_1}, \underbrace{w_2(y_1, y_2)}_{=x_2}] & (y_1, y_2) \in T \\ 0 & \text{elsewhere}, \end{cases}$$

where $x_1 = w_1(y_1, y_2)$, $x_2 = w_2(y_1, y_2)$ is the single-valued inverse of $y_1 = u_1(x_1, x_2)$, $y_2 = u_2(x_1, x_2)$. From this joint pmf $p_{Y_1, Y_2}(y_1, y_2)$ we may obtain the marginal pmf of Y_1 by summing on y_2 or the marginal pmf of Y_2 by summing on y_1.

In using this change of variable technique, it should be emphasized that we need two "new" variables to replace the two "old" variables. An example helps explain this technique.

Example 2.2.1. Let X_1 and X_2 have the joint pmf

$$p_{X_1, X_2}(x_1, x_2) = \frac{\mu_1^{x_1} \mu_2^{x_2} e^{-\mu_1} e^{-\mu_2}}{x_1! x_2!}, \quad x_1 = 0, 1, 2, 3, \ldots, \quad x_2 = 0, 1, 2, 3, \ldots,$$

and is zero elsewhere, where μ_1 and μ_2 are fixed positive real numbers. Thus the space S is the set of points (x_1, x_2), where each of x_1 and x_2 is a nonnegative integer. We wish to find the pmf of $Y_1 = X_1 + X_2$. If we use the change of variable technique, we need to define a second random variable Y_2. Because Y_2 is of no interest to us, let us choose it in such a way that we have a simple one-to-one transformation. For example, take $Y_2 = X_2$. Then $y_1 = x_1 + x_2$ and $y_2 = x_2$ represent a one-to-one transformation that maps S onto

$\begin{cases} y_1 = x_1 + x_2 \\ y_2 = x_2 \end{cases} \Rightarrow x_1, x_2$

$x_1, x_2 \geq 0$

$$T = \{(y_1, y_2) : y_2 = 0, 1, \ldots, y_1 \quad \text{and} \quad y_1 = 0, 1, 2, \ldots\}.$$

Note that if $(y_1, y_2) \in T$, then $0 \leq y_2 \leq y_1$. The inverse functions are given by $x_1 = y_1 - y_2$ and $x_2 = y_2$. Thus the joint pmf of Y_1 and Y_2 is

$$p_{Y_1, Y_2}(y_1, y_2) = \frac{\mu_1^{y_1 - y_2} \mu_2^{y_2} e^{-\mu_1 - \mu_2}}{(y_1 - y_2)! y_2!}, \quad (y_1, y_2) \in T,$$

当 $(y_1, y_2) \notin T$ 时.

and is zero elsewhere. Consequently, the marginal pmf of Y_1 is given by

$$
\begin{aligned}
p_{Y_1}(y_1) &= \sum_{y_2=0}^{y_1} p_{Y_1, Y_2}(y_1, y_2) \\
&= \frac{e^{-\mu_1 - \mu_2}}{y_1!} \sum_{y_2=0}^{y_1} \frac{y_1!}{(y_1 - y_2)! y_2!} \mu_1^{y_1 - y_2} \mu_2^{y_2} \\
&= \frac{(\mu_1 + \mu_2)^{y_1} e^{-\mu_1 - \mu_2}}{y_1!}, \quad y_1 = 0, 1, 2, \ldots,
\end{aligned}
$$

$\sum_{x=0}^{n} \binom{n}{x} a^x b^{n-x} = (a+b)^n$

$\binom{n}{x} = \frac{n!}{(n-x)! x!}$

and is zero elsewhere, where the third equality follows from the binomial expansion.

∎

For the continuous case we begin with an example which illustrates the cdf technique.

Example 2.2.2. Consider an experiment in which a person chooses at random a point (X, Y) from the unit square $\mathcal{S} = \{(x, y) : 0 < x < 1,\ 0 < y < 1\}$. Suppose that our interest is not in X or in Y but in $Z = X + Y$. Once a suitable probability model has been adopted, we shall see how to find the pdf of Z. To be specific, let the nature of the random experiment be such that it is reasonable to *assume* that the distribution of probability over the unit square is uniform. Then the pdf of X and Y may be written

$$f_{X,Y}(x, y) = \begin{cases} 1 & 0 < x < 1,\ 0 < y < 1 \\ 0 & \text{elsewhere,} \end{cases}$$

and this describes the probability model. Now let the cdf of Z be denoted by $F_Z(z) = P(X + Y \le z)$. Then

$$F_Z(z) = \begin{cases} 0 & z < 0 \\ \int_0^z \int_0^{z-x} dy\,dx = \frac{z^2}{2} & 0 \le z < 1 \\ 1 - \int_{z-1}^1 \int_{z-x}^1 dy\,dx = 1 - \frac{(2-z)^2}{2} & 1 \le z < 2 \\ 1 & 2 \le z. \end{cases}$$

Since $F_Z'(z)$ exists for all values of z, the pmf of Z may then be written

$$f_Z(z) = \begin{cases} z & 0 < z < 1 \\ 2 - z & 1 \le z < 2 \\ 0 & \text{elsewhere.} \end{cases} \quad \blacksquare$$

We now discuss in general the transformation technique for the continuous case. Let (X_1, X_2) have a jointly continuous distribution with pdf $f_{X_1,X_2}(x_1, x_2)$ and support set $\mathcal{S}$. Suppose the random variables Y_1 and Y_2 are given by $Y_1 = u_1(X_1, X_2)$ and $Y_2 = u_2(X_1, X_2)$, where the functions $y_1 = u_1(x_1, x_2)$ and $y_2 = u_2(x_1, x_2)$ define a one-to-one transformation that maps the set $\mathcal{S}$ in R^2 onto a (two-dimensional) set $\mathcal{T}$ in R^2 where $\mathcal{T}$ is the support of (Y_1, Y_2). If we express each of x_1 and x_2 in terms of y_1 and y_2, we can write $x_1 = w_1(y_1, y_2)$, $x_2 = w_2(y_1, y_2)$. The **Jacobian** of the transformation is the determinant of order 2 given by

$$J = \begin{vmatrix} \dfrac{\partial x_1}{\partial y_1} & \dfrac{\partial x_1}{\partial y_2} \\[2mm] \dfrac{\partial x_2}{\partial y_1} & \dfrac{\partial x_2}{\partial y_2} \end{vmatrix}.$$

It is assumed that these first-order partial derivatives are continuous and that the Jacobian J is not identically equal to zero in $\mathcal{T}$.

We can find, by use of a theorem in analysis, the joint pdf of (Y_1, Y_2). Let A be a subset of $\mathcal{S}$, and let B denote the mapping of A under the one-to-one transformation (see Figure 2.2.1). Because the transformation is one-to-one, the events $\{(X_1, X_2) \in A\}$ and $\{(Y_1, Y_2) \in B\}$ are equivalent. Hence

$$P[(Y_1, Y_2) \in B] = P[(X_1, X_2) \in A]$$
$$= \int\!\!\int_A f_{X_1,X_2}(x_1, x_2)\,dx_1\,dx_2.$$

Figure 2.2.1: A general sketch of the supports of (X_1, X_2), $(\mathcal{S})$, and (Y_1, Y_2), $(\mathcal{T})$.

We wish now to change variables of integration by writing $y_1 = u_1(x_1, x_2)$, $y_2 = u_2(x_1, x_2)$, or $x_1 = w_1(y_1, y_2)$, $x_2 = w_2(y_1, y_2)$. It has been proved in analysis, [see, e.g., page 304 of Buck (1965)], that this change of variables requires

$$\int\int_A f_{X_1,X_2}(x_1, x_2)\, dx_1 dx_2 = \int\int_B f_{X_1,X_2}[w_1(y_1,y_2), w_2(y_1,y_2)]|J|\, dy_1 dy_2.$$

Thus, for every set B in $\mathcal{T}$,

$$P[(Y_1, Y_2) \in B] = \int\int_B f_{X_1,X_2}[w_1(y_1,y_2), w_2(y_1,y_2)]|J|\, dy_1 dy_2,$$

which implies that the joint pdf $f_{Y_1,Y_2}(y_1, y_2)$ of Y_1 and Y_2 is

$$f_{Y_1,Y_2}(y_1, y_2) = \begin{cases} f_{X_1,X_2}[w_1(y_1,y_2), w_2(y_1,y_2)]|J| & (y_1, y_2) \in \mathcal{T} \\ 0 & \text{elsewhere.} \end{cases}$$

Accordingly, the marginal pdf $f_{Y_1}(y_1)$ of Y_1 can be obtained from the joint pdf $f_{Y_1,Y_2}(y_1, y_2)$ in the usual manner by integrating on y_2. Several examples of this result are given.

Example 2.2.3. Suppose (X_1, X_2) have the joint pdf

$$f_{X_1,X_2}(x_1, x_2) = \begin{cases} 1 & 0 < x_1 < 1, 0 < x_2 < 1 \\ 0 & \text{elsewhere.} \end{cases}$$

The support of (X_1, X_2) is then the set $\mathcal{S} = \{(x_1, x_2) : 0 < x_1 < 1, 0 < x_2 < 1\}$ depicted in Figure 2.2.2.

Suppose $Y_1 = X_1 + X_2$ and $Y_2 = X_1 - X_2$. The transformation is given by

$$y_1 = u_1(x_1, x_2) = x_1 + x_2$$
$$y_2 = u_2(x_1, x_2) = x_1 - x_2.$$

若先要求 $f(x_1+x_2)$, 则亦可通过设 $\begin{cases} y_1=x_1+x_2 \\ y_2=x_1 \end{cases}$ 来去之:

$\begin{cases} y_1=x_1+x_2 \\ y_2=x_1 \end{cases}$ $\begin{cases} x_1=y_2=w_1(y_1,y_2) \\ x_2=y_1-y_2=w_2(y_1,y_2) \end{cases}$

$\therefore J=\begin{vmatrix} \frac{\partial x_1}{\partial y_1} & \frac{\partial x_1}{\partial y_2} \\ \frac{\partial x_2}{\partial y_1} & \frac{\partial x_2}{\partial y_2} \end{vmatrix}=\begin{vmatrix} 0 & 1 \\ 1 & -1 \end{vmatrix}=-1\neq0$

$\therefore$ 套用式:

$f_{X_1,Y_2}(y_1,y_2)=f_{X_1,X_2}(w_1(y_1,y_2),w_2(y_1,y_2))\cdot|J|$

$=f_{X_1,X_2}(y_2,y_1-y_2)\cdot|J|$

$=1$

由 $\begin{cases} 0<x_1<1 \\ 0<x_2<1 \end{cases}$ $\Rightarrow \begin{cases} 0<x_1=y_2<1 \\ 0<x_2=y_1-y_2<1 \end{cases}$

$\Rightarrow \begin{cases} 0<y_2<1 \\ y_1<y_2, y_1<1+y_2 \end{cases}$

y_1, y_2 的图为:

$\therefore f_Y(y_1)$

$=\int_{-\infty}^{\infty}f(y_1,y_2)dy_2=\int_{-\infty}^{\infty}1\cdot dy_2$

$=\begin{cases} 在0<y_1<1上: 为\int_0^{y_1}dy_2=y_1 \\ 在1<y_1<2上: 为\int_{y_1-1}^1 dy_2=2-y_1 \\ elsewhere: 为0 \end{cases}$

上结果与

设 $\begin{cases} y_1=x_1+x_2 \\ y_2=x_1-x_2 \end{cases}$

而得之 $f(x_1+x_2)$ 即 $f_{Y_1}(y_1)$ 的结果一样!

Figure 2.2.2: The support of (X_1, X_2) of Example 2.2.3.

This transformation is one-to-one. We first determine the set $\mathcal{T}$ in the y_1y_2-plane that is the mapping of $\mathcal{S}$ under this transformation. Now

$$x_1 = w_1(y_1, y_2) = \tfrac{1}{2}(y_1 + y_2)$$
$$x_2 = w_2(y_1, y_2) = \tfrac{1}{2}(y_1 - y_2).$$

To determine the set $\mathcal{S}$ in the y_1y_2-plane onto which $\mathcal{T}$ is mapped under the transformation, note that the boundaries of $\mathcal{S}$ are transformed as follows into the boundaries of $\mathcal{T}$:

$$x_1 = 0 \quad \text{into} \quad 0 = \tfrac{1}{2}(y_1 + y_2)$$
$$x_1 = 1 \quad \text{into} \quad 1 = \tfrac{1}{2}(y_1 + y_2)$$
$$x_2 = 0 \quad \text{into} \quad 0 = \tfrac{1}{2}(y_1 - y_2)$$
$$x_2 = 1 \quad \text{into} \quad 1 = \tfrac{1}{2}(y_1 - y_2).$$

Accordingly, $\mathcal{T}$ is shown in Figure 2.2.3. Next, the Jacobian is given by

$$J = \begin{vmatrix} \dfrac{\partial x_1}{\partial y_1} & \dfrac{\partial x_1}{\partial y_2} \\ \dfrac{\partial x_2}{\partial y_1} & \dfrac{\partial x_2}{\partial y_2} \end{vmatrix} = \begin{vmatrix} \tfrac{1}{2} & \tfrac{1}{2} \\ \tfrac{1}{2} & -\tfrac{1}{2} \end{vmatrix} = -\tfrac{1}{2}.$$

Although we suggest transforming the boundaries of $\mathcal{S}$, others might want to use the inequalities

$$0 < x_1 < 1 \quad \text{and} \quad 0 < x_2 < 1$$

directly. These four inequalities become

$$x_1 = \tfrac{1}{2}(y_1+y_2) \qquad x_2=\tfrac{1}{2}(y_1-y_2)$$

$$0 < \tfrac{1}{2}(y_1 + y_2) < 1 \quad \text{and} \quad 0 < \tfrac{1}{2}(y_1 - y_2) < 1.$$

$\Rightarrow 0<y_1+y_2<2$

$\begin{cases} 0<y_1+y_2 \Rightarrow -y_1<y_2 (或 -y_2<y_1) \\ y_1+y_2<2 \Rightarrow y_2<2-y_1 (或 y_1<2-y_2) \end{cases}$

$\Rightarrow 0<y_1-y_2<2 \begin{cases} 0<y_1-y_2 \Rightarrow y_2<y_1 \\ y_1-y_2<2 \Rightarrow y_1<2+y_2 \\ (或 y_1-2<y_2) \end{cases}$

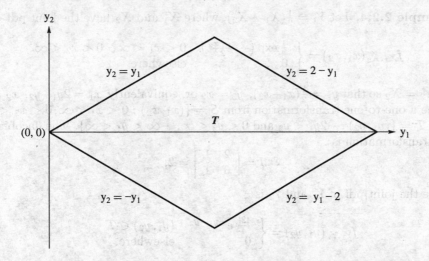

Figure 2.2.3: The support of (Y_1, Y_2) of Example 2.2.3.

It is easy to see that these are equivalent to

$$-y_1 < y_2, \quad y_2 < 2 - y_1, \quad y_2 < y_1 \quad y_1 - 2 < y_2;$$

and they define the set $\mathcal{T}$.

Hence, the joint pdf of (Y_1, Y_2) is given by

$$f_{Y_1,Y_2}(y_1, y_2) = \begin{cases} f_{X_1,X_2}[\frac{1}{2}(y_1 + y_2), \frac{1}{2}(y_1 - y_2)]|J| = \frac{1}{2} & (y_1, y_2) \in \mathcal{T} \\ 0 & \text{elsewhere.} \end{cases}$$

The marginal pdf of Y_1 is given by

$$f_{Y_1}(y_1) = \int_{-\infty}^{\infty} f_{Y_1,Y_2}(y_1, y_2)\, dy_2.$$

If we refer to Figure 2.2.3, we can see that

$$f_{Y_1}(y_1) = \begin{cases} \int_{-y_1}^{y_1} \frac{1}{2}\, dy_2 = y_1 & 0 < y_1 \le 1 \\ \int_{y_1-2}^{2-y_1} \frac{1}{2}\, dy_2 = 2 - y_1 & 1 < y_1 < 2 \\ 0 & \text{elsewhere.} \end{cases}$$

In a similar manner, the marginal pdf $f_{Y_2}(y_2)$ is given by

$$f_{Y_2}(y_2) = \begin{cases} \int_{-y_2}^{y_2+2} \frac{1}{2}\, dy_1 = y_2 + 1 & -1 < y_2 \le 0 \\ \int_{y_2}^{2-y_2} \frac{1}{2}\, dy_1 = 1 - y_2 & 0 < y_2 < 1 \\ 0 & \text{elsewhere.} \end{cases} \quad \blacksquare$$

Example 2.2.4. Let $Y_1 = \frac{1}{2}(X_1 - X_2)$, where X_1 and X_2 have the joint pdf

$$f_{X_1, X_2}(x_1, x_2) = \begin{cases} \frac{1}{4} \exp\left(-\frac{x_1 + x_2}{2}\right) & 0 < x_1 < \infty, \ 0 < x_2 < \infty \\ 0 & \text{elsewhere.} \end{cases}$$

Let $Y_2 = X_2$ so that $y_1 = \frac{1}{2}(x_1 - x_2)$, $y_2 = x_2$ or, equivalently, $x_1 = 2y_1 + y_2$, $x_2 = y_2$ define a one-to-one transformation from $S = \{(x_1, x_2) : 0 < x_1 < \infty, 0 < x_2 < \infty\}$ onto $T = \{(y_1, y_2) : -2y_1 < y_2 \text{ and } 0 < y_2 < \infty, \ -\infty < y_1 < \infty\}$. The Jacobian of the transformation is

$$J = \begin{vmatrix} 2 & 1 \\ 0 & 1 \end{vmatrix} = 2;$$

hence the joint pdf of Y_1 and Y_2 is

$$f_{Y_1, Y_2}(y_1, y_2) = \begin{cases} \frac{|2|}{4} e^{-y_1 - y_2} & (y_1, y_2) \in T \\ 0 & \text{elsewhere.} \end{cases}$$

Thus the pdf of Y_1 is given by

$$f_{Y_1}(y_1) = \begin{cases} \int_{-2y_1}^{\infty} \frac{1}{2} e^{-y_1 - y_2} \, dy_2 = \frac{1}{2} e^{y_1} & -\infty < y_1 < 0 \\ \int_{0}^{\infty} \frac{1}{2} e^{-y_1 - y_2} \, dy_2 = \frac{1}{2} e^{-y_1} & 0 \le y_1 < \infty, \end{cases}$$

or

$$f_{Y_1}(y_1) = \frac{1}{2} e^{-|y_1|}, \quad -\infty < y_1 < \infty. \tag{2.2.1}$$

This pdf is frequently called the **double exponential** or **Laplace** pdf. ∎

Example 2.2.5. Let X_1 and X_2 have the joint pdf

$$f_{X_1, X_2}(x_1, x_2) = \begin{cases} 10 x_1 x_2^2 & 0 < x_1 < x_2 < 1 \\ 0 & \text{elsewhere.} \end{cases}$$

Suppose $Y_1 = X_1 / X_2$ and $Y_2 = X_2$. Hence, the inverse transformation is $x_1 = y_1 y_2$ and $x_2 = y_2$, which has the Jacobian

$$J = \begin{vmatrix} y_2 & y_1 \\ 0 & 1 \end{vmatrix} = y_2.$$

The inequalities defining the support S of (X_1, X_2) become

$$0 < y_1 y_2, \ y_1 y_2 < y_2, \text{ and } y_2 < 1.$$

These inequalities are equivalent to

$$0 < y_1 < 1 \text{ and } 0 < y_2 < 1,$$

which defines the support set T of (Y_1, Y_2). Hence, the joint pdf of (Y_1, Y_2) is

$$f_{Y_1, Y_2}(y_1, y_2) = 10 y_1 y_2 y_2^2 |y_2| = 10 y_1 y_2^4, \quad (y_1, y_2) \in T.$$

The marginal pdfs are

$$f_{Y_1}(y_1) = \int_0^1 10 y_1 y_2^4 \, dy_2 = 2y_1, \quad 0 < y_1 < 1,$$

zero elsewhere, and

$$f_{Y_2}(y_2) = \int_0^1 10 y_1 y_2^4 \, dy_1 = 5y_2^4, \quad 0 < y_1 < 1,$$

zero elsewhere. ∎

In addition to the change-of-variable and cdf techniques for finding distributions of functions of random variables, there is another method, called the moment generating function (mgf) technique, which works well for linear functions of random variables. In Subsection 2.1.1, we pointed out that if $Y = g(X_1, X_2)$, then $E(Y)$, if it exists, could be found by

$$E(Y) = \int_{-\infty}^{\infty} \int_{-\infty}^{\infty} g(x_1, x_2) f_{X_1, X_2}(x_1, x_2) \, dx_1 dx_2$$

in the continuous case, with summations replacing integrals in the discrete case. Certainly, that function $g(X_1, X_2)$ could be $\exp\{tu(X_1, X_2)\}$, so that in reality we would be finding the mgf of the function $Z = u(X_1, X_2)$. If we could then recognize this mgf as belonging to a certain distribution, then Z would have that distribution. We give two illustrations that demonstrate the power of this technique by reconsidering Examples 2.2.1 and 2.2.4.

Example 2.2.6 (Continuation of Example 2.2.1). Here X_1 and X_2 have the joint pmf

$$p_{X_1, X_2}(x_1, x_2) = \begin{cases} \dfrac{\mu_1^{x_1} \mu_2^{x_2} e^{-\mu_1} e^{-\mu_2}}{x_1! x_2!} & x_1 = 0, 1, 2, 3, \ldots, \quad x_2 = 0, 1, 2, 3, \ldots \\ 0 & \text{elsewhere,} \end{cases}$$

where μ_1 and μ_2 are fixed positive real numbers. Let $Y = X_1 + X_2$ and consider

$$
\begin{aligned}
E(e^{tY}) &= \sum_{x_1=0}^{\infty} \sum_{x_2=0}^{\infty} e^{t(x_1+x_2)} p_{X_1, X_2}(x_1, x_2) \\
&= \sum_{x_1=0}^{\infty} e^{tx_1} \frac{\mu^{x_1} e^{-\mu_1}}{x_1!} \sum_{x_2=0}^{\infty} e^{tx_2} \frac{\mu^{x_2} e^{-\mu_2}}{x_2!} \\
&= \left[e^{-\mu_1} \sum_{x_1=0}^{\infty} \frac{(e^t \mu_1)^{x_1}}{x_1!} \right] \left[e^{-\mu_2} \sum_{x_2=0}^{\infty} \frac{(e^t \mu_2)^{x_2}}{x_2!} \right] \\
&= \left[e^{\mu_1(e^t-1)} \right] \left[e^{\mu_2(e^t-1)} \right] \\
&= e^{(\mu_1+\mu_2)(e^t-1)}.
\end{aligned}
$$

Notice that the factors in the brackets in the next-to-last equality are the mgfs of X_1 and X_2, respectively. Hence, the mgf of Y is the same as that of X_1 except μ_1 has been replaced by $\mu_1 + \mu_2$. Therefore, by the uniqueness of mgfs, the pmf of Y must be

$$p_Y(y) = e^{-(\mu_1+\mu_2)} \frac{(\mu_1 + \mu_2)^y}{y!}, \quad y = 0, 1, 2, \ldots,$$

which is the same pmf that was obtained in Example 2.2.1. ■

Example 2.2.7 (Continuation of Example 2.2.4). Here X_1 and X_2 have the joint pdf

$$f_{X_1,X_2}(x_1, x_2) = \begin{cases} \frac{1}{4} \exp\left(-\frac{x_1+x_2}{2}\right) & 0 < x_1 < \infty, \ 0 < x_2 < \infty \\ 0 & \text{elsewhere.} \end{cases}$$

So the mgf of $Y = (1/2)(X_1 - X_2)$ is given by

$$\begin{aligned}
E(e^{tY}) &= \int_0^\infty \int_0^\infty e^{t(x_1-x_2)/2} \frac{1}{4} e^{-(x_1+x_2)/2} \, dx_1 dx_2 \\
&= \left[\int_0^\infty \frac{1}{2} e^{-x_1(1-t)/2} \, dx_1 \right] \left[\int_0^\infty \frac{1}{2} e^{-x_2(1+t)/2} \, dx_2 \right] \\
&= \left[\frac{1}{1-t} \right] \left[\frac{1}{1+t} \right] = \frac{1}{1-t^2}
\end{aligned}$$

provided that $1 - t > 0$ and $1 + t > 0$; i.e., $-1 < t < 1$. However, the mgf of a double exponential distribution is

$$\begin{aligned}
\int_{-\infty}^\infty e^{tx} \frac{e^{-|x|}}{2} \, dx &= \int_{-\infty}^0 \frac{e^{(1+t)x}}{2} \, dx + \int_0^\infty \frac{e^{(t-1)x}}{2} \, dx \\
&= \frac{1}{2(1+t)} + \frac{1}{2(1-t)} = \frac{1}{1-t^2},
\end{aligned}$$

provided $-1 < t < 1$. Thus, by the uniqueness of mgfs, Y has the double exponential distribution. ■

EXERCISES

2.2.1. If $p(x_1, x_2) = (\frac{2}{3})^{x_1+x_2}(\frac{1}{3})^{2-x_1-x_2}$, $(x_1, x_2) = (0,0), (0,1), (1,0), (1,1)$, zero elsewhere, is the joint pmf of X_1 and X_2, find the joint pmf of $Y_1 = X_1 - X_2$ and $Y_2 = X_1 + X_2$.

2.2.2. Let X_1 and X_2 have the joint pmf $p(x_1, x_2) = x_1 x_2/36$, $x_1 = 1, 2, 3$ and $x_2 = 1, 2, 3$, zero elsewhere. Find first the joint pmf of $Y_1 = X_1 X_2$ and $Y_2 = X_2$, and then find the marginal pmf of Y_1.

2.2.3. Let X_1 and X_2 have the joint pdf $h(x_1, x_2) = 2e^{-x_1-x_2}$, $0 < x_1 < x_2 < \infty$, zero elsewhere. Find the joint pdf of $Y_1 = 2X_1$ and $Y_2 = X_2 - X_1$.

√ **2.2.4.** Let X_1 and X_2 have the joint pdf $h(x_1, x_2) = 8x_1x_2$, $0 < x_1 < x_2 < 1$, zero elsewhere. Find the joint pdf of $Y_1 = X_1/X_2$ and $Y_2 = X_2$.
Hint: Use the inequalities $0 < y_1y_2 < y_2 < 1$ in considering the mapping from $\mathcal{S}$ onto $\mathcal{T}$.

2.2.5. Let X_1 and X_2 be continuous random variables with the joint probability density function $f_{X_1,X_2}(x_1, x_2)$, $-\infty < x_i < \infty$, $i = 1, 2$. Let $Y_1 = X_1 + X_2$ and $Y_2 = X_2$.

(a) Find the joint pdf f_{Y_1,Y_2}.

(b) Show that

$$f_{Y_1}(y_1) = \int_{-\infty}^{\infty} f_{X_1,X_2}(y_1 - y_2, y_2)\, dy_2, \qquad (2.2.2)$$

which is sometimes called the **convolution formula**.

2.2.6. Suppose X_1 and X_2 have the joint pdf $f_{X_1,X_2}(x_1, x_2) = e^{-(x_1+x_2)}$, $0 < x_i < \infty$, $i = 1, 2$, zero elsewhere.

(a) Use formula (2.2.2) to find the pdf of $Y_1 = X_1 + X_2$.

(b) Find the mgf of Y_1.

2.2.7. Use the formula (2.2.2) to find the pdf of $Y_1 = X_1 + X_2$, where X_1 and X_2 have the joint pdf $f_{X_1,X_2}(x_1, x_2) = 2e^{-(x_1+x_2)}$, $0 < x_1 < x_2 < \infty$, zero elsewhere.

2.2.8. Suppose X_1 and X_2 have the joint pdf

$$f(x_1, x_2) = \begin{cases} e^{-x_1}e^{-x_2} & x_1 > 0, x_2 > 0 \\ 0 & \text{elsewhere.} \end{cases}$$

For constants $w_1 > 0$ and $w_2 > 0$, let $W = w_1X_1 + w_2X_2$.

(a) Show that the pdf of W is

$$f_W(w) = \begin{cases} \frac{1}{w_1-w_2}(e^{-w/w_1} - e^{-w/w_2}) & w > 0 \\ 0 & \text{elsewhere.} \end{cases}$$

(b) Verify that $f_W(w) > 0$ for $w > 0$.

(c) Note that the pdf $f_W(w)$ has an indeterminate form when $w_1 = w_2$. Rewrite $f_W(w)$ using h defined as $w_1 - w_2 = h$. Then use l'Hôpital's rule to show that when $w_1 = w_2$, the pdf is given by $f_W(w) = (w/w_1^2)\exp\{-w/w_1\}$ for $w > 0$ and zero elsewhere.

2.3 Conditional Distributions and Expectations

In Section 2.1 we introduced the joint probability distribution of a pair of random variables. We also showed how to recover the individual (marginal) distributions for the random variables from the joint distribution. In this section, we discuss conditional distributions, i.e., the distribution of one of the random variables when the other has assumed a specific value. We discuss this first for the discrete case, which follows easily from the concept of conditional probability presented in Section 1.4.

Let X_1 and X_2 denote random variables of the discrete type, which have the joint pmf $p_{X_1,X_2}(x_1, x_2)$ that is positive on the support set S and is zero elsewhere. Let $p_{X_1}(x_1)$ and $p_{X_2}(x_2)$ denote, respectively, the marginal probability mass functions of X_1 and X_2. Let x_1 be a point in the support of X_1; hence, $p_{X_1}(x_1) > 0$. Using the definition of conditional probability, we have

$$P(X_2 = x_2 | X_1 = x_1) = \frac{P(X_1 = x_1, X_2 = x_2)}{P(X_1 = x_1)} = \frac{p_{X_1,X_2}(x_1, x_2)}{p_{X_1}(x_1)}$$

for all x_2 in the support S_{X_2} of X_2. Define this function as

$$p_{X_2|X_1}(x_2|x_1) = \frac{p_{X_1,X_2}(x_1, x_2)}{p_{X_1}(x_1)}, \quad x_2 \in S_{X_2}. \tag{2.3.1}$$

For any fixed x_1 with $p_{X_1}(x_1) > 0$, this function $p_{X_2|X_1}(x_2|x_1)$ satisfies the conditions of being a pmf of the discrete type because $p_{X_2|X_1}(x_2|x_1)$ is nonnegative and

$$\sum_{x_2} p_{X_2|X_1}(x_2|x_1) = \sum_{x_2} \frac{p_{X_1,X_2}(x_1, x_2)}{p_{X_1}(x_1)}$$

$$= \frac{1}{p_{X_1}(x_1)} \sum_{x_2} p_{X_1,X_2}(x_1, x_2) = \frac{p_{X_1}(x_1)}{p_{X_1}(x_1)} = 1.$$

We call $p_{X_2|X_1}(x_2|x_1)$ the **conditional pmf** of the discrete type of random variable X_2, given that the discrete type of random variable $X_1 = x_1$. In a similar manner, provided $x_2 \in S_{X_2}$, we define the symbol $p_{X_1|X_2}(x_1|x_2)$ by the relation

$$p_{X_1|X_2}(x_1|x_2) = \frac{p_{X_1,X_2}(x_1, x_2)}{p_{X_2}(x_2)}, \quad x_1 \in S_{X_1},$$

and we call $p_{X_1|X_2}(x_1|x_2)$ the conditional pmf of the discrete type of random variable X_1, given that the discrete type of random variable $X_2 = x_2$. We often abbreviate $p_{X_1|X_2}(x_1|x_2)$ by $p_{1|2}(x_1|x_2)$ and $p_{X_2|X_1}(x_2|x_1)$ by $p_{2|1}(x_2|x_1)$. Similarly, $p_1(x_1)$ and $p_2(x_2)$ are used to denote the respective marginal pmfs.

Now let X_1 and X_2 denote random variables of the continuous type and have the joint pdf $f_{X_1,X_2}(x_1, x_2)$ and the marginal probability density functions $f_{X_1}(x_1)$ and $f_{X_2}(x_2)$, respectively. We use the results of the preceding paragraph to motivate a definition of a conditional pdf of a continuous type of random variable. When $f_{X_1}(x_1) > 0$, we define the symbol $f_{X_2|X_1}(x_2|x_1)$ by the relation

$$f_{X_2|X_1}(x_2|x_1) = \frac{f_{X_1,X_2}(x_1,x_2)}{f_{X_1}(x_1)}. \qquad (2.3.2)$$

可配记记为为: $f_{2|1} = \dfrac{f_{21}或f_{12}}{f_1}$

即 $f_{X_2|X_1}(x_2 | X_1 = x_1)$

In this relation, x_1 is to be thought of as having a fixed (but any fixed) value for which $f_{X_1}(x_1) > 0$. It is evident that $f_{X_2|X_1}(x_2|x_1)$ is nonnegative and that

$$
\begin{aligned}
\int_{-\infty}^{\infty} f_{X_2|X_1}(x_2|x_1)\, dx_2 &= \int_{-\infty}^{\infty} \frac{f_{X_1,X_2}(x_1,x_2)}{f_{X_1}(x_1)}\, dx_2 \\
&= \frac{1}{f_{X_1}(x_1)} \int_{-\infty}^{\infty} f_{X_1,X_2}(x_1,x_2)\, dx_2 \\
&= \frac{1}{f_{X_1}(x_1)} f_{X_1}(x_1) = 1.
\end{aligned}
$$

即 $\begin{cases} P(x)>0 \\ \sum\limits_{x} P(x)=1 \end{cases}$ ∴是离散型

有 $E[X]$ 及 $\sigma(x)$,

若 $\begin{cases} f_{X_1|X_2}(x_1|x_2)>0 \\ \sum\limits_{X_1} f_{X_1|X_2}(x_1|x_2)=1 \end{cases}$ 则

同样, $X_1|X_2$ 也存在 $E[X_1|X_2]$ 及 $\sigma(X_1|X_2)$

That is, $f_{X_2|X_1}(x_2|x_1)$ has the properties of a pdf of one continuous type of random variable. It is called the **conditional pdf** of the continuous type of random variable X_2, given that the continuous type of random variable X_1 has the value x_1. When $f_{X_2}(x_2) > 0$, the conditional pdf of the continuous random variable X_1, given that the continuous type of random variable X_2 has the value x_2, is defined by

$$f_{X_1|X_2}(x_1|x_2) = \frac{f_{X_1,X_2}(x_1,x_2)}{f_{X_2}(x_2)}, \quad f_{X_2}(x_2) > 0.$$

We often abbreviate these conditional pdfs by $f_{1|2}(x_1|x_2)$ and $f_{2|1}(x_2|x_1)$, respectively. Similarly, $f_1(x_1)$ and $f_2(x_2)$ are used to denote the respective marginal pdfs.

Since each of $f_{2|1}(x_2|x_1)$ and $f_{1|2}(x_1|x_2)$ is a pdf of one random variable, each has all the properties of such a pdf. Thus we can compute probabilities and mathematical expectations. If the random variables are of the continuous type, the probability

$$P(a < X_2 < b|X_1 = x_1) = \int_a^b f_{2|1}(x_2|x_1)\, dx_2$$

is called "the conditional probability that $a < X_2 < b$, given that $X_1 = x_1$." If there is no ambiguity, this may be written in the form $P(a < X_2 < b|x_1)$. Similarly, the conditional probability that $c < X_1 < d$, given $X_2 = x_2$, is

即, $P(c<X_1<d | X_2=x_2)=\int f_{1|2} dx_1$
X_1 的范围

$$P(c < X_1 < d|X_2 = x_2) = \int_c^d f_{1|2}(x_1|x_2)\, dx_1.$$

If $u(X_2)$ is a function of X_2, the conditional expectation of $u(X_2)$, given that $X_1 = x_1$, if it exists, is given by

$$E[u(X_2)|x_1] = \int_{-\infty}^{\infty} u(x_2) f_{2|1}(x_2|x_1)\, dx_2.$$

简记为 $\int\limits_{X_2的范围} u(x_2) f_{2|1}\, dx_2$

Note that $E[u(X_2)|x_1]$ is a function of x_1. If they do exist, then $E(X_2|x_1)$ is the mean and $E\{[X_2 - E(X_2|x_1)]^2|x_1\}$ is the variance of the conditional distribution

→ 可理解为: 事件 X_2 的 赵收敛 的 期望值 = 事件 X_1 发生的条件下, 发生事件 X_2, 再乘上 X_2 的函数值 $u(x_2)$.
= 即 $u(x_2)$ 起让 X_2 发生的权重.

$$E\{[X_2 - \underbrace{E(X_2|X_1)}_{u(X_2)}]^2|X_1\} = \int_{-\infty}^{+\infty} [X_2 - \underbrace{E(X_2|Y_1)}_{u(X_2)}]^2 f(X_2|X_1)\, dX_2$$

$$= \int \{X_2^2 - 2E(X_2|X_1)] \cdot X_2 + [E(X_2|X_1)]^2\} f(X_2|X_1)\, dX_2$$

$$= \int X_2^2\, f(X_2|X_1)\, dX_2 - 2E(X_2|X_1) \cdot \int X_2 \cdot f(X_2|X_1)\, dX_2 + [E(X_2|X_1)]^2 \int f(X_2|X_1)\, dX_2 \nearrow$$

$$\begin{aligned} &= \int 1 \cdot f(X_2|X_1)\, dX_2 \\ &= E(1|X_1) = E(1) = 1 \end{aligned}$$

$E(X_2|X_1)$ 是个常数，可提取到∫外。

96 $= E(X_2^2|X_1) - 2E(X_2|X_1) \cdot E(X_2|X_1) + [E(X_2|X_1)]^2$

$= E(X_2^2|X_1) - [E(X_2|X_1)]^2$

of X_2, given $X_1 = x_1$, which can be written more simply as $\text{Var}(X_2|x_1)$. It is convenient to refer to these as the "conditional mean" and the "conditional variance" of X_2, given $X_1 = x_1$. Of course, we have

$E(X_2|X_1) = \int_{-\infty}^{+\infty} X_2 \cdot f_{2|1}\, dX_2$

相比较于 $\text{Var}(X) = E(X^2) - (E(X))^2$

$$\text{Var}(X_2|x_1) = \underbrace{E(X_2^2|x_1)} - \underbrace{[E(X_2|x_1)]^2}$$

from an earlier result. In a like manner, the conditional expectation of $u(X_1)$, given $X_2 = x_2$, if it exists, is given by

$$E[u(X_1)|x_2] = \int_{-\infty}^{\infty} u(x_1) f_{1|2}(x_1|x_2)\, dx_1.$$

With random variables of the discrete type, these conditional probabilities and conditional expectations are computed by using summation instead of integration. An illustrative example follows.

即 $E(X_2|X_1) = \sum_{X_2} X_2 \cdot P(X_2|X_1)$.

Example 2.3.1. Let X_1 and X_2 have the joint pdf

$$f(x_1, x_2) = \begin{cases} 2 & 0 < x_1 < x_2 < 1 \\ 0 & \text{elsewhere.} \end{cases}$$

Then the marginal probability density functions are, respectively,

$$f_1(x_1) = \begin{cases} \int_{x_1}^{1} 2\, dx_2 = 2(1 - x_1) & 0 < x_1 < 1 \\ 0 & \text{elsewhere,} \end{cases}$$

and

$$f_2(x_2) = \begin{cases} \int_{0}^{x_2} 2\, dx_1 = 2x_2 & 0 < x_2 < 1 \\ 0 & \text{elsewhere.} \end{cases}$$

The conditional pdf of X_1, given $X_2 = x_2$, $0 < x_2 < 1$, is

$$f_{1|2}(x_1|x_2) = \begin{cases} \dfrac{2}{2x_2} = \dfrac{1}{x_2} & 0 < x_1 < x_2 < 1 \\ 0 & \text{elsewhere.} \end{cases}$$

Here the conditional mean and the conditional variance of X_1, given $X_2 = x_2$, are respectively,

(指 X_1 值乘与该值概率的比重) 之和

$$\begin{aligned} E(X_1|x_2) &= \int_{-\infty}^{\infty} x_1 f_{1|2}(x_1|x_2)\, dx_1 \\ &= \int_{0}^{x_2} x_1 \left(\frac{1}{x_2}\right) dx_1 \\ &= \frac{x_2}{2}, \quad 0 < x_2 < 1, \end{aligned}$$

and

$= E\{[X_1 - E[X_1|x_2]]|x_2\}^2 = \int_{-\infty}^{+\infty} (X_1 - \frac{X_2}{2})^2 \cdot f_{1|2}\, dX_1$

$$\begin{aligned} \text{Var}(X_1|x_2) &= \int_{0}^{x_2} \left(x_1 - \frac{x_2}{2}\right)^2 \left(\frac{1}{x_2}\right) dx_1 + \int \text{其余区间}\ldots \\ &= \frac{x_2^2}{12}, \quad 0 < x_2 < 1. \end{aligned}$$

在那些区间，$f_{1|2} = 0$

$\therefore = 0$.

Finally, we compare the values of

$$P(0 < X_1 < \tfrac{1}{2} | X_2 = \tfrac{3}{4}) \quad \text{and} \quad P(0 < X_1 < \tfrac{1}{2}).$$

[handwritten: 前已 $f_{1|2} = \frac{1}{X_2}$; 当 $X_2 = \frac{3}{4}$ 时: $f_{1|2}(X_1|X_2 = x_2 = \frac{3}{4}) = \frac{1}{3/4} = \frac{4}{3}$]

We have

[handwritten: $P(0 < X_1 < \tfrac{1}{2} | X_2 = x_2 = \tfrac{3}{4}) = \int_{X_1 = 0}^{X_1 = \frac{1}{2}} f_{1|2}(X_1 | X_2 = x_2) dx_1$]

$$= P(0 < X_1 < \tfrac{1}{2} | X_2 = \tfrac{3}{4}) = \int_0^{1/2} f_{1|2}(x_1 | \tfrac{3}{4}) dx_1 = \int_0^{1/2} \left(\tfrac{4}{3}\right) dx_1 = \tfrac{2}{3},$$

but

$$P(0 < X_1 < \tfrac{1}{2}) = \int_0^{1/2} f_1(x_1) dx_1 = \int_0^{1/2} 2(1 - x_1) dx_1 = \tfrac{3}{4}. \quad \blacksquare$$

[handwritten: 其中把 X_1 设定为某一固定的值 ... 其中把 X_1 视为一个变量]

Since $E(X_2 | x_1)$ is a function of x_1, then $E(X_2 | X_1)$ is a random variable with its own distribution, mean, and variance. Let us consider the following illustration of this.

Example 2.3.2. Let X_1 and X_2 have the joint pdf

$$f_{12} = f(x_1, x_2) = \begin{cases} 6x_2 & 0 < x_2 < x_1 < 1 \\ 0 & \text{elsewhere.} \end{cases}$$

Then the marginal pdf of X_1 is

[handwritten sketch with axes labeled X_2, X_1, line $x_2 = x_1$]

$$f_1(x_1) = \int_0^{x_1} 6x_2 \, dx_2 = 3x_1^2, \quad 0 < x_1 < 1,$$

zero elsewhere. The conditional pdf of X_2, given $X_1 = x_1$, is $= f_{2|1} = \dfrac{f_{21}}{f_1} = \dfrac{f_{12}}{f_1}$

$$= f_{2|1}(x_2 | x_1) = \frac{6x_2}{3x_1^2} - \frac{2x_2}{x_1^2}, \quad 0 < x_2 < x_1,$$

zero elsewhere, where $0 < x_1 < 1$. The conditional mean of X_2, given $X_1 = x_1$, is

[handwritten: $E[X_2 | X_1 = x_1] = \int_{X_2 \text{范围}} x_2 \cdot f_{2|1} dx_2 =$]

$$E(X_2 | x_1) = \int_0^{x_1} x_2 \underbrace{\left(\frac{2x_2}{x_1^2}\right)}_{f_{2|1}} dx_2 = \frac{2}{3}x_1, \quad 0 < x_1 < 1.$$

Now $E(X_2 | X_1) = 2X_1/3$ is a random variable, say Y. The cdf of $Y = 2X_1/3$ is

[handwritten: $G(y) = F_Y(y) = P(Y \le y) = P(\frac{2}{3}X_1 \le y) = P(X_1 \le \frac{3}{2}y) = F_{X_1}(\frac{3}{2}y) = \int f_1(x_1) dx_1$; X_1的范围]

$$G(y) = P(Y \le y) = P\left(X_1 \le \frac{3y}{2}\right), \quad 0 \le y < \frac{2}{3}.$$

From the pdf $f_1(x_1)$, we have

[handwritten: $\left.\begin{array}{l} y = \frac{2}{3}X_1 \\ 0 < X_1 < 1 \end{array}\right\} \Rightarrow 0 < y < \frac{2}{3}$]

$$G(y) = \int_0^{3y/2} 3x_1^2 \, dx_1 = \frac{27y^3}{8}, \quad 0 \le y < \frac{2}{3}.$$

Of course, $G(y) = 0$ if $y < 0$, and $G(y) = 1$ if $\frac{2}{3} < y$. The pdf, mean, and variance of $Y = 2X_1/3$ are

[handwritten: $P_Y(y) = F_Y'(y)$]

$$g(y) = \frac{81y^2}{8}, \quad 0 \le y < \frac{2}{3},$$

zero elsewhere,

$$E(Y) = \int_Y y \cdot P_y(y)\, dy \quad (\text{handwritten})$$

$$E(Y) = \int_0^{2/3} y\left(\frac{81y^2}{8}\right) dy = \frac{1}{2},$$

and

$$\text{Var}(Y) = E(Y^2) - (E(Y))^2 \quad (\text{handwritten})$$
$$= \int_y y^2 \cdot P_y(y)\,dy - \left(\tfrac{1}{2}\right)^2 = \quad (\text{handwritten})$$

$$\text{Var}(Y) = \int_0^{2/3} y^2\left(\frac{81y^2}{8}\right) dy - \frac{1}{4} = \frac{1}{60}.$$

Since the marginal pdf of X_2 is $= \int_{X_1} f_{12}\, dx_1$ (handwritten)

$$f_2(x_2) = \int_{x_2}^1 6x_2\, dx_1 = 6x_2(1 - x_2), \quad 0 < x_2 < 1,$$

(handwritten left margin:)
$$E[X_2] = \int_{X_2} x_2 \cdot f_{X_2}\, dx_2$$
$$= \int_0^1 x_2 \cdot 6x_2(1-x_2)\, dx_2$$
$$= \frac{1}{2}.$$
$$\text{Var}(X_2) = E(X_2^2) - (E(X_2))^2$$
$$= \int_{X_2} x_2^2 \cdot 6x_2(1-x_2)\, dx_2 - \left(\tfrac{1}{2}\right)^2 = \frac{1}{20}.$$

zero elsewhere, it is easy to show that $E(X_2) = \frac{1}{2}$ and $\text{Var}(X_2) = \frac{1}{20}$. That is, here

$$E(Y) = E[E(X_2|X_1)] = E(X_2)$$

and

$$\text{Var}(Y) = \text{Var}[E(X_2|X_1)] \leq \text{Var}(X_2). \quad \blacksquare$$

Example 2.3.2 is excellent, as it provides us with the opportunity to apply many of these new definitions as well as review the cdf technique for finding the distribution of a function of a random variable, namely $Y = 2X_1/3$. Moreover, the two observations at the end of this example are no accident because they are true in general.

Theorem 2.3.1. *Let (X_1, X_2) be a random vector such that the variance of X_2 is finite. Then,*

(a) $E[E(X_2|X_1)] = E(X_2).$

(b) $Var[E(X_2|X_1)] \leq Var(X_2).$

Proof: The proof is for the continuous case. To obtain it for the discrete case, exchange summations for integrals. We first prove (a). Note that

(handwritten left margin:)
$E(X_2|X_1)$ 结果是是 X_1 的函数,
即 $E(X_2|X_1) = g(X_1).$
∴ $E[E(X_2|X_1)] = E(g(X_1))$
$= \int g(x_1) \cdot f(x_1)\, dx_1$
$= \int E(X_2|X_1) \cdot f(x_1)\, dx_1$

(handwritten top:) $= \int_{X_2} x_2 \cdot f_{X_2}\, dx_2 = \int_{X_2} x_2 \left(\int_{X_1} f_{X_1 X_2}\, dx_1\right) dx_2 =$

$$E(X_2) = \int_{-\infty}^{\infty}\int_{-\infty}^{\infty} x_2 f(x_1, x_2)\, dx_2\, dx_1$$

(handwritten:) $= f_{2|1}(x_2|x_1)$

$$= \int_{-\infty}^{\infty}\left[\int_{-\infty}^{\infty} x_2 \frac{f(x_1, x_2)}{f_1(x_1)}\, dx_2\right] f_1(x_1)\, dx_1$$

$$= \int_{-\infty}^{\infty} E(X_2|x_1) f_1(x_1)\, dx_1$$

$$= E[E(X_2|X_1)],$$

which is the first result.

Next we show (b). Consider with $\mu_2 = E(X_2)$,

$$\begin{aligned}
\text{Var}(X_2) &= E[(X_2 - \mu_2)^2] \\
&= E\{[X_2 - E(X_2|X_1) + E(X_2|X_1) - \mu_2]^2\} \\
&= E\{[X_2 - E(X_2|X_1)]^2\} + E\{[E(X_2|X_1) - \mu_2]^2\} \\
&\quad + 2E\{[X_2 - E(X_2|X_1)][E(X_2|X_1) - \mu_2]\}.
\end{aligned}$$

We show that the last term of the right-hand member of the immediately preceding equation is zero. It is equal to

结果为 x_1 的函数，与 x_2 无关，可提出到 dx_2 外

$$2 \int_{-\infty}^{\infty} \int_{-\infty}^{\infty} [x_2 - E(X_2|x_1)][E(X_2|x_1) - \mu_2] f(x_1, x_2)\, dx_2 dx_1$$

$$= 2 \int_{-\infty}^{\infty} [E(X_2|x_1) - \mu_2] \left\{ \int_{-\infty}^{\infty} [x_2 - E(X_2|x_1)] \frac{f(x_1, x_2)}{f_1(x_1)}\, dx_2 \right\} f_1(x_1)\, dx_1.$$

But $E(X_2|x_1)$ is the conditional mean of X_2, given $X_1 = x_1$. Since the expression in the inner braces is equal to

$$E(X_2|x_1) - E(X_2|x_1) = 0,$$

$\mu_2 = E(X_2) = E[E(X_2|X_1)].$

So, the double integral is equal to zero. Accordingly, we have

$$\mathrm{Var}(X_2) = E\{[X_2 - E(X_2|X_1)]^2\} + E\{[E(X_2|X_1) - \mu_2]^2\}.$$

The first term in the right-hand member of this equation is nonnegative because it is the expected value of a nonnegative function, namely $[X_2 - E(X_2|X_1)]^2$. Since $E[E(X_2|X_1)] = \mu_2$, the second term is $\mathrm{Var}[E(X_2|X_1)]$. Hence we have

$E[X_2]$

$$\mathrm{Var}(X_2) \geq \mathrm{Var}[E(X_2|X_1)],$$

which completes the proof. ∎

解释: $\mathrm{Var}(X_2)$ 更大，说明 X_2 两误差比 $E(X_2|X_1)$ 的误差大。

   Intuitively, this result could have this useful interpretation. Both the random variables X_2 and $E(X_2|X_1)$ have the same mean μ_2. If we did not know μ_2, we could use either of the two random variables to guess at the unknown μ_2. Since, however, $\mathrm{Var}(X_2) \geq \mathrm{Var}[E(X_2|X_1)]$, we would put more reliance in $E(X_2|X_1)$ as a guess. That is, if we observe the pair (X_1, X_2) to be (x_1, x_2), we could prefer to use $E(X_2|x_1)$ to x_2 as a guess at the unknown μ_2. When studying the use of sufficient statistics in estimation in Chapter 7, we make use of this famous result, attributed to C. R. Rao and David Blackwell.

   We finish this section with an example illustrating Theorem 2.3.1.

Example 2.3.3. Let X_1 and X_2 be discrete random variables. Suppose the conditional pmf of X_1 given X_2 and the marginal distribution of X_2 are given by

$P(X_1|X_2 = x_2)$ *$P_{X_2}(x_2)$*

$$\begin{cases} p(x_1|x_2) = \binom{x_2}{x_1}\left(\frac{1}{2}\right)^{x_2}, & x_1 = 0, 1, \ldots, x_2 \\[2mm] p(x_2) = \frac{2}{3}\left(\frac{1}{3}\right)^{x_2-1}, & x_2 = 1, 2, 3 \ldots. \end{cases}$$

Let us determine the mgf of X_1. For fixed x_2, by the binomial theorem,

$$E\left(e^{tX_1}|x_2\right) = \sum_{x_1=0}^{x_2} \binom{x_2}{x_1} e^{tx_1} \left(\frac{1}{2}\right)^{x_2-x_1} \left(\frac{1}{2}\right)^{x_1}$$

$= \sum_{x_1} e^{tx_1} p(x_1|x_2)$

$= \sum_{x_1=0}^{x_2} e^{tx_1}.$ $= \left(\frac{1}{2} + \frac{1}{2}e^t\right)^{x_2}.$

Hence, by the geometric series and Theorem 2.3.1,

$$
\begin{aligned}
E\left(e^{tX_1}\right) &= E\left[E\left(e^{tX_1}|X_2\right)\right] \\
&= \sum_{x_2=1}^{\infty} \left(\frac{1}{2}+\frac{1}{2}e^t\right)^{x_2} \frac{2}{3}\left(\frac{1}{3}\right)^{x_2-1} \\
&= \frac{2}{3}\left(\frac{1}{2}+\frac{1}{2}e^t\right) \sum_{x_2=1}^{\infty} \left(\frac{1}{6}+\frac{1}{6}e^t\right)^{x_2-1} \\
&= \frac{2}{3}\left(\frac{1}{2}+\frac{1}{2}e^t\right) \frac{1}{1-[(1/6)+(1/6)e^t]},
\end{aligned}
$$

provided $(1/6)+(1/6)e^t < 1$ or $t < \log 5$ (which includes $t=0$). ∎

EXERCISES

2.3.1. Let X_1 and X_2 have the joint pdf $f(x_1,x_2) = x_1 + x_2$, $0 < x_1 < 1$, $0 < x_2 < 1$, zero elsewhere. Find the conditional mean and variance of X_2, given $X_1 = x_1$, $0 < x_1 < 1$.

$\checkmark$ **2.3.2.** Let $f_{1|2}(x_1|x_2) = c_1 x_1/x_2^2$, $0 < x_1 < x_2$, $0 < x_2 < 1$, zero elsewhere, and $f_2(x_2) = c_2 x_2^4$, $0 < x_2 < 1$, zero elsewhere, denote, respectively, the conditional pdf of X_1, given $X_2 = x_2$, and the marginal pdf of X_2. Determine:

(a) The constants c_1 and c_2.

(b) The joint pdf of X_1 and X_2.

(c) $P(\frac{1}{4} < X_1 < \frac{1}{2}|X_2 = \frac{5}{8})$.

(d) $P(\frac{1}{4} < X_1 < \frac{1}{2})$.

2.3.3. Let $f(x_1,x_2) = 21x_1^2 x_2^3$, $0 < x_1 < x_2 < 1$, zero elsewhere, be the joint pdf of X_1 and X_2.

(a) Find the conditional mean and variance of X_1, given $X_2 = x_2$, $0 < x_2 < 1$.

(b) Find the distribution of $Y = E(X_1|X_2)$.

(c) Determine $E(Y)$ and $\text{Var}(Y)$ and compare these to $E(X_1)$ and $\text{Var}(X_1)$, respectively.

2.3.4. Suppose X_1 and X_2 are random variables of the discrete type which have the joint pmf $p(x_1,x_2) = (x_1 + 2x_2)/18$, $(x_1,x_2) = (1,1),(1,2),(2,1),(2,2)$, zero elsewhere. Determine the conditional mean and variance of X_2, given $X_1 = x_1$, for $x_1 = 1$ or 2. Also, compute $E(3X_1 - 2X_2)$.

2.3.5. Let X_1 and X_2 be two random variables such that the conditional distributions and means exist. Show that:

(a) $E(X_1 + X_2 \,|\, X_2) = E(X_1 \,|\, X_2) + X_2,$

(b) $E(u(X_2) \,|\, X_2) = u(X_2).$

2.3.6. Let the joint pdf of X and Y be given by

$$f(x,y) = \begin{cases} \frac{2}{(1+x+y)^3} & 0 < x < \infty,\ 0 < y < \infty \\ 0 & \text{elsewhere.} \end{cases}$$

(a) Compute the marginal pdf of X and the conditional pdf of Y, given $X = x$.

(b) For a fixed $X = x$, compute $E(1 + x + Y|x)$ and use the result to compute $E(Y|x)$.

2.3.7. Suppose X_1 and X_2 are discrete random variables which have the joint pmf $p(x_1, x_2) = (3x_1 + x_2)/24$, $(x_1, x_2) = (1,1), (1,2), (2,1), (2,2)$, zero elsewhere. Find the conditional mean $E(X_2|x_1)$, when $x_1 = 1$.

2.3.8. Let X and Y have the joint pdf $f(x,y) = 2\exp\{-(x+y)\}$, $0 < x < y < \infty$, zero elsewhere. Find the conditional mean $E(Y|x)$ of Y, given $X = x$.

2.3.9. Five cards are drawn at random and without replacement from an ordinary deck of cards. Let X_1 and X_2 denote, respectively, the number of spades and the number of hearts that appear in the five cards.

(a) Determine the joint pmf of X_1 and X_2.

(b) Find the two marginal pmfs.

(c) What is the conditional pmf of X_2, given $X_1 = x_1$?

2.3.10. Let X_1 and X_2 have the joint pmf $p(x_1, x_2)$ described as follows:

(x_1, x_2)	$(0,0)$	$(0,1)$	$(1,0)$	$(1,1)$	$(2,0)$	$(2,1)$
$p(x_1, x_2)$	$\frac{1}{18}$	$\frac{3}{18}$	$\frac{4}{18}$	$\frac{3}{18}$	$\frac{6}{18}$	$\frac{1}{18}$

and $p(x_1, x_2)$ is equal to zero elsewhere. Find the two marginal probability mass functions and the two conditional means.
Hint: Write the probabilities in a rectangular array.

2.3.11. Let us choose at random a point from the interval $(0, 1)$ and let the random variable X_1 be equal to the number which corresponds to that point. Then choose a point at random from the interval $(0, x_1)$, where x_1 is the experimental value of X_1; and let the random variable X_2 be equal to the number which corresponds to this point.

(a) Make assumptions about the marginal pdf $f_1(x_1)$ and the conditional pdf $f_{2|1}(x_2|x_1)$.

(b) Compute $P(X_1 + X_2 \geq 1)$.

(c) Find the conditional mean $E(X_1|x_2)$.

2.3.12. Let $f(x)$ and $F(x)$ denote, respectively, the pdf and the cdf of the random variable X. The conditional pdf of X, given $X > x_0$, x_0 a fixed number, is defined by $f(x|X > x_0) = f(x)/[1-F(x_0)]$, $x_0 < x$, zero elsewhere. This kind of conditional pdf finds application in a problem of time until death, given survival until time x_0.

(a) Show that $f(x|X > x_0)$ is a pdf.

(b) Let $f(x) = e^{-x}$, $0 < x < \infty$, and zero elsewhere. Compute $P(X > 2|X > 1)$.

2.4   The Correlation Coefficient

Because the result that we obtain in this section is more familiar in terms of X and Y, we use X and Y rather than X_1 and X_2 as symbols for our two random variables. Rather than discussing these concepts separately for continuous and discrete cases, we use continuous notation in our discussion. But the same properties hold for the discrete case also. Let X and Y have the joint pdf $f(x, y)$. If $u(x, y)$ is a function of x and y, then $E[u(X, Y)]$ was defined, subject to its existence, in Section 2.1. The existence of all mathematical expectations is assumed in this discussion. The means of X and Y, say μ_1 and μ_2, are obtained by taking $u(x, y)$ to be x and y, respectively; and the variances of X and Y, say σ_1^2 and σ_2^2, are obtained by setting the function $u(x, y)$ equal to $(x - \mu_1)^2$ and $(y - \mu_2)^2$, respectively. Consider the mathematical expectation

$$
\begin{aligned}
E[(X - \mu_1)(Y - \mu_2)] &= E(XY - \mu_2 X - \mu_1 Y + \mu_1 \mu_2) \\
&= E(XY) - \mu_2 E(X) - \mu_1 E(Y) + \mu_1 \mu_2 \\
&= E(XY) - \mu_1 \mu_2.
\end{aligned}
$$

This number is called the **covariance** of X and Y and is often denoted by $\mathrm{cov}(X, Y)$. If each of σ_1 and σ_2 is positive, the number

$$
\rho = \frac{E[(X - \mu_1)(Y - \mu_2)]}{\sigma_1 \sigma_2} = \frac{\mathrm{cov}(X, Y)}{\sigma_1 \sigma_2}
$$

is called the **correlation coefficient** of X and Y. It should be noted that the expected value of the product of two random variables is equal to the product of their expectations plus their covariance; that is, $E(XY) = \mu_1 \mu_2 + \rho \sigma_1 \sigma_2 = \mu_1 \mu_2 + \mathrm{cov}(X, Y)$.

Example 2.4.1. Let the random variables X and Y have the joint pdf

$$
f(x, y) = \begin{cases} x + y & 0 < x < 1, \ 0 < y < 1, \\ 0 & \text{elsewhere.} \end{cases}
$$

We next compute the correlation coefficient ρ of X and Y. Now

$$
\mu_1 = E(X) = \int_0^1 \int_0^1 x(x + y)\, dx\, dy = \frac{7}{12}.
$$

$E(g(x,y)) = \iint g(x,y) f(x,y)\, dx\, dy$

and $\frac{1}{2} g(x,y) = x^2$

$$\sigma_1^2 = E(X^2) - \mu_1^2 = \int_0^1 \int_0^1 x^2(x+y)\, dx\, dy - \left(\frac{7}{12}\right)^2 = \frac{11}{144}.$$

Similarly,

$$\mu_2 = E(Y) = \frac{7}{12} \quad \text{and} \quad \sigma_2^2 = E(Y^2) - \mu_2^2 = \frac{11}{144}.$$

The covariance of X and Y is

$$\text{Cov}(X,Y) = E(XY) - \mu_1\mu_2 = \int_0^1 \int_0^1 xy(x+y)\, dx\, dy - \left(\frac{7}{12}\right)^2 = -\frac{1}{144}.$$

Accordingly, the correlation coefficient of X and Y is

$$\rho = \frac{-\frac{1}{144}}{\sqrt{\left(\frac{11}{144}\right)\left(\frac{11}{144}\right)}} = -\frac{1}{11}. \quad \blacksquare$$

Remark 2.4.1. For certain kinds of distributions of two random variables, say X and Y, the correlation coefficient ρ proves to be a very useful characteristic of the distribution. Unfortunately, the formal definition of ρ does not reveal this fact. At this time we make some observations about ρ, some of which will be explored more fully at a later stage. It will soon be seen that if a joint distribution of two variables has a correlation coefficient (that is, if both of the variances are positive), then ρ satisfies $-1 \leq \rho \leq 1$. If $\rho = 1$, there is a line with equation $y = a + bx$, $b > 0$, the graph of which contains all of the probability of the distribution of X and Y. In this extreme case, we have $P(Y = a + bX) = 1$. If $\rho = -1$, we have the same state of affairs except that $b < 0$. This suggests the following interesting question: When ρ does not have one of its extreme values, is there a line in the xy-plane such that the probability for X and Y tends to be concentrated in a band about this line? Under certain restrictive conditions this is, in fact, the case, and under those conditions we can look upon ρ as a measure of the intensity of the concentration of the probability for X and Y about that line. $\blacksquare$

Next, let $f(x,y)$ denote the joint pdf of two random variables X and Y and let $f_1(x)$ denote the marginal pdf of X. Recall from Section 2.3 that the conditional pdf of Y, given $X = x$, is

$$f_{2|1}(y|x) = \frac{f(x,y)}{f_1(x)} \qquad \text{何为: } \tilde{f}_{2|1} = \frac{f_{21}}{f_1}$$

at points where $f_1(x) > 0$, and the conditional mean of Y, given $X = x$, is given by

$$E(Y|x) = \int_{-\infty}^{\infty} y f_{2|1}(y|x)\, dy = \frac{\int_{-\infty}^{\infty} y f(x,y)\, dy}{f_1(x)},$$

when dealing with random variables of the continuous type. This conditional mean of Y, given $X = x$, is, of course, a function of x, say $u(x)$. In a like vein, the conditional mean of X, given $Y = y$, is a function of y, say $v(y)$.

In case $u(x)$ is a linear function of x, say $u(x) = a + bx$, we say the conditional mean of Y is linear in x; or that Y is a linear conditional mean. When $u(x) = a+bx$, the constants a and b have simple values which we summarize in the following theorem.

Theorem 2.4.1. *Suppose (X, Y) have a joint distribution with the variances of X and Y finite and positive. Denote the means and variances of X and Y by μ_1, μ_2 and σ_1^2, σ_2^2, respectively, and let ρ be the correlation coefficient between X and Y. If $E(Y|X)$ is linear in X then*

$$E(Y|X) = \mu_2 + \rho\frac{\sigma_2}{\sigma_1}(X - \mu_1) \tag{2.4.1}$$

and

$$E(Var(Y|X)) = \sigma_2^2(1 - \rho^2). \tag{2.4.2}$$

Proof: The proof is given in the continuous case. The discrete case follows similarly by changing integrals to sums. Let $E(Y|x) = a + bx$. From

$$E(Y|x) = \frac{\int_{-\infty}^{\infty} y f(x,y)\, dy}{f_1(x)} = a + bx,$$

we have

$$\int_{-\infty}^{\infty} y f(x,y)\, dy = (a + bx) f_1(x). \tag{2.4.3}$$

If both members of Equation (2.4.3) are integrated on x, it is seen that

$$\int_{-\infty}^{+\infty}\left(\int_{-\infty}^{+\infty} y f(x,y)\, dy\right) dx = \int_{-\infty}^{+\infty}\left[(a+bx) f_1(x)\right] dx.$$

$$\int_{-\infty}^{\infty}\int_{-\infty}^{\infty} y f(x,y)\, dx\, dy = \int_{-\infty}^{\infty} a f_1(x)\, dx + \int_{-\infty}^{\infty} b x f_1(x)\, dx.$$

$$E(Y) = a + bE(X)$$

or $E(Y) = E(a) + E(bX)$
$$= a + bE(X)$$

$$\mu_2 = a + b\mu_1, \tag{2.4.4}$$

where $\mu_1 = E(X)$ and $\mu_2 = E(Y)$. If both members of Equation (2.4.3) are first multiplied by x and then integrated on x, we have

$$E(XY) = aE(X) + bE(X^2),$$

or

$$\rho\sigma_1\sigma_2 + \mu_1\mu_2 = a\mu_1 + b(\sigma_1^2 + \mu_1^2), \tag{2.4.5}$$

where $\rho\sigma_1\sigma_2$ is the covariance of X and Y. The simultaneous solution of equations (2.4.4) and (2.4.5) yields

$$a = \mu_2 - \rho\frac{\sigma_2}{\sigma_1}\mu_1 \quad \text{and} \quad b = \rho\frac{\sigma_2}{\sigma_1}.$$

These values give the first result (2.4.1).

The conditional variance of Y is given by

$$\mathrm{Var}(Y|x) = \int_{-\infty}^{\infty} \left[y - \mu_2 - \rho \frac{\sigma_2}{\sigma_1}(x - \mu_1) \right]^2 f_{2|1}(y|x)\, dy$$

$$= \frac{\int_{-\infty}^{\infty} \left[(y - \mu_2) - \rho \frac{\sigma_2}{\sigma_1}(x - \mu_1) \right]^2 f(x, y)\, dy}{f_1(x)}. \qquad (2.4.6)$$

This variance is nonnegative and is at most a function of x alone. If it is multiplied by $f_1(x)$ and integrated on x, the result obtained is nonnegative. This result is

$$\int_{-\infty}^{\infty} \int_{-\infty}^{\infty} \left[(y - \mu_2) - \rho \frac{\sigma_2}{\sigma_1}(x - \mu_1) \right]^2 f(x, y)\, dy dx$$

$$= \int_{-\infty}^{\infty} \int_{-\infty}^{\infty} \left[(y - \mu_2)^2 - 2\rho \frac{\sigma_2}{\sigma_1}(y - \mu_2)(x - \mu_1) + \rho^2 \frac{\sigma_2^2}{\sigma_1^2}(x - \mu_1)^2 \right] f(x, y)\, dy dx$$

$$= E[(Y - \mu_2)^2] - 2\rho \frac{\sigma_2}{\sigma_1} E[(X - \mu_1)(Y - \mu_2)] + \rho^2 \frac{\sigma_2^2}{\sigma_1^2} E[(X - \mu_1)^2]$$

$$= \sigma_2^2 - 2\rho \frac{\sigma_2}{\sigma_1} \rho \sigma_1 \sigma_2 + \rho^2 \frac{\sigma_2^2}{\sigma_1^2} \sigma_1^2$$

$$= \sigma_2^2 - 2\rho^2 \sigma_2^2 + \rho^2 \sigma_2^2 = \sigma_2^2(1 - \rho^2),$$

which is the desired result. ∎

Note that if the variance, Equation (2.4.6), is denoted by $k(x)$, then $E[k(X)] = \sigma_2^2(1 - \rho^2) \geq 0$. Accordingly, $\rho^2 \leq 1$, or $-1 \leq \rho \leq 1$. It is left as an exercise to prove that $-1 \leq \rho \leq 1$ whether the conditional mean is or is not linear; see Exercise 2.4.7.

Suppose that the variance, Equation (2.4.6), is positive but not a function of x; that is, the variance is a constant $k > 0$. Now if k is multiplied by $f_1(x)$ and integrated on x, the result is k, so that $k = \sigma_2^2(1 - \rho^2)$. Thus, in this case, the variance of each conditional distribution of Y, given $X = x$, is $\sigma_2^2(1 - \rho^2)$. If $\rho = 0$, the variance of each conditional distribution of Y, given $X = x$, is σ_2^2, the variance of the marginal distribution of Y. On the other hand, if ρ^2 is near 1, the variance of each conditional distribution of Y, given $X = x$, is relatively small, and there is a high concentration of the probability for this conditional distribution near the mean $E(Y|x) = \mu_2 + \rho(\sigma_2/\sigma_1)(x - \mu_1)$. Similar comments can be made about $E(X|y)$ if it is linear. In particular, $E(X|y) = \mu_1 + \rho(\sigma_1/\sigma_2)(y - \mu_2)$ and $E[\mathrm{Var}(X|Y)] = \sigma_1^2(1 - \rho^2)$.

Example 2.4.2. Let the random variables X and Y have the linear conditional means $E(Y|x) = 4x + 3$ and $E(X|y) = \frac{1}{16}y - 3$. In accordance with the general formulas for the linear conditional means, we see that $E(Y|x) = \mu_2$ if $x = \mu_1$ and $E(X|y) = \mu_1$ if $y = \mu_2$. Accordingly, in this special case, we have $\mu_2 = 4\mu_1 + 3$ and $\mu_1 = \frac{1}{16}\mu_2 - 3$ so that $\mu_1 = -\frac{15}{4}$ and $\mu_2 = -12$. The general formulas for the linear conditional means also show that the product of the coefficients of x and y, respectively, is equal to ρ^2 and that the quotient of these coefficients is equal to

σ_2^2/σ_1^2. Here $\rho^2 = 4(\frac{1}{16}) = \frac{1}{4}$ with $\rho = \frac{1}{2}$ (not $-\frac{1}{2}$), and $\sigma_2^2/\sigma_1^2 = 64$. Thus, from the two linear conditional means, we are able to find the values of μ_1, μ_2, ρ, and σ_2/σ_1, but not the values of σ_1 and σ_2. ∎

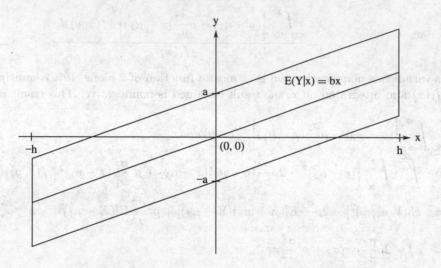

Figure 2.4.1: Illustration for Example 2.4.3.

Example 2.4.3. To illustrate how the correlation coefficient measures the intensity of the concentration of the probability for X and Y about a line, let these random variables have a distribution that is uniform over the area depicted in Figure 2.4.1. That is, the joint pdf of X and Y is

$$f(x,y) = \begin{cases} \frac{1}{4ah} & -a+bx < y < a+bx, \quad -h < x < h \\ 0 & \text{elsewhere.} \end{cases}$$

We assume here that $b \geq 0$, but the argument can be modified for $b \leq 0$. It is easy to show that the pdf of X is uniform, namely

$$f_1(x) = \begin{cases} \int_{-a+bx}^{a+bx} \frac{1}{4ah}\, dy = \frac{1}{2h} & -h < x < h \\ 0 & \text{elsewhere.} \end{cases}$$

The conditional mean and variance are

$$E(Y|x) = bx \quad \text{and} \quad \text{var}(Y|x) = \frac{a^2}{3}.$$

From the general expressions for those characteristics we know that

$$b = \rho\frac{\sigma_2}{\sigma_1} \quad \text{and} \quad \frac{a^2}{3} = \sigma_2^2(1-\rho^2).$$

Additionally, we know that $\sigma_1^2 = h^2/3$. If we solve these three equations, we obtain an expression for the correlation coefficient, namely

$$\rho = \frac{bh}{\sqrt{a^2 + b^2h^2}}.$$

Referring to Figure 2.4.1, we note

1. As a gets small (large), the straight-line effect is more (less) intense and ρ is closer to 1 (0).

2. As h gets large (small), the straight-line effect is more (less) intense and ρ is closer to 1 (0).

3. As b gets large (small), the straight-line effect is more (less) intense and ρ is closer to 1 (0).   ■

Recall that in Section 2.1 we introduced the mgf for the random vector (X, Y). As for random variables, the joint mgf also gives explicit formulas for certain moments. In the case of random variables of the continuous type,

$$\frac{\partial^{k+m} M(t_1, t_2)}{\partial t_1^k \partial t_2^m} = \int_{-\infty}^{\infty} \int_{-\infty}^{\infty} x^k y^m e^{t_1 x + t_2 y} f(x, y)\, dxdy,$$

so that

$$\left. \frac{\partial^{k+m} M(t_1, t_2)}{\partial t_1^k \partial t_2^m} \right|_{t_1 = t_2 = 0} = \int_{-\infty}^{\infty} \int_{-\infty}^{\infty} x^k y^m f(x, y)\, dxdy = E(X^k Y^m).$$

For instance, in a simplified notation that appears to be clear,

$$\mu_1 = E(X) = \frac{\partial M(0,0)}{\partial t_1}$$

$$\mu_2 = E(Y) = \frac{\partial M(0,0)}{\partial t_2}$$

$$\sigma_1^2 = E(X^2) - \mu_1^2 = \frac{\partial^2 M(0,0)}{\partial t_1^2} - \mu_1^2$$

$$\sigma_2^2 = E(Y^2) - \mu_2^2 = \frac{\partial^2 M(0,0)}{\partial t_2^2} - \mu_2^2$$

$$E[(X - \mu_1)(Y - \mu_2)] = \frac{\partial^2 M(0,0)}{\partial t_1 \partial t_2} - \mu_1 \mu_2, \tag{2.4.7}$$

and from these we can compute the correlation coefficient ρ.

It is fairly obvious that the results of equations (2.4.7) hold if X and Y are random variables of the discrete type. Thus the correlation coefficients may be computed by using the mgf of the joint distribution if that function is readily available. An illustrative example follows.

Example 2.4.4 (Example 2.1.7, Continued). In Example 2.1.7, we considered the joint density

$$f(x,y) = \begin{cases} e^{-y} & 0 < x < y < \infty \\ 0 & \text{elsewhere,} \end{cases}$$

and showed that the mgf was

$$M(t_1, t_2) = \frac{1}{(1 - t_1 - t_2)(1 - t_2)},$$

for $t_1 + t_2 < 1$ and $t_2 < 1$. For this distribution, equations (2.4.7) become

$$\begin{aligned} \mu_1 = 1, \quad \mu_2 &= 2 \\ \sigma_1^2 = 1, \quad \sigma_2^2 &= 2 \\ E[(X - \mu_1)(Y - \mu_2)] &= 1. \end{aligned} \tag{2.4.8}$$

Verification of (2.4.8) is left as an exercise; see Exercise 2.4.5. If, momentarily, we accept these results, the correlation coefficient of X and Y is $\rho = 1/\sqrt{2}$. ∎

EXERCISES

2.4.1. Let the random variables X and Y have the joint pmf

(a) $p(x,y) = \frac{1}{3}$, $(x,y) = (0,0),(1,1),(2,2)$, zero elsewhere.

(b) $p(x,y) = \frac{1}{3}$, $(x,y) = (0,2),(1,1),(2,0)$, zero elsewhere.

(c) $p(x,y) = \frac{1}{3}$, $(x,y) = (0,0),(1,1),(2,0)$, zero elsewhere.

In each case compute the correlation coefficient of X and Y.

2.4.2. Let X and Y have the joint pmf described as follows:

(x,y)	$(1,1)$	$(1,2)$	$(1,3)$	$(2,1)$	$(2,2)$	$(2,3)$
$p(x,y)$	$\frac{2}{15}$	$\frac{4}{15}$	$\frac{3}{15}$	$\frac{1}{15}$	$\frac{1}{15}$	$\frac{4}{15}$

and $p(x,y)$ is equal to zero elsewhere.

(a) Find the means μ_1 and μ_2, the variances σ_1^2 and σ_2^2, and the correlation coefficient ρ.

(b) Compute $E(Y|X = 1)$, $E(Y|X = 2)$, and the line $\mu_2 + \rho(\sigma_2/\sigma_1)(x - \mu_1)$. Do the points $[k, E(Y|X = k)]$, $k = 1, 2$, lie on this line?

2.4.3. Let $f(x,y) = 2$, $0 < x < y$, $0 < y < 1$, zero elsewhere, be the joint pdf of X and Y. Show that the conditional means are, respectively, $(1+x)/2$, $0 < x < 1$, and $y/2$, $0 < y < 1$. Show that the correlation coefficient of X and Y is $\rho = \frac{1}{2}$.

2.4.4. Show that the variance of the conditional distribution of Y, given $X = x$, in Exercise 2.4.3, is $(1 - x)^2/12$, $0 < x < 1$, and that the variance of the conditional distribution of X, given $Y = y$, is $y^2/12$, $0 < y < 1$.

2.4.5. Verify the results of equations (2.4.8) of this section.

2.4.6. Let X and Y have the joint pdf $f(x, y) = 1$, $-x < y < x$, $0 < x < 1$, zero elsewhere. Show that, on the set of positive probability density, the graph of $E(Y|x)$ is a straight line, whereas that of $E(X|y)$ is not a straight line.

2.4.7. If the correlation coefficient ρ of X and Y exists, show that $-1 \leq \rho \leq 1$. *Hint:* Consider the discriminant of the nonnegative quadratic function

$$h(v) = E\{[(X - \mu_1) + v(Y - \mu_2)]^2\},$$

where v is real and is not a function of X nor of Y.

2.4.8. Let $\psi(t_1, t_2) = \log M(t_1, t_2)$, where $M(t_1, t_2)$ is the mgf of X and Y. Show that

$$\frac{\partial \psi(0,0)}{\partial t_i}, \quad \frac{\partial^2 \psi(0,0)}{\partial t_i^2}, \quad i = 1, 2,$$

and

$$\frac{\partial^2 \psi(0,0)}{\partial t_1 \partial t_2}$$

yield the means, the variances, and the covariance of the two random variables. Use this result to find the means, the variances, and the covariance of X and Y of Example 2.4.4.

2.4.9. Let X and Y have the joint pmf $p(x, y) = \frac{1}{7}$, $(0,0), (1,0), (0,1), (1,1), (2,1),$ $(1,2), (2,2)$, zero elsewhere. Find the correlation coefficient ρ.

2.4.10. Let X_1 and X_2 have the joint pmf described by the following table:

(x_1, x_2)	$(0,0)$	$(0,1)$	$(0,2)$	$(1,1)$	$(1,2)$	$(2,2)$
$p(x_1, x_2)$	$\frac{1}{12}$	$\frac{2}{12}$	$\frac{1}{12}$	$\frac{3}{12}$	$\frac{4}{12}$	$\frac{1}{12}$

Find $p_1(x_1), p_2(x_2), \mu_1, \mu_2, \sigma_1^2, \sigma_2^2$, and ρ.

2.4.11. Let $\sigma_1^2 = \sigma_2^2 = \sigma^2$ be the common variance of X_1 and X_2 and let ρ be the correlation coefficient of X_1 and X_2. Show for $k > 0$ that

$$P[|(X_1 - \mu_1) + (X_2 - \mu_2)| \geq k\sigma] \leq \frac{2(1 + \rho)}{k^2}.$$

2.5 Independent Random Variables

Let X_1 and X_2 denote the random variables of the continuous type which have the joint pdf $f(x_1, x_2)$ and marginal probability density functions $f_1(x_1)$ and $f_2(x_2)$, respectively. In accordance with the definition of the conditional pdf $f_{2|1}(x_2|x_1)$, we may write the joint pdf $f(x_1, x_2)$ as

对阿干: $f(AB) = f(B|A) f(A)$.

$$f(x_1, x_2) = f_{2|1}(x_2|x_1)f_1(x_1).$$

Suppose that we have an instance where $f_{2|1}(x_2|x_1)$ does not depend upon x_1. Then the marginal pdf of X_2 is, for random variables of the continuous type,

(据定义) $\int_{-\infty}^{\infty} f(x_1, x_2)\, dx_1$

$$f_2(x_2) = \int_{-\infty}^{\infty} f_{2|1}(x_2|x_1)f_1(x_1)\, dx_1$$

∵ $f_{2|1}(x_2|x_1)$ does not depend on x_1,
即 $f_{2|1}(x_2|x_1)$ 结果与 x_1 无关.

$$= f_{2|1}(x_2|x_1)\int_{-\infty}^{\infty} f_1(x_1)\, dx_1 = 1.$$

∴ $f_{2|1}(x_2|x_1)$ 可提取出来到 ∫ 外.

$$= f_{2|1}(x_2|x_1).$$

其余还有:
$\int_{-\infty}^{\infty} f_2(x_2)\, dx_2 = 1$
$\int_{-\infty}^{\infty} f_{2|1}(x_2|x_1)\, dx_2 = 1$
$\int_{-\infty}^{\infty} f_{1|2}(x_1|x_2)\, dx_1 = 1$

均为.

Accordingly,

$$f_2(x_2) = f_{2|1}(x_2|x_1) \quad \text{and} \quad f(x_1, x_2) = f_1(x_1)f_2(x_2),$$

when $f_{2|1}(x_2|x_1)$ does not depend upon x_1. That is, if the conditional distribution of X_2, given $X_1 = x_1$, is independent of any assumption about x_1, then $f(x_1, x_2) = f_1(x_1)f_2(x_2)$.

The same discussion applies to the discrete case too, which we summarize in parentheses in the following definition.

Definition 2.5.1 (Independence). *Let the random variables X_1 and X_2 have the joint pdf $f(x_1, x_2)$ [joint pmf $p(x_1, x_2)$] and the marginal pdfs [pmfs] $f_1(x_1)$ [$p_1(x_1)$] and $f_2(x_2)$ [$p_2(x_2)$], respectively. The random variables X_1 and X_2 are said to be* **independent** *if, and only if, $f(x_1, x_2) \equiv f_1(x_1)f_2(x_2)$ [$p(x_1, x_2) \equiv p_1(x_1)p_2(x_2)$]. Random variables that are not independent are said to be* **dependent**.

Remark 2.5.1. Two comments should be made about the preceding definition. First, the product of two positive functions $f_1(x_1)f_2(x_2)$ means a function that is positive on the product space. That is, if $f_1(x_1)$ and $f_2(x_2)$ are positive on, and only on, the respective spaces $\mathcal{S}_1$ and $\mathcal{S}_2$, then the product of $f_1(x_1)$ and $f_2(x_2)$ is positive on, and only on, the product space $\mathcal{S} = \{(x_1, x_2) : x_1 \in \mathcal{S}_1,\ x_2 \in \mathcal{S}_2\}$. For instance, if $\mathcal{S}_1 = \{x_1 : 0 < x_1 < 1\}$ and $\mathcal{S}_2 = \{x_2 : 0 < x_2 < 3\}$, then $\mathcal{S} = \{(x_1, x_2) : 0 < x_1 < 1,\ 0 < x_2 < 3\}$. The second remark pertains to the identity. The identity in Definition 2.5.1 should be interpreted as follows. There may be certain points $(x_1, x_2) \in \mathcal{S}$ at which $f(x_1, x_2) \neq f_1(x_1)f_2(x_2)$. However, if A is the set of points (x_1, x_2) at which the equality does not hold, then $P(A) = 0$. In subsequent theorems and the subsequent generalizations, a product of nonnegative functions and an identity should be interpreted in an analogous manner. ∎

Example 2.5.1. Let the joint pdf of X_1 and X_2 be

$$f(x_1, x_2) = \begin{cases} x_1 + x_2 & 0 < x_1 < 1, \ 0 < x_2 < 1 \\ 0 & \text{elsewhere.} \end{cases}$$

We show that X_1 and X_2 are dependent. Here the marginal probability density functions are

$$f_1(x_1) = \begin{cases} \int_{-\infty}^{\infty} f(x_1, x_2)\, dx_2 = \int_0^1 (x_1 + x_2)\, dx_2 = x_1 + \frac{1}{2} & 0 < x_1 < 1 \\ 0 & \text{elsewhere,} \end{cases}$$

and

$$f_2(x_2) = \begin{cases} \int_{-\infty}^{\infty} f(x_1, x_2)\, dx_1 = \int_0^1 (x_1 + x_2)\, dx_1 = \frac{1}{2} + x_2 & 0 < x_2 < 1 \\ 0 & \text{elsewhere.} \end{cases}$$

Since $f(x_1, x_2) \not\equiv f_1(x_1) f_2(x_2)$, the random variables X_1 and X_2 are dependent. ∎

The following theorem makes it possible to assert that the random variables X_1 and X_2 of Example 2.5.1 are dependent, without computing the marginal probability density functions.

Theorem 2.5.1. *Let the random variables X_1 and X_2 have supports $\mathcal{S}_1$ and $\mathcal{S}_2$, respectively, and have the joint pdf $f(x_1, x_2)$. Then X_1 and X_2 are independent if and only if $f(x_1, x_2)$ can be written as a product of a nonnegative function of x_1 and a nonnegative function of x_2. That is,*

$$f(x_1, x_2) \equiv g(x_1) h(x_2),$$

where $g(x_1) > 0$, $x_1 \in \mathcal{S}_1$, zero elsewhere, and $h(x_2) > 0$, $x_2 \in \mathcal{S}_2$, zero elsewhere.

Proof. If X_1 and X_2 are independent, then $f(x_1, x_2) \equiv f_1(x_1) f_2(x_2)$, where $f_1(x_1)$ and $f_2(x_2)$ are the marginal probability density functions of X_1 and X_2, respectively. Thus the condition $f(x_1, x_2) \equiv g(x_1) h(x_2)$ is fulfilled.

Conversely, if $f(x_1, x_2) \equiv g(x_1) h(x_2)$, then, for random variables of the continuous type, we have

$$f_1(x_1) = \int_{-\infty}^{\infty} g(x_1) h(x_2)\, dx_2 = g(x_1) \int_{-\infty}^{\infty} h(x_2)\, dx_2 = c_1 g(x_1)$$

and

$$f_2(x_2) = \int_{-\infty}^{\infty} g(x_1) h(x_2)\, dx_1 = h(x_2) \int_{-\infty}^{\infty} g(x_1)\, dx_1 = c_2 h(x_2),$$

where c_1 and c_2 are constants, not functions of x_1 or x_2. Moreover, $c_1 c_2 = 1$ because

$$1 = \int_{-\infty}^{\infty} \int_{-\infty}^{\infty} g(x_1) h(x_2)\, dx_1 dx_2 = \left[\int_{-\infty}^{\infty} g(x_1)\, dx_1 \right] \left[\int_{-\infty}^{\infty} h(x_2)\, dx_2 \right] = c_2 c_1.$$

These results imply that

$$f(x_1, x_2) \equiv g(x_1) h(x_2) \equiv c_1 g(x_1) c_2 h(x_2) \equiv f_1(x_1) f_2(x_2).$$

取值范围不
能凑起在
一起!(即不能
有函数关系!)

Accordingly, X_1 and X_2 are independent. ∎

This theorem is true for the discrete case also. Simply replace the joint pdf by the joint pmf.

If we now refer to Example 2.5.1, we see that the joint pdf

$$f(x_1, x_2) = \begin{cases} x_1 + x_2 & 0 < x_1 < 1, \ 0 < x_2 < 1 \\ 0 & \text{elsewhere} \end{cases}$$

cannot be written as the product of a nonnegative function of x_1 and a nonnegative function of x_2. Accordingly, X_1 and X_2 are dependent.

$f(x_1, x_2) = 8x_1 x_2$
$\Rightarrow$
$f(x_1) = \int_{-\infty}^{\infty} f(x_1, x_2) dx_2$
$= \int_{x_1}^{1} f(x_1, x_2) dx_2$
$= 4x_1(1 - x_1^2)$

同样
$f(x_2) = 4x_2(1 - x_2^2)$
$\therefore f(x_1, x_2) \neq f(x_1) f(x_2)$
$\therefore x_1, x_2$ 是 dependent.

Example 2.5.2. Let the pdf of the random variable X_1 and X_2 be $f(x_1, x_2) = 8x_1 x_2$, $0 < x_1 < x_2 < 1$, zero elsewhere. The formula $8x_1 x_2$ might suggest to some that X_1 and X_2 are independent. However, if we consider the space $\mathcal{S} = \{(x_1, x_2) : 0 < x_1 < x_2 < 1\}$, we see that it is not a product space. This should make it clear that, in general, X_1 and X_2 must be dependent if the space of positive probability density of X_1 and X_2 is bounded by a curve that is neither a horizontal nor a vertical line. ∎

只有当 x_1、x_2 分别只由水平线或垂直线 bounded 时 (例：$0 < x_1 < 1$, $2 < x_2 < 4$), x_1 与 x_2 之间才可能是 independent 的。
即 x_1与x_2 的关系曲线, 如 $x_2 = x_1$

$x_2 = x_1$

Instead of working with pdfs (or pmfs) we could have presented independence in terms of cumulative distribution functions. The following theorem shows the equivalence.

x_1 被 $x_1 = 0$ 与 $x_1 = x_2$ 两线 bounded 住.
$\Rightarrow$ 若 x_1, x_2 由 x_1, x_2 之间的关系曲线 bounded 住(例如, $0 < x_1 < x_2$), 则 x_1, x_2 之间一定是 dependent 的.

Theorem 2.5.2. *Let (X_1, X_2) have the joint cdf $F(x_1, x_2)$ and let X_1 and X_2 have the marginal cdfs $F_1(x_1)$ and $F_2(x_2)$, respectively. Then X_1 and X_2 are independent if and only if*

$$F(x_1, x_2) = F_1(x_1)F_2(x_2) \quad \text{for all } (x_1, x_2) \in R^2 . \tag{2.5.1}$$

Proof: We give the proof for the continuous case. Suppose expression (2.5.1) holds. Then the mixed second partial is

$$\frac{\partial^2}{\partial x_1 \partial x_2} F(x_1, x_2) = f_1(x_1)f_2(x_2).$$

$\Rightarrow \frac{\partial^2}{\partial x_1 \partial x_2}(F_1(x_1)F_2(x_2)) = \frac{\partial}{\partial x_2}\left(\frac{\partial}{\partial x_1}(F_1(x_1)F_2(x_2))\right)$
$= \frac{\partial}{\partial x_2}\left[F_2(x_2)\frac{\partial}{\partial x_1}(F_1(x_1))\right]$
$= \frac{\partial}{\partial x_2}[F_2(x_2) \cdot f_1(x_1)]$
$= f_1(x_1) \cdot \frac{\partial}{\partial x_2}(F_2(x_2)) = f_1(x_1) \cdot f_2(x_2)$

Hence, X_1 and X_2 are independent. Conversely, suppose X_1 and X_2 are independent. Then by the definition of the joint cdf, (P74 ~ P75)

(精定义) $\stackrel{\downarrow}{=} \int_{-\infty}^{x_1}\int_{-\infty}^{x_2} f_{X_1, X_2}(w_1, w_2) dw_1 dw_2$

$$F(x_1, x_2) \stackrel{\downarrow}{=} \int_{-\infty}^{x_1}\int_{-\infty}^{x_2} f_1(w_1)f_2(w_2) \, dw_2 dw_1$$

w_1, w_2 indep.
$\Rightarrow f(w_1, w_2) = f(w_1)f(w_2)$

$$= \int_{-\infty}^{x_1} f_1(w_1) \, dw_1 \cdot \int_{-\infty}^{x_2} f_2(w_2) \, dw_2 = F_1(x_1)F_2(x_2).$$

Hence, condition (2.5.1) is true. ∎

We now give a theorem that frequently simplifies the calculations of probabilities of events which involve independent variables.

Theorem 2.5.3. *The random variables X_1 and X_2 are independent random variables if and only if the following condition holds,*

$$P(a < X_1 \leq b, c < X_2 \leq d) = P(a < X_1 \leq b)P(c < X_2 \leq d) \qquad (2.5.2)$$

for every $a < b$ and $c < d$, where $a, b, c,$ and d are constants.

Proof: If X_1 and X_2 are independent, then an application of the last theorem and expression (2.1.2) shows that

$$
\begin{aligned}
P(a < X_1 \leq b, c < X_2 \leq d) &= F(b,d) - F(a,d) - F(b,c) + F(a,c) \\
&= F_1(b)F_2(d) - F_1(a)F_2(d) - F_1(b)F_2(c) \\
&\quad + F_1(a)F_2(c) \\
&= [F_1(b) - F_1(a)][F_2(d) - F_2(c)],
\end{aligned}
$$

which is the right side of expression (2.5.2). Conversely, condition (2.5.2) implies that the joint cdf of (X_1, X_2) factors into a product of the marginal cdfs, which in turn by Theorem 2.5.2 implies that X_1 and X_2 are independent. ∎

Example 2.5.3 (Example 2.5.1, Continued). Independence is necessary for condition (2.5.2). For example, consider the dependent variables X_1 and X_2 of Example 2.5.1. For these random variables, we have

$$P(0 < X_1 < \tfrac{1}{2}, 0 < X_2 < \tfrac{1}{2}) = \int_0^{1/2} \int_0^{1/2} (x_1 + x_2)\, dx_1 dx_2 = \tfrac{1}{8},$$

whereas

$$P(0 < X_1 < \tfrac{1}{2}) = \int_0^{1/2} (x_1 + \tfrac{1}{2})\, dx_1 = \tfrac{3}{8}$$

and

$$P(0 < X_2 < \tfrac{1}{2}) = \int_0^{1/2} (\tfrac{1}{2} + x_1)\, dx_2 = \tfrac{3}{8}.$$

Hence, condition (2.5.2) does not hold. ∎

Not merely are calculations of some probabilities usually simpler when we have independent random variables, but many expectations, including certain moment generating functions, have comparably simpler computations. The following result proves so useful that we state it in the form of a theorem.

Theorem 2.5.4. *Suppose X_1 and X_2 are independent and that $E(u(X_1))$ and $E(v(X_2))$ exist. Then*

$$E[u(X_1)v(X_2)] = E[u(X_1)]E[v(X_2)].$$

Proof. We give the proof in the continuous case. The independence of X_1 and X_2 implies that the joint pdf of X_1 and X_2 is $f_1(x_1)f_2(x_2)$. Thus we have, by definition of expectation,

$$
\begin{aligned}
E[u(X_1)v(X_2)] &= \int_{-\infty}^{\infty} \int_{-\infty}^{\infty} u(x_1)v(x_2)f_1(x_1)f_2(x_2)\, dx_1 dx_2 \\
&= \left[\int_{-\infty}^{\infty} u(x_1)f_1(x_1)\, dx_1 \right]\left[\int_{-\infty}^{\infty} v(x_2)f_2(x_2)\, dx_2 \right] \\
&= E[u(X_1)]E[v(X_2)].
\end{aligned}
$$

Hence, the result is true. ∎

Upon taking the functions $u(\cdot)$ and $v(\cdot)$ to be the identity functions in Theorem 2.5.4, we have that for independent random variables X_1 and X_2,

$$E(X_1 X_2) = E(X_1) E(X_2). \tag{2.5.3}$$

Example 2.5.4. Let X and Y be two independent random variables with means μ_1 and μ_2 and positive variances σ_1^2 and σ_2^2, respectively. We show that the independence of X and Y implies that the correlation coefficient of X and Y is zero. This is true because the covariance of X and Y is equal to

$$E[(X - \mu_1)(Y - \mu_2)] = E(X - \mu_1) E(Y - \mu_2) = 0. \quad ∎$$

We next prove a very useful theorem about independent random variables. The proof of the theorem relies heavily upon our assertion that an mgf, when it exists, is unique and that it uniquely determines the distribution of probability.

Theorem 2.5.5. *Suppose the joint mgf, $M(t_1, t_2)$, exists for the random variables X_1 and X_2. Then X_1 and X_2 are independent if and only if*

$$M(t_1, t_2) = M(t_1, 0) M(0, t_2);$$

that is, the joint mgf is identically equal to the product of the marginal mgfs.

Proof. If X_1 and X_2 are independent, then

$$
\begin{aligned}
M(t_1, t_2) &= E(e^{t_1 X_1 + t_2 X_2}) \\
&= E(e^{t_1 X_1} e^{t_2 X_2}) \\
&= E(e^{t_1 X_1}) E(e^{t_2 X_2}) \\
&= M(t_1, 0) M(0, t_2).
\end{aligned}
$$

Thus the independence of X_1 and X_2 implies that the mgf of the joint distribution factors into the product of the moment-generating functions of the two marginal distributions.

Suppose next that the mgf of the joint distribution of X_1 and X_2 is given by $M(t_1, t_2) = M(t_1, 0) M(0, t_2)$. Now X_1 has the unique mgf, which, in the continuous case, is given by

$$M(t_1, 0) = \int_{-\infty}^{\infty} e^{t_1 x_1} f_1(x_1) \, dx_1.$$

Similarly, the unique mgf of X_2, in the continuous case, is given by

$$M(0, t_2) = \int_{-\infty}^{\infty} e^{t_2 x_2} f_2(x_2) \, dx_2.$$

Thus we have

$$
\begin{aligned}
M(t_1, 0) M(0, t_2) &= \left[\int_{-\infty}^{\infty} e^{t_1 x_1} f_1(x_1) \, dx_1 \right] \left[\int_{-\infty}^{\infty} e^{t_2 x_2} f_2(x_2) \, dx_2 \right] \\
&= \int_{-\infty}^{\infty} \int_{-\infty}^{\infty} e^{t_1 x_1 + t_2 x_2} f_1(x_1) f_2(x_2) \, dx_1 dx_2.
\end{aligned}
$$

We are given that $M(t_1, t_2) = M(t_1, 0)M(0, t_2)$; so

$$M(t_1, t_2) = \int_{-\infty}^{\infty} \int_{-\infty}^{\infty} e^{t_1 x_1 + t_2 x_2} f_1(x_1) f_2(x_2) \, dx_1 dx_2.$$

But $M(t_1, t_2)$ is the mgf of X_1 and X_2. Thus

$$M(t_1, t_2) = \int_{-\infty}^{\infty} \int_{-\infty}^{\infty} e^{t_1 x_1 + t_2 x_2} f(x_1, x_2) \, dx_1 dx_2.$$

The uniqueness of the mgf implies that the two distributions of probability that are described by $f_1(x_1)f_2(x_2)$ and $f(x_1, x_2)$ are the same. Thus

$$f(x_1, x_2) \equiv f_1(x_1) f_2(x_2).$$

That is, if $M(t_1, t_2) = M(t_1, 0)M(0, t_2)$, then X_1 and X_2 are independent. This completes the proof when the random variables are of the continuous type. With random variables of the discrete type, the proof is made by using summation instead of integration. ∎

Example 2.5.5 (Example 2.1.7, Continued). Let (X, Y) be a pair of random variables with the joint pdf

$$f(x, y) = \begin{cases} e^{-y} & 0 < x < y < \infty \\ 0 & \text{elsewhere.} \end{cases}$$

In Example 2.1.7, we showed that the mgf of (X, Y) is

$$
\begin{aligned}
M(t_1, t_2) &= \int_0^{\infty} \int_x^{\infty} \exp(t_1 x + t_2 y - y) \, dy dx \\
&= \frac{1}{(1 - t_1 - t_2)(1 - t_2)},
\end{aligned}
$$

provided that $t_1 + t_2 < 1$ and $t_2 < 1$. Because $M(t_1, t_2) \neq M(t_1, 0)M(t_1, 0)$, the random variables are dependent. ∎

Example 2.5.6 (Exercise 2.1.14, Continued). For the random variable X_1 and X_2 defined in Exercise 2.1.14, we showed that the joint mgf is

$$M(t_1, t_2) = \left[\frac{\exp\{t_1\}}{2 - \exp\{t_1\}} \right] \left[\frac{\exp\{t_2\}}{2 - \exp\{t_2\}} \right], \quad t_i < \log 2, \, i = 1, 2.$$

We showed further that $M(t_1, t_2) = M(t_1, 0)M(0, t_2)$. Hence, X_1 and X_2 are independent random variables. ∎

EXERCISES

2.5.1. Show that the random variables X_1 and X_2 with joint pdf

$$f(x_1, x_2) = \begin{cases} 12x_1x_2(1-x_2) & 0 < x_1 < 1, \ 0 < x_2 < 1 \\ 0 & \text{elsewhere} \end{cases}$$

are independent.

2.5.2. If the random variables X_1 and X_2 have the joint pdf $f(x_1, x_2) = 2e^{-x_1-x_2}$, $0 < x_1 < x_2$, $0 < x_2 < \infty$, zero elsewhere, show that X_1 and X_2 are dependent.

2.5.3. Let $p(x_1, x_2) = \frac{1}{16}$, $x_1 = 1, 2, 3, 4$, and $x_2 = 1, 2, 3, 4$, zero elsewhere, be the joint pmf of X_1 and X_2. Show that X_1 and X_2 are independent.

2.5.4. Find $P(0 < X_1 < \frac{1}{3}, 0 < X_2 < \frac{1}{3})$ if the random variables X_1 and X_2 have the joint pdf $f(x_1, x_2) = 4x_1(1-x_2)$, $0 < x_1 < 1$, $0 < x_2 < 1$, zero elsewhere.

2.5.5. Find the probability of the union of the events $a < X_1 < b$, $-\infty < X_2 < \infty$, and $-\infty < X_1 < \infty$, $c < X_2 < d$ if X_1 and X_2 are two independent variables with $P(a < X_1 < b) = \frac{2}{3}$ and $P(c < X_2 < d) = \frac{5}{8}$.

2.5.6. If $f(x_1, x_2) = e^{-x_1-x_2}$, $0 < x_1 < \infty$, $0 < x_2 < \infty$, zero elsewhere, is the joint pdf of the random variables X_1 and X_2, show that X_1 and X_2 are independent and that $M(t_1, t_2) = (1-t_1)^{-1}(1-t_2)^{-1}$, $t_2 < 1$, $t_1 < 1$. Also show that

$$E(e^{t(X_1+X_2)}) = (1-t)^{-2}, \quad t < 1.$$

Accordingly, find the mean and the variance of $Y = X_1 + X_2$.

2.5.7. Let the random variables X_1 and X_2 have the joint pdf $f(x_1, x_2) = 1/\pi$, for $(x_1 - 1)^2 + (x_2 + 2)^2 < 1$, zero elsewhere. Find $f_1(x_1)$ and $f_2(x_2)$. Are X_1 and X_2 independent?

2.5.8. Let X and Y have the joint pdf $f(x, y) = 3x$, $0 < y < x < 1$, zero elsewhere. Are X and Y independent? If not, find $E(X|y)$.

2.5.9. Suppose that a man leaves for work between 8:00 a.m. and 8:30 a.m. and takes between 40 and 50 minutes to get to the office. Let X denote the time of departure and let Y denote the time of travel. If we assume that these random variables are independent and uniformly distributed, find the probability that he arrives at the office before 9:00 a.m.

2.5.10. Let X and Y be random variables with the space consisting of the four points $(0,0), (1,1), (1,0), (1,-1)$. Assign positive probabilities to these four points so that the correlation coefficient is equal to zero. Are X and Y independent?

2.5.11. Two line segments, each of length two units, are placed along the x-axis. The midpoint of the first is between $x = 0$ and $x = 14$ and that of the second is between $x = 6$ and $x = 20$. Assuming independence and uniform distributions for these midpoints, find the probability that the line segments overlap.

2.5.12. Cast a fair die and let $X = 0$ if $1, 2$, or 3 spots appear, let $X = 1$ if 4 or 5 spots appear, and let $X = 2$ if 6 spots appear. Do this two independent times, obtaining X_1 and X_2. Calculate $P(|X_1 - X_2| = 1)$.

2.5.13. For X_1 and X_2 in Example 2.5.6, show that the mgf of $Y = X_1 + X_2$ is $e^{2t}/(2 - e^t)^2$, $t < \log 2$, and then compute the mean and variance of Y.

2.6 Extension to Several Random Variables

The notions about two random variables can be extended immediately to n random variables. We make the following definition of the space of n random variables.

Definition 2.6.1. *Consider a random experiment with the sample space C. Let the random variable X_i assign to each element $c \in C$ one and only one real number $X_i(c) = x_i$, $i = 1, 2, \ldots, n$. We say that $(X_1, \ldots, X_n)$ is an n-dimensional* **random vector.** *The* **space** *of this random vector is the set of ordered n-tuples $\mathcal{D} = \{(x_1, x_2, \ldots, x_n) : x_1 = X_1(c), \ldots, x_n = X_n(c), c \in C\}$. Furthermore, let A be a subset of the space $\mathcal{D}$. Then $P[(X_1, \ldots, X_n) \in A] = P(C)$, where $C = \{c : c \in C \text{ and } (X_1(c), X_2(c), \ldots, X_n(c)) \in A\}$.*

In this section, we often use vector notation. We denote $(X_1, \ldots, X_n)'$ by the n-dimensional column vector $\mathbf{X}$ and the observed values $(x_1, \ldots, x_n)'$ of the random variables by $\mathbf{x}$. The joint cdf is defined to be

$$F_{\mathbf{X}}(\mathbf{x}) = P[X_1 \leq x_1, \ldots, X_n \leq x_n]. \tag{2.6.1}$$

We say that the n random variables $X_1, X_2, \ldots, X_n$ are of the discrete type or of the continuous type and have a distribution of that type according to whether the joint cdf can be expressed as

$$F_{\mathbf{X}}(\mathbf{x}) = \sum \cdots \sum_{w_1 \leq x_1, \ldots, w_n \leq x_n} p(w_1, \ldots, w_n),$$

or as

$$F_{\mathbf{X}}(\mathbf{x}) = \int_{-\infty}^{x_1} \int_{-\infty}^{x_2} \cdots \int_{-\infty}^{x_n} f(w_1, \ldots, w_n) \, dw_n \cdots dw_1.$$

For the continuous case,

$$\frac{\partial^n}{\partial x_1 \cdots \partial x_n} F_{\mathbf{X}}(\mathbf{x}) = f(\mathbf{x}), \tag{2.6.2}$$

except possibly on points that have probability zero.

In accordance with the convention of extending the definition of a joint pdf, it is seen that a continuous function f essentially satisfies the conditions of being a pdf if (a) f is defined and is nonnegative for all real values of its argument(s) and (b) its integral over all real values of its argument(s) is 1. Likewise, a point function p essentially satisfies the conditions of being a joint pmf if (a) p is defined and is nonnegative for all real values of its argument(s) and (b) its sum over all real values of its argument(s) is 1. As in previous sections, it is sometimes convenient to speak of the support set of a random vector. For the discrete case, this would be all points in $\mathcal{D}$ which have positive mass, while for the continuous case these would be all points in $\mathcal{D}$ which can be embedded in an open set of positive probability. We use $\mathcal{S}$ to denote support sets.

Example 2.6.1. Let

$$f(x, y, z) = \begin{cases} e^{-(x+y+z)} & 0 < x, y, z < \infty \\ 0 & \text{elsewhere} \end{cases}$$

be the pdf of the random variables X, Y, and Z. Then the distribution function of X, Y, and Z is given by

$$\begin{aligned} F(x, y, z) &= P(X \leq x, Y \leq y, Z \leq z) \\ &= \int_0^z \int_0^y \int_0^x e^{-u-v-w} \, du\,dv\,dw \\ &= (1 - e^{-x})(1 - e^{-y})(1 - e^{-z}), \quad 0 \leq x, y, z < \infty, \end{aligned}$$

and is equal to zero elsewhere. The relationship (2.6.2) can easily be verified. ∎

Let $(X_1, X_2, \ldots, X_n)$ be a random vector and let $Y = u(X_1, X_2, \ldots, X_n)$ for some function u. As in the bivariate case, the expected value of the random variable exists if the n-fold integral

$$\int_{-\infty}^{\infty} \cdots \int_{-\infty}^{\infty} |u(x_1, x_2, \ldots, x_n)| f(x_1, x_2, \ldots, x_n) \, dx_1 dx_2 \cdots dx_n$$

exists when the random variables are of the continuous type, or if the n-fold sum

$$\sum_{x_n} \cdots \sum_{x_1} |u(x_1, x_2, \ldots, x_n)| p(x_1, x_2, \ldots, x_n)$$

exists when the random variables are of the discrete type. If the expected value of Y exists, then its expectation is given by

$$E(Y) = \int_{-\infty}^{\infty} \cdots \int_{-\infty}^{\infty} u(x_1, x_2, \ldots, x_n) f(x_1, x_2, \ldots, x_n) \, dx_1 dx_2 \cdots dx_n \qquad (2.6.3)$$

for the continuous case, and by

$$E(Y) = \sum_{x_n} \cdots \sum_{x_1} u(x_1, x_2, \ldots, x_n) p(x_1, x_2, \ldots, x_n) \qquad (2.6.4)$$

for the discrete case. The properties of expectation discussed in Section 2.1 hold for the n-dimensional case also. In particular, E is a linear operator. That is, if $Y_j = u_j(X_1, \ldots, X_n)$ for $j = 1, \ldots, m$ and each $E(Y_i)$ exists, then

$$E\left[\sum_{j=1}^{m} k_j Y_j\right] = \sum_{j=1}^{m} k_j E[Y_j], \qquad (2.6.5)$$

where $k_1, \ldots, k_m$ are constants.

We next discuss the notions of marginal and conditional probability density functions from the point of view of n random variables. All of the preceding definitions can be directly generalized to the case of n variables in the following manner. Let the random variables $X_1, X_2, \ldots, X_n$ be of the continuous type with the joint pdf $f(x_1, x_2, \ldots, x_n)$. By an argument similar to the two-variable case, we have for every b,

$$F_{X_1}(b) = P(X_1 \leq b) = \int_{-\infty}^{b} f_1(x_1)\, dx_1,$$

where $f_1(x_1)$ is defined by the $(n-1)$-fold integral

$$f_1(x_1) = \int_{-\infty}^{\infty} \cdots \int_{-\infty}^{\infty} f(x_1, x_2, \ldots, x_n)\, dx_2 \cdots dx_n.$$

Therefore, $f_1(x_1)$ is the pdf of the random variable X_1 and $f_1(x_1)$ is called the marginal pdf of X_1. The marginal probability density functions $f_2(x_2), \ldots, f_n(x_n)$ of $X_2, \ldots, X_n$, respectively, are similar $(n-1)$-fold integrals.

Up to this point, each marginal pdf has been a pdf of one random variable. It is convenient to extend this terminology to joint probability density functions, which we do now. Let $f(x_1, x_2, \ldots, x_n)$ be the joint pdf of the n random variables $X_1, X_2, \ldots, X_n$, just as before. Now, however, let us take any group of $k < n$ of these random variables and let us find the joint pdf of them. This joint pdf is called the marginal pdf of this particular group of k variables. To fix the ideas, take $n = 6$, $k = 3$, and let us select the group X_2, X_4, X_5. Then the marginal pdf of X_2, X_4, X_5 is the joint pdf of this particular group of three variables, namely,

$$\int_{-\infty}^{\infty} \int_{-\infty}^{\infty} \int_{-\infty}^{\infty} f(x_1, x_2, x_3, x_4, x_5, x_6)\, dx_1 dx_3 dx_6,$$

if the random variables are of the continuous type.

Next we extend the definition of a conditional pdf. Suppose $f_1(x_1) > 0$. Then we define the symbol $f_{2,\ldots,n|1}(x_2, \ldots, x_n | x_1)$ by the relation

$$f_{2,\ldots,n|1}(x_2, \ldots, x_n | x_1) = \frac{f(x_1, x_2, \ldots, x_n)}{f_1(x_1)},$$

and $f_{2,\ldots,n|1}(x_2, \ldots, x_n | x_1)$ is called the **joint conditional pdf** of $X_2, \ldots, X_n$, given $X_1 = x_1$. The joint conditional pdf of any $n-1$ random variables, say $X_1, \ldots, X_{i-1}, X_{i+1}, \ldots, X_n$, given $X_i = x_i$, is defined as the joint pdf of $X_1, \ldots, X_n$ divided by the marginal pdf $f_i(x_i)$, provided that $f_i(x_i) > 0$. More generally, the joint conditional pdf of $n-k$ of the random variables, for given values of the remaining k variables, is defined as the joint pdf of the n variables divided by the marginal pdf of the particular group of k variables, provided that the latter pdf is positive. We remark that there are many other conditional probability density functions; for instance, see Exercise 2.3.12.

Because a conditional pdf is a pdf of a certain number of random variables, the expectation of a function of these random variables has been defined. To emphasize the fact that a conditional pdf is under consideration, such expectations are called conditional expectations. For instance, the conditional expectation of $u(X_2, \ldots, X_n)$, given $X_1 = x_1$, is, for random variables of the continuous type, given by

$$E[u(X_2, \ldots, X_n)|x_1] = \int_{-\infty}^{\infty} \cdots \int_{-\infty}^{\infty} u(x_2, \ldots, x_n) f_{2,\ldots,n|1}(x_2, \ldots, x_n|x_1) \, dx_2 \cdots dx_n$$

provided $f_1(x_1) > 0$ and the integral converges (absolutely). A useful random variable is given by $h(X_1) = E[u(X_2, \ldots, X_n)|X_1)]$.

The above discussion of marginal and conditional distributions generalizes to random variables of the discrete type by using pmfs and summations instead of integrals.

Let the random variables $X_1, X_2, \ldots, X_n$ have the joint pdf $f(x_1, x_2, \ldots, x_n)$ and the marginal probability density functions $f_1(x_1), f_2(x_2), \ldots, f_n(x_n)$, respectively. The definition of the independence of X_1 and X_2 is generalized to the mutual independence of $X_1, X_2, \ldots, X_n$ as follows: The random variables $X_1, X_2, \ldots, X_n$ are said to be **mutually independent** if and only if

$$f(x_1, x_2, \ldots, x_n) \equiv f_1(x_1) f_2(x_2) \cdots f_n(x_n),$$

for the continuous case. In the discrete case, $X_1, X_2, \ldots, X_n$ are said to be **mutually independent** if and only if

$$p(x_1, x_2, \ldots, x_n) \equiv p_1(x_1) p_2(x_2) \cdots p_n(x_n).$$

Suppose $X_1, X_2, \ldots, X_n$ are mutually independent. Then

$$P(a_1 < X_1 < b_1, \, a_2 < X_2 < b_2, \ldots, a_n < X_n < b_n)$$
$$= \quad P(a_1 < X_1 < b_1)P(a_2 < X_2 < b_2) \cdots P(a_n < X_n < b_n)$$
$$= \quad \prod_{i=1}^{n} P(a_i < X_i < b_i),$$

where the symbol $\prod_{i=1}^{n} \varphi(i)$ is defined to be

$$\prod_{i=1}^{n} \varphi(i) = \varphi(1)\varphi(2) \cdots \varphi(n).$$

The theorem that
$$E[u(X_1)v(X_2)] = E[u(X_1)]E[v(X_2)]$$

for independent random variables X_1 and X_2 becomes, for mutually independent random variables $X_1, X_2, \ldots, X_n$,

$$E[u_1(X_1)u_2(X_2) \cdots u_n(X_n)] = E[u_1(X_1)]E[u_2(X_2)] \cdots E[u_n(X_n)],$$

or

$$E\left[\prod_{i=1}^{n} u_i(X_i)\right] = \prod_{i=1}^{n} E[u_i(X_i)].$$

The moment-generating function (mgf) of the joint distribution of n random variables $X_1, X_2, \ldots, X_n$ is defined as follows. Let

$$E[\exp(t_1 X_1 + t_2 X_2 + \cdots + t_n X_n)]$$

exists for $-h_i < t_i < h_i$, $i = 1, 2, \ldots, n$, where each h_i is positive. This expectation is denoted by $M(t_1, t_2, \ldots, t_n)$ and it is called the mgf of the joint distribution of $X_1, \ldots, X_n$ (or simply the mgf of $X_1, \ldots, X_n$). As in the cases of one and two variables, this mgf is unique and uniquely determines the joint distribution of the n variables (and hence all marginal distributions). For example, the mgf of the marginal distributions of X_i is $M(0, \ldots, 0, t_i, 0, \ldots, 0)$, $i = 1, 2, \ldots, n$; that of the marginal distribution of X_i and X_j is $M(0, \ldots, 0, t_i, 0, \ldots, 0, t_j, 0, \ldots, 0)$; and so on. Theorem 2.5.5 of this chapter can be generalized, and the factorization

$$M(t_1, t_2, \ldots, t_n) = \prod_{i=1}^{n} M(0, \ldots, 0, t_i, 0, \ldots, 0) \qquad (2.6.6)$$

is a necessary and sufficient condition for the mutual independence of $X_1, X_2, \ldots, X_n$. Note that we can write the joint mgf in vector notation as

$$M(\mathbf{t}) = E[\exp(\mathbf{t}'\mathbf{X})], \quad \text{for } \mathbf{t} \in B \subset R^n,$$

where $B = \{\mathbf{t} : -h_i < t_i < h_i, i = 1, \ldots, n\}$.

The following is a theorem that proves useful in the sequel. It gives the mgf of a linear combination of independent random variables.

Theorem 2.6.1. *Suppose $X_1, X_2, \ldots, X_n$ are n mutually independent random variables. Suppose, for all $i = 1, 2, \ldots, n$, X_i has mgf $M_i(t)$, for $-h_i < t < h_i$, where $h_i > 0$. Let $T = \sum_{i=1}^{n} k_i X_i$, where $k_1, k_2, \ldots, k_n$ are constants. Then T has the mgf given by*

$$M_T(t) = \prod_{i=1}^{n} M_i(k_i t), \quad -\min_i\{h_i\} < t < \min_i\{h_i\}. \qquad (2.6.7)$$

Proof. Assume t is in the interval $(-\min_i\{h_i\}, \min_i\{h_i\})$. Then, by independence,

$$
\begin{aligned}
M_T(t) &= E\left[e^{\sum_{i=1}^{n} t k_i X_i}\right] = E\left[\prod_{i=1}^{n} e^{(t k_i) X_i}\right] \\
&= \prod_{i=1}^{n} E\left[e^{t k_i X_i}\right] = \prod_{i=1}^{n} M_i(k_i t),
\end{aligned}
$$

which completes the proof. ∎

Example 2.6.2. Let X_1, X_2, and X_3 be three mutually independent random variables and let each have the pdf

$$f(x) = \begin{cases} 2x & 0 < x < 1 \\ 0 & \text{elsewhere.} \end{cases} \qquad (2.6.8)$$

The joint pdf of X_1, X_2, X_3 is $f(x_1)f(x_2)f(x_3) = 8x_1x_2x_3$, $0 < x_i < 1$, $i = 1, 2, 3$, zero elsewhere. Then, for illustration, the expected value of $5X_1X_2^3 + 3X_2X_3^4$ is

$$\int_0^1 \int_0^1 \int_0^1 (5x_1x_2^3 + 3x_2x_3^4)8x_1x_2x_3 \, dx_1 dx_2 dx_3 = 2.$$

Let Y be the maximum of X_1, X_2, and X_3. Then, for instance, we have

$$
\begin{aligned}
P(Y \le \tfrac{1}{2}) &= P(X_1 \le \tfrac{1}{2}, X_2 \le \tfrac{1}{2}, X_3 \le \tfrac{1}{2}) \\
&= \int_0^{1/2} \int_0^{1/2} \int_0^{1/2} 8x_1x_2x_3 \, dx_1 dx_2 dx_3 \\
&= (\tfrac{1}{2})^6 = \tfrac{1}{64}.
\end{aligned}
$$

In a similar manner, we find that the cdf of Y is

$$G(y) = P(Y \le y) = \begin{cases} 0 & y < 0 \\ y^6 & 0 \le y < 1 \\ 1 & 1 \le y. \end{cases}$$

Accordingly, the pdf of Y is

$$g(y) = \begin{cases} 6y^5 & 0 < y < 1 \\ 0 & \text{elsewhere.} \end{cases} \quad \blacksquare$$

Remark 2.6.1. If X_1, X_2, and X_3 are mutually independent, they are **pairwise independent** (that is, X_i and X_j, $i \ne j$, where $i, j = 1, 2, 3$, are independent). However, the following example, attributed to S. Bernstein, shows that pairwise independence does not necessarily imply mutual independence. Let X_1, X_2, and X_3 have the joint pmf

$$p(x_1, x_2, x_3) = \begin{cases} \tfrac{1}{4} & (x_1, x_2, x_3) \in \{(1,0,0),(0,1,0),(0,0,1),(1,1,1)\} \\ 0 & \text{elsewhere.} \end{cases}$$

The joint pmf of X_i and X_j, $i \ne j$, is

$$p_{ij}(x_i, x_j) = \begin{cases} \tfrac{1}{4} & (x_i, x_j) \in \{(0,0),(1,0),(0,1),(1,1)\} \\ 0 & \text{elsewhere,} \end{cases}$$

whereas the marginal pmf of X_i is

$$p_i(x_i) = \begin{cases} \tfrac{1}{2} & x_i = 0, 1 \\ 0 & \text{elsewhere.} \end{cases}$$

Obviously, if $i \ne j$, we have

$$p_{ij}(x_i, x_j) \equiv p_i(x_i)p_j(x_j),$$

and thus X_i and X_j are independent. However,

$$p(x_1, x_2, x_3) \not\equiv p_1(x_1)p_2(x_2)p_3(x_3).$$

Thus X_1, X_2, and X_3 are not mutually independent.

Unless there is a possible misunderstanding between *mutual* and *pairwise* independence, we usually drop the modifier *mutual*. Accordingly, using this practice in Example 2.6.2, we say that X_1, X_2, X_3 are independent random variables, meaning that they are mutually independent. Occasionally, for emphasis, we use *mutually independent* so that the reader is reminded that this is different from *pairwise independence*.

In addition, if several random variables are mutually independent and have the same distribution, we say that they are **independent and identically distributed**, which we abbreviate as **iid**. So the random variables in Example 2.6.2 are iid with the common pdf given in expression (2.6.8). ∎

The following is a useful corollary to Theorem 2.6.1 for iid random variables. Its proof is asked for in Exercise 2.6.7.

Corollary 2.6.1. *Suppose $X_1, X_2, \ldots, X_n$ are iid random variables with the common mgf $M(t)$, for $-h < t < h$, where $h > 0$. Let $T = \sum_{i=1}^{n} X_i$. Then T has the mgf given by*

$$M_T(t) = [M(t)]^n, \quad -h < t < h. \tag{2.6.9}$$

2.6.1 *Multivariate Variance-Covariance Matrix

In Section 2.4 we discussed the covariance between two random variables. In this section we want to extend this discussion to the n-variate case. Let $\mathbf{X} = (X_1, \ldots, X_n)'$ be an n-dimensional random vector. Recall that we defined $E(\mathbf{X}) = (E(X_1), \ldots, E(X_n))'$, that is, the expectation of a random vector is just the vector of the expectations of its components. Now suppose $\mathbf{W}$ is an $m \times n$ matrix of random variables, say, $\mathbf{W} = [W_{ij}]$ for the random variables $W_{ij}, 1 \leq i \leq m$ and $1 \leq j \leq n$. Note that we can always string out the matrix into an $mn \times 1$ random vector. Hence, we define the expectation of a random matrix

$$E[\mathbf{W}] = [E(W_{ij})]. \tag{2.6.10}$$

As the following theorem shows, the linearity of the expectation operator easily follows from this definition:

Theorem 2.6.2. *Let $\mathbf{W}_1$ and $\mathbf{W}_2$ be $m \times n$ matrices of random variables, let $\mathbf{A}_1$ and $\mathbf{A}_2$ be $k \times m$ matrices of constants, and let $\mathbf{B}$ be an $n \times l$ matrix of constants. Then*

$$E[\mathbf{A}_1 \mathbf{W}_1 + \mathbf{A}_2 \mathbf{W}_2] = \mathbf{A}_1 E[\mathbf{W}_1] + \mathbf{A}_2 E[\mathbf{W}_2] \tag{2.6.11}$$

$$E[\mathbf{A}_1 \mathbf{W}_1 \mathbf{B}] = \mathbf{A}_1 E[\mathbf{W}_1]\mathbf{B}. \tag{2.6.12}$$

Proof: Because of the linearity of the operator E on random variables, we have for the (i, j)th components of expression (2.6.11) that

$$E\left[\sum_{s=1}^{m} a_{1is}W_{1sj} + \sum_{s=1}^{m} a_{2is}W_{2sj}\right] = \sum_{s=1}^{m} a_{1is}E[W_{1sj}] + \sum_{s=1}^{m} a_{2is}E[W_{2sj}].$$

Hence by (2.6.10), expression (2.6.11) is true. The derivation of expression (2.6.12) follows in the same manner. ∎

Let $\mathbf{X} = (X_1, \dots, X_n)'$ be an n-dimensional random vector, such that $\sigma_i^2 = \text{Var}(X_i) < \infty$. The **mean** of $\mathbf{X}$ is $\boldsymbol{\mu} = E[\mathbf{X}]$ and we define its **variance-covariance matrix** to be,

$$\text{Cov}(\mathbf{X}) = E[(\mathbf{X} - \boldsymbol{\mu})(\mathbf{X} - \boldsymbol{\mu})'] = [\sigma_{ij}], \tag{2.6.13}$$

where σ_{ii} denotes σ_i^2. As Exercise 2.6.8 shows, the ith diagonal entry of $\text{Cov}(\mathbf{X})$ is $\sigma_i^2 = \text{Var}(X_i)$ and the (i, j)th off diagonal entry is $\text{Cov}(X_i, X_j)$. So the name, variance-covariance matrix is appropriate.

Example 2.6.3 (Example 2.4.4, Continued). In Example 2.4.4, we considered the joint pdf

$$f(x, y) = \begin{cases} e^{-y} & 0 < x < y < \infty \\ 0 & \text{elsewhere,} \end{cases}$$

and showed that the first two moments are

$$\begin{aligned} \mu_1 &= 1, \quad \mu_2 = 2 \\ \sigma_1^2 &= 1, \quad \sigma_2^2 = 2 \\ E[(X - \mu_1)(Y - \mu_2)] &= 1. \end{aligned} \tag{2.6.14}$$

Let $\mathbf{Z} = (X, Y)'$. Then using the present notation, we have

$$E[\mathbf{Z}] = \begin{bmatrix} 1 \\ 2 \end{bmatrix} \text{ and } \text{Cov}(\mathbf{Z}) = \begin{bmatrix} 1 & 1 \\ 1 & 2 \end{bmatrix}. \quad \blacksquare$$

Two properties of $\text{Cov}(X_i, X_j)$ which we need later are summarized in the following theorem,

Theorem 2.6.3. *Let $\mathbf{X} = (X_1, \dots, X_n)'$ be an n-dimensional random vector, such that $\sigma_i^2 = \sigma_{ii} = \text{Var}(X_i) < \infty$. Let $\mathbf{A}$ be an $m \times n$ matrix of constants. Then*

$$\begin{cases} \text{Cov}(\mathbf{X}) &= E[\mathbf{X}\mathbf{X}'] - \boldsymbol{\mu}\boldsymbol{\mu}' \tag{2.6.15} \\ \text{Cov}(\mathbf{A}\mathbf{X}) &= \mathbf{A}\,\text{Cov}(\mathbf{X})\mathbf{A}'. \end{cases}$$
$$\tag{2.6.16}$$

Proof. Use Theorem 2.6.2 to derive (2.6.15); i.e.,

$$\begin{aligned} \text{Cov}(\mathbf{X}) &= E[(\mathbf{X} - \boldsymbol{\mu})(\mathbf{X} - \boldsymbol{\mu})'] \\ &= E[\mathbf{X}\mathbf{X}' - \boldsymbol{\mu}\mathbf{X}' - \mathbf{X}\boldsymbol{\mu}' + \boldsymbol{\mu}\boldsymbol{\mu}'] \\ &= E[\mathbf{X}\mathbf{X}'] - \boldsymbol{\mu}E[\mathbf{X}'] - E[\mathbf{X}]\boldsymbol{\mu}' + \boldsymbol{\mu}\boldsymbol{\mu}', \end{aligned}$$

which is the desired result. The proof of (2.6.16) is left as an exercise. ∎

All variance-covariance matrices are **positive semi-definite** matrices; that is, $\mathbf{a}'\text{Cov}(\mathbf{X})\mathbf{a} \geq 0$, for all vectors $\mathbf{a} \in R^n$. To see this let $\mathbf{X}$ be a random vector and let $\mathbf{a}$ be any $n \times 1$ vector of constants. Then $Y = \mathbf{a}'\mathbf{X}$ is a random variable and, hence, has nonnegative variance; i.e.,

$$0 \leq \text{Var}(Y) = \text{Var}(\mathbf{a}'\mathbf{X}) = \mathbf{a}'\text{Cov}(\mathbf{X})\mathbf{a}; \tag{2.6.17}$$

hence, $\text{Cov}(\mathbf{X})$ is positive semi-definite.

EXERCISES

2.6.1. Let X, Y, Z have joint pdf $f(x, y, z) = 2(x + y + z)/3$, $0 < x < 1$, $0 < y < 1$, $0 < z < 1$, zero elsewhere.

(a) Find the marginal probability density functions of X, Y, and Z.

(b) Compute $P(0 < X < \frac{1}{2}, 0 < Y < \frac{1}{2}, 0 < Z < \frac{1}{2})$ and $P(0 < X < \frac{1}{2}) = P(0 < Y < \frac{1}{2}) = P(0 < Z < \frac{1}{2})$.

(c) Are X, Y, and Z independent?

(d) Calculate $E(X^2 Y Z + 3 X Y^4 Z^2)$.

(e) Determine the cdf of X, Y, and Z.

(f) Find the conditional distribution of X and Y, given $Z = z$, and evaluate $E(X + Y | z)$.

(g) Determine the conditional distribution of X, given $Y = y$ and $Z = z$, and compute $E(X | y, z)$.

2.6.2. Let $f(x_1, x_2, x_3) = \exp[-(x_1 + x_2 + x_3)]$, $0 < x_1 < \infty$, $0 < x_2 < \infty$, $0 < x_3 < \infty$, zero elsewhere, be the joint pdf of X_1, X_2, X_3.

(a) Compute $P(X_1 < X_2 < X_3)$ and $P(X_1 = X_2 < X_3)$.

(b) Determine the joint mgf of X_1, X_2, and X_3. Are these random variables independent?

2.6.3. Let X_1, X_2, X_3, and X_4 be four independent random variables, each with pdf $f(x) = 3(1 - x)^2$, $0 < x < 1$, zero elsewhere. If Y is the minimum of these four variables, find the cdf and the pdf of Y.
Hint: $P(Y > y) = P(X_i > y, i = 1, \ldots, 4)$.

2.6.4. A fair die is cast at random three independent times. Let the random variable X_i be equal to the number of spots that appear on the ith trial, $i = 1, 2, 3$. Let the random variable Y be equal to $\max(X_i)$. Find the cdf and the pmf of Y.
Hint: $P(Y \le y) = P(X_i \le y, i = 1, 2, 3)$.

2.6.5. Let $M(t_1, t_2, t_3)$ be the mgf of the random variables X_1, X_2, and X_3 of Bernstein's example, described in the remark following Example 2.6.2. Show that

$$M(t_1, t_2, 0) = M(t_1, 0, 0)M(0, t_2, 0), \quad M(t_1, 0, t_3) = M(t_1, 0, 0)M(0, 0, t_3),$$

and

$$M(0, t_2, t_3) = M(0, t_2, 0)M(0, 0, t_3)$$

are true, but that

$$M(t_1, t_2, t_3) \neq M(t_1, 0, 0)M(0, t_2, 0)M(0, 0, t_3).$$

Thus X_1, X_2, X_3 are pairwise independent but not mutually independent.

2.6.6. Let X_1, X_2, and X_3 be three random variables with means, variances, and correlation coefficients, denoted by $\mu_1, \mu_2, \mu_3; \sigma_1^2, \sigma_2^2, \sigma_3^2;$ and $\rho_{12}, \rho_{13}, \rho_{23}$, respectively. For constants b_2 and b_3, suppose $E(X_1 - \mu_1 | x_2, x_3) = b_2(x_2 - \mu_2) + b_3(x_3 - \mu_3)$. Determine b_2 and b_3 in terms of the variances and the correlation coefficients.

2.6.7. Prove Corollary 2.6.1.

2.6.8. Let $\mathbf{X} = (X_1, \ldots, X_n)'$ be an n-dimensional random vector, with the variance-covariance matrix given in display (2.6.13). Show that the ith diagonal entry of $\text{Cov}(\mathbf{X})$ is $\sigma_i^2 = \text{Var}(X_i)$ and that the (i, j)th off diagonal entry is $\text{Cov}(X_i, X_j)$.

2.6.9. Let X_1, X_2, X_3 be iid with common pdf $f(x) = \exp(-x)$, $0 < x < \infty$, zero elsewhere. Evaluate:

(a) $P(X_1 < X_2 | X_1 < 2X_2)$.

(b) $P(X_1 < X_2 < X_3 | X_3 < 1)$.

2.7 Transformations for Several Random Variables

In Section 2.2 it was seen that the determination of the joint pdf of two functions of two random variables of the continuous type was essentially a corollary to a theorem in analysis having to do with the change of variables in a twofold integral. This theorem has a natural extension to n-fold integrals. This extension is as follows. Consider an integral of the form

$$\int \cdots \int_A f(x_1, x_2, \ldots, x_n) \, dx_1 \, dx_2 \cdots dx_n$$

taken over a subset A of an n-dimensional space $\mathcal{S}$. Let

$$y_1 = u_1(x_1, x_2, \ldots, x_n), \quad y_2 = u_2(x_1, x_2, \ldots, x_n), \ldots, y_n = u_n(x_1, x_2, \ldots, x_n),$$

together with the inverse functions

$$x_1 = w_1(y_1, y_2, \ldots, y_n), \quad x_2 = w_2(y_1, y_2, \ldots, y_n), \ldots, x_n = w_n(y_1, y_2, \ldots, y_n)$$

define a one-to-one transformation that maps $\mathcal{S}$ onto $\mathcal{T}$ in the $y_1, y_2, \ldots, y_n$ space and, hence, maps the subset A of $\mathcal{S}$ onto a subset B of $\mathcal{T}$. Let the first partial derivatives of the inverse functions be continuous and let the n by n determinant (called the Jacobian)

$$J = \begin{vmatrix} \frac{\partial x_1}{\partial y_1} & \frac{\partial x_1}{\partial y_2} & \cdots & \frac{\partial x_1}{\partial y_n} \\ \frac{\partial x_2}{\partial y_1} & \frac{\partial x_2}{\partial y_2} & \cdots & \frac{\partial x_2}{\partial y_n} \\ \vdots & \vdots & & \vdots \\ \frac{\partial x_n}{\partial y_1} & \frac{\partial x_n}{\partial y_2} & \cdots & \frac{\partial x_n}{\partial y_n} \end{vmatrix}$$

not be identically zero in $\mathcal{T}$. Then

$$\int \cdots \int_A f(x_1, x_2, \ldots, x_n)\, dx_1 dx_2 \cdots dx_n$$

$$= \int \cdots \int_B f[w_1(y_1, \ldots, y_n), w_2(y_1, \ldots, y_n), \ldots, w_n(y_1, \ldots, y_n)] |J|\, dy_1 dy_2 \cdots dy_n.$$

Whenever the conditions of this theorem are satisfied, we can determine the joint pdf of n functions of n random variables. Appropriate changes of notation in Section 2.2 (to indicate n-space as opposed to 2-space) are all that are needed to show that the joint pdf of the random variables $Y_1 = u_1(X_1, X_2, \ldots, X_n)$, $\ldots$, $Y_n = u_n(X_1, X_2, \ldots, X_n)$, where the joint pdf of $X_1, \ldots, X_n$ is $f(x_1, \ldots, x_n)$, is given by

$$g(y_1, y_2, \ldots, y_n) = f[w_1(y_1, \ldots, y_n), \ldots, w_n(y_1, \ldots, y_n)] |J|,$$

where $(y_1, y_2, \ldots, y_n) \in \mathcal{T}$, and is zero elsewhere.

Example 2.7.1. Let X_1, X_2, X_3 have the joint pdf

$$f(x_1, x_2, x_3) = \begin{cases} 48x_1 x_2 x_3 & 0 < x_1 < x_2 < x_3 < 1 \\ 0 & \text{elsewhere.} \end{cases} \qquad (2.7.1)$$

If $Y_1 = X_1/X_2$, $Y_2 = X_2/X_3$, and $Y_3 = X_3$, then the inverse transformation is given by

$$x_1 = y_1 y_2 y_3, \quad x_2 = y_2 y_3, \quad \text{and} \quad x_3 = y_3.$$

The Jacobian is given by

$$J = \begin{vmatrix} y_2 y_3 & y_1 y_3 & y_1 y_2 \\ 0 & y_3 & y_2 \\ 0 & 0 & 1 \end{vmatrix} = y_2 y_3^2.$$

Moreover, inequalities defining the support are equivalent to

$$0 < y_1 y_2 y_3, \quad y_1 y_2 y_3 < y_2 y_3, \quad y_2 y_3 < y_3, \quad \text{and} \quad y_3 < 1,$$

which reduces to the support $\mathcal{T}$ of Y_1, Y_2, Y_3 of

$$\mathcal{T} = \{(y_1, y_2, y_3) : 0 < y_i < 1, i = 1, 2, 3\}.$$

Hence the joint pdf of Y_1, Y_2, Y_3 is

$$\begin{aligned} g(y_1, y_2, y_3) &= 48(y_1 y_2 y_3)(y_2 y_3) y_3 |y_2 y_3^2| \\ &= \begin{cases} 48 y_1 y_2^3 y_3^5 & 0 < y_i < 1, i = 1, 2, 3 \\ 0 & \text{elsewhere.} \end{cases} \end{aligned} \qquad (2.7.2)$$

The marginal pdfs are

$$\begin{aligned} g_1(y_1) &= 2y_1, 0 < y_1 < 1, \text{zero elsewhere} \\ g_2(y_2) &= 4y_2^3, 0 < y_2 < 1, \text{zero elsewhere} \\ g_3(y_3) &= 6y_3^5, 0 < y_3 < 1, \text{zero elsewhere.} \end{aligned}$$

Because $g(y_1, y_2, y_3) = g_1(y_1) g_2(y_2) g_3(y_3)$, the random variables Y_1, Y_2, Y_3 are mutually independent. ■

Example 2.7.2. Let X_1, X_2, X_3 be iid with common pdf

$$f(x) = \begin{cases} e^{-x} & 0 < x < \infty \\ 0 & \text{elsewhere.} \end{cases}$$

Consequently, the joint pdf of X_1, X_2, X_3 is

$$f_{X_1,X_2,X_3}(x_1, x_2, x_3) = \begin{cases} e^{-\sum_{i=1}^3 x_i} & 0 < x_i < \infty, i = 1, 2, 3 \\ 0 & \text{elsewhere.} \end{cases}$$

Consider the random variables Y_1, Y_2, Y_3 defined by

$$Y_1 = \frac{X_1}{X_1+X_2+X_3}, \ Y_2 = \frac{X_2}{X_1+X_2+X_3}, \text{ and } Y_3 = X_1 + X_2 + X_3.$$

Hence, the inverse transformation is given by

$$x_1 = y_1 y_3, \ x_2 = y_2 y_3, \text{ and } x_3 = y_3 - y_1 y_3 - y_2 y_3,$$

with the Jacobian

$$J = \begin{vmatrix} y_3 & 0 & y_1 \\ 0 & y_3 & y_2 \\ -y_3 & -y_3 & 1 - y_1 - y_2 \end{vmatrix} = y_3^2.$$

The support of X_1, X_2, X_3 maps onto

$$0 < y_1 y_3 < \infty, \ 0 < y_2 y_3 < \infty, \text{ and } 0 < y_3(1 - y_1 - y_2) < \infty,$$

which is equivalent to the support $\mathcal{T}$ given by

$$\mathcal{T} = \{(y_1, y_2, y_3) : 0 < y_1, 0 < y_2, 0 < 1 - y_1 - y_2, 0 < y_3 < \infty\}.$$

Hence the joint pdf of Y_1, Y_2, Y_3 is

$$g(y_1, y_2, y_3) = y_3^2 e^{-y_3}, \quad (y_1, y_2, y_3) \in \mathcal{T}.$$

The marginal pdf of Y_1 is

$$g_1(y_1) = \int_0^{1-y_1} \int_0^\infty y_3^2 e^{-y_3} \, dy_3 \, dy_2 = 2(1 - y_1), \quad 0 < y_1 < 1,$$

zero elsewhere. Likewise the marginal pdf of Y_2 is

$$g_2(y_2) = 2(1 - y_2), \quad 0 < y_2 < 1,$$

zero elsewhere, while the pdf of Y_3 is

$$g_3(y_3) = \int_0^1 \int_0^{1-y_1} y_3^2 e^{-y_3} \, dy_2 \, dy_1 = \frac{1}{2} y_3^2 e^{-y_3}, \quad 0 < y_3 < \infty,$$

zero elsewhere. Because $g(y_1, y_2, y_3) \neq g_1(y_1)g_2(y_2)g_3(y_3)$, Y_1, Y_2, Y_3 are dependent random variables.

$\int_0^\infty y_3^2 e^{-y_3} dy_3 = -\int_0^\infty y_3^2 de^{-y_3} = -(y_3^2 e^{-y_3}\big|_0^\infty - \int e^{-y_3} dy_3^2) = -[(\frac{\infty^2}{e^{-\infty}} - \frac{0^2}{e^{-0}}) - 2\int_0^\infty e^{-y_3} y_3 dy_3]$

$= 2\int_0^\infty e^{-y_3} \cdot y_3 dy_3 = -2\int_0^\infty y_3 de^{-y_3}$

$= -2(y_3 \cdot e^{-y_3}\big|_0^\infty - \int_0^\infty e^{-y_3} dy_3)$

2.7. Transformations for Several Random Variables

$$= -2[0 - (-\int_0^\infty de^{-y_3})] = -2e^{-y_3}\big|_0^\infty = 2.$$

Note, however, that the joint pdf of Y_1 and Y_3 is

$$g_{13}(y_1, y_3) = \int_0^{1-y_1} y_3^2 e^{-y_3} dy_2 = (1-y_1)y_3^2 e^{-y_3}, \quad 0 < y_1 < 1, 0 < y_3 < \infty,$$

zero elsewhere. Hence Y_1 and Y_3 are independent. In a similar manner, Y_2 and Y_3 are also independent. Because the joint pdf of Y_1 and Y_2 is

$$g_{12}(y_1, y_2) = \int_0^\infty y_3^2 e^{-y_3} dy_3 = 2, \quad 0 < y_1, 0 < y_2, y_1 + y_2 < 1,$$

zero elsewhere, Y_1 and Y_2 are seen to be dependent. ∎

We now consider some other problems that are encountered when transforming variables. Let X have the Cauchy pdf

$$f(x) = \frac{1}{\pi(1 + x^2)}, \quad -\infty < x < \infty,$$

and let $Y = X^2$. We seek the pdf $g(y)$ of Y. Consider the transformation $y = x^2$. This transformation maps the space of X, namely $\mathcal{S} = \{x : -\infty < x < \infty\}$, onto $\mathcal{T} = \{y : 0 \le y < \infty\}$. However, the transformation is not one-to-one. To each $y \in \mathcal{T}$, with the exception of $y = 0$, there correspond two points $x \in \mathcal{S}$. For example, if $y = 4$, we may have either $x = 2$ or $x = -2$. In such an instance, we represent $\mathcal{S}$ as the union of two disjoint sets A_1 and A_2 such that $y = x^2$ defines a one-to-one transformation that maps each of A_1 and A_2 onto $\mathcal{T}$. If we take A_1 to be $\{x : -\infty < x < 0\}$ and A_2 to be $\{x : 0 < x < \infty\}$, we see that A_1 is mapped onto $\{y : 0 < y < \infty\}$, whereas A_2 is mapped onto $\{y : 0 \le y < \infty\}$, and these sets are not the same. Our difficulty is caused by the fact that $x = 0$ is an element of $\mathcal{S}$. Why, then, do we not return to the Cauchy pdf and take $f(0) = 0$? Then our new $\mathcal{S}$ is $\mathcal{S} = \{-\infty < x < \infty \text{ but } x \ne 0\}$. We then take $A_1 = \{x : -\infty < x < 0\}$ and $A_2 = \{x : 0 < x < \infty\}$. Thus $y = x^2$, with the inverse $x = -\sqrt{y}$, maps A_1 onto $\mathcal{T} = \{y : 0 < y < \infty\}$ and the transformation is one-to-one. Moreover, the transformation $y = x^2$, with inverse $x = \sqrt{y}$, maps A_2 onto $\mathcal{T} = \{y : 0 < y < \infty\}$ and the transformation is one-to-one. Consider the probability $P(Y \in B)$, where $B \subset \mathcal{T}$. Let $A_3 = \{x : x = -\sqrt{y}, y \in B\} \subset A_1$ and let $A_4 = \{x : x = \sqrt{y}, y \in B\} \subset A_2$. Then $Y \in B$ when and only when $X \in A_3$ or $X \in A_4$. Thus we have

$$\begin{aligned} P(Y \in B) &= P(X \in A_3) + P(X \in A_4) \\ &= \int_{A_3} f(x)\,dx + \int_{A_4} f(x)\,dx. \end{aligned}$$

In the first of these integrals, let $x = -\sqrt{y}$. Thus the Jacobian, say J_1, is $-1/2\sqrt{y}$; furthermore, the set A_3 is mapped onto B. In the second integral let $x = \sqrt{y}$. Thus the Jacobian, say J_2, is $1/2\sqrt{y}$; furthermore, the set A_4 is also mapped onto B.

$$P(Y \in B) = P(X \in A_3) + P(X \in A_4) = \int_{A_3} f(x)\,dx + \int_{A_4} f(x)\,dx$$

Finally,

$$P(Y \in B) = \int_B f(-\sqrt{y}) \left| -\frac{1}{2\sqrt{y}} \right| dy + \int_B f(\sqrt{y}) \frac{1}{2\sqrt{y}} dy$$

$$= \int_B [f(-\sqrt{y}) + f(\sqrt{y})] \frac{1}{2\sqrt{y}} dy.$$

Hence the pdf of Y is given by

$$g(y) = \frac{1}{2\sqrt{y}}[f(-\sqrt{y}) + f(\sqrt{y})], \quad y \in \mathcal{T}.$$

With $f(x)$ the Cauchy pdf we have

$$g(y) = \begin{cases} \frac{1}{\pi(1+y)\sqrt{y}} & 0 < y < \infty \\ 0 & \text{elsewhere.} \end{cases}$$

In the preceding discussion of a random variable of the continuous type, we had two inverse functions, $x = -\sqrt{y}$ and $x = \sqrt{y}$. That is why we sought to partition S (or a modification of S) into two disjoint subsets such that the transformation $y = x^2$ maps each onto the same $\mathcal{T}$. Had there been three inverse functions, we would have sought to partition S (or a modified form of S) into three disjoint subsets, and so on. It is hoped that this detailed discussion makes the following paragraph easier to read.

Let $f(x_1, x_2, \ldots, x_n)$ be the joint pdf of $X_1, X_2, \ldots, X_n$, which are random variables of the continuous type. Let S denote the n-dimensional space where this joint pdf $f(x_1, x_2, \ldots, x_n) > 0$, and consider the transformation $y_1 = u_1(x_1, x_2, \ldots, x_n)$, $\ldots, y_n = u_n(x_1, x_2, \ldots, x_n)$, which maps S onto $\mathcal{T}$ in the $y_1, y_2, \ldots, y_n$ space. To each point of S there corresponds, of course, only one point in $\mathcal{T}$; but to a point in $\mathcal{T}$ there may correspond more than one point in S. That is, the transformation may not be one-to-one. Suppose, however, that we can represent S as the union of a finite number, say k, of mutually disjoint sets $A_1, A_2, \ldots, A_k$ so that

$$y_1 = u_1(x_1, x_2, \ldots, x_n), \ldots, y_n = u_n(x_1, x_2, \ldots, x_n)$$

define a one-to-one transformation of each A_i onto $\mathcal{T}$. Thus to each point in $\mathcal{T}$ there corresponds exactly one point in each of $A_1, A_2, \ldots, A_k$. For $i = 1, \ldots, k$, let

$$x_1 = w_{1i}(y_1, y_2, \ldots, y_n), x_2 = w_{2i}(y_1, y_2, \ldots, y_n), \ldots, x_n = w_{ni}(y_1, y_2, \ldots, y_n),$$

denote the k groups of n inverse functions, one group for each of these k transformations. Let the first partial derivatives be continuous and let each

$$J_i = \begin{vmatrix} \frac{\partial w_{1i}}{\partial y_1} & \frac{\partial w_{1i}}{\partial y_2} & \cdots & \frac{\partial w_{1i}}{\partial y_n} \\ \frac{\partial w_{2i}}{\partial y_1} & \frac{\partial w_{2i}}{\partial y_2} & \cdots & \frac{\partial w_{2i}}{\partial y_n} \\ \vdots & \vdots & & \vdots \\ \frac{\partial w_{ni}}{\partial y_1} & \frac{\partial w_{ni}}{\partial y_2} & \cdots & \frac{\partial w_{ni}}{\partial y_n} \end{vmatrix}, \quad i = 1, 2, \ldots, k,$$

be not identically equal to zero in $\mathcal{T}$. Considering the probability of the union of k mutually exclusive events and by applying the change-of-variable technique to the probability of each of these events, it can be seen that the joint pdf of $Y_1 = u_1(X_1, X_2, \ldots, X_n)$, $Y_2 = u_2(X_1, X_2, \ldots, X_n), \ldots, Y_n = u_n(X_1, X_2, \ldots, X_n)$, is given by

$$g(y_1, y_2, \ldots, y_n) = \sum_{i=1}^{k} f[w_{1i}(y_1, \ldots, y_n), \ldots, w_{ni}(y_1, \ldots, y_n)]|J_i|,$$

provided that $(y_1, y_2, \ldots, y_n) \in \mathcal{T}$, and equals zero elsewhere. The pdf of any Y_i, say Y_1, is then

$$g_1(y_1) = \int_{-\infty}^{\infty} \cdots \int_{-\infty}^{\infty} g(y_1, y_2, \ldots, y_n)\, dy_2 \cdots dy_n.$$

Example 2.7.3. Let X_1 and X_2 have the joint pdf defined over the unit circle given by

$$f(x_1, x_2) = \begin{cases} \frac{1}{\pi} & 0 < x_1^2 + x_2^2 < 1 \\ 0 & \text{elsewhere.} \end{cases}$$

Let $Y_1 = X_1^2 + X_2^2$ and $Y_2 = X_1^2/(X_1^2 + X_2^2)$. Thus $y_1 y_2 = x_1^2$ and $x_2^2 = y_1(1 - y_2)$. The support $\mathcal{S}$ maps onto $\mathcal{T} = \{(y_1, y_2) : 0 < y_i < 1, i = 1, 2\}$. For each ordered pair $(y_1, y_2) \in \mathcal{T}$, there are four points in $\mathcal{S}$, given by

$$(x_1, x_2) \quad \text{such that} \quad x_1 = \sqrt{y_1 y_2} \text{ and } x_2 = \sqrt{y_1(1 - y_2)}$$
$$(x_1, x_2) \quad \text{such that} \quad x_1 = \sqrt{y_1 y_2} \text{ and } x_2 = -\sqrt{y_1(1 - y_2)}$$
$$(x_1, x_2) \quad \text{such that} \quad x_1 = -\sqrt{y_1 y_2} \text{ and } x_2 = \sqrt{y_1(1 - y_2)}$$
$$\text{and } (x_1, x_2) \quad \text{such that} \quad x_1 = -\sqrt{y_1 y_2} \text{ and } x_2 = -\sqrt{y_1(1 - y_2)}.$$

The value of the first Jacobian is

$$J_1 = \begin{vmatrix} \frac{1}{2}\sqrt{y_2/y_1} & \frac{1}{2}\sqrt{y_1/y_2} \\ \frac{1}{2}\sqrt{(1 - y_2)/y_1} & -\frac{1}{2}\sqrt{y_1/(1 - y_2)} \end{vmatrix}$$

$$= \frac{1}{4}\left\{ -\sqrt{\frac{1 - y_2}{y_2}} - \sqrt{\frac{y_2}{1 - y_2}} \right\} = -\frac{1}{4}\frac{1}{\sqrt{y_2(1 - y_2)}}.$$

It is easy to see that the absolute value of each of the four Jacobians equals $1/4\sqrt{y_2(1 - y_2)}$. Hence, the joint pdf of Y_1 and Y_2 is the sum of four terms and can be written as

$$g(y_1, y_2) = 4\frac{1}{\pi}\frac{1}{4\sqrt{y_2(1 - y_2)}} = \frac{1}{\pi\sqrt{y_2(1 - y_2)}}, \quad (y_1, y_2) \in \mathcal{T}.$$

Thus Y_1 and Y_2 are independent random variables by Theorem 2.5.1. ∎

Of course, as in the bivariate case, we can use the mgf technique by noting that if $Y = g(X_1, X_2, \ldots, X_n)$ is a function of the random variables, then the mgf of Y is given by

$$E\left(e^{tY}\right) = \int_{-\infty}^{\infty} \int_{-\infty}^{\infty} \cdots \int_{-\infty}^{\infty} e^{tg(x_1, x_2, \ldots, x_n)} f(x_1, x_2, \ldots, x_n)\, dx_1 dx_2 \cdots dx_n,$$

in the continuous case, where $f(x_1, x_2, \ldots, x_n)$ is the joint pdf. In the discrete case, summations replace the integrals. This procedure is particularly useful in cases in which we are dealing with linear functions of independent random variables.

Example 2.7.4 (Extension of Example 2.2.6). Let X_1, X_2, X_3 be independent random variables with joint pmf

$$p(x_1, x_2, x_3) = \begin{cases} \frac{\mu_1^{x_1} \mu_2^{x_2} \mu_3^{x_3} e^{-\mu_1 - \mu_2 - \mu_3}}{x_1! x_2! x_3!} & x_i = 0, 1, 2, \ldots, i = 1, 2, 3 \\ 0 & \text{elsewhere.} \end{cases}$$

If $Y = X_1 + X_2 + X_3$, the mgf of Y is

$$\begin{aligned} E\left(e^{tY}\right) &= E\left(e^{t(X_1 + X_2 + X_3)}\right) \\ &= E\left(e^{tX_1} e^{tX_2} e^{tX_3}\right) \\ &= E\left(e^{tX_1}\right) E\left(e^{tX_2}\right) E\left(e^{tX_3}\right), \end{aligned}$$

because of the independence of X_1, X_2, X_3. In Example 2.2.6, we found that

$$E\left(e^{tX_i}\right) = \exp\{\mu_i(e^t - 1)\}, \quad i = 1, 2, 3.$$

Hence,

$$E\left(e^{tY}\right) = \exp\{(\mu_1 + \mu_2 + \mu_3)(e^t - 1)\}.$$

This, however, is the mgf of the pmf

$$p_Y(y) = \begin{cases} \frac{(\mu_1 + \mu_2 + \mu_3)^y e^{-(\mu_1 + \mu_2 + \mu_3)}}{y!} & y = 0, 1, 2 \ldots \\ 0 & \text{elsewhere,} \end{cases}$$

so $Y = X_1 + X_2 + X_3$ has this distribution. ∎

Example 2.7.5. Let X_1, X_2, X_3, X_4 be independent random variables with common pdf

$$f(x) = \begin{cases} e^{-x} & x > 0 \\ 0 & \text{elsewhere.} \end{cases}$$

If $Y = X_1 + X_2 + X_3 + X_4$, then similar to the argument in the last example, the independence of X_1, X_2, X_3, X_4 implies that

$$E\left(e^{tY}\right) = E\left(e^{tX_1}\right) E\left(e^{tX_2}\right) E\left(e^{tX_3}\right) E\left(e^{tX_4}\right).$$

In Section 1.9, we saw that

$$E\left(e^{tX_i}\right) = (1 - t)^{-1}, \quad t < 1, \, i = 1, 2, 3, 4.$$

Hence,

$$E\left(e^{tY}\right) = (1-t)^{-4}.$$

In Section 3.3, we find that this is the mgf of a distribution with pdf

$$f_Y(y) = \begin{cases} \frac{1}{3!} y^3 e^{-y} & 0 < y < \infty \\ 0 & \text{elsewhere.} \end{cases}$$

Accordingly, Y has this distribution. ∎

EXERCISES

2.7.1. Let X_1, X_2, X_3 be iid, each with the distribution having pdf $f(x) = e^{-x}$, $0 < x < \infty$, zero elsewhere. Show that

$$Y_1 = \frac{X_1}{X_1 + X_2}, \quad Y_2 = \frac{X_1 + X_2}{X_1 + X_2 + X_3}, \quad Y_3 = X_1 + X_2 + X_3$$

are mutually independent.

2.7.2. If $f(x) = \frac{1}{2}$, $-1 < x < 1$, zero elsewhere, is the pdf of the random variable X, find the pdf of $Y = X^2$.

2.7.3. If X has the pdf of $f(x) = \frac{1}{4}$, $-1 < x < 3$, zero elsewhere, find the pdf of $Y = X^2$.
Hint: Here $T = \{y : 0 \le y < 9\}$ and the event $Y \in B$ is the union of two mutually exclusive events if $B = \{y : 0 < y < 1\}$.

2.7.4. Let X_1, X_2, X_3 be iid with common pdf $f(x) = e^{-x}$, $x > 0$, 0 elsewhere. Find the joint pdf of $Y_1 = X_1$, $Y_2 = X_1 + X_2$, and $Y_3 = X_1 + X_2 + X_3$.

2.7.5. Let X_1, X_2, X_3 be iid with common pdf $f(x) = e^{-x}$, $x > 0$, 0 elsewhere. Find the joint pdf of $Y_1 = X_1/X_2$, $Y_2 = X_3/(X_1 + X_2)$, and $Y_3 = X_1 + X_2$. Are Y_1, Y_2, Y_3 mutually independent?

2.7.6. Let X_1, X_2 have the joint pdf $f(x_1, x_2) = 1/\pi$, $0 < x_1^2 + x_2^2 < 1$. Let $Y_1 = X_1^2 + X_2^2$ and $Y_2 = X_2$. Find the joint pdf of Y_1 and Y_2.

2.7.7. Let X_1, X_2, X_3, X_4 have the joint pdf $f(x_1, x_2, x_3, x_4) = 24$, $0 < x_1 < x_2 < x_3 < x_4 < 1$, 0 elsewhere. Find the joint pdf of $Y_1 = X_1/X_2$, $Y_2 = X_2/X_3$, $Y_3 = X_3/X_4$, $Y_4 = X_4$ and show that they are mutually independent.

2.7.8. Let X_1, X_2, X_3 be iid with common mgf $M(t) = ((3/4) + (1/4)e^t)^2$, for all $t \in R$.

(a) Determine the probabilities, $P(X_1 = k), k = 0, 1, 2$.

(b) Find the mgf of $Y = X_1 + X_2 + X_3$ and then determine the probabilities, $P(Y = k), k = 0, 1, 2, \dots, 6$.

2.8 Linear Combinations of Random Variables

Let $(X_1, \ldots, X_n)'$ denote a random vector from some experiment. Often we are interested in a function of $T = T(X_1, \ldots, X_n)$. In this section, we consider linear combinations of these variables, i.e., functions of the form

$$T = \sum_{i=1}^{n} a_i X_i,$$

for a specified vector $\mathbf{a} = (a_1, \ldots, a_n)'$.

The mean of T follows immediately from the linearity of the expectation operator, E, but for easy reference we state this as a theorem:

Theorem 2.8.1. *Let* $T = \sum_{i=1}^{n} a_i X_i$. *Provided* $E[|X_i|] < \infty$, *for* $i = 1, \ldots, n$,

$$E(T) = \sum_{i=1}^{n} a_i E(X_i).$$

$E(a_1 X_1 + a_2 X_2 + \cdots)$
$= a_1 E(X_1) + a_2 E(X_2) + \cdots$

For the variance of T, we first state a very general result involving covariances.

Theorem 2.8.2. *Let* $T = \sum_{i=1}^{n} a_i X_i$ *and let* $W = \sum_{i=1}^{m} b_i Y_i$. *If* $E[X_i^2] < \infty$, *and* $E[Y_j^2] < \infty$ *for* $i = 1, \ldots, n$ *and* $j = 1, \ldots, m$, *then*

$$Cov(T, W) = \sum_{i=1}^{n} \sum_{j=1}^{m} a_i b_j \, Cov(X_i, Y_j).$$

Proof: Using the definition of the covariance and Theorem 2.8.1, we have the first equality below, while the second equality follows from the linearity of E:

$$Cov(T, W) = E\left[\sum_{i=1}^{n} \sum_{j=1}^{m} (a_i X_i - a_i E(X_i))(b_j Y_j - b_j E(Y_j)) \right]$$

$$= \sum_{i=1}^{n} \sum_{j=1}^{m} a_i b_j E[(X_i - E(X_i))(Y_j - E(Y_j))],$$

which is the desired result. ∎

To obtain the variance of T, simply replace W by T in Theorem 2.8.2. We state the result as a corollary:

Corollary 2.8.1. *Let* $T = \sum_{i=1}^{n} a_i X_i$. *Provided* $E[X_i^2] < \infty$, *for* $i = 1, \ldots, n$,

$$Var(T) = Cov(T, T) = \sum_{i=1}^{n} a_i^2 \, Var(X_i) + 2 \sum_{i<j} a_i a_j \, Cov(X_i, X_j). \tag{2.8.1}$$

Note that if $X_1, \ldots, X_n$ are independent random variables, then the covariance $Cov(X_i, X_j) = 0$; see Example 2.5.4. This leads to a simplification of (2.8.1), which we record in the following corollary.

Corollary 2.8.2. *If $X_1, \ldots, X_n$ are independent random variables with finite variances, then*

$$Var(T) = \sum_{i=1}^{n} a_i^2 \, Var(X_i). \qquad (2.8.2)$$

[handwritten: $Var(a_1 x_1 + a_2 x_2 + \cdots) = a_1^2 Var(x_1) + a_2^2 Var(x_2) + \cdots$]

Note that we need only X_i and X_j to be uncorrelated for all $i \neq j$ to obtain this result; for example, $Cov(X_i, X_j) = 0$, $i \neq j$, which is true when $X_1, \ldots, X_n$ are independent.

If the random variables $X_1, X_2, \ldots, X_n$ are independent and identically distributed (iid), we often say that these random variables constitute a **random sample** of size n from that common distribution. In the next two examples, we find some properties of two statistics of the random sample, namely the sample mean and variance.

Example 2.8.1 (Sample Mean). Let $X_1, \ldots, X_n$ be independent and identically distributed random variables with common mean μ and variance σ^2. The **sample mean** is defined by $\overline{X} = n^{-1} \sum_{i=1}^{n} X_i$. This is a linear combination of the sample observations with $a_i \equiv n^{-1}$; hence, by Theorem 2.8.1 and Corollary 2.8.2, we have

[handwritten: $E(\overline{x}) = E(\frac{1}{n}\sum x_i) = E(\frac{1}{n}x_1 + \frac{1}{n}x_2 + \cdots)$
$= \frac{1}{n}E(x_1) + \frac{1}{n}E(x_2) + \cdots + \frac{1}{n}E(x_n)$
$= \frac{1}{n}\mu + \cdots + \frac{1}{n}\mu = \frac{1}{n}\cdot n\mu = \mu. \quad (\because E(x_1) = E(x_2) = \cdots = \mu).$]

$$E(\overline{X}) = \mu \quad \text{and} \quad Var(\overline{X}) = \frac{\sigma^2}{n}. \qquad (2.8.3)$$

By Definition 4.1.3 of Chapter 4, we say that $\overline{X}$ is an **unbiased estimator** of μ. ∎

[handwritten: 同理, $Var(\overline{x}) = Var(\frac{1}{n}\sum x_i) = \frac{1}{n^2}(Var(x_1) + \cdots + Var(x_n)) = \frac{1}{n^2}\cdot n\sigma^2 = \frac{\sigma^2}{n}$]

Example 2.8.2 (Sample Variance). Define the **sample variance** by

$$S^2 = (n-1)^{-1} \sum_{i=1}^{n} (X_i - \overline{X})^2 = (n-1)^{-1}\left(\sum_{i=1}^{n} X_i^2 - n\overline{X}^2 \right), \qquad (2.8.4)$$

where the second equality follows after some algebra; see Exercise 2.8.1. Using the above theorems, the results of the last example, and the fact that $E(X^2) = \sigma^2 + \mu^2$, we have the following:

[handwritten right: $Var(\overline{x}) = E(\overline{x}^2) - [E(\overline{x})]^2$
$E(\overline{x}^2) = Var(\overline{x}) + [E(\overline{x})]^2 = \frac{\sigma^2}{n} + \mu^2$]

[handwritten left: $E(x_i^2) - [E(x_i)]^2 = Var(x_i)$
$\Rightarrow E(x_i^2) = Var(x_i) + [E(x_i)]^2 = \sigma^2 + \mu^2$]

$$E(S^2) = (n-1)^{-1}\left(\sum_{i=1}^{n} E(X_i^2) - nE(\overline{X}^2) \right)$$

$$= (n-1)^{-1}\left\{ n\sigma^2 + n\mu^2 - n[(\sigma^2/n) + \mu^2] \right\}$$

$$= \sigma^2. \qquad (2.8.5)$$

Hence, S^2 is an unbiased estimator of σ^2. ∎

[handwritten: 单号, 只有 x 这个变量, x 为所有可能取值为 $x_1, \cdots, x_n$. → 是一个 size 为 n 的一个 sample, 里面的值记为 $\overline{x}_1, \overline{x}_2, \cdots, \overline{x}_n$, 是]

[handwritten: (注: 以下有些地方想 $Var(x)$ 与 $Var(\overline{x})$ 两区别!]
$Var(x) = E[(x-\mu)^2] = \sum_{x=x_1,\cdots x_n}(x-\mu)^2 \cdot f(x) = (x_1-\mu)^2 f(x_1) + \cdots + (x_n-\mu)^2 \cdot f(x)$]

EXERCISES

[handwritten: $Var(\overline{x}) = ? = \frac{1}{n^2}(Var(x_1) + \cdots + Var(x_n)) = \frac{\sigma^2}{n}$] *[handwritten: n 个相互独立但又具有相同分布的变量, $\because E(\overline{x}_1) = E(\overline{x}_2) = \cdots = \mu.$]*

2.8.1. Derive the second equality in expression (2.8.4). *[handwritten: (下接 P137.)]*

2.8.2. Let X_1, X_2, X_3, X_4 be four iid random variables having the same pdf $f(x) = 2x$, $0 < x < 1$, zero elsewhere. Find the mean and variance of the sum Y of these four random variables. *[handwritten: $Var(x_i) = \sigma^2$.]*

2.8.3. Let X_1 and X_2 be two independent random variables so that the variances of X_1 and X_2 are $\sigma_1^2 = k$ and $\sigma_2^2 = 2$, respectively. Given that the variance of $Y = 3X_2 - X_1$ is 25, find k.

2.8.4. If the independent variables X_1 and X_2 have means μ_1, μ_2 and variances σ_1^2, σ_2^2, respectively, show that the mean and variance of the product $Y = X_1 X_2$ are $\mu_1 \mu_2$ and $\sigma_1^2 \sigma_2^2 + \mu_1^2 \sigma_2^2 + \mu_2^2 \sigma_1^2$, respectively.

2.8.5. Find the mean and variance of the sum $Y = \sum_{i=1}^{5} X_i$, where $X_1, \ldots, X_5$ are iid, having pdf $f(x) = 6x(1-x)$, $0 < x < 1$, zero elsewhere.

2.8.6. Determine the mean and variance of the sample mean $\overline{X} = 5^{-1} \sum_{i=1}^{5} X_i$, where $X_1, \ldots, X_5$ is a random sample from a distribution having pdf $f(x) = 4x^3$, $0 < x < 1$, zero elsewhere.

2.8.7. Let X and Y be random variables with $\mu_1 = 1$, $\mu_2 = 4$, $\sigma_1^2 = 4$, $\sigma_2^2 = 6$, $\rho = \frac{1}{2}$. Find the mean and variance of the random variable $Z = 3X - 2Y$.

2.8.8. Let X and Y be independent random variables with means μ_1, μ_2 and variances σ_1^2, σ_2^2. Determine the correlation coefficient of X and $Z = X - Y$ in terms of μ_1, $\mu_2, \sigma_1^2, \sigma_2^2$.

2.8.9. Let μ and σ^2 denote the mean and variance of the random variable X. Let $Y = c + bX$, where b and c are real constants. Show that the mean and variance of Y are, respectively, $c + b\mu$ and $b^2 \sigma^2$.

2.8.10. Determine the correlation coefficient of the random variables X and Y if $\mathrm{var}(X) = 4$, $\mathrm{var}(Y) = 2$, and $\mathrm{var}(X + 2Y) = 15$.

2.8.11. Let X and Y be random variables with means μ_1, μ_2; variances σ_1^2, σ_2^2; and correlation coefficient ρ. Show that the correlation coefficient of $W = aX + b$, $a > 0$, and $Z = cY + d$, $c > 0$, is ρ.

2.8.12. A person rolls a die, tosses a coin, and draws a card from an ordinary deck. He receives \$3 for each point up on the die, \$10 for a head and \$0 for a tail, and \$1 for each spot on the card (jack = 11, queen = 12, king = 13). If we assume that the three random variables involved are independent and uniformly distributed, compute the mean and variance of the amount to be received.

2.8.13. Let X_1 and X_2 be independent random variables with nonzero variances. Find the correlation coefficient of $Y = X_1 X_2$ and X_1 in terms of the means and variances of X_1 and X_2.

2.8.14. Let X_1 and X_2 have a joint distribution with parameters μ_1, μ_2, σ_1^2, σ_2^2, and ρ. Find the correlation coefficient of the linear functions of $Y = a_1 X_1 + a_2 X_2$ and $Z = b_1 X_1 + b_2 X_2$ in terms of the real constants a_1, a_2, b_1, b_2, and the parameters of the distribution.

2.8.15. Let X_1, X_2, and X_3 be random variables with equal variances but with correlation coefficients $\rho_{12} = 0.3$, $\rho_{13} = 0.5$, and $\rho_{23} = 0.2$. Find the correlation coefficient of the linear functions $Y = X_1 + X_2$ and $Z = X_2 + X_3$.

2.8.16. Find the variance of the sum of 10 random variables if each has variance 5 and if each pair has correlation coefficient 0.5.

2.8.17. Let X and Y have the parameters μ_1, μ_2, σ_1^2, σ_2^2, and ρ. Show that the correlation coefficient of X and $[Y - \rho(\sigma_2/\sigma_1)X]$ is zero.

2.8.18. Let S^2 be the sample variance of a random sample from a distribution with variance $\sigma^2 > 0$. Since $E(S^2) = \sigma^2$, why isn't $E(S) = \sigma$?
Hint: Use Jensen's inequality to show that $E(S) < \sigma$.

根据var定义   乙才推E$(\frac{\Sigma x_i}{n}) = E(\bar{x}) = \mu.$

$$var(\bar{x}) = var(\frac{\Sigma x_i}{n}) \underset{\text{①}}{=} E\left[(\frac{\Sigma x_i}{n} - E(\frac{\Sigma x_i}{n}))^2\right] \underset{\text{②}}{=} E\left[(\frac{\Sigma x_i}{n} - \mu)^2\right]$$

$$= E\left(\left(\frac{\Sigma x_i}{n}\right)^2 - 2\mu\frac{\Sigma x_i}{n} + \mu^2\right) = E\left[\left(\frac{\Sigma x_i}{n}\right)^2\right] - 2\mu\underbrace{\left(E(\frac{\Sigma x_i}{n})\right)}_{=\mu} + \mu^2$$

$$= \frac{1}{n^2}E\left[(\Sigma x_i)^2\right] - \mu^2 = \frac{1}{n^2}E\left[(x_1 + x_2 + \cdots + x_n)^2\right] - \mu^2$$

$$= ? \longrightarrow$$ 到此，可看到，若直接从variance的定义 $= E[(\cdots - \cdots)^2]$ 将会很难得出生最后结果.

应如前面 2.8.11中那样 利用公式来计算 $var(\bar{x}) = \frac{\sigma^2}{n}$

（另，可利用 $var(\bar{x}) = \frac{\sigma^2}{n}$ 这个结果间接得出 $E[(x_1 + \cdots + x_n)^2]$ 的值来！）

$$var(\bar{x}) = E(\bar{x}^2) - [E(\bar{x})]^2 \Rightarrow \frac{\sigma^2}{n} = E(\bar{x}^2) - \mu^2$$

$$\Rightarrow E(\bar{x}^2) = \frac{\sigma^2}{n} + \mu^2$$

Chapter 3

Some Special Distributions

3.1 The Binomial and Related Distributions

In Chapter 1 we introduced the *uniform distribution* and the *hypergeometric distribution*. In this chapter we discuss some other important distributions of random variables frequently used in statistics. We begin with the binomial and related distributions.

A **Bernoulli experiment** is a random experiment, the outcome of which can be classified in but one of two mutually exclusive and exhaustive ways, for instance, success or failure (e.g., female or male, life or death, nondefective or defective). A sequence of **Bernoulli trials** occurs when a Bernoulli experiment is performed several independent times so that the probability of success, say p, remains the same from trial to trial. That is, in such a sequence, we let p denote the probability of success on each trial.

Let X be a random variable associated with a Bernoulli trial by defining it as follows:

$$X(\text{success}) = 1 \quad \text{and} \quad X(\text{failure}) = 0.$$

That is, the two outcomes, success and failure, are denoted by one and zero, respectively. The pmf of X can be written as

$$p(x) = p^x(1-p)^{1-x}, \quad x = 0, 1, \tag{3.1.1}$$

and we say that X has a *Bernoulli distribution*. The expected value of X is

$$\mu = E(X) = (0)(1-p) + (1)(p) = p,$$

and the variance of X is

$$\sigma^2 = \text{var}(X) = p^2(1-p) + (1-p)^2 p = p(1-p).$$

It follows that the standard deviation of X is $\sigma = \sqrt{p(1-p)}$.

In a sequence of n Bernoulli trials, let X_i denote the Bernoulli random variable associated with the ith trial. An observed sequence of n Bernoulli trials is then an n-tuple of zeros and ones. In such a sequence of Bernoulli trials, we are often interested

139

in the total number of successes and not in the order of their occurrence. If we let the random variable X equal the number of observed successes in n Bernoulli trials, the possible values of X are $0, 1, 2, \ldots, n$. If x successes occur, where $x = 0, 1, 2, \ldots, n$, then $n - x$ failures occur. The number of ways of selecting the x positions for the x successes in the n trials is

$$\binom{n}{x} = \frac{n!}{x!(n-x)!}.$$

Since the trials are independent and the probabilities of success and failure on each trial are, respectively, p and $1 - p$, the probability of each of these ways is $p^x(1-p)^{n-x}$. Thus the pmf of X, say $p(x)$, is the sum of the probabilities of these $\binom{n}{x}$ mutually exclusive events; that is,

$$p(x) = \begin{cases} \binom{n}{x}p^x(1-p)^{n-x} & x = 0, 1, 2, \ldots, n \\ 0 & \text{elsewhere.} \end{cases} \qquad (3.1.2)$$

Recall, if n is a positive integer, that

$$(a+b)^n = \sum_{x=0}^{n} \binom{n}{x} b^x a^{n-x}.$$

Thus it is clear that $p(x) \geq 0$ and that

$$\begin{aligned} \sum_x p(x) &= \sum_{x=0}^{n} \binom{n}{x} p^x (1-p)^{n-x} \\ &= [(1-p)+p]^n = 1. \end{aligned}$$

Therefore, $p(x)$ satisfies the conditions of being a pmf of a random variable X of the discrete type. A random variable X that has a pmf of the form of $p(x)$ is said to have a **binomial distribution**, and any such $p(x)$ is called a **binomial pmf**. A binomial distribution is denoted by the symbol $b(n, p)$. The constants n and p are called the **parameters** of the binomial distribution. Thus, if we say that X is $b(5, \frac{1}{3})$, we mean that X has the binomial pmf

$$p(x) = \begin{cases} \binom{5}{x} \left(\frac{1}{3}\right)^x \left(\frac{2}{3}\right)^{5-x} & x = 0, 1, \ldots, 5 \\ 0 & \text{elsewhere.} \end{cases} \qquad (3.1.3)$$

The mgf of a binomial distribution is easily obtained as follows:

$$\begin{aligned} M(t) &= \sum_x e^{tx} p(x) = \sum_{x=0}^{n} e^{tx} \binom{n}{x} p^x (1-p)^{n-x} \\ &= \sum_{x=0}^{n} \binom{n}{x} (pe^t)^x (1-p)^{n-x} \\ &= [(1-p) + pe^t]^n \end{aligned}$$

for all real values of t. The mean μ and the variance σ^2 of X may be computed from $M(t)$. Since

$$M'(t) = n[(1-p) + pe^t]^{n-1}(pe^t) \quad , \quad M'(t)\big|_{t=0} = \tilde{E}(x)$$

and

$$M''(t) = n[(1-p) + pe^t]^{n-1}(pe^t) + n(n-1)[(1-p) + pe^t]^{n-2}(pe^t)^2, \quad M''(t)\big|_{t=0} = E(x^2)$$

if follows that

$$\mu = M'(0) = np$$

and

$$\sigma^2 = M''(0) - \mu^2 = np + n(n-1)p^2 - (np)^2 = np(1-p). = npq$$

Example 3.1.1. Let X be the number of heads (successes) in $n = 7$ independent tosses of an unbiased coin. The pmf of X is

$\therefore p = \frac{1}{2}$ $= \binom{n}{x} p^x (1-p)^{n-x}$

$$p(x) = \begin{cases} = \binom{7}{x} \left(\frac{1}{2}\right)^x \left(1 - \frac{1}{2}\right)^{7-x} & x = 0, 1, 2, \dots, 7 \\ 0 & \text{elsewhere.} \end{cases}$$

Then X has the mgf

$$M(t) = \left(\tfrac{1}{2} + \tfrac{1}{2}e^t\right)^7,$$

has mean $\mu = np = \frac{7}{2}$, and has variance $\sigma^2 = np(1-p) = \frac{7}{4}$. Furthermore, we have

$= p(0) + p(1) = \binom{7}{0}\frac{1}{2}^0 (1-\frac{1}{2})^7 + \binom{7}{1}\frac{1}{2}^1 (1-\frac{1}{2})^6$

$$P(0 < X < 1) = \sum_{x=0}^{1} p(x) = \frac{1}{128} + \frac{7}{128} = \frac{8}{128}$$

and

$$P(X = 5) = p(5) = \frac{7!}{5!2!} \left(\frac{1}{2}\right)^5 \left(\frac{1}{2}\right)^2 = \frac{21}{128}. \quad \blacksquare$$

Most computer packages have commands which obtain the binomial probabilities. To give the R (Ihaka and Gentleman, 1996) commands, suppose X has a $b(n, p)$ distribution. Then the command dbinom(k,n,p) returns $P(X = k)$, while the command pbinom(k,n,p) returns the cumulative probability $P(X \le k)$.

Example 3.1.2. If the mgf of a random variable X is

$$M(t) = \left(\tfrac{2}{3} + \tfrac{1}{3}e^t\right)^5, \quad = (1-p + pe^t)^n$$

$\swarrow = 1 - p \Rightarrow p = \frac{1}{3}$

then X has a binomial distribution with $n = 5$ and $p = \frac{1}{3}$; that is, the pmf of X is

$$p(x) = \begin{cases} \binom{5}{x} \left(\frac{1}{3}\right)^x \left(\frac{2}{3}\right)^{5-x} & x = 0, 1, 2, \dots, 5 \\ 0 & \text{elsewhere.} \end{cases}$$

Here $\mu = np = \frac{5}{3}$ and $\sigma^2 = np(1-p) = \frac{10}{9}$. $\blacksquare$

Example 3.1.3. If Y is $b(n, \frac{1}{3})$, then $P(Y \geq 1) = 1 - P(Y = 0) = 1 - (\frac{2}{3})^n$. Suppose that we wish to find the smallest value of n that yields $P(Y \geq 1) > 0.80$. We have $1 - (\frac{2}{3})^n > 0.80$ and $0.20 > (\frac{2}{3})^n$. Either by inspection or by use of logarithms, we see that $n = 4$ is the solution. That is, the probability of at least one success throughout $n = 4$ independent repetitions of a random experiment with probability of success $p = \frac{1}{3}$ is greater than 0.80. ∎

Example 3.1.4. Let the random variable Y be equal to the number of successes throughout n independent repetitions of a random experiment with probability p of success. That is, Y is $b(n, p)$. The ratio Y/n is called the relative frequency of success. Recall expression (1.10.3), the second version of Chebyshev's inequality (Theorem 1.10.3). Applying this result, we have for all $\epsilon > 0$ that

$$P\left(\left|\frac{Y}{n} - p\right| \geq \epsilon\right) \leq \frac{\text{Var}(Y/n)}{\epsilon^2} = \frac{p(1-p)}{n\epsilon^2}$$

[Exercise 3.1.3 asks for the determination of $\text{Var}(Y/n)$]. Now, for every fixed $\epsilon > 0$, the right-hand member of the preceding inequality is close to zero for sufficiently large n. That is,

$$\lim_{n \to \infty} P\left(\left|\frac{Y}{n} - p\right| \geq \epsilon\right) = 0$$

and

$$\lim_{n \to \infty} P\left(\left|\frac{Y}{n} - p\right| < \epsilon\right) = 1.$$

Since this is true for every fixed $\epsilon > 0$, we see, in a certain sense, that the relative frequency of success is for large values of n, close to the probability of p of success. This result is one form of the *Weak Law of Large Numbers*. It was alluded to in the initial discussion of probability in Chapter 1 and is considered again, along with related concepts, in Chapter 5. ∎

Example 3.1.5. Let the independent random variables X_1, X_2, X_3 have the same cdf $F(x)$. Let Y be the middle value of X_1, X_2, X_3. To determine the cdf of Y, say $F_Y(y) = P(Y \leq y)$, we note that $Y \leq y$ if and only if at least two of the random variables X_1, X_2, X_3 are less than or equal to y. Let us say that the ith "trial" is a success if $X_i \leq y$, $i = 1, 2, 3$; here each "trial" has the probability of success $F(y)$. In this terminology, $F_Y(y) = P(Y \leq y)$ is then the probability of at least two successes in three independent trials. Thus

$$F_Y(y) = \binom{3}{2}[F(y)]^2[1 - F(y)] + [F(y)]^3.$$

If $F(x)$ is a continuous cdf so that the pdf of X is $F'(x) = f(x)$, then the pdf of Y is

$$f_Y(y) = F_Y'(y) = 6[F(y)][1 - F(y)]f(y). \quad ∎$$

Example 3.1.6. Consider a sequence of independent repetitions of a random experiment with constant probability p of success. Let the random variable Y denote the total number of failures in this sequence before the rth success, that is,

$Y + r$ is equal to the number of trials necessary to produce exactly r successes. Here r is a fixed positive integer. To determine the pmf of Y, let y be an element of $\{y : y = 0, 1, 2, \ldots\}$. Then, by the multiplication rule of probabilities, $P(Y = y) = g(y)$ is equal to the product of the probability

$$\binom{y + r - 1}{r - 1} p^{r-1}(1 - p)^y$$

of obtaining exactly $r - 1$ successes in the first $y + r - 1$ trials and the probability p of a success on the $(y + r)$th trial. Thus the pmf of Y is

$$p_Y(y) = \begin{cases} \binom{y+r-1}{r-1} p^r (1-p)^y & y = 0, 1, 2, \ldots \\ 0 & \text{elsewhere.} \end{cases} \tag{3.1.4}$$

A distribution with a pmf of the form $p_Y(y)$ is called a **negative binomial distribution**; and any such $p_Y(y)$ is called a negative binomial pmf. The distribution derives its name from the fact that $p_Y(y)$ is a general term in the expansion of $p^r[1 - (1 - p)]^{-r}$. It is left as an exercise to show that the mgf of this distribution is $M(t) = p^r[1 - (1 - p)e^t]^{-r}$, for $t < -\log(1 - p)$. If $r - 1$, then Y has the pmf

$$p_Y(y) = p(1-p)^y, \quad y = 0, 1, 2, \ldots, \tag{3.1.5}$$

zero elsewhere, and the mgf $M(t) = p[1 - (1 - p)e^t]^{-1}$. In this special case, $r = 1$, we say that Y has a **geometric distribution**. ■

Suppose we have several independent binomial distributions with the same probability of success. Then it makes sense that the sum of these random variables is binomial, as shown in the following theorem.

Theorem 3.1.1. *Let $X_1, X_2, \ldots, X_m$ be independent random variables such that X_i has binomial $b(n_i, p)$ distribution, for $i = 1, 2, \ldots, m$. Let $Y = \sum_{i=1}^m X_i$. Then Y has a binomial $b(\sum_{i=1}^m n_i, p)$ distribution.*

Proof: The mgf of X_i is $M_{X_i}(t) = (1 - p + pe^t)^{n_i}$. By independence it follows from Theorem 2.6.1 that

$$M_Y(t) = \prod_{i=1}^m (1 - p + pe^t)^{n_i} = (1 - p + pe^t)^{\sum_{i=1}^m n_i}.$$

Hence, Y has a binomial $b(\sum_{i=1}^m n_i, p)$ distribution. ■

The binomial distribution is generalized to the multinomial distribution as follows. Let a random experiment be repeated n independent times. On each repetition, the experiment results in but one of k mutually exclusive and exhaustive ways, say $C_1, C_2, \ldots, C_k$. Let p_i be the probability that the outcome is an element of C_i and let p_i remain constant throughout the n independent repetitions, $i = 1, 2, \ldots, k$. Define the random variable X_i to be equal to the number of outcomes that are elements of C_i, $i = 1, 2, \ldots, k - 1$. Furthermore, let $x_1, x_2, \ldots, x_{k-1}$ be nonnegative integers so that $x_1 + x_2 + \cdots + x_{k-1} \leq n$. Then the probability that exactly x_1 terminations of the experiment are in $C_1, \ldots$, exactly x_{k-1} terminations are in C_{k-1}, and hence exactly $n - (x_1 + \cdots + x_{k-1})$ terminations are in C_k is

$$\frac{n!}{x_1! \cdots x_{k-1}! x_k!} p_1^{x_1} \cdots p_{k-1}^{x_{k-1}} p_k^{x_k},$$

where x_k is merely an abbreviation for $n - (x_1 + \cdots + x_{k-1})$. This is the **multinomial pmf** of $k - 1$ random variables $X_1, X_2, \ldots, X_{k-1}$ of the discrete type. To see that this is correct, note that the number of distinguishable arrangements of $x_1 \, C_1\text{s}, x_2 \, C_2\text{s}, \ldots, x_k \, C_k\text{s}$ is

$$\binom{n}{x_1}\binom{n - x_1}{x_2} \cdots \binom{n - x_1 - \cdots - x_{k-2}}{x_{k-1}} = \frac{n!}{x_1! x_2! \cdots x_k!}$$

and the probability of each of these distinguishable arrangements is

$$p_1^{x_1} p_2^{x_2} \cdots p_k^{x_k}.$$

Hence the product of these two latter expressions gives the correct probability, which is an agreement with the formula for the multinomial pmf.

When $k = 3$, we often let $X = X_1$ and $Y = X_2$; then $n - X - Y = X_3$. We say that X and Y have a **trinomial distribution**. The joint pmf of X and Y is

$$p(x, y) = \frac{n!}{x! y! (n - x - y)!} p_1^x p_2^y p_3^{n-x-y},$$

where x and y are nonnegative integers with $x + y \leq n$, and p_1, p_2, and p_3 are positive proper fractions with $p_1 + p_2 + p_3 = 1$; and let $p(x, y) = 0$ elsewhere. Accordingly, $p(x, y)$ satisfies the conditions of being a joint pmf of two random variables X and Y of the discrete type; that is, $p(x, y)$ is nonnegative and its sum over all points (x, y) at which $p(x, y)$ is positive is equal to $(p_1 + p_2 + p_3)^n = 1$.

If n is a positive integer and a_1, a_2, a_3 are fixed constants, we have

$$\sum_{x=0}^{n} \sum_{y=0}^{n-x} \frac{n!}{x! y! (n - x - y)!} a_1^x a_2^y a_3^{n-x-y}$$

$$= \sum_{x=0}^{n} \frac{n! a_1^x}{x! (n - x)!} \sum_{y=0}^{n-x} \frac{(n - x)!}{y! (n - x - y)!} a_2^y a_3^{n-x-y}$$

$$= \sum_{x=0}^{n} \frac{n!}{x! (n - x)!} a_1^x (a_2 + a_3)^{n-x}$$

$$= (a_1 + a_2 + a_3)^n. \tag{3.1.6}$$

Consequently, the mgf of a trinomial distribution, in accordance with Equation (3.1.6), is given by

$$M(t_1, t_2) = \sum_{x=0}^{n} \sum_{y=0}^{n-x} \frac{n!}{x! y! (n - x - y)!} (p_1 e^{t_1})^x (p_2 e^{t_2})^y p_3^{n-x-y}$$

$$= (p_1 e^{t_1} + p_2 e^{t_2} + p_3)^n,$$

for all real values of t_1 and t_2. The moment-generating functions of the marginal distributions of X and Y are, respectively,

$$M(t_1, 0) = (p_1 e^{t_1} + p_2 + p_3)^n = [(1 - p_1) + p_1 e^{t_1}]^n$$

and

$$M(0, t_2) = (p_1 + p_2 e^{t_2} + p_3)^n = [(1 - p_2) + p_2 e^{t_2}]^n.$$

We see immediately, from Theorem 2.5.5, that X and Y are dependent random variables. In addition, X is $b(n, p_1)$ and Y is $b(n, p_2)$. Accordingly, the means and variances of X and Y are, respectively, $\mu_1 = np_1$, $\mu_2 = np_2$, $\sigma_1^2 = np_1(1 - p_1)$, and $\sigma_2^2 = np_2(1 - p_2)$.

Consider next the conditional pmf of Y, given $X = x$. We have

$$p_{2|1}(y|x) = \begin{cases} \frac{(n-x)!}{y!(n-x-y)!} \left(\frac{p_2}{1-p_1}\right)^y \left(\frac{p_3}{1-p_1}\right)^{n-x-y} & y = 0, 1, \ldots, n - x \\ 0 & \text{elsewhere.} \end{cases}$$

Thus the conditional distribution of Y, given $X = x$, is $b[n - x, p_2/(1 - p_1)]$. Hence the conditional mean of Y, given $X = x$, is the linear function

$$E(Y|x) = (n - x)\left(\frac{p_2}{1 - p_1}\right).$$

Also, the conditional distribution of X, given $Y = y$, is $b[n - y, p_1/(1 - p_2)]$ and thus

$$E(X|y) = (n - y)\left(\frac{p_1}{1 - p_2}\right).$$

Now recall from Example 2.4.2 that the square of the correlation coefficient ρ^2 is equal to the product of $-p_2/(1 - p_1)$ and $-p_1/(1 - p_2)$, the coefficients of x and y in the respective conditional means. Since both of these coefficients are negative (and thus ρ is negative), we have

$$\rho = -\sqrt{\frac{p_1 p_2}{(1 - p_1)(1 - p_2)}}.$$

In general, the mgf of a multinomial distribution is given by

$$M(t_1, \ldots, t_{k-1}) = (p_1 e^{t_1} + \cdots + p_{k-1} e^{t_{k-1}} + p_k)^n$$

for all real values of $t_1, t_2, \ldots, t_{k-1}$. Thus each one-variable marginal pmf is binomial, each two-variable marginal pmf is trinomial, and so on.

In Chapter 1, we introduced the hypergeometric distribution; see expression (1.6.4) for the definition of the pmf. As the next example shows, it is related to the binomial distribution.

Example 3.1.7 (Hypergeometric Distribution). A frequently used application of the hypergeometric distribution is in acceptance sampling. Suppose we have a lot of N items of which D are defective. Let X denote the number of defective items in a sample of size n. If the sampling is done with replacement and the items are chosen at random, then X has a binomial distribution with parameters n and D/N. In this case the mean and variance of X are $n(D/N)$ and $n(D/N)[(N-D)/N]$, respectively. Suppose, however, that the sampling is without replacement, which is often the case in practice. The pmf of X follows by noting in this case that each of the $\binom{N}{n}$ samples are equilikely and that there are $\binom{N-D}{n-x}\binom{D}{x}$ samples which have x defective items. Hence, the pmf of X is

$$p(x) = \frac{\binom{N-D}{n-x}\binom{D}{x}}{\binom{N}{n}}, \quad x = 0, 1, \ldots, n, \tag{3.1.7}$$

where, as usual, a binomial coefficient is taken to be 0 when the top value is less than the bottom value. We say that X has a **hypergeometric distribution** with parameters (N, D, n). The mean of X is

$$
\begin{aligned}
E(X) &= \sum_{x=0}^{n} xp(x) = \sum_{x=1}^{n} x \frac{\binom{N-D}{n-x}[D(D-1)!]/[x(x-1)!(D-x)!]}{[N(N-1)!]/[(N-n)!n(n-1)!]} \\
&= n\frac{D}{N} \sum_{x=1}^{n} \binom{(N-1)-(D-1)}{(n-1)-(x-1)}\binom{D-1}{x-1}\binom{N-1}{n-1}^{-1} = n\frac{D}{N}.
\end{aligned}
$$

In the next-to-last step, we used the fact that the probabilities of a hypergeometric $(N-1, D-1, n-1)$ distribution summed over its entire range is 1. So the mean for both types of sampling is the same. The variances, though, differ. As Exercise 3.1.28 shows, the variance of a hypergeometric (N, D, n) is

$$\text{Var}(X) = n\frac{D}{N}\frac{N-D}{N}\frac{N-n}{N-1}. \tag{3.1.8}$$

The last term is often thought of as the correction term when sampling without replacement. Note that it is close to 1 if N is much larger than n. ∎

EXERCISES

3.1.1. If the mgf of a random variable X is $(\frac{1}{3} + \frac{2}{3}e^t)^5$, find $P(X = 2$ or $3)$.

3.1.2. The mgf of a random variable X is $(\frac{2}{3} + \frac{1}{3}e^t)^9$. Show that

$$P(\mu - 2\sigma < X < \mu + 2\sigma) = \sum_{x=1}^{5} \binom{9}{x} \left(\frac{1}{3}\right)^x \left(\frac{2}{3}\right)^{9-x}.$$

3.1.3. If X is $b(n, p)$, show that

$$E\left(\frac{X}{n}\right) = p \quad \text{and} \quad E\left[\left(\frac{X}{n} - p\right)^2\right] = \frac{p(1-p)}{n}.$$

3.1.4. Let the independent random variables X_1, X_2, X_3 have the same pdf $f(x) = 3x^2$, $0 < x < 1$, zero elsewhere. Find the probability that exactly two of these three variables exceed $\frac{1}{2}$.

3.1.5. Let Y be the number of successes in n independent repetitions of a random experiment having the probability of success $p = \frac{2}{3}$. If $n = 3$, compute $P(2 \leq Y)$; if $n = 5$, compute $P(3 \leq Y)$.

3.1.6. Let Y be the number of successes throughout n independent repetitions of a random experiment with probability of success $p = \frac{1}{4}$. Determine the smallest value of n so that $P(1 \leq Y) \geq 0.70$.

3.1.7. Let the independent random variables X_1 and X_2 have binomial distribution with parameters $n_1 = 3$, $p = \frac{2}{3}$ and $n_2 = 4$, $p = \frac{1}{2}$, respectively. Compute $P(X_1 = X_2)$.
Hint: List the four mutually exclusive ways that $X_1 = X_2$ and compute the probability of each.

3.1.8. For this exercise, the reader must have access to a statistical package that obtains the binomial distribution. Hints are given for R code, but other packages can be used too.

(a) Obtain the plot of the pmf for the $b(15, 0.2)$ distribution. Using R, the following commands return the plot:

```
x<-0:15
y<-dbinom(x,15,.2)
plot(x,y)
```

(b) Repeat part (a) for the binomial distributions with $n = 15$ and with $p = 0.10, 0.20, \ldots, 0.90$. Comment on the plots.

(c) Let $Y = \frac{X}{n}$, where X has a $b(n, 0.05)$ distribution. Obtain the plots of the pmfs of Y for $n = 10, 20, 50, 200$. Comment on the plots (what do the plots seem to be converging to as n gets large?).

3.1.9. Toss two nickels and three dimes at random. Make appropriate assumptions and compute the probability that there are more heads showing on the nickels than on the dimes.

3.1.10. Let $X_1, X_2, \ldots, X_{k-1}$ have a multinomial distribution.

(a) Find the mgf of $X_2, X_3, \ldots, X_{k-1}$.

(b) What is the pmf of $X_2, X_3, \ldots, X_{k-1}$?

(c) Determine the conditional pmf of X_1 given that $X_2 = x_2, \ldots, X_{k-1} = x_{k-1}$.

(d) What is the conditional expectation $E(X_1 | x_2, \ldots, x_{k-1})$?

3.1.11. Let X be $b(2, p)$ and let Y be $b(4, p)$. If $P(X \geq 1) = \frac{5}{9}$, find $P(Y \geq 1)$.

3.1.12. If $x = r$ is the unique mode of a distribution that is $b(n, p)$, show that

$$(n+1)p - 1 < r < (n+1)p.$$

Hint: Determine the values of x for which the ratio $p(x+1)/p(x) > 1$.

3.1.13. Let X have a binomial distribution with parameters n and $p = \frac{1}{3}$. Determine the smallest integer n can be such that $P(X \geq 1) \geq 0.85$.

3.1.14. Let X have the pmf $p(x) = (\frac{1}{3})(\frac{2}{3})^x$, $x = 0, 1, 2, 3, \ldots$, zero elsewhere. Find the conditional pmf of X given that $X \geq 3$.

3.1.15. One of the numbers $1, 2, \ldots, 6$ is to be chosen by casting an unbiased die. Let this random experiment be repeated five independent times. Let the random variable X_1 be the number of terminations in the set $\{x : x = 1, 2, 3\}$ and let the random variable X_2 be the number of terminations in the set $\{x : x = 4, 5\}$. Compute $P(X_1 = 2, X_2 = 1)$.

3.1.16. Show that the moment generating function of the negative binomial distribution is $M(t) = p^r[1 - (1 - p)e^t]^{-r}$. Find the mean and the variance of this distribution.
Hint: In the summation representing $M(t)$, make use of the Maclaurin's series for $(1 - w)^{-r}$.

3.1.17. Let X_1 and X_2 have a trinomial distribution. Differentiate the moment-generating function to show that their covariance is $-np_1p_2$.

3.1.18. If a fair coin is tossed at random five independent times, find the conditional probability of five heads given that there are at least four heads.

3.1.19. Let an unbiased die be cast at random seven independent times. Compute the conditional probability that each side appears at least once given that side 1 appears exactly twice.

3.1.20. Compute the measures of skewness and kurtosis of the binomial distribution $b(n, p)$.

3.1.21. Let

$$p(x_1, x_2) = \binom{x_1}{x_2}\left(\frac{1}{2}\right)^{x_1}\left(\frac{x_1}{15}\right), \qquad \begin{matrix} x_2 = 0, 1, \ldots, x_1 \\ x_1 = 1, 2, 3, 4, 5, \end{matrix}$$

zero elsewhere, be the joint pmf of X_1 and X_2. Determine

(a) $E(X_2)$.

(b) $u(x_1) = E(X_2|x_1)$.

(c) $E[u(X_1)]$.

Compare the answers of parts (a) and (c).
Hint: Note that $E(X_2) = \sum_{x_1=1}^{5}\sum_{x_2=0}^{x_1} x_2 p(x_1, x_2)$.

3.1.22. Three fair dice are cast. In 10 independent casts, let X be the number of times all three faces are alike and let Y be the number of times only two faces are alike. Find the joint pmf of X and Y and compute $E(6XY)$.

3.1.23. Let X have a geometric distribution. Show that

$$P(X \geq k+j \mid X \geq k) = P(X \geq j), \qquad (3.1.9)$$

where k and j are nonnegative integers. Note that we sometimes say in this situation that X is *memoryless*.

3.1.24. Let X equal the number of independent tosses of a fair coin that are required to observe heads on consecutive tosses. Let u_n equal the nth Fibonacci number, where $u_1 = u_2 = 1$ and $u_n = u_{n-1} + u_{n-2}$, $n = 3, 4, 5, \ldots$.

(a) Show that the pmf of X is

$$p(x) = \frac{u_{x-1}}{2^x}, \quad x = 2, 3, 4, \ldots.$$

(b) Use the fact that

$$u_n = \frac{1}{\sqrt{5}} \left[\left(\frac{1+\sqrt{5}}{2} \right)^n - \left(\frac{1-\sqrt{5}}{2} \right)^n \right]$$

to show that $\sum_{x=2}^{\infty} p(x) = 1$.

3.1.25. Let the independent random variables X_1 and X_2 have binomial distributions with parameters n_1, $p_1 = \frac{1}{2}$ and n_2, $p_2 = \frac{1}{2}$, respectively. Show that $Y = X_1 - X_2 + n_2$ has a binomial distribution with parameters $n = n_1 + n_2$, $p = \frac{1}{2}$.

3.1.26. Consider a standard deck of 52 cards. Let X equal the number of aces in a sample of size 2.

(a) If the sampling is with replacement, obtain the pmf of X.

(b) If the sampling is without replacement, obtain the pmf of X.

3.1.27. Consider a shipment of 1000 items into a factory. Suppose the factory can tolerate about 5% defective items. Let X be the number of defective items in a sample without replacement of size $n = 10$. Suppose the factory returns the shipment if $X \geq 2$.

(a) Obtain the probability that the factory returns a shipment of items which has 5% defective items.

(b) Suppose the shipment has 10% defective items. Obtain the probability that the factory returns such a shipment.

(c) Obtain approximations to the probabilities in parts (a) and (b) using appropriate binomial distributions.

Note: If you do not have access to a computer package with a hypergeometric command, obtain the answer to (c) only. This is what would have been done in practice 20 years ago. If you have access to R, then the command dhyper(x,D,N-D,n) returns the probability in expression (3.1.7).

3.1.28. Show that the variance of a hypergeometric (N, D, n) distribution is given by expression (3.1.8).

Hint: First obtain $E[X(X-1)]$ by proceeding in the same way as the derivation of the mean given in Example 3.1.7.

3.2   The Poisson Distribution

Recall that the series

$$1 + m + \frac{m^2}{2!} + \frac{m^3}{3!} + \cdots = \sum_{x=0}^{\infty} \frac{m^x}{x!} = e^m$$

converges, for all values of m, to e^m. Consider the function $p(x)$ defined by

$$p(x) = \begin{cases} \frac{m^x e^{-m}}{x!} & x = 0, 1, 2, \ldots \\ 0 & \text{elsewhere,} \end{cases} \tag{3.2.1}$$

where $m > 0$. Since $m > 0$, then $p(x) \geq 0$ and

$$\sum_x p(x) = \sum_{x=0}^{\infty} \frac{m^x e^{-m}}{x!} = e^{-m} \sum_{x=0}^{\infty} \frac{m^x}{x!} = e^{-m} e^m = 1;$$

that is, $p(x)$ satisfies the conditions of being a pmf of a discrete type of random variable. A random variable that has a pmf of the form $p(x)$ is said to have a **Poisson distribution** with parameter m, and any such $p(x)$ is called a **Poisson pmf** with parameter m.

Remark 3.2.1. Experience indicates that the Poisson pmf may be used in a number of applications with quite satisfactory results. For example, let the random variable X denote the number of alpha particles emitted by a radioactive substance that enter a prescribed region during a prescribed interval of time. With a suitable value of m, it is found that X may be assumed to have a Poisson distribution. Again let the random variable X denote the number of defects on a manufactured article, such as a refrigerator door. Upon examining many of these doors, it is found, with an appropriate value of m, that X may be said to have a Poisson distribution. The number of automobile accidents in a unit of time (or the number of insurance claims in some unit of time) is often assumed to be a random variable which has a Poisson distribution. Each of these instances can be thought of as a process that generates a number of changes (accidents, claims, etc.) in a fixed interval (of time or space, etc.). A process which leads to a Poisson distribution is called a **Poisson process**. Some assumptions that ensure a Poisson process are now enumerated.

Let $g(x, w)$ denote the probability of x changes in each interval of length w. Let the symbol $o(h)$ represent any function such that $\lim_{h \to 0}[o(h)/h] = 0$; for example, $h^2 = o(h)$ and $o(h) + o(h) = o(h)$. The Poisson postulates are the following:

1. $g(1, h) = \lambda h + o(h)$, where λ is a positive constant and $h > 0$.

2. $\sum_{x=2}^{\infty} g(x, h) = o(h)$.

3. The numbers of changes in nonoverlapping intervals are independent.

Postulates 1 and 3 state, in effect, that the probability of one change in a short interval h is independent of changes in other nonoverlapping intervals and is approximately proportional to the length of the interval. The substance of postulate 2 is that the probability of two or more changes in the same short interval h is essentially equal to zero. If $x = 0$, we take $g(0, 0) = 1$. In accordance with postulates 1 and 2, the probability of at least one change in an interval h is $\lambda h + o(h) + o(h) = \lambda h + o(h)$. Hence the probability of zero changes in this interval of length h is $1 - \lambda h - o(h)$. Thus the probability $g(0, w + h)$ of zero changes in an interval of length $w + h$ is, in accordance with postulate 3, equal to the product of the probability $g(0, w)$ of zero changes in an interval of length w and the probability $[1 - \lambda h - o(h)]$ of zero changes in a nonoverlapping interval of length h. That is,

$$g(0, w + h) = g(0, w)[1 - \lambda h - o(h)].$$

Then

$$\frac{g(0, w + h) - g(0, w)}{h} = -\lambda g(0, w) - \frac{o(h) g(0, w)}{h}.$$

If we take the limit as $h \to 0$, we have

$$D_w[g(0, w)] = -\lambda g(0, w). \tag{3.2.2}$$

The solution of this differential equation is

$$g(0, w) = ce^{-\lambda w};$$

that is, the function $g(0, w) = cc^{-\lambda w}$ satisfies Equation (3.2.2). The condition $g(0, 0) = 1$ implies that $c = 1$; thus

$$g(0, w) = e^{-\lambda w}.$$

If x is a positive integer, we take $g(x, 0) = 0$. The postulates imply that

$$g(x, w + h) = [g(x, w)][1 - \lambda h - o(h)] + [g(x - 1, w)][\lambda h + o(h)] + o(h).$$

Accordingly, we have

$$\frac{g(x, w + h) - g(x, w)}{h} = -\lambda g(x, w) + \lambda g(x - 1, w) + \frac{o(h)}{h}$$

and

$$D_w[g(x, w)] = -\lambda g(x, w) + \lambda g(x - 1, w),$$

for $x = 1, 2, 3, \ldots$. It can be shown, by mathematical induction, that the solutions to these differential equations, with boundary conditions $g(x, 0) = 0$ for $x = 1, 2, 3, \ldots$, are, respectively,

$$g(x, w) = \frac{(\lambda w)^x e^{-\lambda w}}{x!}, \quad x = 1, 2, 3, \ldots.$$

Hence the number of changes in X in an interval of length w has a Poisson distribution with parameter $m = \lambda w$. ∎

The mgf of a Poisson distribution is given by

$$M(t) = \sum_x e^{tx} p(x) = \sum_{x=0}^{\infty} e^{tx} \frac{m^x e^{-m}}{x!}$$

$$= e^{-m} \sum_{x=0}^{\infty} \frac{(me^t)^x}{x!}$$

$$= e^{-m} e^{me^t} = e^{m(e^t - 1)}$$

for all real values of t. Since

$$M'(t) = e^{m(e^t - 1)} (me^t)$$

and

$$M''(t) = e^{m(e^t - 1)} (me^t) + e^{m(e^t - 1)} (me^t)^2,$$

then

$$\mu = M'(0) = m$$

and

$$\sigma^2 = M''(0) - \mu^2 = m + m^2 - m^2 = m.$$

That is, a Poisson distribution has $\mu = \sigma^2 = m > 0$. On this account, a Poisson pmf is frequently written as

$$p(x) = \begin{cases} \frac{\mu^x e^{-\mu}}{x!} & x = 0, 1, 2, \ldots \\ 0 & \text{elsewhere.} \end{cases}$$

Thus the parameter m in a Poisson pmf is the mean μ. Table I in Appendix C gives approximately the distribution for various values of the parameter $m = \mu$. On the other hand, if X has a Poisson distribution with parameter $m = \mu$, then the R command dpois(k,m) returns the value that $P(X = k)$. The cumulative probability $P(X \leq k)$ is given by ppois(k,m).

Example 3.2.1. Suppose that X has a Poisson distribution with $\mu = 2$. Then the pmf of X is

$$p(x) = \begin{cases} \frac{2^x e^{-2}}{x!} & x = 0, 1, 2, \ldots \\ 0 & \text{elsewhere.} \end{cases}$$

The variance of this distribution is $\sigma^2 = \mu = 2$. If we wish to compute $P(1 \leq X)$, we have

$$P(1 \leq X) = 1 - P(X = 0)$$
$$= 1 - p(0) = 1 - e^{-2} = 0.865,$$

approximately, by Table I of Appendix C. ∎

Example 3.2.2. If the mgf of a random variable X is

$$M(t) = e^{4(e^t - 1)},$$

then X has a Poisson distribution with $\mu = 4$. Accordingly, by way of example,

$$P(X = 3) = \frac{4^3 e^{-4}}{3!} = \frac{32}{3} e^{-4},$$

or, by Table I,

$$P(X = 3) = P(X \le 3) - P(X \le 2) = 0.433 - 0.238 = 0.195. \quad \blacksquare$$

Example 3.2.3. Let the probability of exactly one blemish in 1 foot of wire be about $\frac{1}{1000}$ and let the probability of two or more blemishes in that length be, for all practical purposes, zero. Let the random variable X be the number of blemishes in 3000 feet of wire. If we assume the independence of the number of blemishes in nonoverlapping intervals, then the postulates of the Poisson process are approximated, with $\lambda = \frac{1}{1000}$ and $w = 3000$. Thus X has an approximate Poisson distribution with mean $3000(\frac{1}{1000}) = 3$. For example, the probability that there are five or more blemishes in 3000 feet of wire is

$$P(X \ge 5) = \sum_{k=5}^{\infty} \frac{3^k e^{-3}}{k!}$$

and by Table I,

$$P(X \ge 5) = 1 - P(X \le 4) = 1 - 0.815 = 0.185,$$

approximately. $\quad \blacksquare$

The Poisson distribution satisfies the following important additive property.

Theorem 3.2.1. *Suppose $X_1, \ldots, X_n$ are independent random variables and suppose X_i has a Poisson distribution with parameter m_i. Then $Y = \sum_{i=1}^{n} X_i$ has a Poisson distribution with parameter $\sum_{i=1}^{n} m_i$.* $\quad X_i \sim \text{Poisson}(m_i) \Rightarrow \Sigma X_i \sim \text{Poisson}(\Sigma m_i).$

Proof: We obtain the result by determining the mgf of Y, which by Theorem 2.6.1 is given by

$$
\begin{aligned}
M_Y(t) &= E\left(e^{tY}\right) = \prod_{i=1}^{n} e^{m_i(e^t - 1)} \\
&= e^{\sum_{i=1}^{n} m_i(e^t - 1)}.
\end{aligned}
$$

By the uniqueness of mgfs, we conclude that Y has a Poisson distribution with parameter $\sum_{i=1}^{n} m_i$. $\quad \blacksquare$

Example 3.2.4 (Example 3.2.3, Continued). Suppose in Example 3.2.3 that a bail of wire consists of 3000 feet. Based on the information in the example, we expect three blemishes in a bail of wire, and the probability of five or more blemishes is 0.185. Suppose in a sampling plan, three bails of wire are selected at random and we compute the mean number of blemishes in the wire. Now suppose we want to determine the probability that the mean of the three observations has five or more blemishes. Let X_i be the number of blemishes in the ith bail of wire for $i = 1, 2, 3$. Then X_i has a Poisson distribution with parameter 3. The mean of X_1, X_2, and X_3 is $\overline{X} = 3^{-1} \sum_{i=1}^{3} X_i$, which can also be expressed as $Y/3$, where $Y = \sum_{i=1}^{3} X_i$. By the last theorem, because the bails are independent of one another, Y has a Poisson distribution with parameter $\sum_{i=1}^{3} 3 = 9$. Hence, by Table I, the desired probability is

$$P(\overline{X} \geq 5) = P(Y \geq 15) = 1 - P(Y \leq 14) = 1 - 0.959 = 0.041.$$

Hence, while it is not too odd that a bail has five or more blemishes (probability is 0.185), it is unusual (probability is 0.041) that three independent bails of wire average five or more blemishes. ∎

EXERCISES

3.2.1. If the random variable X has a Poisson distribution such that $P(X = 1) = P(X = 2)$, find $P(X = 4)$.

3.2.2. The mgf of a random variable X is $e^{4(e^t-1)}$. Show that $P(\mu - 2\sigma < X < \mu + 2\sigma) = 0.931$.

3.2.3. In a lengthy manuscript, it is discovered that only 13.5 percent of the pages contain no typing errors. If we assume that the number of errors per page is a random variable with a Poisson distribution, find the percentage of pages that have exactly one error.

3.2.4. Let the pmf $p(x)$ be positive on and only on the nonnegative integers. Given that $p(x) = (4/x)p(x - 1)$, $x = 1, 2, 3, \ldots$, find the formula for $p(x)$.
Hint: Note that $p(1) = 4p(0)$, $p(2) = (4^2/2!)p(0)$, and so on. That is, find each $p(x)$ in terms of $p(0)$ and then determine $p(0)$ from

$$1 = p(0) + p(1) + p(2) + \cdots.$$

3.2.5. Let X have a Poisson distribution with $\mu = 100$. Use Chebyshev's inequality to determine a lower bound for $P(75 < X < 125)$.

3.2.6. Suppose that $g(x, 0) = 0$ and that

$$D_w[g(x, w)] = -\lambda g(x, w) + \lambda g(x - 1, w)$$

for $x = 1, 2, 3, \ldots$. If $g(0, w) = e^{-\lambda w}$, show by mathematical induction that

$$g(x, w) = \frac{(\lambda w)^x e^{-\lambda w}}{x!}, \quad x = 1, 2, 3, \ldots.$$

3.2.7. Using the computer, obtain an overlay plot of the pmfs following two distributions:

(a) Poisson distribution with $\lambda = 2$.

(b) Binomial distribution with $n = 100$ and $p = 0.02$.

Why would these distributions be approximately the same? Discuss.

3.2.8. Let the number of chocolate chips in a certain type of cookie have a Poisson distribution. We want the probability that a cookie of this type contains at least two chocolate chips to be greater than 0.99. Find the smallest value of the mean that the distribution can take.

3.2.9. Compute the measures of skewness and kurtosis of the Poisson distribution with mean μ.

3.2.10. On the average, a grocer sells three of a certain article per week. How many of these should he have in stock so that the chance of his running out within a week is less than 0.01? Assume a Poisson distribution.

3.2.11. Let X have a Poisson distribution. If $P(X - 1) = P(X = 3)$, find the mode of the distribution.

3.2.12. Let X have a Poisson distribution with mean 1. Compute, if it exists, the expected value $E(X!)$.

3.2.13. Let X and Y have the joint pmf $p(x, y) = e^{-2}/[x!(y - x)!]$, $y = 0, 1, 2, \ldots$, $x = 0, 1, \ldots, y$, zero elsewhere.

(a) Find the mgf $M(t_1, t_2)$ of this joint distribution.

(b) Compute the means, the variances, and the correlation coefficient of X and Y.

(c) Determine the conditional mean $E(X|y)$.
   Hint: Note that

$$\sum_{x=0}^{y} [\exp(t_1 x)] y! / [x!(y - x)!] = [1 + \exp(t_1)]^y.$$

Why?

3.2.14. Let X_1 and X_2 be two independent random variables. Suppose that X_1 and $Y = X_1 + X_2$ have Poisson distributions with means μ_1 and $\mu > \mu_1$, respectively. Find the distribution of X_2.

3.3 The Γ, χ^2, and β Distributions

In this section we introduce the gamma (Γ), chi-square (χ^2), and beta (β) distributions. It is proved in books on advanced calculus that the integral

$$\int_0^\infty y^{\alpha-1}e^{-y}\,dy$$

exists for $\alpha > 0$ and that the value of the integral is a positive number. The integral is called the gamma function of α, and we write

$$\Gamma(\alpha) = \int_0^\infty y^{\alpha-1}e^{-y}\,dy.$$

If $\alpha = 1$, clearly

$$\Gamma(1) = \int_0^\infty e^{-y}\,dy = 1.$$

If $\alpha > 1$, an integration by parts shows that

$$\Gamma(\alpha) = (\alpha-1)\int_0^\infty y^{\alpha-2}e^{-y}\,dy = (\alpha-1)\Gamma(\alpha-1).$$

Accordingly, if α is a positive integer greater than 1,

$$\Gamma(\alpha) = (\alpha-1)(\alpha-2)\cdots(3)(2)(1)\Gamma(1) = (\alpha-1)!.$$

Since $\Gamma(1) = 1$, this suggests we take $0! = 1$, as we have done.

In the integral that defines $\Gamma(\alpha)$, let us introduce a new variable by writing $y = x/\beta$, where $\beta > 0$. Then

$$\Gamma(\alpha) = \int_0^\infty \left(\frac{x}{\beta}\right)^{\alpha-1}e^{-x/\beta}\left(\frac{1}{\beta}\right)\,dx,$$

or, equivalently,

$$1 = \int_0^\infty \frac{1}{\Gamma(\alpha)\beta^\alpha}x^{\alpha-1}e^{-x/\beta}\,dx.$$

Since $\alpha > 0$, $\beta > 0$, and $\Gamma(\alpha) > 0$, we see that

$$f(x) = \begin{cases} \frac{1}{\Gamma(\alpha)\beta^\alpha}x^{\alpha-1}e^{-x/\beta} & 0 < x < \infty \\ 0 & \text{elsewhere} \end{cases} \tag{3.3.1}$$

is a pdf of a random variable of the continuous type. A random variable X that has a pdf of this form is said to have a **gamma** distribution with parameters α and β. We write this as X has a $\Gamma(\alpha, \beta)$ distribution.

Remark 3.3.1 (Poisson Processes). The gamma distribution is frequently a probability model for waiting times; for instance, in life testing, the waiting time until "death" is a random variable which is frequently modeled with a gamma distribution. To see this, let us assume the postulates of a Poisson process and let the interval of length w be a time interval. Specifically, let the random variable W be the time that is needed to obtain exactly k changes (possibly deaths), where k is a fixed positive integer. Then the cdf of W is

$$G(w) = P(W \le w) = 1 - P(W > w).$$

However, the event $W > w$, for $w > 0$, is equivalent to the event in which there are fewer than k changes in a time interval of length w. That is, if the random variable X is the number of changes in an interval of length w, then

$$P(W > w) = \sum_{x=0}^{k-1} P(X = x) = \sum_{x=0}^{k-1} \frac{(\lambda w)^x e^{-\lambda w}}{x!}.$$

In Exercise 3.3.5, the reader is asked to prove that

$$\int_{\lambda w}^{\infty} \frac{z^{k-1} e^{-z}}{(k-1)!} \, dz = \sum_{x=0}^{k-1} \frac{(\lambda w)^x e^{-\lambda w}}{x!}.$$

If, momentarily, we accept this result, we have, for $w > 0$,

$$G(w) = 1 - \int_{\lambda w}^{\infty} \frac{z^{k-1} e^{-z}}{\Gamma(k)} \, dz = \int_{0}^{\lambda w} \frac{z^{k-1} e^{-z}}{\Gamma(k)} \, dz,$$

and for $w \le 0$, $G(w) = 0$. If we change the variable of integration in the integral that defines $G(w)$ by writing $z = \lambda y$, then

$$G(w) = \int_{0}^{w} \frac{\lambda^k y^{k-1} e^{-\lambda y}}{\Gamma(k)} \, dy, \quad w > 0,$$

and $G(w) = 0$ for $w \le 0$. Accordingly, the pdf of W is

$$g(w) = G'(w) = \begin{cases} \frac{\lambda^k w^{k-1} e^{-\lambda w}}{\Gamma(k)} & 0 < w < \infty \\ 0 & \text{elsewhere.} \end{cases}$$

That is, W has a gamma distribution with $\alpha = k$ and $\beta = 1/\lambda$.

If W is the waiting time until the first change, i.e., $k = 1$, then the pdf of W is

$$g(w) = \begin{cases} \lambda e^{-\lambda w} & 0 < w < \infty \\ 0 & \text{elsewhere,} \end{cases} \tag{3.3.2}$$

and W is said to have an **exponential distribution** with parameter λ. We continue this discussion in Remark 3.3.3. Also, two other important properties of the exponential distribution are discussed in Exercises 3.3.25 and 3.3.26. These and further properties make the exponential distribution an important distribution in applications. ∎

We now find the mgf of a gamma distribution. Since

$$M(t) = \int_0^\infty e^{tx} \frac{1}{\Gamma(\alpha)\beta^\alpha} x^{\alpha-1} e^{-x/\beta}\, dx$$

$$= \int_0^\infty \frac{1}{\Gamma(\alpha)\beta^\alpha} x^{\alpha-1} e^{-x(1-\beta t)/\beta}\, dx,$$

we may set $y = x(1-\beta t)/\beta$, $t < 1/\beta$, or $x = \beta y/(1-\beta t)$, to obtain

$$M(t) = \int_0^\infty \frac{\beta/(1-\beta t)}{\Gamma(\alpha)\beta^\alpha} \left(\frac{\beta y}{1-\beta t}\right)^{\alpha-1} e^{-y}\, dy.$$

That is,

$$M(t) = \left(\frac{1}{1-\beta t}\right)^\alpha \int_0^\infty \frac{1}{\Gamma(\alpha)} y^{\alpha-1} e^{-y}\, dy$$

$$= \frac{1}{(1-\beta t)^\alpha}, \quad t < \frac{1}{\beta}.$$

Now

$$M'(t) = (-\alpha)(1-\beta t)^{-\alpha-1}(-\beta)$$

and

$$M''(t) = (-\alpha)(-\alpha-1)(1-\beta t)^{-\alpha-2}(-\beta)^2.$$

Hence, for a gamma distribution, we have

$$\mu = M'(0) = \alpha\beta$$

and

$$\sigma^2 = M''(0) - \mu^2 = \alpha(\alpha+1)\beta^2 - \alpha^2\beta^2 = \alpha\beta^2.$$

To calculate probabilities for gamma distributions with the program R, suppose X has a gamma distribution with parameters $\alpha = a$ and $\beta = b$. Then the command pgamma(x,shape=a,scale=b) returns $P(X \le x)$, while the value of the pdf of X at x is returned by the command dgamma(x,shape=a,scale=b).

Example 3.3.1. Let the waiting time W have a gamma pdf with $\alpha = k$ and $\beta = 1/\lambda$. Accordingly, $E(W) = k/\lambda$. If $k = 1$, then $E(W) = 1/\lambda$; that is, the expected waiting time for $k = 1$ changes is equal to the reciprocal of λ. ■

Example 3.3.2. Let X be a random variable such that

$$E(X^m) = \frac{(m+3)!}{3!} 3^m, \quad m = 1, 2, 3, \ldots.$$

Then the mgf of X is given by the series

$$M(t) = 1 + \frac{4!}{3!}\frac{3}{1!}t + \frac{5!}{3!}\frac{3^2}{2!}t^2 + \frac{6!}{3!}\frac{3^3}{3!}t^3 + \cdots.$$

This, however, is the Maclaurin's series for $(1-3t)^{-4}$, provided that $-1 < 3t < 1$. Accordingly, X has a gamma distribution with $\alpha = 4$ and $\beta = 3$. ■

Remark 3.3.2. The gamma distribution is not only a good model for waiting times, but one for many nonnegative random variables of the continuous type. For illustration, the distribution of certain incomes could be modeled satisfactorily by the gamma distribution, since the two parameters α and β provide a great deal of flexibility. Several gamma probability density functions are depicted in Figure 3.3.1. ∎

Figure 3.3.1: Several gamma densities

Let us now consider a special case of the gamma distribution in which $\alpha = r/2$, where r is a positive integer, and $\beta = 2$. A random variable X of the continuous type that has the pdf

$$f(x) = \begin{cases} \frac{1}{\Gamma(r/2)2^{r/2}}x^{r/2-1}e^{-x/2} & 0 < x < \infty \\ 0 & \text{elsewhere,} \end{cases} \tag{3.3.3}$$

and the mgf

$$M(t) = (1-2t)^{-r/2}, \quad t < \tfrac{1}{2},$$

is said to have a **chi-square distribution**, and any $f(x)$ of this form is called a **chi-square pdf**. The mean and the variance of a chi-square distribution are $\mu = \alpha\beta = (r/2)2 = r$ and $\sigma^2 = \alpha\beta^2 = (r/2)2^2 = 2r$, respectively. For no obvious reason, we call the parameter r the number of degrees of freedom of the chi-square distribution (or of the chi-square pdf). Because the chi-square distribution has an important role in statistics and occurs so frequently, we write, for brevity, that X is $\chi^2(r)$ to mean that the random variable X has a chi-square distribution with r degrees of freedom.

Example 3.3.3. If X has the pdf

$$f(x) = \begin{cases} \frac{1}{4}xe^{-x/2} & 0 < x < \infty \\ 0 & \text{elsewhere,} \end{cases}$$

then X is $\chi^2(4)$. Hence $\mu = 4$, $\sigma^2 = 8$, and $M(t) = (1 - 2t)^{-2}$, $t < \frac{1}{2}$. ∎

Example 3.3.4. If X has the mgf $M(t) = (1 - 2t)^{-8}$, $t < \frac{1}{2}$, then X is $\chi^2(16)$. ∎

If the random variable X is $\chi^2(r)$, then, with $c_1 < c_2$, we have

$$P(c_1 < X < c_2) = P(X \le c_2) - P(X \le c_1),$$

since $P(X = c_2) = 0$. To compute such a probability, we need the value of an integral like

$$P(X \le x) = \int_0^x \frac{1}{\Gamma(r/2)2^{r/2}} w^{r/2-1} e^{-w/2} \, dw.$$

Tables of this integral for selected values of r and x have been prepared and are partially reproduced in Table II in Appendix C. If, on the other hand, the package R is available, then the command `pchisq(x,r)` returns $P(X \le x)$ and the command `dchisq(x,r)` returns the value of the pdf of X at x when X has a chi-squared distribution with r degrees of freedom.

The following result is used several times in the sequel; hence, we record it as a theorem.

Theorem 3.3.1. *Let X have a $\chi^2(r)$ distribution. If $k > -r/2$, then $E(X^k)$ exists and it is given by*

$$E(X^k) = \frac{2^k \Gamma\left(\frac{r}{2} + k\right)}{\Gamma\left(\frac{r}{2}\right)}, \quad \text{if } k > -r/2. \tag{3.3.4}$$

Proof: Note that

$$E(X^k) = \int_0^\infty \frac{1}{\Gamma\left(\frac{r}{2}\right)2^{r/2}} x^{(r/2)+k-1} e^{-x/2} \, dx.$$

Make the change of variable $u = x/2$ in the above integral. This results in

$$E(X^k) = \int_0^\infty \frac{1}{\Gamma\left(\frac{r}{2}\right)2^{(r/2)-1}} 2^{(r/2)+k-1} u^{(r/2)+k-1} e^{-u} \, du.$$

This yields the desired result provided that $k > -(r/2)$. ∎

Notice that if k is a nonnegative integer, then $k > -(r/2)$ is always true. Hence, all moments of a χ^2 distribution exist and the kth moment is given by (3.3.4).

Example 3.3.5. Let X be $\chi^2(10)$. Then, by Table II of Appendix C, with $r = 10$,

$$\begin{aligned} P(3.25 \le X \le 20.5) &= P(X \le 20.5) - P(X \le 3.5) \\ &\cong 0.975 - 0.025 = 0.95. \end{aligned}$$

Again, as an example, if $P(a < X) = 0.05$, then $P(X \le a) = 0.95$, and thus $a = 18.3$ from Table II with $r = 10$. ∎

Example 3.3.6. Let X have a gamma distribution with $\alpha = r/2$, where r is a positive integer, and $\beta > 0$. Define the random variable $Y = 2X/\beta$. We seek the pdf of Y. Now the cdf of Y is

$$= P(Y = \frac{2X}{\beta} \le y)$$

$$G(y) = P(Y \le y) = P\left(X \le \frac{\beta y}{2}\right).$$

If $y \le 0$, then $G(y) = 0$; but if $y > 0$, then

$$G(y) = \int_0^{\beta y/2} \frac{1}{\Gamma(r/2)\beta^{r/2}} x^{r/2-1} e^{-x/\beta} \, dx.$$

Accordingly, the pdf of Y is

$$
\begin{aligned}
g(y) &= G'(y) = \frac{\beta/2}{\Gamma(r/2)\beta^{r/2}} (\beta y/2)^{r/2-1} e^{-y/2} \\
&= \frac{1}{\Gamma(r/2)2^{r/2}} y^{r/2-1} e^{-y/2}
\end{aligned}
$$

if $y > 0$. That is, Y is $\chi^2(r)$. ∎

One of the most important properties of the gamma distribution is its additive property.

Theorem 3.3.2. *Let $X_1, \ldots, X_n$ be independent random variables. Suppose, for $i = 1, \ldots, n$, that X_i has a $\Gamma(\alpha_i, \beta)$ distribution. Let $Y = \sum_{i=1}^n X_i$. Then Y has a $\Gamma(\sum_{i=1}^n \alpha_i, \beta)$ distribution.*

$X_i \sim \Gamma(\alpha_i, \beta) \Rightarrow \sum X_i \sim \Gamma(\sum \alpha_i, \beta)$.

Proof: Using the assumed independence and the mgf of a gamma distribution, we have by Theorem 2.6.1 that for $t < 1/\beta$,

$$M_Y(t) = \prod_{i=1}^n (1 - \beta t)^{-\alpha_i} = (1 - \beta t)^{-\sum_{i=1}^n \alpha_i},$$

which is the mgf of a $\Gamma(\sum_{i=1}^n \alpha_i, \beta)$ distribution. ∎

In the sequel, we often use this property for the χ^2 distribution. For convenience, we state the result as a corollary, since here $\beta = 2$ and $\sum \alpha_i = \sum r_i/2$.

Corollary 3.3.1. *Let $X_1, \ldots, X_n$ be independent random variables. Suppose, for $i = 1, \ldots, n$, that X_i has a $\chi^2(r_i)$ distribution. Let $Y = \sum_{i=1}^n X_i$. Then Y has a $\chi^2(\sum_{i=1}^n r_i)$ distribution.*

$X_i \sim \chi^2(r_i) \Rightarrow \sum X_i \sim \chi^2(\sum r_i)$

The following remark on Poisson processes proves useful in the simulation of these processes as discussed in Chapter 4.

Remark 3.3.3 (Poisson Processes, Continued). We continue the discussion of Remark 3.3.1 concerning the Poisson process with parameter λ. Recall that the Poisson process is counting the number of occurrences of an event over an interval of time.

Let $T_1, T_2, T_3, \ldots$ denote the interarrival times of these events. For instance, T_1 is the time until the first occurrence, T_2 is the time between the first and second occurrences, and so on. From Remark 3.3.1, we know that T_1 has an exponential distribution with parameter λ. Note that Postulates (1) and (2) of the Poisson process only depend on λ and the length of the interval; in particular, they do not depend on the endpoints of the interval. Further, occurrences in nonoverlapping intervals are independent of one another. Hence, the same reasoning found in Remark 3.3.1 can be applied to show that T_j, $j \geq 2$, also has an exponential distribution with parameter λ and that, further, $T_1, T_2, T_3, \ldots$ are independent. Let W_n be the waiting time until the nth occurrence. Then $W_n = T_1 + \cdots + T_n$. Thus by Theorem 3.3.2, W_n has a $\Gamma(n, \lambda)$ distribution, confirming the derivation of its distribution given in Remark 3.3.1. Although this discussion has been intuitive, it can be made rigorous; see, for example, Parzen (1962). ∎

We conclude this section with another important distribution called the **beta** distribution, which we derive from a pair of independent Γ random variables. Let X_1 and X_2 be two independent random variables that have Γ distributions and the joint pdf

$$h(x_1, x_2) = \frac{1}{\Gamma(\alpha)\Gamma(\beta)} x_1^{\alpha-1} x_2^{\beta-1} e^{-x_1 - x_2}, \quad 0 < x_1 < \infty, \ 0 < x_2 < \infty,$$

zero elsewhere, where $\alpha > 0$, $\beta > 0$. Let $Y_1 = X_1 + X_2$ and $Y_2 = X_1/(X_1 + X_2)$. We next show that Y_1 and Y_2 are independent.

The space $\mathcal{S}$ is, exclusive of the points on the coordinate axes, the first quadrant of the $x_1 x_2$-plane. Now

$$y_1 = u_1(x_1, x_2) = x_1 + x_2$$

$$y_2 = u_2(x_1, x_2) = \frac{x_1}{x_1 + x_2}$$

may be written $x_1 = y_1 y_2$, $x_2 = y_1(1 - y_2)$, so

$$J = \begin{vmatrix} y_2 & y_1 \\ 1 - y_2 & -y_1 \end{vmatrix} = -y_1 \not\equiv 0.$$

The transformation is one-to-one, and it maps $\mathcal{S}$ onto $\mathcal{T} = \{(y_1, y_2) : 0 < y_1 < \infty, \ 0 < y_2 < 1\}$ in the $y_1 y_2$-plane. The joint pdf of Y_1 and Y_2 is then

$$
\begin{aligned}
g(y_1, y_2) &= (y_1) \frac{1}{\Gamma(\alpha)\Gamma(\beta)} (y_1 y_2)^{\alpha-1} [y_1(1 - y_2)]^{\beta-1} e^{-y_1} \\
&= \begin{cases} \frac{y_2^{\alpha-1}(1-y_2)^{\beta-1}}{\Gamma(\alpha)\Gamma(\beta)} y_1^{\alpha+\beta-1} e^{-y_1} & 0 < y_1 < \infty, \ 0 < y_2 < 1 \\ 0 & \text{elsewhere.} \end{cases}
\end{aligned}
$$

In accordance with Theorem 2.5.1 the random variables are independent. The marginal pdf of Y_2 is

$$
\begin{aligned}
g_2(y_2) &= \frac{y_2^{\alpha-1}(1-y_2)^{\beta-1}}{\Gamma(\alpha)\Gamma(\beta)} \int_0^\infty y_1^{\alpha+\beta-1} e^{-y_1} \, dy_1 \\
&= \begin{cases} \frac{\Gamma(\alpha+\beta)}{\Gamma(\alpha)\Gamma(\beta)} y_2^{\alpha-1}(1-y_2)^{\beta-1} & 0 < y_2 < 1 \\ 0 & \text{elsewhere.} \end{cases}
\end{aligned} \tag{3.3.5}
$$

This pdf is that of the **beta distribution** with parameters α and β. Since $g(y_1, y_2) \equiv g_1(y_1)g_2(y_2)$, it must be that the pdf of Y_1 is

$$
g_1(y_1) = \begin{cases} \frac{1}{\Gamma(\alpha+\beta)} y_1^{\alpha+\beta-1} e^{-y_1} & 0 < y_1 < \infty \\ 0 & \text{elsewhere,} \end{cases}
$$

which is that of a gamma distribution with parameter values of $\alpha + \beta$ and 1.

It is an easy exercise to show that the mean and the variance of Y_2, which has a beta distribution with parameters α and β, are, respectively,

$$
\mu = \frac{\alpha}{\alpha+\beta}, \quad \sigma^2 = \frac{\alpha\beta}{(\alpha+\beta+1)(\alpha+\beta)^2}.
$$

The program R calculates probabilities for the beta distribution. If X has a beta distribution with parameters $\alpha = a$ and $\beta = b$, then the command `pbeta(x,a,b)` returns $P(X \le x)$ and the command `dbeta(x,a,b)` returns the value of the pdf of X at x.

We close this section with another example of a random variable whose distribution is derived from a transformation of gamma random variables.

Example 3.3.7 (Dirichlet Distribution). Let $X_1, X_2, \ldots, X_{k+1}$ be independent random variables, each having a gamma distribution with $\beta = 1$. The joint pdf of these variables may be written as

$$
h(x_1, x_2, \ldots, x_{k+1}) = \begin{cases} \prod_{i=1}^{k+1} \frac{1}{\Gamma(\alpha_i)} x_i^{\alpha_i-1} e^{-x_i} & 0 < x_i < \infty \\ 0 & \text{elsewhere.} \end{cases}
$$

Let

$$
Y_i = \frac{X_i}{X_1 + X_2 + \cdots + X_{k+1}}, \quad i = 1, 2, \ldots, k,
$$

and $Y_{k+1} = X_1 + X_2 + \cdots + X_{k+1}$ denote $k+1$ new random variables. The associated transformation maps $\mathcal{A} = \{(x_1, \ldots, x_{k+1}) : 0 < x_i < \infty, \ i = 1, \ldots, k+1\}$ onto the space:

$$
\mathcal{B} = \{(y_1, \ldots, y_k, y_{k+1}) : 0 < y_i, \ i = 1, \ldots, k, \ y_1 + \cdots + y_k < 1, \ 0 < y_{k+1} < \infty\}.
$$

The single-valued inverse functions are $x_1 = y_1 y_{k+1}, \ldots, x_k = y_k y_{k+1}, x_{k+1} = y_{k+1}(1 - y_1 - \cdots - y_k)$, so that the Jacobian is

$$
J = \begin{vmatrix} y_{k+1} & 0 & \cdots & 0 & y_1 \\ 0 & y_{k+1} & \cdots & 0 & y_2 \\ \vdots & \vdots & & \vdots & \vdots \\ 0 & 0 & \cdots & y_{k+1} & y_k \\ -y_{k+1} & -y_{k+1} & \cdots & -y_{k+1} & (1 - y_1 - \cdots - y_k) \end{vmatrix} = y_{k+1}^k.
$$

Hence the joint pdf of $Y_1, \ldots, Y_k, Y_{k+1}$ is given by

$$\frac{y_{k+1}^{\alpha_1 + \cdots + \alpha_{k+1} - 1} y_1^{\alpha_1 - 1} \cdots y_k^{\alpha_k - 1} (1 - y_1 - \cdots - y_k)^{\alpha_{k+1} - 1} e^{-y_{k+1}}}{\Gamma(\alpha_1) \cdots \Gamma(\alpha_k) \Gamma(\alpha_{k+1})},$$

provided that $(y_1, \ldots, y_k, y_{k+1}) \in \mathcal{B}$ and is equal to zero elsewhere. By integrating out y_{k+1}, the joint pdf of $Y_1, \ldots, Y_k$ is seen to be

$$g(y_1, \ldots, y_k) = \frac{\Gamma(\alpha_1 + \cdots + \alpha_{k+1})}{\Gamma(\alpha_1) \cdots \Gamma(\alpha_{k+1})} y_1^{\alpha_1 - 1} \cdots y_k^{\alpha_k - 1} (1 - y_1 - \cdots - y_k)^{\alpha_{k+1} - 1}, \quad (3.3.6)$$

when $0 < y_i$, $i = 1, \ldots, k$, $y_1 + \cdots + y_k < 1$, while the function g is equal to zero elsewhere. Random variables $Y_1, \ldots, Y_k$ that have a joint pdf of this form are said to have a **Dirichlet pdf**. It is seen, in the special case of $k = 1$, that the Dirichlet pdf becomes a beta pdf. Moreover, it is also clear from the joint pdf of $Y_1, \ldots, Y_k, Y_{k+1}$ that Y_{k+1} has a gamma distribution with parameters $\alpha_1 + \cdots + \alpha_k + \alpha_{k+1}$ and $\beta = 1$ and that Y_{k+1} is independent of $Y_1, Y_2, \ldots, Y_k$. ∎

EXERCISES

3.3.1. If $(1 - 2t)^{-6}$, $t < \frac{1}{2}$, is the mgf of the random variable X, find $P(X < 5.23)$.

3.3.2. If X is $\chi^2(5)$, determine the constants c and d so that $P(c < X < d) = 0.95$ and $P(X < c) = 0.025$.

3.3.3. Find $P(3.28 < X < 25.2)$ if X has a gamma distribution with $\alpha = 3$ and $\beta = 4$.
Hint: Consider the probability of the equivalent event $1.64 < Y < 12.6$, where $Y = 2X/4 = X/2$.

3.3.4. Let X be a random variable such that $E(X^m) = (m+1)!2^m$, $m = 1, 2, 3, \ldots$. Determine the mgf and the distribution of X.

√ **3.3.5.** Show that

$$\int_\mu^\infty \frac{1}{\Gamma(k)} z^{k-1} e^{-z} \, dz = \sum_{x=0}^{k-1} \frac{\mu^x e^{-\mu}}{x!}, \quad k = 1, 2, 3, \ldots.$$

This demonstrates the relationship between the cdfs of the gamma and Poisson distributions.
Hint: Either integrate by parts $k-1$ times or obtain the "antiderivative" by showing that

$$\frac{d}{dz}\left[-e^{-z} \sum_{j=0}^{k-1} \frac{\Gamma(k)}{(k-j-1)!} z^{k-j-1} \right] = z^{k-1} e^{-z}.$$

3.3.6. Let X_1, X_2, and X_3 be iid random variables, each with pdf $f(x) = e^{-x}$, $0 < x < \infty$, zero elsewhere.

(a) Find the distribution of $Y = \text{minimum}(X_1, X_2, X_3)$.
   Hint: $P(Y \leq y) = 1 - P(Y > y) = 1 - P(X_i > y, i = 1, 2, 3)$.

(b) Find the distribution of $Y = \text{maximum}(X_1, X_2, X_3)$.

3.3.7. Let X have a gamma distribution with pdf

$$f(x) = \frac{1}{\beta^2} x e^{-x/\beta}, \quad 0 < x < \infty,$$

zero elsewhere. If $x = 2$ is the unique mode of the distribution, find the parameter β and $P(X < 9.49)$.

3.3.8. Compute the measures of skewness and kurtosis of a gamma distribution which has parameters α and β.

3.3.9. Let X have a gamma distribution with parameters α and β. Show that $P(X \geq 2\alpha\beta) \leq (2/e)^\alpha$.
Hint: Use the result of Exercise 1.10.4.

3.3.10. Give a reasonable definition of a chi-square distribution with zero degrees of freedom.
Hint: Work with the mgf of a distribution that is $\chi^2(r)$ and let $r = 0$.

3.3.11. Using the computer, obtain plots of the pdfs of chi-squared distributions with degrees of freedom $r = 1, 2, 5, 10, 20$. Comment on the plots.

3.3.12. Using the computer, plot the cdf of $\Gamma(5, 4)$ and use it to guess the median. Confirm it with a computer command which returns the median [In R, use the command `qgamma(.5,shape=5,scale=4)`].

3.3.13. Using the computer, obtain plots of beta pdfs for $\alpha = 1, 5, 10$ and $\beta = 1, 2, 5, 10, 20$.

3.3.14. In the Poisson postulates of Remark 3.2.1, let λ be a nonnegative function of w, say $\lambda(w)$, such that $D_w[g(0, w)] = -\lambda(w)g(0, w)$. Suppose that $\lambda(w) = krw^{r-1}$, $r \geq 1$.

(a) Find $g(0, w)$, using the boundary condition $g(0, 0) = 1$.

(b) Let W be the time that is needed to obtain exactly one change. Find the distribution function of W, i.e., $G(w) = P(W \leq w) = 1 - P(W > w) = 1 - g(0, w)$, $0 \leq w$, and then find the pdf of W. This pdf is that of the **Weibull distribution**, which is used in the study of breaking strengths of materials.

3.3.15. Let X have a Poisson distribution with parameter m. If m is an experimental value of a random variable having a gamma distribution with $\alpha = 2$ and $\beta = 1$, compute $P(X = 0, 1, 2)$.
Hint: Find an expression that represents the joint distribution of X and m. Then integrate out m to find the marginal distribution of X.

3.3.16. Let X have the uniform distribution with pdf $f(x) = 1$, $0 < x < 1$, zero elsewhere. Find the cdf of $Y = -2 \log X$. What is the pdf of Y?

3.3.17. Find the uniform distribution of the continuous type on the interval (b, c) that has the same mean and the same variance as those of a chi-square distribution with 8 degrees of freedom. That is, find b and c.

3.3.18. Find the mean and variance of the β distribution.
Hint: From the pdf, we know that

$$\int_0^1 y^{\alpha-1}(1 - y)^{\beta-1}\, dy = \frac{\Gamma(\alpha)\Gamma(\beta)}{\Gamma(\alpha + \beta)}$$

for all $\alpha > 0$, $\beta > 0$.

3.3.19. Determine the constant c in each of the following so that each $f(x)$ is a β pdf:

(a) $f(x) = cx(1 - x)^3$, $0 < x < 1$, zero elsewhere.

(b) $f(x) = cx^4(1 - x)^5$, $0 < x < 1$, zero elsewhere.

(c) $f(x) = cx^2(1 - x)^8$, $0 < x < 1$, zero elsewhere.

3.3.20. Determine the constant c so that $f(x) = cx(3 - x)^4$, $0 < x < 3$, zero elsewhere, is a pdf.

3.3.21. Show that the graph of the β pdf is symmetric about the vertical line through $x = \frac{1}{2}$ if $\alpha = \beta$.

3.3.22. Show, for $k = 1, 2, \ldots, n$, that

$$\int_p^1 \frac{n!}{(k - 1)!(n - k)!} z^{k-1}(1 - z)^{n-k}\, dz = \sum_{x=0}^{k-1} \binom{n}{x} p^x (1 - p)^{n-x}.$$

This demonstrates the relationship between the cdfs of the β and binomial distributions.

3.3.23. Let X_1 and X_2 be independent random variables. Let X_1 and $Y = X_1 + X_2$ have chi-square distributions with r_1 and r degrees of freedom, respectively. Here $r_1 < r$. Show that X_2 has a chi-square distribution with $r - r_1$ degrees of freedom.
Hint: Write $M(t) = E(e^{t(X_1+X_2)})$ and make use of the independence of X_1 and X_2.

3.3.24. Let X_1, X_2 be two independent random variables having gamma distributions with parameters $\alpha_1 = 3$, $\beta_1 = 3$ and $\alpha_2 = 5$, $\beta_2 = 1$, respectively.

(a) Find the mgf of $Y = 2X_1 + 6X_2$.

(b) What is the distribution of Y?

3.3.25. Let X have an exponential distribution.

(a) For $x > 0$ and $y > 0$, show that

$$P(X > x + y \mid X > x) = P(X > y). \qquad (3.3.7)$$

Hence, the exponential distribution has the **memoryless** property. Recall from (3.1.9) that the discrete geometric distribution had a similar property.

(b) Let $F(x)$ be the cdf of a continuous random variable Y. Assume that $F(0) = 0$ and $0 < F(y) < 1$ for $y > 0$. Suppose property (3.3.7) holds for Y. Show that $F_Y(y) = 1 - e^{-\lambda y}$ for $y > 0$.

Hint: Show that $g(y) = 1 - F_Y(y)$ satisfies the equation

$$g(y + z) = g(y)g(z),$$

3.3.26. Consider a random variable X of the continuous type with cdf $F(x)$ and pdf $f(x)$. The **hazard rate** (or **failure rate** or **force of mortality**) is defined by

$$r(x) = \lim_{\Delta \to 0} \frac{P(x \le X < x + \Delta \mid X \ge x)}{\Delta}. \qquad (3.3.8)$$

In the case that X represents the failure time of an item, the above conditional probability represents the failure of an item in the interval $[x, x + \Delta]$ given that it has survived until time x. Viewed this way, $r(x)$ is the rate of instantaneous failure at time $x > 0$.

(a) Show that $r(x) = f(x)/(1 - F(x))$.

(b) If $r(x) = c$, where c is a positive constant, show that the underlying distribution is exponential. Hence, exponential distributions have constant failure rates over all time.

(c) If $r(x) = cx^b$; where c and b are positive constants, show that X has a **Weibull** distribution; i.e.,

$$f(x) = \begin{cases} cx^b \exp\left\{-\frac{cx^{b+1}}{b+1}\right\} & 0 < x < \infty \\ 0 & \text{elsewhere.} \end{cases} \qquad (3.3.9)$$

(d) If $r(x) = ce^{bx}$, where c and b are positive constants, show that X has a **Gompertz** cdf given by

$$F(x) = \begin{cases} 1 - \exp\left\{\frac{c}{b}(1 - e^{bx})\right\} & 0 < x < \infty \\ 0 & \text{elsewhere.} \end{cases} \qquad (3.3.10)$$

This is frequently used by actuaries as a distribution of "length of life."

3.3.27. Let $Y_1, \ldots, Y_k$ have a Dirichlet distribution with parameters $\alpha_1, \ldots, \alpha_k, \alpha_{k+1}$.

(a) Show that Y_1 has a beta distribution with parameters $\alpha = \alpha_1$ and $\beta = \alpha_2 + \cdots + \alpha_{k+1}$.

(b) Show that $Y_1 + \cdots + Y_r$, $r \leq k$, has a beta distribution with parameters $\alpha = \alpha_1 + \cdots + \alpha_r$ and $\beta = \alpha_{r+1} + \cdots + \alpha_{k+1}$.

(c) Show that $Y_1 + Y_2$, $Y_3 + Y_4$, $Y_5, \ldots, Y_k$, $k \geq 5$, have a Dirichlet distribution with parameters $\alpha_1 + \alpha_2$, $\alpha_3 + \alpha_4$, $\alpha_5, \ldots, \alpha_k, \alpha_{k+1}$.

   Hint: Recall the definition of Y_i in Example 3.3.7 and use the fact that the sum of several independent gamma variables with $\beta = 1$ is a gamma variable.

3.4 The Normal Distribution

Motivation for the normal distribution is found in the Central Limit Theorem, which is presented in Section 5.3. This theorem shows that normal distributions provide an important family of distributions for applications and for statistical inference, in general. We proceed by first introducing the standard normal distribution and through it the general normal distribution.

   Consider the integral

$$I = \int_{-\infty}^{\infty} \frac{1}{\sqrt{2\pi}} \exp\left(\frac{-z^2}{2}\right) dz. \tag{3.4.1}$$

This integral exists because the integrand is a positive continuous function which is bounded by an integrable function; that is,

$$0 < \exp\left(\frac{-z^2}{2}\right) < \exp(-|z| + 1), \quad -\infty < z < \infty,$$

and

$$\int_{-\infty}^{\infty} \exp(-|z| + 1)\, dz = 2e.$$

To evaluate the integral I, we note that $I > 0$ and that I^2 may be written

$$I^2 = \frac{1}{2\pi} \int_{-\infty}^{\infty} \int_{-\infty}^{\infty} \exp\left(-\frac{z^2 + w^2}{2}\right) dz\, dw.$$

This iterated integral can be evaluated by changing to polar coordinates. If we set $z = r\cos\theta$ and $w = r\sin\theta$, we have

$$
\begin{aligned}
I^2 &= \frac{1}{2\pi} \int_0^{2\pi} \int_0^{\infty} e^{-r^2/2} r\, dr\, d\theta \\
&= \frac{1}{2\pi} \int_0^{2\pi} d\theta = 1.
\end{aligned}
$$

Because the integrand of display (3.4.1) is positive on R and integrates to 1 over R, it is a pdf of a continuous random variable with support R. We denote this random variable by Z. In summary, Z has the pdf

$$f(z) = \frac{1}{\sqrt{2\pi}} \exp\left(\frac{-z^2}{2}\right), \quad -\infty < z < \infty. \tag{3.4.2}$$

For $t \in R$, the mgf of Z can be derived by a completion of a square as follows:

$$
\begin{aligned}
E[\exp\{tZ\}] &= \int_{-\infty}^{\infty} \exp\{tz\}\frac{1}{\sqrt{2\pi}}\exp\left\{-\frac{1}{2}z^2\right\}\,dz \\
&= \exp\left\{\frac{1}{2}t^2\right\}\int_{-\infty}^{\infty}\frac{1}{\sqrt{2\pi}}\exp\left\{-\frac{1}{2}(z-t)^2\right\}\,dz \\
&= \exp\left\{\frac{1}{2}t^2\right\}\int_{-\infty}^{\infty}\frac{1}{\sqrt{2\pi}}\exp\left\{-\frac{1}{2}w^2\right\}\,dw, \tag{3.4.3}
\end{aligned}
$$

$\left[= \int_{-\infty}^{\infty}\frac{1}{\sqrt{2\pi}} e^{-\frac{z^2}{2}}\,dz = 1 \quad \text{由} (3.4.1) \right]$

where for the last integral we made the one-to-one change of variable $w = z - t$. By the identity (3.4.2), the integral in expression (3.4.3) has value 1. Thus the mgf of Z is

$$M_Z(t) = \exp\left\{\frac{1}{2}t^2\right\}, \quad \text{for } -\infty < t < \infty. \tag{3.4.4}$$

The first two derivatives of $M_Z(t)$ are easily shown to be

$$M_Z'(t) = t\exp\left\{\frac{1}{2}t^2\right\} \quad \Rightarrow E(Z) = M_z'(t)\big|_{t=0} = 0 = \mu_z$$

$$M_Z''(t) = \exp\left\{\frac{1}{2}t^2\right\} + t^2\exp\left\{\frac{1}{2}t^2\right\}. \quad \Rightarrow E(Z^2) = M_z''(t)\big|_{t=0} = 1+0 = 1$$
$$\therefore \sigma^2 = E(Z^2) - (E(Z))^2 = 1 - 0 = 0.$$

Upon evaluating these derivatives at $t = 0$, the mean and variance of Z are

$$E(Z) = 0 \text{ and } \operatorname{Var}(Z) = 1. \tag{3.4.5}$$

Next, define the continuous random variable X by

$$X = bZ + a,$$

$X = a + bz = g(z) \Rightarrow z = g^{-1}(x) = \frac{x-a}{b} \Rightarrow \frac{\partial z}{\partial x} = \frac{1}{b}$

$f_X(x) = f_z(g^{-1}(x)) \cdot |J| = f_z(g^{-1}(x)) \cdot \left|\frac{\partial z}{\partial x}\right| = \frac{1}{b} f_z(g^{-1}(x))$

for $b > 0$. This is a one-to-one transformation. To derive the pdf of X, note that the inverse of the transformation and the Jacobian are $z = b^{-1}(x - a)$ and $J = b^{-1}$, respectively. Because $b > 0$, it follows from (3.4.2) that the pdf of X is

$$f_X(x) = \frac{1}{\sqrt{2\pi}b}\exp\left\{-\frac{1}{2}\left(\frac{x-a}{b}\right)^2\right\}, \quad -\infty < x < \infty.$$

$E(X) = E(bZ+a) = bE(Z)+a = 0+a = a \qquad \operatorname{Var}(X) = \operatorname{Var}(a+bZ) = \operatorname{Var}(a) + \operatorname{Var}(bZ)$
$= 0 + b^2\cdot\operatorname{Var}(Z)$
$= 0 + b^2\cdot 1$
$= b^2.$

By (3.4.5), we immediately have $E(X) = a$ and $\operatorname{Var}(X) = b^2$. Hence, in the expression for the pdf of X, we can replace a by $\mu = E(X)$ and b^2 by $\sigma^2 = \operatorname{Var}(X)$. We make this formal in the following definition,

Definition 3.4.1 (Normal Distribution). *We say a random variable X has a **normal distribution** if its pdf is*

$$f(x) = \frac{1}{\sqrt{2\pi}\sigma}\exp\left\{-\frac{1}{2}\left(\frac{x-\mu}{\sigma}\right)^2\right\}, \quad \text{for } -\infty < x < \infty. \tag{3.4.6}$$

若 $X \sim N(\mu, \sigma^2)$，则 $Z = \frac{x-\mu}{\sigma} \sim N(0,1)$：

证明： $f(x) = \frac{1}{\sqrt{2\pi}\sigma} e^{-\frac{1}{2}\left(\frac{x-\mu}{\sigma}\right)^2}$, $\quad z = \frac{x-\mu}{\sigma} \Rightarrow x = Z\sigma+\mu$, $\frac{\partial x}{\partial z} = \sigma$

$\therefore f_z(z) = f_X(Z\sigma+\mu)\cdot\left|\frac{\partial x}{\partial z}\right| = \frac{1}{\sqrt{2\pi}\sigma} e^{-\frac{1}{2}\left(\frac{Z\sigma+\mu-\mu}{\sigma}\right)^2}\cdot\sigma = \frac{1}{\sqrt{2\pi}} e^{-\frac{z^2}{2}}$ 此式是标准差于 $\mu=0, \sigma^2=1$ 的 Normal pdf 表达式

$\therefore Z = \frac{x-\mu}{\sigma} \sim N(0,1).$

The parameters μ and σ^2 are the mean and variance of X, respectively. We often write that X has a $N(\mu, \sigma^2)$ distribution.

In this notation, the random variable Z with pdf (3.4.2) has a $N(0, 1)$ distribution. We call Z a **standard normal** random variable.

For the mgf of X, use the relationship $X = \sigma Z + \mu$ and the mgf for Z, (3.4.4), to obtain

$$E[\exp\{tX\}] = E[\exp\{t(\sigma Z + \mu)\}] = \exp\{\mu t\} E[\exp\{t\sigma Z\}]$$

$$= \exp\{\mu t\} \exp\left\{\frac{1}{2}\sigma^2 t^2\right\} = \exp\left\{\mu t + \frac{1}{2}\sigma^2 t^2\right\}, \qquad (3.4.7)$$

for $-\infty < t < \infty$.

We summarize the above discussion, by noting the relationship between Z and X:

X has a $N(\mu, \sigma^2)$ distribution if and only if $Z = \frac{X-\mu}{\sigma}$ has a $N(0, 1)$ distribution.

$$\qquad (3.4.8)$$

Example 3.4.1. If X has the mgf

$$M(t) = e^{2t + 32t^2},$$

then X has a normal distribution with $\mu = 2$ and $\sigma^2 = 64$. Furthermore, the random variable $Z = \frac{X-2}{8}$ has a $N(0, 1)$ distribution. ∎

Example 3.4.2. Recall Example 1.9.6. In that example we derived all the moments of a standard normal random variable by using its moment generating function. We can use this to obtain all the moments of X, where X has a $N(\mu, \sigma^2)$ distribution. From above, we can write $X = \sigma Z + \mu$, where Z has a $N(0, 1)$ distribution. Hence, for all nonnegative integers k a simple application of the binomial theorem yields

$$E(X^k) = E[(\sigma Z + \mu)^k] = \sum_{j=0}^{k} \binom{k}{j} \sigma^j E(Z^j) \mu^{k-j}. \qquad (3.4.9)$$

Recall from Example 1.9.6 that all the odd moments of Z are 0, while all the even moments are given by expression (1.9.2). These can be substituted into expression (3.4.9) to derive the moments of X. ∎

The graph of the normal pdf, (3.4.6), is seen in Figure 3.4.1 to have the following characteristics: (1) symmetry about a vertical axis through $x = \mu$; (2) having its maximum of $1/(\sigma\sqrt{2\pi})$ at $x = \mu$; and (3) having the x-axis as a horizontal asymptote. It should also be verified that (4) there are points of inflection at $x = \mu \pm \sigma$; see Exercise 3.4.7.

As we discussed at the beginning of this section, many practical applications involve normal distributions. In particular, we need to be able to readily compute probabilities concerning them. Normal pdfs, however, contain some factor such as $\exp\{-s^2\}$. Hence, their antiderivatives cannot be obtained in closed form

Figure 3.4.1: The normal density $f(x)$, (3.4.6).

and numerical integration techniques must be used. Because of the relationship between normal and standard normal random variables, (3.4.8), we need only compute probabilities for standard normal random variables. To see this, denote the cdf of a standard normal random variable, Z, by

$$\Phi(z) = \int_{-\infty}^{z} \frac{1}{\sqrt{2\pi}} \exp\left\{ \frac{-w^2}{2} \right\} dw. \qquad (3.4.10)$$

Let X have a $N(\mu, \sigma^2)$ distribution. If we want to compute $F_X(x) = P(X \le x)$ for a specified x, then for $Z = (X - \mu)/\sigma$, expression (3.4.8) implies that

$$F_X(x) = P(X \le x) = P\left(Z \le \frac{x - \mu}{\sigma} \right) = \Phi\left(\frac{x - \mu}{\sigma} \right).$$

Thus we only need numerical integration computations for $\Phi(z)$. Normal quantiles can also be computed by using quantiles based on Z. For example, suppose we wanted the value x_p, such that $p = F_X(x_p)$, for a specified value of p. Take $z_p = \Phi^{-1}(p)$. Then by (3.4.8), $x_p = \sigma z_p + \mu$.

Figure 3.4.2 shows the standard normal density. The area under the density function to the left of z_p is p; that is, $\Phi(z_p) = p$. Table III in Appendix C offers an abbreviated table of probabilities for a standard normal distribution. Note that the table only gives probabilities for $z > 0$. Suppose we need to compute $\Phi(-z)$, where $z > 0$. Because the pdf of Z is symmetric about 0, we have

$$\Phi(-z) = 1 - \Phi(z); \qquad (3.4.11)$$

see Exercise 3.4.1. In the examples ahead, we illustrate the computation of normal probabilities and quantiles.

Most computer packages offer functions for computation of these probabilities. For example, the R command `pnorm(x,a,b)` calculates $P(X \le x)$ when X has a normal distribution with mean a and standard deviation b, while the command $\mathtt{dnorm(x,a,b)}$ returns the value of the pdf of X at x.

density function
distribution function

Figure 3.4.2: The standard normal density: $p = \Phi(z_p)$ is the area under the curve to the left of z_p.

Example 3.4.3. Let X be $N(2, 25)$. Then, by Table III,

$$
\begin{aligned}
P(0 < X < 10) &= \Phi\left(\frac{10-2}{5}\right) - \Phi\left(\frac{0-2}{5}\right) \\
&= \Phi(1.6) - \Phi(-0.4) \\
&= 0.945 - (1 - 0.655) = 0.600
\end{aligned}
$$

and

$$
\begin{aligned}
P(-8 < X < 1) &= \Phi\left(\frac{1-2}{5}\right) - \Phi\left(\frac{-8-2}{5}\right) \\
&= \Phi(-0.2) - \Phi(-2) \\
&= (1 - 0.579) - (1 - 0.977) = 0.398. \quad \blacksquare
\end{aligned}
$$

Example 3.4.4. Let X be $N(\mu, \sigma^2)$. Then, by Table III,

$$
\begin{aligned}
P(\mu - 2\sigma < X < \mu + 2\sigma) &= \Phi\left(\frac{\mu + 2\sigma - \mu}{\sigma}\right) - \Phi\left(\frac{\mu - 2\sigma - \mu}{\sigma}\right) \\
&= \Phi(2) - \Phi(-2) \\
&= 0.977 - (1 - 0.977) = 0.954. \quad \blacksquare
\end{aligned}
$$

Example 3.4.5. Suppose that 10% of the probability for a certain distribution that is $N(\mu, \sigma^2)$ is below 60 and that 5% is above 90. What are the values of μ and σ? We are given that the random variable X is $N(\mu, \sigma^2)$ and that $P(X \leq 60) = 0.10$ and $P(X \leq 90) = 0.95$. Thus $\Phi[(60 - \mu)/\sigma] = 0.10$ and $\Phi[(90 - \mu)/\sigma] = 0.95$. From Table III we have

$$\frac{60 - \mu}{\sigma} = -1.28, \quad \frac{90 - \mu}{\sigma} = 1.64.$$

These conditions require that $\mu = 73.1$ and $\sigma = 10.2$ approximately. ∎

Remark 3.4.1. In this chapter we have illustrated three types of **parameters** associated with distributions. The mean μ of $N(\mu, \sigma^2)$ is called a **location parameter** because changing its value simply changes the location of the middle of the normal pdf; that is, the graph of the pdf looks exactly the same except for a shift in location. The standard deviation σ of $N(\mu, \sigma^2)$ is called a **scale parameter** because changing its value changes the spread of the distribution. That is, a small value of σ requires the graph of the normal pdf to be tall and narrow, while a large value of σ requires it to spread out and not be so tall. No matter what the values of μ and σ, however, the graph of the normal pdf is that familiar "bell shape." Incidentally, the β of the gamma distribution is also a scale parameter. On the other hand, the α of the gamma distribution is called a **shape parameter**, as changing its value modifies the shape of the graph of the pdf, as can be seen by referring to Figure 3.3.1. The parameters p and μ of the binomial and Poisson distributions, respectively, are also shape parameters. ∎

We close this part of the section with two important theorems.

Theorem 3.4.1. *If the random variable X is $N(\mu, \sigma^2)$, $\sigma^2 > 0$, then the random variable $V = (X - \mu)^2/\sigma^2$ is $\chi^2(1)$.*

Proof. Because $V = W^2$, where $W = (X - \mu)/\sigma$ is $N(0, 1)$, the cdf $G(v)$ for V is, for $v \geq 0$,

$$G(v) = P(W^2 \leq v) = P(-\sqrt{v} \leq W \leq \sqrt{v}).$$

That is,

$$G(v) = 2 \int_0^{\sqrt{v}} \frac{1}{\sqrt{2\pi}} e^{-w^2/2} \, dw, \quad 0 \leq v,$$

and

$$G(v) = 0, \quad v < 0.$$

If we change the variable of integration by writing $w = \sqrt{y}$, then

$$G(v) = \int_0^v \frac{1}{\sqrt{2\pi}\sqrt{y}} e^{-y/2} \, dy, \quad 0 \leq v.$$

Hence the pdf $g(v) = G'(v)$ of the continuous-type random variable V is

$$g(v) = \begin{cases} \frac{1}{\sqrt{\pi}\sqrt{2}} v^{1/2-1} e^{-v/2} & 0 < v < \infty \\ 0 & \text{elsewhere.} \end{cases}$$

Since $g(v)$ is a pdf and hence

$$\int_0^\infty g(v)\,dv = 1,$$

符合这个族分区而 $g(v)$ 也是这
个 α、β 分别为半面的 gamma 分布
pdf 函数。

it must be that $\Gamma(\frac{1}{2}) = \sqrt{\pi}$ and thus V is $\chi^2(1)$. ∎

$\therefore \alpha=\frac{1}{2}, \therefore r=2\alpha=1 \quad \therefore$ 是 $\chi^2(r)$ 即 $\chi^2(1)$.

One of the most important properties of the normal distribution is its additivity under independence.

$X_i \sim N(\mu_i, \sigma_i^2) \Rightarrow \Sigma a_i X_i \sim N(\Sigma a_i \mu_i, \Sigma a_i^2 \sigma_i^2)$

Theorem 3.4.2. *Let $X_1, \ldots, X_n$ be independent random variables such that, for $i = 1, \ldots, n$, X_i has a $N(\mu_i, \sigma_i^2)$ distribution. Let $Y = \sum_{i=1}^n a_i X_i$, where $a_1, \ldots, a_n$ are constants. Then the distribution of Y is $N(\sum_{i=1}^n a_i\mu_i, \sum_{i=1}^n a_i^2\sigma_i^2)$.*

$y = a_1 X_1 + \cdots + a_n X_n$.
$y \sim N(a_1\mu_1 + \cdots + a_n\mu_n,$
$a_1^2\sigma_1^2 + \cdots + a_n^2\sigma_n^2)$

Proof: By Theorem 2.6.1, for $t \in R$, the mgf of Y is

$$M_Y(t) = \prod_{i=1}^n \exp\left\{ta_i\mu_i + (1/2)t^2 a_i^2\sigma_i^2\right\}$$

$$= \exp\left\{t\sum_{i=1}^n a_i\mu_i + (1/2)t^2\sum_{i=1}^n a_i^2\sigma_i^2\right\},$$

which is the mgf of a $N(\sum_{i=1}^n a_i\mu_i, \sum_{i=1}^n a_i^2\sigma_i^2)$ distribution. ∎

A simple corollary to this result gives the distribution of the sample mean $\overline{X} = n^{-1}\sum_{i=1}^n X_i$ when $X_1, X_2, \ldots X_n$ represents a random sample from a $N(\mu, \sigma^2)$.

Corollary 3.4.1. *Let $X_1, \ldots, X_n$ be iid random variables with a common $N(\mu, \sigma^2)$ distribution. Let $\overline{X} = n^{-1}\sum_{i=1}^n X_i$. Then $\overline{X}$ has a $N(\mu, \sigma^2/n)$ distribution.*

To prove this corollary, simply take $a_i = (1/n)$, $\mu_i = \mu$, and $\sigma_i^2 = \sigma^2$, for $i = 1, 2, \ldots, n$, in Theorem 3.4.2.

3.4.1 Contaminated Normals (未看！)

We next discuss a random variable whose distribution is a mixture of normals. As with the normal, we begin with a standardized random variable.

Suppose we are observing a random variable that most of the time follows a standard normal distribution but occasionally follows a normal distribution with a larger variance. In applications, we might say that most of the data are "good" but that there are occasional outliers. To make this precise let Z have a $N(0,1)$ distribution; let $I_{1-\epsilon}$ be a discrete random variable defined by

$$I_{1-\epsilon} = \begin{cases} 1 & \text{with probability } 1 - \epsilon \\ 0 & \text{with probability } \epsilon, \end{cases}$$

and assume that Z and $I_{1-\epsilon}$ are independent. Let $W = ZI_{1-\epsilon} + \sigma_c Z(1 - I_{1-\epsilon})$. Then W is the random variable of interest.

The independence of Z and $I_{1-\epsilon}$ imply that the cdf of W is

$$
\begin{aligned}
F_W(w) = P[W \le w] &= P[W \le w, I_{1-\epsilon} = 1] + P[W \le w, I_{1-\epsilon} = 0] \\
&= P[W \le w | I_{1-\epsilon} = 1]P[I_{1-\epsilon} = 1] \\
&\quad + P[W \le w | I_{1-\epsilon} = 0]P[I_{1-\epsilon} = 0] \\
&= P[Z \le w](1 - \epsilon) + P[Z \le w/\sigma_c]\epsilon. \\
&= \Phi(w)(1 - \epsilon) + \Phi(w/\sigma_c)\epsilon \qquad (3.4.12)
\end{aligned}
$$

Therefore, we have shown that the distribution of W is a mixture of normals. Further, because $W = ZI_{1-\epsilon} + \sigma_c Z(1 - I_{1-\epsilon})$, we have

$$
E(W) = 0 \text{ and } \mathrm{Var}(W) = 1 + \epsilon(\sigma_c^2 - 1); \qquad (3.4.13)
$$

see Exercise 3.4.25. Upon differentiating (3.4.12), the pdf of W is

$$
f_W(w) = \phi(w)(1 - \epsilon) + \phi(w/\sigma_c)\frac{\epsilon}{\sigma_c}, \qquad (3.4.14)
$$

where ϕ is the pdf of a standard normal.

Suppose, in general, that the random variable of interest is $X = a + bW$, where $b > 0$. Based on (3.4.13), the mean and variance of X are

$$
E(X) = a \text{ and } \mathrm{Var}(X) = b^2(1 + \epsilon(\sigma_c^2 - 1)). \qquad (3.4.15)
$$

From expression (3.4.12), the cdf of X is

$$
F_X(x) = \Phi\left(\frac{x - a}{b}\right)(1 - \epsilon) + \Phi\left(\frac{x - a}{b\sigma_c}\right)\epsilon, \qquad (3.4.16)
$$

which is a mixture of normal cdfs.

Based on expression (3.4.16) it is easy to obtain probabilities for contaminated normal distributions using R. For example, suppose, as above, W has cdf (3.4.12). Then $P(W \le w)$ is obtained by the R command (1-eps)*pnorm(w) + eps*pnorm(w/sigc), where eps and sigc denote ϵ and σ_c, respectively. Similarly, the pdf of W at w is returned by (1-eps)*dnorm(w) + eps*dnorm(w/sigc)/sigc. In Section 3.7, we explore mixture distributions in general.

EXERCISES

3.4.1. If

$$
\Phi(z) = \int_{-\infty}^{z} \frac{1}{\sqrt{2\pi}} e^{-w^2/2} \, dw,
$$

show that $\Phi(-z) = 1 - \Phi(z)$.

3.4.2. If X is $N(75, 100)$, find $P(X < 60)$ and $P(70 < X < 100)$ by using either Table III or, if R is available, the command pnorm.

3.4.3. If X is $N(\mu, \sigma^2)$, find b so that $P[-b < (X - \mu)/\sigma < b] = 0.90$, by using either Table III of Appendix C or, if R is available, the command pnorm.

3.4.4. Let X be $N(\mu, \sigma^2)$ so that $P(X < 89) = 0.90$ and $P(X < 94) = 0.95$. Find μ and σ^2.

3.4.5. Show that the constant c can be selected so that $f(x) = c2^{-x^2}$, $-\infty < x < \infty$, satisfies the conditions of a normal pdf.
Hint: Write $2 = e^{\log 2}$.

3.4.6. If X is $N(\mu, \sigma^2)$, show that $E(|X - \mu|) = \sigma\sqrt{2/\pi}$.

3.4.7. Show that the graph of a pdf $N(\mu, \sigma^2)$ has points of inflection at $x = \mu - \sigma$ and $x = \mu + \sigma$.

3.4.8. Evaluate $\int_2^3 \exp[-2(x-3)^2]\,dx$.

3.4.9. Determine the 90th percentile of the distribution, which is $N(65, 25)$.

3.4.10. If e^{3t+8t^2} is the mgf of the random variable X, find $P(-1 < X < 9)$.

3.4.11. Let the random variable X have the pdf

$$f(x) = \frac{2}{\sqrt{2\pi}}e^{-x^2/2}, \quad 0 < x < \infty, \quad \text{zero elsewhere.}$$

Find the mean and the variance of X.
Hint: Compute $E(X)$ directly and $E(X^2)$ by comparing the integral with the integral representing the variance of a random variable that is $N(0, 1)$.

3.4.12. Let X be $N(5, 10)$. Find $P[0.04 < (X - 5)^2 < 38.4]$.

3.4.13. If X is $N(1, 4)$, compute the probability $P(1 < X^2 < 9)$.

3.4.14. If X is $N(75, 25)$, find the conditional probability that X is greater than 80 given that X is greater than 77. See Exercise 2.3.12.

3.4.15. Let X be a random variable such that $E(X^{2m}) = (2m)!/(2^m m!)$, $m = 1, 2, 3, \ldots$ and $E(X^{2m-1}) = 0$, $m = 1, 2, 3, \ldots$. Find the mgf and the pdf of X.

3.4.16. Let the mutually independent random variables X_1, X_2, and X_3 be $N(0, 1)$, $N(2, 4)$, and $N(-1, 1)$, respectively. Compute the probability that exactly two of these three variables are less than zero.

3.4.17. Let X have a $N(\mu, \sigma^2)$ distribution. Use expression (3.4.9) to derive the third and fourth moments of X.

3.4.18. Compute the measures of skewness and kurtosis of a distribution which is $N(\mu, \sigma^2)$. See Exercises 1.9.14 and 1.9.15 for the definitions of skewness and kurtosis, respectively.

3.4.19. Let the random variable X have a distribution that is $N(\mu, \sigma^2)$.

(a) Does the random variable $Y = X^2$ also have a normal distribution?

(b) Would the random variable $Y = aX + b$, a and b nonzero constants have a normal distribution?
Hint: In each case, first determine $P(Y \leq y)$.

3.4.20. Let the random variable X be $N(\mu, \sigma^2)$. What would this distribution be if $\sigma^2 = 0$?
Hint: Look at the mgf of X for $\sigma^2 > 0$ and investigate its limit as $\sigma^2 \to 0$.

3.4.21. Let Y have a **truncated** distribution with pdf $g(y) = \phi(y)/[\Phi(b) - \Phi(a)]$, for $a < y < b$, zero elsewhere, where $\phi(x)$ and $\Phi(x)$ are, respectively, the pdf and distribution function of a standard normal distribution. Show then that $E(Y)$ is equal to $[\phi(a) - \phi(b)]/[\Phi(b) - \Phi(a)]$.

3.4.22. Let $f(x)$ and $F(x)$ be the pdf and the cdf, respectively, of a distribution of the continuous type such that $f'(x)$ exists for all x. Let the mean of the truncated distribution that has pdf $g(y) = f(y)/F(b)$, $-\infty < y < b$, zero elsewhere, be equal to $-f(b)/F(b)$ for all real b. Prove that $f(x)$ is a pdf of a standard normal distribution.

3.4.23. Let X and Y be independent random variables, each with a distribution that is $N(0, 1)$. Let $Z = X + Y$. Find the integral that represents the cdf $G(z) = P(X + Y \leq z)$ of Z. Determine the pdf of Z.
Hint: We have that $G(z) = \int_{-\infty}^{\infty} H(x, z)\, dx$, where

$$H(x, z) = \int_{-\infty}^{z-x} \frac{1}{2\pi} \exp[-(x^2 + y^2)/2]\, dy.$$

Find $G'(z)$ by evaluating $\int_{-\infty}^{\infty}[\partial H(x, z)/\partial z]\, dx$.

3.4.24. Suppose X is a random variable with the pdf $f(x)$ which is symmetric about 0; i.e., $f(-x) = f(x)$. Show that $F(-x) = 1 - F(x)$, for all x in the support of X.

3.4.25. Derive the mean and variance of a contaminated normal random variable. They are given in expression (3.4.13).

3.4.26. Assuming a computer is available, investigate the probabilities of an "outlier" for a contaminated normal random variable and a normal random variable. Specifically, determine the probability of observing the event $\{|X| \geq 2\}$ for the following random variables:

(a) X has a standard normal distribution.

(b) X has a contaminated normal distribution with cdf (3.4.12), where $\epsilon = 0.15$ and $\sigma_c = 10$.

(c) X has a contaminated normal distribution with cdf (3.4.12), where $\epsilon = 0.15$ and $\sigma_c = 20$.

(d) X has a contaminated normal distribution with cdf (3.4.12), where $\epsilon = 0.25$ and $\sigma_c = 20$.

3.4.27. Assuming a computer is available, plot the pdfs of the random variables defined in parts (a)–(d) of the last exercise. Obtain an overlay plot of all four pdfs also. In R the domain values of the pdfs can easily be obtained by using the seq command. For instance, the command x<-seq(-6,6,.1) returns a vector of values between -6 and 6 in jumps of 0.1.

3.4.28. Let X_1 and X_2 be independent with normal distributions $N(6,1)$ and $N(7,1)$, respectively. Find $P(X_1 > X_2)$.
Hint: Write $P(X_1 > X_2) = P(X_1 - X_2 > 0)$ and determine the distribution of $X_1 - X_2$.

3.4.29. Compute $P(X_1 + 2X_2 - 2X_3 > 7)$ if X_1, X_2, X_3 are iid with common distribution $N(1,4)$.

3.4.30. A certain job is completed in three steps in series. The means and standard deviations for the steps are (in minutes)

Step	Mean	Standard Deviation
1	17	2
2	13	1
3	13	2

Assuming independent steps and normal distributions, compute the probability that the job takes less than 40 minutes to complete.

3.4.31. Let X be $N(0,1)$. Use the moment generating function technique to show that $Y = X^2$ is $\chi^2(1)$.
Hint: Evaluate the integral that represents $E(e^{tX^2})$ by writing $w = x\sqrt{1 - 2t}$, $t < \frac{1}{2}$.

3.4.32. Suppose X_1, X_2 are iid with a common standard normal distribution. Find the joint pdf of $Y_1 = X_1^2 + X_2^2$ and $Y_2 = X_2$ and the marginal pdf of Y_1.
Hint: Note that the space of Y_1 and Y_2 is given by $-\sqrt{y_1} < y_2 < \sqrt{y_1}, 0 < y_1 < \infty$.

3.5 The Multivariate Normal Distribution

In this section we present the multivariate normal distribution. We introduce it in general for an n-dimensional random vector, but we offer detailed examples for the bivariate case when $n = 2$. As with Section 3.4 on the normal distribution, the derivation of the distribution is simplified by first discussing the standard case and then proceeding to the general case. Also, vector and matrix notation is used.

Consider the random vector $\mathbf{Z} = (Z_1, \ldots, Z_n)'$, where $Z_1, \ldots, Z_n$ are iid $N(0,1)$ random variables. Then the density of $\mathbf{Z}$ is

$$
\begin{aligned}
f_{\mathbf{Z}}(\mathbf{z}) &= \prod_{i=1}^n \frac{1}{\sqrt{2\pi}} \exp\left\{-\frac{1}{2}z_i^2\right\} = \left(\frac{1}{2\pi}\right)^{n/2} \exp\left\{-\frac{1}{2}\sum_{i=1}^n z_i^2\right\} \\
&= \left(\frac{1}{2\pi}\right)^{n/2} \exp\left\{-\frac{1}{2}\mathbf{z}'\mathbf{z}\right\}, \tag{3.5.1}
\end{aligned}
$$

for $\mathbf{z} \in R^n$. Because the Z_is have mean 0, have variance 1, and are uncorrelated, the mean and covariance matrix of $\mathbf{Z}$ are

$$
E[\mathbf{Z}] = \mathbf{0} \quad \text{and} \quad \text{Cov}[\mathbf{Z}] = \mathbf{I}_n, \tag{3.5.2}
$$

where $\mathbf{I}_n$ denotes the identity matrix of order n. Recall that the mgf of Z_i evaluated at t_i is $\exp\{t_i^2/2\}$. Hence, because the Z_is are independent, the mgf of $\mathbf{Z}$ is

$$
M_{\mathbf{Z}}(\mathbf{t}) = E\left[\exp\{\mathbf{t}'\mathbf{Z}\}\right] = E\left[\prod_{i=1}^n \exp\{t_i Z_i\}\right] = \prod_{i=1}^n E\left[\exp\{t_i Z_i\}\right]
$$

$$
= \exp\left\{\frac{1}{2}\sum_{i=1}^n t_i^2\right\} = \exp\left\{\frac{1}{2}\mathbf{t}'\mathbf{t}\right\}, \tag{3.5.3}
$$

for all $\mathbf{t} \in R^n$. We say that $\mathbf{Z}$ has a **multivariate normal distribution** with mean vector $\mathbf{0}$ and covariance matrix $\mathbf{I}_n$. We abbreviate this by saying that $\mathbf{Z}$ has an $N_n(\mathbf{0}, \mathbf{I}_n)$ distribution.

For the general case, suppose $\boldsymbol{\Sigma}$ is an $n \times n$, symmetric, and positive semi-definite matrix. Then from linear algebra, we can always decompose $\boldsymbol{\Sigma}$ as

$$
\boldsymbol{\Sigma} = \boldsymbol{\Gamma}'\boldsymbol{\Lambda}\boldsymbol{\Gamma}, \tag{3.5.4}
$$

where $\boldsymbol{\Lambda}$ is the diagonal matrix $\boldsymbol{\Lambda} = \text{diag}(\lambda_1, \lambda_2, \ldots, \lambda_n)$, $\lambda_1 \geq \lambda_2 \geq \cdots \geq \lambda_n \geq 0$ are the eigenvalues of $\boldsymbol{\Sigma}$, and the columns of $\boldsymbol{\Gamma}'$, $\mathbf{v}_1, \mathbf{v}_2, \ldots, \mathbf{v}_n$, are the corresponding eigenvectors. This decomposition is called the **spectral decomposition** of $\boldsymbol{\Sigma}$. The matrix $\boldsymbol{\Gamma}$ is orthogonal, i.e., $\boldsymbol{\Gamma}^{-1} = \boldsymbol{\Gamma}'$, and, hence, $\boldsymbol{\Gamma}\boldsymbol{\Gamma}' = \mathbf{I}$. As Exercise 3.5.19 shows, we can write the spectral decomposition in another way, as

$$
\boldsymbol{\Sigma} = \boldsymbol{\Gamma}'\boldsymbol{\Lambda}\boldsymbol{\Gamma} = \sum_{i=1}^n \lambda_i \mathbf{v}_i \mathbf{v}_i'. \tag{3.5.5}
$$

Because the λ_is are nonnegative, we can define the diagonal matrix $\boldsymbol{\Lambda}^{1/2} = \text{diag}\{\sqrt{\lambda_1}, \ldots, \sqrt{\lambda_n}\}$. Then the orthogonality of $\boldsymbol{\Gamma}$ implies

$$
\boldsymbol{\Sigma} = \boldsymbol{\Gamma}'\boldsymbol{\Lambda}^{1/2}\boldsymbol{\Gamma}\boldsymbol{\Gamma}'\boldsymbol{\Lambda}^{1/2}\boldsymbol{\Gamma}.
$$

Define the **square root** of the positive semi-definite matrix $\boldsymbol{\Sigma}$ as

$$
\boldsymbol{\Sigma}^{1/2} = \boldsymbol{\Gamma}'\boldsymbol{\Lambda}^{1/2}\boldsymbol{\Gamma}. \tag{3.5.6}
$$

Note that $\Sigma^{1/2}$ is symmetric and positive semi-definite. Suppose Σ is positive definite; that is, all of its eigenvalues are strictly positive. Based on this, it is then easy to show that

$$\left(\Sigma^{1/2}\right)^{-1} = \Gamma'\Lambda^{-1/2}\Gamma; \tag{3.5.7}$$

see Exercise 3.5.11. We write the left side of this equation as $\Sigma^{-1/2}$. These matrices enjoy many additional properties of the law of exponents for numbers; see, for example, Arnold (1981). Here, though, all we need are the properties given above.

Let $\mathbf{Z}$ have a $N_n(\mathbf{0}, \mathbf{I}_n)$ distribution. Let Σ be a positive semi-definite, symmetric matrix and let $\boldsymbol{\mu}$ be an $n \times 1$ vector of constants. Define the random vector $\mathbf{X}$ by

$$\mathbf{X} = \Sigma^{1/2}\mathbf{Z} + \boldsymbol{\mu}. \tag{3.5.8}$$

By (3.5.2) and Theorem 2.6.3, we immediately have

$$E[\mathbf{X}] = \boldsymbol{\mu} \quad \text{and} \quad \text{Cov}[\mathbf{X}] = \Sigma^{1/2}\Sigma^{1/2} = \Sigma. \tag{3.5.9}$$

Further, the mgf of $\mathbf{X}$ is given by

$$
\begin{aligned}
M_{\mathbf{X}}(\mathbf{t}) = E\left[\exp\{\mathbf{t}'\mathbf{X}\}\right] &= E\left[\exp\{\mathbf{t}'\Sigma^{1/2}\mathbf{Z} + \mathbf{t}'\boldsymbol{\mu}\}\right] \\
&= \exp\{\mathbf{t}'\boldsymbol{\mu}\}E\left[\exp\left\{\left(\Sigma^{1/2}\mathbf{t}\right)'\mathbf{Z}\right\}\right] \\
&= \exp\{\mathbf{t}'\boldsymbol{\mu}\}\exp\left\{(1/2)\left(\Sigma^{1/2}\mathbf{t}\right)'\Sigma^{1/2}\mathbf{t}\right\} \\
&= \exp\{\mathbf{t}'\boldsymbol{\mu}\}\exp\{(1/2)\mathbf{t}'\Sigma\mathbf{t}\}. \tag{3.5.10}
\end{aligned}
$$

This leads to the following definition:

Definition 3.5.1 (Multivariate Normal). *We say an n-dimensional random vector $\mathbf{X}$ has a* **multivariate normal distribution** *if its mgf is*

$$M_{\mathbf{X}}(\mathbf{t}) = \exp\left\{\mathbf{t}'\boldsymbol{\mu} + (1/2)\mathbf{t}'\Sigma\mathbf{t}\right\}, \tag{3.5.11}$$

for all $\mathbf{t} \in R^n$ and where Σ is a symmetric, positive semi-definite matrix and $\boldsymbol{\mu} \in R^n$. We abbreviate this by saying that $\mathbf{X}$ has a $N_n(\boldsymbol{\mu}, \Sigma)$ distribution.

Note that our definition is for positive semi-definite matrices Σ. Usually Σ is positive definite, in which case we can further obtain the density of $\mathbf{X}$. If Σ is positive definite, then so is $\Sigma^{1/2}$ and, as discussed above, its inverse is given by expression (3.5.7). Thus the transformation between $\mathbf{X}$ and $\mathbf{Z}$, (3.5.8), is one-to-one with the inverse transformation

$$\mathbf{Z} = \Sigma^{-1/2}(\mathbf{X} - \boldsymbol{\mu}),$$

with Jacobian $|\Sigma^{-1/2}| = |\Sigma|^{-1/2}$. Hence, upon simplification, the pdf of $\mathbf{X}$ is given by

$$f_{\mathbf{X}}(\mathbf{x}) = \frac{1}{(2\pi)^{n/2}|\Sigma|^{1/2}}\exp\left\{-\frac{1}{2}(\mathbf{x} - \boldsymbol{\mu})'\Sigma^{-1}(\mathbf{x} - \boldsymbol{\mu})\right\}, \quad \text{for } \mathbf{x} \in R^n. \tag{3.5.12}$$

The following two theorems are very useful. The first says that a linear transformation of a multivariate normal random vector has a multivariate normal distribution.

$$\therefore \vec{X} = \vec{u} + \Sigma^{1/2} \cdot \vec{Z}$$

Theorem 3.5.1. *Suppose* $\mathbf{X}$ *has a* $N_n(\boldsymbol{\mu}, \boldsymbol{\Sigma})$ *distribution. Let* $\mathbf{Y} = \mathbf{AX} + \mathbf{b}$, *where* $\mathbf{A}$ *is an* $m \times n$ *matrix and* $\mathbf{b} \in R^m$. *Then* $\mathbf{Y}$ *has a* $N_m(\mathbf{A\boldsymbol{\mu}} + \mathbf{b}, \mathbf{A\boldsymbol{\Sigma}A'})$ *distribution.*

对指于是 $y = ax + b,$
$R_y, E(y) = E(ax+b) = aE(x) = a\mu$
$var(y) = Var(ax+b) = a^2\sigma^2.$

Proof: From (3.5.11), for $\mathbf{t} \in R^m$, the mgf of $\mathbf{Y}$ is

$$
\begin{aligned}
M_\mathbf{Y}(\mathbf{t}) &= E\left[\exp\{\mathbf{t'Y}\}\right] &&\rightarrow \mathbf{t'AX} = (\mathbf{t'A})\mathbf{X} = (\mathbf{A't})'\mathbf{X} \\
&= E\left[\exp\{\mathbf{t'(AX + b)}\}\right] \\
&= \exp\{\mathbf{t'b}\}\,E\left[\exp\{(\mathbf{A't})'\mathbf{X}\}\right] &&\therefore \vec{X} = \vec{u} + \Sigma^{1/2} \cdot \vec{Z} \\
&= \exp\{\mathbf{t'b}\}\exp\{(\mathbf{A't})'\boldsymbol{\mu} + (1/2)(\mathbf{A't})'\boldsymbol{\Sigma}(\mathbf{A't})\} \\
&= \exp\{\mathbf{t'(A\boldsymbol{\mu} + b)} + (1/2)\mathbf{t'A\boldsymbol{\Sigma}A't}\},
\end{aligned}
$$

which is the mgf of an $N_m(\mathbf{A\boldsymbol{\mu}} + \mathbf{b}, \mathbf{A\boldsymbol{\Sigma}A'})$ distribution. ∎

A simple corollary to this theorem gives marginal distributions of a multivariate normal random variable. Let $\mathbf{X}_1$ be any subvector of $\mathbf{X}$, say of dimension $m < n$. Because we can always rearrange means and correlations, there is no loss in generality in writing $\mathbf{X}$ as

$$\mathbf{X} = \left[\begin{array}{c} \mathbf{X}_1 \\ \hline \mathbf{X}_2 \end{array}\right], \qquad (3.5.13)$$

where $\mathbf{X}_2$ is of dimension $p = n - m$. In the same way, partition the mean and covariance matrix of $\mathbf{X}$; that is,

$= cov(\vec{X_1}, \vec{X_1})$ $= cov(\vec{X_1}, \vec{X_2})$

$$\boldsymbol{\mu} = \left[\begin{array}{c} \boldsymbol{\mu}_1 \\ \boldsymbol{\mu}_2 \end{array}\right] \quad \text{and} \quad \boldsymbol{\Sigma} = \left[\begin{array}{cc} \boldsymbol{\Sigma}_{11} & \boldsymbol{\Sigma}_{12} \\ \boldsymbol{\Sigma}_{21} & \boldsymbol{\Sigma}_{22} \end{array}\right] \qquad (3.5.14)$$

$= cov(\vec{X_2}, \vec{X_2})$
$= cov(\vec{X_2}, \vec{X_1})$

with the same dimensions as in expression (3.5.13). Note, for instance, that $\boldsymbol{\Sigma}_{11}$ is the covariance matrix of $\mathbf{X}_1$ and $\boldsymbol{\Sigma}_{12}$ contains all the covariances between the components of $\mathbf{X}_1$ and $\mathbf{X}_2$. Now define $\mathbf{A}$ to be the matrix

$m \times m$ $m \times p$

$$\mathbf{A} = [\mathbf{I}_m \vdots \mathbf{O}_{mp}],$$

$= m \times (m+p)$ 矩阵
$= m \times n$ 矩阵. $p = n - m.$

where $\mathbf{O}_{mp}$ is an $m \times p$ matrix of zeroes. Then $\mathbf{X}_1 = \mathbf{AX}$. Hence, applying Theorem 3.5.1 to this transformation, along with some matrix algebra, we have the following corollary:

Corollary 3.5.1. *Suppose* $\mathbf{X}$ *has a* $N_n(\boldsymbol{\mu}, \boldsymbol{\Sigma})$ *distribution, partitioned as in expressions (3.5.13) and (3.5.14). Then* $\mathbf{X}_1$ *has a* $N_m(\boldsymbol{\mu}_1, \boldsymbol{\Sigma}_{11})$ *distribution.*

This is a useful result because it says that any marginal distribution of $\mathbf{X}$ is also normal and, further, its mean and covariance matrix are those associated with that partial vector.

Example 3.5.1. In this example, we explore the multivariate normal case when $n = 2$. The distribution in this case is called the bivariate normal. We also use the customary notation of (X, Y) instead of (X_1, X_2). So, suppose (X, Y) has a $N_2(\boldsymbol{\mu}, \boldsymbol{\Sigma})$ distribution, where

$$\boldsymbol{\mu} = \begin{bmatrix} \mu_1 \\ \mu_2 \end{bmatrix} \text{ and } \boldsymbol{\Sigma} = \begin{bmatrix} \sigma_1^2 & \sigma_{12} \\ \sigma_{12} & \sigma_2^2 \end{bmatrix}. \tag{3.5.15}$$

Hence, μ_1 and σ_1^2 are the mean and variance, respectively, of X; μ_2 and σ_2^2 are the mean and variance, respectively, of Y; and σ_{12} is the covariance between X and Y. Recall that $\sigma_{12} = \rho\sigma_1\sigma_2$, where ρ is the correlation coefficient between X and Y. Substituting $\rho\sigma_1\sigma_2$ for σ_{12} in $\boldsymbol{\Sigma}$, it is easy to see that the determinant of $\boldsymbol{\Sigma}$ is $\sigma_1^2\sigma_2^2(1-\rho^2)$. Recall that $\rho^2 \le 1$. For the remainder of this example, assume that $\rho^2 < 1$. In this case, $\boldsymbol{\Sigma}$ is invertible (it is also positive definite). Further, since $\boldsymbol{\Sigma}$ is a 2×2 matrix, its inverse can easily be determined to be

若 $\rho^2 < 1$, 而不 $= 1$,
则 $\det(\Sigma) \neq 0$.
则 Σ^{-1} 存在.

$\det(\Sigma) = \sigma_1^2 \sigma_2^2 (1-\rho^2)$

$$\boldsymbol{\Sigma}^{-1} = \frac{1}{\sigma_1^2\sigma_2^2(1-\rho^2)} \begin{bmatrix} \sigma_2^2 & -\rho\sigma_1\sigma_2 \\ -\rho\sigma_1\sigma_2 & \sigma_1^2 \end{bmatrix}. \tag{3.5.16}$$

Using this expression, the pdf of (X, Y), expression (3.5.12), can be written as

$f(x,y) = \frac{1}{2\pi^{n/2} \cdot \sqrt{\det\Sigma}} \times \exp\left(-\frac{1}{2}(\vec{x}-\vec{\mu})' \Sigma^{-1} (\vec{x}-\vec{\mu})\right) = ?$

$$f(x, y) = \frac{1}{2\pi\sigma_1\sigma_2\sqrt{1-\rho^2}} e^{-q/2}, \quad -\infty < x < \infty, \quad -\infty < y < \infty, \tag{3.5.17}$$

$(\vec{x}-\vec{\mu})' \Sigma^{-1} (\vec{x}-\vec{\mu}) = ?$

$= (x-\mu_1 \quad y-\mu_2)\begin{pmatrix}\sigma_2^2 & -\rho\sigma_1\sigma_2 \\ -\rho\sigma_1\sigma_2 & \sigma_1^2\end{pmatrix}\begin{pmatrix}x-\mu_1 \\ y-\mu_2\end{pmatrix}$ where σ_{12}

$= \left[(x-\mu_1)\sigma_2^2 + (y-\mu_2)(-\rho\sigma_1\sigma_2)\right] \times (x-\mu_1)$ $+ \left((x-\mu_1)(-\rho\sigma_1\sigma_2) + (y-\mu_2)\sigma_1^2\right)\times(y-\mu_2) \times \frac{1}{\sigma_1^2\sigma_2^2(1-\rho^2)}$

$=$

$$q = \frac{1}{1-\rho^2}\left[\left(\frac{x-\mu_1}{\sigma_1}\right)^2 - 2\rho\left(\frac{x-\mu_1}{\sigma_1}\right)\left(\frac{y-\mu_2}{\sigma_2}\right) + \left(\frac{y-\mu_2}{\sigma_2}\right)^2\right]; \tag{3.5.18}$$

see Exercise 3.5.12.

Recall in general, that if X and Y are independent random variables then their correlation coefficient is 0. If they are normal, by Corollary 3.5.1, X has a $N(\mu_1, \sigma_1^2)$ distribution and Y has a $N(\mu_2, \sigma_2^2)$ distribution. Further, based on the expression (3.5.17) for the joint pdf of (X, Y), we see that if the correlation coefficient is 0, then X and Y are independent. That is, for the bivariate normal case, independence is equivalent to $\rho = 0$. The generalization is true for the multivariate normal as shown by Theorem 3.5.2. ∎

n维 covariance $= 0 \Rightarrow$ indep.

Recall in Section 2.5, Example 2.5.4, that if two random variables are independent then their covariance is 0. In general, the converse is not true. However, as the following theorem shows, it is true for the multivariate normal distribution.

Theorem 3.5.2. *Suppose $\mathbf{X}$ has a $N_n(\boldsymbol{\mu}, \boldsymbol{\Sigma})$ distribution, partitoned as in the expressions (3.5.13) and (3.5.14). Then $\mathbf{X}_1$ and $\mathbf{X}_2$ are independent if and only if $\boldsymbol{\Sigma}_{12} = \mathbf{O}$.*

Proof: First note that $\boldsymbol{\Sigma}_{21} = \boldsymbol{\Sigma}_{12}'$. The joint mgf of $\mathbf{X}_1$ and $\mathbf{X}_2$ is given by

$$M_{\mathbf{X}_1, \mathbf{X}_2}(\mathbf{t}_1, \mathbf{t}_2) = \exp\left\{\mathbf{t}_1'\boldsymbol{\mu}_1 + \mathbf{t}_2'\boldsymbol{\mu}_2 + \frac{1}{2}(\mathbf{t}_1'\boldsymbol{\Sigma}_{11}\mathbf{t}_1 + \mathbf{t}_2'\boldsymbol{\Sigma}_{22}\mathbf{t}_2 + \mathbf{t}_2'\boldsymbol{\Sigma}_{21}\mathbf{t}_1 + \mathbf{t}_1'\boldsymbol{\Sigma}_{12}\mathbf{t}_2)\right\}$$

$\Sigma_{12} = \left[cov(X_i, X_{m+1})\cdots\right]$

$$\tag{3.5.19}$$

$\begin{bmatrix} \Sigma_{11} & \\ \Sigma_{21} = \begin{bmatrix}cov(X_{m+1}, X_1)\cdots\end{bmatrix} & \Sigma_{22} \end{bmatrix}$

$\Sigma_{21} = \Sigma_{12}'$

where $t' = (t_1', t_2')$ is partitioned the same as μ. By Corollary 3.5.1, X_1 has a $N_m(\mu_1, \Sigma_{11})$ distribution and X_2 has a $N_p(\mu_2, \Sigma_{22})$ distribution. Hence, the product of their marginal mgfs is

$$M_{X_1}(t_1)M_{X_2}(t_2) = \exp\left\{ t_1'\mu_1 + t_2'\mu_2 + \frac{1}{2}\left(t_1'\Sigma_{11}t_1 + t_2'\Sigma_{22}t_2\right) \right\}. \qquad (3.5.20)$$

By (2.6.6) of Section 2.6, X_1 and X_2 are independent if and only if the expressions (3.5.19) and (3.5.20) are the same. If $\Sigma_{12} = O'$ and, hence, $\Sigma_{21} = O$, then the expressions are the same and X_1 and X_2 are independent. If X_1 and X_2 are independent, then the covariances between their components are all 0; i.e., $\Sigma_{12} = O'$ and $\Sigma_{21} = O$. ∎

Corollary 3.5.1 showed that the marginal distributions of a multivariate normal are themselves normal. This is true for conditional distributions, too. As the following proof shows, we can combine the results of Theorems 3.5.1 and 3.5.2 to obtain the following theorem.

Theorem 3.5.3. *Suppose X has a $N_n(\mu, \Sigma)$ distribution, which is partitioned as in expressions (3.5.13) and (3.5.14). Assume that Σ is positive definite. Then the conditional distribution of $X_1 \mid X_2$ is*

$$N_m(\mu_1 + \Sigma_{12}\Sigma_{22}^{-1}(X_2 - \mu_2), \Sigma_{11} - \Sigma_{12}\Sigma_{22}^{-1}\Sigma_{21}). \qquad (3.5.21)$$

Proof: Consider first the joint distribution of the random vector $W = X_1 - \Sigma_{12}\Sigma_{22}^{-1}X_2$ and X_2. This distribution is obtained from the transformation

$$\begin{bmatrix} W \\ X_2 \end{bmatrix} = \begin{bmatrix} I_m & -\Sigma_{12}\Sigma_{22}^{-1} \\ O & I_p \end{bmatrix} \begin{bmatrix} X_1 \\ X_2 \end{bmatrix}.$$

Because this is a linear transformation, it follows from Theorem 3.5.1 that the joint distribution is multivariate normal, with $E[W] = \mu_1 - \Sigma_{12}\Sigma_{22}^{-1}\mu_2$, $E[X_2] = \mu_2$, and covariance matrix

$$\begin{bmatrix} I_m & -\Sigma_{12}\Sigma_{22}^{-1} \\ O & I_p \end{bmatrix} \begin{bmatrix} \Sigma_{11} & \Sigma_{12} \\ \Sigma_{21} & \Sigma_{22} \end{bmatrix} \begin{bmatrix} I_m & O' \\ -\Sigma_{22}^{-1}\Sigma_{21} & I_p \end{bmatrix} =$$
$$\begin{bmatrix} \Sigma_{11} - \Sigma_{12}\Sigma_{22}^{-1}\Sigma_{21} & O' \\ O & \Sigma_{22} \end{bmatrix}.$$

Hence, by Theorem 3.5.2 the random vectors W and X_2 are independent. Thus the conditional distribution of $W \mid X_2$ is the same as the marginal distribution of W; that is,

$$W \mid X_2 \text{ is } N_m(\mu_1 - \Sigma_{12}\Sigma_{22}^{-1}\mu_2, \Sigma_{11} - \Sigma_{12}\Sigma_{22}^{-1}\Sigma_{21}).$$

Further, because of this independence, $W + \Sigma_{12}\Sigma_{22}^{-1}X_2$ given X_2 is distributed as

$$N_m(\mu_1 - \Sigma_{12}\Sigma_{22}^{-1}\mu_2 + \Sigma_{12}\Sigma_{22}^{-1}X_2, \Sigma_{11} - \Sigma_{12}\Sigma_{22}^{-1}\Sigma_{21}), \qquad (3.5.22)$$

which is the desired result. ∎

Example 3.5.2 (Continuation of Example 3.5.1). Consider once more the bivariate normal distribution that was given in Example 3.5.1. For this case, reversing the roles so that $Y = X_1$ and $X = X_2$, expression (3.5.21) shows that the conditional distribution of Y given $X = x$ is

$$N\left[\mu_2 + \rho\frac{\sigma_2}{\sigma_1}(x - \mu_1), \sigma_2^2(1 - \rho^2)\right]. \qquad (3.5.23)$$

Thus, with a bivariate normal distribution, the conditional mean of Y, given that $X = x$, is linear in x and is given by

$$E(Y|x) = \mu_2 + \rho\frac{\sigma_2}{\sigma_1}(x - \mu_1).$$

Since the coefficient of x in this linear conditional mean $E(Y|x)$ is $\rho\sigma_2/\sigma_1$, and since σ_1 and σ_2 represent the respective standard deviations, ρ is the correlation coefficient of X and Y. This follows from the result, established in Section 2.4, that the coefficient of x in a general linear conditional mean $E(Y|x)$ is the product of the correlation coefficient and the ratio σ_2/σ_1.

Although the mean of the conditional distribution of Y, given $X = x$, depends upon x (unless $\rho = 0$), the variance $\sigma_2^2(1 - \rho^2)$ is the same for all real values of x. Thus, by way of example, given that $X = x$, the conditional probability that Y is within $(2.576)\sigma_2\sqrt{1 - \rho^2}$ units of the conditional mean is 0.99, whatever the value of x may be. In this sense, most of the probability for the distribution of X and Y lies in the band

$$\mu_2 + \rho\frac{\sigma_2}{\sigma_1}(x - \mu_1) \pm 2.576\sigma_2\sqrt{1 - \rho^2}$$

about the graph of the linear conditional mean. For every fixed positive σ_2, the width of this band depends upon ρ. Because the band is narrow when ρ^2 is nearly 1, we see that ρ does measure the intensity of the concentration of the probability for X and Y about the linear conditional mean. We alluded to this fact in the remark of Section 2.4.

In a similar manner we can show that the conditional distribution of X, given $Y = y$, is the normal distribution

$$N\left[\mu_1 + \rho\frac{\sigma_1}{\sigma_2}(y - \mu_2), \sigma_1^2(1 - \rho^2)\right]. \quad \blacksquare$$

Example 3.5.3. Let us assume that in a certain population of married couples the height X_1 of the husband and the height X_2 of the wife have a bivariate normal distribution with parameters $\mu_1 = 5.8$ feet, $\mu_2 = 5.3$ feet, $\sigma_1 = \sigma_2 = 0.2$ foot, and $\rho = 0.6$. The conditional pdf of X_2, given $X_1 = 6.3$, is normal, with mean $5.3 + (0.6)(6.3 - 5.8) = 5.6$ and standard deviation $(0.2)\sqrt{(1 - 0.36)} = 0.16$. Accordingly, given that the height of the husband is 6.3 feet, the probability that his wife has a height between 5.28 and 5.92 feet is

$$P(5.28 < X_2 < 5.92|X_1 = 6.3) = \Phi(2) - \Phi(-2) = 0.954.$$

The interval $(5.28, 5.92)$ could be thought of as a 95.4% *prediction interval* for the wife's height, given $X_1 = 6.3$. $\blacksquare$

Recall that if the random variable X has a $N(\mu, \sigma^2)$ distribution, then the random variable $[(X - \mu)/\sigma]^2$ has a $\chi^2(1)$ distribution. The multivariate analog of this fact is given in the next theorem.

Theorem 3.5.4. *Suppose* $\mathbf{X}$ *has a* $N_n(\boldsymbol{\mu}, \boldsymbol{\Sigma})$ *distribution, where* $\boldsymbol{\Sigma}$ *is positive definite. Then the random variable* $W = (\mathbf{X} - \boldsymbol{\mu})' \boldsymbol{\Sigma}^{-1} (\mathbf{X} - \boldsymbol{\mu})$ *has a* $\chi^2(n)$ *distribution.*

Proof: Write $\boldsymbol{\Sigma} = \boldsymbol{\Sigma}^{1/2} \boldsymbol{\Sigma}^{1/2}$, where $\boldsymbol{\Sigma}^{1/2}$ is defined as in (3.5.6). Then $\mathbf{Z} = \boldsymbol{\Sigma}^{-1/2}(\mathbf{X} - \boldsymbol{\mu})$ is $N_n(\mathbf{0}, \mathbf{I}_n)$. Let $W = \mathbf{Z}'\mathbf{Z} = \sum_{i=1}^n Z_i^2$. Because, for $i = 1, 2, \ldots, n$, Z_i has a $N(0,1)$ distribution, it follows from Theorem 3.4.1 that Z_i^2 has a $\chi^2(1)$ distribution. Because $Z_1, \ldots, Z_n$ are independent standard normal random variables, by Corollary 3.3.1 $\sum_{i=1}^n Z_i^2 = W$ has a $\chi^2(n)$ distribution. ∎

3.5.1 *Applications

In this section, we consider several applications of the multivariate normal distribution. These the reader may have already encountered in an applied course in statistics. The first is *principal components*, which results in a linear function of a multivariate normal random vector that has independent components and preserves the "total" variation in the problem.

Let the random vector $\mathbf{X}$ have the multivariate normal distribution $N_n(\boldsymbol{\mu}, \boldsymbol{\Sigma})$ where $\boldsymbol{\Sigma}$ is positive definite. As in (3.5.4), write the spectral decomposition of $\boldsymbol{\Sigma}$ as $\boldsymbol{\Sigma} = \boldsymbol{\Gamma}' \boldsymbol{\Lambda} \boldsymbol{\Gamma}$. Recall that the columns, $\mathbf{v}_1, \mathbf{v}_2, \ldots, \mathbf{v}_n$, of $\boldsymbol{\Gamma}'$ are the eigenvectors corresponding to the eigenvalues $\lambda_1, \lambda_2, \ldots, \lambda_n$ which form the main diagonal of the matrix $\boldsymbol{\Lambda}$. Assume without loss of generality that the eigenvalues are decreasing; i.e., $\lambda_1 \geq \lambda_2 \geq \cdots \geq \lambda_n > 0$. Define the random vector $\mathbf{Y} = \boldsymbol{\Gamma}(\mathbf{X} - \boldsymbol{\mu})$. Since $\boldsymbol{\Gamma} \boldsymbol{\Sigma} \boldsymbol{\Gamma}' = \boldsymbol{\Lambda}$, by Theorem 3.5.1 $\mathbf{Y}$ has a $N_n(\mathbf{0}, \boldsymbol{\Lambda})$ distribution. Hence the components $Y_1, Y_2, \ldots, Y_n$ are independent random variables and, for $i = 1, 2, \ldots, n$, Y_i has a $N(0, \lambda_i)$ distribution. The random vector $\mathbf{Y}$ is called the vector of **principal components**.

We say the **total variation**, (TV), of a random vector is the sum of the variances of its components. For the random vector $\mathbf{X}$, because $\boldsymbol{\Gamma}$ is an orthogonal matrix

$$\text{TV}(\mathbf{X}) = \sum_{i=1}^n \sigma_i^2 = \text{tr}\, \boldsymbol{\Sigma} = \text{tr}\, \boldsymbol{\Gamma}' \boldsymbol{\Lambda} \boldsymbol{\Gamma} = \text{tr}\, \boldsymbol{\Lambda} \boldsymbol{\Gamma} \boldsymbol{\Gamma}' = \sum_{i=1}^n \lambda_i = \text{TV}(\mathbf{Y}).$$

Hence, $\mathbf{X}$ and $\mathbf{Y}$ have the same total variation.

Next, consider the first component of $\mathbf{Y}$, which is given by $Y_1 = \mathbf{v}_1'(\mathbf{X} - \boldsymbol{\mu})$. This is a linear combination of the components of $\mathbf{X} - \boldsymbol{\mu}$ with the property $\|\mathbf{v}_1\|^2 = \sum_{j=1}^n v_{1j}^2 = 1$, because $\boldsymbol{\Gamma}'$ is orthogonal. Consider any other linear combination of $(\mathbf{X} - \boldsymbol{\mu})$, say $\mathbf{a}'(\mathbf{X} - \boldsymbol{\mu})$ such that $\|\mathbf{a}\|^2 = 1$. Because $\mathbf{a} \in R^n$ and $\{\mathbf{v}_1, \ldots, \mathbf{v}_n\}$ forms a basis for R^n, we must have $\mathbf{a} = \sum_{j=1}^n a_j \mathbf{v}_j$ for some set of scalars $a_1, \ldots, a_n$. Furthermore, because the basis $\{\mathbf{v}_1, \ldots, \mathbf{v}_n\}$ is orthonormal

$$\mathbf{a}' \mathbf{v}_i = \left(\sum_{j=1}^n a_j \mathbf{v}_j \right)' \mathbf{v}_i = \sum_{j=1}^n a_j \mathbf{v}_j' \mathbf{v}_i = a_i.$$

Using (3.5.5) and the fact that $\lambda_i > 0$, we have the inequality

$$
\begin{aligned}
\text{Var}(\mathbf{a}'\mathbf{X}) &= \mathbf{a}'\Sigma\mathbf{a} \\
&= \sum_{i=1}^{n} \lambda_i (\mathbf{a}'\mathbf{v}_i)^2 \\
&= \sum_{i=1}^{n} \lambda_i a_i^2 \leq \lambda_1 \sum_{i=1}^{n} a_i^2 = \lambda_1 = \text{Var}(Y_1). \qquad (3.5.24)
\end{aligned}
$$

Hence, Y_1 has the maximum variance of any linear combination $\mathbf{a}'(\mathbf{X} - \boldsymbol{\mu})$, such that $\|\mathbf{a}\| = 1$. For this reason, Y_1 is called the **first principal component** of $\mathbf{X}$.

What about the other components, $Y_2, \ldots, Y_n$? As the following theorem shows, they share a similar property relative to the order of their associated eigenvalue. For this reason, they are called the **second**, **third**, through the **nth principal components**, respectively.

Theorem 3.5.5. *Consider the situation described above. For $j = 2, \ldots, n$ and $i = 1, 2, \ldots, j-1$, $\text{Var}[\mathbf{a}'\mathbf{X}] \leq \lambda_j = \text{Var}(Y_j)$, for all vectors $\mathbf{a}$ such that $\mathbf{a} \perp \mathbf{v}_i$ and $\|\mathbf{a}\| = 1$.*

The proof of this theorem is similar to that for the first principal component and is left as Exercise 3.5.20. A second application concerning linear regression is offered in Exercise 3.5.22.

EXERCISES

3.5.1. Let X and Y have a bivariate normal distribution with respective parameters $\mu_x = 2.8$, $\mu_y = 110$, $\sigma_x^2 = 0.16$, $\sigma_y^2 = 100$, and $\rho = 0.6$. Compute

(a) $P(106 < Y < 124)$.

(b) $P(106 < Y < 124 | X = 3.2)$.

3.5.2. Let X and Y have a bivariate normal distribution with parameters $\mu_1 = 3$, $\mu_2 = 1$, $\sigma_1^2 = 16$, $\sigma_2^2 = 25$, and $\rho = \frac{3}{5}$. Determine the following probabilities:

(a) $P(3 < Y < 8)$.

(b) $P(3 < Y < 8 | X = 7)$.

(c) $P(-3 < X < 3)$.

(d) $P(-3 < X < 3 | Y = -4)$.

3.5.3. If $M(t_1, t_2)$ is the mgf of a bivariate normal distribution, compute the covariance by using the formula

$$
\frac{\partial^2 M(0,0)}{\partial t_1 \partial t_2} - \frac{\partial M(0,0)}{\partial t_1} \frac{\partial M(0,0)}{\partial t_2}.
$$

Now let $\psi(t_1, t_2) = \log M(t_1, t_2)$. Show that $\partial^2 \psi(0,0)/\partial t_1 \partial t_2$ gives this covariance directly.

3.5.4. Let U and V be independent random variables, each having a standard normal distribution. Show that the mgf $E(e^{t(UV)})$ of the random variable UV is $(1-t^2)^{-1/2}$, $-1 < t < 1$.

Hint: Compare $E(e^{tUV})$ with the integral of a bivariate normal pdf that has means equal to zero.

3.5.5. Let X and Y have a bivariate normal distribution with parameters $\mu_1 = 5$, $\mu_2 = 10$, $\sigma_1^2 = 1$, $\sigma_2^2 = 25$, and $\rho > 0$. If $P(4 < Y < 16|X = 5) = 0.954$, determine ρ.

3.5.6. Let X and Y have a bivariate normal distribution with parameters $\mu_1 = 20$, $\mu_2 = 40$, $\sigma_1^2 = 9$, $\sigma_2^2 = 4$, and $\rho = 0.6$. Find the shortest interval for which 0.90 is the conditional probability that Y is in the interval, given that $X = 22$.

3.5.7. Say the correlation coefficient between the heights of husbands and wives is 0.70 and the mean male height is 5 feet 10 inches with standard deviation 2 inches, and the mean female height is 5 feet 4 inches with standard deviation $1\frac{1}{2}$ inches. Assuming a bivariate normal distribution, what is the best guess of the height of a woman whose husband's height is 6 feet? Find a 95% prediction interval for her height.

3.5.8. Let

$$f(x,y) = (1/2\pi) \exp\left[-\frac{1}{2}(x^2 + y^2)\right]\left\{1 + xy\exp\left[-\frac{1}{2}(x^2 + y^2 - 2)\right]\right\},$$

where $-\infty < x < \infty$, $-\infty < y < \infty$. If $f(x,y)$ is a joint pdf, it is not a normal bivariate pdf. Show that $f(x,y)$ actually is a joint pdf and that each marginal pdf is normal. Thus the fact that each marginal pdf is normal does not imply that the joint pdf is bivariate normal.

3.5.9. Let X, Y, and Z have the joint pdf

$$\left(\frac{1}{2\pi}\right)^{3/2}\exp\left(-\frac{x^2 + y^2 + z^2}{2}\right)\left[1 + xyz\exp\left(-\frac{x^2 + y^2 + z^2}{2}\right)\right],$$

where $-\infty < x < \infty$, $-\infty < y < \infty$, and $-\infty < z < \infty$. While X, Y, and Z are obviously dependent, show that X, Y, and Z are pairwise independent and that each pair has a bivariate normal distribution.

3.5.10. Let X and Y have a bivariate normal distribution with parameters $\mu_1 = \mu_2 = 0$, $\sigma_1^2 = \sigma_2^2 = 1$, and correlation coefficient ρ. Find the distribution of the random variable $Z = aX + bY$ in which a and b are nonzero constants.

3.5.11. Establish formula (3.5.7) by a direct multiplication.

3.5.12. Show that the expression (3.5.12) becomes that of (3.5.17) in the bivariate case.

3.5.13. Show that expression (3.5.21) simplifies to expression (3.5.23) for the bivariate normal case.

3.5.14. Let $\mathbf{X} = (X_1, X_2, X_3)$ have a multivariate normal distribution with mean vector $\mathbf{0}$ and variance-covariance matrix

$$\Sigma = \begin{bmatrix} 1 & 0 & 0 \\ 0 & 2 & 1 \\ 0 & 1 & 2 \end{bmatrix}.$$

Find $P(X_1 > X_2 + X_3 + 2)$.

Hint: Find the vector $\mathbf{a}$ so that $\mathbf{aX} = X_1 - X_2 - X_3$ and make use of Theorem 3.5.1.

3.5.15. Suppose $\mathbf{X}$ is distributed $N_n(\boldsymbol{\mu}, \Sigma)$. Let $\overline{X} = n^{-1} \sum_{i=1}^{n} X_i$.

  (a) Write $\overline{X}$ as $\mathbf{aX}$ for an appropriate vector $\mathbf{a}$ and apply Theorem 3.5.1 to find the distribution of $\overline{X}$.

  (b) Determine the distribution of $\overline{X}$ if all of its component random variables X_i have the same mean μ.

含有 X_1, X_2 iid 这些?

✓ **3.5.16.** Suppose $\mathbf{X}$ is distributed $N_2(\boldsymbol{\mu}, \Sigma)$. Determine the distribution of the random vector $(X_1 + X_2, X_1 - X_2)$. Show that $X_1 + X_2$ and $X_1 - X_2$ are independent if $\text{Var}(X_1) = \text{Var}(X_2)$.

3.5.17. Suppose $\mathbf{X}$ is distributed $N_3(\mathbf{0}, \Sigma)$, where

$$\Sigma = \begin{bmatrix} 3 & 2 & 1 \\ 2 & 2 & 1 \\ 1 & 1 & 3 \end{bmatrix}.$$

Find $P((X_1 - 2X_2 + X_3)^2 > 15.36)$.

3.5.18. Let X_1, X_2, X_3 be iid random variables each having a standard normal distribution. Let the random variables Y_1, Y_2, Y_3 be defined by

$$X_1 = Y_1 \cos Y_2 \sin Y_3, \quad X_2 = Y_1 \sin Y_2 \sin Y_3, \quad X_3 = Y_1 \cos Y_3,$$

where $0 \le Y_1 < \infty$, $0 \le Y_2 < 2\pi$, $0 \le Y_3 \le \pi$. Show that Y_1, Y_2, Y_3 are mutually independent.

3.5.19. Show that expression (3.5.5) is true.

3.5.20. Prove Theorem 3.5.5.

3.5.21. Suppose $\mathbf{X}$ has a multivariate normal distribution with mean $\mathbf{0}$ and covariance matrix

$$\Sigma = \begin{bmatrix} 283 & 215 & 277 & 208 \\ 215 & 213 & 217 & 153 \\ 277 & 217 & 336 & 236 \\ 208 & 153 & 236 & 194 \end{bmatrix}.$$

  (a) Find the total variation of $\mathbf{X}$.

(b) Find the principal component vector $\mathbf{Y}$.

(c) Show that the first principal component accounts for 90% of the total variation.

(d) Show that the first principal component Y_1 is essentially a rescaled $\overline{X}$. Determine the variance of $(1/2)\overline{X}$ and compare it to that of Y_1.

Note if R is available, the command `eigen(amat)` obtains the spectral decomposition of the matrix `amat`.

3.5.22. Readers may have encountered the multiple regression model in a previous course in statistics. We can briefly write it as follows. Suppose we have a vector of n observations $\mathbf{Y}$ which has the distribution $N_n(\mathbf{X}\boldsymbol{\beta}, \sigma^2\mathbf{I})$, where $\mathbf{X}$ is an $n \times p$ matrix of known values, which has full column rank p, and $\boldsymbol{\beta}$ is a $p \times 1$ vector of unknown parameters. The least squares estimator of $\boldsymbol{\beta}$ is

$$\widehat{\boldsymbol{\beta}} = (\mathbf{X}'\mathbf{X})^{-1}\mathbf{X}'\mathbf{Y}.$$

(a) Determine the distribution of $\widehat{\boldsymbol{\beta}}$.

(b) Let $\widehat{\mathbf{Y}} = \mathbf{X}\widehat{\boldsymbol{\beta}}$. Determine the distribution of $\widehat{\mathbf{Y}}$.

(c) Let $\widehat{\mathbf{e}} = \mathbf{Y} - \widehat{\mathbf{Y}}$. Determine the distribution of $\widehat{\mathbf{e}}$.

(d) By writing the random vector $(\widehat{\mathbf{Y}}', \widehat{\mathbf{e}}')'$ as a linear function of $\mathbf{Y}$, show that the random vectors $\widehat{\mathbf{Y}}$ and $\widehat{\mathbf{e}}$ are independent.

(e) Show that $\widehat{\boldsymbol{\beta}}$ solves the least squares problem; that is,

$$\|\mathbf{Y} - \mathbf{X}\widehat{\boldsymbol{\beta}}\|^2 = \min_{\mathbf{b} \in R^p} \|\mathbf{Y} - \mathbf{X}\mathbf{b}\|^2.$$

3.6 t- and F-Distributions

It is the purpose of this section to define two additional distributions that are quite useful in certain problems of statistical inference. These are called, respectively, the (Student's) t-distribution and the F-distribution.

3.6.1 The t-distribution

Let W denote a random variable that is $N(0,1)$; let V denote a random variable that is $\chi^2(r)$; and let W and V be independent. Then the joint pdf of W and V, say $h(w,v)$, is the product of the pdf of W and that of V or $h(w,v) = f(w) \cdot f(v)$ $\therefore w, v$ indep.

$$h(w,v) = \begin{cases} \frac{1}{\sqrt{2\pi}}e^{-w^2/2}\frac{1}{\Gamma(r/2)2^{r/2}}v^{r/2-1}e^{-v/2} & -\infty < w < \infty, \quad 0 < v < \infty \\ 0 & \text{elsewhere.} \end{cases}$$

Define a new random variable T by writing

$$T = \frac{W}{\sqrt{V/r}}.$$

The change-of-variable technique is used to obtain the pdf $g_1(t)$ of T. The equations

$$t = \frac{w}{\sqrt{v/r}} \quad \text{and} \quad u = v$$

define a transformation that maps $\mathcal{S} = \{(w,v) : -\infty < w < \infty, \ 0 < v < \infty\}$ one-to-one and onto $\mathcal{T} = \{(t,u) : -\infty < t < \infty, \ 0 < u < \infty\}$. Since $w = t\sqrt{u}/\sqrt{r}$, $v = u$, the absolute value of the Jacobian of the transformation is $|J| = \sqrt{u}/\sqrt{r}$. Accordingly, the joint pdf of T and $U = V$ is given by

$$
\begin{aligned}
g(t,u) &= h\left(\frac{t\sqrt{u}}{\sqrt{r}}, u\right)|J| \\
&= \begin{cases} \frac{1}{\sqrt{2\pi}\Gamma(r/2)2^{r/2}} u^{r/2-1} \exp\left[-\frac{u}{2}\left(1 + \frac{t^2}{r}\right)\right] \frac{\sqrt{u}}{\sqrt{r}} & |t| < \infty, \ 0 < u < \infty \\ 0 & \text{elsewhere.} \end{cases}
\end{aligned}
$$

The marginal pdf of T is then

$$
\begin{aligned}
g_1(t) &= \int_{-\infty}^{\infty} g(t,u)\, du \\
&= \int_0^{\infty} \frac{1}{\sqrt{2\pi r}\Gamma(r/2)2^{r/2}} u^{(r+1)/2-1} \exp\left[-\frac{u}{2}\left(1 + \frac{t^2}{r}\right)\right] du.
\end{aligned}
$$

In this integral let $z = u[1 + (t^2/r)]/2$, and it is seen that

$$
\begin{aligned}
g_1(t) &= \int_0^{\infty} \frac{1}{\sqrt{2\pi r}\Gamma(r/2)2^{r/2}} \left(\frac{2z}{1+t^2/r}\right)^{(r+1)/2-1} e^{-z} \left(\frac{2}{1+t^2/r}\right) dz \\
&= \frac{\Gamma[(r+1)/2]}{\sqrt{\pi r}\Gamma(r/2)} \frac{1}{(1+t^2/r)^{(r+1)/2}}, \quad -\infty < t < \infty. \quad (3.6.1)
\end{aligned}
$$

Thus, if W is $N(0,1)$, if V is $\chi^2(r)$, and if W and V are independent, then

$$T = \frac{W}{\sqrt{V/r}} \quad\quad\quad\quad (3.6.2)$$

has the immediately preceding pdf $g_1(t)$. The distribution of the random variable T is usually called a *t-distribution*. It should be observed that a t-distribution is completely determined by the parameter r, the number of degrees of freedom of the random variable that has the chi-square distribution. Some approximate values of

$$P(T \le t) = \int_{-\infty}^{t} g_1(w)\, dw$$

[handwritten: t 's $\overset{DF \to \infty}{\longrightarrow} \sim N(0,1)$]

for selected values of r and t can be found in Table IV in Appendix C. Note that the last line of the this table, which is labeled ∞, contains the $N(0,1)$ critical values. This is because as the degrees of freedom approach ∞, the t-distribution converges to the $N(0,1)$ distribution; see Example 5.2.3 of Chapter 5.

The R computer package can also be used to obtain critical values as well as probabilities concerning the t-distribution. For instance, the command qt(.975,15) returns the 97.5th percentile of the t-distribution with 15 degrees of freedom; the command pt(2.0,15) returns the probability that a t-distributed random variable with 15 degrees of freedom is less that 2.0; and the command dt(2.0,15) returns the value of the pdf of this distribution at 2.0.

Remark 3.6.1. This distribution was first discovered by W. S. Gosset when he was working for an Irish brewery. Gosset published under the pseudonym Student. Thus this distribution is often known as Student's t-distribution. ∎

Example 3.6.1 (Mean and Variance of the t-Distribution). Let the random variable T have a t-distribution with r degrees of freedom. Then, as in (3.6.2), we can write $T = W(V/r)^{-1/2}$, where W has a $N(0,1)$ distribution, V has a $\chi^2(r)$ distribution, and W and V are independent random variables. Independence of W and V and expression (3.3.4), provided $(r/2) - (k/2) > 0$ (i.e., $k < r$), implies the following:

[handwritten: $\because E(T)=0.$]
[handwritten: $E(T^2)= E(T^k)\big|_{k=2}$]

$$E(T^k) = E\left[W^k \left(\frac{V}{r}\right)^{-k/2}\right] = E(W^k)E\left[\left(\frac{V}{r}\right)^{-k/2}\right] \tag{3.6.3}$$

[handwritten: $= E(W^2)\cdot \frac{2^{-1}\cdot\Gamma(\frac{r}{2}-1)}{\Gamma(\frac{r}{2})\cdot r^{-1}}$]

$$= E(W^k)\frac{2^{-k/2}\Gamma\left(\frac{r}{2}-\frac{k}{2}\right)}{\Gamma\left(\frac{r}{2}\right)r^{-k/2}} \quad \text{if } k < r. \tag{3.6.4}$$

[handwritten: $= 1 \times \frac{(\frac{r}{2}-2)!\cdot r}{(\frac{r}{2}-1)!\cdot 2}$]
[handwritten: $k<r$ 即 $r>k$, 而 $k\geq 1$, ∴ $r\geq 1$]

For the mean of T, use $k = 1$. Because $E(W) = 0$, as long as the degrees of freedom of T exceed 1, the mean of T is 0. For the variance, use $k = 2$. In this case *[handwritten: $E(T)=0$]* the condition $r > k$ becomes $r > 2$. Since $E(W^2) = 1$, by expression (3.6.4), the variance of T is given by

[handwritten: $Var(T) = E(T^2) - (E(T))^2 = E(T^2) - 0 = E(T^2).$]

[handwritten left: $= \frac{1}{(\frac{r}{2}-1)}\cdot\frac{r}{2}$]

$$Var(T) = E(T^2) = \frac{r}{r-2}. \tag{3.6.5}$$

[handwritten: $= \frac{2}{r-2}\cdot\frac{r}{2} = \frac{r}{r-2} =$]

Therefore, a t-distribution with $r > 2$ degrees of freedom has a mean of 0 and a variance of $r/(r-2)$. ∎

3.6.2 The F-distribution

Next consider two independent chi-square random variables U and V having r_1 and r_2 degrees of freedom, respectively. The joint pdf $h(u,v)$ of U and V is then

$$h(u,v) = \begin{cases} \frac{1}{\Gamma(r_1/2)\Gamma(r_2/2)2^{(r_1+r_2)/2}}u^{r_1/2-1}v^{r_2/2-1}e^{-(u+v)/2} & 0 < u,v < \infty \\ 0 & \text{elsewhere.} \end{cases}$$

We define the new random variable

$$W = \frac{U/r_1}{V/r_2}$$

[handwritten: $\begin{cases} U \sim \chi^2(r_1) \\ V \sim \chi^2(r_2) \end{cases}$]

and we propose finding the pdf $g_1(w)$ of W. The equations

$$w = \frac{u/r_1}{v/r_2}, \quad z = v,$$

define a one-to-one transformation that maps the set $\mathcal{S} = \{(u,v) : 0 < u < \infty, \, 0 < v < \infty\}$ onto the set $\mathcal{T} = \{(w,z) : 0 < w < \infty, \, 0 < z < \infty\}$. Since $u = (r_1/r_2)zw$, $v = z$, the absolute value of the Jacobian of the transformation is $|J| = (r_1/r_2)z$. The joint pdf $g(w,z)$ of the random variables W and $Z = V$ is then

$$g(w,z) = \frac{1}{\Gamma(r_1/2)\Gamma(r_2/2)2^{(r_1+r_2)/2}} \left(\frac{r_1 zw}{r_2}\right)^{\frac{r_1-2}{2}} z^{\frac{r_2-2}{2}} \exp\left[-\frac{z}{2}\left(\frac{r_1 w}{r_2}+1\right)\right]\frac{r_1 z}{r_2},$$

provided that $(w,z) \in \mathcal{T}$, and zero elsewhere. The marginal pdf $g_1(w)$ of W is then

$$\begin{aligned}
g_1(w) &= \int_{-\infty}^{\infty} g(w,z)\,dz \\
&= \int_0^{\infty} \frac{(r_1/r_2)^{r_1/2}(w)^{r_1/2-1}}{\Gamma(r_1/2)\Gamma(r_2/2)2^{(r_1+r_2)/2}} z^{(r_1+r_2)/2-1} \exp\left[-\frac{z}{2}\left(\frac{r_1 w}{r_2}+1\right)\right]dz.
\end{aligned}$$

If we change the variable of integration by writing

$$y = \frac{z}{2}\left(\frac{r_1 w}{r_2}+1\right),$$

it can be seen that

$$\begin{aligned}
g_1(w) &= \int_0^{\infty} \frac{(r_1/r_2)^{r_1/2}(w)^{r_1/2-1}}{\Gamma(r_1/2)\Gamma(r_2/2)2^{(r_1+r_2)/2}} \left(\frac{2y}{r_1 w/r_2+1}\right)^{(r_1+r_2)/2-1} e^{-y} \\
&\quad \times \left(\frac{2}{r_1 w/r_2+1}\right)dy \\
&= \begin{cases} \dfrac{\Gamma[(r_1+r_2)/2](r_1/r_2)^{r_1/2}}{\Gamma(r_1/2)\Gamma(r_2/2)} \dfrac{(w)^{r_1/2-1}}{(1+r_1 w/r_2)^{(r_1+r_2)/2}} & 0 < w < \infty \\ 0 & \text{elsewhere.} \end{cases}
\end{aligned} \qquad (3.6.6)$$

Accordingly, if U and V are independent chi-square variables with r_1 and r_2 degrees of freedom, respectively, then

$$W = \frac{U/r_1}{V/r_2}$$

has the immediately preceding pdf $g(w)$. The distribution of this random variable is usually called an *F-distribution*; and we often call the ratio, which we have denoted by W, F. That is,

$$F = \frac{U/r_1}{V/r_2}. \qquad (3.6.7)$$

It should be observed that an F-distribution is completely determined by the two parameters r_1 and r_2. For selected values of r_1, r_2, and b, Table V in Appendix C gives some approximate values of

$$P(F \leq b) = \int_0^b g_1(w)\, dw.$$

The R package can also be used to find critical values and probabilities for F-distributed random variables. Suppose we want the 0.025 upper critical point for an F random variable with a and b degrees of freedom. This can be obtained by the command qf(.975,a,b). Also, the probability that this F-distributed random variable is less than x is returned by the command pf(x,a,b), while the command df(x,a,b) returns the value of its pdf at x.

Example 3.6.2 (Moments of F-Distributions). Let F have an F-distribution with r_1 and r_2 degrees of freedom. Then, as in expression (3.6.7), we can write $F = (r_2/r_1)(U/V)$, where U and V are independent χ^2 random variables with r_1 and r_2 degrees of freedom, respectively. Hence, for the kth moment of F, by independence we have

$$E\left(F^k\right) = \left(\frac{r_2}{r_1}\right)^k E\left(U^k\right) E\left(V^{-k}\right),$$

provided, of course, that both expectations on the right side exist. By Theorem 3.3.1, because $k > -(r_1/2)$ is always true, the first expectation always exists. The second expectation, however, exists if $r_2 > 2k$; i.e., the denominator degrees of freedom must exceed twice k. Assuming this is true, it follows from (3.3.4) that the mean of F is given by

$$E(F) = \frac{r_2}{r_1} r_1 \frac{2^{-1}\Gamma\left(\frac{r_2}{2} - 1\right)}{\Gamma\left(\frac{r_2}{2}\right)} = \frac{r_2}{r_2 - 2}. \tag{3.6.8}$$

If r_2 is large, then $E(F)$ is about 1. In Exercise 3.6.6, a general expression for $E(F^k)$ is derived. ∎

3.6.3 Student's Theorem

Our final note in this section concerns an important result for the later chapters on inference for normal random variables. It is a corollary to the t-distribution derived above and is often referred to as Student's Theorem.

Theorem 3.6.1. *Let $X_1, \ldots, X_n$ be iid random variables each having a normal distribution with mean μ and variance σ^2. Define the random variables*

$$\overline{X} = \frac{1}{n}\sum_{i=1}^n X_i \quad and \quad S^2 = \frac{1}{n-1}\sum_{i=1}^n (X_i - \overline{X})^2.$$

Then

(a) *$\overline{X}$ has a $N\left(\mu, \frac{\sigma^2}{n}\right)$ distribution.*

(b) $\overline{X}$ and S^2 are independent.

(c) $(n-1)S^2/\sigma^2$ has a $\chi^2(n-1)$ distribution.

(d) The random variable

$$T = \frac{\overline{X} - \mu}{S/\sqrt{n}} \tag{3.6.9}$$

has a Student t-distribution with $n-1$ degrees of freedom.

Proof: Note that we have proved part (a) in Corollary 3.4.1. Let $\mathbf{X} = (X_1, \ldots, X_n)'$. Because $X_1, \ldots, X_n$ are iid $N(\mu, \sigma^2)$ random variables, $\mathbf{X}$ has a multivariate normal distribution $N(\mu\mathbf{1}, \sigma^2\mathbf{I})$, where $\mathbf{1}$ denotes a vector whose components are all 1. Let $\mathbf{v}' = (1/n, \ldots, 1/n) = (1/n)\mathbf{1}'$. Note that $\overline{X} = \mathbf{v}'\mathbf{X}$. Define the random vector $\mathbf{Y}$ by $\mathbf{Y} = (X_1 - \overline{X}, \ldots, X_n - \overline{X})'$. Consider the following transformation:

$$\mathbf{W} = \begin{bmatrix} \overline{X} \\ \mathbf{Y} \end{bmatrix} = \begin{bmatrix} \mathbf{v}' \\ \mathbf{I} - \mathbf{1}\mathbf{v}' \end{bmatrix} \mathbf{X}. \tag{3.6.10}$$

Because $\mathbf{W}$ is a linear transformation of multivariate normal random vector, by Theorem 3.5.1 it has a multivariate normal distribution with mean

$$E[\mathbf{W}] = \begin{bmatrix} \mathbf{v}' \\ \mathbf{I} - \mathbf{1}\mathbf{v}' \end{bmatrix} \mu\mathbf{1} = \begin{bmatrix} \mu \\ \mathbf{0}_n \end{bmatrix}, \tag{3.6.11}$$

where $\mathbf{0}_n$ denotes a vector whose components are all 0, and covariance matrix

$$\begin{aligned} \mathbf{\Sigma} &= \begin{bmatrix} \mathbf{v}' \\ \mathbf{I} - \mathbf{1}\mathbf{v}' \end{bmatrix} \sigma^2\mathbf{I} \begin{bmatrix} \mathbf{v}' \\ \mathbf{I} - \mathbf{1}\mathbf{v}' \end{bmatrix}' \\ &= \sigma^2 \begin{bmatrix} \frac{1}{n} & \mathbf{0}'_n \\ \mathbf{0}_n & \mathbf{I} - \mathbf{1}\mathbf{v}' \end{bmatrix}. \end{aligned} \tag{3.6.12}$$

Because $\overline{X}$ is the first component of $\mathbf{W}$, we can also obtain part (a) by Theorem 3.5.1. Next, because the covariances are 0, $\overline{X}$ is independent of $\mathbf{Y}$. But $S^2 = (n-1)^{-1}\mathbf{Y}'\mathbf{Y}$. Hence, $\overline{X}$ is independent of S^2, also. Thus part (b) is true.

Consider the random variable

$$V = \sum_{i=1}^{n} \left(\frac{X_i - \mu}{\sigma} \right)^2.$$

Each term in this sum is the square of a $N(0, 1)$ random variable and, hence, has a $\chi^2(1)$ distribution (Theorem 3.4.1). Because the summands are independent, it follows from Corollary 3.3.1 that V is a $\chi^2(n)$ random variable. Note the following identity:

$$\begin{aligned} V &= \sum_{i=1}^{n} \left(\frac{(X_i - \overline{X}) + (\overline{X} - \mu)}{\sigma} \right)^2 \\ &= \sum_{i=1}^{n} \left(\frac{X_i - \overline{X}}{\sigma} \right)^2 + \left(\frac{\overline{X} - \mu}{\sigma/\sqrt{n}} \right)^2 \\ &= \frac{(n-1)S^2}{\sigma^2} + \left(\frac{\overline{X} - \mu}{\sigma/\sqrt{n}} \right)^2. \end{aligned} \tag{3.6.13}$$

By part (b), the two terms on the right side of the last equation are independent. Further, the second term is the square of a standard normal random variable and, hence, has a $\chi^2(1)$ distribution. Taking mgfs of both sides, we have

$$(1-2t)^{-n/2} \; = \; E\left[\exp\{t(n-1)S^2/\sigma^2\}\right](1-2t)^{-1/2}. \qquad (3.6.14)$$

Solving for the mgf of $(n-1)S^2/\sigma^2$ on the right side we obtain part (c). Finally, part (d) follows immediately from parts (a)–(c) upon writing T, (3.6.9), as

$$T = \frac{(\overline{X}-\mu)/(\sigma/\sqrt{n})}{\sqrt{(n-1)S^2/(\sigma^2(n-1))}}. \qquad \blacksquare$$

$\begin{cases} W = \frac{\overline{X}-\mu}{\sigma/\sqrt{n}} \sim N(0,1) \\ V = (n-1)\frac{S^2}{\sigma^2} \sim \chi^2(n-1) \end{cases}$

$\Rightarrow T = \frac{W}{\sqrt{V/r}} = \frac{\overline{X}-\mu}{\sigma/\sqrt{n}} \Big/ \sqrt{(n-1)\frac{S^2}{\sigma^2}}$

$= \frac{\overline{X}-\mu}{S/\sqrt{n}} \sim T(n-1).$

EXERCISES

3.6.1. Let T have a t-distribution with 10 degrees of freedom. Find $P(|T| > 2.228)$ from either Table IV or, if available, by using R.

3.6.2. Let T have a t-distribution with 14 degrees of freedom. Determine b so that $P(-b < T < b) = 0.90$. Use either Table IV or, if available, by using R.

3.6.3. Let T have a t-distribution with $r > 4$ degrees of freedom. Use expression (3.6.4) to determine the kurtosis of T. See Exercise 1.9.15 for the definition of kurtosis.

3.6.4. Assuming a computer is available, plot the pdfs of the random variables defined in parts (a)–(e) below. Obtain an overlay plot of all five pdfs, also. In R the domain values of the pdfs can easily be obtained by using the **seq** command. For instance, the command **x<-seq(-6,6,.1)** returns in **x** a vector of values between -6 and 6 in jumps of 0.1.

(a) X has a standard normal distribution.

(b) X has a t-distribution with 1 degree of freedom.

(c) X has a t-distribution with 3 degrees of freedom.

(d) X has a t-distribution with 10 degrees of freedom.

(e) X has a t-distribution with 30 degrees of freedom.

3.6.5. Assuming a computer is available, investigate the probabilities of an "outlier" for a t-random variable and a normal random variable. Specifically, determine the probability of observing the event $\{|X| \geq 2\}$ for the following random variables:

(a) X has a standard normal distribution.

(b) X has a t-distribution with 1 degree of freedom.

(c) X has a t-distribution with 3 degrees of freedom.

(d) X has a t-distribution with 10 degrees of freedom.

(e) X has a t-distribution with 30 degrees of freedom.

3.6.6. Let F have an F-distribution with parameters r_1 and r_2. Assuming that $r_2 > 2k$, continue with Example 3.6.2 and derive the $E(F^k)$.

3.6.7. Let F have an F-distribution with parameters r_1 and r_2. Using the results of the last exercise, determine the kurtosis of F, assuming that $r_2 > 8$.

3.6.8. Let F have an F-distribution with parameters r_1 and r_2. Argue that $1/F$ has an F-distribution with parameters r_2 and r_1.

3.6.9. If F has an F-distribution with parameters $r_1 = 5$ and $r_2 = 10$, find a and b so that $P(F \leq a) = 0.05$ and $P(F \leq b) = 0.95$, and, accordingly, $P(a < F < b) = 0.90$.

Hint: Write $P(F \leq a) = P(1/F \geq 1/a) = 1 - P(1/F \leq 1/a)$, and use the result of Exercise 3.6.8 and Table V or, if available, use R.

3.6.10. Let $T = W/\sqrt{V/r}$, where the independent variables W and V are, respectively, normal with mean zero and variance 1 and chi-square with r degrees of freedom. Show that T^2 has an F-distribution with parameters $r_1 = 1$ and $r_2 = r$.
Hint: What is the distribution of the numerator of T^2?

3.6.11. Show that the t-distribution with $r = 1$ degree of freedom and the Cauchy distribution are the same.

3.6.12. Show that

$$Y = \frac{1}{1 + (r_1/r_2)W},$$

where W has an F-distribution with parameters r_1 and r_2, has a beta distribution.

3.6.13. Let X_1, X_2 be iid with common distribution having the pdf $f(x) = e^{-x}$, $0 < x < \infty$, zero elsewhere. Show that $Z = X_1/X_2$ has an F-distribution.

3.6.14. Let X_1, X_2, and X_3 be three independent chi-square variables with r_1, r_2, and r_3 degrees of freedom, respectively.

(a) Show that $Y_1 = X_1/X_2$ and $Y_2 = X_1 + X_2$ are independent and that Y_2 is $\chi^2(r_1 + r_2)$.

(b) Deduce that

$$\frac{X_1/r_1}{X_2/r_2} \quad \text{and} \quad \frac{X_3/r_3}{(X_1 + X_2)/(r_1 + r_2)}$$

are independent F-variables.

3.7 Mixture Distributions

Recall the discussion on the contaminated normal distribution given in Section 3.4.1. This was an example of a mixture of normal distributions. In this section, we extend this to mixtures of distributions in general. Generally, we use continuous-type notation for the discussion, but discrete pmfs can be handled the same way.

Suppose that we have k distributions with respective pdfs $f_1(x), f_2(x), \ldots, f_k(x)$, with supports $\mathcal{S}_1, \mathcal{S}_2, \ldots, \mathcal{S}_k$, means $\mu_1, \mu_2, \ldots, \mu_k$, and variances $\sigma_1^2, \sigma_2^2, \ldots, \sigma_k^2$, with positive mixing probabilities $p_1, p_2, \ldots, p_k$, where $p_1 + p_2 + \cdots + p_k = 1$. Let $\mathcal{S} = \cup_{i=1}^k \mathcal{S}_i$ and consider the function

$$f(x) = p_1 f_1(x) + p_2 f_2(x) + \cdots + p_k f_k(x) = \sum_{i=1}^k p_i f_i(x), \quad x \in \mathcal{S}. \qquad (3.7.1)$$

Note that $f(x)$ is nonnegative and it is easy to see that it integrates to one over $(-\infty, \infty)$; hence, $f(x)$ is a pdf for some continuous-type random variable X. The mean of X is given by

$$E(X) = \sum_{i=1}^k p_i \int_{-\infty}^{\infty} x f_i(x)\, dx = \sum_{i=1}^k p_i \mu_i = \overline{\mu}, \qquad (3.7.2)$$

a weighted average of $\mu_1, \mu_2, \ldots, \mu_k$, and the variance equals

$$
\begin{aligned}
\text{var}(X) &= \sum_{i=1}^k p_i \int_{-\infty}^{\infty} (x - \overline{\mu})^2 f_i(x)\, dx \\
&= \sum_{i=1}^k p_i \int_{-\infty}^{\infty} [(x - \mu_i) + (\mu_i - \overline{\mu})]^2 f_i(x)\, dx \\
&= \sum_{i=1}^k p_i \int_{-\infty}^{\infty} (x - \mu_i)^2 f_i(x)\, dx + \sum_{i=1}^k p_i (\mu_i - \overline{\mu})^2 \int_{-\infty}^{\infty} f_i(x)\, dx,
\end{aligned}
$$

because the cross-product terms integrate to zero. That is,

$$\text{var}(X) = \sum_{i=1}^k p_i \sigma_i^2 + \sum_{i=1}^k p_i (\mu_i - \overline{\mu})^2. \qquad (3.7.3)$$

Note that the variance is not simply the weighted average of the k variances, but it also includes a positive term involving the weighted variance of the means.

Remark 3.7.1. It is extremely important to note these characteristics are associated with a mixture of k distributions and have nothing to do with a linear combination, say $\sum a_i X_i$, of k random variables. ∎

For the next example, we need the following distribution. We say that X has a **loggamma** pdf with parameters $\alpha > 0$ and $\beta > 0$ if it has pdf

$$f_1(x) = \begin{cases} \frac{1}{\Gamma(\alpha)\beta^\alpha} x^{-(1+\beta)/\beta} (\log x)^{\alpha-1} & x > 1 \\ 0 & \text{elsewhere.} \end{cases} \qquad (3.7.4)$$

The derivation of this pdf is given in Exercise 3.7.1, where its mean and variance are also derived. We denote this distribution of X by $\log \Gamma(\alpha, \beta)$.

Example 3.7.1. Actuaries have found that a mixture of the loggamma and gamma distributions is an important model for claim distributions. Suppose, then, that X_1 is $\log \Gamma(\alpha_1, \beta_1)$, X_2 is $\Gamma(\alpha_2, \beta_2)$, and the mixing probabilities are p and $(1-p)$. Then the pdf of the mixture distribution is

$$f(x) = \begin{cases} \frac{1-p}{\beta_2^{\alpha_2} \Gamma(\alpha_2)} x^{\alpha_2 - 1} e^{-x/\beta_2} & 0 < x \leq 1 \\ \frac{p}{\beta_1^{\alpha_1} \Gamma(\alpha_1)} (\log x)^{\alpha_1 - 1} x^{-(\beta_1 + 1)/\beta_1} + \frac{1-p}{\beta_2^{\alpha_2} \Gamma(\alpha_2)} x^{\alpha_2 - 1} e^{-x/\beta_2} & 1 < x \\ 0 & \text{elsewhere.} \end{cases}$$

(3.7.5)

Provided $\beta_1 < 2^{-1}$, the mean and the variance of this mixture distribution are

$$\mu = p(1 - \beta_1)^{-\alpha_1} + (1-p)\alpha_2 \beta_2 \tag{3.7.6}$$

$$\sigma^2 = p[(1 - 2\beta_1)^{-\alpha_1} - (1 - \beta_1)^{-2\alpha_1}]$$
$$+ (1-p)\alpha_2 \beta_2^2 + p(1-p)[(1 - \beta_1)^{-\alpha_1} - \alpha_2 \beta_2]^2; \tag{3.7.7}$$

see Exercise 3.7.2. ∎

The mixture of distributions is sometimes called **compounding**. Moreover, it does not need to be restricted to a finite number of distributions. As demonstrated in the following example, a continuous weighting function, which is of course a pdf, can replace $p_1, p_2, \ldots, p_k$; i.e., integration replaces summation.

Example 3.7.2. Let X_θ be a Poisson random variable with parameter θ. We want to mix an infinite number of Poisson distributions, each with a different value of θ. We let the weighting function be a pdf of θ, namely, a gamma with parameters α and β. For $x = 0, 1, 2, \ldots$, the pmf of the compound distribution is

$$\begin{aligned} p(x) &= \int_0^\infty \left[\frac{1}{\beta^\alpha \Gamma(\alpha)} \theta^{\alpha - 1} e^{-\theta/\beta} \right] \left[\frac{\theta^x e^{-\theta}}{x!} \right] d\theta \\ &= \frac{1}{\Gamma(\alpha)\beta^\alpha x!} \int_0^\infty \theta^{\alpha + x - 1} e^{-\theta(1+\beta)/\beta} \, d\theta \\ &= \frac{\Gamma(\alpha + x)\beta^x}{\Gamma(\alpha) x! (1 + \beta)^{\alpha + x}}, \end{aligned}$$

where the third line follows from the change of variable $t = \theta(1 + \beta)/\beta$ to solve the integral of the second line.

An interesting case of this compound occurs when $\alpha = r$, a positive integer, and $\beta = (1-p)/p$, where $0 < p < 1$. In this case the pmf becomes

$$p(x) = \frac{(r + x - 1)!}{(r-1)!} \frac{p^r (1-p)^x}{x!}, \quad x = 0, 1, 2, \ldots.$$

That is, this compound distribution is the same as that of the number of excess trials needed to obtain r successes in a sequence of independent trials, each with probability p of success; this is one form of the **negative binomial distribution**. The negative binomial distribution has been used successfully as a model for the number of accidents (see Weber, 1971). ∎

In compounding, we can think of the original distribution of X as being a conditional distribution given θ, whose pdf is denoted by $f(x|\theta)$. Then the weighting function is treated as a pdf for θ, say $g(\theta)$. Accordingly, the joint pdf is $f(x|\theta)g(\theta)$, and the compound pdf can be thought of as the marginal (unconditional) pdf of X,

$$h(x) = \int_\theta g(\theta) f(x|\theta) \, d\theta,$$

where a summation replaces integration in case θ has a discrete distribution. For illustration, suppose we know that the mean of the normal distribution is zero but the variance σ^2 equals $1/\theta > 0$, where θ has been selected from some random model. For convenience, say this latter is a gamma distribution with parameters α and β. Thus, given that θ, X is conditionally $N(0, 1/\theta)$ so that the joint distribution of X and θ is

$$f(x|\theta)g(\theta) = \left[\frac{\sqrt{\theta}}{\sqrt{2\pi}} \exp\left(\frac{-\theta x^2}{2} \right) \right] \left[\frac{1}{\beta^\alpha \Gamma(\alpha)} \theta^{\alpha-1} \exp(-\theta/\beta) \right],$$

for $-\infty < x < \infty$, $0 < \theta < \infty$. Therefore, the marginal (unconditional) pdf $h(x)$ of X is found by integrating out θ; that is,

$$h(x) = \int_0^\infty \frac{\theta^{\alpha+1/2-1}}{\beta^\alpha \sqrt{2\pi} \Gamma(\alpha)} \exp\left[-\theta \left(\frac{x^2}{2} + \frac{1}{\beta} \right) \right] \, d\theta.$$

By comparing this integrand with a gamma pdf with parameters $\alpha + \frac{1}{2}$ and $[(1/\beta) + (x^2/2)]^{-1}$, we see that the integral equals

$$h(x) = \frac{\Gamma(\alpha + \frac{1}{2})}{\beta^\alpha \sqrt{2\pi} \Gamma(\alpha)} \left(\frac{2\beta}{2 + \beta x^2} \right)^{\alpha+1/2}, \quad -\infty < x < \infty.$$

It is interesting to note that if $\alpha = r/2$ and $\beta = 2/r$, where r is a positive integer, then X has an unconditional distribution, which is Student's t, with r degrees of freedom. That is, we have developed a generalization of Student's distribution through this type of mixing or compounding. We note that the resulting distribution (a generalization of Student's t) has much thicker tails than those of the conditional normal with which we started.

The next two examples offer two additional illustrations of this type of compounding.

Example 3.7.3. Suppose that we have a binomial distribution, but we are not certain about the probability p of success on a given trial. Suppose p has been selected first by some random process which has a beta pdf with parameters α and

β. Thus X, the number of successes on n independent trials, has a conditional binomial distribution so that the joint pdf of X and p is

$$p(x|p)g(p) = \frac{n!}{x!(n-x)!}p^x(1-p)^{n-x}\frac{\Gamma(\alpha+\beta)}{\Gamma(\alpha)\Gamma(\beta)}p^{\alpha-1}(1-p)^{\beta-1},$$

for $x = 0, 1, \ldots, n$, $0 < p < 1$. Therefore, the unconditional pmf of X is given by the integral

$$h(x) = \int_0^1 \frac{n!\Gamma(\alpha+\beta)}{x!(n-x)!\Gamma(\alpha)\Gamma(\beta)}p^{x+\alpha-1}(1-p)^{n-x+\beta-1}\,dp$$

$$= \frac{n!\Gamma(\alpha+\beta)\Gamma(x+\alpha)\Gamma(n-x+\beta)}{x!(n-x)!\Gamma(\alpha)\Gamma(\beta)\Gamma(n+\alpha+\beta)}, \quad x = 0, 1, 2, \ldots, n.$$

Now suppose α and β are positive integers; since $\Gamma(k) = (k-1)!$, this unconditional (marginal or compound) pdf can be written

$$h(x) = \frac{n!(\alpha+\beta-1)!(x+\alpha-1)!(n-x+\beta-1)!}{x!(n-x)!(\alpha-1)!(\beta-1)!(n+\alpha+\beta-1)!}, \quad x = 0, 1, 2, \ldots, n.$$

Because the conditional mean $E(X|p) = np$, the unconditional mean is $n\alpha/(\alpha+\beta)$ since $E(p)$ equals the mean $\alpha/(\alpha+\beta)$ of the beta distribution. ∎

Example 3.7.4. In this example, we develop by compounding a heavy-tailed skewed distribution. Assume X has a conditional gamma pdf with parameters k and θ^{-1}. The weighting function for θ is a gamma pdf with parameters α and β. Thus the unconditional (marginal or compounded) pdf of X is

$$h(x) = \int_0^\infty \left[\frac{\theta^{\alpha-1}e^{-\theta/\beta}}{\beta^\alpha\Gamma(\alpha)}\right]\left[\frac{\theta^k x^{k-1}e^{-\theta x}}{\Gamma(k)}\right]d\theta$$

$$= \int_0^\infty \frac{x^{k-1}\theta^{\alpha+k-1}}{\beta^\alpha\Gamma(\alpha)\Gamma(k)}e^{-\theta(1+\beta x)/\beta}\,d\theta.$$

Comparing this integrand to the gamma pdf with parameters $\alpha+k$ and $\beta/(1+\beta x)$, we see that

$$h(x) = \frac{\Gamma(\alpha+k)\beta^k x^{k-1}}{\Gamma(\alpha)\Gamma(k)(1+\beta x)^{\alpha+k}}, \quad 0 < x < \infty,$$

which is the pdf of the **generalized Pareto distribution** (and a generalization of the F distribution). Of course, when $k = 1$ (so that X has a conditional exponential distribution), the pdf is

$$h(x) = \alpha\beta(1+\beta x)^{-(\alpha+1)}, \quad 0 < x < \infty,$$

which is the **Pareto pdf**. Both of these compound pdfs have thicker tails than the original (conditional) gamma distribution.

While the cdf of the generalized Pareto distribution cannot be expressed in a simple closed form, that of the Pareto distribution is

$$H(x) = \int_0^x \alpha\beta(1+\beta t)^{-(\alpha+1)}\,dt = 1 - (1+\beta x)^{-\alpha}, \quad 0 \le x < \infty.$$

From this, we can create another useful long-tailed distribution by letting $X = Y^\tau$, $0 < \tau$. Thus Y has the cdf

$$G(y) = P(Y \le y) = P[X^{1/\tau} \le y] = P[X \le y^\tau].$$

Hence, this probability is equal to

$$G(y) = H(y^\tau) = 1 - (1 + \beta y^\tau)^{-\alpha}, \quad 0 < y < \infty,$$

with corresponding pdf

$$G'(y) = g(y) = \frac{\alpha\beta\tau y^{\tau-1}}{(1 + \beta y^\tau)^{\alpha+1}}, \quad 0 < y < \infty.$$

We call the associated distribution the **transformed Pareto distribution** or the **Burr distribution** (Burr, 1942), and it has proved to be a useful one in modeling thicker-tailed distributions. ∎

EXERCISES

3.7.1. Suppose Y has a $\Gamma(\alpha, \beta)$ distribution. Let $X = e^Y$. Show that the pdf of X is given by expression (3.7.4). Derive the mean and variance of X.

3.7.2. In Example 3.7.1, derive the pdf of the mixture distribution given in expression (3.7.5), then obtain its mean and variance as given in expressions (3.7.6) and (3.7.7).

3.7.3. Consider the mixture distribution, $(9/10)N(0,1) + (1/10)N(0,9)$. Show that its kurtosis is 8.34.

3.7.4. Let X have the conditional geometric pmf $\theta(1-\theta)^{x-1}$, $x = 1, 2, \ldots$, where θ is a value of a random variable having a beta pdf with parameters α and β. Show that the marginal (unconditional) pmf of X is

$$\frac{\Gamma(\alpha+\beta)\Gamma(\alpha+1)\Gamma(\beta+x-1)}{\Gamma(\alpha)\Gamma(\beta)\Gamma(\alpha+\beta+x)}, \quad x = 1, 2, \ldots.$$

If $\alpha = 1$, we obtain

$$\frac{\beta}{(\beta+x)(\beta+x-1)}, \quad x = 1, 2, \ldots,$$

which is one form of **Zipf's law**.

3.7.5. Repeat Exercise 3.7.4, letting X have a conditional negative binomial distribution instead of the geometric one.

3.7.6. Let X have a generalized Pareto distribution with parameters k, α, and β. Show, by change of variables, that $Y = \beta X/(1 + \beta X)$ has a beta distribution.

3.7.7. Show that the failure rate (hazard function) of the Pareto distribution is

$$\frac{h(x)}{1 - H(x)} = \frac{\alpha}{\beta^{-1} + x}.$$

Find the failure rate (hazard function) of the Burr distribution with cdf

$$G(y) = 1 - \left(\frac{1}{1 + \beta y^\tau} \right)^\alpha, \quad 0 \le y < \infty.$$

In each of these two failure rates, note what happens as the value of the variable increases.

3.7.8. For the Burr distribution, show that

$$E(X^k) = \frac{1}{\beta^{k/\tau}} \Gamma \left(\alpha - \frac{k}{\tau} \right) \Gamma \left(\frac{k}{\tau} + 1 \right) \Big/ \Gamma(\alpha),$$

provided $k < \alpha\tau$.

3.7.9. Let the number X of accidents have a Poisson distribution with mean $\lambda\theta$. Suppose λ, the liability to have an accident, has, given θ, a gamma pdf with parameters $\alpha = h$ and $\beta = h^{-1}$; and θ, an accident proneness factor, has a generalized Pareto pdf with parameters α, $\lambda = h$, and k. Show that the unconditional pdf of X is

$$\frac{\Gamma(\alpha + k)\Gamma(\alpha + h)\Gamma(\alpha + h + k)\Gamma(h + k)\Gamma(k + x)}{\Gamma(\alpha)\Gamma(\alpha + k + h)\Gamma(h)\Gamma(k)\Gamma(\alpha + h + k + x)x!}, \quad x = 0, 1, 2, \ldots,$$

sometimes called the **generalized Waring** pmf.

3.7.10. Let X have a conditional Burr distribution with fixed parameters β and τ, given parameter α.

(a) If α has the geometric pmf $p(1 - p)^\alpha$, $\alpha = 0, 1, 2, \ldots$, show that the unconditional distribution of X is a Burr distribution.

(b) If α has the exponential pdf $\beta^{-1} e^{-\alpha/\beta}$, $\alpha > 0$, find the unconditional pdf of X.

3.7.11. Let X have the conditional Weibull pdf

$$f(x|\theta) = \theta\tau x^{\tau-1} e^{-\theta x^\tau}, \quad 0 < x < \infty,$$

and let the pdf (weighting function) $g(\theta)$ be gamma with parameters α and β. Show that the compound (marginal) pdf of X is that of Burr.

3.7.12. If X has a Pareto distribution with parameters α and β and if c is a positive constant, show that $Y = cX$ has a Pareto distribution with parameters α and β/c.

Chapter 4

Some Elementary Statistical Inferences

4.1 Sampling and Statistics

In Chapter 2, we introduced the concepts of samples and statistics. We continue with this development in this chapter while introducing the main tools of inference: confidence intervals and tests of hypotheses.

In a typical statistical problem, we have a random variable X of interest, but its pdf $f(x)$ or pmf $p(x)$ is not known. Our ignorance about $f(x)$ or $p(x)$ can roughly be classified in one of two ways:

1. $f(x)$ or $p(x)$ is completely unknown.

2. The form of $f(x)$ or $p(x)$ is known down to a parameter θ, where θ may be a vector.

For now, we consider the second classification, although some of our discussion pertains to the first classification also. Some examples are the following:

(a) X has an exponential distribution, $\text{Exp}(\theta)$, (3.3.2), where θ is unknown.

(b) X has a binomial distribution $b(n,p)$, (3.1.2), where n is known but p is unknown.

(c) X has a gamma distribution $\Gamma(\alpha, \beta)$, (3.3.1), where both α and β are unknown.

(d) X has a normal distribution $N(\mu, \sigma^2)$, (3.4.6), where both the mean μ and the variance σ^2 of X are unknown.

We often denote this problem by saying that the random variable X has a density or mass function of the form $f(x; \theta)$ or $p(x; \theta)$, where $\theta \in \Omega$ for a specified set Ω. For example, in (a) above, $\Omega = \{\theta \mid \theta > 0\}$. We call θ a parameter of the distribution. Because θ is unknown, we want to estimate it.

即利用 $x_1, x_2, \cdots, x_n$ 的值去估计 θ 目的值，即得出 θ 与 $x_1, x_2, \cdots x_n$ 的关系式：$\theta = g(x_1, x_2, \cdots x_n)$，这即是 θ 的 estimator。θ 必是 $x_1, x_2, \cdots x_n$ 的 pdf 203 函数 $f(x)$ 的表达式中的一个参数！

In this process, our information about the unknown distribution of X or the unknown parameters of the distribution of X comes from a sample on X. The sample observations have the same distribution as X, and we denote them as the random variables $X_1, X_2, \ldots, X_n$, where n denotes the **sample size**. When the sample is actually drawn, we use lower case letters $x_1, x_2, \ldots, x_n$ as the values or **realizations** of the sample. Often we assume that the sample observations $X_1, X_2, \ldots, X_n$ are also mutually independent, in which case we call the sample a random sample, which we now formally define:

Definition 4.1.1. *If the random variables $X_1, X_2, \ldots, X_n$ are independent and identically distributed (iid), then these random variables constitute a **random sample** of size n from the common distribution.*

Often, functions of the sample are used to summarize the information in a sample. These are called statistics, which we define as

Definition 4.1.2. *Let $X_1, X_2, \ldots, X_n$ denote a sample on a random variable X. Let $T = T(X_1, X_2, \ldots, X_n)$ be a function of the sample. Then T is called a **statistic**.*

Once the sample is drawn, then t is called the realization of T, where $t = T(x_1, x_2, \ldots, x_n)$ and $x_1, x_2, \ldots, x_n$ is the realization of the sample.

Using this terminology, the problem we discuss in this chapter is phrased as: Let $X_1, X_2, \ldots, X_n$ denote a random sample on a random variable X with a density or mass function of the form $f(x; \theta)$ or $p(x; \theta)$, where $\theta \in \Omega$ for a specified set Ω. In this situation, it makes sense to consider a statistic T, which is an **estimator** of θ. More formally, T is called a **point estimator** of θ. While we call T an estimator of θ, we call its realization t an **estimate** of θ.

There are several properties of point estimators that we discuss in this book. We begin with a simple one, unbiasedness.

Definition 4.1.3 (Unbiasedness). *Let $X_1, X_2, \ldots, X_n$ denote a sample on a random variable X with pdf $f(x; \theta)$, $\theta \in \Omega$. Let $T = T(X_1, X_2, \ldots, X_n)$ be a statistic. We say that T is an **unbiased** estimator of θ if $E(T) = \theta$.*

In Chapters 6 and 7, we discuss several theories of estimation in general. The purpose of this chapter, though, is an introduction to inference, so we briefly discuss the **maximum likelihood estimator**, (mle) and then use it to obtain point estimators for some of the examples cited above. We expand on this theory in Chapter 6. Our discussion is for the continuous case. For the discrete case, simply replace the pdf with the pmf.

In our problem, the information in the sample and the parameter θ are involved in the joint distribution of the random sample; i.e., $\prod_{i=1}^{n} f(x_i; \theta)$. We want to view this as a function of θ, so we write it as

$$L(\theta) = L(\theta; x_1, x_2, \ldots, x_n) = \prod_{i=1}^{n} f(x_i; \theta). \tag{4.1.1}$$

This is called the **likelihood function** of the random sample. As an estimate of θ, a measure of the center of $L(\theta)$ seems appropriate. An often-used estimate is that value of θ which provides a maximum of $L(\theta)$. If it is unique, this is called the **maximum likelihood estimator** (mle), and we denote it as $\widehat{\theta}$; i.e.,

$$\widehat{\theta} = \text{Argmax}\,L(\theta). \qquad (4.1.2)$$

In practice, it is often much easier to work with the log of the likelihood, that is, the function $l(\theta) = \log L(\theta)$. Because the log is a strictly increasing function, the value which maximizes $l(\theta)$ is the same as the value which maximizes $L(\theta)$. Furthermore, for most of the models discussed in this book, the pdf (or pmf) is a differentiable function of θ, and frequently $\widehat{\theta}$ solves the equation

$$\frac{\partial l(\theta)}{\partial \theta} = 0. \qquad (4.1.3)$$

利用该式最后老可得到一个关于 $\Sigma x_i = \theta$ 的关系式,

If θ is a vector of parameters, this results in a system of equations to be solved simultaneously; see Example 4.1.3.

查验后,
可得 $\theta = g(x_i)$.

As we show in Chapter 6, under general conditions, mles have some good properties. One property that we need at the moment concerns the situation where, besides the parameter θ, we are also interested in the parameter $\eta = g(\theta)$ for a specified function g. Then, as Theorem 6.1.2 of Chapter 6 shows, the mle of η is $\widehat{\eta} = g(\widehat{\theta})$, where $\widehat{\theta}$ is the mle of θ. We now proceed with some examples.

本例应 pdf 函数中涉及到了两个参数 α 与 β, 其中以 $\alpha = 1$, β 设为 θ.

Example 4.1.1 (Exponential Distribution). Suppose the common pdf of the random sample $X_1, X_2, \ldots, X_n$ is the $\Gamma(1, \theta)$ density given in expression (3.3.1) of Chapter 3. The log of the likelihood function is given by

$f(x) = \frac{1}{\Gamma(\alpha)\beta^\alpha} x^{\alpha-1} e^{-x/\beta}$, $\Gamma(1,\theta) \Rightarrow \begin{cases} \alpha=1 \\ \beta=\theta \end{cases}$

$\therefore f(x) = \frac{1}{\Gamma(1)\theta^1} x^0 \cdot e^{-x/\theta} = \frac{1}{\theta} e^{-x/\theta}$

$\therefore f(x_1) = \frac{1}{\theta} e^{-x_1/\theta}$ —写作 $f(x_1;\theta)$

$$l(\theta) = \log \prod_{i=1}^{n} \frac{1}{\theta} e^{-x_i/\theta} = -n \log \theta - \theta^{-1} \sum_{i=1}^{n} x_i.$$

$f(x_2) = \frac{1}{\theta} e^{-x_2/\theta}$ —写作 $f(x_2;\theta)$

The first partial of the log-likelihood with respect to θ is

$\frac{\partial l}{\partial \theta}$

$\therefore L(\theta) = f(x_1;\theta) \times f(x_2;\theta) \times \cdots \times f(x_n;\theta)$
$= \frac{1}{\theta} e^{-\frac{x_1}{\theta}} \times \cdots \times \frac{1}{\theta} e^{-x_n/\theta}$

$$\frac{\partial l(\theta)}{\partial \theta} = -n\theta^{-1} + \theta^{-2} \sum_{i=1}^{n} x_i.$$

$\therefore l(\theta) = \log L(\theta) = \cdots$

$\frac{\partial l}{\partial \theta} = \cdots = 0 \Rightarrow \Sigma x_i = n\theta \Rightarrow \bar{x} = \frac{\Sigma x_i}{n} = \theta$

Setting this partial to 0 and solving for θ, we obtain the solution $\overline{x}$. There is only one critical value and, furthermore, the second partial of the log-likelihood evaluated at $\overline{x}$ is strictly negative, verifying that it provides a maximum. Hence, for this example, the statistic $\widehat{\theta} = \overline{X}$ is the mle of θ. Because $E(X) = \theta$, we have that $E(\overline{X}) = \theta$ and, hence, $\widehat{\theta}$ is an unbiased estimator of θ. ∎

Example 4.1.2 (Binomial Distribution). Let X be one or zero if, respectively, the outcome of a Bernoulli experiment is success or failure. Let θ, $0 < \theta < 1$, denote the probability of success. Then by (3.1.1), the pmf of X is

令 $P = \theta$.

$$p(x; \theta) = \theta^x (1-\theta)^{1-x}, \quad x = 0 \text{ or } 1.$$

$P(x; P) = P^x (1-P)^{1-x}$.

If $X_1, X_2, \ldots, X_n$ is a random sample on X, then the likelihood function is

$$L(\theta) = \prod_{i=1}^{n} p(x_i; \theta) = \theta^{\sum_{i=1}^{n} x_i}(1-\theta)^{n-\sum_{i=1}^{n} x_i}, \quad x_i = 0 \text{ or } 1.$$

Taking logs, we have

$$l(\theta) = \sum_{i=1}^{n} x_i \log \theta + \left(n - \sum_{i=1}^{n} x_i\right) \log(1-\theta), \quad x_i = 0 \text{ or } 1.$$

The partial derivative of $l(\theta)$ is

$$\frac{\partial l(\theta)}{\partial \theta} = \frac{\sum_{i=1}^{n} x_i}{\theta} - \frac{n - \sum_{i=1}^{n} x_i}{1-\theta}.$$

Setting this to 0 and solving for θ, we obtain $\widehat{\theta} = n^{-1}\sum_{i=1}^{n} X_i = \overline{X}$; i.e., the mle is the proportion of successes in the n trials. Because $E(X) = \theta$, $\widehat{\theta}$ is an unbiased estimator of θ. ∎

Example 4.1.3 (Normal Distribution). Let X have a $N(\mu, \sigma^2)$ distribution with the pdf given in expression (3.4.6). In this case, $\boldsymbol{\theta}$ is the vector $\boldsymbol{\theta} = (\mu, \sigma)$. If $X_1, X_2, \ldots, X_n$ is a random sample on X, then the log of the likelihood function simplifies to

$$l(\mu, \sigma) = -\frac{n}{2}\log 2\pi - n\log \sigma - \frac{1}{2}\sum_{i=1}^{n}\left(\frac{x_i - \mu}{\sigma}\right)^2. \tag{4.1.4}$$

The two partial derivatives simplify to

$$\frac{\partial l(\mu, \sigma)}{\partial \mu} = -\sum_{i=1}^{n}\left(\frac{x_i - \mu}{\sigma}\right)\left(-\frac{1}{\sigma}\right) \tag{4.1.5}$$

$$\frac{\partial l(\mu, \sigma)}{\partial \sigma} = -\frac{n}{\sigma} + \frac{1}{\sigma^3}\sum_{i=1}^{n}(x_i - \mu)^2. \tag{4.1.6}$$

Setting these to 0 and solving simultaneously, we see that the mles are

$$\widehat{\mu} = \overline{X} \tag{4.1.7}$$

$$\widehat{\sigma}^2 = n^{-1}\sum_{i=1}^{n}(X_i - \overline{X})^2. \tag{4.1.8}$$

Notice that we have used the property that the mle of $\widehat{\sigma}^2$ is the mle of σ squared. From the discussion around expressions (2.8.3) and (2.8.4) of Chapter 2, we see that $\widehat{\mu}$ is an unbiased estimator of μ, while $\widehat{\sigma}^2$ is a biased estimator of σ^2. By (2.8.4), though, the bias of $\widehat{\sigma}^2$ is $E(\widehat{\sigma}^2 - \sigma^2) = -\sigma^2/n$, which converges to 0 as $n \to \infty$. ∎

In all three of these examples, standard differential calculus methods led us to the solution. For the next example, the support of the random variable involves θ and, hence, it is not surprising that for this case differential calculus is not useful.

Example 4.1.4 (Uniform Distribution). Let $X_1, \ldots, X_n$ be iid with the uniform $(0, \theta)$ density; i.e., $f(x) = 1/\theta$ for $0 < x < \theta$, 0 elsewhere. Because θ is in the support, differentiation is not helpful here. The likelihood function can be written as

$$L(\theta) = \theta^{-n} I(\max\{x_i\}, \theta), \quad \text{for all } \theta > 0,$$

where $I(a, b)$ is 1 or 0 if $a \leq b$ or $a > b$, respectively. The function $L(\theta)$ is a decreasing function of θ for all $\theta \geq \max\{x_i\}$ and is 0 otherwise [sketch the graph of $L(\theta)$]. So the maximum occurs at the smallest value that θ can assume; i.e., the mle is $\widehat{\theta} = \max\{X_i\}$. ∎

4.1.1   Histogram Estimates of pmfs and pdfs

Let $X_1, \ldots, X_n$ be a random sample on a random variable X with cdf $F(x)$. In this section, we briefly discuss a histogram of the sample, which is an estimate of the pmf, $p(x)$, or the pdf, $f(x)$, of X depending on whether X is discrete or continuous. Other than X being a discrete or continuous random variable, we make no assumptions on the form of the distribution of X. In particular, we do not assume a parametric form of the distribution as we did for the above discussion on maximum likelihood estimates; hence, the histogram that we present is often called a **nonparametric** estimator. See Chapter 10 for a general discussion of nonparametric inference. We discuss the discrete situation first.

The Distribution of X Is Discrete

Assume that X is a discrete random variable with pmf $p(x)$. Suppose first that the space of X is finite, say, $\mathcal{D} = \{a_1, \ldots, a_m\}$. An intuitive estimator of $p(a_j)$ is the relative frequency of sample observations, which are equal to a_j. For $j = 1, 2, \ldots, m$, define the statistics

$$I_j(X_i) = \begin{cases} 1 & X_i = a_j \\ 0 & X_i \neq a_j. \end{cases}$$

Then the intuitive estimate of $p(a_j)$ can be expressed by the average

$$\widehat{p}(a_j) = \frac{1}{n} \sum_{i=1}^{n} I_j(X_i). \tag{4.1.9}$$

Thus the estimates $\{\widehat{p}(a_1), \ldots, \widehat{p}(a_m)\}$ constitute the nonparametric estimate of the pmf $p(x)$. Note that $I_j(X_i)$ has a Bernoulli distribution with probability of success $p(a_j)$. As Exercise 4.1.6 shows, our estimator of the pmf is unbiased.

Suppose next that the space of X is infinite, say, $\mathcal{D} = \{a_1, a_2, \ldots\}$. In practice, we select a value, say, a_m, and make the groupings

$$\{a_1\}, \{a_2\}, \ldots, \{a_m\}, \tilde{a}_{m+1} = \{a_{m+1}, a_{m+2}, \ldots\}. \tag{4.1.10}$$

Let $\widehat{p}(\tilde{a}_{m+1})$ be the proportion of sample items that are greater than or equal to a_{m+1}. Then the estimates $\{\widehat{p}(a_1), \ldots, \widehat{p}(a_m), \widehat{p}(\tilde{a}_{m+1})\}$ form our estimate of

$p(x)$. For the merging of groups, a rule of thumb is to select m so that the frequency of the category a_m exceeds twice the combined frequencies of the categories $a_{m+1}, a_{m+2}, \ldots$.

A histogram is a **barplot** of $\widehat{p}(a_j)$ versus a_j. There are two cases to consider. For the first case, suppose the values a_j represent qualitative categories, for example, hair colors of a population. In this case, there is no ordinal information in the a_js. The usual histogram for such data are nonabutting bars with heights $\widehat{p}(a_j)$ that are plotted in decreasing order of the $\widehat{p}(a_1)$s. Such histograms are usually called **bar charts**. An example is helpful here.

Example 4.1.5 (Hair Color of Scottish Schoolchildren). Kendall and Sturat (1979) presented data on the hair color of Scottish schoolchildren in the early 1900s. Five hair colors were recorded for this sample of size $n = 22{,}361$. The frequency distribution of this sample and the estimate of the pmf are

	Fair	Red	Medium	Dark	Black
Count	5789	1319	9418	5678	157
$\widehat{p}(a_j)$	0.259	0.059	0.421	0.254	0.007

The bar chart of this sample is shown in Figure 4.1.1. ∎

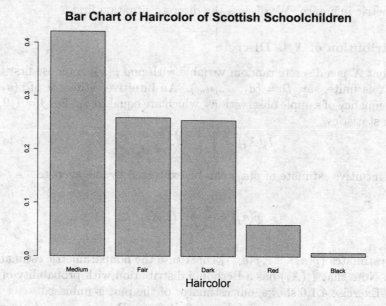

Bar Chart of Haircolor of Scottish Schoolchildren

Figure 4.1.1: Bar chart of the Scottish hair color data discussed in Example 4.1.5.

For the second case, assume that the values in the space $\mathcal{D}$ are **ordinal** in nature; i.e., the natural ordering of the a_js is numerically meaningful. In this case, the usual histogram is an abutting bar chart with heights $\widehat{p}(a_j)$ that are plotted in the natural order of the a_js, as in the following example.

Example 4.1.6 (Simulated Poisson Variates). The following 30 data points are simulated values drawn from a Poisson distribution with mean $\lambda = 2$; see Example 4.8.2 for the generation of Poisson variates.

$$2 \quad 1 \quad 1 \quad 1 \quad 1 \quad 5 \quad 1 \quad 1 \quad 3 \quad 0 \quad 2 \quad 1 \quad 1 \quad 3 \quad 4$$
$$2 \quad 1 \quad 2 \quad 2 \quad 6 \quad 5 \quad 2 \quad 3 \quad 2 \quad 4 \quad 1 \quad 3 \quad 1 \quad 3 \quad 0$$

The nonparametric estimate of the pmf is

j	0	1	2	3	4	5	≥ 6
$\widehat{p}(j)$	0.067	0.367	0.233	0.167	0.067	0.067	0.033

The histogram for this data set is given in Figure 4.1.2. Note that counts are used for the vertical axis. ∎

Figure 4.1.2: Histogram of the Poisson variates of Example 4.1.6.

The Distribution of X Is Continuous

For this section, assume that the random sample $X_1, \ldots, X_n$ is from a continuous random variable X with continuous pdf $f(t)$. We first sketch an estimate for this pdf at a specified value of x. Then we use this estimate to develop a histogram estimate of the pdf. For an arbitrary but fixed point x and a given $h > 0$, consider the interval $(x - h, x + h)$. By the mean value theorem for integrals, we have for some ξ, $|x - \xi| < h$, that

$$P(x - h < X < x + h) = \int_{x-h}^{x+h} f(t)\, dt = f(\xi)2h \approx f(x)2h.$$

The nonparametric estimate of the leftside is the proportion of the sample items that fall in the interval $(x - h, x + h)$. This suggests the following nonparametric estimate of $f(x)$ at a given x:

$$\widehat{f}(x) = \frac{\#\{x - h < X_i < x + h\}}{2hn}. \qquad (4.1.11)$$

To write this more formally, consider the indicator statistic

$$I_i(x) = \begin{cases} 1 & x - h < X_i < x + h \\ 0 & \text{otherwise}, \end{cases} \qquad i = 1, \dots, n.$$

Then a nonparametric estimator of $f(x)$ is

$$\widehat{f}(x) = \frac{1}{2hn} \sum_{i=1}^{n} I_h(X_i). \qquad (4.1.12)$$

Since the sample items are identically distributed,

$$E[\widehat{f}(x)] = \frac{1}{2hn} n f(\xi) 2h = f(\xi) \to f(x),$$

as $h \to 0$. Hence $\widehat{f}(x)$ is approximately an unbiased estimator of the density $f(x)$. In density estimation terminology, the indicator function I_i is called a **rectangular kernel** with **bandwidth** $2h$. See Chapter 6 of Lehmann (1999) for a discussion of density estimation.

Let $x_1, \dots, x_n$ be the realized values of the random sample. Our histogram estimate of $f(x)$ is obtained as follows. For the discrete case, there are natural classes for the histogram, namely, the domain values. For the continuous case, though, classes must be selected. One way of doing this is to select a positive integer m, an $h > 0$, and a value a such that $a < \min x_i$, so that the m intervals

$$(a - h, a + h], (a + h, a + 3h], (a + 3h, a + 5h], \dots, (a + (2m - 3)h, a + (2m - 1)h] \quad (4.1.13)$$

cover the range of the sample $[\min x_i, \max x_i]$. These intervals form our classes. For the histogram, over the interval $(a + (2i - 3)h, a + (2i - 1)h]$, $i = 1, \dots, m$, let the height of the bar be the density estimate given in expression (4.1.12) at the midpoint of the interval, i.e., $\widehat{f}[a + 2(i - 1)h]$. The height of the bar is thus proportional to the number of x_is that fall in the interval $(a + (2i - 3)h, a + (2i - 1)h]$. Over the interval $(a + (2i - 3)h, a + (2i - 1)h]$, our histigram estimate of the density is $\widehat{f}[a + 2(i - 1)h]$. To complete the histogram estimate of $f(x)$, take it to be 0 for $x \leq a$ and for $x > a + (2m - 1)h$. Denote the intervals of the partition by $I_i = (a + (2i - 3)h, a + (2i - 1)h]$, $i = 1, \dots, m$. Then we can summarize our histogram estimate of the pdf by

$$\widehat{f}(x) = \begin{cases} \#\{a + (2i - 3)h < X_i \leq a + (2i - 1)h\}/(2hn) & x \in I_i, \ i = 1, \dots, m \\ 0 & \text{elsewehere}. \end{cases}$$
$$(4.1.14)$$

Hence the estimator is nonnegative and, as Exercise 4.1.9 shows, it integrates to 1 over $(-\infty, \infty)$. So it satisfies the properties of a pdf.

Example 4.1.7 (Histogram for Normally Generated Data). The following data are the rounded values of a generated set of data from a $N(50, 100)$ distribution.

$$\begin{array}{cccccccccc} 63 & 58 & 60 & 60 & 39 & 41 & 57 & 49 & 44 & 36 \\ 52 & 48 & 44 & 19 & 42 & 67 & 44 & 64 & 34 & 46 \end{array}$$

See Example 4.8.5 for details on generating a sample from a normal distribution. To construct a histogram for this data, we selected six intervals of length 10, by setting $a = 15$ and $h = 5$. The resulting histogram is displayed in Figure 4.1.3. Counts, not relative frequency, are used for the vertical axis. Note that the two values of 60 are included in the interval $(50, 60]$. The sample size is too small to guess the probability model which generated the data. ∎

Figure 4.1.3: Histogram of the normal variates discussed in Example 4.1.7.

For the discrete case, except when classes are merged, the histogram is unique. For the continuous case, though, the histogram depends on the classes chosen. The resulting picture can be quite different if the classes are changed. If the histogram is not appealing, then a different set of classes may be used. This would seem to mean obtaining a new frequency distribution. There is a simple way, however. First choose classes so that the numbers in each class begin with the same digits. These digits are the **stems** and should be thought of as the classes. The trailing digits are called the **leaves**. A histogram can be constructed by writing the stems in a single column and then attaching the leaves. This is called a **stem-leaf plot**; see Tukey (1977). Consider, for instance, the data of Example 4.1.7. As stems we take 1, 2, ..., 6. Then the stem-leaf plot is

```
1 | 9
2 |
3 | 469
4 | 12444689
5 | 278
6 | 00347
```

The leaf 9 in the first row represents the data point 19. The leaves are in order because this stem-leaf plot was computed by the R command hist. If the stem-leaf plot is done by hand, then the leaves should be attached in the order that the data are read, and, hence, they may not necessarily be in order. Notice that if we rotate it 90°, it is similar to the histogram given in Figure 4.1.3, except that three values of 60 were placed in the interval with midpoint 55 in the histogram. For our histogram, although there appear to be enough stems (classes), suppose we think that there are too few. Then we can easily split each stem to obtain a new histogram. For example, the stem 4 splits into low-4 (leaves: 0–4) and high-4 (leaves: 5–9). Thus we need not obtain a new frequency distribution.

EXERCISES

4.1.1. Twenty motors were put on test under a high-temperature setting. The lifetimes in hours of the motors under these conditions are given below. Suppose we assume that the lifetime of a motor under these conditions, X, has a $\Gamma(1, \theta)$ distribution.

1	4	5	21	22	28	40	42	51	53
58	67	95	124	124	160	202	260	303	363

(a) Obtain a frequency distribution and a histogram or a stem-leaf plot of the data. Use the intervals $[0, 50), [50, 100), \ldots$. Based on this plot, do you think that the $\Gamma(1, \theta)$ model is credible?

(b) Obtain the maximum likelihood estimate of θ and locate it on your plot.

(c) Obtain the sample median of the data, which is an estimate of the median lifetime of a motor. What parameter is it estimating (i.e., determine the median of X)?

(d) Based on the mle, what is another estimate of the median of X?

4.1.2. The weights of 26 professional baseball pitchers are given below; [see page 76 of Hettmansperger and McKean (2011) for the complete data set]. Suppose we assume that the weight of a professional baseball pitcher is normally distributed with mean μ and variance σ^2.

160	175	180	185	185	185	190	190	195	195	195	200	200
200	200	205	205	210	210	218	219	220	222	225	225	232

(a) Obtain a frequency distribution and a histogram or a stem-leaf plot of the data. Use 5-pound intervals. Based on this plot, is a normal probability model credible?

(b) Obtain the maximum likelihood estimates of μ, σ^2, σ, and μ/σ. Locate your estimate of μ on your plot in part (a).

(c) Using the binomial model, obtain the maximum likelihood estimate of the proportion p of professional baseball pitchers who weigh over 215 pounds.

(d) Determine the mle of p assuming that the weight of a professional baseball player follows the normal probability model $N(\mu, \sigma^2)$ with μ and σ unknown.

4.1.3. Suppose the number of customers X that enter a store between the hours 9:00 a.m. and 10:00 a.m. follows a Poisson distribution with parameter θ. Suppose a random sample of the number of customers that enter the store between 9:00 a.m. and 10:00 a.m. for 10 days results in the values

$$9 \quad 7 \quad 9 \quad 15 \quad 10 \quad 13 \quad 11 \quad 7 \quad 2 \quad 12$$

(a) Determine the maximum likelihood estimate of θ. Show that it is an unbiased estimator.

(b) Based on these data, obtain the realization of your estimator in part (a). Explain the meaning of this estimate in terms of the number of customers.

4.1.4. For Example 4.1.3, verify equations (4.1.4)-(4.1.8).

4.1.5. Let $X_1, X_2, \ldots, X_n$ be a random sample from a continuous-type distribution.

(a) Find $P(X_1 \leq X_2), P(X_1 \leq X_2, X_1 \leq X_3), \ldots, P(X_1 \leq X_i, i = 2, 3, \ldots, n)$.

(b) Suppose the sampling continues until X_1 is no longer the smallest observation (i.e., $X_j < X_1 \leq X_i, i = 2, 3, \ldots, j-1$). Let Y equal the number of trials, not including X_1, until X_1 is no longer the smallest observation (i.e., $Y = j - 1$). Show that the distribution of Y is

$$P(Y = y) = \frac{1}{y(y+1)}, \quad y = 1, 2, 3, \ldots.$$

(c) Compute the mean and variance of Y if they exist.

4.1.6. Show that the estimate of the pmf in expression (4.1.9) is an unbiased estimate. Find the variance of the estimator also.

4.1.7. The data set on Scottish schoolchildren discussed in Example 4.1.5 included the eye colors of the children also. The frequencies of their eye colors are

Blue	Light	Medium	Dark
2978	6697	7511	5175

Use these frequencies to obtain a bar chart and an estimate of the associated pmf.

4.1.8. Recall that for the parameter $\eta = g(\theta)$, the mle of η is $g(\widehat{\theta})$, where $\widehat{\theta}$ is the mle of θ. Assuming that the data in Example 4.1.6 were drawn from a Poisson distribution with mean λ, obtain the mle of λ and then use it to obtain the mle of the pmf. Compare the mle of the pmf to the nonparametric estimate. Note: For the domain value 6, obtain the mle of $P(X \geq 6)$.

4.1.9. Show that the nonparametric estimate of a pdf $f(x)$ given in expression (4.1.14) integrates to 1 over $(-\infty, \infty)$.

4.1.10. Consider the histogram for the sample of size 20 in Example 4.1.7.

 (a) Compute the nonparametric estimator (4.1.12) of the density at the point $x = 45$.

 (b) Assuming a normal, $N(\mu, \sigma^2)$, distribution, compute the mles of μ and σ.

 (c) Compute the mle of the density at the point $x = 45$ and compare it with your answer in part (b).

 (d) Compute $f(45)$, where f is the density from a $N(50, 100)$ distribution and compare the nonparametric and mle estimates with it.

4.1.11. For the nonparametric estimator (4.1.12) of a pdf,

 (a) Obtain its mean and determine the bias of the estimator.

 (b) Obtain its variance.

4.2 Confidence Intervals

Let us continue with the statistical problem that we were discussing in Section 4.1. Recall that the random variable of interest X has density $f(x; \theta), \theta \in \Omega$, where θ is unknown. In that section, we discussed estimating θ by a statistic $\widehat{\theta} = \widehat{\theta}(X_1, \ldots, X_n)$, where $X_1, \ldots, X_n$ is a sample from the distribution of X. When the sample is drawn, it is unlikely that the value of $\widehat{\theta}$ is the true value of the parameter. In fact, if $\widehat{\theta}$ has a continuous distribution, then $P_\theta(\widehat{\theta} = \theta) = 0$. What is needed is an estimate of the error of the estimation i.e., by how much did $\widehat{\theta}$ miss θ? In this section, we embody this estimate of error in terms of a confidence interval, which we now formally define:

Definition 4.2.1 (Confidence Interval). *Let $X_1, X_2, \ldots, X_n$ be a sample on a random variable X, where X has pdf $f(x; \theta)$, $\theta \in \Omega$. Let $0 < \alpha < 1$ be specified. Let $L = L(X_1, X_2, \ldots, X_n)$ and $U = U(X_1, X_2, \ldots, X_n)$ be two statistics. We say that the interval (L, U) is a $(1 - \alpha)100\%$ **confidence interval** for θ if*

$$1 - \alpha = P_\theta[\theta \in (L, U)]. \tag{4.2.1}$$

That is, the probability that the interval includes θ is $1 - \alpha$, which is called the **confidence coefficient** *of the interval.*

Once the sample is drawn, the realized value of the confidence interval is (l, u), an interval of real numbers. Either the interval (l, u) traps θ or it does not. One way of thinking of a confidence interval is in terms of Bernoulli trials with probability of success $1 - \alpha$. If one makes, say, M independent confidence intervals over a period of time, then one would expect to have $(1 - \alpha)M$ successful confidence intervals (those that trap θ) over this period of time. Hence one feels $(1 - \alpha)100\%$ confident that the true value of θ lies in the interval (l, u).

A measure of efficiency based on confidence intervals is their expected length. Suppose (L_1, U_1) and (L_2, U_2) are two confidence intervals for θ that have the same confidence coefficient. Then we say that (L_1, U_1) is more efficient than (L_2, U_2) if $E_\theta(U_1 - L_1) \leq E_\theta(U_2 - L_2)$ for all $\theta \in \Omega$.

There are several procedures for obtaining confidence intervals. We explore one of them in this section. It is based on a pivot random variable. The pivot is usually a function of an estimator of θ and the parameter and, further, the distribution of the pivot is known. Using this information, an algebraic derivation can often be used to obtain a confidence interval. The next several examples illustrate the pivot method. A second way to obtain a confidence interval involves distribution free techniques, as used in Section 4.4.2 to determine confidence intervals for quantiles.

Example 4.2.1 (Confidence Interval for μ Under Normality). Suppose the random variables $X_1, \ldots, X_n$ are a random sample from a $N(\mu, \sigma^2)$ distribution. Let $\overline{X}$ and S^2 denote the sample mean and sample variance, respectively. Recall from the last section that $\overline{X}$ is the mle of μ and $[(n - 1)/n]S^2$ is the mle of σ^2. By part (d) of Theorem 3.6.1, the random variable $T = (\overline{X} - \mu)/(S/\sqrt{n})$ has a t-distribution with $n - 1$ degrees of freedom. The random variable T is our pivot variable.

For $0 < \alpha < 1$, define $t_{\alpha/2, n-1}$ to be the upper $\alpha/2$ critical point of a t-distribution with $n - 1$ degrees of freedom; i.e., $\alpha/2 = P(T > t_{\alpha/2, n-1})$. Using a simple algebraic derivation, we obtain

$$1 - \alpha = P(-t_{\alpha/2, n-1} < T < t_{\alpha/2, n-1})$$

$$= P\left(-t_{\alpha/2, n-1} < \frac{\overline{X} - \mu}{S/\sqrt{n}} < t_{\alpha/2, n-1}\right)$$

$$= P\left(-t_{\alpha/2, n-1}\frac{S}{\sqrt{n}} < \overline{X} - \mu < t_{\alpha/2, n-1}\frac{S}{\sqrt{n}}\right)$$

$$= P\left(\overline{X} - t_{\alpha/2, n-1}\frac{S}{\sqrt{n}} < \mu < \overline{X} + t_{\alpha/2, n-1}\frac{S}{\sqrt{n}}\right). \quad (4.2.2)$$

Once the sample is drawn, let $\overline{x}$ and s denote the realized values of the statistics $\overline{X}$ and S, respectively. Then a $(1 - \alpha)100\%$ confidence interval for μ is given by

$$(\overline{x} - t_{\alpha/2, n-1}s/\sqrt{n}, \overline{x} + t_{\alpha/2, n-1}s/\sqrt{n}). \quad (4.2.3)$$

This interval is often referred to as the $(1 - \alpha)100\%$ **t-interval** for μ. The estimate of the standard deviation of $\overline{X}$, $s/\sqrt{n}$, is referred to as the **standard error** of $\overline{X}$.

∎

The distribution of the pivot random variable $T = (\overline{X} - \mu)/(s/\sqrt{n})$ of the last example depends on the normality of the sampled items; however, this is approximately true even if the sampled items are not drawn from a normal distribution. The **Central Limit Theorem** (CLT) shows that the distribution of T is approximately $N(0,1)$. In order to use this result now, we state the CLT now and leave its proof to Chapter 5; see Theorem 5.3.1.

Theorem 4.2.1 (Central Limit Theorem). *Let* $X_1, X_2, \ldots, X_n$ *denote the observations of a random sample from a distribution that has mean* μ *and finite variance* σ^2. *Then the distribution function of the random variable* $W_n = (\overline{X} - \mu)/(\sigma/\sqrt{n})$ *converges to* Φ, *the distribution function of the* $N(0,1)$ *distribution, as* $n \to \infty$.

即若 $X_1, \cdots X_n$ 是
以同一分布 (μ, σ^2)
中取出的一个 random
sample, 不管是什
什么样的分布,
则当 $W = \frac{\overline{X} - \mu}{\sigma/\sqrt{n}}$
都服从 $W \sim N(0,1)$,
当 $n \to \infty$ 时!

As we further show in Chapter 5, the result stays the same if we replace σ by the sample standard deviation S; that is, under the assumptions of Theorem 4.2.1, the distribution of

$$Z_n = \frac{\overline{X} - \mu}{S/\sqrt{n}} = \frac{\overline{x} - E(\overline{x})}{\sqrt{var(\overline{x})}} \quad (4.2.4)$$

$\begin{cases} E(\overline{x}) = E(\frac{\sum X_i}{n}) = \mu \\ var(\overline{x}) = var(\frac{\sum X_i}{n}) \\ = \frac{\sigma^2}{n} \approx \frac{s^2}{n} \end{cases}$

is approximately $N(0,1)$. For the nonnormal case, as the next example shows, with this result we can obtain an approximate confidence interval for μ.

Example 4.2.2 (Large Sample Confidence Interval for the Mean μ). Suppose $X_1, X_2, \ldots, X_n$ is a random sample on a random variable X with mean μ and variance σ^2, but, unlike the last example, the distribution of X is not normal. However, from the above discussion we know that the distribution of Z_n, (4.2.4), is approximately $N(0,1)$. Hence

$$1 - \alpha \approx P\left(-z_{\alpha/2} < \frac{\overline{X} - \mu}{S/\sqrt{n}} < z_{\alpha/2}\right).$$

Using the same algebraic derivation as in the last example, we obtain

$$1 - \alpha \approx P\left(\overline{X} - z_{\alpha/2}\frac{S}{\sqrt{n}} < \mu < \overline{X} + z_{\alpha/2}\frac{S}{\sqrt{n}}\right). \quad (4.2.5)$$

Again, letting $\overline{x}$ and s denote the realized values of the statistics $\overline{X}$ and S, respectively, after the sample is drawn, an approximate $(1 - \alpha)100\%$ confidence interval for μ is given by

$$(\overline{x} - z_{\alpha/2}s/\sqrt{n}, \overline{x} + z_{\alpha/2}s/\sqrt{n}). \quad (4.2.6)$$

This is called a **large sample** confidence interval for μ. ∎

In practice, we often do not know if the population is normal. Which confidence interval should we use? Generally, for the same α, the intervals based on $t_{\alpha/2,n-1}$ are larger than those based on $z_{\alpha/2}$. Hence the interval (4.2.3) is generally more conservative than the interval (4.2.6). So in practice, statisticians generally prefer the interval (4.2.3).

Occasionally in practice, the standard deviation σ is assumed known. In this case, the confidence interval generally used for μ is (4.2.6) with s replaced by σ.

小结: · 通常, (4.2.3)式比(4.2.6)更保守, 因此, 首选采用t分布的(4.2.3)式作为 CI 的计算公式.
· 若 σ 已知, 则能选利用正态分布的(4.2.6)式计算 CI.

(handwritten annotations at top): $X_1, \cdots, X_n$ 是从同一'分布 (Bernoulli 分布 with 参数 p) 中产生出来一个 random sample, 记分布为 $B(P, P段)$, 即其 $u=P$, $\sigma^2 = P段 = P(1-P)$.

设 $W = \dfrac{\bar{X}-\mu}{\sigma/\sqrt{n}} = \dfrac{\bar{X}-P}{\sqrt{P段}/\sqrt{n}}$ 渐近为 $N(0,1)$ 分布. $\therefore W = \dfrac{\bar{X}-P}{\sqrt{P段/n}} = \dfrac{\hat{P}-P}{\sqrt{P段/n}}$

其中 $\bar{X} = \frac{1}{n}\Sigma X_i = (X_1+X_2+\cdots+X_n)\times\frac{1}{n}$ = the sample portion of success

($\because X_i$ 只能取值 1 或 0, success时取 1, fail 取 0) $= \hat{P}$

Example 4.2.3 (Large Sample Confidence Interval for p). Let X be a Bernoulli random variable with probability of success p, where X is 1 or 0 if the outcome is success or failure, respectively. Suppose $X_1, \ldots, X_n$ is a random sample from the distribution of X. Let $\hat{p} = \overline{X}$ be the sample proportion of successes. Note that $\hat{p} = n^{-1}\sum_{i=1}^{n} X_i$ is a sample average and that $\text{Var}(\hat{p}) = p(1-p)/n$. It follows immediately from the CLT that the distribution of $Z = (\hat{p} - p)/\sqrt{p(1-p)/n}$ is approximately $N(0,1)$. Referring to Example 5.1.1 of Chapter 5, we replace $p(1-p)$ with its estimate $\hat{p}(1-\hat{p})$. Then proceeding as in the last example, an approximate $(1-\alpha)100\%$ confidence interval for p is given by

$$(\hat{p} - z_{\alpha/2}\sqrt{\hat{p}(1-\hat{p})/n}, \hat{p} + z_{\alpha/2}\sqrt{\hat{p}(1-\hat{p})/n}), \qquad (4.2.7)$$

where $\sqrt{\hat{p}(1-\hat{p})/n}$ is called the standard error of $\hat{p}$. ∎

4.2.1 Confidence Intervals for Difference in Means

A practical problem of interest is the comparison of two distributions, that is, comparing the distributions of two random variables, say X and Y. In this section, we compare the means of X and Y. Denote the means of X and Y by μ_1 and μ_2, respectively. In particular, we obtain confidence intervals for the difference $\Delta = \mu_1 - \mu_2$. Assume that the variances of X and Y are finite and denote them as $\sigma_1^2 = \text{Var}(X)$ and $\sigma_2^2 = \text{Var}(Y)$. Let $X_1, \ldots, X_{n_1}$ be a random sample from the distribution of X and let $Y_1, \ldots, Y_{n_2}$ be a random sample from the distribution of Y. Assume that the samples were gathered independently of one another. Let $\overline{X} = n_1^{-1}\sum_{i=1}^{n_1} X_i$ and $\overline{Y} = n_2^{-1}\sum_{i=1}^{n_2} Y_i$ be the sample means. Let $\widehat{\Delta} = \overline{X} - \overline{Y}$. The statistic $\widehat{\Delta}$ is an unbiased estimator of Δ. This difference, $\widehat{\Delta} - \Delta$, is the numerator of the pivot random variable. By independence of the samples,

(handwritten left): $\text{Var}(\hat{\Delta}) = \text{Var}(\bar{X}-\bar{Y})$
$= \text{Var}(\bar{X}) + \text{Var}(\bar{Y})$
$= \dfrac{\sigma_1^2}{n_1} + \dfrac{\sigma_2^2}{n_2}$ ($\because \text{Var}(\bar{X}) = \text{Var}(\frac{1}{n}\Sigma X_i) = \frac{1}{n^2}\text{Var}(X_1+\cdots+X_n) = \frac{1}{n^2}\cdot n\cdot\text{Var}(X_1) = \frac{1}{n}\text{Var}(X_1) = \frac{\sigma_1^2}{n_1}$ 同样 $\text{Var}(\bar{Y}) = \frac{\sigma_2^2}{n_2}$)

$$\text{Var}(\widehat{\Delta}) = \frac{\sigma_1^2}{n_1} + \frac{\sigma_2^2}{n_2}.$$

Let $S_1^2 = (n_1 - 1)^{-1}\sum_{i=1}^{n_1}(X_i - \overline{X})^2$ and $S_2^2 = (n_2 - 1)^{-1}\sum_{i=1}^{n_2}(Y_i - \overline{Y})^2$ be the sample variances. Then estimating the variances by the sample variances, consider the random variable

(handwritten right): $\begin{cases} E(\hat{\Delta}) = E(\bar{X}-\bar{Y}) = E(\bar{X}) - E(\bar{Y}) = \mu_1 - \mu_2 \\ \text{Var}(\hat{\Delta}) = \dfrac{\sigma_1^2}{n_1} + \dfrac{\sigma_2^2}{n_2} \end{cases}$

$$Z = \frac{\widehat{\Delta} - \Delta}{\sqrt{\dfrac{S_1^2}{n_1} + \dfrac{S_2^2}{n_2}}}. \qquad (4.2.8)$$

By the independence of the samples and Theorem 4.2.1, this pivot variable has an approximate $N(0,1)$ distribution. This leads to the approximate $(1-\alpha)100\%$ confidence interval for $\Delta = \mu_1 - \mu_2$ given by

$$\left((\overline{x} - \overline{y}) - z_{\alpha/2}\sqrt{\frac{s_1^2}{n_1} + \frac{s_2^2}{n_2}}, (\overline{x} - \overline{y}) + z_{\alpha/2}\sqrt{\frac{s_1^2}{n_1} + \frac{s_2^2}{n_2}}\right), \qquad (4.2.9)$$

where $\sqrt{(s_1^2/n_1) + (s_2^2/n_2)}$ is the standard error of $\overline{X} - \overline{Y}$. This is a large sample $(1-\alpha)100\%$ confidence interval for $\mu_1 - \mu_2$.

The above confidence interval is approximate. In this situation we can obtain exact confidence intervals if we assume that the distributions of X and Y are normal with the same variance; i.e., $\sigma_1^2 = \sigma_2^2$. Thus the distributions can differ only in location, i.e., a **location model**. Assume then that X is distributed $N(\mu_1, \sigma^2)$ and Y is distributed $N(\mu_2, \sigma^2)$, where σ^2 is the common variance of X and Y. As above, let $X_1, \ldots, X_{n_1}$ be a random sample from the distribution of X, let $Y_1, \ldots, Y_{n_2}$ be a random sample from the distribution of Y, and assume that the samples are independent of one another. Let $n = n_1 + n_2$ be the total sample size. Our estimator of Δ is $\overline{X} - \overline{Y}$. Our goal is to show that a pivot random variable, defined below, has a t-distribution, which is defined in Section 3.6.

Because $\overline{X}$ is distributed $N(\mu_1, \sigma^2/n_1)$, $\overline{Y}$ is distributed $N(\mu_2, \sigma^2/n_2)$, and $\overline{X}$ and $\overline{Y}$ are independent, we have the result

$$\frac{(\overline{X} - \overline{Y}) - (\mu_1 - \mu_2)}{\sigma\sqrt{\frac{1}{n_1} + \frac{1}{n_2}}} \text{ has a } N(0,1) \text{ distribution.} \tag{4.2.10}$$

This serves as the numerator of our T-statistic.

Let

$$S_p^2 = \frac{(n_1 - 1)S_1^2 + (n_2 - 1)S_2^2}{n_1 + n_2 - 2}. \tag{4.2.11}$$

Note that S_p^2 is a weighted average of S_1^2 and S_2^2. It is easy to see that S_p^2 is an unbiased estimator of σ^2. It is called the **pooled estimator** of σ^2. Also, because $(n_1 - 1)S_1^2/\sigma^2$ has a $\chi^2(n_1 - 1)$ distribution, $(n_2 - 1)S_2^2/\sigma^2$ has a $\chi^2(n_2 - 1)$ distribution, and S_1^2 and S_2^2 are independent, we have that $(n - 2)S_p^2/\sigma^2$ has a $\chi^2(n - 2)$ distribution; see Corollary 3.3.1. Finally, because S_1^2 is independent of $\overline{X}$ and S_2^2 is independent of $\overline{Y}$, and the random samples are independent of each other, it follows that S_p^2 is independent of expression (4.2.10). Therefore, from the result of Section 3.6.1 concerning Student's t-distribution, we have that

$$T = \frac{[(\overline{X} - \overline{Y}) - (\mu_1 - \mu_2)]/\sigma\sqrt{n_1^{-1} + n_2^{-1}}}{\sqrt{(n - 2)S_p^2/(n - 2)\sigma^2}}$$

$$= \frac{(\overline{X} - \overline{Y}) - (\mu_1 - \mu_2)}{S_p\sqrt{\frac{1}{n_1} + \frac{1}{n_2}}} \tag{4.2.12}$$

has a t-distribution with $n - 2$ degrees of freedom. From this last result, it is easy to see that the following interval is an exact $(1 - \alpha)100\%$ confidence interval for $\Delta = \mu_1 - \mu_2$:

$$\left((\overline{x} - \overline{y}) - t_{(\alpha/2, n-2)} s_p \sqrt{\frac{1}{n_1} + \frac{1}{n_2}}, (\overline{x} - \overline{y}) + t_{(\alpha/2, n-2)} s_p \sqrt{\frac{1}{n_1} + \frac{1}{n_2}} \right). \tag{4.2.13}$$

A consideration of the difficulty encountered when the unknown variances of the two normal distributions are not equal is assigned to one of the exercises.

Example 4.2.4. Suppose $X_1, \ldots, X_{10}$ is a random sample from a $N(\mu_1, \sigma^2)$ distribution, $Y_1, \ldots, Y_7$ is a random sample from a $N(\mu_2, \sigma^2)$ distribution, and the samples are independent. Suppose the realizations of the samples result in the sample means $\overline{x} = 4.2$ and $\overline{y} = 3.4$ and the sample standard deviations $s_1^2 = 49$ and $s_2^2 = 32$. Then, using (4.2.13), a 90% confidence interval for $\mu_1 - \mu_2$ is $(-4.81, 6.41)$. ∎

Remark 4.2.1. Suppose X and Y are not normally distributed but that their distributions differ only in location. As we show in Chapter 5, the above interval, (4.2.13), is then approximate and not exact. ∎

4.2.2 Confidence Interval for Difference in Proportions

Let X and Y be two independent random variables with Bernoulli distributions $b(1, p_1)$ and $b(1, p_2)$, respectively. Let us now turn to the problem of finding a confidence interval for the difference $p_1 - p_2$. Let $X_1, \ldots, X_{n_1}$ be a random sample from the distribution of X and let $Y_1, \ldots, Y_{n_2}$ be a random sample from the distribution of Y. As above, assume that the samples are independent of one another and let $n = n_1 + n_2$ be the total sample size. Our estimator of $p_1 - p_2$ is the difference in sample proportions, which, of course, is given by $\overline{X} - \overline{Y}$. We use the traditional notation and write $\hat{p}_1$ and $\hat{p}_2$ instead of $\overline{X}$ and $\overline{Y}$, respectively. Hence, from the above discussion, an interval such as (4.2.9) serves as an approximate confidence interval for $p_1 - p_2$. Here, $\sigma_1^2 = p_1(1 - p_1)$ and $\sigma_2^2 = p_2(1 - p_2)$. In the interval, we estimate these by $\hat{p}_1(1 - \hat{p}_1)$ and $\hat{p}_2(1 - \hat{p}_2)$, respectively. Thus our approximate $(1 - \alpha)100\%$ confidence interval for $p_1 - p_2$ is

$$\hat{p}_1 - \hat{p}_2 \pm z_{\alpha/2} \sqrt{\frac{\hat{p}_1(1 - \hat{p}_1)}{n_1} + \frac{\hat{p}_2(1 - \hat{p}_2)}{n_2}}. \tag{4.2.14}$$

Example 4.2.5. If, in the preceding discussion, we take $n_1 = 100$, $n_2 = 400$, $y_1 = 30$, and $y_2 = 80$, then the observed values of $Y_1/n_1 - Y_2/n_2$ and its standard error are 0.1 and $\sqrt{(0.3)(0.7)/100 + (0.2)(0.8)/400} = 0.05$, respectively. Thus the interval $(0, 0.2)$ is an approximate 95.4% confidence interval for $p_1 - p_2$. ∎

EXERCISES

4.2.1. Let the observed value of the mean $\overline{X}$ and of the sample variance of a random sample of size 20 from a distribution that is $N(\mu, \sigma^2)$ be 81.2 and 26.5, respectively. Find respectively 90%, 95% and 99% confidence intervals for μ. Note how the lengths of the confidence intervals increase as the confidence increases.

4.2.2. Consider the data on the lifetimes of motors given in Exercise 4.1.1. Obtain a large sample confidence interval for the mean lifetime of a motor.

4.2.3. As in the last exercise, refer to Exercise 4.1.1. Using expression (4.4.8), obtain a confidence interval (with confidence close to 90%) for the median lifetime of a motor.

4.2.4. Suppose we assume that $X_1, X_2, \ldots, X_n$ is a random sample from a $\Gamma(1, \theta)$ distribution.

(a) Show that the random variable $(2/\theta) \sum_{i=1}^{n} X_i$ has a χ^2-distribution with $2n$ degrees of freedom.

(b) Using the random variable in part (a) as a pivot random variable, find a $(1 - \alpha)100\%$ confidence interval for θ.

(c) Obtain the confidence interval in part (b) for the data of Exercise 4.1.1 and compare it with the interval you obtained in Exercise 4.2.2.

4.2.5. In Exercise 4.1.2, the weights of 26 professional baseball pitchers were given. From the same data set, the weights of 33 professional baseball hitters (not pitchers) are given below. Assume that the data sets are independent of one another.

155	155	160	160	160	166	170	175	175	175	180	185	185
185	185	185	185	185	190	190	190	190	190	195	195	195
195	200	205	207	210	211	230						

Use expression (4.2.13) to find a 95% confidence interval for the difference in mean weights between the pitches and the hitters. Which group (on the average) appears to be heavier? Why would this be so?
(The sample means and variances for the weights of the pitchers and hitters are, respectively, Pitchers 201, 305.68 and Hitters 185.4, 298.13.)

4.2.6. In the baseball data set discussed in the last exercise, it was found that out of the 59 baseball players, 15 were left-handed. Is this odd, since the proportion of left-handed males in America is about 11%? Answer by using (4.2.7) to construct a 95% approximate confidence interval for p, the proportion of left-handed baseball players.

4.2.7. Let $\overline{X}$ be the mean of a random sample of size n from a distribution that is $N(\mu, 9)$. Find n such that $P(\overline{X} - 1 < \mu < \overline{X} + 1) = 0.90$, approximately.

4.2.8. Let a random sample of size 17 from the normal distribution $N(\mu, \sigma^2)$ yield $\overline{x} = 4.7$ and $s^2 = 5.76$. Determine a 90% confidence interval for μ.

4.2.9. Let $\overline{X}$ denote the mean of a random sample of size n from a distribution that has mean μ and variance $\sigma^2 = 10$. Find n so that the probability is approximately 0.954 that the random interval $(\overline{X} - \frac{1}{2}, \overline{X} + \frac{1}{2})$ includes μ.

4.2.10. Let $X_1, X_2, \ldots, X_9$ be a random sample of size 9 from a distribution that is $N(\mu, \sigma^2)$.

(a) If σ is known, find the length of a 95% confidence interval for μ if this interval is based on the random variable $\sqrt{9}(\overline{X} - \mu)/\sigma$.

(b) If σ is unknown, find the expected value of the length of a 95% confidence interval for μ if this interval is based on the random variable $\sqrt{9}(\overline{X} - \mu)/S$. *Hint:* Write $E(S) = (\sigma/\sqrt{n-1})E[((n-1)S^2/\sigma^2)^{1/2}]$.

(c) Compare these two answers.

4.2.11. Let $X_1, X_2, \ldots, X_n, X_{n+1}$ be a random sample of size $n+1$, $n > 1$, from a distribution that is $N(\mu, \sigma^2)$. Let $\overline{X} = \sum_1^n X_i/n$ and $S^2 = \sum_1^n (X_i - \overline{X})^2/(n-1)$. Find the constant c so that the statistic $c(\overline{X} - X_{n+1})/S$ has a t-distribution. If $n = 8$, determine k such that $P(\overline{X} - kS < X_9 < \overline{X} + kS) = 0.80$. The observed interval $(\overline{x} - ks, \ \overline{x} + ks)$ is often called an 80% **prediction interval** for X_9.

4.2.12. Let Y be $b(300, p)$. If the observed value of Y is $y = 75$, find an approximate 90% confidence interval for p.

4.2.13. Let $\overline{X}$ be the mean of a random sample of size n from a distribution that is $N(\mu, \sigma^2)$, where the positive variance σ^2 is known. Because $\Phi(2) - \Phi(-2) = 0.954$, find, for each μ, $c_1(\mu)$ and $c_2(\mu)$ such that $P[c_1(\mu) < \overline{X} < c_2(\mu)] = 0.954$. Note that $c_1(\mu)$ and $c_2(\mu)$ are increasing functions of μ. Solve for the respective functions $d_1(\overline{x})$ and $d_2(\overline{x})$; thus, we also have that $P[d_2(\overline{X}) < \mu < d_1(\overline{X})] = 0.954$. Compare this with the answer obtained previously in the text.

4.2.14. Let $\overline{X}$ denote the mean of a random sample of size 25 from a gamma-type distribution with $\alpha = 4$ and $\beta > 0$. Use the Central Limit Theorem to find an approximate 0.954 confidence interval for μ, the mean of the gamma distribution. *Hint:* Use the random variable $(\overline{X} - 4\beta)/(4\beta^2/25)^{1/2} = 5\overline{X}/2\beta - 10$.

4.2.15. Let $\overline{x}$ be the observed mean of a random sample of size n from a distribution having mean μ and known variance σ^2. Find n so that $\overline{x} - \sigma/4$ to $\overline{x} + \sigma/4$ is an approximate 95% confidence interval for μ.

4.2.16. Assume a binomial model for a certain random variable. If we desire a 90% confidence interval for p that is at most 0.02 in length, find n.
Hint: Note that $\sqrt{(y/n)(1 - y/n)} \leq \sqrt{(\frac{1}{2})(1 - \frac{1}{2})}$.

4.2.17. It is known that a random variable X has a Poisson distribution with parameter μ. A sample of 200 observations from this distribution has a mean equal to 3.4. Construct an approximate 90% confidence interval for μ.

4.2.18. Let $X_1, X_2, \ldots, X_n$ be a random sample from $N(\mu, \sigma^2)$, where both parameters μ and σ^2 are unknown. A *confidence interval* for σ^2 can be found as follows. We know that $(n-1)S^2/\sigma^2$ is a random variable with a $\chi^2(n-1)$ distribution. Thus we can find constants a and b so that $P((n-1)S^2/\sigma^2 < b) = 0.975$ and $P(a < (n-1)S^2/\sigma^2 < b) = 0.95$.

(a) Show that this second probability statement can be written as

$$P((n-1)S^2/b < \sigma^2 < (n-1)S^2/a) = 0.95.$$

(b) If $n = 9$ and $s^2 = 7.93$, find a 95% confidence interval for σ^2.

(c) If μ is known, how would you modify the preceding procedure for finding a confidence interval for σ^2?

4.2.19. Let $X_1, X_2, \ldots, X_n$ be a random sample from a gamma distribution with known parameter $\alpha = 3$ and unknown $\beta > 0$. Discuss the construction of a confidence interval for β.
Hint: What is the distribution of $2 \sum_1^n X_i/\beta$? Follow the procedure outlined in Exercise 4.2.18.

4.2.20. When 100 tacks were thrown on a table, 60 of them landed point up. Obtain a 95% confidence interval for the probability that a tack of this type lands point up. Assume independence.

4.2.21. Let two independent random samples, each of size 10, from two normal distributions $N(\mu_1, \sigma^2)$ and $N(\mu_2, \sigma^2)$ yield $\overline{x} = 4.8$, $s_1^2 = 8.64$, $\overline{y} = 5.6$, $s_2^2 = 7.88$. Find a 95% confidence interval for $\mu_1 - \mu_2$.

4.2.22. Let two independent random variables, Y_1 and Y_2, with binomial distributions that have parameters $n_1 = n_2 = 100$, p_1, and p_2, respectively, be observed to be equal to $y_1 = 50$ and $y_2 = 40$. Determine an approximate 90% confidence interval for $p_1 - p_2$.

4.2.23. Discuss the problem of finding a confidence interval for the difference $\mu_1 - \mu_2$ between the two means of two normal distributions if the variances σ_1^2 and σ_2^2 are known but not necessarily equal.

4.2.24. Discuss Exercise 4.2.23 when it is assumed that the variances are unknown and unequal. This is a very difficult problem, and the discussion should point out exactly where the difficulty lies. If, however, the variances are unknown but their ratio σ_1^2/σ_2^2 is a known constant k, then a statistic that is a T random variable can again be used. Why?

4.2.25. To illustrate Exercise 4.2.24, let $X_1, X_2, \ldots, X_9$ and $Y_1, Y_2, \ldots, Y_{12}$ represent two independent random samples from the respective normal distributions $N(\mu_1, \sigma_1^2)$ and $N(\mu_2, \sigma_2^2)$. It is given that $\sigma_1^2 = 3\sigma_2^2$, but σ_2^2 is unknown. Define a random variable that has a t-distribution that can be used to find a 95% confidence interval for $\mu_1 - \mu_2$.

4.2.26. Let $\overline{X}$ and $\overline{Y}$ be the means of two independent random samples, each of size n, from the respective distributions $N(\mu_1, \sigma^2)$ and $N(\mu_2, \sigma^2)$, where the common variance is known. Find n such that

$$P(\overline{X} - \overline{Y} - \sigma/5 < \mu_1 - \mu_2 < \overline{X} - \overline{Y} + \sigma/5) = 0.90.$$

4.2.27. Let $X_1, X_2, \ldots, X_n$ and $Y_1, Y_2, \ldots, Y_m$ be two independent random samples from the respective normal distributions $N(\mu_1, \sigma_1^2)$ and $N(\mu_2, \sigma_2^2)$, where the four parameters are unknown. To construct a *confidence interval for the ratio*, σ_1^2/σ_2^2, of the variances, form the quotient of the two independent χ^2 variables, each divided by its degrees of freedom, namely,

$$F = \frac{\frac{(m-1)S_2^2}{\sigma_2^2}/(m-1)}{\frac{(n-1)S_1^2}{\sigma_1^2}/(n-1)} = \frac{S_2^2/\sigma_2^2}{S_1^2/\sigma_1^2},$$

where S_1^2 and S_2^2 are the respective sample variances.

(a) What kind of distribution does F have?

(b) From the appropriate table, a and b can be found so that $P(F < b) = 0.975$ and $P(a < F < b) = 0.95$.

(c) Rewrite the second probability statement as

$$P\left[a\frac{S_1^2}{S_2^2} < \frac{\sigma_1^2}{\sigma_2^2} < b\frac{S_1^2}{S_2^2}\right] = 0.95.$$

The observed values, s_1^2 and s_2^2, can be inserted in these inequalities to provide a 95% confidence interval for σ_1^2/σ_2^2.

4.3 Confidence Intervals for Parameters of Discrete Distributions

In this section, we outline a procedure that can be used to obtain exact confidence intervals for the parameters of discrete random variables. Let $X_1, X_2, \ldots, X_n$ be a random sample on a discrete random variable X with pmf $p(x;\theta)$, $\theta \in \Omega$, where Ω is an interval of real numbers. Let $T = T(X_1, X_2, \ldots, X_n)$ be an estimator of θ with cdf $F_T(t;\theta)$. Assume that $F_T(t;\theta)$ is a nonincreasing and continuous function of θ for every t in the support of T. Let $\alpha_1 > 0$ and $\alpha_2 > 0$ be given such that $\alpha = \alpha_1 + \alpha_2 < 0.50$. Let $\underline{\theta}$ and $\overline{\theta}$ be the solutions of the equations

$$F_T(T-;\underline{\theta}) = 1 - \alpha_2 \quad \text{and} \quad F_T(T;\overline{\theta}) = \alpha_1, \tag{4.3.1}$$

where $T-$ is the statistic whose support lags by one value of T's support. For instance, if $t_i < t_{i+1}$ are consecutive support values of T, then $T = t_{i+1}$ if and only if $T- = t_i$. Under these conditions, the interval $(\underline{\theta}, \overline{\theta})$ is a confidence interval for θ with confidence coefficient of at least $1 - \alpha$. We sketch a proof of this below, but, for now, we present two examples.

In general, iterative algorithms are needed to solve equations (4.3.1). In practice, the function $F_T(T;\theta)$ is often strictly decreasing and continuous in θ, so a simple algorithm often suffices. We illustrate the examples below by using the simple **bisection algorithm**, which we now briefly discuss.

Remark 4.3.1 (Bisection Algorithm). Suppose we want to solve the equation $g(x) = d$, where $g(x)$ is strictly decreasing. Assume on a given step of the algorithm that $a < b$ bracket the solution; i.e., $g(a) > d$ and $g(b) < d$. Let $c = (a+b)/2$. Then on the next step of the algorithm, the new bracket values a and b are determined by

$$\text{if}(g(c) > d) \quad \text{then} \quad \{a \leftarrow c \text{ and } b \leftarrow b\}$$
$$\text{if}(g(c) < d) \quad \text{then} \quad \{a \leftarrow a \text{ and } b \leftarrow c\}.$$

The algorithm continues until $a - b < \epsilon$, where $\epsilon > 0$ is a specified tolerance. ∎

Example 4.3.1 (Confidence Interval for a Bernoulli Proportion). Let X have a Bernoulli distribution with θ as the probability of success. Let $\Omega = (0, 1)$. Suppose $X_1, X_2, \ldots, X_n$ is a random sample on X. As our point estimator of θ, we consider $\overline{X}$, which is the sample proportion of successes. The cdf of $n\overline{X}$ is binomial$(n.\theta)$. Thus

$$
\begin{aligned}
F_{\overline{X}}(\overline{x}; \theta) &= P(n\overline{X} \leq n\overline{x}) \\
&= \sum_{j=0}^{n\overline{x}} \binom{n}{j} \theta^j (1-\theta)^{n-j} \\
&= 1 - \sum_{j=n\overline{x}+1}^{n} \binom{n}{j} \theta^j (1-\theta)^{n-j} \\
&= 1 - \int_0^\theta \frac{n!}{(n\overline{x})![n - (n\overline{x}+1]!} z^{n\overline{x}} (1-z)^{n-(n\overline{x}+1)} \, dz, \quad (4.3.2)
\end{aligned}
$$

where the last equality, involving the incomplete β-function, follows from Exercise 4.3.1. By the fundamental theorem of calculus and expression (4.3.2),

$$
\frac{d}{d\theta} F_{\overline{X}}(\overline{x}; \theta) = -\frac{n!}{(n\overline{x})![n - (n\overline{x}+1]!} \theta^{n\overline{x}} (1-\theta)^{n-(n\overline{x}+1)} < 0;
$$

hence, $F_{\overline{X}}(\overline{x}; \theta)$ is a strictly decreasing function of θ, for each $\overline{x}$. Next, let $\alpha_1, \alpha_2 > 0$ be specified constants such that $\alpha_1 + \alpha_2 < 1/2$ and let $\underline{\theta}$ and $\overline{\theta}$ solve the equations

$$
F_{\overline{X}}(\overline{X}-; \underline{\theta}) = 1 - \alpha_2 \text{ and } F_{\overline{X}}(\overline{X}; \overline{\theta}) = \alpha_1. \quad (4.3.3)
$$

Then $(\underline{\theta}, \overline{\theta})$ is a confidence interval for θ with confidence coefficient at least $1 - \alpha$, where $\alpha = \alpha_1 + \alpha_2$. These equations can be solved iteratively, as discussed in the following numerical illustration.

Numerical Illustration. Suppose $n = 30$, $\overline{x} = 0.60$, and $\alpha_1 = \alpha_2 = 0.05$ Because the support of the binomial consists of integers and $n\overline{x} = 18$, we can write the first equation in (4.3.3) as

$$
\sum_{j=0}^{17} \binom{n}{j} \underline{\theta}^j (1-\underline{\theta})^{n-j} = 0.95.
$$

Let $bin(n, p)$ denote a random variable with binomial distribution with parameters n and p. Because $P(bin(30, 0.4) \leq 17) = 0.9787$ and $P(bin(30, 0.45) \leq 17) = 0.9286$, the values 0.4 and 0.45 bracket the solution to the first equation. We used the R command `pbinom` to do these computations. Using these bracket values as input to the R function `binomci.r` (see Appendix B) the solution to the first equation is $\underline{\theta} = 0.434$. In the same way, because $P(bin(30, 0.7) \leq 18) = 0.1593$ and $P(bin(30, 0.8) \leq 18) = 0.0094$, the values 0.7 and 0.8 bracket the solution to the second equation. This leads to the solution $\overline{\theta} = 0.750$. Thus the confidence interval is $(0.434, 0.750)$, with a confidence of at least 90%. For comparison, the asymptotic 90% confidence interval of expression (4.2.7) is $(0.453, 0.747)$; see Exercise 4.3.2. ∎

Example 4.3.2 (Confidence Interval for the Mean of a Poisson Distribution). Let $X_1, X_2, \ldots, X_n$ be a random sample on a random variable X which has a Poisson distribution with mean θ. Let $\overline{X} = n^{-1} \sum_{i=1}^{n} X_i$ be our point estimator of θ. As with the Bernoulli confidence interval in the last example, we can work with $n\overline{X}$, which, in this case, has a Poisson distribution with mean $n\theta$. The cdf of $\overline{X}$ is

$$
\begin{aligned}
F_{\overline{X}}(\overline{x}; \theta) &= \sum_{j=0}^{n\overline{x}} e^{-n\theta} \frac{(n\theta)^j}{j!} \\
&= \frac{1}{\Gamma(n\overline{x}+1)} \int_{n\theta}^{\infty} x^{n\overline{x}} e^{-x} \, dx,
\end{aligned} \tag{4.3.4}
$$

where the integral equation is obtained in Exercise 4.3.4. From expression (4.3.4), we immediately have

$$
\frac{d}{d\theta} F_{\overline{X}}(\overline{x}; \theta) = \frac{-n}{\Gamma(n\overline{x}+1)} (n\theta)^{n\overline{x}} e^{-n\theta} < 0.
$$

Therefore, $F_{\overline{X}}(\overline{x}; \theta)$ is a strictly decreasing function of θ for every fixed $\overline{x}$. Hence, as discussed above, for $\alpha_1, \alpha_2 > 0$ such that $\alpha_1 + \alpha_2 < 1/2$, the confidence interval is given by $(\underline{\theta}, \overline{\theta})$, where

$$
\sum_{j=0}^{n\overline{X}-1} e^{-n\underline{\theta}} \frac{(n\underline{\theta})^j}{j!} = 1 - \alpha_2 \tag{4.3.5}
$$

$$
\sum_{j=0}^{n\overline{X}} e^{-n\overline{\theta}} \frac{(n\overline{\theta})^j}{j!} = \alpha_1. \tag{4.3.6}
$$

The confidence coefficient of the interval $(\underline{\theta}, \overline{\theta})$ is at least $1 - \alpha = 1 - (\alpha_1 + \alpha_2)$. As with the Bernoulli proportion, these equations can be solved iteratively.

Numerical Illustration. Suppose $n = 25$ and the realized value of $\overline{X}$ is $\overline{x} = 5$; hence, $n\overline{x} = 125$. We select $\alpha_1 = \alpha_2 = 0.05$. Then, by (4.3.5) and (4.3.6), our confidence interval solves the equations

$$
\sum_{j=0}^{124} e^{-n\underline{\theta}} \frac{(n\underline{\theta})^j}{j!} = 0.95 \tag{4.3.7}
$$

$$
\sum_{j=0}^{125} e^{-n\overline{\theta}} \frac{(n\overline{\theta})^j}{j!} = 0.05. \tag{4.3.8}
$$

As with the Bernoulli confidence interval, we use the simple bisection algorithm to solve these equations. Let $poi(x, \theta)$ denote the probability that a Poisson random variable with mean θ is less than or equal to x. Using a simple computer package, we have $poi(124, 25 \cdot 4) = 0.9912$ and $poi(124, 25 \cdot 4.4) = 0.9145$. Thus, $\theta = 4$ and $\theta = 4.4$ bracket the solution to the first equation. The simple R function `poissonci.r` given in Appendix B returns the solution $\underline{\theta} = 4.287$. For the second equation, $poi(125, 25 \cdot 5.5) = 0.1528$ and $poi(125, 25 \cdot 6) = 0.0204$. Using the bracket values 5.5 and 6, `poissonci.r` obtains the solution $\overline{\theta} = 5.8$. So the confidence interval is $(4.287, 5.8)$, with confidence at least 90%. Note that the confidence interval is right-skewed, similar to the Poisson distribution. ∎

A brief sketch of the theory behind this confidence interval follows. Consider the general setup in the first paragraph of this section, where T is an estimator of the unknown parameter θ and $F_T(t; \theta)$ is the cdf of T. Define

$$\overline{\theta} = \sup\{\theta : F_T(T; \theta) \geq \alpha_1\} \tag{4.3.9}$$
$$\underline{\theta} = \inf\{\theta : F_T(T-; \theta) \leq 1 - \alpha_2\}. \tag{4.3.10}$$

Hence, we have

$$\theta > \overline{\theta} \;\Rightarrow\; F_T(T; \theta) \leq \alpha_1$$
$$\theta < \underline{\theta} \;\Rightarrow\; F_T(T-; \theta) \geq 1 - \alpha_2.$$

These implications lead to

$$\begin{aligned}
P[\underline{\theta} < \theta < \overline{\theta}] &= 1 - P[\{\theta < \underline{\theta}\} \cup \{\theta > \overline{\theta}\}] \\
&= 1 - P[\theta < \underline{\theta}] - P[\theta > \overline{\theta}] \\
&\geq 1 - P[F_T(T-; \theta) \geq 1 - \alpha_2] - P[F_T(T; \theta) \leq \alpha_1] \\
&\geq 1 - \alpha_1 - \alpha_2,
\end{aligned}$$

where the last inequality is evident from equations (4.3.9) and (4.3.10). A rigorous proof can be based on Exercise 4.8.13; see page 425 of Shao (1998) for details.

EXERCISES

4.3.1. Using Exercise 3.3.22, show that

$$\int_0^p \frac{n!}{(k-1)!(n-k)!} z^{k-1}(1-z)^{n-k}\,dz = \sum_{w=k}^{n} \binom{n}{w} p^w (1-p)^{n-w},$$

where $0 < p < 1$, and k and n are positive integers such that $k \leq n$.

4.3.2. In Example 4.3.1, verify the result for the asymptotic confidence interval for θ.

4.3.3. Suppose $X_1, X_2, \ldots, X_{10}$ is a random sample on a random variable X which has a Poisson distribution with mean θ. Say the realized value of the sample mean is 0.5; i.e., $n\overline{x} = 5$. Suppose we want to compute the confidence interval $(\underline{\theta}, \overline{\theta})$ as determined by equations (4.3.5) and (4.3.6). Using Table I in Appendix C, show that 0.2 and 0.3 bracket $\underline{\theta}$ and that 0.9 and 1.0 bracket $\overline{\theta}$. If R is available, use the R function `poissonci.r` to compute the solutions to the equations.

4.3.4. This exercise obtains a useful identity for the cdf of a Poisson cdf.

(a) Use Exercise 3.3.5 to show that this identity is true:

$$\frac{\lambda^n}{\Gamma(n)} \int_1^{\infty} x^{n-1} e^{-x\lambda} \, dx = \sum_{j=n}^{\infty} e^{-\lambda} \frac{\lambda^j}{j!},$$

for $\lambda > 0$ and n a positive integer.

Hint: Just consider a Poisson process on the unit interval with mean λ. Let W_n be the waiting time until the nth event. Then the left side is $P(W_n \leq 1)$. Why?

(b) Obtain the identity used in Example 4.3.2, by making the transformation $z = \lambda x$ in the above integral.

4.4 Order Statistics

In this section the notion of an order statistic is defined and some of its simple properties are investigated. These statistics have in recent times come to play an important role in statistical inference partly because some of their properties do not depend upon the distribution from which the random sample is obtained.

Let $X_1, X_2, \ldots, X_n$ denote a random sample from a distribution of the *continuous type* having a pdf $f(x)$ that has support $\mathcal{S} = (a, b)$, where $-\infty \leq a < b \leq \infty$. Let Y_1 be the smallest of these X_i, Y_2 the next X_i in order of magnitude, ..., and Y_n the largest of X_i. That is, $Y_1 < Y_2 < \cdots < Y_n$ represent $X_1, X_2, \ldots, X_n$ when the latter are arranged in ascending order of magnitude. We call Y_i, $i = 1, 2, \ldots, n$, the ith order statistic of the random sample $X_1, X_2, \ldots, X_n$. Then the joint pdf of $Y_1, Y_2, \ldots, Y_n$ is given in the following theorem.

Theorem 4.4.1. *Using the above notation, let $Y_1 < Y_2 < \cdots < Y_n$ denote the n order statistics based on the random sample $X_1, X_2, \ldots, X_n$ from a continuous distribution with pdf $f(x)$ and support (a, b). Then the joint pdf of $Y_1, Y_2, \ldots, Y_n$ is given by*

$$g(y_1, y_2, \ldots, y_n) = \begin{cases} n! f(y_1) f(y_2) \cdots f(y_n) & a < y_1 < y_2 < \cdots < y_n < b \\ 0 & elsewhere. \end{cases} \tag{4.4.1}$$

Proof: Note that the support of $X_1, X_2, \ldots, X_n$ can be partitioned into $n!$ mutually disjoint sets which map onto the support of $Y_1, Y_2, \ldots, Y_n$, namely, $\{(y_1, y_2, \ldots, y_n) : a < y_1 < y_2 < \cdots < y_n < b\}$. One of these $n!$ sets is $a < x_1 < x_2 < \cdots < x_n < b$, and the others can be found by permuting the n xs in all possible ways. The transformation associated with the one listed is $x_1 = y_1, x_2 = y_2, \ldots, x_n = y_n$, which has a Jacobian equal to 1. However, the Jacobian of each of the other transformations is either ± 1. Thus

$$g(y_1, y_2, \ldots, y_n) = \sum_{i=1}^{n!} |J_i| f(y_1) f(y_2) \cdots f(y_n)$$

$$= \begin{cases} n! f(y_1) f(y_2) \cdots f(y_n) & a < y_1 < y_2 < \cdots < y_n < b \\ 0 & elsewhere, \end{cases}$$

as was to be proved. ∎

Example 4.4.1. Let X denote a random variable of the continuous type with a pdf $f(x)$ that is positive and continuous, with support $\mathcal{S} = (a, b)$, $-\infty \le a < b \le \infty$. The distribution function $F(x)$ of X may be written

$$F(x) = \int_a^x f(w)\,dw, \quad a < x < b.$$

If $x \le a$, $F(x) = 0$; and if $b \le x$, $F(x) = 1$. Thus there is a unique median m of the distribution with $F(m) = \frac{1}{2}$. Let X_1, X_2, X_3 denote a random sample from this distribution and let $Y_1 < Y_2 < Y_3$ denote the order statistics of the sample. Note that Y_2 is the sample median. We compute the probability that $Y_2 \le m$. The joint pdf of the three order statistics is

$$g(y_1, y_2, y_3) = \begin{cases} 6f(y_1)f(y_2)f(y_3) & a < y_1 < y_2 < y_3 < b \\ 0 & \text{elsewhere.} \end{cases}$$

The pdf of Y_2 is then

$$
\begin{aligned}
h(y_2) &= 6f(y_2)\int_{y_2}^b \int_a^{y_2} f(y_1)f(y_3)\,dy_1 dy_3 \\
&= \begin{cases} 6f(y_2)F(y_2)[1 - F(y_2)] & a < y_2 < b \\ 0 & \text{elsewhere.} \end{cases}
\end{aligned}
$$

Accordingly,

$$
\begin{aligned}
P(Y_2 \le m) &= 6\int_a^m \{F(y_2)f(y_2) - [F(y_2)]^2 f(y_2)\}\,dy_2 \\
&= 6\left\{\frac{[F(y_2)]^2}{2} - \frac{[F(y_2)]^3}{3}\right\}_a^m = \frac{1}{2}.
\end{aligned}
$$

Hence, for this situation, the median of the sample median Y_2 is the population median m. ∎

Once it is observed that

$$\int_a^x [F(w)]^{\alpha - 1} f(w)\,dw = \frac{[F(x)]^\alpha}{\alpha}, \quad \alpha > 0,$$

and that

$$\int_y^b [1 - F(w)]^{\beta - 1} f(w)\,dw = \frac{[1 - F(y)]^\beta}{\beta}, \quad \beta > 0,$$

it is easy to express the marginal pdf of any order statistic, say Y_k, in terms of $F(x)$ and $f(x)$. This is done by evaluating the integral

$$g_k(y_k) = \int_a^{y_k} \cdots \int_a^{y_2} \int_{y_k}^b \cdots \int_{y_{n-1}}^b n! f(y_1)f(y_2) \cdots f(y_n)\,dy_n \cdots dy_{k+1}\,dy_1 \cdots dy_{k-1}.$$

The result is

$$g_k(y_k) = \begin{cases} \frac{n!}{(k-1)!(n-k)!}[F(y_k)]^{k-1}[1-F(y_k)]^{n-k}f(y_k) & a < y_k < b \\ 0 & \text{elsewhere.} \end{cases} \quad (4.4.2)$$

Example 4.4.2. Let $Y_1 < Y_2 < Y_3 < Y_4$ denote the order statistics of a random sample of size 4 from a distribution having pdf

$$f(x) = \begin{cases} 2x & 0 < x < 1 \\ 0 & \text{elsewhere.} \end{cases}$$

We express the pdf of Y_3 in terms of $f(x)$ and $F(x)$ and then compute $P(\frac{1}{2} < Y_3)$. Here $F(x) = x^2$, provided that $0 < x < 1$, so that

$$g_3(y_3) = \begin{cases} \frac{4!}{2!\,1!}(y_3^2)^2(1-y_3^2)(2y_3) & 0 < y_3 < 1 \\ 0 & \text{elsewhere.} \end{cases}$$

Thus

$$\begin{aligned} P(\tfrac{1}{2} < Y_3) &= \int_{1/2}^{\infty} g_3(y_3)\,dy_3 \\ &= \int_{1/2}^{1} 24(y_3^5 - y_3^7)\,dy_3 = \frac{243}{256}. \end{aligned}$$

Finally, the joint pdf of any two order statistics, say $Y_i < Y_j$, is easily expressed in terms of $F(x)$ and $f(x)$. We have

$$g_{ij}(y_i, y_j) = \int_a^{y_i} \cdots \int_a^{y_2} \int_{y_i}^{y_j} \cdots \int_{y_{j-2}}^{y_j} \int_{y_j}^{b} \cdots \int_{y_{n-1}}^{b} n!\, f(y_1) \times \cdots$$
$$\times f(y_n)\,dy_n \cdots dy_{j+1}dy_{j-1} \cdots dy_{i+1}dy_1 \cdots dy_{i-1}.$$

Since, for $\gamma > 0$,

$$\begin{aligned} \int_x^{y} [F(y) - F(w)]^{\gamma-1} f(w)\,dw &= \left. -\frac{[F(y) - F(w)]^{\gamma}}{\gamma} \right|_x^{y} \\ &= \frac{[F(y) - F(x)]^{\gamma}}{\gamma}, \end{aligned}$$

it is found that

$$g_{ij}(y_i, y_j) = \begin{cases} \frac{n!}{(i-1)!(j-i-1)!(n-j)!}[F(y_i)]^{i-1}[F(y_j) - F(y_i)]^{j-i-1} \\ \qquad \times [1 - F(y_j)]^{n-j} f(y_i) f(y_j) & a < y_i < y_j < b \\ 0 & \text{elsewhere.} \quad \blacksquare \end{cases}$$
$$(4.4.3)$$

Remark 4.4.1 (Heuristic Derivation). There is an easy method of remembering the pdf of a vector of order statistics such as the one given in formula (4.4.3). The probability $P(y_i < Y_i < y_i + \Delta_i,\ y_j < Y_j < y_j + \Delta_j)$, where Δ_i and Δ_j are small, can be approximated by the following multinomial probability. In n independent trials, $i-1$ outcomes must be less than y_i [an event that has probability $p_1 = F(y_i)$ on each trial]; $j-i-1$ outcomes must be between $y_i + \Delta_i$ and y_j [an event with approximate probability $p_2 = F(y_j) - F(y_i)$ on each trial]; $n-j$ outcomes must be greater than $y_j + \Delta_j$ [an event with approximate probability $p_3 = 1 - F(y_j)$ on each trial]; one outcome must be between y_i and $y_i + \Delta_i$ [an event with approximate probability $p_4 = f(y_i)\Delta_i$ on each trial]; and, finally, one outcome must be between y_j and $y_j + \Delta_j$ [an event with approximate probability $p_5 = f(y_j)\Delta_j$ on each trial]. This multinomial probability is

$$\frac{n!}{(i-1)!(j-i-1)!(n-j)!\,1!\,1!}p_1^{i-1}p_2^{j-i-1}p_3^{n-j}p_4p_5,$$

which is $g_{i,j}(y_i, y_j)\Delta_i\Delta_j$, where $g_{i,j}(y_i, y_j)$ is given in expression (4.4.3). ∎

Certain functions of the order statistics $Y_1, Y_2, \ldots, Y_n$ are important statistics themselves. A few of these are (a) $Y_n - Y_1$, which is called the **range** of the random sample; (b) $(Y_1 + Y_n)/2$, which is called the **midrange** of the random sample; and (c) if n is odd, $Y_{(n+1)/2}$, which is called the **median** of the random sample.

Example 4.4.3. Let Y_1, Y_2, Y_3 be the order statistics of a random sample of size 3 from a distribution having pdf

$$f(x) = \begin{cases} 1 & 0 < x < 1 \\ 0 & \text{elsewhere.} \end{cases}$$

We seek the pdf of the sample range $Z_1 = Y_3 - Y_1$. Since $F(x) = x$, $0 < x < 1$, the joint pdf of Y_1 and Y_3 is

$$g_{13}(y_1, y_3) = \begin{cases} 6(y_3 - y_1) & 0 < y_1 < y_3 < 1 \\ 0 & \text{elsewhere.} \end{cases}$$

In addition to $Z_1 = Y_3 - Y_1$, let $Z_2 = Y_3$. The functions $z_1 = y_3 - y_1$, $z_2 = y_3$ have respective inverses $y_1 = z_2 - z_1$, $y_3 = z_2$, so that the corresponding Jacobian of the one-to-one transformation is

$$J = \begin{vmatrix} \frac{\partial y_1}{\partial z_1} & \frac{\partial y_1}{\partial z_2} \\ \frac{\partial y_3}{\partial z_1} & \frac{\partial y_3}{\partial z_2} \end{vmatrix} = \begin{vmatrix} -1 & 1 \\ 0 & 1 \end{vmatrix} = -1.$$

Thus the joint pdf of Z_1 and Z_2 is

$$h(z_1, z_2) = \begin{cases} |-1|6z_1 = 6z_1 & 0 < z_1 < z_2 < 1 \\ 0 & \text{elsewhere.} \end{cases}$$

Accordingly, the pdf of the range $Z_1 = Y_3 - Y_1$ of the random sample of size 3 is

$$h_1(z_1) = \begin{cases} \int_{z_1}^1 6z_1\, dz_2 = 6z_1(1 - z_1) & 0 < z_1 < 1 \\ 0 & \text{elsewhere.} \end{cases}$$
∎

4.4.1   Quantiles

Let X be a random variable with a continuous cdf $F(x)$. For $0 < p < 1$, define the pth **quantile** of X to be $\xi_p = F^{-1}(p)$. For example, $\xi_{0.5}$, the median of X, is the 0.5 quantile. Let $X_1, X_2, \ldots, X_n$ be a random sample from the distribution of X and let $Y_1 < Y_2 < \cdots < Y_n$ be the corresponding order statistics. Let k be the greatest integer less than or equal to $[p(n+1)]$. We next define an estimator of ξ_p after making the following observation. The area under the pdf $f(x)$ to the left of Y_k is $F(Y_k)$. The expected value of this area is

$$E(F(Y_k)) = \int_a^b F(y_k) g_k(y_k)\, dy_k,$$

where $g_k(y_k)$ is the pdf of Y_k given in expression (4.4.2). If, in this integral, we make a change of variables through the transformation $z = F(y_k)$, we have

$$E(F(Y_k)) = \int_0^1 \frac{n!}{(k-1)!(n-k)!} z^k (1-z)^{n-k}\, dz.$$

Comparing this to the integral of a beta pdf, we see that it is equal to

$$E(F(Y_k)) = \frac{n!k!(n-k)!}{(k-1)!(n-k)!(n+1)!} = \frac{k}{n+1}.$$

On the average, there is $k/(n+1)$ of the total area to the left of Y_k. Because $p \doteq k/(n+1)$, it seems reasonable to take Y_k as an estimator of the quantile ξ_p. Hence, we call Y_k the pth **sample quantile** It is also called the $100p$th **percentile of the sample.**

Remark 4.4.2. Some statisticians define sample quantiles slightly differently from what we have. For one modification with $1/(n+1) < p < n/(n+1)$, if $(n+1)/p$ is not equal to an integer, then the pth quantile of the sample may be defined as follows. Write $(n+1)p = k + r$, where $k = [(n+1)p]$ and r is a proper fraction, using the weighted average. Then the pth quantile of the sample is the weighted average

$$(1-r)Y_k + rY_{k+1},$$

which is an estimator of the pth quantile. As n becomes large, however, all these modified definitions are essentially the same. ∎

Sample quantiles are useful descriptive statistics. For instance, if Y_k is the pth quantile of the sample, then we know that approximately $p100\%$ of the data are less than or equal to Y_k and approximately $(1-p)100\%$ of the data are greater than or equal to Y_k. Next we discuss two statistical applications of quantiles.

A **five-number** summary of the data consist of the following five sample quantiles: the minimum (Y_1), the first quartile $(Y_{.25(n+1)})$, the median $(Y_{.50(n+1)})$, the third quartile $(Y_{.75(n+1)})$, and the maximum (Y_n). Note that the median given is for odd sample sizes. In the case that n is even, we use the traditional $[Y_{n/2} + Y_{(n/2)+1}]/2$ as our estimator of the median $\xi_{.5}$. For this section, we use the notation Q_1, Q_2, and Q_3 to denote, respectively, the first quartile, median, and third quartile of the sample.

The five-number summary divides the data into their quartiles, offering a simple and easily interpretable description of the data. Five-number summaries were made popular by the work of the late Professor John Tukey [see Tukey (1977) and Mosteller and Tukey (1977)]. He used slightly different quantities in place of the first and third quartiles which he called *hinges*. We prefer to use the sample quartiles.

Example 4.4.4. The following data are the ordered realizations of a random sample of size 15 on a random variable X.

$$
\begin{array}{cccccccc}
56 & 70 & 89 & 94 & 96 & 101 & 102 & 102 \\
102 & 105 & 106 & 108 & 110 & 113 & 116 &
\end{array}
$$

For these data, since $n + 1 = 16$, the realizations of the five-number summary are $y_1 = 56$, $Q_1 = y_4 = 94$, $Q_2 = y_8 = 102$, $Q_3 = y_{12} = 108$, and $y_{15} = 116$. Hence, based on the five-number summary, the data range from 56 to 116; the middle 50% of the data range from 94 to 108; and the middle of the data occurred at 102. ∎

The five-number summary is the basis for a useful and quick plot of the data. This is called a **boxplot** of the data. The box encloses the middle 50% of the data and a line segment is usually used to indicate the median. The extreme order statistics, however, are very sensitive to outlying points. So care must be used in placing these on the plot. We make use of the **box and whisker** plots defined by John Tukey. In order to define this plot, we need to define a potential outlier. Let $h = 1.5(Q_3 - Q_1)$ and define the **lower fence** (LF) and the **upper fence** (UF) by

$$
LF = Q_1 - h \text{ and } UF = Q_3 + h. \tag{4.4.4}
$$

Points that lie outside the fences, i.e., outside the interval (LF, UF), are called **potential outliers** and they are denoted by the symbol "0" on the boxplot. The whiskers then protrude from the sides of the box to what are called the **adjacent points**, which are the points within the fences but closest to the fences. Exercise 4.4.2 shows that the probability of an observation from a normal distribution being a potential outlier is 0.006977.

Example 4.4.5 (Example 4.4.4, Continued). Consider the data given in Example 4.4.4. For these data, $h = 1.5(108 - 94) = 21$, $LF = 73$, and $UF = 129$. Hence the observations 56 and 70 are potential outliers. There are no outliers on the high side of the data. The lower adjacent point is 89. Hence the boxplot of data is given by Panel A of Figure 4.4.1.

Note that the point 56 is over $2h$ from Q_1. Some statisticians call such a point an "outlier" and label it with a symbol other than "O," but we do not make this distinction. ∎

In practice, we often assume that the data follow a certain distribution. For example, we may assume that $X_1, \ldots, X_n$ are a random sample from a normal distribution with unknown mean and variance. Thus the form of the distribution of X is known, but the specific parameters are not. Such an assumption needs to

Figure 4.4.1: Boxplot and quantile plots for the data of Example 4.4.4.

be checked and there are many statistical tests which do so; see D'Agostino and Stephens (1986) for a thorough discussion of such tests. As our second statistical application of quantiles, we discuss one such diagnostic plot in this regard.

We consider the location and scale family. Suppose X is a random variable with cdf $F((x - a)/b)$, where $F(x)$ is known but a and $b > 0$ may not be. Let $Z = (X - a)/b$; then Z has cdf $F(z)$. Let $0 < p < 1$ and let $\xi_{X,p}$ be the pth quantile of X. Let $\xi_{Z,p}$ be the pth quantile of $Z = (X - a)/b$. Because $F(z)$ is known, $\xi_{Z,p}$ is known. But

$$p = P[X \leq \xi_{X,p}] = P\left[Z \leq \frac{\xi_{X,p} - a}{b}\right],$$

from which we have the linear relationship

$$\xi_{X,p} = b\xi_{Z,p} + a. \qquad (4.4.5)$$

Thus, if X has a cdf of the form of $F((x - a)/b)$, then the quantiles of X are linearly related to the quantiles of Z. Of course, in practice, we do not know the quantiles of X, but we can estimate them. Let $X_1, \ldots, X_n$ be a random sample from the distribution of X and let $Y_1 < \cdots < Y_n$ be the order statistics. For $k = 1, \ldots, n$, let $p_k = k/(n + 1)$. Then Y_k is an estimator of ξ_{X,p_k}. Denote the corresponding quantiles of the cdf $F(z)$ by $\xi_{Z,p_k} = F^{-1}(p_k)$. The plot of Y_k versus ξ_{Z,p_k} is called a **q−q plot**, as it plots one set of quantiles from the sample against another set from the theoretical cdf $F(z)$. Based on the above discussion, the linearity of such a plot indicates that the cdf of X is of the form $F((x - a)/b)$.

Example 4.4.6 (Example 4.4.5, Continued). Panels B, C, and D of Figure 4.4.1 contain $q − q$ plots of the data of Example 4.4.4 for three different distributions.

The quantiles of a standard normal random variable are used for the plot in Panel B. Hence, as described above, this is the plot of Y_k versus $\Phi^{-1}(k/(n+1))$, for $k = 1, 2, \ldots, n$. For Panel C, the population quantiles of the standard **Laplace** distribution are used; that is, the density of Z is $f(z) = (1/2)e^{-|z|}$, $-\infty < z < \infty$. For Panel D, the quantiles were generated from an exponential distribution with density $f(z) = e^{-z}$, $0 < z < \infty$, zero elsewhere. The generation of these quantiles is discussed in Exercise 4.4.1.

The plot farthest from linearity is that of Panel D. Note that this plot gives an indication of a more correct distribution. For the points to lie on a line, the lower quantiles of Z must be spread out as are the higher quantiles; i.e., symmetric distributions may be more appropriate. The plots in Panels B and C are more linear than that of Panel D, but they still contain some curvature. Of the two, Panel C appears to be more linear. Actually, the data were generated from a Laplace distribution, so one would expect that Panel C would be the most linear of the three plots.

Many computer packages have commands to obtain the population quantiles used in this example. In Appendix B, the R function `qqplotc4s2` obtains the normal, Laplace, and exponential quantiles used for Figure 4.4.1. It also obtains an R version of the figure. ∎

The $q-q$ plot using normal quantiles is often called a **normal** $q-q$ plot.

4.4.2 Confidence Intervals for Quantiles

Let X be a continuous random variable with cdf $F(x)$. For $0 < p < 1$, define the $100p$th distribution percentile to be ξ_p, where $F(\xi_p) = p$. For a sample of size n on X, let $Y_1 < Y_2 < \cdots < Y_n$ be the order statistics. Let $k = [(n+1)p]$. Then the $100p$th sample percentile Y_k is a point estimate of ξ_p.

We now derive a **distribution free** confidence interval for ξ_p, meaning it is a confidence interval for ξ_p which is free of any assumptions about $F(x)$ other than it is of the continuous type. Let $i < [(n+1)p] < j$, and consider the order statistics $Y_i < Y_j$ and the event $Y_i < \xi_p < Y_j$. For the ith order statistic Y_i to be less than ξ_p, it must be true that at least i of the X values are less than ξ_p. Moreover, for the jth order statistic to be greater than ξ_p, fewer than j of the X values are less than ξ_p. To put this in the context of a binomial distribution, the probability of success is $P(X < \xi_p) = F(\xi_p) = p$. Further, the event $Y_i < \xi_p < Y_j$ is equivalent to obtaining between i (inclusive) and j (exclusive) successes in n independent trials. Thus, taking probabilities, we have

$$P(Y_i < \xi_p < Y_j) = \sum_{w=i}^{j-1} \binom{n}{w} p^w (1-p)^{n-w}. \qquad (4.4.6)$$

When particular values of n, i, and j are specified, this probability can be computed. By this procedure, suppose that it has been found that $\gamma = P(Y_i < \xi_p < Y_j)$. Then the probability is γ that the random interval (Y_i, Y_j) includes the quantile of order p. If the experimental values of Y_i and Y_j are, respectively, y_i and y_j, the interval

(y_i, y_j) serves as a $100\gamma\%$ confidence interval for ξ_p, the quantile of order p. We use this in the next example to find a confidence interval for the median.

Example 4.4.7 (Confidence Interval for the Median). Let X be a continuous random variable with cdf $F(x)$. Let $\xi_{1/2}$ denote the median of $F(x)$; i.e., $\xi_{1/2}$ solves $F(\xi_{1/2}) = 1/2$. Suppose $X_1, X_2, \ldots, X_n$ is a random sample from the distribution of X with corresponding order statistics $Y_1 < Y_2 < \cdots < Y_n$. As before, let Q_2 denote the sample median, which is a point estimator of $\xi_{1/2}$. Select α, so that $0 < \alpha < 1$. Take $c_{\alpha/2}$ to be the $\alpha/2$th quantile of a binomial $b(n, 1/2)$ distribution; that is, $P[S \leq c_{\alpha/2}] = \alpha/2$, where S is distributed $b(n, 1/2)$. Then note also that $P[S \geq n - c_{\alpha/2}] = \alpha/2$. (Because of the discreteness of the binomial distribution, either take a value of α for which these probabilities are correct or change the equalities to approximations.) Thus it follows from expression (4.4.6) that

$$P[Y_{c_{\alpha/2}+1} < \xi_{1/2} < Y_{n-c_{\alpha/2}}] = 1 - \alpha. \tag{4.4.7}$$

Hence, when the sample is drawn, if $y_{c_{\alpha/2}+1}$ and $y_{n-c_{\alpha/2}}$ are the realized values of the order statistics $Y_{c_{\alpha/2}+1}$ and $Y_{n-c_{\alpha/2}}$, then the interval

$$(y_{c_{\alpha/2}+1}, y_{n-c_{\alpha/2}}) \tag{4.4.8}$$

is a $(1 - \alpha)100\%$ confidence interval for $\xi_{1/2}$.

To illustrate this confidence interval, consider the data of Example 4.4.4. Suppose we want an 88% confidence interval for $\xi_{1/2}$. Then $\alpha/2 = 0.060$. Then $c_{\alpha/2} = 4$ because $P[S \leq 4] = 0.059$, where the distribution of S is binomial with $n = 15$ and $p = 0.5$. Therefore, an 88% confidence interval for $\xi_{1/2}$ is $(y_5, y_{11}) = (96, 106)$. ∎

Note that because of the discreteness of the binomial distribution, only certain confidence levels are possible for this confidence interval for the median. If we further assume that $f(x)$ is symmetric about ξ, Chapter 10 presents other distribution free confidence intervals where this discreteness is much less of a problem.

EXERCISES

4.4.1. Obtain closed-form expressions for the distribution quantiles based on the exponential and Laplace distributions as discussed in Example 4.4.6.

4.4.2. Obtain the probability that an observation is a potential outlier for the following distributions.

(a) The underlying distribution is normal.

(b) The underlying distribution is *logistic*; that is, the pdf is given by

$$f(x) = \frac{e^{-x}}{(1 + e^{-x})^2}, \quad -\infty < x < \infty. \tag{4.4.9}$$

(c) The underlying distribution is Laplace, with the pdf

$$f(x) = \frac{1}{2}e^{-|x|}, \quad -\infty < x < \infty. \tag{4.4.10}$$

4.4.3. Consider the sample of data:

13	5	202	15	99	4	67	83	36	11	301
23	213	40	66	106	78	69	166	84	64	

(a) Obtain the five-number summary of these data.

(b) Determine if there are any outliers.

(c) Boxplot the data. Comment on the plot.

4.4.4. Consider the data in Exercise 4.4.3. Obtain the normal $q-q$ plot for these data. Does the plot suggest that the underlying distribution is normal? Use the plot to determine, if any, what quantiles associated with a different theoretical distribution would lead to a more linear plot. Then obtain the plot.

4.4.5. Let $Y_1 < Y_2 < Y_3 < Y_4$ be the order statistics of a random sample of size 4 from the distribution having pdf $f(x) = e^{-x}$, $0 < x < \infty$, zero elsewhere. Find $P(Y_4 \geq 3)$.

4.4.6. Let X_1, X_2, X_3 be a random sample from a distribution of the continuous type having pdf $f(x) = 2x$, $0 < x < 1$, zero elsewhere.

(a) Compute the probability that the smallest of X_1, X_2, X_3 exceeds the median of the distribution.

(b) If $Y_1 < Y_2 < Y_3$ are the order statistics, find the correlation between Y_2 and Y_3.

4.4.7. Let $f(x) = \frac{1}{6}$, $x = 1, 2, 3, 4, 5, 6$, zero elsewhere, be the pmf of a distribution of the discrete type. Show that the pmf of the smallest observation of a random sample of size 5 from this distribution is

$$g_1(y_1) = \left(\frac{7 - y_1}{6}\right)^5 - \left(\frac{6 - y_1}{6}\right)^5, \quad y_1 = 1, 2, \ldots, 6,$$

zero elsewhere. Note that in this exercise the random sample is from a distribution of the discrete type. All formulas in the text were derived under the assumption that the random sample is from a distribution of the continuous type and are not applicable. Why?

4.4.8. Let $Y_1 < Y_2 < Y_3 < Y_4 < Y_5$ denote the order statistics of a random sample of size 5 from a distribution having pdf $f(x) = e^{-x}$, $0 < x < \infty$, zero elsewhere. Show that $Z_1 = Y_2$ and $Z_2 = Y_4 - Y_2$ are independent.
Hint: First find the joint pdf of Y_2 and Y_4.

4.4.9. Let $Y_1 < Y_2 < \cdots < Y_n$ be the order statistics of a random sample of size n from a distribution with pdf $f(x) = 1$, $0 < x < 1$, zero elsewhere. Show that the kth order statistic Y_k has a beta pdf with parameters $\alpha = k$ and $\beta = n - k + 1$.

4.4.10. Let $Y_1 < Y_2 < \cdots < Y_n$ be the order statistics from a Weibull distribution, Exercise 3.3.26. Find the distribution function and pdf of Y_1.

4.4.11. Find the probability that the range of a random sample of size 4 from the uniform distribution having the pdf $f(x) = 1$, $0 < x < 1$, zero elsewhere, is less than $\frac{1}{2}$.

4.4.12. Let $Y_1 < Y_2 < Y_3$ be the order statistics of a random sample of size 3 from a distribution having the pdf $f(x) = 2x$, $0 < x < 1$, zero elsewhere. Show that $Z_1 = Y_1/Y_2$, $Z_2 = Y_2/Y_3$, and $Z_3 = Y_3$ are mutually independent.

4.4.13. Suppose a random sample of size 2 is obtained from a distribution that has pdf $f(x) = 2(1 - x)$, $0 < x < 1$, zero elsewhere. Compute the probability that one sample observation is at least twice as large as the other.

4.4.14. Let $Y_1 < Y_2 < Y_3$ denote the order statistics of a random sample of size 3 from a distribution with pdf $f(x) = 1$, $0 < x < 1$, zero elsewhere. Let $Z = (Y_1 + Y_3)/2$ be the midrange of the sample. Find the pdf of Z.

4.4.15. Let $Y_1 < Y_2$ denote the order statistics of a random sample of size 2 from $N(0, \sigma^2)$.

(a) Show that $E(Y_1) = -\sigma/\sqrt{\pi}$.
   Hint: Evaluate $E(Y_1)$ by using the joint pdf of Y_1 and Y_2 and first integrating on y_1.

(b) Find the covariance of Y_1 and Y_2.

4.4.16. Let $Y_1 < Y_2$ be the order statistics of a random sample of size 2 from a distribution of the continuous type which has pdf $f(x)$ such that $f(x) > 0$, provided that $x \geq 0$, and $f(x) = 0$ elsewhere. Show that the independence of $Z_1 = Y_1$ and $Z_2 = Y_2 - Y_1$ characterizes the gamma pdf $f(x)$, which has parameters $\alpha = 1$ and $\beta > 0$. That is, show that Y_1 and Y_2 are independent if and only if $f(x)$ is the pdf of a $\Gamma(1, \beta)$ distribution.
Hint: Use the change-of-variable technique to find the joint pdf of Z_1 and Z_2 from that of Y_1 and Y_2. Accept the fact that the functional equation $h(0)h(x + y) \equiv h(x)h(y)$ has the solution $h(x) = c_1 e^{c_2 x}$, where c_1 and c_2 are constants.

4.4.17. Let $Y_1 < Y_2 < Y_3 < Y_4$ be the order statistics of a random sample of size $n = 4$ from a distribution with pdf $f(x) = 2x$, $0 < x < 1$, zero elsewhere.

(a) Find the joint pdf of Y_3 and Y_4.

(b) Find the conditional pdf of Y_3, given $Y_4 = y_4$.

(c) Evaluate $E(Y_3|y_4)$.

4.4.18. Two numbers are selected at random from the interval $(0, 1)$. If these values are uniformly and independently distributed, by cutting the interval at these numbers, compute the probability that the three resulting line segments can form a triangle.

4.4.19. Let X and Y denote independent random variables with respective probability density functions $f(x) = 2x$, $0 < x < 1$, zero elsewhere, and $g(y) = 3y^2$, $0 < y < 1$, zero elsewhere. Let $U = \min(X, Y)$ and $V = \max(X, Y)$. Find the joint pdf of U and V.

Hint: Here the two inverse transformations are given by $x = u$, $y = v$ and $x = v$, $y = u$.

4.4.20. Let the joint pdf of X and Y be $f(x, y) = \frac{12}{7}x(x+y)$, $0 < x < 1$, $0 < y < 1$, zero elsewhere. Let $U = \min(X, Y)$ and $V = \max(X, Y)$. Find the joint pdf of U and V.

4.4.21. Let $X_1, X_2, \ldots, X_n$ be a random sample from a distribution of either type. A measure of spread is *Gini's mean difference*

$$G = \sum_{j=2}^{n} \sum_{i=1}^{j-1} |X_i - X_j| / \binom{n}{2}. \qquad (4.4.11)$$

(a) If $n = 10$, find $a_1, a_2, \ldots, a_{10}$ so that $G = \sum_{i=1}^{10} a_i Y_i$, where $Y_1, Y_2, \ldots, Y_{10}$ are the order statistics of the sample.

(b) Show that $E(G) = 2\sigma/\sqrt{\pi}$ if the sample arises from the normal distribution $N(\mu, \sigma^2)$.

4.4.22. Let $Y_1 < Y_2 < \cdots < Y_n$ be the order statistics of a random sample of size n from the exponential distribution with pdf $f(x) = e^{-x}$, $0 < x < \infty$, zero elsewhere.

(a) Show that $Z_1 = nY_1$, $Z_2 = (n-1)(Y_2 - Y_1)$, $Z_3 = (n-2)(Y_3 - Y_2), \ldots, Z_n = Y_n - Y_{n-1}$ are independent and that each Z_i has the exponential distribution.

(b) Demonstrate that all linear functions of $Y_1, Y_2, \ldots, Y_n$, such as $\sum_1^n a_i Y_i$, can be expressed as linear functions of independent random variables.

4.4.23. In the Program Evaluation and Review Technique (PERT), we are interested in the total time to complete a project that is comprised of a large number of subprojects. For illustration, let X_1, X_2, X_3 be three independent random times for three subprojects. If these subprojects are in series (the first one must be completed before the second starts, etc.), then we are interested in the sum $Y = X_1 + X_2 + X_3$. If these are in parallel (can be worked on simultaneously), then we are interested in $Z = \max(X_1, X_2, X_3)$. In the case each of these random variables has the uniform distribution with pdf $f(x) = 1$, $0 < x < 1$, zero elsewhere, find (a) the pdf of Y and (b) the pdf of Z.

4.4.24. Let Y_n denote the nth order statistic of a random sample of size n from a distribution of the continuous type. Find the smallest value of n for which the inequality $P(\xi_{0.9} < Y_n) \geq 0.75$ is true.

4.4.25. Let $Y_1 < Y_2 < Y_3 < Y_4 < Y_5$ denote the order statistics of a random sample of size 5 from a distribution of the continuous type. Compute:

(a) $P(Y_1 < \xi_{0.5} < Y_5)$.

(b) $P(Y_1 < \xi_{0.25} < Y_3)$.

(c) $P(Y_4 < \xi_{0.80} < Y_5)$.

4.4.26. Compute $P(Y_3 < \xi_{0.5} < Y_7)$ if $Y_1 < \cdots < Y_9$ are the order statistics of a random sample of size 9 from a distribution of the continuous type.

4.4.27. Find the smallest value of n for which $P(Y_1 < \xi_{0.5} < Y_n) \geq 0.99$, where $Y_1 < \cdots < Y_n$ are the order statistics of a random sample of size n from a distribution of the continuous type.

4.4.28. Let $Y_1 < Y_2$ denote the order statistics of a random sample of size 2 from a distribution that is $N(\mu, \sigma^2)$, where σ^2 is known.

(a) Show that $P(Y_1 < \mu < Y_2) = \frac{1}{2}$ and compute the expected value of the random length $Y_2 - Y_1$.

(b) If $\overline{X}$ is the mean of this sample, find the constant c that solves the equation $P(\overline{X} - c\sigma < \mu < \overline{X} + c\sigma) = \frac{1}{2}$, and compare the length of this random interval with the expected value of that of part (a).

4.4.29. Let $y_1 < y_2 < y_3$ be the observed values of the order statistics of a random sample of size $n = 3$ from a continuous type distribution. Without knowing these values, a statistician is given these values in a random order, and she wants to select the largest; but once she refuses an observation, she cannot go back. Clearly, if she selects the first one, her probability of getting the largest is $1/3$. Instead, she decides to use the following algorithm: She looks at the first but refuses it and then takes the second if it is larger than the first, or else she takes the third. Show that this algorithm has probability of $1/2$ of selecting the largest.

4.4.30. Refer to Exercise 4.1.1. Using expression (4.4.8), obtain a confidence interval (with confidence close to 90%) for the median lifetime of a motor. What does the interval mean?

4.4.31. Let $Y_1 < Y_2 < \cdots < Y_n$ denote the order statistics of a random sample of size n from a distribution that has pdf $f(x) = 3x^2/\theta^3$, $0 < x < \theta$, zero elsewhere.

(a) Show that $P(c < Y_n/\theta < 1) = 1 - c^{3n}$, where $0 < c < 1$.

(b) If n is 4 and if the observed value of Y_4 is 2.3, what is a 95% confidence interval for θ?

4.4.32. In Exercises 4.1.2 and 4.2.5 samples of the weights of professional baseball pitchers and hitters are displayed. Obtain comparison (on the same real line) boxplots of the two data sets. Comment on the plots. In particular, how similar are the interquartile ranges?

4.5   Introduction to Hypothesis Testing

Point estimation and confidence intervals are useful statistical inference procedures. Another type of inference that is frequently used concerns tests of hypotheses. As in Sections 4.1 through 4.3, suppose our interest centers on a random variable X that has density function $f(x; \theta)$, where $\theta \in \Omega$. Suppose we think, due to theory or a preliminary experiment, that $\theta \in \omega_0$ or $\theta \in \omega_1$, where ω_0 and ω_1 are disjoint subsets of Ω and $\omega_0 \cup \omega_1 = \Omega$. We label these hypotheses as

$$H_0 : \ \theta \in \omega_0 \text{ versus } H_1 : \ \theta \in \omega_1. \tag{4.5.1}$$

The hypothesis H_0 is referred to as the **null hypothesis**, while H_1 is referred to as the **alternative hypothesis**. Often the null hypothesis represents no change or no difference from the past, while the alternative represents change or difference. The alternative is often referred to as the research worker's hypothesis. The decision rule to take H_0 or H_1 is based on a sample $X_1, \ldots, X_n$ from the distribution of X and, hence, the decision could be wrong. For instance, we could decide that $\theta \in \omega_1$ when really $\theta \in \omega_0$ or we could decide that $\theta \in \omega_0$ when, in fact, $\theta \in \omega_1$. We label these errors Type I and Type II errors, respectively, later in this section. As we show in Chapter 8, a careful analysis of these errors can lead in certain situations to optimal decision rules. In this section, though, we simply want to introduce the elements of hypothesis testing. To set ideas, consider the following example.

Example 4.5.1 (*Zea mays* Data). In 1878 Charles Darwin recorded some data on the heights of *Zea mays* plants to determine what effect cross-fertilization or self-fertilization had on the height of *Zea mays*. The experiment was to select one cross-fertilized plant and one self-fertilized plant, grow them in the same pot, and then later measure their heights. An interesting hypothesis for this example would be that the cross-fertilized plants are generally taller than the self-fertilized plants. This is the alternative hypothesis, i.e., the research worker's hypothesis. The null hypothesis is that the plants generally grow to the same height regardless of whether they were self- or cross-fertilized. Data for 15 pots were recorded.

We represent the data as $(Y_1, Z_1), \ldots, (Y_{15}, Z_{15})$, where Y_i and Z_i are the heights of the cross-fertilized and self-fertilized plants, respectively, in the ith pot. Let $X_i = Y_i - Z_i$. Due to growing in the same pot, Y_i and Z_i may be dependent random variables, but it seems appropriate to assume independence between pots, i.e., independence between the paired random vectors. So we assume that $X_1, \ldots, X_{15}$ form a random sample. As a tentative model, consider

$$X_i = \mu + e_i, \quad i = 1, \ldots, 15,$$

where the random variables e_i are iid with continuous density $f(x)$. For this model, there is no loss in generality in assuming that the mean of e_i is 0, for, otherwise, we can simply redefine μ. Hence, $E(X_i) = \mu$. Further, the density of X_i is $f_X(x; \mu) = f(x - \mu)$. In practice, the goodness of the model is always a concern and diagnostics based on the data would be run to confirm the quality of the model.

If $\mu = E(X_i) = 0$, then $E(Y_i) = E(Z_i)$; i.e., on average, the cross-fertilized plants grow to the same height as the self-fertilized plants. While, if $\mu > 0$ then

Table 4.5.1: 2×2 Decision Table for a Hypothesis Test

Decision	True State of Nature	
	H_0 is True	H_1 is True
Reject H_0	Type I Error	Correct Decision
Accept H_0	Correct Decision	Type II Error

$E(Y_i) > E(Z_i)$; i.e., on average the cross-fertilized plants are taller than the self-fertilized plants. Under this model, our hypotheses are

$$H_0 : \mu = 0 \text{ versus } H_1 : \mu > 0. \tag{4.5.2}$$

Hence, $\omega_0 = \{0\}$ represents no difference in the treatments, while $\omega_1 = (0, \infty)$ represents that the mean height of cross-fertilized *Zea mays* exceeds the mean height of self-fertilized *Zea mays*. ■

To complete the testing structure for the general problem described at the beginning of this section, we need to discuss decision rules. Recall that $X_1, \ldots, X_n$ is a random sample from the distribution of a random variable X which has density $f(x; \theta)$, where $\theta \in \Omega$. Consider testing the hypotheses $H_0 : \theta \in \omega_0$ versus $H_1 : \theta \in \omega_1$, where $\omega_0 \cup \omega_1 = \Omega$. Denote the space of the sample by $\mathcal{D}$; that is, $\mathcal{D} = \text{space}\{(X_1, \ldots, X_n)\}$. A **test** of H_0 versus H_1 is based on a subset C of $\mathcal{D}$. This set C is called the **critical region** and its corresponding decision rule (test) is

$$\text{Reject } H_0 \text{ (Accept } H_1) \quad \text{if } (X_1, \ldots, X_n) \in C \tag{4.5.3}$$
$$\text{Retain } H_0 \text{ (Reject } H_1) \quad \text{if } (X_1, \ldots, X_n) \in C^c.$$

For a given critical region, the 2×2 decision table as shown in Table 4.5.1, summarizes the results of the hypothesis test in terms of the true state of nature. Besides the correct decisions, two errors can occur. A **Type I** error occurs if H_0 is rejected when it is true, while a **Type II** error occurs if H_0 is accepted when H_1 is true.

The goal, of course, is to select a critical region from all possible critical regions which minimizes the probabilities of these errors. In general, this is not possible. The probabilities of these errors often have a see saw effect. This can be seen immediately in an extreme case. Simply let $C = \phi$. With this critical region, we would never reject H_0, so the probability of Type I error would be 0, but the probability of Type II error is 1. Often we consider Type I error to be the worse of the two errors. We then proceed by selecting critical regions which bound the probability of Type I error and then among these critical regions we try to select one which minimizes the probability of Type II error.

Definition 4.5.1. *We say a critical region C is of* **size** α *if*

$$\alpha = \max_{\theta \in \omega_0} P_\theta[(X_1, \ldots, X_n) \in C]. \tag{4.5.4}$$

Over all critical regions of size α, we want to consider critical regions which have lower probabilities of Type II error. We also can look at the complement of a Type II error, namely, rejecting H_0 when H_1 is true, which is a correct decision, as marked in Table 4.5.1. Since we desire to maximize the probability of this latter decision, we want the probability of it to be as large as possible. That is, for $\theta \in \omega_1$, we want to maximize

$$1 - P_\theta[\text{Type II Error}] = P_\theta[(X_1, \ldots, X_n) \in C].$$

The probability on the right side of this equation is called the **power** of the test at θ. It is the probability that the test detects the alternative θ when $\theta \in \omega_1$ is the true parameter. So minimizing the probability of Type II error is equivalent to maximizing power.

We define the **power function** of a critical region to be

$$\gamma_C(\theta) = P_\theta[(X_1, \ldots, X_n) \in C]; \quad \theta \in \omega_1. \tag{4.5.5}$$

Hence, given two critical regions C_1 and C_2, which are both of size α, C_1 is better than C_2 if $\gamma_{C_1}(\theta) \geq \gamma_{C_2}(\theta)$ for all $\theta \in \omega_1$. In Chapter 8, we obtain optimal critical regions for specific situations. In this section, we want to illustrate these concepts of hypotheses testing with several examples.

Example 4.5.2 (Test for a Binomial Proportion of Success). Let X be a Bernoulli random variable with probability of success p. Suppose we want to test, at size α,

$$H_0 : p = p_0 \text{ versus } H_1 : p < p_0, \tag{4.5.6}$$

where p_0 is specified. As an illustration, suppose "success" is dying from a certain disease and p_0 is the probability of dying with some standard treatment. A new treatment is used on several (randomly chosen) patients, and it is hoped that the probability of dying under this new treatment is less than p_0. Let $X_1, \ldots, X_n$ be a random sample from the distribution of X and let $S = \sum_{i=1}^{n} X_i$ be the total number of successes in the sample. An intuitive decision rule (critical region) is

Reject H_0 in favor of H_1 if $S \leq k$, $\tag{4.5.7}$

where k is such that $\alpha = P_{H_0}[S \leq k]$. Since S has a $b(n, p_0)$ distribution under H_0, k is determined by $\alpha = P_{p_0}[S \leq k]$. Because the binomial distribution is discrete, however, it is likely that there is no integer k which solves this equation. For example, suppose $n = 20$, $p_0 = 0.7$, and $\alpha = 0.15$. Then under H_0, S has a binomial $b(20, 0.7)$ distribution. Hence, computationally, $P_{H_0}[S \leq 11] = 0.1133$ and $P_{H_0}[S \leq 12] = 0.2277$. Hence, erring on the conservative side, we would probably choose k to be 11 and $\alpha = 0.1133$. As n increases, this is less of a problem; see, also, the later discussion on p-values. In general, the power of the test for the hypotheses (4.5.6) is

$$\gamma(p) = P_p[S \leq k], \quad p < p_0. \tag{4.5.8}$$

The curve labeled Test 1 in Figure 4.5.1 is the power function for the case $n = 20$, $p_0 = 0.7$, and $\alpha = 0.1133$. Notice that the power function is decreasing. The power is higher to detect the alternative $p = 0.2$ than $p = 0.6$. In Section 8.2, we prove in general the monotonicity of the power function for binomial tests of these hypotheses. Using this monotonicity, we extend our test to the more general null hypothesis $H_0 : p \geq p_0$ rather than simply $H_0 : p = p_0$. Using the same decision rule as we used for the hypotheses (4.5.6), the definition of the size of a test (4.5.4), and the monotonicity of the power curve, we have

$$\max_{p \geq p_0} P_p[S \leq k] = P_{p_0}[S \leq k] = \alpha,$$

i.e., the same size as for the original null hypothesis.

Figure 4.5.1: Power curves for tests 1 and 2; see Example 4.5.2.

Denote by Test 1 the test for the situation with $n = 20$, $p_0 = 0.70$, and size $\alpha = 0.1133$. Suppose we have a second test (Test 2) with an increased size. How does the power function of Test 2 compare to Test 1? As an example, suppose for Test 2, we select $\alpha = 0.2277$. Hence, for Test 2, we reject H_0 if $S \leq 12$. Figure 4.5.1 displays the resulting power function. Note that while Test 2 has a higher probability of committing a Type I error, it also has a higher power at each alternative $p < 0.7$. Exercise 4.5.7 shows this is true for these binomial tests. It is true in general; that is, if the size of the test increases, power does too. For this example, the R function `binpower.r` of Appendix B produces a version of Figure 4.5.1. ∎

Remark 4.5.1 (Nomenclature). Since in Example 4.5.2, the first null hypothesis $H_0 : p = p_0$ completely specifies the underlying distribution, it is called a **simple** hypothesis. Most hypotheses, such as $H_1 : p < p_0$, are **composite** hypotheses, because they are composed of many simple hypotheses and hence do not completely specify the distribution.

As we study more and more statistics, we find out that often other names are used for the size, α, of the critical region. Frequently, α is also called the **signifi-**

cance level of the test associated with that critical region. Moreover, sometimes α is called the "maximum of probabilities of committing an error of Type I" and the "maximum of the power of the test when H_0 is true." It is disconcerting to the student to discover that there are so many names for the same thing. However, all of them are used in the statistical literature, and we feel obligated to point out this fact. ∎

The test in the last example is based on the exact distribution of its test statistic, i.e., the binomial distribution. Often we cannot obtain the distribution of the test statistic in closed form. As with approximate confidence intervals, however, we can frequently appeal to the Central Limit Theorem to obtain an approximate test; see Theorem 4.2.1. Such is the case for the next example.

Example 4.5.3 (Large Sample Test for the Mean). Let X be a random variable with mean μ and finite variance σ^2. We want to test the hypotheses

$$H_0 : \mu = \mu_0 \text{ versus } H_1 : \mu > \mu_0, \qquad (4.5.9)$$

where μ_0 is specified. To illustrate, suppose μ_0 is the mean level on a standardized test of students who have been taught a course by a standard method of teaching. Suppose it is hoped that a new method which incorporates computers has a mean level $\mu > \mu_0$, where $\mu = E(X)$ and X is the score of a student taught by the new method. This conjecture is tested by having n students (randomly selected) taught under this new method.

Let $X_1, \ldots, X_n$ be a random sample from the distribution of X and denote the sample mean and variance by $\overline{X}$ and S^2, respectively. Because $\overline{X}$ is an unbiased estimate of μ, an intuitive decision rule is given by

$$\text{Reject } H_0 \text{ in favor of } H_1 \text{ if } \overline{X} \text{ is much larger than } \mu_0. \qquad (4.5.10)$$

In general, the distribution of the sample mean cannot be obtained in closed form. In Example 4.5.4, under the strong assumption of normality for the distribution of X, we obtain an exact test. For now, the Central Limit Theorem (Theorem 4.2.1) shows that the distribution of $(\overline{X} - \mu)/(S/\sqrt{n})$ is approximately $N(0,1)$. Using this, we obtain a test with an approximate size α, with the decision rule

$$\text{Reject } H_0 \text{ in favor of } H_1 \text{ if } \frac{\overline{X}-\mu_0}{S/\sqrt{n}} \geq z_\alpha. \qquad (4.5.11)$$

The test is intuitive. To reject H_0, $\overline{X}$ must exceed μ_0 by at least $z_\alpha S/\sqrt{n}$. To approximate the power function of the test, we use the Central Limit Theorem. Upon substituting σ for S, it readily follows that the approximate power function is

$$
\begin{aligned}
\gamma(\mu) &= P_\mu(\overline{X} \geq \mu_0 + z_\alpha \sigma/\sqrt{n}) \\
&= P_\mu\left(\frac{\overline{X}-\mu}{\sigma/\sqrt{n}} \geq \frac{\mu_0-\mu}{\sigma/\sqrt{n}} + z_\alpha\right) \\
&\approx 1 - \Phi\left(z_\alpha + \frac{\sqrt{n}(\mu_0-\mu)}{\sigma}\right) \\
&= \Phi\left(-z_\alpha - \frac{\sqrt{n}(\mu_0-\mu)}{\sigma}\right). \qquad (4.5.12)
\end{aligned}
$$

So if we have some reasonable idea of what σ equals, we can compute the approximate power function. As Exercise 4.5.1 shows, this approximate power function is strictly increasing in μ, so as in the last example, we can change the null hypotheses to

$$H_0 : \mu \leq \mu_0 \text{ versus } H_1 : \mu > \mu_0. \tag{4.5.13}$$

Our asymptotic test has approximate size α for these hypotheses. ∎

Example 4.5.4 (Test for μ Under Normality). Let X have a $N(\mu, \sigma^2)$ distribution. As in Example 4.5.3, consider the hypotheses

$$H_0 : \mu = \mu_0 \text{ versus } H_1 : \mu > \mu_0, \tag{4.5.14}$$

where μ_0 is specified. Assume that the desired size of the test is α, for $0 < \alpha < 1$, Suppose $X_1, \ldots, X_n$ is a random sample from a $N(\mu, \sigma^2)$ distribution. Let $\overline{X}$ and S^2 denote the sample mean and variance, respectively. Our intuitive rejection rule is to reject H_0 in favor of H_1 if $\overline{X}$ is much larger than μ_0. Unlike Example 4.5.3, we now know the distribution of the statistic $\overline{X}$. In particular, by Part (d) of Theorem 3.6.1, under H_0 the statistic $T = (\overline{X} - \mu_0)/(S/\sqrt{n})$ has a t-distribution with $n - 1$ degrees of freedom. Using the distribution of T, it follows that this rejection rule has exact level α:

$$\text{Reject } H_0 \text{ in favor of } H_1 \text{ if } T = \frac{\overline{X} - \mu_0}{S/\sqrt{n}} \geq t_{\alpha, n-1}, \tag{4.5.15}$$

where $t_{\alpha, n-1}$ is the upper α critical point of a t-distribution with $n - 1$ degrees of freedom; i.e., $\alpha = P(T > t_{\alpha, n-1})$. This is often called the **t-test** of $H_0 : \mu = \mu_0$.

Note the differences between this rejection rule and the large sample rule, (4.5.11). The large sample rule has approximate level α, while this has exact level α. Of course, we now have to assume that X has a normal distribution. In practice, we may not be willing to assume that the population is normal. Usually t-critical values are larger than z-critical values; hence, the t-test is conservative relative to the large sample test. So, in practice, many statisticians often use the t-test. ∎

Example 4.5.5 (Example 4.5.1, Continued). The data for Darwin's experiment on *Zea mays* are recorded in Table 4.5.2. A boxplot and a normal $q-q$ plot of the 15 differences, $x_i = y_i - z_i$, are found in Figure 4.5.2. Based on these plots, we can see that there seem to be two outliers, Pots 2 and 15. In these two pots, the self-fertilized *Zea mays* are much taller than their cross-fertilized pairs. Except for these two outliers, the differences, $y_i - z_i$, are positive, indicating that the cross-fertilization leads to taller plants. We proceed to conduct a test of hypotheses (4.5.2), as discussed in Example 4.5.4. We use the decision rule given by (4.5.15) with $\alpha = 0.05$. As Exercise 4.5.2 shows, the values of the sample mean and standard deviation for the differences, x_i, are $\overline{x} = 2.62$ and $s_x = 4.72$. Hence the t-test statistic is 2.15, which exceeds the t-critical value, $t_{.05,14} = 1.76$. Thus we reject H_0 and conclude that cross-fertilized *Zea mays* are on the average taller than self-fertilized *Zea mays*. Because of the outliers, normality of the error distribution is somewhat dubious, and we use the test in a conservative manner, as discussed at the end of Example 4.5.4. ∎

Table 4.5.2: Plant Growth

Pot	1	2	3	4	5	6	7	8
Cross	23.500	12.000	21.000	22.000	19.125	21.500	22.125	20.375
Self	17.375	20.375	20.000	20.000	18.375	18.625	18.625	15.250
Pot	9	10	11	12	13	14	15	
Cross	18.250	21.625	23.250	21.000	22.125	23.000	12.000	
Self	16.500	18.000	16.250	18.000	12.750	15.500	18.000	

Figure 4.5.2: Boxplot and normal $q-q$ plot for the data of Example 4.5.5.

EXERCISES

4.5.1. Show that the approximate power function given in expression (4.5.12) of Example 4.5.3 is a strictly increasing function of μ. Show then that the test discussed in this example has approximate size α for testing

$$H_0 : \mu \leq \mu_0 \text{ versus } H_1 : \mu > \mu_0.$$

4.5.2. For the Darwin data tabled in Example 4.5.5, verify that the Student t-test statistic is 2.15.

4.5.3. Let X have a pdf of the form $f(x; \theta) = \theta x^{\theta-1}$, $0 < x < 1$, zero elsewhere, where $\theta \in \{\theta : \theta = 1, 2\}$. To test the simple hypothesis $H_0 : \theta = 1$ against the alternative simple hypothesis $H_1 : \theta = 2$, use a random sample X_1, X_2 of size $n = 2$ and define the critical region to be $C = \{(x_1, x_2) : \frac{3}{4} \leq x_1 x_2\}$. Find the power function of the test.

4.5.4. Let X have a binomial distribution with the number of trials $n = 10$ and with p either 1/4 or 1/2. The simple hypothesis $H_0 : p = \frac{1}{2}$ is rejected, and the alternative simple hypothesis $H_1 : p = \frac{1}{4}$ is accepted, if the observed value of X_1, a random sample of size 1, is less than or equal to 3. Find the significance level and the power of the test.

4.5.5. Let X_1, X_2 be a random sample of size $n = 2$ from the distribution having pdf $f(x; \theta) = (1/\theta)e^{-x/\theta}$, $0 < x < \infty$, zero elsewhere. We reject $H_0 : \theta = 2$ and accept $H_1 : \theta = 1$ if the observed values of X_1, X_2, say x_1, x_2, are such that

$$\frac{f(x_1; 2)f(x_2; 2)}{f(x_1; 1)f(x_2; 1)} \le \frac{1}{2}.$$

Here $\Omega = \{\theta : \theta = 1, 2\}$. Find the significance level of the test and the power of the test when H_0 is false.

4.5.6. Consider the tests Test 1 and Test 2 for the situation discussed in Example 4.5.2. Consider the test which rejects H_0 if $S \le 10$. Find the level of significance for this test and sketch its power curve as in Figure 4.5.1.

4.5.7. Consider the situation described in Example 4.5.2. Suppose we have two tests A and B defined as follows. For Test A, H_0 is rejected if $S \le k_A$, while for Test B, H_0 is rejected if $S \le k_B$. If Test A has a higher level of significance than Test B, show that Test A has higher power than Test B at each alternative.

4.5.8. Let us say the life of a tire in miles, say X, is normally distributed with mean θ and standard deviation 5000. Past experience indicates that $\theta = 30{,}000$. The manufacturer claims that the tires made by a new process have mean $\theta > 30{,}000$. It is possible that $\theta = 35{,}000$. Check his claim by testing $H_0 : \theta = 30{,}000$ against $H_1 : \theta > 30{,}000$. We observe n independent values of X, say $x_1, \ldots, x_n$, and we reject H_0 (thus accept H_1) if and only if $\overline{x} \ge c$. Determine n and c so that the power function $\gamma(\theta)$ of the test has the values $\gamma(30{,}000) = 0.01$ and $\gamma(35{,}000) = 0.98$.

4.5.9. Let X have a Poisson distribution with mean θ. Consider the simple hypothesis $H_0 : \theta = \frac{1}{2}$ and the alternative composite hypothesis $H_1 : \theta < \frac{1}{2}$. Thus $\Omega = \{\theta : 0 < \theta \le \frac{1}{2}\}$. Let $X_1, \ldots, X_{12}$ denote a random sample of size 12 from this distribution. We reject H_0 if and only if the observed value of $Y = X_1 + \cdots + X_{12} \le 2$. If $\gamma(\theta)$ is the power function of the test, find the powers $\gamma(\frac{1}{2})$, $\gamma(\frac{1}{3})$, $\gamma(\frac{1}{4})$, $\gamma(\frac{1}{6})$, and $\gamma(\frac{1}{12})$. Sketch the graph of $\gamma(\theta)$. What is the significance level of the test?

4.5.10. Let Y have a binomial distribution with parameters n and p. We reject $H_0 : p = \frac{1}{2}$ and accept $H_1 : p > \frac{1}{2}$ if $Y \ge c$. Find n and c to give a power function $\gamma(p)$ which is such that $\gamma(\frac{1}{2}) = 0.10$ and $\gamma(\frac{2}{3}) = 0.95$, approximately.

4.5.11. Let $Y_1 < Y_2 < Y_3 < Y_4$ be the order statistics of a random sample of size $n = 4$ from a distribution with pdf $f(x; \theta) = 1/\theta$, $0 < x < \theta$, zero elsewhere, where $0 < \theta$. The hypothesis $H_0 : \theta = 1$ is rejected and $H_1 : \theta > 1$ is accepted if the observed $Y_4 \ge c$.

(a) Find the constant c so that the significance level is $\alpha = 0.05$.

(b) Determine the power function of the test.

4.5.12. Let $X_1, X_2, \ldots, X_8$ be a random sample of size $n = 8$ from a Poisson distribution with mean μ. Reject the simple null hypothesis $H_0 : \mu = 0.5$ and accept $H_1 : \mu > 0.5$ if the observed sum $\sum_{i=1}^{8} x_i \ge 8$.

(a) Compute the significance level α of the test.

(b) Find the power function $\gamma(\mu)$ of the test as a sum of Poisson probabilities.

(c) Using Table I of Appendix C, determine $\gamma(0.75)$, $\gamma(1)$, and $\gamma(1.25)$.

4.5.13. Let p denote the probability that, for a particular tennis player, the first serve is good. Since $p = 0.40$, this player decided to take lessons in order to increase p. When the lessons are completed, the hypothesis $H_0 : p = 0.40$ is tested against $H_1 : p > 0.40$ based on $n = 25$ trials. Let y equal the number of first serves that are good, and let the critical region be defined by $C = \{y : y \geq 13\}$.

(a) Determine $\alpha = P(Y \geq 13; p = 0.40)$.

(b) Find $\beta = P(Y < 13)$ when $p = 0.60$; that is, $\beta = P(Y \leq 12; \ p = 0.60)$ so that $1 - \beta$ is the power at $p = 0.60$.

4.6 Additional Comments About Statistical Tests

All of the alternative hypotheses considered in Section 4.5 were **one-sided hypotheses**. For illustration, in Exercise 4.5.8 we tested $H_0 : \mu = 30{,}000$ against the one-sided alternative $H_1 : \mu > 30{,}000$, where μ is the mean of a normal distribution having standard deviation $\sigma = 5000$. Perhaps in this situation, though, we think the manufacturer's process has changed but are unsure of the direction. That is, we are interested in the alternative $H_1 : \ \mu \neq 30{,}000$. In this section, we further explore hypotheses testing and we begin with the construction of a test for a two-sided alternative involving the mean of a random variable.

Example 4.6.1 (Large Sample Two-Sided Test for the Mean). In order to see how to construct a test for a two-sided alternative, reconsider Example 4.5.3, where we constructed a large sample one-sided test for the mean of a random variable. As in Example 4.5.3, let X be a random variable with mean μ and finite variance σ^2. Here, though, we want to test

$$H_0 : \ \mu = \mu_0 \text{ versus } H_1 : \ \mu \neq \mu_0, \qquad (4.6.1)$$

where μ_0 is specified. Let $X_1, \ldots, X_n$ be a random sample from the distribution of X and denote the sample mean and variance by $\overline{X}$ and S^2, respectively. For the one-sided test, we rejected H_0 if $\overline{X}$ was too large; hence, for the hypotheses (4.6.1), we use the decision rule

$$\text{Reject } H_0 \text{ in favor of } H_1 \text{ if } \overline{X} \leq h \text{ or } \overline{X} \geq k, \qquad (4.6.2)$$

where h and k are such that $\alpha = P_{H_0}[\overline{X} \leq h \text{ or } \overline{X} \geq k]$. Clearly, $h < k$; hence, we have

$$\alpha = P_{H_0}[\overline{X} \leq h \text{ or } \overline{X} \geq k] = P_{H_0}[\overline{X} \leq h] + P_{H_0}[\overline{X} \geq k].$$

Since, at least for large samples, the distribution of $\overline{X}$ is symmetrically distributed about μ_0, under H_0, an intuitive rule is to divide α equally between the two terms on the right side of the above expression; that is, h and k are chosen by

$$P_{H_0}[\overline{X} \le h] = \alpha/2 \text{ and } P_{H_0}[\overline{X} \ge k] = \alpha/2. \tag{4.6.3}$$

From Theorem 4.2.1, it follows that $(\overline{X} - \mu_0)/(S/\sqrt{n})$ is approximately $N(0,1)$. This and (4.6.3) lead to the approximate decision rule

$$\text{Reject } H_0 \text{ in favor of } H_1 \text{ if } \left| \frac{\overline{X}-\mu_0}{S/\sqrt{n}} \right| \ge z_{\alpha/2}. \tag{4.6.4}$$

Upon substituting σ for S, it readily follows that the approximate power function is

$$\gamma(\mu) = P_\mu(\overline{X} \le \mu_0 - z_{\alpha/2}\sigma/\sqrt{n}) + P_\mu(\overline{X} \ge \mu_0 + z_{\alpha/2}\sigma/\sqrt{n})$$

$$= \Phi\left(\frac{\sqrt{n}(\mu_0 - \mu)}{\sigma} - z_{\alpha/2} \right) + 1 - \Phi\left(\frac{\sqrt{n}(\mu_0 - \mu)}{\sigma} + z_{\alpha/2} \right), \tag{4.6.5}$$

where $\Phi(z)$ is the cdf of a standard normal random variable; see (3.4.10). So if we have some reasonable idea of what σ equals, we can compute the approximate power function. Note that the derivative of the power function is

$$\gamma'(\mu) = \frac{\sqrt{n}}{\sigma} \left[\phi\left(\frac{\sqrt{n}(\mu_0 - \mu)}{\sigma} + z_{\alpha/2} \right) - \phi\left(\frac{\sqrt{n}(\mu_0 - \mu)}{\sigma} - z_{\alpha/2} \right) \right], \tag{4.6.6}$$

where $\phi(z)$ is the pdf of a standard normal random variable. Note that $\gamma(\mu)$ has a critical value at μ_0. As Exercise 4.6.2 shows, this gives the minimum of $\gamma(\mu)$. Further, $\gamma(\mu)$ is strictly decreasing for $\mu < \mu_0$ and strictly increasing for $\mu > \mu_0$. ∎

Consider again the situation at the beginning of this section. Suppose we want to test

$$H_0 : \mu = 30,000 \text{ versus } H_1 : \mu \ne 30,000. \tag{4.6.7}$$

Suppose $n = 20$ and $\alpha = 0.01$. Then the rejection rule (4.6.4) becomes

$$\text{Reject } H_0 \text{ in favor of } H_1 \text{ if } \left| \frac{\overline{X}-30,000}{S/\sqrt{20}} \right| \ge 2.575. \tag{4.6.8}$$

Figure 4.6.1 shows the power curve for this test when $\sigma = 5000$, as in Exercise 4.5.8, is substituted in for S. For comparison, the power curve for the test with level $\alpha = 0.05$ is also shown; see Exercise 4.6.1.

The two-sided test for the mean is approximate. If we assume that X has a normal distribution, then, as Exercise 4.6.3 shows, the following test has exact size α for testing $H_0 : \mu = \mu_0$ versus $H_1 : \mu \ne \mu_0$:

$$\text{Reject } H_0 \text{ in favor of } H_1 \text{ if } \left| \frac{\overline{X}-\mu_0}{S/\sqrt{n}} \right| \ge t_{\alpha/2,n-1}. \tag{4.6.9}$$

It too has a bowl-shaped power curve similar to Figure 4.6.1, although it is not as easy to show; see Lehmann (1986).

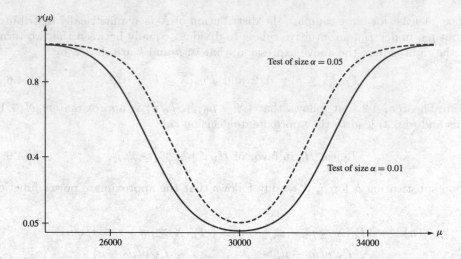

Figure 4.6.1: Power curves for the tests of the hypotheses (4.6.7).

There exists a relationship between two-sided tests and confidence intervals. Consider the two-sided t-test (4.6.9). Here, we use the rejection rule with "if and only if" replacing "if." Hence, in terms of acceptance, we have

Accept H_0 if and only if $\mu_0 - t_{\alpha/2,n-1}S/\sqrt{n} < \overline{X} < \mu_0 + t_{\alpha/2,n-1}S/\sqrt{n}$.

But this is easily shown to be

Accept H_0 if and only if $\mu_0 \in (\overline{X} - t_{\alpha/2,n-1}S/\sqrt{n}, \overline{X} + t_{\alpha/2,n-1}S/\sqrt{n})$;   (4.6.10)

that is, we accept H_0 at significance level α if and only if μ_0 is in the $(1-\alpha)100\%$ confidence interval for μ. Equivalently, we reject H_0 at significance level α if and only if μ_0 is not in the $(1-\alpha)100\%$ confidence interval for μ. This is true for all the two-sided tests and hypotheses discussed in this text. There is also a similar relationship between one-sided tests and one-sided confidence intervals.

Once we recognize this relationship between confidence intervals and tests of hypothesis, we can use all those statistics that we used to construct confidence intervals to test hypotheses, not only against two-sided alternatives but one-sided ones as well. Without listing all of these in a table, we present enough of them so that the principle can be understood.

Example 4.6.2. Let independent random samples be taken from $N(\mu_1, \sigma^2)$ and $N(\mu_2, \sigma^2)$, respectively. Say these have the respective sample characteristics n_1, $\overline{X}$, S_1^2 and n_2, $\overline{Y}$, S_2^2. Let $n = n_1 + n_2$ denote the combined sample size and let $S_p^2 = [(n_1-1)S_1^2 + (n_2-1)S_2^2]/(n-2)$, (4.2.11), be the pooled estimator of the common variance. At $\alpha = 0.05$, reject $H_0 : \mu_1 = \mu_2$ and accept the one-sided alternative $H_1 : \mu_1 > \mu_2$ if

$$T = \frac{\overline{X} - \overline{Y} - 0}{S_p\sqrt{\frac{1}{n_1} + \frac{1}{n_2}}} \geq t_{.05,n-2},$$

because, under $H_0 : \mu_1 = \mu_2$, T has a $t(n-2)$-distribution. A rigorous development of this test is given in Example 8.3.1. ∎

Example 4.6.3. Say X is $b(1,p)$. Consider testing $H_0 : p = p_0$ against $H_1 : p < p_0$. Let $X_1 \ldots, X_n$ be a random sample from the distribution of X and let $\widehat{p} = \overline{X}$. To test H_0 versus H_1, we use either

$$Z_1 = \frac{\widehat{p} - p_0}{\sqrt{p_0(1-p_0)/n}} \leq c \quad \text{or} \quad Z_2 = \frac{\widehat{p} - p_0}{\sqrt{\widehat{p}(1-\widehat{p})/n}} \leq c.$$

If n is large, both Z_1 and Z_2 have approximate standard normal distributions provided that $H_0 : p = p_0$ is true. Hence, if c is set at -1.645, then the approximate significance level is $\alpha = 0.05$. Some statisticians use Z_1 and others Z_2. We do not have strong preferences one way or the other because the two methods provide about the same numerical results. As one might suspect, using Z_1 provides better probabilities for power calculations if the true p is close to p_0, while Z_2 is better if H_0 is clearly false. However, with a two-sided alternative hypothesis, Z_2 does provide a better relationship with the confidence interval for p. That is, $|Z_2| < z_{\alpha/2}$ is equivalent to p_0 being in the interval from

$$\widehat{p} - z_{\alpha/2}\sqrt{\frac{\widehat{p}(1-\widehat{p})}{n}} \quad \text{to} \quad \widehat{p} + z_{\alpha/2}\sqrt{\frac{\widehat{p}(1-\widehat{p})}{n}},$$

which is the interval that provides a $(1-\alpha)100\%$ approximate confidence interval for p as considered in Section 4.2. ∎

In closing this section, we introduce the concepts of **randomized tests** and **p-values** through an example and remarks that follow the example.

Example 4.6.4. Let $X_1, X_2, \ldots, X_{10}$ be a random sample of size $n = 10$ from a Poisson distribution with mean θ. A critical region for testing $H_0 : \theta = 0.1$ against $H_1 : \theta > 0.1$ is given by $Y = \sum_1^{10} X_i \geq 3$. The statistic Y has a Poisson distribution with mean 10θ. Thus, with $\theta = 0.1$ so that the mean of Y is 1, the significance level of the test is

$$P(Y \geq 3) = 1 - P(Y \leq 2) = 1 - 0.920 = 0.080.$$

If the critical region defined by $\sum_1^{10} x_i \geq 4$ is used, the significance level is

$$\alpha = P(Y \geq 4) = 1 - P(Y \leq 3) = 1 - 0.981 = 0.019.$$

For instance, if a significance level of about $\alpha = 0.05$, say, is desired, most statisticians would use one of these tests; that is, they would adjust the significance level to that of one of these convenient tests. However, a significance level of $\alpha = 0.05$ can be achieved in the following way. Let W have a Bernoulli distribution with probability of success equal to

$$P(W = 1) = \frac{0.050 - 0.019}{0.080 - 0.019} = \frac{31}{61}.$$

Assume that W is selected independently of the sample. Consider the rejection rule

Reject H_0 if $\sum_1^{10} x_i \geq 4$ or if $\sum_1^{10} x_i = 3$ and $W = 1$.

The significance level of this rule is

$$
\begin{aligned}
P_{H_0}(Y \geq 4) + P_{H_0}(\{Y = 3\} \cap \{W = 1\}) &= P_{H_0}(Y \geq 4) \\
&\quad + P_{H_0}(Y = 3)P(W = 1) \\
&= 0.019 + 0.061\frac{31}{61} = 0.05;
\end{aligned}
$$

hence, the decision rule has exactly level 0.05. The process of performing the auxiliary experiment to decide whether to reject or not when $Y = 3$ is sometimes referred to as a **randomized test**. ∎

Remark 4.6.1 (Observed Significance Level). Not many statisticians like randomized tests in practice, because the use of them means that two statisticians could make the same assumptions, observe the same data, apply the same test, and yet make different decisions. Hence, they usually adjust their significance level so as not to randomize. As a matter of fact, many statisticians report what are commonly called **observed significance levels** or *p*-**values** (for *probability values*). For illustration, if in Example 4.6.4 the observed Y is $y = 4$, the *p*-value is 0.019; and if it is $y = 3$, the *p*-value is 0.080. That is, the *p*-value is the observed "tail" probability of a statistic being at least as extreme as the particular observed value when H_0 is true. Hence, more generally, if $Y = u(X_1, X_2, \ldots, X_n)$ is the statistic to be used in a test of H_0 and if the critical region is of the form

$$
u(x_1, x_2, \ldots, x_n) \leq c,
$$

an observed value $u(x_1, x_2, \ldots, x_n) = d$ means that the

$$
p\text{-value} = P_{H_0}(Y \leq d).
$$

That is, if $G(y)$ is the distribution function of $Y = u(X_1, X_2, \ldots, X_n)$, provided that H_0 is true, the *p*-value is equal to $G(d)$ in this case. However, $G(Y)$, in the continuous case, is uniformly distributed on the unit interval, so an observed value $G(d) \leq 0.05$ is equivalent to selecting c, so that

$$
P_{H_0}[u(X_1, X_2, \ldots, X_n) \leq c] = 0.05
$$

and observing that $d \leq c$. Most computer programs automatically print out the *p*-value of a test. ∎

Example 4.6.5. Let $X_1, X_2, \ldots, X_{25}$ be a random sample from $N(\mu, \sigma^2 = 4)$. To test $H_0 : \mu = 77$ against the one-sided alternative hypothesis $H_1 : \mu < 77$, say we observe the 25 values and determine that $\bar{x} = 76.1$. The variance of $\overline{X}$ is $\sigma^2/n = 4/25 = 0.16$; so we know that $Z = (\overline{X} - 77)/0.4$ is $N(0, 1)$ provided that $\mu = 77$. Since the observed value of this test statistic is $z = (76.1 - 77)/0.4 = -2.25$, the *p*-value of the test is $\Phi(-2.25) = 1 - 0.988 = 0.012$. Accordingly, if we were using a significance level of $\alpha = 0.05$, we would reject H_0 and accept $H_1 : \mu < 77$ because $0.012 < 0.05$. ∎

EXERCISES

4.6.1. For the test at level 0.05 of the hypotheses given by (4.6.1) with $\mu_0 = 30,000$ and $n = 20$, obtain the power function, (use $\sigma = 5000$). Evaluate the power function for the following values: $\mu = 25,000; 27,500; 30,000; 32,500$; and $35,000$. Then sketch this power function and see if it agrees with Figure 4.6.1.

4.6.2. Consider the power function $\gamma(\mu)$ and its derivative $\gamma'(\mu)$ given by (4.6.5) and (4.6.6). Show that $\gamma'(\mu)$ is strictly negative for $\mu < \mu_0$ and strictly positive for $\mu > \mu_0$.

4.6.3. Show that the test defined by 4.6.9 has exact size α for testing $H_0 : \mu = \mu_0$ versus $H_1 : \mu \neq \mu_0$.

4.6.4. Consider the one-sided t-test for $H_0 : \mu = \mu_0$ versus $H_{A1} : \mu > \mu_0$ constructed in Example 4.5.4 and the two-sided t-test for t-test for $H_0 : \mu = \mu_0$ versus $H_1 : \mu \neq \mu_0$ given in (4.6.9). Assume that both tests are of size α. Show that for $\mu > \mu_0$, the power function of the one-sided test is larger than the power function of the two-sided test.

4.6.5. Assume that the weight of cereal in a "10-ounce box" is $N(\mu, \sigma^2)$. To test $H_0 : \mu = 10.1$ against $H_1 : \mu > 10.1$, we take a random sample of size $n = 16$ and observe that $\bar{x} = 10.4$ and $s = 0.4$.

(a) Do we accept or reject H_0 at the 5% significance level?

(b) What is the approximate p-value of this test?

4.6.6. Each of 51 golfers hit three golf balls of brand X and three golf balls of brand Y in a random order. Let X_i and Y_i equal the averages of the distances traveled by the brand X and brand Y golf balls hit by the ith golfer, $i = 1, 2, \ldots, 51$. Let $W_i = X_i - Y_i$, $i = 1, 2, \ldots, 51$. Test $H_0 : \mu_W = 0$ against $H_1 : \mu_W > 0$, where μ_W is the mean of the differences. If $w = 2.07$ and $s_W^2 = 84.63$, would H_0 be accepted or rejected at an $\alpha = 0.05$ significance level? What is the p-value of this test?

4.6.7. Among the data collected for the World Health Organization air quality monitoring project is a measure of suspended particles in $\mu g/m^3$. Let X and Y equal the concentration of suspended particles in $\mu g/m^3$ in the city center (commercial district) for Melbourne and Houston, respectively. Using $n = 13$ observations of X and $m = 16$ observations of Y, we test $H_0 : \mu_X = \mu_Y$ against $H_1 : \mu_X < \mu_Y$.

(a) Define the test statistic and critical region, assuming that the unknown variances are equal. Let $\alpha = 0.05$.

(b) If $\bar{x} = 72.9$, $s_x = 25.6$, $\bar{y} = 81.7$, and $s_y = 28.3$, calculate the value of the test statistic and state your conclusion.

4.6.8. Let p equal the proportion of drivers who use a seat belt in a country that does not have a mandatory seat belt law. It was claimed that $p = 0.14$. An advertising campaign was conducted to increase this proportion. Two months after the campaign, $y = 104$ out of a random sample of $n = 590$ drivers were wearing their seat belts. Was the campaign successful?

(a) Define the null and alternative hypotheses.

(b) Define a critical region with an $\alpha = 0.01$ significance level.

(c) Determine the approximate p-value and state your conclusion.

4.6.9. In Exercise 4.2.18 we found a confidence interval for the variance σ^2 using the variance S^2 of a random sample of size n arising from $N(\mu, \sigma^2)$, where the mean μ is unknown. In testing $H_0 : \sigma^2 = \sigma_0^2$ against $H_1 : \sigma^2 > \sigma_0^2$, use the critical region defined by $(n-1)S^2/\sigma_0^2 \geq c$. That is, reject H_0 and accept H_1 if $S^2 \geq c\sigma_0^2/(n-1)$. If $n = 13$ and the significance level $\alpha = 0.025$, determine c.

4.6.10. In Exercise 4.2.27, in finding a confidence interval for the ratio of the variances of two normal distributions, we used a statistic S_1^2/S_2^2, which has an F-distribution when those two variances are equal. If we denote that statistic by F, we can test $H_0 : \sigma_1^2 = \sigma_2^2$ against $H_1 : \sigma_1^2 > \sigma_2^2$ using the critical region $F \geq c$. If $n = 13$, $m = 11$, and $\alpha = 0.05$, find c.

4.7 Chi-Square Tests

In this section we introduce tests of statistical hypotheses called **chi-square tests**. A test of this sort was originally proposed by Karl Pearson in 1900, and it provided one of the earlier methods of statistical inference.

Let the random variable X_i be $N(\mu_i, \sigma_i^2)$, $i = 1, 2, \ldots, n$, and let $X_1, X_2, \ldots, X_n$ be mutually independent. Thus the joint pdf of these variables is

$$\frac{1}{\sigma_1 \sigma_2 \cdots \sigma_n (2\pi)^{n/2}} \exp\left[-\frac{1}{2}\sum_1^n \left(\frac{x_i - \mu_i}{\sigma_i}\right)^2\right], \quad -\infty < x_i < \infty.$$

The random variable that is defined by the exponent (apart from the coefficient $-\frac{1}{2}$) is $\sum_1^n [(X_i - \mu_i)/\sigma_i]^2$, and this random variable has a $\chi^2(n)$ distribution. In Section 3.5 we generalized this joint normal distribution of probability to n random variables that are *dependent* and we called the distribution a *multivariate normal distribution*. In Section 9.8, we show that a certain exponent in the joint pdf (apart from a coefficient of $-1/2$) defines a random variable that is $\chi^2(n)$. This fact is the mathematical basis of the chi-square tests.

Let us now discuss some random variables that have approximate chi-square distributions. Let X_1 be $b(n, p_1)$. Consider the random variable

$$Y = \frac{X_1 - np_1}{\sqrt{np_1(1 - p_1)}},$$

which has, as $n \to \infty$, an approximate $N(0, 1)$ distribution (see Theorem 4.2.1). Furthermore, as discussed in Example 5.3.6, the distribution of Y^2 is approximately $\chi^2(1)$. Let $X_2 = n - X_1$ and let $p_2 = 1 - p_1$. Let $Q_1 = Y^2$. Then Q_1 may be written as

$$Q_1 = \frac{(X_1 - np_1)^2}{np_1(1 - p_1)} = \frac{(X_1 - np_1)^2}{np_1} + \frac{(X_1 - np_1)^2}{n(1 - p_1)}$$

$$= \frac{(X_1 - np_1)^2}{np_1} + \frac{(X_2 - np_2)^2}{np_2} \qquad (4.7.1)$$

because $(X_1 - np_1)^2 = (n - X_2 - n + np_2)^2 = (X_2 - np_2)^2$. This result can be generalized as follows.

Let $X_1, X_2, \ldots, X_{k-1}$ have a multinomial distribution with the parameters n and $p_1, \ldots, p_{k-1}$, as in Section 3.1. Let $X_k = n - (X_1 + \cdots + X_{k-1})$ and let $p_k = 1 - (p_1 + \cdots + p_{k-1})$. Define Q_{k-1} by

$$Q_{k-1} = \sum_{i=1}^{k} \frac{(X_i - np_i)^2}{np_i}.$$

It is proved in a more advanced course that, as $n \to \infty$, Q_{k-1} has an approximate $\chi^2(k - 1)$ distribution. Some writers caution the user of this approximation to be certain that n is large enough so that each np_i, $i = 1, 2, \ldots, k$, is at least equal to 5. In any case, it is important to realize that Q_{k-1} does not have a chi-square distribution, only an approximate chi-square distribution.

The random variable Q_{k-1} may serve as the basis of the tests of certain statistical hypotheses which we now discuss. Let the sample space $\mathcal{A}$ of a random experiment be the union of a finite number k of mutually disjoint sets $A_1, A_2, \ldots, A_k$. Furthermore, let $P(A_i) = p_i$, $i = 1, 2, \ldots, k$, where $p_k = 1 - p_1 - \cdots - p_{k-1}$, so that p_i is the probability that the outcome of the random experiment is an element of the set A_i. The random experiment is to be repeated n independent times and X_i represents the number of times the outcome is an element of set A_i. That is, $X_1, X_2, \ldots, X_k = n - X_1 - \cdots - X_{k-1}$ are the frequencies with which the outcome is, respectively, an element of $A_1, A_2, \ldots, A_k$. Then the joint pmf of $X_1, X_2, \ldots, X_{k-1}$ is the multinomial pmf with the parameters n, $p_1, \ldots, p_{k-1}$. Consider the simple hypothesis (concerning this multinomial pmf) $H_0 : p_1 = p_{10}$, $p_2 = p_{20}, \ldots, p_{k-1} = p_{k-1,0}$ $(p_k = p_{k0} = 1 - p_{10} - \cdots - p_{k-1,0})$, where $p_{10}, \ldots, p_{k-1,0}$ are specified numbers. It is desired to test H_0 against all alternatives.

If the hypothesis H_0 is true, the random variable

$$Q_{k-1} = \sum_{1}^{k} \frac{(X_i - np_{i0})^2}{np_{i0}}$$

has an approximate chi-square distribution with $k - 1$ degrees of freedom. Since, when H_0 is true, np_{i0} is the expected value of X_i, one would feel intuitively that observed values of Q_{k-1} should not be too large if H_0 is true. With this in mind, we may use Table II of Appendix C, with $k - 1$ degrees of freedom, and find c so that $P(Q_{k-1} \geq c) = \alpha$, where α is the desired significance level of the test. If, then, the hypothesis H_0 is rejected when the observed value of Q_{k-1} is at least as great as c, the test of H_0 has a significance level that is approximately equal to α. This is frequently called a **goodness-of-fit test**. Some illustrative examples follow.

Example 4.7.1. One of the first six positive integers is to be chosen by a random experiment (perhaps by the cast of a die). Let $A_i = \{x : x = i\}$, $i = 1, 2, \ldots, 6$. The hypothesis $H_0 : P(A_i) = p_{i0} = \frac{1}{6}$, $i = 1, 2, \ldots, 6$, is tested, at the approximate 5% significance level, against all alternatives. To make the test, the random experiment is repeated under the same conditions, 60 independent times. In this example, $k = 6$ and $np_{i0} = 60(\frac{1}{6}) = 10$, $i = 1, 2, \ldots, 6$. Let X_i denote the frequency with which the random experiment terminates with the outcome in A_i, $i = 1, 2, \ldots, 6$, and let $Q_5 = \sum_1^6 (X_i - 10)^2/10$. If H_0 is true, Table II, with $k - 1 = 6 - 1 = 5$ degrees of freedom, shows that we have $P(Q_5 \geq 11.1) = 0.05$. Now suppose that the experimental frequencies of $A_1, A_2, \ldots, A_6$ are, respectively, 13, 19, 11, 8, 5, and 4. The observed value of Q_5 is

$$\frac{(13 - 10)^2}{10} + \frac{(19 - 10)^2}{10} + \frac{(11 - 10)^2}{10} + \frac{(8 - 10)^2}{10} + \frac{(5 - 10)^2}{10} + \frac{(4 - 10)^2}{10} = 15.6.$$

Since $15.6 > 11.1$, the hypothesis $P(A_i) = \frac{1}{6}$, $i = 1, 2, \ldots, 6$, is rejected at the (approximate) 5% significance level. ∎

Example 4.7.2. A point is to be selected from the unit interval $\{x : 0 < x < 1\}$ by a random process. Let $A_1 = \{x : 0 < x \leq \frac{1}{4}\}$, $A_2 = \{x : \frac{1}{4} < x \leq \frac{1}{2}\}$, $A_3 = \{x : \frac{1}{2} < x \leq \frac{3}{4}\}$, and $A_4 = \{x : \frac{3}{4} < x < 1\}$. Let the probabilities p_i, $i = 1, 2, 3, 4$, assigned to these sets under the hypothesis be determined by the pdf $2x$, $0 < x < 1$, zero elsewhere. Then these probabilities are, respectively,

$$p_{10} = \int_0^{1/4} 2x \, dx = \frac{1}{16}, \quad p_{20} = \frac{3}{16}, \quad p_{30} = \frac{5}{16}, \quad p_{40} = \frac{7}{16}.$$

Thus the hypothesis to be tested is that p_1, p_2, p_3, and $p_4 = 1 - p_1 - p_2 - p_3$ have the preceding values in a multinomial distribution with $k = 4$. This hypothesis is to be tested at an approximate 0.025 significance level by repeating the random experiment $n = 80$ independent times under the same conditions. Here the np_{i0} for $i = 1, 2, 3, 4$, are, respectively, 5, 15, 25, and 35. Suppose the observed frequencies of A_1, A_2, A_3, and A_4 are 6, 18, 20, and 36, respectively. Then the observed value of $Q_3 = \sum_1^4 (X_i - np_{i0})^2/(np_{i0})$ is

$$\frac{(6 - 5)^2}{5} + \frac{(18 - 15)^2}{15} + \frac{(20 - 25)^2}{25} + \frac{(36 - 35)^2}{35} = \frac{64}{35} = 1.83,$$

approximately. From Table II, with $4 - 1 = 3$ degrees of freedom, the value corresponding to a 0.025 significance level is $c = 9.35$. Since the observed value of Q_3 is less than 9.35, the hypothesis is accepted at the (approximate) 0.025 level of significance. ∎

Thus far we have used the chi-square test when the hypothesis H_0 is a simple hypothesis. More often we encounter hypotheses H_0 in which the multinomial probabilities $p_1, p_2, \ldots, p_k$ are not completely specified by the hypothesis H_0. That is, under H_0, these probabilities are functions of unknown parameters. For an illustration, suppose that a certain random variable Y can take on any real value. Let us partition the space $\{y : -\infty < y < \infty\}$ into k mutually disjoint sets $A_1, A_2, \ldots, A_k$ so that the events $A_1, A_2, \ldots, A_k$ are mutually exclusive and exhaustive. Let H_0 be the hypothesis that Y is $N(\mu, \sigma^2)$ with μ and σ^2 unspecified. Then each

$$p_i = \int_{A_i} \frac{1}{\sqrt{2\pi}\sigma} \exp[-(y-\mu)^2/2\sigma^2]\, dy, \quad i = 1, 2, \ldots, k,$$

is a function of the unknown parameters μ and σ^2. Suppose that we take a random sample $Y_1, \ldots, Y_n$ of size n from this distribution. If we let X_i denote the frequency of A_i, $i = 1, 2, \ldots, k$, so that $X_1 + X_2 + \cdots + X_k = n$, the random variable

$$Q_{k-1} = \sum_{i=1}^{k} \frac{(X_i - np_i)^2}{np_i}$$

cannot be computed once $X_1, \ldots, X_k$ have been observed, since each p_i, and hence Q_{k-1}, is a function of μ and σ^2. Accordingly, choose the values of μ and σ^2 that minimize Q_{k-1}. These values depend upon the observed $X_1 = x_1, \ldots, X_k = x_k$ and are called **minimum chi-square estimates** of μ and σ^2. These point estimates of μ and σ^2 enable us to compute numerically the estimates of each p_i. Accordingly, if these values are used, Q_{k-1} can be computed once $Y_1, Y_2, \ldots, Y_n$, and hence $X_1, X_2, \ldots, X_k$, are observed. However, a very important aspect of the fact, which we accept without proof, is that now Q_{k-1} is approximately $\chi^2(k-3)$. That is, the number of degrees of freedom of the approximate chi-square distribution of Q_{k-1} is reduced by one for each parameter estimated by the observed data. This statement applies not only to the problem at hand but also to more general situations. Two examples are now be given. The first of these examples deals with the test of the hypothesis that two multinomial distributions are the same.

Remark 4.7.1. In many cases, such as that involving the mean μ and the variance σ^2 of a normal distribution, minimum chi-square estimates are difficult to compute. Other estimates, such as the maximum likelihood estimates (Chapter 6), $\hat{\mu} = \overline{Y}$ and $\hat{\sigma^2} = V = (n-1)S^2/n$, are used to evaluate p_i and Q_{k-1}. In general, Q_{k-1} is not minimized by maximum likelihood estimates, and thus its computed value is somewhat greater than it would be if minimum chi-square estimates are used. Hence, when comparing it to a critical value listed in the chi-square table with $k-3$ degrees of freedom, there is a greater chance of rejection than there would be if the actual minimum of Q_{k-1} is used. Accordingly, the approximate significance level of such a test is somewhat higher than the value found in the table. This modification should be kept in mind and, if at all possible, each p_i should be estimated using the frequencies $X_1, \ldots, X_k$ rather than directly using the observations $Y_1, Y_2, \ldots, Y_n$ of the random sample. ∎

Example 4.7.3. In this example, we consider two multinomial distributions with parameters $n_j, p_{1j}, p_{2j}, \ldots, p_{kj}$ and $j = 1, 2$, respectively. Let X_{ij}, $i = 1, 2, \ldots, k$, $j = 1, 2$, represent the corresponding frequencies. If n_1 and n_2 are large and the

observations from one distribution are independent of those from the other, the
random variable

$$\sum_{j=1}^{2}\sum_{i=1}^{k}\frac{(X_{ij}-n_j p_{ij})^2}{n_j p_{ij}}$$

is the sum of two independent random variables each of which we treat as though it
were $\chi^2(k-1)$; that is, the random variable is approximately $\chi^2(2k-2)$. Consider
the hypothesis

$$H_0 : p_{11} = p_{12}, p_{21} = p_{22}, \ldots, p_{k1} = p_{k2},$$

where each $p_{i1} = p_{i2}$, $i = 1, 2, \ldots, k$, is unspecified. Thus we need point estimates
of these parameters. The maximum likelihood estimator of $p_{i1} = p_{i2}$, based upon
the frequencies X_{ij}, is $(X_{i1} + X_{i2})/(n_1 + n_2)$, $i = 1, 2, \ldots, k$. Note that we need
only $k-1$ point estimates, because we have a point estimate of $p_{k1} = p_{k2}$ once we
have point estimates of the first $k-1$ probabilities. In accordance with the fact
that has been stated, the random variable

$$\sum_{j=1}^{2}\sum_{i=1}^{k}\frac{\{X_{ij}-n_j[(X_{i1}+X_{i2})/(n_1+n_2)]\}^2}{n_j[(X_{i1}+X_{i2})/(n_1+n_2)]}$$

has an approximate χ^2 distribution with $2k-2-(k-1) = k-1$ degrees of freedom.
Thus we are able to test the hypothesis that two multinomial distributions are the
same; this hypothesis is rejected when the computed value of this random variable
is at least as great as an appropriate number from Table II, with $k-1$ degrees of
freedom. This test is often called the chi-square test for *homogeneity*, (the null is
equivalent to homogeneous distributions). ∎

The second example deals with the subject of **contingency tables**.

Example 4.7.4. Let the result of a random experiment be classified by two attributes (such as the color of the hair and the color of the eyes). That is, one
attribute of the outcome is one and only one of certain mutually exclusive and
exhaustive events, say $A_1, A_2, \ldots, A_a$; and the other attribute of the outcome is
also one and only one of certain mutually exclusive and exhaustive events, say
$B_1, B_2, \ldots, B_b$. Let $p_{ij} = P(A_i \cap B_j)$, $i = 1, 2, \ldots, a$; $j = 1, 2, \ldots, b$. The random
experiment is repeated n independent times and X_{ij} denotes the frequency of the
event $A_i \cap B_j$. Since there are $k = ab$ such events as $A_i \cap B_j$, the random variable

$$Q_{ab-1} = \sum_{j=1}^{b}\sum_{i=1}^{a}\frac{(X_{ij}-n p_{ij})^2}{n p_{ij}}$$

has an approximate chi-square distribution with $ab-1$ degrees of freedom, provided
that n is large. Suppose that we wish to test the independence of the A and the B
attributes, i.e., the hypothesis $H_0 : P(A_i \cap B_j) = P(A_i)P(B_j)$, $i = 1, 2, \ldots, a$; $j =
1, 2, \ldots, b$. Let us denote $P(A_i)$ by $p_{i.}$ and $P(B_j)$ by $p_{.j}$. It follows that

$$p_{i.} = \sum_{j=1}^{b} p_{ij}, \quad p_{.j} = \sum_{i=1}^{a} p_{ij}, \quad \text{and} \quad 1 = \sum_{j=1}^{b}\sum_{i=1}^{a} p_{ij} = \sum_{j=1}^{b} p_{.j} = \sum_{i=1}^{a} p_{i.}.$$

Then the hypothesis can be formulated as $H_0 : p_{ij} = p_{i.}p_{.j}$, $i = 1, 2, \ldots, a$; $j = 1, 2, \ldots, b$. To test H_0, we can use Q_{ab-1} with p_{ij} replaced by $p_{i.}p_{.j}$. But if $p_{i.}$, $i = 1, 2, \ldots, a$, and $p_{.j}$, $j = 1, 2, \ldots, b$, are unknown, as they frequently are in applications, we cannot compute Q_{ab-1} once the frequencies are observed. In such a case, we estimate these unknown parameters by

$$\hat{p}_{i.} = \frac{X_{i.}}{n}, \text{ where } X_{i.} = \sum_{j=1}^{b} X_{ij}, \text{ for } i = 1, 2, \ldots, a,$$

and

$$\hat{p}_{.j} = \frac{X_{.j}}{n}, \text{ where } X_{.j} = \sum_{i=1}^{a} X_{ij}, \text{ for } j = 1, 2, \ldots, b.$$

Since $\sum_i p_{i.} = \sum_j p_{.j} = 1$, we have estimated only $a-1+b-1 = a+b-2$ parameters. So if these estimates are used in Q_{ab-1}, with $p_{ij} = p_{i.}p_{.j}$, then, according to the rule that has been stated in this section, the random variable

$$\sum_{j=1}^{b} \sum_{i=1}^{a} \frac{[X_{ij} - n(X_{i.}/n)(X_{.j}/n)]^2}{n(X_{i.}/n)(X_{.j}/n)}$$

has an approximate chi-square distribution with $ab - 1 - (a+b-2) = (a-1)(b-1)$ degrees of freedom provided that H_0 is true. The hypothesis H_0 is then rejected if the computed value of this statistic exceeds the constant c, where c is selected from Table II so that the test has the desired significance level α. This is the *chi-square test* for independence. ∎

In each of the four examples of this section, we have indicated that the statistic used to test the hypothesis H_0 has an approximate chi-square distribution, provided that n is sufficiently large and H_0 is true. To compute the power of any of these tests for values of the parameters not described by H_0, we need the distribution of the statistic when H_0 is not true. In each of these cases, the statistic has an approximate distribution called a **noncentral chi-square distribution**. The noncentral chi-square distribution is discussed later in Section 9.3.

EXERCISES

4.7.1. A number is to be selected from the interval $\{x : 0 < x < 2\}$ by a random process. Let $A_i = \{x : (i - 1)/2 < x \le i/2\}$, $i = 1, 2, 3$, and let $A_4 = \{x : \frac{3}{2} < x < 2\}$. For $i = 1, 2, 3, 4$, suppose a certain hypothesis assigns probabilities p_{i0} to these sets in accordance with $p_{i0} = \int_{A_i} (\frac{1}{2})(2 - x)\, dx$, $i = 1, 2, 3, 4$. This hypothesis (concerning the multinomial pdf with $k = 4$) is to be tested at the 5% level of significance by a chi-square test. If the observed frequencies of the sets A_i, $i = 1, 2, 3, 4$, are respectively, 30, 30, 10, 10, would H_0 be accepted at the (approximate) 5% level of significance?

4.7.2. Define the sets $A_1 = \{x : -\infty < x \le 0\}$, $A_i = \{x : i - 2 < x \le i - 1\}$, $i = 2, \ldots, 7$, and $A_8 = \{x : 6 < x < \infty\}$. A certain hypothesis assigns probabilities p_{i0} to these sets A_i in accordance with

$$p_{i0} = \int_{A_i} \frac{1}{2\sqrt{2\pi}} \exp\left[-\frac{(x-3)^2}{2(4)}\right] \, dx, \quad i = 1, 2, \ldots, 7, 8.$$

This hypothesis (concerning the multinomial pdf with $k = 8$) is to be tested, at the 5% level of significance, by a chi-square test. If the observed frequencies of the sets A_i, $i = 1, 2, \ldots, 8$, are, respectively, 60, 96, 140, 210, 172, 160, 88, and 74, would H_0 be acccpted at the (approximate) 5% level of significance?

4.7.3. A die was cast $n = 120$ independent times and the following data resulted:

Spots Up	1	2	3	4	5	6
Frequency	b	20	20	20	20	$40 - b$

If we use a chi-square test, for what values of b would the hypothesis that the die is unbiased be rejected at the 0.025 significance level?

4.7.4. Consider the problem from genetics of crossing two types of peas. The Mendelian theory states that the probabilities of the classifications (a) round and yellow, (b) wrinkled and yellow, (c) round and green, and (d) wrinkled and green are $\frac{9}{16}$, $\frac{3}{16}$, $\frac{3}{16}$, and $\frac{1}{16}$, respectively. If, from 160 independent observations, the observed frequencies of these respective classifications are 86, 35, 26, and 13, are these data consistent with the Mendelian theory? That is, test, with $\alpha = 0.01$, the hypothesis that the respective probabilities are $\frac{9}{16}$, $\frac{3}{16}$, $\frac{3}{16}$, and $\frac{1}{16}$.

4.7.5. Two different teaching procedures were used on two different groups of students. Each group contained 100 students of about the same ability. At the end of the term, an evaluating team assigned a letter grade to each student. The results were tabulated as follows.

Group	Grade					
	A	B	C	D	F	Total
I	15	25	32	17	11	100
II	9	18	29	28	16	100

If we consider these data to be independent observations from two respective multinomial distributions with $k = 5$, test at the 5% significance level the hypothesis that the two distributions are the same (and hence the two teaching procedures are equally effective).

4.7.6. Let the result of a random experiment be classified as one of the mutually exclusive and exhaustive ways A_1, A_2, A_3 and also as one of the mutually exclusive and exhaustive ways B_1, B_2, B_3, B_4. Two hundred independent trials of the experiment result in the following data:

	B_1	B_2	B_3	B_4
A_1	10	21	15	6
A_2	11	27	21	13
A_3	6	19	27	24

Test, at the 0.05 significance level, the hypothesis of independence of the A attribute and the B attribute, namely, $H_0 : P(A_i \cap B_j) = P(A_i)P(B_j)$, $i = 1, 2, 3$ and $j = 1, 2, 3, 4$, against the alternative of dependence.

4.7.7. A certain genetic model suggests that the probabilities of a particular trinomial distribution are, respectively, $p_1 = p^2$, $p_2 = 2p(1-p)$, and $p_3 = (1-p)^2$, where $0 < p < 1$. If X_1, X_2, X_3 represent the respective frequencies in n independent trials, explain how we could check on the adequacy of the genetic model.

4.7.8. Let the result of a random experiment be classified as one of the mutually exclusive and exhaustive ways A_1, A_2, A_3 and also as one of the mutually exhaustive ways B_1, B_2, B_3, B_4. Say that 180 independent trials of the experiment result in the following frequencies:

	B_1	B_2	B_3	B_4
A_1	$15 - 3k$	$15 - k$	$15 + k$	$15 + 3k$
A_2	15	15	15	15
A_3	$15 + 3k$	$15 + k$	$15 - k$	$15 - 3k$

where k is one of the integers $0, 1, 2, 3, 4, 5$. What is the smallest value of k that leads to the rejection of the independence of the A attribute and the B attribute at the $\alpha = 0.05$ significance level?

4.7.9. It is proposed to fit the Poisson distribution to the following data:

x	0	1	2	3	$3 < x$
Frequency	20	40	16	18	6

(a) Compute the corresponding chi-square goodness-of-fit statistic.
   Hint: In computing the mean, treat $3 < x$ as $x = 4$.

(b) How many degrees of freedom are associated with this chi-square?

(c) Do these data result in the rejection of the Poisson model at the $\alpha = 0.05$ significance level?

4.8 The Method of Monte Carlo

In this section we introduce the concept of generating observations from a specified distribution or sample. This is often called **Monte Carlo** generation. This technique has been used for simulating complicated processes and investigating finite sample properties of statistical methodology for some time now. In the last 20 years, however, this has become a very important concept in modern statistics in the realm of inference based on the bootstrap (resampling) and modern Bayesian methods. We repeatedly make use of this concept throughout the book.

For the most part, a generator of random uniform observations is all that is needed. It is not easy to construct a device which generates random uniform observations. However, there has been considerable work done in this area, not only in the construction of such generators, but in the testing of their accuracy as well.

Most statistical software packages have reliable uniform generators. We make use of this fact in the text. For the examples and exercises, we often use *simple* algorithms written in R code (Ihaka and Gentleman, 1996), which are almost *self-explanatory*. Most of these additional R functions can be found in Appendix B. The package R is freeware and runs on most platforms. Besides R, there are other excellent statistical computing packages such as S-PLUS and Maple which can be easily used.

Suppose then we have a device capable of generating a stream of independent and identically distributed observations from a uniform $(0, 1)$ distribution. For example, the following command generates 10 such observations in the language R: `runif(10)`. In this command the r stands for random, the unif stands for uniform, the 10 stands for the number of observations requested, and the lack of additional arguments means that the standard uniform $(0, 1)$ generator is used.

For observations from a discrete distribution, often a uniform generator suffices. For a simple example, consider an experiment where a fair six-sided die is rolled and the random variable X is 1 if the upface is a "low number," namely $\{1, 2\}$; otherwise, $X = 0$. Note that the mean of X is $\mu = 1/3$. If U has a uniform $(0, 1)$ distribution, then X can be realized as

$$X = \begin{cases} 1 & \text{if } 0 < U \leq 1/3 \\ 0 & \text{if } 1/3 < U < 1. \end{cases}$$

Using the command above, we used the following R code to generate 10 observations from this experiment:

```
n = 10
u = runif(n)
x = rep(0,n)
cut = 1/3
for(i in 1:n){if(u[i] <= cut){x[i]=1}}
x
```

The following table displays the results.

u_i	0.4743	0.7891	0.5550	0.9693	0.0299
x_i	0	0	0	0	1
u_i	0.8425	0.6012	0.1009	0.0545	0.4677
x_i	0	0	1	1	0

Note that observations form a realization of a random sample $X_1, \ldots, X_{10}$ drawn from the distribution of X. For these 10 observations, the realized value of the statistic $\overline{X}$ is $\overline{x} = 0.3$.

Example 4.8.1 (Estimation of π). Consider the experiment where a pair of numbers (U_1, U_2) is chosen at random in the unit square, as shown in Figure 4.8.1; that is, U_1 and U_2 are iid uniform $(0, 1)$ random variables. Since the point is chosen at random, the probability of (U_1, U_2) lying within the unit circle is $\pi/4$. Let X be the random variable,

$$X = \begin{cases} 1 & \text{if } U_1^2 + U_2^2 < 1 \\ 0 & \text{otherwise.} \end{cases}$$

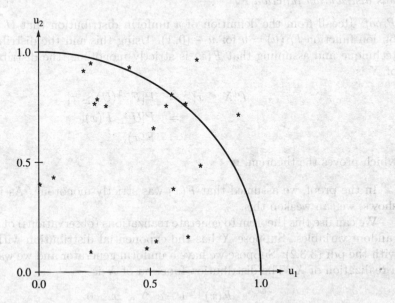

Figure 4.8.1: Unit square with the first quadrant of the unit circle, Example 4.8.1.

Hence the mean of X is $\mu = \pi/4$. Now suppose π is unknown. One way of estimating π is to repeat the experiment n independent times, hence, obtaining a random sample $X_1, \ldots, X_n$ on X. The statistic $4\overline{X}$ is an unbiased estimator of π. In Appendix B, a simple R routine, `piest`, is found which repeats the experiment n times and returns the estimate of π. Figure 4.8.1 shows 20 realizations of this experiment. Note that of the 20 points, 15 fall within the unit circle. Hence our estimate of π is $4(15/20) = 3.00$. We ran this code for various values of n with the following results:

n	100	500	1000	10,000	100,000
$4\overline{x}$	3.24	3.072	3.132	3.138	3.13828
$1.96 \cdot 4\sqrt{\overline{x}(1-\overline{x})/n}$	0.308	0.148	0.102	0.032	0.010

We can use the large sample confidence interval derived in Section 4.2 to estimate the error of estimation. The corresponding 95% confidence interval for π is

$$\left(4\overline{x} - 1.96 \cdot 4\sqrt{\overline{x}(1-\overline{x})/n},\, 4\overline{x} + 1.96 \cdot 4\sqrt{\overline{x}(1-\overline{x})/n}\right). \qquad (4.8.1)$$

The last row of the above table contains the error part of the confidence intervals. Notice that all five confidence intervals trapped the true value of π. ∎

What about continuous random variables? For these we have the following theorem:

Theorem 4.8.1. *Suppose the random variable U has a uniform $(0,1)$ distribution. Let F be a continuous distribution function. Then the random variable $X = F^{-1}(U)$ has distribution function F.*

Proof: Recall from the definition of a uniform distribution that U has the distribution function $F_U(u) = u$ for $u \in (0,1)$. Using this and the distribution-function technique and assuming that $F(x)$ is strictly monotone, the distribution function of X is

$$
\begin{aligned}
P[X \le x] &= P[F^{-1}(U) \le x] \\
&= P[U \le F(x)] \\
&= F(x),
\end{aligned}
$$

which proves the theorem. ∎

In the proof, we assumed that $F(x)$ was strictly monotone. As Exercise 4.8.13 shows, we can weaken this.

We can use this theorem to generate realizations (observations) of many different random variables. Suppose X has the exponential distribution with parameter λ with the pdf (3.3.2). Suppose we have a uniform generator and we want to generate a realization of X. The distribution function of X is

$$ F(x) = 1 - e^{-\lambda x}, \quad x > 0. $$

Hence the inverse of the distribution function is given by

$$ F^{-1}(u) = -(1/\lambda)\log(1-u), \quad 0 < u < 1. \tag{4.8.2} $$

So if U has uniform $(0,1)$ distribution, then $X = -(1/\lambda)\log(1-U)$ has an exponential distribution with pdf (3.3.2). For instance, suppose $\lambda = 1$ and our uniform generator generated the following stream of uniform observations:

$$ 0.473, 0.858, 0.501, 0.676, 0.240. $$

Then the corresponding stream of exponential observations is

$$ 0.641, 1.95, 0.696, 1.13, 0.274. $$

As the next example shows, we can generate Poisson realizations using this exponential generation.

Example 4.8.2 (Simulating Poisson Processes). Let X be the number of occurrences of an event over a unit of time and assume that it has a Poisson distribution with mean $m = \lambda$, (3.2.1). Let $T_1, T_2, T_3, \ldots$ be the interarrival times of the occurrences. Recall from Remark 3.3.3 that $T_1, T_2, T_3, \ldots$ are iid with an exponential λ distribution, (3.3.2). Note that $X = k$ if and only if $\sum_{j=1}^{k} T_j \le 1$ and $\sum_{j=1}^{k+1} T_j > 1$. Using this fact and the generation of exponential (λ) variates discussed above, the following algorithm generates a realization of X (assume that the uniforms generated are independent of one another).

1. Set $X = 0$ and $T = 0$.
2. Generate U uniform $(0, 1)$ and let $Y = -(1/\lambda) \log(1 - U)$.
3. Set $T = T + Y$.
4. If $T > 1$, output X;
   else set $X = X + 1$ and go to step 2.

The program `poisrand` found in Appendix B provides an R coding of this algorithm for generating n simulations of a Poisson distribution with parameter λ. As an illustration, we obtained 1000 realizations from a Poisson distribution with $\lambda = 5$ by running R with the command `temp = poisrand(1000,5)`. This stores the realizations in the vector `temp`. The sample average of these realizations is found by the command `mean(temp)`. In our case, the realized mean was 4.895. ∎

Example 4.8.3 (Monte Carlo Integration). Suppose we want to obtain the integral $\int_a^b g(x)\,dx$ for a continuous function g over the closed and bounded interval $[a, b]$. If the antiderivative of g does not exist, then numerical integration is in order. A simple numerical technique is the method of Monte Carlo. We can write the integral as

$$\int_a^b g(x)\,dx = (b - a) \int_a^b g(x) \frac{1}{b - a}\,dx = (b - a)E[g(X)],$$

where X has the uniform (a, b) distribution. The Monte Carlo technique is then to generate a random sample $X_1, \ldots, X_n$ of size n from the uniform (a, b) distribution and compute $Y_i = (b - a)g(X_i)$. Then $\overline{Y}$ is an unbiased estimator of $\int_a^b g(x)\,dx$. ∎

Example 4.8.4 (Estimation of π by Monte Carlo Integration). For a numerical example, reconsider the estimation of π. Instead of the experiment described in Example 4.8.1, we use the method of Monte Carlo integration. Let $g(x) = 4\sqrt{1 - x^2}$ for $0 < x < 1$. Then

$$\pi = \int_0^1 g(x)\,dx = E[g(X)],$$

where X has the uniform $(0, 1)$ distribution. Hence we need to generate a random sample $X_1, \ldots, X_n$ from the uniform $(0, 1)$ distribution and form $Y_i = 4\sqrt{1 - X_i^2}$. Then $\overline{Y}$ is a unbiased estimator of π. Note that $\overline{Y}$ is estimating a mean, so the large sample confidence interval (4.2.6) derived in Example 4.2.2 for means can be used to estimate the error of estimation. Recall that this 95% confidence interval is given by

$$(\overline{y} - 1.96s/\sqrt{n}, \overline{y} + 1.96s/\sqrt{n}),$$

where s is the value of the sample standard deviation. The table below gives the results for estimates of π for various runs of different sample sizes along with the confidence intervals.

n	100	1000	10,000	100,000
$\overline{y}$	3.217849	3.103322	3.135465	3.142066
$\overline{y} - 1.96(s/\sqrt{n})$	3.054664	3.046330	3.118080	3.136535
$\overline{y} + 1.96(s/\sqrt{n})$	3.381034	3.160314	3.152850	3.147597

Note that for each experiment the confidence interval trapped π. See Appendix B, `piest2`, for the actual code used for the computation. ∎

Numerical integration techniques have made great strides over the last 20 years. But the simplicity of integration by Monte Carlo still makes it a powerful technique.

As Theorem 4.8.1 shows, if we can obtain $F_X^{-1}(u)$ in closed form, then we can easily generate observations with cdf F_X. In many cases where this is not possible, techniques have been developed to generate observations. Note that the normal distribution serves as an example of such a case, and, in the next example, we show how to generate normal observations. In Section 4.8.1, we discuss an algorithm which can be adapted for many of these cases.

Example 4.8.5 (Generating Normal Observations). To simulate normal variables, Box and Muller (1958) suggested the following procedure. Let Y_1, Y_2 be a random sample from the uniform distribution over $0 < y < 1$. Define X_1 and X_2 by

$$
\begin{aligned}
X_1 &= (-2\log Y_1)^{1/2}\cos(2\pi Y_2), \\
X_2 &= (-2\log Y_1)^{1/2}\sin(2\pi Y_2).
\end{aligned}
$$

This transformation is one-to-one and maps $\{(y_1, y_2) : 0 < y_1 < 1,\ 0 < y_2 < 1\}$ onto $\{(x_1, x_2) : -\infty < x_1 < \infty,\ -\infty < x_2 < \infty\}$ except for sets involving $x_1 = 0$ and $x_2 = 0$, which have probability zero. The inverse transformation is given by

$$
y_1 = \exp\left(-\frac{x_1^2 + x_2^2}{2}\right),
$$

$$
y_2 = \frac{1}{2\pi}\arctan\frac{x_2}{x_1}.
$$

This has the Jacobian

$$
\begin{aligned}
J &= \begin{vmatrix} (-x_1)\exp\left(-\dfrac{x_1^2 + x_2^2}{2}\right) & (-x_2)\exp\left(-\dfrac{x_1^2 + x_2^2}{2}\right) \\[2ex] \dfrac{-x_2/x_1^2}{(2\pi)(1 + x_2^2/x_1^2)} & \dfrac{1/x_1}{(2\pi)(1 + x_2^2/x_1^2)} \end{vmatrix} \\[3ex]
&= \frac{-(1 + x_2^2/x_1^2)\exp\left(-\dfrac{x_1^2 + x_2^2}{2}\right)}{(2\pi)(1 + x_2^2/x_1^2)} = \frac{-\exp\left(-\dfrac{x_1^2 + x_2^2}{2}\right)}{2\pi}.
\end{aligned}
$$

Since the joint pdf of Y_1 and Y_2 is 1 on $0 < y_1 < 1, 0 < y_2 < 1$, and zero elsewhere, the joint pdf of X_1 and X_2 is

$$
\frac{\exp\left(-\dfrac{x_1^2 + x_2^2}{2}\right)}{2\pi}, \quad -\infty < x_1 < \infty,\ -\infty < x_2 < \infty.
$$

That is, X_1 and X_2 are independent, standard normal random variables. One of the most commonly used normal generators is a variant of the above procedure called the Marsaglia and Bray (1964) algorithm; see Exercise 4.8.21. ∎

Observations from a contaminated normal distribution, discussed in Section 3.4.1, can easily be generated using a normal generator and a uniform generator. We close this section by estimating via Monte Carlo the significance level of a t-test when the underlying distribution is a contaminated normal.

Example 4.8.6. Let X be a random variable with mean μ and consider the hypotheses

$$H_0 : \ \mu = 0 \text{ versus } H_1 : \ \mu > 0. \qquad (4.8.3)$$

Suppose we decide to base this test on a sample of size $n = 20$ from the distribution of X, using the t-test with rejection rule

$$\text{Reject } H_0 : \ \mu = 0 \text{ in favor of } H_1 : \ \mu > 0 \text{ if } t > t_{.05,19} = 1.729, \qquad (4.8.4)$$

where $t = \overline{x}/(s/\sqrt{20})$ and $\overline{x}$ and s are the sample mean and standard deviation, respectively. If X has a normal distribution, then this test has level 0.05. But what if X does not have a normal distribution? In particular, for this example, suppose X has the contaminated normal distribution given by (3.4.14) with $\epsilon = 0.25$ and $\sigma_c = 25$; that is, 75% of the time an observation is generated by a standard normal distribution, while 25% of the time it is generated by a normal distribution with mean 0 and standard deviation 25. Hence the mean of X is 0, so H_0 is true. To obtain the exact significance level of the test would be quite complicated. We would have to obtain the distribution of t when X has this contaminated normal distribution. As an alternative, we estimate the level (and the error of estimation) by simulation. Let N be the number of simulations. The following algorithm gives the steps of our simulation:

1. Set $k = 1$, $I = 0$.

2. Simulate a random sample of size 20 from the distribution of X.

3. Based on this sample, compute the test statistic t.

4. If $t > 1.729$, increase I by 1.

5. If $k = N$; go to step 6; else increase k by 1 and go to step 2.

6. Compute $\widehat{\alpha} = I/N$ and the approximate error $= 1.96\sqrt{\widehat{\alpha}(1 - \widehat{\alpha})/N}$.

Then $\widehat{\alpha}$ is our simulated estimate of α and the half-width of a confidence interval for α serves as our estimate of the error of estimation.

The routine `empalphacn`, found in Appendix B, provides R code for this algorithm. When we ran it for $N = 10,000$ we obtained the results:

No. Simulat.	Empirical $\widehat{\alpha}$	Error	95% CI for α
10,000	0.0412	0.0039	$(0.0373, 0.0451)$

Based on these results, the t-test appears to be slightly conservative when the sample is drawn from this contaminated normal distribution. ∎

4.8.1 Accept–Reject Generation Algorithm

In this section, we develop the **accept–reject** procedure that can often be used to simulate random variables whose inverse cdf cannot be obtained in closed form. Let X be a continuous random variable with pdf $f(x)$. For this discussion, we call this pdf the *target* pdf. Suppose it is relatively easy to generate an observation of the random variable Y which has pdf $g(x)$ and that for some constant M we have

$$f(x) \leq Mg(x), \quad -\infty < x < \infty. \tag{4.8.5}$$

We call $g(x)$ the **instrumental** pdf. For clarity, we write the accept–reject as an algorithm:

Algorithm 4.8.1 (Accept–Reject Algorithm). *Let $f(x)$ be a pdf. Suppose that Y is a random variable with pdf $g(y)$, U is a random variable with a uniform$(0, 1)$ distribution, Y and U are independent, and (4.8.5) holds. The following algorithm generates a random variable X with pdf $f(x)$.*

  1. *Generate Y and U.*

  2. *If $U \leq \frac{f(Y)}{Mg(Y)}$, then take $X = Y$. Otherwise return to step 1.*

  3. *X has pdf $f(x)$.*

Proof of the validity of the algorithm: Let $-\infty < x < \infty$. Then

$$
\begin{aligned}
P[X \leq x] &= P\left[Y \leq x \,\middle|\, U \leq \frac{f(Y)}{Mg(Y)}\right] \\[2mm]
&= \frac{P\left[Y \leq x, U \leq \frac{f(Y)}{Mg(Y)}\right]}{P\left[U \leq \frac{f(Y)}{Mg(Y)}\right]} \\[2mm]
&= \frac{\int_{-\infty}^{x}\left[\int_0^{f(y)/Mg(y)} du\right] g(y)\,dy}{\int_{-\infty}^{\infty}\left[\int_0^{f(y)/Mg(y)} du\right] g(y)\,dy} \\[2mm]
&= \frac{\int_{-\infty}^{x} \frac{f(y)}{Mg(y)} g(y)\,dy}{\int_{-\infty}^{\infty} \frac{f(y)}{Mg(y)} g(y)\,dy} \tag{4.8.6} \\[2mm]
&= \int_{-\infty}^{x} f(y)\,dy. \tag{4.8.7}
\end{aligned}
$$

Hence, by differentiating both sides, we find that the pdf of X is $f(x)$. ∎

As Exercise 4.8.14 shows, from step (4.8.6) of the proof, we can ignore normalizing constants of the two pdfs $f(x)$ and $g(x)$. For example, if $f(x) = kh(x)$ and $g(x) = ct(x)$ for constants c and k, then we can use the rule

$$h(x) \leq M_2 t(x), \quad -\infty < x < \infty, \tag{4.8.8}$$

and change the ratio in step 2 of the algorithm to $U \leq h(Y)/[M_2 t(Y)]$. This often simplifies the use of the accept–reject algorithm.

As an example of the accept–reject algorithm, consider simulating a $\Gamma(\alpha, \beta)$ distribution. There are several approaches to generating gamma observations; see, for instance, Kennedy and Gentle (1980). We present the approach discussed in Robert and Casella (1999). Recall if X has a $\Gamma(\alpha, 1)$ distribution, then the random variable βX has a $\Gamma(\alpha, \beta)$ distribution. So without loss of generality, we can assume that $\beta = 1$. If α is an integer, then by Theorem 3.3.2, $X = \sum_{i=1}^{\alpha} Y_i$, where the Y_is are iid $\Gamma(1, 1)$. In this case, by expression (4.8.2), we see that the inverse cdf of Y_i is easily written in closed form, and, hence, X is easy to generate. Thus the only remaining case is when α is not an integer.

Assume then that X has a $\Gamma(\alpha, 1)$ distribution, where α is not an integer. Let Y have a $\Gamma([\alpha], 1/b)$ distribution, where $b < 1$ is chosen later and, as usual, $[\alpha]$ means the greatest integer less than or equal to α. To establish rule (4.8.8), consider the ratio, with $h(x)$ and $t(x)$ proportional to the pdfs of x and y, respectively, given by

$$\frac{h(x)}{t(x)} = b^{-[\alpha]} x^{\alpha-[\alpha]} e^{-(1-b)x}, \tag{4.8.9}$$

where we have ignored some of the normalizing constants. We next determine the constant b.

As Exercise 4.8.15 shows, the derivative of expression (4.8.9) is

$$\frac{d}{dx} b^{-[\alpha]} x^{\alpha-[\alpha]} e^{-(1-b)x} = b^{-[\alpha]} e^{-(1-b)x} [(\alpha - [\alpha]) - x(1 - b)] x^{\alpha-[\alpha]-1}, \tag{4.8.10}$$

which has a maximum critical value at $x = (\alpha - [\alpha])/(1 - b)$. Hence, using the maximum of $h(x)/t(x)$,

$$\frac{h(x)}{t(x)} \leq b^{-[\alpha]} \left[\frac{\alpha - [\alpha]}{(1 - b)e} \right]^{\alpha-[\alpha]}. \tag{4.8.11}$$

Now, we need to find our choice of b. Differentiating the right side of this inequality with respect to b, we get, as Exercise 4.8.16 shows,

$$\frac{d}{db} b^{-[\alpha]} (1 - b)^{[\alpha]-\alpha} = -b^{-[\alpha]} (1 - b)^{[\alpha]-\alpha} \left[\frac{[\alpha] - \alpha b}{b(1 - b)} \right], \tag{4.8.12}$$

which has a critical value at $b = [\alpha]/\alpha < 1$. As shown in that exercise, this value of b provides a minimum of the right side of expression (4.8.11). Thus, if we take $b = [\alpha]/\alpha < 1$, then equality (4.8.11) holds and it is the tightest inequality possible. The final value of M is the right side of expression (4.8.11) evaluated at $b = [\alpha]/\alpha < 1$.

The following example offers a simpler derivation for a normal generator where the instrumental pdf is the pdf of a Cauchy random variable.

Example 4.8.7. Suppose that X is a normally distributed random variable with pdf $\phi(x) = (2\pi)^{-1/2} \exp\{-x^2/2\}$ and Y has a Cauchy distribution with pdf $g(x) =$

$\pi^{-1}(1+x^2)^{-1}$. As Exercise 4.8.9 shows, the Cauchy distribution is easy to simulate because its inverse cdf is a known function. Ignoring normalizing constants, the ratio to bound is

$$\frac{f(x)}{g(x)} \propto (1+x^2)\exp\{-x^2/2\}, \quad -\infty < x < \infty. \tag{4.8.13}$$

As Exercise 4.8.17 shows, the derivative of this ratio is $-x\exp\{-x^2/2\}(x^2-1)$, which has critical values at ± 1. These values provide maxima to (4.8.13). Hence,

$$(1+x^2)\exp\{-x^2/2\} \le 2\exp\{-1/2\} = 1.213,$$

so $M = 1.213$. ∎

One result of the proof of Algorithm 4.8.1 is that the probability of acceptance in the algorithm is M^{-1}. This follows immediately from the denominator factor in step (4.8.6) of the proof. Note, however, that this holds only for properly normed pdfs. For instance, in the last example, the maximum value of the ratio of properly normed pdfs is

$$\frac{\pi}{\sqrt{2\pi}} 2\exp\{-1/2\} = 1.52.$$

Hence, $1/M = 1.52^{-1} = 0.66$. Therefore, the probability that the algorithm accepts is 0.66.

EXERCISES

4.8.1. Prove the converse of Theorem MCT. That is, let X be a random variable with a continuous cdf $F(x)$. Assume that $F(x)$ is strictly increasing on the space of X. Consider the random variable $Z = F(X)$. Show that Z has a uniform distribution on the interval $(0, 1)$.

4.8.2. Recall that $\log 2 = \int_0^1 \frac{1}{x+1}\, dx$. Hence, by using a uniform$(0, 1)$ generator, approximate $\log 2$. Obtain an error of estimation in terms of a large sample 95% confidence interval. If you have access to the statistical package R, write an R function for the estimate and the error of estimation. Obtain your estimate for 10,000 simulations and compare it to the true value.

4.8.3. Similar to Exercise 4.8.2 but now approximate $\int_0^{1.96} \frac{1}{\sqrt{2\pi}}\exp\left\{-\frac{1}{2}t^2\right\}\, dt$.

4.8.4. Suppose X is a random variable with the pdf $f_X(x) = b^{-1}f((x-a)/b)$, where $b > 0$. Suppose we can generate observations from $f(z)$. Explain how we can generate observations from $f_X(x)$.

4.8.5. Determine a method to generate random observations for the logistic pdf, (4.4.9). If access is available, write an R function which returns a random sample of observations from a logistic distribution.

4.8.6. Determine a method to generate random observations for the following pdf:

$$f(x) = \begin{cases} 4x^3 & 0 < x < 1 \\ 0 & \text{elsewhere.} \end{cases}$$

If access is available, write an R function which returns a random sample of observations from this pdf.

4.8.7. Determine a method to generate random observations for the Laplace pdf, (4.4.10). If access is available, write an R function which returns a random sample of observations from a Laplace distribution.

4.8.8. Determine a method to generate random observations for the extreme-valued pdf which is given by

$$f(x) = \exp\{x - e^x\}, \quad -\infty < x < \infty. \tag{4.8.14}$$

If access is available, write an R function which returns a random sample of observations from an extreme-valued distribution.

4.8.9. Determine a method to generate random observations for the Cauchy distribution with pdf

$$f(x) = \frac{1}{\pi(1 + x^2)}, \quad -\infty < x < \infty. \tag{4.8.15}$$

If access is available, write an R function which returns a random sample of observation from a Cauchy distribution.

4.8.10. Suppose we are interested in a particular Weibull distribution with pdf

$$f(x) = \begin{cases} \frac{1}{\theta^3} 3x^2 e^{-x^3/\theta^3} & 0 < x < \infty \\ 0 & \text{elsewhere.} \end{cases}$$

Determine a method to generate random observations from this Weibull distribution. If access is available, write an R function which returns a random sample of observation from a Weibull distribution.
Hint: Find $F^{-1}(u)$.

4.8.11. Consider the situation in Example 4.8.6 with the hypotheses (4.8.3). Write an algorithm which simulates the power of the test (4.8.4) to detect the alternative $\mu = 0.5$ under the same contaminated normal distribution as in the example. If access is available, modify the R function `empalphacn(N)` to simulate this power and to obtain an estimate of the error of estimation.

4.8.12. For the last exercise, write an algorithm to simulate the significance level and power to detect the alternative $\mu = 0.5$ for the test (4.8.4) when the underling distribution is the logistic distribution (4.4.9).

4.8.13. For the proof of Theorem 4.8.1, we assumed that the cdf was strictly increasing over its support. Consider a random variable X with cdf $F(x)$ which is not strictly increasing. Define as the inverse of $F(x)$ the function

$$F^{-1}(u) = \inf\{x : F(x) \geq u\}, \quad 0 < u < 1.$$

Let U have a uniform $(0, 1)$ distribution. Prove that the random variable $F^{-1}(U)$ has cdf $F(x)$.

4.8.14. Show that the discussion at the end of the proof of Algorithm 4.8.1 does not need to use normalizing constants for the accept–reject algorithm to be true.

4.8.15. Verify the derivative in expression (4.8.10) and show that the function (4.8.9) attains a maximum at the critical value $x = (\alpha - [\alpha])/(1 - b)$.

4.8.16. Derive expression (4.8.12) and show that the resulting critical value $b = [\alpha]/\alpha < 1$ gives a minimum of the function which is the right side of expression (4.8.11).

4.8.17. Show that the derivative of the ratio in expression (4.8.13) is given by the function $-x \exp\{-x^2/2\}(x^2 - 1)$ with critical values ± 1. Show that the critical values provide maxima for expression (4.8.13).

4.8.18. Consider the pdf

$$f(x) = \begin{cases} \beta x^{\beta - 1} & 0 < x < 1 \\ 0 & \text{elsewhere}, \end{cases}$$

for $\beta > 1$.

(a) Use Theorem 4.8.1 to generate an observation from this pdf.

(b) Use the accept–reject algorithm to generate an observation from this pdf.

4.8.19. Proceeding similar to Example 4.8.7, use the accept–reject algorithm to generate an observation from a t distribution with $r > 1$ degrees of freedom when $g(x)$ is the Cauchy pdf.

4.8.20. For $\alpha > 0$ and $\beta > 0$, consider the following accept–reject algorithm:

1. Generate U_1 and U_2 iid uniform$(0, 1)$ random variables. Set $V_1 = U_1^{1/\alpha}$ and $V_2 = U_2^{1/\beta}$.

2. Set $W = V_1 + V_2$. If $W \leq 1$, set $X = V_1/W$; else go to step 1.

3. Deliver X.

Show that X has a beta distribution with parameters α and β, (3.3.5). See Kennedy and Gentle (1980).

4.8.21. Consider the following algorithm:

1. Generate U and V independent uniform $(-1, 1)$ random variables.

2. Set $W = U^2 + V^2$.

3. If $W > 1$ go to step 1.

4. Set $Z = \sqrt{(-2 \log W)/W}$ and let $X_1 = UZ$ and $X_2 = VZ$.

Show that the random variables X_1 and X_2 are iid with a common $N(0, 1)$ distribution. This algorithm was proposed by Marsaglia and Bray (1964).

4.9   Bootstrap Procedures

In the last section, we introduced the method of Monte Carlo and discussed several of its applications. In the last few years, however, Monte Carlo procedures have become increasingly used in statistical inference. In this section, we present the *bootstrap*, one of these procedures. We concentrate on confidence intervals and tests for one- and two-sample problems in this section.

4.9.1   Percentile Bootstrap Confidence Intervals

Let X be a random variable of the continuous type with pdf $f(x; \theta)$, for $\theta \in \Omega$. Suppose $\mathbf{X} = (X_1, X_2, \ldots, X_n)$ is a random sample on X and $\widehat{\theta} = \widehat{\theta}(\mathbf{X})$ is a point estimator of θ. The vector notation, $\mathbf{X}$, proves useful in this section. In Sections 4.2 and 4.3, we discussed the problem of obtaining confidence intervals for θ in certain situations. In this section, we discuss a general method called the **percentile bootstrap** procedure, which is a *resampling* procedure. It was proposed by Efron (1979). Informative discussions of such procedures can be found in the books by Efron and Tibshirani (1993) and Davison and Hinkley (1997).

To motivate the procedure, suppose for the moment that

$$\widehat{\theta} \text{ has a } N(\theta, \sigma_{\widehat{\theta}}^2) \text{ distribution.} \tag{4.9.1}$$

Then as in Section 4.2, a $(1 - \alpha)100\%$ confidence interval for θ is $(\widehat{\theta}_L, \widehat{\theta}_U)$, where

$$\widehat{\theta}_L = \widehat{\theta} - z^{(1-\alpha/2)}\sigma_{\widehat{\theta}} \quad \text{and} \quad \widehat{\theta}_U = \widehat{\theta} - z^{(\alpha/2)}\sigma_{\widehat{\theta}}, \tag{4.9.2}$$

and $z^{(\gamma)}$ denotes the $\gamma 100$th percentile of a standard normal random variable; i.e., $z^{(\gamma)} = \Phi^{-1}(\gamma)$, where Φ is the cdf of a $N(0,1)$ random variable (see also Exercise 4.9.4). We have gone to a superscript notation here to avoid confusion with the usual subscript notation on critical values.

Now suppose that $\widehat{\theta}$ and $\sigma_{\widehat{\theta}}$ are realizations from the sample and $\widehat{\theta}_L$ and $\widehat{\theta}_U$ are calculated as in (4.9.2). Next suppose that $\widehat{\theta}^*$ is a random variable with a $N(\widehat{\theta}, \sigma_{\widehat{\theta}}^2)$ distribution. Then, by (4.9.2),

$$P(\widehat{\theta}^* \leq \widehat{\theta}_L) = P\left(\frac{\widehat{\theta}^* - \widehat{\theta}}{\sigma_{\widehat{\theta}}} \leq -z^{(1-\alpha/2)} \right) = \alpha/2. \tag{4.9.3}$$

Likewise, $P(\widehat{\theta}^* \leq \widehat{\theta}_U) = 1 - (\alpha/2)$. Therefore, $\widehat{\theta}_L$ and $\widehat{\theta}_U$ are the $\frac{\alpha}{2}100$th and $(1 - \frac{\alpha}{2})100$th percentiles of the distribution of $\widehat{\theta}^*$. That is, the percentiles of the $N(\widehat{\theta}, \sigma_{\widehat{\theta}}^2)$ distribution form the $(1 - \alpha)100\%$ confidence interval for θ.

We want our final procedure to be quite general, so the normality assumption (4.9.1) is definitely not desired and, in Remark 4.9.1, we do show that this assumption is not necessary. So, in general, let $H(t)$ denote the cdf of $\widehat{\theta}$.

In practice, though, we do not know the function $H(t)$. Hence the above confidence interval defined by statement (4.9.3) cannot be obtained. But suppose we could take an infinite number of samples $\mathbf{X}_1, \mathbf{X}_2, \ldots$; obtain $\widehat{\theta}^* = \widehat{\theta}(\mathbf{X}^*)$ for each sample $\mathbf{X}^*$; and then form the histogram of these estimates $\widehat{\theta}^*$. The percentiles of this histogram would be the confidence interval defined by expression (4.9.3). Since we only have one sample, this is impossible. It is, however, the idea behind bootstrap procedures.

Bootstrap procedures simply resample from the empirical distribution defined by the one sample. The sampling is done at random and with replacement and the resamples are all of size n, the size of the original sample. That is, suppose $\mathbf{x}' = (x_1, x_2, \ldots, x_n)$ denotes the realization of the sample. Let $\widehat{F}_n$ denote the empirical distribution function of the sample. Recall that $\widehat{F}_n$ is a discrete cdf which puts mass n^{-1} at each point x_i and that $\widehat{F}_n(x)$ is an estimator of $F(x)$. Then a bootstrap sample is a random sample, say $\mathbf{x}^{*'} = (x_1^*, x_2^*, \ldots, x_n^*)$, drawn from $\widehat{F}_n$. As Exercise 4.9.1 shows, $E(x_i^*) = \overline{x}$ and $V(x_i^*) = n^{-1} \sum_{i=1}^{n} (x_i - \overline{x})^2$. At first glance, this resampling the sample seems like it would not work. But our only information on sampling variability is within the sample itself, and by resampling the sample we are simulating this variability.

We now give an algorithm which obtains a bootstrap confidence interval. For clarity, we present a formal algorithm, which can be readily coded into languages such as R. Let $\mathbf{x}' = (x_1, x_2, \ldots, x_n)$ be the realization of a random sample drawn from a cdf $F(x; \theta)$, $\theta \in \Omega$. Let $\widehat{\theta}$ be a point estimator of θ. Let B, an integer, denote the number of bootstrap replications, i.e., the number of resamples. In practice, B is often 3000 or more.

1. Set $j = 1$.

2. While $j \leq B$, do steps 2–5.

3. Let $\mathbf{x}_j^*$ be a random sample of size n drawn from the sample $\mathbf{x}$. That is, the observations $\mathbf{x}_j^*$ are drawn at random from $x_1, x_2, \ldots, x_n$, with replacement.

4. Let $\widehat{\theta}_j^* = \widehat{\theta}(\mathbf{x}_j^*)$.

5. Replace j by $j + 1$.

6. Let $\widehat{\theta}_{(1)}^* \leq \widehat{\theta}_{(2)}^* \leq \cdots \leq \widehat{\theta}_{(B)}^*$ denote the ordered values of $\widehat{\theta}_1^*, \widehat{\theta}_2^*, \ldots, \widehat{\theta}_B^*$. Let $m = [(\alpha/2)B]$, where $[\cdot]$ denotes the greatest integer function. Form the interval

$$(\widehat{\theta}_{(m)}^*, \widehat{\theta}_{(B+1-m)}^*); \tag{4.9.4}$$

that is, obtain the $\frac{\alpha}{2}100\%$ and $(1 - \frac{\alpha}{2})100\%$ percentiles of the sampling distribution of $\widehat{\theta}_1^*, \widehat{\theta}_2^*, \ldots, \widehat{\theta}_B^*$.

The interval in (4.9.4) is called the **percentile bootstrap** confidence interval for θ.

In step 6, the subscripted parenthetical notation is a common notation for order statistics (Section 4.4), which is handy in this section.

Example 4.9.1. In this example, we sample from a known distribution, but, in practice, the distribution is usually unknown. Let $X_1, X_2, \ldots, X_n$ be a random sample from a $\Gamma(1, \beta)$ distribution. Since the mean of this distribution is β, the sample average $\overline{X}$ is an unbiased estimator of β. In this example, $\overline{X}$ serves as our point estimator of β. The following 20 data points are the realizations (rounded) of a random sample of size $n = 20$ from a $\Gamma(1, 100)$ distribution:

131.7	182.7	73.3	10.7	150.4	42.3	22.2	17.9	264.0	154.4
4.3	265.6	61.9	10.8	48.8	22.5	8.8	150.6	103.0	85.9

The value of $\overline{X}$ for this sample is $\overline{x} = 90.59$, which is our point estimate of β. For illustration, we generated one bootstrap sample of these data. This ordered bootstrap sample is

4.3	4.3	4.3	10.8	10.8	10.8	10.8	17.9	22.5	42.3
48.8	48.8	85.9	131.7	131.7	150.4	154.4	154.4	264.0	265.6

As Exercise 4.9.1 shows, in general, the sample mean of a bootstrap sample is an unbiased estimator of original sample mean $\overline{x}$. The sample mean of this particular bootstrap sample is $\overline{x}^* = 78.725$. We wrote an R function to generate bootstrap samples and the percentile confidence interval above; see the program `percentciboot.s` of Appendix B. Figure 4.9.1 displays a histogram of 3000 $\overline{x}^*$s for the above sample. The sample mean of these 3000 values is 90.13, close to $\overline{x} = 90.59$. Our program also obtained a 90% (bootstrap percentile) confidence interval given by $(61.655, 120.48)$, which the reader can locate on the figure. It did trap $\mu = 100$.

Figure 4.9.1: Histogram of the 3000 bootstrap $\overline{x}^*$s. The 90% bootstrap confidence interval is $(61.655, 120.48)$.

Exercise 4.9.2 shows that if we are sampling from a $\Gamma(1, \beta)$ distribution, then the interval $(2n\overline{X}/[\chi^2_{2n}]^{(1-(\alpha/2))}, 2n\overline{X}/[\chi^2_{2n}]^{(\alpha/2)})$ is an exact $(1 - \alpha)100\%$ confidence interval for β. Note that, in keeping with our superscript notation for critical values, $[\chi^2_{2n}]^{(\gamma)}$ denotes the $\gamma100\%$ percentile of a χ^2 distribution with $2n$ degrees of freedom. The 90% confidence interval for our sample is $(64.99, 136.69)$. ∎

Remark 4.9.1. Briefly, we show that the normal assumption on the distribution of $\widehat{\theta}$, (4.9.1), is transparent to the argument. Suppose H is the cdf of $\widehat{\theta}$ and that H depends on θ. Then, using Theorem 4.8.1, we can find an increasing transformation $\phi = m(\theta)$ such that the distribution of $\widehat{\phi} = m(\widehat{\theta})$ is $N(\phi, \sigma_c^2)$, where $\phi = m(\theta)$ and σ_c^2 is some variance. For example, take the transformation to be $m(\theta) = F_c^{-1}(H(\theta))$, where $F_c(x)$ is the cdf of a $N(\phi, \sigma_c^2)$ distribution. Then, as above, $(\widehat{\phi} - z^{(1-\alpha/2)}\sigma_c, \widehat{\phi} - z^{(\alpha/2)}\sigma_c)$ is a $(1-\alpha)100\%$ confidence interval for ϕ. But note that

$$
\begin{aligned}
1 - \alpha &= P\left[\widehat{\phi} - z^{(1-\alpha/2)}\sigma_c < \phi < \widehat{\phi} - z^{(\alpha/2)}\sigma_c\right] \\
&= P\left[m^{-1}(\widehat{\phi} - z^{(1-\alpha/2)}\sigma_c) < \theta < m^{-1}(\widehat{\phi} - z^{(\alpha/2)}\sigma_c)\right]. \quad (4.9.5)
\end{aligned}
$$

Hence, $(m^{-1}(\widehat{\phi} - z^{(1-\alpha/2)}\sigma_c), m^{-1}(\widehat{\phi} - z^{(\alpha/2)}\sigma_c))$ is a $(1-\alpha)100\%$ confidence interval for θ. Now suppose $\widehat{H}$ is the cdf H with a realization $\widehat{\theta}$ substituted in for θ, i.e., analogous to the $N(\widehat{\theta}, \sigma_{\widehat{\theta}}^2)$ distribution above. Suppose $\widehat{\theta}^*$ is a random variable with cdf $\widehat{H}$. Let $\widehat{\phi} = m(\widehat{\theta})$ and $\widehat{\phi}^* = m(\widehat{\theta}^*)$. We have

$$
\begin{aligned}
P\left[\widehat{\theta}^* \leq m^{-1}(\widehat{\phi} - z^{(1-\alpha/2)}\sigma_c)\right] &= P\left[\widehat{\phi}^* \leq \widehat{\phi} - z^{(1-\alpha/2)}\sigma_c\right] \\
&= P\left[\frac{\widehat{\phi}^* - \widehat{\phi}}{\sigma_c} \leq -z^{(1-\alpha/2)}\right] = \alpha/2,
\end{aligned}
$$

similar to (4.9.3). Therefore, $m^{-1}(\widehat{\phi} - z^{(1-\alpha/2)}\sigma_c)$ is the $\frac{\alpha}{2}100$th percentile of the cdf $\widehat{H}$. Likewise, $m^{-1}(\widehat{\phi} - z^{(\alpha/2)}\sigma_c)$ is the $(1 - \frac{\alpha}{2})100$th percentile of the cdf $\widehat{H}$. Therefore, in the general case too, the percentiles of the distribution of $\widehat{H}$ form the confidence interval for θ. ∎

What about the validity of a bootstrap confidence interval? Davison and Hinkley (1997) discuss the theory behind the bootstrap in Chapter 2 of their book. Under some general conditions, they show that the bootstrap confidence interval is asymptotically valid.

One way of improving the bootstrap is to use a pivot random variable, a variable whose distribution is free of other parameters. For instance, in the last example, instead of using $\overline{X}$, use $\overline{X}/\widehat{\sigma}_{\overline{X}}$, where $\widehat{\sigma}_{\overline{X}} = S/\sqrt{n}$ and $S = [\sum(X_i - \overline{X})^2/(n-1)]^{1/2}$; that is, adjust $\overline{X}$ by its standard error. This is discussed in Exercise 4.9.5. Other improvements are discussed in the two books cited earlier.

4.9.2 Bootstrap Testing Procedures

Bootstrap procedures can also be used effectively in testing hypotheses. We begin by discussing these procedures for two-sample problems, which cover many of the nuances of the use of the bootstrap in testing.

Consider a two-sample location problem; that is, $\mathbf{X}' = (X_1, X_2, \ldots, X_{n_1})$ is a random sample from a distribution with cdf $F(x)$ and $\mathbf{Y}' = (Y_1, Y_2, \ldots, Y_{n_2})$ is a random sample from a distribution with the cdf $F(x - \Delta)$, where $\Delta \in R$. The parameter Δ is the shift in locations between the two samples. Hence Δ can be written as the difference in location parameters. In particular, assuming that the means μ_Y and μ_X exist, we have $\Delta = \mu_Y - \mu_X$. We consider the one-sided hypotheses given by

$$H_0 : \Delta = 0 \text{ versus } H_1 : \Delta > 0 . \tag{4.9.6}$$

As our test statistic, we take the difference in sample means, i.e.,

$$V = \overline{Y} - \overline{X}. \tag{4.9.7}$$

Our decision rule is to reject H_0 if $V \geq c$. As is often done in practice, we base our decision on the p-value of the test. Recall if the samples result in the values $x_1, x_2, \ldots, x_{n_1}$ and $y_1, y_2, \ldots, y_{n_2}$ with realized sample means $\overline{x}$ and $\overline{y}$, respectively, then the p-value of the test is

$$\widehat{p} = P_{H_0}[V \geq \overline{y} - \overline{x}]. \tag{4.9.8}$$

Our goal is a bootstrap estimate of the p-value. But, unlike the last section, the bootstraps here have to be performed when H_0 is true. An easy way to do this is to combine the samples into one large sample and then to resample at random and with replacement the combined sample into two samples, one of size n_1 (new xs) and one of size n_2 (new ys). Hence the resampling is performed under one distribution; i.e., H_0 is true. Let B be a positive integer and let $v = \overline{y} - \overline{x}$. Our bootstrap algorithm is

1. Combine the samples into one sample: $\mathbf{z}' = (\mathbf{x}', \mathbf{y}')$.

2. Set $j = 1$.

3. While $j \leq B$, do steps 3–6.

4. Obtain a random sample with replacement of size n_1 from $\mathbf{z}$. Call the sample $\mathbf{x}^{*'} = (x_1^*, x_2^*, \ldots, x_{n_1}^*)$. Compute $\overline{x}_j^*$.

5. Obtain a random sample with replacement of size n_2 from $\mathbf{z}$. Call the sample $\mathbf{y}^{*'} = (y_1^*, y_2^*, \ldots, y_{n_2}^*)$. Compute $\overline{y}_j^*$.

6. Compute $v_j^* = \overline{y}_j^* - \overline{x}_j^*$.

7. The bootstrap estimated p-value is given by

$$\widehat{p}^* = \frac{\#_{j=1}^{B}\{v_j^* \geq v\}}{B}. \tag{4.9.9}$$

Note that the theory cited above for the bootstrap confidence intervals covers this testing situation also. Hence, this bootstrap p-value is valid.

Example 4.9.2. For illustration, we generated data sets from a contaminated normal distribution. Let W be a random variable with the contaminated normal distribution (3.4.14) with proportion of contamination $\epsilon = 0.20$ and $\sigma_c = 4$. Thirty independent observations $W_1, W_2, \ldots, W_{30}$ were generated from this distribution. Then we let $X_i = 10W_i + 100$ for $1 \le i \le 15$ and $Y_i = 10W_{i+15} + 120$ for $1 \le i \le 15$. Hence the true shift parameter is $\Delta = 20$. The actual (rounded) data are

			X variates				
94.2	111.3	90.0	99.7	116.8	92.2	166.0	95.7
109.3	106.0	111.7	111.9	111.6	146.4	103.9	
			Y variates				
125.5	107.1	67.9	98.2	128.6	123.5	116.5	143.2
120.3	118.6	105.0	111.8	129.3	130.8	139.8	

Based on the comparison boxplots below, the scales of the two data sets appear to be the same, while the y-variates (Sample 2) appear to be shifted to the right of x-variates (Sample 1).

```
                                 ---------
Sample 1                     ----I   +I--            *          0
                                 ---------


                                        -----------
Sample 2         *               ------I   +   I---------
                                        -----------

             +---------+---------+---------+---------+---------+------C3
            60        80        100       120       140       160
```

There are three outliers in the data sets.

Our test statistic for these data is $v = \overline{y} - \overline{x} = 117.74 - 111.11 = 6.63$. Computing with the R program **boottesttwo.s** found in Appendix B, we performed the bootstrap algorithm given above for $B = 3000$ bootstrap replications. The bootstrap p-value was $\widehat{p}^* = 0.169$. This means that $(0.169)(3000) = 507$ of the bootstrap test statistics exceeded the value of the test statistic. Furthermore, these bootstrap values were generated under H_0. In practice, H_0 would generally not be rejected for a p-value this high. In Figure 4.9.2, we display a histogram of the 3000 values of the bootstrap test statistic that were obtained. The relative area to the right of the value of the test statistic, 6.63, is approximately equal to $\widehat{p}^*$.

For comparison purposes, we used the two-sample "pooled" t-test discussed in Example 4.6.2 to test these hypotheses. As the reader can obtain in Exercise 4.9.7, for these data, $t = 0.93$ with a p-value of 0.18, which is quite close to the bootstrap p-value. ∎

The above test uses the difference in sample means as the test statistic. Certainly other test statistics could be used. Exercise 4.9.6 asks the reader to obtain the

Figure 4.9.2: Histogram of the 3000 bootstrap v^*s. Locate the value of the test statistic $v = \overline{y} - \overline{x} = 6.63$ on the horizontal axis. The area (proportional to overall area) to the right is the p-value of the bootstrap test.

bootstrap test based on the difference in sample medians. Often, as with confidence intervals, standardizing the test statistic by a scale estimator improves the bootstrap test.

The bootstrap test described above for the two-sample problem is analogous to permutation tests. In the permutation test, the test statistic is calculated for all possible samples of xs and ys drawn without replacement from the combined data. Often, it is approximated by Monte Carlo methods, in which case it is quite similar to the bootstrap test except, in the case of the bootstrap, the sampling is done with replacement; see Exercise 4.9.9. Usually, the permutation tests and the bootstrap tests give very similar solutions; see Efron and Tibshirani (1993) for discussion.

As our second testing situation, consider a one-sample location problem. Suppose $X_1, X_2, \ldots, X_n$ is a random sample from a continuous cdf $F(x)$ with finite mean μ. Suppose we want to test the hypotheses

$$H_0 : \mu = \mu_0 \text{ versus } H_1 : \mu > \mu_0,$$

where μ_0 is specified. As a test statistic we use $\overline{X}$ with the decision rule

Reject H_0 in favor of H_1 if $\overline{X}$ is too large.

Let $x_1, x_2, \ldots, x_n$ be the realization of the random sample. We base our decision on the p-value of the test, namely,

$$\widehat{p} = P_{H_0}[\overline{X} \geq \overline{x}],$$

where $\overline{x}$ is the realized value of the sample average when the sample is drawn. Our bootstrap test is to obtain a bootstrap estimate of this p-value. At first glance, one might proceed by bootstrapping the statistic $\overline{X}$. But note that the p-value must be estimated under H_0. One way of assuring H_0 is true is instead of bootstrapping $x_1, x_2, \ldots, x_n$ is to bootstrap the values:

$$z_i = x_i - \overline{x} + \mu_0, \quad i = 1, 2, \ldots, n. \tag{4.9.10}$$

Our bootstrap procedure is to randomly sample with replacement from $z_1, z_2, \ldots, z_n$. Letting z^* be such an observation, it is easy to see that $E(z^*) = \mu_0$; see Exercise 4.9.10. Hence, using the z_is, the bootstrap resampling is performed under H_0.

To be precise, here is our algorithm to compute this bootstrap test. Let B be a positive integer.

1. Form the vector of shifted observations: $\mathbf{z}' = (z_1, z_2, \ldots, z_n)$, where $z_i = x_i - \overline{x} + \mu_0$.

2. Set $j = 1$.

3. While $j \leq B$, do steps 3–5.

4. Obtain a random sample with replacement of size n from $\mathbf{z}$. Call the sample $\mathbf{z}_j^*$. Compute its sample mean $\overline{z}_j^*$.

5. j is replaced by $j + 1$.

6. The bootstrap estimated p-value is given by

$$\widehat{p}^* = \frac{\#_{j=1}^{B}\{\overline{z}_j^* \geq \overline{x}\}}{B}. \tag{4.9.11}$$

The theory discussed for the bootstrap confidence intervals remains valid for this testing situation also.

Example 4.9.3. To illustrate the bootstrap test described in the last paragraph, consider the following data set. We generated $n = 20$ observations $X_i = 10W_i + 100$, where W_i has a contaminated normal distribution with proportion of contamination 20% and $\sigma_c = 4$. Suppose we are interested in testing

$$H_0 : \mu = 90 \text{ versus } H_1 : \mu > 90.$$

Because the true mean of X_i is 100, the null hypothesis is false. The data generated are

119.7	104.1	92.8	85.4	108.6	93.4	67.1	88.4	101.0	97.2
95.4	77.2	100.0	114.2	150.3	102.3	105.8	107.5	0.9	94.1

The sample mean of these values is $\overline{x} = 95.27$, which exceeds 90, but is it significantly over 90? We wrote an R function to perform the algorithm described above, bootstrapping the values $z_i = x_i - 95.27 + 90$; see the program **boottestonemean** of Appendix B. We obtained 3000 values $\overline{z}_j^*$, which are displayed in the histogram in Figure 4.9.3. The mean of these 3000 values is 89.96, which is quite close to 90. Of

Figure 4.9.3: Histogram of the 3000 bootstrap $\overline{z}^*$s discussed in Example 4.9.3. The bootstrap p-value is the area (relative to the total area) under the histogram to right of the 95.27.

these 3000 values, 563 exceeded $\overline{x} = 95.27$; hence, the p-value of the bootstrap test is 0.188. The fraction of the total area which is to the right of 95.27 in Figure 4.9.3 is approximately equal to 0.188. Such a high p-value is usually deemed nonsignificant; hence, the null hypothesis would not be rejected.

For comparison, the reader is asked to show in Exercise 4.9.11 that the value of the one-sample t-test is $t = 0.84$, which has a p-value of 0.20. A test based on the median is discussed in Exercise 4.9.12. ■

EXERCISES

4.9.1. Let $x_1, x_2, \ldots, x_n$ be the values of a random sample. A bootstrap sample, $\mathbf{x}^{*\prime} = (x_1^*, x_2^*, \ldots, x_n^*)$, is a random sample of $x_1, x_2, \ldots, x_n$ drawn with replacement.

(a) Show that $x_1^*, x_2^*, \ldots, x_n^*$ are iid with common cdf $\widehat{F}_n$, the empirical cdf of $x_1, x_2, \ldots, x_n$.

(b) Show that $E(x_i^*) = \overline{x}$.

(c) If n is odd, show that median $\{x_i^*\} = x_{((n+1)/2)}$.

(d) Show that $V(x_i^*) = n^{-1} \sum_{i=1}^{n} (x_i - \overline{x})^2$.

4.9.2. Let $X_1, X_2, \ldots, X_n$ be a random sample from a $\Gamma(1, \beta)$ distribution.

(a) Show that the confidence interval $(2n\overline{X}/(\chi_{2n}^2)^{(1-(\alpha/2))}, 2n\overline{X}/(\chi_{2n}^2)^{(\alpha/2)})$ is an exact $(1 - \alpha)100\%$ confidence interval for β.

(b) Using part (a), show that the 90% confidence interval for the data of Example 4.9.1 is $(64.99, 136.69)$.

4.9.3. Consider the situation discussed in Example 4.9.1. Suppose we want to estimate the median of X_i using the sample median.

(a) Determine the median for a $\Gamma(1, \beta)$ distribution.

(b) The algorithm for the bootstrap percentile confidence intervals is general and hence can be used for the median. Rewrite the R code in program `percentciboot.s` of Appendix B so the median is the estimator. Using the sample given in the example, obtain a 90% bootstrap percentile confidence interval for the median. Did it trap the true median in this case?

4.9.4. Suppose $X_1, X_2, \ldots, X_n$ is a random sample drawn from a $N(\mu, \sigma^2)$ distribution. As discussed in Example 4.2.1, the pivot random variable for a confidence interval is

$$t = \frac{\overline{X} - \mu}{S/\sqrt{n}}, \tag{4.9.12}$$

where $\overline{X}$ and S are the sample mean and standard deviation, respectively. Recall by Theorem 3.6.1 that t has a Student t-distribution with $n - 1$ degrees of freedom; hence, its distribution is free of all parameters for this normal situation. In the notation of this section, $t_{n-1}^{(\gamma)}$ denotes the $\gamma 100\%$ percentile of a t-distribution with $n - 1$ degrees of freedom. Using this notation, show that a $(1 - \alpha)100\%$ confidence interval for μ is

$$\left(\overline{x} - t^{(1-\alpha/2)} \frac{s}{\sqrt{n}}, \overline{x} - t^{(\alpha/2)} \frac{s}{\sqrt{n}} \right). \tag{4.9.13}$$

4.9.5. Frequently, the bootstrap percentile confidence interval can be improved if the estimator $\widehat{\theta}$ is standardized by an estimate of scale. To illustrate this, consider a bootstrap for a confidence interval for the mean. Let $x_1^*, x_2^*, \ldots, x_n^*$ be a bootstrap sample drawn from the sample $x_1, x_2, \ldots, x_n$. Consider the bootstrap pivot [analog of (4.9.12)]:

$$t^* = \frac{\overline{x}^* - \overline{x}}{s^*/\sqrt{n}}, \tag{4.9.14}$$

where $\overline{x}^* = n^{-1} \sum_{i=1}^n x_i^*$ and

$$s^{*2} = (n - 1)^{-1} \sum_{i=1}^n (x_i^* - \overline{x}^*)^2.$$

(a) Rewrite the percentile bootstrap confidence interval algorithm using the mean and collecting t_j^* for $j = 1, 2, \ldots, B$. Form the interval

$$\left(\overline{x} - t^{*(1-\alpha/2)} \frac{s}{\sqrt{n}}, \overline{x} - t^{*(\alpha/2)} \frac{s}{\sqrt{n}} \right), \tag{4.9.15}$$

where $t^{*(\gamma)} = t_{([\gamma * B])}^*$; that is, order the t_j^*s and pick off the quantiles.

(b) Rewrite the R program `percentciboot.s` of Appendix B and use it to find a 90% confidence interval for μ for the data in Example 4.9.3. Use 3000 bootstraps.

(c) Compare your confidence interval in the last part with the nonstandardized bootstrap confidence interval based on the program `percentciboot.s` of Appendix B.

4.9.6. Consider the algorithm for a two-sample bootstrap test given in Section 4.9.2.

(a) Rewrite the algorithm for the bootstrap test based on the difference in medians.

(b) Consider the data in Example 4.9.2. By substituting the difference in medians for the difference in means in the R program `boottesttwo.s` of Appendix B, obtain the bootstrap test for the algorithm of part (a).

(c) Obtain the estimated p-value of your test for $B = 3000$ and compare it to the estimated p-value of 0.063 which the authors obtained.

4.9.7. Consider the data of Example 4.9.2. The two-sample t-test of Example 4.6.2 can be used to test these hypotheses. The test is not exact here (why?), but it is an approximate test. Show that the value of the test statistic is $t = 0.93$, with an approximate p-value of 0.18.

4.9.8. In Example 4.9.3, suppose we are testing the two-sided hypotheses,

$$H_0 : \mu = 90 \text{ versus } H_1 : \mu \neq 90.$$

(a) Determine the bootstrap p-value for this situation.

(b) Rewrite the R program `boottestonemean` of Appendix B to obtain this p-value.

(c) Compute the p-value based on 3000 bootstraps.

4.9.9. Consider the following permutation test for the two-sample problem with hypotheses (4.9.6). Let $\mathbf{x}' = (x_1, x_2, \ldots, x_{n_1})$ and $\mathbf{y}' = (y_1, y_2, \ldots, y_{n_2})$ be the realizations of the two random samples. The test statistic is the difference in sample means $\bar{y} - \bar{x}$. The estimated p-value of the test is calculated as follows:

1. Combine the data into one sample $\mathbf{z}' = (\mathbf{x}', \mathbf{y}')$.

2. Obtain all possible samples of size n_1 drawn without replacement from $\mathbf{z}$. Each such sample automatically gives another sample of size n_2, i.e., all elements of $\mathbf{z}$ not in the sample of size n_1. There are $M = \binom{n_1 + n_2}{n_1}$ such samples.

3. For each such sample j:

   (a) Label the sample of size n_1 by $\mathbf{x}^*$ and label the sample of size n_2 by $\mathbf{y}^*$.

   (b) Calculate $v_j^* = \bar{y}^* - \bar{x}^*$.

4. The estimated p-value is $\hat{p}^* = \#\{v_j^* \geq \bar{y} - \bar{x}\}/M$.

   (a) Suppose we have two samples each of size 3 which result in the realizations: $\mathbf{x}' = (10, 15, 21)$ and $\mathbf{y}' = (20, 25, 30)$. Determine the test statistic and the permutation test described above along with the p-value.

   (b) If we ignore distinct samples, then we can approximate the permutation test by using the bootstrap algorithm with resampling performed at random and without replacement. Modify the bootstrap program `boottesttwo.s` of Appendix B to do this and obtain this approximate permutation test based on 3000 resamples for the data of Example 4.9.2.

   (c) In general, what is the probability of having distinct samples in the approximate permutation test described in the last part? Assume that the original data are distinct values.

4.9.10. Let z^* be drawn at random from the discrete distribution which has mass n^{-1} at each point $z_i = x_i - \bar{x} + \mu_0$, where $(x_1, x_2, \ldots, x_n)$ is the realization of a random sample. Determine $E(z^*)$ and $V(z^*)$.

4.9.11. For the situation described in Example 4.9.3, show that the value of the one-sample t-test is $t = 0.84$ and its associated p-value is 0.20.

4.9.12. For the situation described in Example 4.9.3, obtain the bootstrap test based on medians. Use the same hypotheses; i.e.,

$$H_0 : \mu = 90 \text{ versus } H_1 : \mu > 90.$$

4.9.13. Consider the Darwin's experiment on *Zea mays* discussed in Examples 4.5.1 and 4.5.5.

   (a) Obtain a bootstrap test for this experimental data. Keep in mind that the data are recorded in pairs. Hence your resampling procedure must keep this dependence intact and still be under H_0.

   (b) Provided computational facilities exist, write an R program that executes your bootstrap test and compare its p-value with that found in Example 4.5.5.

4.10   *Tolerance Limits for Distributions

We propose now to investigate a problem that has something of the same flavor as that treated in Section 4.4. Specifically, can we compute the probability that a certain random interval includes (or *covers*) a preassigned percentage of the probability of the distribution under consideration? And, by appropriate selection of the random interval, can we be led to an additional distribution free method of statistical inference?

Let X be a random variable with distribution function $F(x)$ of the continuous type. Let $Z = F(X)$. Then, as shown in Exercise 4.8.1, Z has a uniform$(0, 1)$ distribution. That is, $Z = F(X)$ has the pdf

$$h(z) = \begin{cases} 1 & 0 < z < 1 \\ 0 & \text{elsewhere.} \end{cases}$$

Then, if $0 < p < 1$, we have

$$P[F(X) \le p] = \int_0^p dz = p.$$

Now $F(x) = P(X \le x)$. Since $P(X = x) = 0$, then $F(x)$ is the fractional part of the probability for the distribution of X that is between $-\infty$ and x. If $F(x) \le p$, then no more than $100p\%$ of the probability for the distribution of X is between $-\infty$ and x. But recall $P[F(X) \le p] = p$. That is, the probability that the random variable $Z = F(X)$ is less than or equal to p is precisely the probability that the random interval $(-\infty, X)$ contains no more than $100p\%$ of the probability for the distribution. For example, if $p = 0.70$, the probability that the random interval $(-\infty, X)$ contains no more than 70% of the probability for the distribution is 0.70; and the probability that the random interval $(-\infty, X)$ contains more than 70% of the probability for the distribution is $1 - 0.70 = 0.30$.

We now consider certain functions of the order statistics. Let $X_1, X_2, \ldots, X_n$ denote a random sample of size n from a distribution that has a positive and continuous pdf $f(x)$ if and only if $a < x < b$, and let $F(x)$ denote the associated distribution function. Consider the random variables $F(X_1), F(X_2), \ldots, F(X_n)$. These random variables are independent and each, in accordance with Exercise 4.8.1, has a uniform distribution on the interval $(0, 1)$. Thus, $F(X_1), F(X_2), \ldots, F(X_n)$ is a random sample of size n from a uniform distribution on the interval $(0, 1)$. Consider the order statistics of this random sample $F(X_1), F(X_2), \ldots, F(X_n)$. Let Z_1 be the smallest of these $F(X_i)$, Z_2 the next $F(X_i)$ in order of magnitude, $\ldots$, and Z_n the largest of $F(X_i)$. If $Y_1, Y_2, \ldots, Y_n$ are the order statistics of the initial random sample $X_1, X_2, \ldots, X_n$, the fact that $F(x)$ is a nondecreasing (here, strictly increasing) function of x implies that $Z_1 = F(Y_1), Z_2 = F(Y_2), \ldots, Z_n = F(Y_n)$. Hence, it follows from (4.4.1) that the joint pdf of $Z_1, Z_2, \ldots, Z_n$ is given by

$$h(z_1, z_2, \ldots, z_n) = \begin{cases} n! & 0 < z_1 < z_2 < \cdots < z_n < 1 \\ 0 & \text{elsewhere.} \end{cases} \tag{4.10.1}$$

This proves a special case of the following theorem.

Theorem 4.10.1. *Let $Y_1, Y_2, \ldots, Y_n$ denote the order statistics of a random sample of size n from a distribution of the continuous type that has pdf $f(x)$ and cdf $F(x)$. The joint pdf of the random variables $Z_i = F(Y_i)$, $i = 1, 2, \ldots, n$, is given by expression (4.10.1).*

Because the distribution function of $Z = F(X)$ is given by z, $0 < z < 1$, it follows from (4.4.2) that the marginal pdf of $Z_k = F(Y_k)$ is the following beta pdf:

$$h_k(z_k) = \begin{cases} \frac{n!}{(k-1)!(n-k)!} z_k^{k-1}(1 - z_k)^{n-k} & 0 < z_k < 1 \\ 0 & \text{elsewhere.} \end{cases} \tag{4.10.2}$$

Moreover, from (4.4.3), the joint pdf of $Z_i = F(Y_i)$ and $Z_j = F(Y_j)$ is, with $i < j$, given by

$$h(z_i, z_j) = \begin{cases} \frac{n! z_i^{i-1}(z_j - z_i)^{j-i-1}(1-z_j)^{n-j}}{(i-1)!(j-i-1)!(n-j)!} & 0 < z_i < z_j < 1 \\ 0 & \text{elsewhere.} \end{cases} \qquad (4.10.3)$$

Consider the difference $Z_j - Z_i = F(Y_j) - F(Y_i)$, $i < j$. Now $F(y_j) = P(X \leq y_j)$ and $F(y_i) = P(X \leq y_i)$. Since $P(X = y_i) = P(X = y_j) = 0$, then the difference $F(y_j) - F(y_i)$ is that fractional part of the probability for the distribution of X that is between y_i and y_j. Let p denote a positive proper fraction. If $F(y_j) - F(y_i) \geq p$, then at least $100p\%$ of the probability for the distribution of X is between y_i and y_j. Let it be given that $\gamma = P[F(Y_j) - F(Y_i) \geq p]$. Then the random interval (Y_i, Y_j) has probability γ of containing at least $100p\%$ of the probability for the distribution of X. Now if y_i and y_j denote, respectively, observational values of Y_i and Y_j, the interval (y_i, y_j) either does or does not contain at least $100p\%$ of the probability for the distribution of X. However, we refer to the interval (y_i, y_j) as a $100\gamma\%$ **tolerance interval** for $100p\%$ of the probability for the distribution of X. In like vein, y_i and y_j are called the $100\gamma\%$ *tolerance limits* for $100p\%$ the probability for the distribution of X.

One way to compute the probability $\gamma = P[F(Y_j) - F(Y_i) \geq p]$ is to use equation (4.10.3), which gives the joint pdf of $Z_i = F(Y_i)$ and $Z_j = F(Y_j)$. The required probability is then given by

$$\gamma = P(Z_j - Z_i \geq p) = \int_0^{1-p} \left[\int_{p+z_i}^1 h_{ij}(z_i, z_j)\, dz_j \right] dz_i.$$

Sometimes, this is a rather tedious computation. For this reason and also for the reason that *coverages* are important in distribution free statistical inference, we choose to introduce at this time the concept of coverage.

Consider the random variables $W_1 = F(Y_1) = Z_1$, $W_2 = F(Y_2) - F(Y_1) = Z_2 - Z_1$, and $W_3 = F(Y_3) - F(Y_2) = Z_3 - Z_2, \ldots, W_n = F(Y_n) - F(Y_{n-1}) = Z_n - Z_{n-1}$. The random variable W_1 is called a *coverage* of the random interval $\{x : -\infty < x < Y_1\}$ and the random variable W_i, $i = 2, 3, \ldots, n$, is called a *coverage* of the random interval $\{x : Y_{i-1} < x < Y_i\}$. We find that the joint pdf of the n coverages $W_1, W_2, \ldots, W_n$. First we note that the inverse functions of the associated transformation are given by

$$z_i = \sum_{j=1}^i w_j, \text{ for } i = 1, 2, \ldots, n.$$

We also note that the Jacobian is equal to 1 and that the space of positive probability density is

$$\{(w_1, w_2, \ldots, w_n) : 0 < w_i, \ i = 1, 2, \ldots, n, \ w_1 + \cdots + w_n < 1\}.$$

Since the joint pdf of $Z_1, Z_2, \ldots, Z_n$ is $n!$, $0 < z_1 < z_2 < \cdots < z_n < 1$, zero elsewhere, the joint pdf of the n coverages is

$$k(w_1, \ldots, w_n) = \begin{cases} n! & 0 < w_i, \ i = 1, \ldots, n, \ w_1 + \cdots w_n < 1 \\ 0 & \text{elsewhere.} \end{cases}$$

Because the pdf $k(w_1, \ldots, w_n)$ is symmetric in $w_1, w_2, \ldots, w_n$, it is evident that the distribution of every sum of r, $r < n$, of these coverages $W_1, \ldots, W_n$ is exactly the same for each fixed value of r. For instance, if $i < j$ and $r = j - i$, the distribution of $Z_j - Z_i = F(Y_j) - F(Y_i) = W_{i+1} + W_{i+2} + \cdots + W_j$ is exactly the same as that of $Z_{j-i} = F(Y_{j-i}) = W_1 + W_2 + \cdots + W_{j-i}$. But we know that the pdf of Z_{j-i} is the beta pdf of the form

$$h_{j-i}(v) = \begin{cases} \frac{\Gamma(n+1)}{\Gamma(j-i)\Gamma(n-j+i+1)} v^{j-i-1}(1-v)^{n-j+i} & 0 < v < 1 \\ 0 & \text{elsewhere.} \end{cases}$$

Consequently, $F(Y_j) - F(Y_i)$ has this pdf and

$$P[F(Y_j) - F(Y_i) \geq p] = \int_p^1 h_{j-i}(v)\,dv.$$

Example 4.10.1. Let $Y_1 < Y_2 < \cdots < Y_6$ be the order statistics of a random sample of size 6 from a distribution of the continuous type. We want to use the observed interval (y_1, y_6) as a tolerance interval for 80% of the distribution. Then

$$\gamma = P[F(Y_6) - F(Y_1) \geq 0.8]$$
$$= 1 - \int_0^{0.8} 30v^4(1-v)\,dv,$$

because the integrand is the pdf of $F(Y_6) - F(Y_1)$. Accordingly,

$$\gamma = 1 - 6(0.8)^5 + 5(0.8)^6 = 0.34,$$

approximately. That is, the observed values of Y_1 and Y_6 define a 34% tolerance interval for 80% the probability for the distribution. ∎

Remark 4.10.1. Tolerance intervals are extremely important and often they are more desirable than confidence intervals. For illustration, consider a "fill" problem in which a manufacturer says that each container has at least 12 ounces of the product. Let X be the amount in a container. The company would be pleased to note that the interval $(12.1, 12.3)$, for instance, is a 95% tolerance interval for 99% of the distribution of X. This would be true in this case, because the federal agency, the FDA, allows a very small fraction of the containers to be less than 12 ounces. ∎

EXERCISES

4.10.1. Let Y_1 and Y_n be, respectively, the first and the nth order statistic of a random sample of size n from a distribution of the continuous type having cdf $F(x)$. Find the smallest value of n such that $P[F(Y_n) - F(Y_1) \geq 0.5]$ is at least 0.95.

4.10.2. Let Y_2 and Y_{n-1} denote the second and the $(n-1)$st order statistics of a random sample of size n from a distribution of the continuous type having a distribution function $F(x)$. Compute $P[F(Y_{n-1}) - F(Y_2) \geq p]$, where $0 < p < 1$.

4.10.3. Let $Y_1 < Y_2 < \cdots < Y_{48}$ be the order statistics of a random sample of size 48 from a distribution of the continuous type. We want to use the observed interval (y_4, y_{45}) as a $100\gamma\%$ tolerance interval for 75% of the distribution.

(a) What is the value of γ?

(b) Approximate the integral in part (a) by noting that it can be written as a partial sum of a binomial pdf, which in turn can be approximated by probabilities associated with a normal distribution (see Section 5.3).

4.10.4. Let $Y_1 < Y_2 < \cdots < Y_n$ be the order statistics of a random sample of size n from a distribution of the continuous type having distribution function $F(x)$.

(a) What is the distribution of $U = 1 - F(Y_j)$?

(b) Determine the distribution of $V = F(Y_n) - F(Y_j) + F(Y_i) - F(Y_1)$, where $i < j$.

4.10.5. Let $Y_1 < Y_2 < \cdots < Y_{10}$ be the order statistics of a random sample from a continuous-type distribution with distribution function $F(x)$. What is the joint distribution of $V_1 = F(Y_4) - F(Y_2)$ and $V_2 = F(Y_{10}) - F(Y_6)$?

Chapter 5

Consistency and Limiting Distributions

In Chapter 4, we introduced some of the main concepts in statistical inference, namely, point estimation, confidence intervals, and hypothesis tests. The theory behind these procedures often depends on the distribution of a pivot random variable. For example, suppose $X_1, X_2, \ldots, X_n$ is a random sample on a random variable X which has a $N(\mu, \sigma^2)$ distribution. Denote the sample mean by $\overline{X}_n = n^{-1} \sum_{i=1}^{n} X_i$. Then the pivot random variable of interest is

$$Z_n = \frac{\overline{X}_n - \mu}{\sigma / \sqrt{n}}.$$

This random variable plays a key role in obtaining exact procedures for the confidence interval for μ and for tests of hypotheses concerning μ. What if X does not have a normal distribution? In this case, in Chapter 4, we discussed inference procedures, which were quite similar to the exact procedures, but they were based on the "approximate" (as the sample size n gets large) distribution of Z_n.

There are several types of convergence used in statistics, and in this chapter we discuss two of the most important: convergence in probability and convergence in distribution. These concepts provide structure to the "approximations" discussed in Chapter 4. Beyond this, though, these concepts play a crucial role in much of statistics and probability. We begin with convergence in probability.

5.1 Convergence in Probability

In this section, we formalize a way of saying that a sequence of random variables $\{X_n\}$ is getting "close" to another random variable X, as $n \to \infty$. We will use this concept throughout the book.

Definition 5.1.1. *Let $\{X_n\}$ be a sequence of random variables and let X be a random variable defined on a sample space. We say that X_n **converges in prob-***

ability *to* X *if, for all* $\epsilon > 0$,

$$\lim_{n \to \infty} P[|X_n - X| \geq \epsilon] = 0,$$

or equivalently,

$$\lim_{n \to \infty} P[|X_n - X| < \epsilon] = 1.$$

If so, we write

$$X_n \xrightarrow{P} X.$$

If $X_n \xrightarrow{P} X$, we often say that the mass of the difference $X_n - X$ is converging to 0. In statistics, often the limiting random variable X is a constant; i.e., X is a degenerate random variable with all its mass at some constant a. In this case, we write $X_n \xrightarrow{P} a$. Also, as Exercise 5.1.1 shows, convergence of the real sequence $a_n \to a$ is equivalent to $a_n \xrightarrow{P} a$.

One way of showing convergence in probability is to use Chebyshev's Theorem (1.10.3). An illustration of this is given in the following proof. To emphasize the fact that we are working with sequences of random variables, we may place a subscript n on random variables, like $\overline{X}$ to read $\overline{X}_n$.

"WLLN"

Theorem 5.1.1 (Weak Law of Large Numbers). *Let* $\{X_n\}$ *be a sequence of iid random variables having common mean* μ *and variance* $\sigma^2 < \infty$. *Let* $\overline{X}_n = n^{-1} \sum_{i=1}^{n} X_i$. *Then*

$$\overline{X}_n \xrightarrow{P} \mu.$$

Proof: From expression (2.8.3) of Example 2.8.1, the mean and variance of $\overline{X}_n$ are μ and σ^2/n, respectively. Hence, by Chebyshev's Theorem, we have for every $\epsilon > 0$,

$$P(|X - \mu| \geq k\sigma) \leq \frac{1}{k^2}$$

$$P[|\overline{X}_n - \mu| \geq \epsilon] = P[|\overline{X}_n - \mu| \geq (\epsilon\sqrt{n}/\sigma)(\sigma/\sqrt{n})] \leq \frac{\sigma^2}{n\epsilon^2} \to 0. \quad \blacksquare$$

$= k \qquad = \sigma_{\overline{X}}$

This theorem says that all the mass of the distribution of $\overline{X}_n$ is converging to μ, as $n \to \infty$. In a sense, for n large, $\overline{X}_n$ is close to μ. But how close? For instance, if we were to estimate μ by $\overline{X}_n$, what can we say about the error of estimation? We answer this in Section 5.3.

Actually, in a more advanced course, a Strong Law of Large Numbers is proved; see page 124 of Chung (1974). One result of this theorem is that we can weaken the hypothesis of Theorem 5.1.1 to the assumption that the random variables X_i are independent and each has finite mean μ. Thus the Strong Law of Large Numbers is a first moment theorem, while the Weak Law requires the existence of the second moment.

There are several theorems concerning convergence in probability which will be useful in the sequel. Together the next two theorems say that convergence in probability is closed under linearity.

Theorem 5.1.2. *Suppose* $X_n \xrightarrow{P} X$ *and* $Y_n \xrightarrow{P} Y$. *Then* $X_n + Y_n \xrightarrow{P} X + Y$.

Special Cases of the WLLN:
- If $X_1, X_2, \cdots$ are iid with $E|X_1|^k < \infty$, then $\frac{1}{n}\sum_{i=1}^{n} X_i^k \xrightarrow{P} E(X_1^k)$.
  That is, sample moments are consistent.
- If $X \sim$ binomial (n, p), then $X/n \xrightarrow{P} p$.

Proof: Let $\epsilon > 0$ be given. Using the triangle inequality, we can write

$$|X_n - X| + |Y_n - Y| \geq |(X_n + Y_n) - (X + Y)| \geq \epsilon.$$

Since P is monotone relative to set containment 遏制, we have

$$
\begin{aligned}
P[|(X_n + Y_n) - (X + Y)| \geq \epsilon] &\leq P[|X_n - X| + |Y_n - Y| \geq \epsilon] \\
&\leq P[|X_n - X| \geq \epsilon/2] + P[|Y_n - Y| \geq \epsilon/2].
\end{aligned}
$$

→0 as n→∞   →0 as n→∞

By the hypothesis of the theorem, the last two terms converge to 0, which gives us the desired result. ∎

Theorem 5.1.3. *Suppose $X_n \xrightarrow{P} X$ and a is a constant. Then $aX_n \xrightarrow{P} aX$.*

Proof: If $a = 0$, the result is immediate. Suppose $a \neq 0$. Let $\epsilon > 0$. The result follows from these equalities:

$$P[|aX_n - aX| \geq \epsilon] = P[|a||X_n - X| \geq \epsilon] = P[|X_n - X| \geq \epsilon/|a|],$$

and by hypotheses the last term goes to 0. ∎

Theorem 5.1.4. *Suppose $X_n \xrightarrow{P} a$* ← *a为常数!* *and the real function g is continuous at a. Then $g(X_n) \xrightarrow{P} g(a)$.*

Proof: Let $\epsilon > 0$. Then since g is continuous at a, there exists a $\delta > 0$ such that if $|x - a| < \delta$, then $|g(x) - g(a)| < \epsilon$. Thus

∵ g is continuous.

$$|g(x) - g(a)| \geq \epsilon \Rightarrow |x - a| \geq \delta.$$

⇒ $P[|g(x)-g(a)|≥ε] ≤ P(|x-a|≥δ)$

Substituting X_n for x in the above implication, we obtain

$$P[|g(X_n) - g(a)| \geq \epsilon] \leq P[|X_n - a| \geq \delta].$$

[handwritten right margin: 前一项可推得(⇒)出后一项, 说明后一项包含了前一项, 即后一项发生的概率大于前一项的. (但不是也可由 |x-a|≥δ 推出 |g(x)-g(a)|≥ε 吗?!)]

By the hypothesis, the last term goes to 0 as $n \to \infty$, which gives us the result. ∎

This theorem gives us many useful results. For instance, if $X_n \xrightarrow{P} a$, then

$$
\left\{
\begin{aligned}
X_n^2 &\xrightarrow{P} a^2 \\
1/X_n &\xrightarrow{P} 1/a, \quad \text{provided } a \neq 0 \\
\sqrt{X_n} &\xrightarrow{P} \sqrt{a}, \quad \text{provided } a \geq 0.
\end{aligned}
\right.
$$

[handwritten: 设 g(x)=x²: 当 X=Xn, g(x)=g(Xn)=Xn² 当 X=a, g(x)=g(a)=a² (该连续函数 g 对∀x∈R) ∴ 当 Xn →a, 则 g(Xn)=Xn² →g(a)=a².]

Actually, in a more advanced class, it is shown that if $X_n \xrightarrow{P} X$ and g is a continuous function, then $g(X_n) \xrightarrow{P} g(X)$; see page 104 of Tucker (1967). We make use of this in the next theorem.

Theorem 5.1.5. *Suppose $X_n \xrightarrow{P} X$ and $Y_n \xrightarrow{P} Y$. Then $X_n Y_n \xrightarrow{P} XY$.*

[handwritten bottom: Theorem (摘自网络上文档): If $X_n \xrightarrow{P} X$ and $Y_n \xrightarrow{P} Y$ and f is continuous, then $f(X_n, Y_n) \xrightarrow{P} f(X,Y)$. If X=a and y=b are constant random variables, then f only need to be continuous at (a,b). Thus, the sum of the limits equals the limits of the sums, the product of the limits equals the limit of the products, etc. | 但是, $X_n \xrightarrow{P} c$ 并不意味 E(Xn)→C 或 Var(Xn)→0.]

Proof: Using the above results, we have

$$X_n Y_n = \frac{1}{2}X_n^2 + \frac{1}{2}Y_n^2 - \frac{1}{2}(X_n - Y_n)^2$$
$$\xrightarrow{P} \frac{1}{2}X^2 + \frac{1}{2}Y^2 - \frac{1}{2}(X - Y)^2 = XY. \quad \blacksquare$$

Let us return to our discussion of sampling and statistics. Consider the situation where we have a random variable X whose distribution has an unknown parameter $\theta \in \Omega$. We seek a statistic based on a sample to estimate θ. In Definition 4.1.3 of Chapter 4, we defined the property of unbiasedness for an estimator. We now introduce consistency:

Definition 5.1.2 (Consistency). *Let X be a random variable with cdf $F(x, \theta)$, $\theta \in \Omega$. Let $X_1, \ldots, X_n$ be a sample from the distribution of X and let T_n denote a statistic. We say T_n is a* **consistent** *estimator of θ if*

$$T_n \xrightarrow{P} \theta.$$

If $X_1, \ldots, X_n$ is a random sample from a distribution with finite mean μ and variance σ^2, then by the Weak Law of Large Numbers, the sample mean, $\overline{X}_n$, is a consistent estimator of μ.

Example 5.1.1 (Sample Variance). Let $X_1, \ldots, X_n$ denote a random sample from a distribution with mean μ and variance σ^2. In Example 2.8.4, we showed that the sample variance is an unbiased estimator of σ^2. We now show that it is a consistent estimator of σ^2. Recall that Theorem 5.1.1 showed that $\overline{X}_n \xrightarrow{P} \mu$. To show that the sample variance converges in probability to σ^2, assume further that $E[X_1^4] < \infty$, so that $\mathrm{Var}(S^2) < \infty$. Using the preceding results, we can show the following:

$$S_n^2 = \frac{1}{n-1}\sum_{i=1}^{n}(X_i - \overline{X}_n)^2 = \frac{n}{n-1}\left(\frac{1}{n}\sum_{i=1}^{n}X_i^2 - \overline{X}_n^2\right)$$
$$\xrightarrow{P} 1 \cdot [E(X_1^2) - \mu^2] = \sigma^2.$$

Hence the sample variance is a consistent estimator of σ^2. From the discussion above, we have immediately that $S_n \xrightarrow{P} \sigma$; that is, the sample standard deviation is a consistent estimator of the population standard deviation. $\blacksquare$

Unlike the last example, sometimes we can obtain the convergence by using the distribution function. We illustrate this with the following example:

Example 5.1.2 (Maximum of a Sample from a Uniform Distribution). Suppose $X_1, \ldots, X_n$ is a random sample from a uniform$(0, \theta)$ distribution. Suppose θ is unknown. An intuitive estimate of θ is the maximum of the sample. Let $Y_n = \max\{X_1, \ldots, X_n\}$. Exercise 5.1.4 shows that the cdf of Y_n is

$$F_{Y_n}(t) = \begin{cases} 1 & t > \theta \\ \left(\frac{t}{\theta}\right)^n & 0 < t \le \theta \\ 0 & t \le 0. \end{cases} \tag{5.1.1}$$

$P(|Y_n - \theta| \geq \varepsilon) = P(\theta - Y_n \geq \varepsilon) = P(\theta - \varepsilon \geq Y_n) = P(Y_n \leq \theta - \varepsilon) = \left(\frac{\theta-\varepsilon}{\theta}\right)^n \xrightarrow{n\to\infty} 0. \; (\because \frac{\theta-\varepsilon}{\theta} < 1).$

$\because Y_n = \max\{x_1, \cdots, x_n\}, \ldots$

$\therefore Y_n < \theta \quad \therefore |Y_n - \theta| = \theta - Y_n$

$E[Y_n] = \int_{-\infty}^{\infty} Y_n \cdot f_{Y_n}(Y_n) \, dY_n = \int_{-\infty}^{\infty} t \cdot f_{Y_n}(t) \, dt = \int_0^\theta t \cdot f_{Y_n}(t) \, dt$

$= \int_0^\theta t \cdot \frac{n}{\theta^n} t^{n-1} \, dt = \frac{n}{n+1} \theta$

Hence the pdf of Y_n is

$$f_{Y_n}(t) = \begin{cases} \frac{n}{\theta^n} t^{n-1} & 0 < t \leq \theta \\ 0 & \text{elsewhere.} \end{cases} \tag{5.1.2}$$

$\therefore E(Y_n) \neq \theta$

Based on its pdf, it is easy to show that $E(Y_n) = (n/(n+1))\theta$. Thus, Y_n is a biased estimator of θ. Note, however, that $((n+1)/n)Y_n$ is an unbiased estimator of θ. Further, based on the cdf of Y_n, it is easily seen that $Y_n \xrightarrow{P} \theta$ and, hence, that the sample maximum is a consistent estimate of θ. Note that the unbiased estimator, $((n+1)/n)Y_n$, is also consistent. ∎

$\mu = \frac{b-a}{2} = \frac{\theta-0}{2} = \frac{\theta}{2}$ $\bar{X}_n \xrightarrow{P} \mu = \frac{\theta-0}{2} = \frac{\theta}{2}$

To expand on Example 5.1.2, by the Weak Law of Large Numbers, Theorem 5.1.1, it follows that $\overline{X}_n$ is a consistent estimator of $\theta/2$, so $2\overline{X}_n$ is a consistent estimator of θ. $2\bar{X}_n \xrightarrow{P} \frac{\theta}{2} \times 2 = \theta$. Note the difference in how we showed that Y_n and $2\overline{X}_n$ converge to θ in probability. For Y_n we used the cdf of Y_n, but for $2\overline{X}_n$ we appealed to the Weak Law of Large Numbers. In fact, the cdf of $2\overline{X}_n$ is quite complicated for the uniform model. In many situations, the cdf of the statistic cannot be obtained, but we can appeal to asymptotic theory to establish the result. There are other estimators of θ. Which is the "best" estimator? In future chapters we will be concerned with such questions.

Consistency is a very important property for an estimator to have. It is a poor estimator that does not approach its target as the sample size gets large. Note that the same cannot be said for the property of unbiasedness. For example, instead of using the sample variance to estimate σ^2, suppose we use $V = n^{-1}\sum_{i=1}^n (X_i - \overline{X})^2$. Then V is consistent for σ^2, but it is biased, because $E(V) = (n-1)\sigma^2/n$. Thus the bias of V is $-\sigma^2/n$, which vanishes as $n \to \infty$.

EXERCISES

5.1.1. Let $\{a_n\}$ be a sequence of real numbers. Hence, we can also say that $\{a_n\}$ is a sequence of constant (degenerate) random variables. Let a be a real number. Show that $a_n \to a$ is equivalent to $a_n \xrightarrow{P} a$.

5.1.2. Let the random variable Y_n have a distribution that is $b(n,p)$.

(a) Prove that Y_n/n converges in probability to p. This result is one form of the weak law of large numbers.

(b) Prove that $1 - Y_n/n$ converges in probability to $1 - p$.

(c) Prove that $(Y_n/n)(1 - Y_n/n)$ converges in probability to $p(1-p)$.

5.1.3. Let W_n denote a random variable with mean μ and variance b/n^p, where $p > 0$, μ, and b are constants (not functions of n). Prove that W_n converges in probability to μ.
Hint: Use Chebyshev's inequality.

5.1.4. Derive the cdf given in expression (5.1.1).

$P\left(\left|\frac{Y_n}{n}\left(1 - \frac{Y_n}{n}\right) - p(1-p)\right| \geq \varepsilon\right)$

$= P\left(\left|\left(\frac{Y_n}{n} - p\right) + \left[-\left(\left(\frac{Y_n}{n}\right)^2 - p^2\right)\right]\right| \geq \varepsilon\right)$

$\leq P\left(\left|\frac{Y_n}{n} - p\right| + \left|\frac{Y_n^2}{n^2} - p^2\right| \geq \varepsilon\right)$

$\leq P\left(\left|\frac{Y_n}{n} - p\right| \geq \frac{\varepsilon}{2}\right) + P\left(\left|\frac{Y_n^2}{n^2} - p^2\right| \geq \frac{\varepsilon}{2}\right)$

$\forall \varepsilon > 0, \begin{cases} P\left(\left|\frac{Y_n}{n} - p\right| \geq \frac{\varepsilon}{2}\right) \xrightarrow{n\to\infty} 0 \\ P\left(\left|\frac{Y_n^2}{n^2} - p^2\right| \geq \frac{\varepsilon}{2}\right) = P\left(\left|\left(\frac{Y_n}{n} - p\right)\left(\frac{Y_n}{n} + p\right)\right| \geq \frac{\varepsilon}{2}\right) \leq P\left(\left|\frac{Y_n}{n} - p\right| \geq \frac{\varepsilon}{2}\right) \xrightarrow{n\to\infty} 0 \end{cases}$

$\therefore \longrightarrow 0.$

✓ **5.1.5.** Let $X_1, \ldots, X_n$ be iid random variables with common pdf

$$f(x) = \begin{cases} e^{-(x-\theta)} & x > \theta \; -\infty < \theta < \infty \\ 0 & \text{elsewhere.} \end{cases} \tag{5.1.3}$$

This pdf is called the **shifted exponential**. Let $Y_n = \min\{X_1, \ldots, X_n\}$. Prove that $Y_n \to \theta$ in probability, by first obtaining the cdf of Y_n.

5.1.6. Using the assumptions behind the confidence interval given in expression (4.2.9), show that

$$\sqrt{\frac{S_1^2}{n_1} + \frac{S_2^2}{n_2}} \Big/ \sqrt{\frac{\sigma_1^2}{n_1} + \frac{\sigma_2^2}{n_2}} \xrightarrow{P} 1.$$

5.1.7. For Exercise 5.1.5, obtain the mean of Y_n. Is Y_n an unbiased estimator of θ? Obtain an unbiased estimator of θ based on Y_n.

5.2 Convergence in Distribution

In the last section, we introduced the concept of convergence in probability. With this concept, we can formally say, for instance, that a statistic converges to a parameter and, furthermore, in many situations we can show this without having to obtain the distribution function of the statistic. But how close is the statistic to the estimator? For instance, can we obtain the error of estimation with some credence? The method of convergence discussed in this section, in conjunction with earlier results, gives us affirmative answers to these questions.

Definition 5.2.1 (Convergence in Distribution). *Let $\{X_n\}$ be a sequence of random variables and let X be a random variable. Let F_{X_n} and F_X be, respectively, the cdfs of X_n and X. Let $C(F_X)$ denote the set of all points where F_X is continuous. We say that X_n converges in distribution to X if*

$$\lim_{n \to \infty} F_{X_n}(x) = F_X(x), \quad \text{for all } x \in C(F_X).$$

We denote this convergence by

$$X_n \xrightarrow{D} X.$$

Remark 5.2.1. This material on convergence in probability and in distribution comes under what statisticians and probabilists refer to as *asymptotic theory*. Often, we say that the distribution of X is the **asymptotic distribution** or the **limiting distribution** of the sequence $\{X_n\}$. We might even refer informally to the asymptotics of certain situations. Moreover, for illustration, instead of saying $X_n \xrightarrow{D} X$, where X has a standard normal distribution, we may write

$$X_n \xrightarrow{D} N(0,1)$$

as an abbreviated way of saying the same thing. Clearly, the right-hand member of this last expression is a distribution and not a random variable as it should be, but we will make use of this convention. In addition, we may say that X_n has a *limiting* standard normal distribution to mean that $X_n \xrightarrow{D} X$, where X has a standard normal random, or equivalently $X_n \xrightarrow{D} N(0,1)$. ∎   比如 $X_n \xrightarrow{D} X \sim N(0,1)$.

Motivation for considering only points of continuity of F_X is given by the following simple example. Let X_n be a random variable with all its mass at $\frac{1}{n}$ and let X be a random variable with all its mass at 0. Then, as Figure 5.2.1 shows, all the mass of X_n is converging to 0, i.e., the distribution of X. At the point of discontinuity of F_X, $\lim F_{X_n}(0) = 0 \neq 1 = F_X(0)$, while at continuity points x of F_X (i.e., , $x \neq 0$), $\lim F_{X_n}(x) = F_X(x)$. Hence, according to the definition, $X_n \xrightarrow{D} X$.

对于X有: $F_X(x) = \begin{cases} 0 & \text{if } x<0 \\ 1 & \text{if } x \geq 0 \end{cases}$ ∴ $F_X(0)=1$.

$f_X(x) = \begin{cases} 1 & x=0 \\ 0 & x \neq 0. \end{cases}$

对于X_n: $f_{X_n}(x) = \begin{cases} 1 & x = \frac{1}{n} \\ 0 & x \neq \frac{1}{n} \end{cases}$

$F_{X_n}(x) = \begin{cases} 0 & x = 0, \\ 0 & x < 0 \\ 1 & x > 0 \end{cases}$

$\{X_n\}_{n=1}^{\infty} = \{X_1, X_2, \cdots \}$

对于X_1: $F_{X_1}(x)$

对于X_2: $F_{X_2}(x)$

对于X_n: $F_{X_n}(x)$

而对于X: $F_X(x)$

Figure 5.2.1: Cdf of X_n, which has all its mass at n^{-1}.

Convergence in probability is a way of saying that a sequence of random variables X_n is getting close to another random variable X. On the other hand, convergence in distribution is only concerned with the cdfs F_{X_n} and F_X. A simple example illustrates this. Let X be a continuous random variable with a pdf $f_X(x)$ which is symmetric about 0; i.e., $f_X(-x) = f_X(x)$. Then it is easy to show that the density of the random variable $-X$ is also $f_X(x)$. Thus, X and $-X$ have the same distributions. Define the sequence of random variables X_n as

n odd时, $X_n = X$ ∴ $f_{X_n}(x) = f_X(x)$

n even时, $X_n = -X$, $x = -x_n$ ⇒ Jacobian $= \frac{\partial x}{\partial x_n} = -1$

$$X_n = \begin{cases} X & \text{if } n \text{ is odd} \\ -X & \text{if } n \text{ is even.} \end{cases} \tag{5.2.1}$$

∴ $f_{X_n}(x) = f_X(x) \cdot |J| = f_X(x)$

∴ $f_{X_n}(x) \leq f_X(x)$ 处处相等, ∴ 它们所属 cdf 也处处相等!

Clearly, $F_{X_n}(x) = F_X(x)$ for all x in the support of X, so that $X_n \xrightarrow{D} X$. On the other hand, the sequence X_n does not get close to X. In particular, $X_n \not\to X$ in probability.

$|X_n - X| = |X-X| = 0 < \forall \varepsilon.$ 当 n is odd. $\Rightarrow X_n \xrightarrow{P} X$.

$|X_n - X| = |-X-X| = |2X| \leq 3\varepsilon.$ 当 n is even

Example 5.2.1. Let $\overline{X}_n$ have the cdf

$$F_n(\overline{x}) = \int_{-\infty}^{\overline{x}} \frac{1}{\sqrt{1/n}\sqrt{2\pi}} e^{-nw^2/2}\, dw.$$

(注: $F_n(\overline{x})$ 即 $F_{\overline{X}_n}(x)$ 的简写法。)

If the change of variable $v = \sqrt{n}w$ is made, we have

当 $n \to \infty$ 时,
若 $\overline{x} > 0$, $\sqrt{n}\,\overline{x} \to +\infty$, $\therefore F_n(\overline{x}) = \int_{-\infty}^{+\infty} \cdots = 1$
若 $\overline{x} = 0$, $\sqrt{n}\,\overline{x} = 0$, $\therefore F_n(\overline{x}) = \int_{-\infty}^{0} \cdots = \frac{1}{2}$
若 $\overline{x} < 0$, $\sqrt{n}\,\overline{x} \to -\infty$, $\therefore F_n(\overline{x}) = \int_{-\infty}^{-\infty} \cdots = 0$.

此式正好与 std. normal 分布的 cdf 一致。

$$F_n(\overline{x}) = \int_{-\infty}^{\sqrt{n}\overline{x}} \frac{1}{\sqrt{2\pi}} e^{-v^2/2}\, dv.$$

It is clear that

$\therefore \overline{x} < 0$ 时, $F_{\overline{X}_n}(\overline{x}) = 0 = F_{\overline{X}}(\overline{x})$
$\overline{x} > 0$ 时, $F_{\overline{X}_n}(\overline{x}) = 1 = F_{\overline{X}}(\overline{x})$

$\int_{-\infty}^{0} \cdots = \int_{0}^{+\infty}$
$\int_{-\infty}^{+\infty} = 1$
$\therefore \int_{-\infty}^{0} \cdots = \int_{0}^{+\infty} = \frac{1}{2}$

$$\lim_{n\to\infty} F_n(\overline{x}) = \begin{cases} 0 & \overline{x} < 0 \\ \frac{1}{2} & \overline{x} = 0 \\ 1 & \overline{x} > 0. \end{cases}$$

$\therefore \overline{X}_n \xrightarrow{D} \overline{X}$ Now the function

($F_{\overline{X}_n}(\overline{x}) \ne F_{\overline{X}}(\overline{x})$ 仅发生在 $\overline{x} = 0$ 时,
但 $\overline{x} = 0$ 不是 $F_{\overline{X}}(\overline{x})$ continuous 的点, 不纳入的!)

$$F(\overline{x}) = \begin{cases} 0 & \overline{x} < 0 \\ 1 & \overline{x} \ge 0 \end{cases}$$

is a cdf and $\lim_{n\to\infty} F_n(\overline{x}) = F(\overline{x})$ at every point of continuity of $F(\overline{x})$. To be sure, $\lim_{n\to\infty} F_n(0) \ne F(0)$, but $F(\overline{x})$ is not continuous at $\overline{x} = 0$. Accordingly, the sequence $\overline{X}_1, \overline{X}_2, \overline{X}_3, \ldots$ converges in distribution to a random variable that has a degenerate distribution at $\overline{x} = 0$. ∎

Example 5.2.2. Even if a sequence $X_1, X_2, X_3, \ldots$ converges in distribution to a random variable X, we cannot in general determine the distribution of X by taking the limit of the pmf of X_n. This is illustrated by letting X_n have the pmf

BP:
$\int_{-\infty}^{+\infty} \lim_{n\to\infty} f_{X_n}(x)dx \ne \lim_{n\to\infty} F_{X_n}(x) \cdots (x)$

$$p_n(x) = \begin{cases} 1 & x = 2 + n^{-1} \\ 0 & \text{elsewhere.} \end{cases}$$

? why (在 $x = 2 + \frac{1}{n}$ 上, $p_n(x) = 1$, 即总有某点 x 能让 $p_n(x) = 1$.)

Clearly, $\lim_{n\to\infty} p_n(x) = 0$ for all values of x. This may suggest that X_n, for $n = 1, 2, 3, \ldots$, does not converge in distribution. However, the cdf of X_n is

$n \to \infty$ 时,
$\therefore$ 若 $p_n(x)$ 在任何 x 值上都趋于 0
则 $F_n(x) = \sum p_n(x)$ 也趋于 0.
这不可能, 没有任何一个分布的 cdf 会趋于 0.
(cdf 应该趋于 1.)

(to any x)

$$F_n(x) = \begin{cases} 0 & x < 2 + n^{-1} \\ 1 & x \ge 2 + n^{-1}, \end{cases}$$

and

$$\lim_{n\to\infty} F_n(x) = \begin{cases} 0 & x \le 2 \\ 1 & x > 2. \end{cases}$$

$\Rightarrow X_n$ converges to X in dist.,
$X_n \xrightarrow{D} X$.

BP $\lim_{n\to\infty} F_n(x) = F(x)$
for all values of x (除了存在非连续点 $x = 2$ 上。)

Since

$$F(x) = \begin{cases} 0 & x < 2 \\ 1 & x \ge 2 \end{cases}$$

is a cdf, and since $\lim_{n\to\infty} F_n(x) = F(x)$ at all points of continuity of $F(x)$, the sequence $X_1, X_2, X_3, \ldots$ converges in distribution to a random variable with cdf $F(x)$. ∎

$x = 2$ 是个非 continuity 的点。

The last example showed in general that we cannot determine limiting distributions by considering pmfs or pdfs. But under certain conditions we can determine convergence in distribution by considering the sequence of pdfs as the following example shows.

determining limiting distribution 即求 $X_n \xrightarrow{D}$?

Example 5.2.3. Let T_n have a t-distribution with n degrees of freedom, $n = 1, 2, 3, \ldots$. Thus its cdf is

$$F_{T_n}(t) = F_n(t) = \int_{-\infty}^{t} \frac{\Gamma[(n+1)/2]}{\sqrt{\pi n}\,\Gamma(n/2)} \frac{1}{(1+y^2/n)^{(n+1)/2}}\, dy,$$

where the integrand is the pdf $f_n(y)$ of T_n. Accordingly,

$$\lim_{n\to\infty} F_n(t) = \lim_{n\to\infty} \int_{-\infty}^{t} f_n(y)\, dy = \int_{-\infty}^{t} \lim_{n\to\infty} f_n(y)\, dy,$$

by a result in analysis (the Lebesgue Dominated Convergence Theorem) that allows us to interchange the order of the limit and integration provided $|f_n(y)|$ is dominated by a function which is integrable. This is true because

$$|f_n(y)| \le 10 f_1(y)$$

and

$$\int_{-\infty}^{t} 10 f_1(y)\, dy = \frac{10}{\pi} \arctan t < \infty,$$

for all real t. Hence we can find the limiting distribution by finding the limit of the pdf of T_n. It is

$$\lim_{n\to\infty} f_n(y) = \lim_{n\to\infty} \left\{ \frac{\Gamma[(n+1)/2]}{\sqrt{n/2}\,\Gamma(n/2)} \right\} \lim_{n\to\infty} \left\{ \frac{1}{(1+y^2/n)^{1/2}} \right\}$$

$$\times \lim_{n\to\infty} \left\{ \frac{1}{\sqrt{2\pi}} \left[\left(1 + \frac{y^2}{n} \right) \right]^{n/2} \right\}.$$

Using the fact from elementary calculus that

$$\lim_{n\to\infty} \left(1 + \frac{y^2}{n} \right)^n = e^{y^2},$$

the limit associated with the third factor is clearly the pdf of the standard normal distribution. The second limit obviously equals 1. By Remark 5.2.2, the first limit also equals 1. Thus, we have

$$\lim_{n\to\infty} F_n(t) = \int_{-\infty}^{t} \frac{1}{\sqrt{2\pi}} e^{-y^2/2}\, dy,$$

and hence T_n has a limiting standard normal distribution. ∎

Remark 5.2.2 (Stirling's Formula). In advanced calculus the following approximation is derived:

$$\Gamma(k+1) \approx \sqrt{2\pi} k^{k+1/2} e^{-k}. \tag{5.2.2}$$

This is known as *Stirling's formula* and it is an excellent approximation when k is large. Because $\Gamma(k+1) = k!$, for k an integer, this formula gives one an idea of how fast $k!$ grows. As Exercise 5.2.20 shows, this approximation can be used to show that the first limit in Example 5.2.3 is 1. ∎

$\longrightarrow$ 已知的 $P_{y_n}(t)$, 要求 $P_{z_n}(t)$.

Example 5.2.4 (Maximum of a Sample from a Uniform Distribution, Continued). Recall Example 5.1.2, where $X_1, \ldots, X_n$ is a random sample from a uniform$(0, \theta)$ distribution. Again, let $Y_n = \max\{X_1, \ldots, X_n\}$, but now consider the random variable $Z_n = n(\theta - Y_n)$. Let $t \in (0, n\theta)$. Then, using the cdf of Y_n, (5.1.1), the cdf of Z_n is

$\left.\begin{array}{c} Z_n \le t \\ Z_n = n(\theta - y_n) \end{array}\right\} \Rightarrow n(\theta - y_n) \le t \Rightarrow \theta - \frac{t}{n} \le y_n$

$$F_{Z_n}(t) = P[Z_n \le t] = P[Y_n \ge \theta - (t/n)] = 1 - P_{y_n}(\theta - \frac{t}{n})$$

$$= 1 - \left(\frac{\theta - (t/n)}{\theta}\right)^n$$

$$= 1 - \left(1 - \frac{t/\theta}{n}\right)^n$$

表示 $\lim\limits_{n \to \infty} F_{Z_n}(t) = 1 - e^{-\frac{t}{\theta}}$ $\longleftarrow$

而 $1 - e^{-\frac{t}{\theta}}$ 正好是 $\exp(\theta)$ 的 cdf

$$\to 1 - e^{-t/\theta}.$$

Note that the last quantity is the cdf of an exponential random variable with mean θ, (3.3.2). So we would say that $Z_n \xrightarrow{D} Z$, where Z is distributed $\exp(\theta)$. ∎

Remark 5.2.3. To simplify several of the proofs of this section, we make use of the $\underline{\lim}$ and $\overline{\lim}$ of a sequence. For readers who are unfamiliar with these concepts, we discuss them in Appendix A. In this brief remark, we highlight the properties needed for understanding the proofs. Let $\{a_n\}$ be a sequence of real numbers and define the two subsequences

$$b_n = \sup\{a_n, a_{n+1}, \ldots\}, \quad n = 1, 2, 3 \ldots, \tag{5.2.3}$$

$$c_n = \inf\{a_n, a_{n+1}, \ldots\}, \quad n = 1, 2, 3 \ldots. \tag{5.2.4}$$

The sequences $\{b_n\}$ and $\{c_n\}$ are nonincreasing and nondecreasing, respectively. Hence their limits always exist (may be $\pm\infty$) and are denoted respectively by $\overline{\lim}_{n \to \infty} a_n$ and $\underline{\lim}_{n \to \infty} a_n$. Further, $c_n \le a_n \le b_n$, for all n. Hence, by the Sandwich Theorem (see Theorem A.2.1 of Appendix A), if $\underline{\lim}_{n \to \infty} a_n = \overline{\lim}_{n \to \infty} a_n$, then $\lim_{n \to \infty} a_n$ exists and is given by $\lim_{n \to \infty} a_n = \overline{\lim}_{n \to \infty} a_n$.

As discussed in Appendix A, several other properties of these concepts are useful. For example, suppose $\{p_n\}$ is a sequence of probabilities and $\overline{\lim}_{n \to \infty} p_n = 0$. Then, by the Sandwich Theorem, since $0 \le p_n \le \sup\{p_n, p_{n+1}, \ldots\}$ for all n, we have [= $\overline{\lim} P_n = 0$.] $\Rightarrow \underline{\lim}_{n \to \infty} p_n = 0$. Also, for any two sequences $\{a_n\}$ and $\{b_n\}$, it easily follows that $\overline{\lim}_{n \to \infty}(a_n + b_n) \le \overline{\lim}_{n \to \infty} a_n + \overline{\lim}_{n \to \infty} b_n$. ∎

怎么得出的?

As the following theorem shows, convergence in distribution is weaker than convergence in probability. Thus convergence in distribution is often called weak convergence.

Theorem 5.2.1. *If X_n converges to X in probability, then X_n converges to X in distribution.* 即 $X_n \xrightarrow{P} X \Rightarrow X_n \xrightarrow{D} X.$

Proof: Let x be a point of continuity of $F_X(x)$. For every $\epsilon > 0$,

$$
\begin{aligned}
F_{X_n}(x) &= P[X_n \le x] \\
&= P[\{X_n \le x\} \cap \{|X_n - X| < \epsilon\}] + P[\{X_n \le x\} \cap \{|X_n - X| \ge \epsilon\}] \\
&\le P[X \le x + \epsilon] + P[|X_n - X| \ge \epsilon].
\end{aligned}
$$

设 $K_n = \sup\{P_n, P_{n+1}, \ldots\}$

P_n 为 Probability $\Rightarrow 0 \le P_n \le 1$ ∴ P_n bounded below $\bigg\} \Rightarrow \lim\limits_{n \to \infty} K_n = \overline{\lim}\limits_{n \to \infty} P_n = P_n$ 的 Lower bound $= 0$. ∴ $\overline{\lim}\limits_{n \to \infty} P_n = 0$.

$P[\{X_n \le x\} \cap \{|X_n - X| < \epsilon\}] = P[\{X_n \le x\} \cap \{-\epsilon \le X_n - X \le \epsilon\}] = P[\{X_n \le x\} \cap \{X_n - \epsilon \le X \le X_n + \epsilon\}]$

$\le P[\{X_n \le x\} \cap \{X < X_n + \epsilon\}] \le P(X < x + \epsilon)$

$P[\{X_n \le x\} \cap \{|X_n - X| \ge \epsilon\}] \le P[|X_n - X| \ge \epsilon]$

Based on this inequality and the fact that $X_n \xrightarrow{P} X$, we see that

$$\overline{\lim_{n \to \infty}} F_{X_n}(x) \le F_X(x + \epsilon). \tag{5.2.5}$$

To get a lower bound, we proceed similarly with the complement to show that

$$P[X_n > x] \le P[X \ge x - \epsilon] + P[|X_n - X| \ge \epsilon].$$

Hence

$$\underline{\lim_{n \to \infty}} F_{X_n}(x) \ge F_X(x - \epsilon). \tag{5.2.6}$$

Using a relationship between $\overline{\lim}$ and $\underline{\lim}$, it follows from (5.2.5) and (5.2.6) that

$$F_X(x - \epsilon) \le \underline{\lim_{n \to \infty}} F_{X_n}(x) \le \overline{\lim_{n \to \infty}} F_{X_n}(x) \le F_X(x + \epsilon).$$

Letting $\epsilon \downarrow 0$ gives us the desired result. ∎

Reconsider the sequence of random variables $\{X_n\}$ defined by expression (5.2.1). Here, $X_n \xrightarrow{D} X$ but $X_n \xrightarrow{P} X$. So, in general, the converse of the above theorem is not true. However, it is true if X is degenerate, as shown by the following theorem.

Theorem 5.2.2. *If X_n converges to the constant b in distribution, then X_n converges to b in probability.*

Proof: Let $\epsilon > 0$ be given. Then

$$\lim_{n \to \infty} P[|X_n - b| \le \epsilon] = \lim_{n \to \infty} F_{X_n}(b + \epsilon) - \lim_{n \to \infty} F_{X_n}[(b - \epsilon) - 0] = 1 - 0 = 1,$$

which is the desired result. ∎

A result that will prove quite useful is the following:

Theorem 5.2.3. *Suppose X_n converges to X in distribution and Y_n converges in probability to 0. Then $X_n + Y_n$ converges to X in distribution.*

The proof is similar to that of Theorem 5.2.2 and is left to Exercise 5.2.12. We often use this last result as follows. Suppose it is difficult to show that X_n converges to X in distribution, but it is easy to show that Y_n converges in distribution to X and that $X_n - Y_n$ converges to 0 in probability. Hence, by this last theorem, $X_n = Y_n + (X_n - Y_n) \xrightarrow{D} X$, as desired.

The next two theorems state general results. A proof of the first result can be found in a more advanced text, while the second, Slutsky's Theorem, follows similarly to that of Theorem 5.2.1.

Theorem 5.2.4. *Suppose X_n converges to X in distribution and g is a continuous function on the support of X. Then $g(X_n)$ converges to $g(X)$ in distribution.*

An often-used application of this theorem occurs when we have a sequence of random variables Z_n which converges in distribution to a standard normal random variable Z. Because the distribution of Z^2 is $\chi^2(1)$, it follows by Theorem 5.2.4 that Z_n^2 converges in distribution to a $\chi^2(1)$ distribution.

Theorem 5.2.5 (Slutsky's Theorem). *Let X_n, X, A_n, and B_n be random variables and let a and b be constants. If $X_n \xrightarrow{D} X$, $A_n \xrightarrow{P} a$, and $B_n \xrightarrow{P} b$, then*

$$A_n + B_n X_n \xrightarrow{D} a + bX.$$

5.2.1 Bounded in Probability

Another useful concept, related to convergence in distribution, is boundedness in probability of a sequence of random variables.

First consider any random variable X with cdf $F_X(x)$. Then given $\epsilon > 0$, we can bound X in the following way. Because the lower limit of F_X is 0 and its upper limit is 1, we can find η_1 and η_2 such that

$$F_X(x) < \epsilon/2 \text{ for } x \leq \eta_1 \text{ and } F_X(x) > 1 - (\epsilon/2) \text{ for } x \geq \eta_2.$$

Let $\eta = \max\{|\eta_1|, |\eta_2|\}$, then

$$P[|X| \leq \eta] = F_X(\eta) - F_X(-\eta - 0) \geq 1 - (\epsilon/2) - (\epsilon/2) = 1 - \epsilon. \qquad (5.2.7)$$

Thus random variables which are not bounded [e.g., X is $N(0,1)$] are still bounded in this way. This is a useful concept for sequences of random variables, which we define next.

Definition 5.2.2 (Bounded in Probability). *We say that the sequence of random variables $\{X_n\}$ is bounded in probability if, for all $\epsilon > 0$, there exist a constant $B_\epsilon > 0$ and an integer N_ϵ such that*

$$n \geq N_\epsilon \Rightarrow P[|X_n| \leq B_\epsilon] \geq 1 - \epsilon.$$

Next, consider a sequence of random variables $\{X_n\}$ which converge in distribution to a random variable X which has cdf F. Let $\epsilon > 0$ be given and choose η so that (5.2.7) holds for X. We can always choose η so that η and $-\eta$ are continuity points of F. We then have

$$\lim_{n\to\infty} P[|X_n| \leq \eta] \geq \lim_{n\to\infty} F_{X_n}(\eta) - \lim_{n\to\infty} F_{X_n}(-\eta - 0) = F_X(\eta) - F_X(-\eta) \geq 1 - \epsilon.$$

To be precise, we can then choose N so large that $P[|X_n| \leq \eta] \geq 1 - \epsilon$, for $n \geq N$. We have thus proved the following theorem

Theorem 5.2.6. *Let $\{X_n\}$ be a sequence of random variables and let X be a random variable. If $X_n \to X$ in distribution, then $\{X_n\}$ is bounded in probability.*

As the following example shows, the converse of this theorem is not true.

Example 5.2.5. Take $\{X_n\}$ to be the following sequence of degenerate random variables. For $n = 2m$ even, $X_{2m} = 2 + (1/(2m))$ with probability 1. For $n = 2m-1$ odd, $X_{2m-1} = 1 + (1/(2m))$ with probability 1. Then the sequence $\{X_2, X_4, X_6, \ldots\}$ converges in distribution to the degenerate random variable $Y = 2$, while the sequence $\{X_1, X_3, X_5, \ldots\}$ converges in distribution to the degenerate random variable $W = 1$. Since the distributions of Y and W are not the same, the sequence $\{X_n\}$ does not converge in distribution. Because all of the mass of the sequence $\{X_n\}$ is in the interval $[1, 5/2]$, however, the sequence $\{X_n\}$ is bounded in probability. ∎

One way of thinking of a sequence which is bounded in probability (or one which is converging to a random variable in distribution) is that the probability mass of $|X_n|$ is not escaping to ∞. At times we can use boundedness in probability instead of convergence in distribution. A property we will need later is given in the following theorem,

Theorem 5.2.7. *Let $\{X_n\}$ be a sequence of random variables bounded in probability and let $\{Y_n\}$ be a sequence of random variables which converge to 0 in probability. Then*

$$X_n Y_n \xrightarrow{P} 0.$$

Proof: Let $\epsilon > 0$ be given. Choose $B_\epsilon > 0$ and an integer N_ϵ such that

$$n \geq N_\epsilon \Rightarrow P[|X_n| \leq B_\epsilon] \geq 1 - \epsilon. \quad \Rightarrow P(|X_n| \geq B_\epsilon) = 1 - (1-\epsilon) = \epsilon.$$

Then

$$\varlimsup_{n \to \infty} P[|X_n Y_n| \geq \epsilon] \leq \varlimsup_{n \to \infty} P[|X_n Y_n| \geq \epsilon, |X_n| \leq B_\epsilon]$$

$$+ \varlimsup_{n \to \infty} P[|X_n Y_n| \geq \epsilon, |X_n| > B_\epsilon]$$

$$\leq \varlimsup_{n \to \infty} P[|Y_n| \geq \epsilon/B_\epsilon] + \epsilon = \epsilon, \quad (5.2.8)$$

from which the desired result follows. ∎

$= 0. \quad \therefore Y_n \xrightarrow{P} 0.$

$\therefore \lim_{n \to \infty} P(|Y_n - 0| > \epsilon) = 0, \quad \lim_{n \to \infty} P(|X_n - 0| > \frac{\epsilon}{B_\epsilon}) = 0.$

将 ϵ 换为 ϵ/B_ϵ 得同样结果

或 $\lim_{n \to \infty} P(|Y_n - 0| < \epsilon) = 1$

5.2.2 Δ-Method

Recall a common problem discussed in the last three chapters is the situation where we know the distribution of a random variable, but we want to determine the distribution of a function of it. This is also true in asymptotic theory, and Theorems 5.2.4 and 5.2.5 are illustrations of this. Another such result is called the **Δ-method**. To establish this result, we need a convenient form of the mean value theorem with remainder, sometimes called Young's Theorem; see Hardy (1992) or Lehmann (1999). Suppose $g(x)$ is differentiable at x. Then we can write

$$g(y) = g(x) + g'(x)(y - x) + o(|y - x|), \quad (5.2.9)$$

where the notation o means

$$a = o(b) \text{ if and only if } \frac{a}{b} \to 0, \text{ as } b \to 0.$$

The *little-o* notation is used in terms of convergence in probability, also. We often write $o_p(X_n)$, which means

$$Y_n = o_p(X_n) \text{ if and only if } \frac{Y_n}{X_n} \xrightarrow{P} 0, \text{ as } n \to \infty. \quad (5.2.10)$$

There is a corresponding O_p notation, which is given by

$$Y_n = O_p(X_n) \text{ if and only if } \frac{Y_n}{X_n} \text{ is bounded in probability as } n \to \infty. \quad (5.2.11)$$

The following theorem illustrates the little-o notation, but it also serves as a lemma for Theorem 5.2.9.

Theorem 5.2.8. *Suppose $\{Y_n\}$ is a sequence of random variables which is bounded in probability. Suppose $X_n = o_p(Y_n)$. Then $X_n \overset{P}{\to} 0$, as $n \to \infty$.*

$\to$ 也同于 $\lim\limits_{n\to\infty} P(|X_n - 0| \geq \varepsilon) = 0$

Proof: Let $\epsilon > 0$ be given. Because the sequence $\{Y_n\}$ is bounded in probability, there exist positive constants N_ϵ and B_ϵ such that

$$n \geq N_\epsilon \implies P[|Y_n| \leq B_\epsilon] \geq 1 - \epsilon. \tag{5.2.12}$$

Also, because $X_n = o_p(Y_n)$, we have

$$\frac{X_n}{Y_n} \overset{P}{\to} 0, \tag{5.2.13}$$

as $n \to \infty$. We then have

$$
\begin{aligned}
P[|X_n| \geq \epsilon] &= P[|X_n| \geq \epsilon, |Y_n| \leq B_\epsilon] + P[|X_n| \geq \epsilon, |Y_n| > B_\epsilon] \\
&\leq P\left[\frac{X_n}{|Y_n|} \geq \frac{\epsilon}{B_\epsilon}\right] + P[|Y_n| > B_\epsilon].
\end{aligned}
$$

$\therefore P(|X_n| \geq \varepsilon) \leq \varepsilon$

$n \to \infty$ 时, $\varepsilon \to 0$., $P(|X_n| \geq \varepsilon) \to 0$

故 $\lim\limits_{n\to\infty} P(|X_n| \geq \varepsilon) = 0 \Rightarrow X_n \overset{P}{\to} 0$

By (5.2.13) and (5.2.12), respectively, the first and second terms on the right side can be made arbitrarily small by choosing n sufficiently large. Hence the result is true. ∎

We can now prove the theorem about the asymptotic procedure, which is often called the Δ method.

Theorem 5.2.9. *Let $\{X_n\}$ be a sequence of random variables such that*

$$\sqrt{n}(X_n - \theta) \overset{D}{\to} N(0, \sigma^2). \tag{5.2.14}$$

Suppose the function $g(x)$ is differentiable at θ and $g'(\theta) \neq 0$. Then

$$\sqrt{n}(g(X_n) - g(\theta)) \overset{D}{\to} N(0, \sigma^2 (g'(\theta))^2). \tag{5.2.15}$$

Proof: Using expression (5.2.9), we have

$$g(X_n) = g(\theta) + g'(\theta)(X_n - \theta) + o_p(|X_n - \theta|),$$

where o_p is interpreted as in (5.2.10). Rearranging, we have

$$\sqrt{n}(g(X_n) - g(\theta)) = g'(\theta)\sqrt{n}(X_n - \theta) + o_p(\sqrt{n}|X_n - \theta|).$$

Because (5.2.14) holds, Theorem 5.2.6 implies that $\sqrt{n}|X_n - \theta|$ is bounded in probability. Therefore, by Theorem 5.2.8, $o_p(\sqrt{n}|X_n - \theta|) \to 0$, in probability. Hence, by (5.2.14) and Theorem 5.2.1, the result follows. ∎

Illustrations of the Δ-method can be found in Example 5.2.8 and the exercises.

5.2.3 Moment Generating Function Technique

To find the limiting distribution function of a random variable X_n by using the definition obviously requires that we know $F_{X_n}(x)$ for each positive integer n. But it is often difficult to obtain $F_{X_n}(x)$ in closed form. Fortunately, if it exists, the mgf that corresponds to the cdf $F_{X_n}(x)$ often provides a convenient method of determining the limiting cdf.

The following theorem, which is essentially Curtiss' (1942) modification of a theorem of Lévy and Cramér, explains how the mgf may be used in problems of limiting distributions. A proof of the theorem is beyond of the scope of this book. It can readily be found in more advanced books; see, for instance, page 171 of Breiman (1968) for a proof based on characteristic functions.

Theorem 5.2.10. *Let $\{X_n\}$ be a sequence of random variables with mgf $M_{X_n}(t)$ that exists for $-h < t < h$ for all n. Let X be a random variable with mgf $M(t)$, which exists for $|t| \leq h_1 \leq h$. If $\lim_{n\to\infty} M_{X_n}(t) = M(t)$ for $|t| \leq h_1$, then $X_n \xrightarrow{D} X$.*

In this and the subsequent sections are several illustrations of the use of Theorem 5.2.10. In some of these examples it is convenient to use a certain limit that is established in some courses in advanced calculus. We refer to a limit of the form

$$\lim_{n\to\infty} \left[1 + \frac{b}{n} + \frac{\psi(n)}{n} \right]^{cn},$$

where b and c do not depend upon n and where $\lim_{n\to\infty} \psi(n) = 0$. Then

$$\lim_{n\to\infty} \left[1 + \frac{b}{n} + \frac{\psi(n)}{n} \right]^{cn} = \lim_{n\to\infty} \left(1 + \frac{b}{n} \right)^{cn} = e^{bc}. \qquad (5.2.16)$$

For example,

$$\lim_{n\to\infty} \left(1 - \frac{t^2}{n} + \frac{t^2}{n^{3/2}} \right)^{-n/2} = \lim_{n\to\infty} \left(1 - \frac{t^2}{n} + \frac{t^2/\sqrt{n}}{n} \right)^{-n/2}.$$

Here $b = -t^2, c = -\frac{1}{2}$, and $\psi(n) = t^2/\sqrt{n}$. Accordingly, for every fixed value of t, the limit is $e^{t^2/2}$.

Example 5.2.6. Let Y_n have a distribution that is $b(n, p)$. Suppose that the mean $\mu = np$ is the same for every n; that is, $p = \mu/n$, where μ is a constant. We shall find the limiting distribution of the binomial distribution, when $p = \mu/n$, by finding the limit of $M_{Y_n}(t)$. Now

$$M_{Y_n}(t) = E(e^{tY_n}) = [(1-p) + pe^t]^n = \left[1 + \frac{\mu(e^t - 1)}{n} \right]^n$$

for all real values of t. Hence we have

$$\lim_{n\to\infty} M_{Y_n}(t) = e^{\mu(e^t - 1)}$$

for all real values of t. Since there exists a distribution, namely the Poisson distribution with mean μ, that has mgf $e^{\mu(e^t-1)}$, then, in accordance with the theorem and under the conditions stated, it is seen that Y_n has a limiting Poisson distribution with mean μ.

Whenever a random variable has a limiting distribution, we may, if we wish, use the limiting distribution as an approximation to the exact distribution function. The result of this example enables us to use the Poisson distribution as an approximation to the binomial distribution when n is large and p is small. To illustrate the use of the approximation, let Y have a binomial distribution with $n = 50$ and $p = \frac{1}{25}$. Then

$$Pr(Y \leq 1) = (\tfrac{24}{25})^{50} + 50(\tfrac{1}{25})(\tfrac{24}{25})^{49} = 0.400,$$

approximately. Since $\mu = np = 2$, the Poisson approximation to this probability is

$$e^{-2} + 2e^{-2} = 0.406. \quad \blacksquare$$

Example 5.2.7. Let Z_n be $\chi^2(n)$. Then the mgf of Z_n is $(1-2t)^{-n/2}$, $t < \frac{1}{2}$. The mean and the variance of Z_n are, respectively, n and $2n$. The limiting distribution of the random variable $Y_n = (Z_n - n)/\sqrt{2n}$ will be investigated. Now the mgf of Y_n is

$$
\begin{aligned}
M_{Y_n}(t) &= E\left\{\exp\left[t\left(\frac{Z_n - n}{\sqrt{2n}}\right)\right]\right\} \\
&= e^{-tn/\sqrt{2n}} E(e^{tZ_n/\sqrt{2n}}) \\
&= \exp\left[-\left(t\sqrt{\frac{2}{n}}\right)\left(\frac{n}{2}\right)\right]\left(1 - 2\frac{t}{\sqrt{2n}}\right)^{-n/2}, \quad t < \frac{\sqrt{2n}}{2}.
\end{aligned}
$$

This may be written in the form

$$M_{Y_n}(t) = \left(e^{t\sqrt{2/n}} - t\sqrt{\frac{2}{n}}e^{t\sqrt{2/n}}\right)^{-n/2}, \quad t < \sqrt{\frac{n}{2}}.$$

In accordance with Taylor's formula, there exists a number $\xi(n)$, between 0 and $t\sqrt{2/n}$, such that

$$e^{t\sqrt{2/n}} = 1 + t\sqrt{\frac{2}{n}} + \frac{1}{2}\left(t\sqrt{\frac{2}{n}}\right)^2 + \frac{e^{\xi(n)}}{6}\left(t\sqrt{\frac{2}{n}}\right)^3.$$

If this sum is substituted for $e^{t\sqrt{2/n}}$ in the last expression for $M_{Y_n}(t)$, it is seen that

$$M_{Y_n}(t) = \left(1 - \frac{t^2}{n} + \frac{\psi(n)}{n}\right)^{-n/2},$$

where

$$\psi(n) = \frac{\sqrt{2}t^3 e^{\xi(n)}}{3\sqrt{n}} - \frac{\sqrt{2}t^3}{\sqrt{n}} - \frac{2t^4 e^{\xi(n)}}{3n}.$$

Since $\xi(n) \to 0$ as $n \to \infty$, then $\lim \psi(n) = 0$ for every fixed value of t. In accordance with the limit proposition cited earlier in this section, we have

$$\lim_{n \to \infty} M_{Y_n}(t) = e^{t^2/2}$$

[handwritten: $Y_n \xrightarrow{D} N(0,1)$. $\therefore Y_n \sim N(0,1)$]

for all real values of t. That is, the random variable $Y_n = (Z_n - n)/\sqrt{2n}$ has a limiting standard normal distribution. ∎

[handwritten: $\frac{(Z_n - n)}{\sqrt{2n}} = \frac{Z_n}{\sqrt{2n}} - \frac{n}{\sqrt{2n}} = \sqrt{n}\left(\frac{Z_n}{\sqrt{2}n} - \frac{1}{\sqrt{2}}\right)$]

Example 5.2.8 (Example 5.2.7, Continued). In the notation of the last example, we showed that *[handwritten: 相對于 Theorem 5.2.9中的 X_n.]*

$$\sqrt{n}\left[\frac{1}{\sqrt{2n}}Z_n - \frac{1}{\sqrt{2}}\right] \xrightarrow{D} N(0,1). \qquad (5.2.17)$$

For this situation, though, there are times when we are interested in the square root of Z_n. Let $g(t) = \sqrt{t}$ and let $W_n = g(Z_n/(\sqrt{2}n)) = (Z_n/(\sqrt{2}n))^{1/2}$. Note that $g(1/\sqrt{2}) = 1/2^{1/4}$ and $g'(1/\sqrt{2}) = 2^{-3/4}$. Therefore, by the Δ-method, Theorem 5.2.9, and (5.2.17), we have

[handwritten: $\sqrt{n}(X_n - \theta) \xrightarrow{D} N(0, \sigma^2)$ $\Rightarrow \sqrt{n}(g(X_n) - g(\theta)) \xrightarrow{D} N(0, \sigma^2 (g'(\theta))^2)$.]

$$\sqrt{n}\left[W_n - 1/2^{1/4}\right] \xrightarrow{D} N(0, 2^{-3/2}). \quad \blacksquare \qquad (5.2.18)$$

EXERCISES

[handwritten: $g(x) = \sqrt{x} \Rightarrow g'(x) = \frac{1}{2\sqrt{x}}$ $\therefore g'(\frac{1}{\sqrt{2}}) = g'(x)\big|_{x=1/\sqrt{2}} = \frac{1}{2 \cdot (\frac{1}{2})^{\frac{1}{4}}} = 2^{-\frac{3}{4}}$.]

5.2.1. Let $\overline{X}_n$ denote the mean of a random sample of size n from a distribution that is $N(\mu, \sigma^2)$. Find the limiting distribution of $\overline{X}_n$.

5.2.2. Let Y_1 denote the minimum of a random sample of size n from a distribution that has pdf $f(x) = e^{-(x-\theta)}$, $\theta < x < \infty$, zero elsewhere. Let $Z_n = n(Y_1 - \theta)$. Investigate the limiting distribution of Z_n.

5.2.3. Let Y_n denote the maximum of a random sample of size n from a distribution of the continuous type that has cdf $F(x)$ and pdf $f(x) = F'(x)$. Find the limiting distribution of $Z_n = n[1 - F(Y_n)]$.

5.2.4. Let Y_2 denote the second smallest item of a random sample of size n from a distribution of the continuous type that has cdf $F(x)$ and pdf $f(x) = F'(x)$. Find the limiting distribution of $W_n = nF(Y_2)$.

5.2.5. Let the pmf of Y_n be $p_n(y) = 1$, $y = n$, zero elsewhere. Show that Y_n does not have a limiting distribution. (In this case, the probability has "escaped" to infinity.)

5.2.6. Let $X_1, X_2, \ldots, X_n$ be a random sample of size n from a distribution that is $N(\mu, \sigma^2)$, where $\sigma^2 > 0$. Show that the sum $Z_n = \sum_1^n X_i$ does not have a limiting distribution.

5.2.7. Let X_n have a gamma distribution with parameter $\alpha = n$ and β, where β is not a function of n. Let $Y_n = X_n/n$. Find the limiting distribution of Y_n.

5.2.8. Let Z_n be $\chi^2(n)$ and let $W_n = Z_n/n^2$. Find the limiting distribution of W_n.

5.2.9. Let X be $\chi^2(50)$. Approximate $P(40 < X < 60)$.

5.2.10. Let $p = 0.95$ be the probability that a man, in a certain age group, lives at least 5 years.

(a) If we are to observe 60 such men and if we assume independence, find the probability that at least 56 of them live 5 or more years.

(b) Find an approximation to the result of part (a) by using the Poisson distribution.
   Hint: Redefine p to be 0.05 and $1 - p = 0.95$.

5.2.11. Let the random variable Z_n have a Poisson distribution with parameter $\mu = n$. Show that the limiting distribution of the random variable $Y_n = (Z_n - n)/\sqrt{n}$ is normal with mean zero and variance 1.

5.2.12. Prove Theorem 5.2.3.

5.2.13. Let X_n and Y_n have a bivariate normal distribution with parameters $\mu_1, \mu_2, \sigma_1^2, \sigma_2^2$ (free of n) but $\rho = 1 - 1/n$. Consider the conditional distribution of Y_n, given $X_n = x$. Investigate the limit of this conditional distribution as $n \to \infty$. What is the limiting distribution if $\rho = -1 + 1/n$? Reference to these facts is made in the remark of Section 2.4.

✓ **5.2.14.** Let $\overline{X}_n$ denote the mean of a random sample of size n from a Poisson distribution with parameter $\mu = 1$.

(a) Show that the mgf of $Y_n = \sqrt{n}(\overline{X}_n - \mu)/\sigma = \sqrt{n}(\overline{X}_n - 1)$ is given by $\exp[-t\sqrt{n} + n(e^{t/\sqrt{n}} - 1)]$.

(b) Investigate the limiting distribution of Y_n as $n \to \infty$.
   Hint: Replace, by its MacLaurin's series, the expression $e^{t/\sqrt{n}}$, which is in the exponent of the mgf of Y_n.

5.2.15. Using Exercise 5.2.14 and the Δ-method, find the limiting distribution of $\sqrt{n}(\sqrt{\overline{X}_n} - 1)$.

✓ **5.2.16.** Let $\overline{X}_n$ denote the mean of a random sample of size n from a distribution that has pdf $f(x) = e^{-x}$, $0 < x < \infty$, zero elsewhere.

(a) Show that the mgf $M_{Y_n}(t)$ of $Y_n = \sqrt{n}(\overline{X}_n - 1)$ is

$$M_{Y_n}(t) = [e^{t/\sqrt{n}} - (t/\sqrt{n})e^{t/\sqrt{n}}]^{-n}, \quad t < \sqrt{n}.$$

(b) Find the limiting distribution of Y_n as $n \to \infty$.

Exercises 5.2.14 and 5.2.16 are special instances of an important theorem that will be proved in the next section.

5.2.17. Continuing with Exercise 5.2.16, use the Δ-method to find the limiting distribution of $\sqrt{n}(\sqrt{\overline{X}_n} - 1)$.

5.2.18. Let $Y_1 < Y_2 < \cdots < Y_n$ be the order statistics of a random sample (see Section 5.2) from a distribution with pdf $f(x) = e^{-x}, 0 < x < \infty$, zero elsewhere. Determine the limiting distribution of $Z_n = (Y_n - \log n)$.

5.2.19. Let $Y_1 < Y_2 < \cdots < Y_n$ be the order statistics of a random sample (see Section 5.2) from a distribution with pdf $f(x) = 5x^4, 0 < x < 1$, zero elsewhere. Find p so that $Z_n = n^p Y_1$ converges in distribution.

5.2.20. Use Stirling's formula, (5.2.2), to show that the first limit in Example 5.2.3 is 1.

5.3 Central Limit Theorem

It was seen in Section 3.4 that if $X_1, X_2, \ldots, X_n$ is a random sample from a normal distribution with mean μ and variance σ^2, the random variable

$$\frac{\sum_{i=1}^{n} X_i - n\mu}{\sigma\sqrt{n}} = \frac{\sqrt{n}(\overline{X}_n - \mu)}{\sigma}$$

is, for every positive integer n, normally distributed with zero mean and unit variance. In probability theory there is a very elegant theorem called the **Central Limit Theorem (CLT)**. A special case of this theorem asserts the remarkable and important fact that if $X_1, X_2, \ldots, X_n$ denote the observations of a random sample of size n from any distribution having finite variance $\sigma^2 > 0$ (and hence finite mean μ), then the random variable $\sqrt{n}(\overline{X}_n - \mu)/\sigma$ converges in distribution to a random variable having a standard normal distribution. Thus, whenever the conditions of the theorem are satisfied, for large n the random variable $\sqrt{n}(\overline{X}_n - \mu)/\sigma$ has an approximate normal distribution with mean zero and variance 1. It is then possible to use this approximate normal distribution to compute approximate probabilities concerning $\overline{X}$.

We often use the notation "Y_n has a limiting standard normal distribution" to mean that Y_n converges in distribution to a standard normal random variable; see Remark 5.2.1.

The more general form of the theorem is stated, but it is proved only in the modified case. However, this is exactly the proof of the theorem that would be given if we could use the characteristic function in place of the mgf.

Theorem 5.3.1 (Central Limit Theorem). *Let $X_1, X_2, \ldots, X_n$ denote the observations of a random sample from a distribution that has mean μ and positive variance σ^2. Then the random variable $Y_n = (\sum_{i=1}^{n} X_i - n\mu)/\sqrt{n}\sigma = \sqrt{n}(\overline{X}_n - \mu)/\sigma$ converges in distribution to a random variable which has a normal distribution with mean zero and variance 1.*

Proof: For this proof, additionally assume that the mgf $M(t) = E(e^{tX})$ exists for $-h < t < h$. If one replaces the mgf by the characteristic function $\varphi(t) = E(e^{itX})$, which always exists, then our proof is essentially the same as the proof in a more advanced course which uses characteristic functions.

The function
$$m(t) = E[e^{t(X-\mu)}] = e^{-\mu t} M(t)$$

also exists for $-h < t < h$. Since $m(t)$ is the mgf for $X - \mu$, it must follow that $m(0) = 1$, $m'(0) = E(X - \mu) = 0$, and $m''(0) = E[(X - \mu)^2] = \sigma^2$. By Taylor's formula there exists a number ξ between 0 and t such that

$$
\begin{aligned}
m(t) &= m(0) + m'(0)t + \frac{m''(\xi)t^2}{2} \\
     &= 1 + \frac{m''(\xi)t^2}{2}.
\end{aligned}
$$

If $\sigma^2 t^2 / 2$ is added and subtracted, then

$$m(t) = 1 + \frac{\sigma^2 t^2}{2} + \frac{[m''(\xi) - \sigma^2]t^2}{2} \qquad (5.3.1)$$

Next consider $M(t;n)$, where

$$
\begin{aligned}
M(t;n) &= E\left[\exp\left(t\frac{\sum X_i - n\mu}{\sigma\sqrt{n}}\right)\right] \\
       &= E\left[\exp\left(t\frac{X_1 - \mu}{\sigma\sqrt{n}}\right)\exp\left(t\frac{X_2 - \mu}{\sigma\sqrt{n}}\right)\cdots\exp\left(t\frac{X_n - \mu}{\sigma\sqrt{n}}\right)\right] \\
       &= E\left[\exp\left(t\frac{X_1 - \mu}{\sigma\sqrt{n}}\right)\right]\cdots E\left[\exp\left(t\frac{X_n - \mu}{\sigma\sqrt{n}}\right)\right] \\
       &= \left\{E\left[\exp\left(t\frac{X - \mu}{\sigma\sqrt{n}}\right)\right]\right\}^n \\
       &= \left[m\left(\frac{t}{\sigma\sqrt{n}}\right)\right]^n, \quad -h < \frac{t}{\sigma\sqrt{n}} < h.
\end{aligned}
$$

In equation (5.3.1), replace t by $t/\sigma\sqrt{n}$ to obtain

$$m\left(\frac{t}{\sigma\sqrt{n}}\right) = 1 + \frac{t^2}{2n} + \frac{[m''(\xi) - \sigma^2]t^2}{2n\sigma^2},$$

where now ξ is between 0 and $t/\sigma\sqrt{n}$ with $-h\sigma\sqrt{n} < t < h\sigma\sqrt{n}$. Accordingly,

$$M(t;n) = \left\{1 + \frac{t^2}{2n} + \frac{[m''(\xi) - \sigma^2]t^2}{2n\sigma^2}\right\}^n.$$

Since $m''(t)$ is continuous at $t = 0$ and since $\xi \to 0$ as $n \to \infty$, we have

$$\lim_{n\to\infty}[m''(\xi) - \sigma^2] = 0.$$

The limit proposition (5.2.16) cited in Section 5.2 shows that

$$\lim_{n\to\infty} M(t;n) = e^{t^2/2},$$

for all real values of t. This proves that the random variable $Y_n = \sqrt{n}(\overline{X}_n - \mu)/\sigma$ has a limiting standard normal distribution. ∎

As cited in Remark 5.2.1, we say that Y_n has a limiting standard normal distribution. We interpret this theorem as saying that when n is a large, fixed positive integer, the random variable $\overline{X}$ has an approximate normal distribution with mean μ and variance σ^2/n; and in applications we often use the approximate normal pdf as though it were the exact pdf of $\overline{X}$.

Example 5.3.1 (Large Sample Inference for μ). Let $X_1, X_2, \ldots, X_n$ be a random sample from a distribution with mean μ and variance σ^2, where μ and σ^2 are unknown. Let $\overline{X}$ and S be the sample mean and sample standard deviation, respectively. In Examples 4.2.2 and 4.5.3 of Chapter 4, we presented large sample confidence intervals and tests for μ. These were based on the fact that

$$\frac{\overline{X} - \mu}{S/\sqrt{n}} \xrightarrow{D} N(0,1). \tag{5.3.2}$$

To see this, write the left side as

$$\frac{\overline{X} - \mu}{S/\sqrt{n}} = \left(\frac{\sigma}{S}\right) \frac{(\overline{X} - \mu)}{\sigma/\sqrt{n}}.$$

Example 5.1.1 shows that S converges in probability to σ and, hence, by the theorems of Section 5.2, that σ/S converges in probability to 1. The result (5.3.2) follows from the CLT and Slutsky's Theorem, Theorem 5.2.5. ∎

Some illustrative examples, here and below, help show the importance of this version of the CLT.

Example 5.3.2. Let $\overline{X}$ denote the mean of a random sample of size 75 from the distribution that has the pdf

$$f(x) = \begin{cases} 1 & 0 < x < 1 \\ 0 & \text{elsewhere.} \end{cases}$$

For this situation, it can be shown that the pdf of $\overline{X}$, $g(\overline{x})$, has a graph when $0 < \overline{x} < 1$ that is composed of arcs of 75 different polynomials of degree 74. The computation of such a probability as $P(0.45 < \overline{X} < 0.55)$ would be extremely laborious. The conditions of the theorem are satisfied, since $M(t)$ exists for all real values of t. Moreover, $\mu = \frac{1}{2}$ and $\sigma^2 = \frac{1}{12}$, so that we have approximately

$$
\begin{aligned}
P(0.45 < \overline{X} < 0.55) &= P\left[\frac{\sqrt{n}(0.45 - \mu)}{\sigma} < \frac{\sqrt{n}(\overline{X} - \mu)}{\sigma} < \frac{\sqrt{n}(0.55 - \mu)}{\sigma}\right] \\
&= P[-1.5 < 30(\overline{X} - 0.5) < 1.5] \\
&\approx 0.866,
\end{aligned}
$$

from Table III in Appendix C. ∎

Example 5.3.3 (Normal Approximation to the Binomial Distribution). Suppose that $X_1, X_2, \ldots, X_n$ is a random sample from a distribution that is $b(1, p)$. Here $\mu = p$, $\sigma^2 = p(1 - p)$, and $M(t)$ exists for all real values of t. If $Y_n = X_1 + \cdots + X_n$, it is known that Y_n is $b(n, p)$. Calculations of probabilities for Y_n, when we do not use the Poisson approximation, are simplified by making use of the fact that $(Y_n - np)/\sqrt{np(1 - p)} = \sqrt{n}(\overline{X}_n - p)/\sqrt{p(1 - p)} = \sqrt{n}(\overline{X}_n - \mu)/\sigma$ has a limiting distribution that is normal with mean zero and variance 1.

Frequently, statisticians say that Y_n, or more simply Y, has an approximate normal distribution with mean np and variance $np(1 - p)$. Even with n as small as 10, with $p = \frac{1}{2}$ so that the binomial distribution is symmetric about $np = 5$, we note in Figure 5.3.1 how well the normal distribution, $N(5, \frac{5}{2})$, fits the binomial distribution, $b(10, \frac{1}{2})$, where the heights of the rectangles represent the probabilities of the respective integers $0, 1, 2, \ldots, 10$. Note that the area of the rectangle whose base is $(k - 0.5, k + 0.5)$ and the area under the normal pdf between $k - 0.5$ and $k + 0.5$ are *approximately* equal for each $k = 0, 1, 2, \ldots, 10$, even with $n = 10$. This example should help the reader understand Example 5.3.4. ∎

Figure 5.3.1: The $b\left(10, \frac{1}{2}\right)$ pmf overlaid by the $N\left(5, \frac{5}{2}\right)$ pdf.

Example 5.3.4. With the background of Example 5.3.3, let $n = 100$ and $p = \frac{1}{2}$, and suppose that we wish to compute $P(Y = 48, 49, 50, 51, 52)$. Since Y is a random variable of the discrete type, $\{Y = 48, 49, 50, 51, 52\}$ and $\{47.5 < Y < 52.5\}$ are equivalent events. That is, $P(Y = 48, 49, 50, 51, 52) = P(47.5 < Y < 52.5)$. Since $np = 50$ and $np(1 - p) = 25$, the latter probability may be written

$$P(47.5 < Y < 52.5) = P\left(\frac{47.5 - 50}{5} < \frac{Y - 50}{5} < \frac{52.5 - 50}{5}\right)$$

$$= P\left(-0.5 < \frac{Y - 50}{5} < 0.5\right).$$

Since $(Y - 50)/5$ has an approximate normal distribution with mean zero and variance 1, Table III show this probability to be approximately 0.382.

The convention of selecting the event $47.5 < Y < 52.5$, instead of another event, say, $47.8 < Y < 52.3$, as the event equivalent to the event $Y = 48, 49, 50, 51, 52$ seems to have originated as: The probability, $P(Y = 48, 49, 50, 51, 52)$, can be interpreted as the sum of five rectangular areas where the rectangles have widths 1 but the heights are, respectively, $P(Y = 48), \ldots, P(Y = 52)$. If these rectangles are so located that the midpoints of their bases are, respectively, at the points $48, 49, \ldots, 52$ on a horizontal axis, then in approximating the sum of these areas by an area bounded by the horizontal axis, the graph of a normal pdf, and two ordinates, it seems reasonable to take the two ordinates at the points 47.5 and 52.5. This is called the **continuity correction**. ∎

We next present two examples concerning large sample inference for proportions.

Example 5.3.5 (Large Sample Inference for Proportions). Let $X_1, X_2, \ldots, X_n$ be a random sample from a Bernoulli distribution with p as the probability of success. Let $\widehat{p}$ be the sample proportion of successes. Then $\widehat{p} = \overline{X}$. In Examples 4.2.3 and 4.5.2 of Chapter 4, we presented large sample confidence intervals and tests for p. A fact used in these derivations is

$$\frac{\widehat{p} - p}{\sqrt{\widehat{p}(1 - \widehat{p})/n}} \xrightarrow{D} N(0, 1). \tag{5.3.3}$$

This is readily established by using the CLT and the same reasoning as in Example 5.3.1; see Exercise 5.3.13. ∎

Example 5.3.6 (Large Sample Inference for χ^2-Tests). Another extension of Example 5.3.3 that was used in Section 4.7 follows quickly from the Central Limit Theorem and Theorem 5.2.4. Using the notation of Example 5.3.3, suppose Y_n has a binomial distribution with parameters n and p. Then, as in Example 5.3.3, $(Y_n - np)/\sqrt{np(1 - p)}$ converges in distribution to a random variable Z with the $N(0, 1)$ distribution. Hence, by Theorem 5.2.4,

$$\left(\frac{Y_n - np}{\sqrt{np(1 - p)}}\right)^2 \xrightarrow{D} \chi^2(1). \tag{5.3.4}$$

This was the result referenced in Chapter 4; see expression (4.7.1). ∎

We know that $\overline{X}$ and $\sum_1^n X_i$ have approximately normal distributions, provided that n is large enough. Later, we find that other statistics also have approximate normal distributions, and this is the reason that the normal distribution is so important to statisticians. That is, while not many underlying distributions are normal, the distributions of statistics calculated from random samples arising from these distributions are often very close to being normal.

Frequently, we are interested in functions of statistics that have approximately normal distributions. To illustrate, consider the sequence of random variable Y_n of Example 5.3.3. As discussed there, Y_n has an approximate $N[np, np(1-p)]$. So $np(1-p)$ is an important function of p, as it is the variance of Y_n. Thus, if p is unknown, we might want to estimate the variance of Y_n. Since $E(Y_n/n) = p$, we might use $n(Y_n/n)(1 - Y_n/n)$ as such an estimator and would want to know something about the latter's distribution. In particular, does it also have an approximate normal distribution? If so, what are its mean and variance? To answer questions like these, we can apply the Δ-method, Theorem 5.2.9.

As an illustration of the Δ-method, we consider a function of the sample mean. We know that $\overline{X}_n$ converges in probability to μ and $\overline{X}_n$ is approximately $N(\mu, \sigma^2/n)$. Suppose that we are interested in a function of $\overline{X}_n$, say $u(\overline{X}_n)$, where u is differentiable at μ and $u'(\mu) \neq 0$. By Theorem 5.2.9, $u(\overline{X}_n)$ is approximately distributed as $N\{u(\mu), [u'(\mu)]^2 \sigma^2/n\}$. More formally, we could say that

$$\frac{u(\overline{X}_n) - u(\mu)}{\sqrt{[u'(\mu)]^2 \sigma^2/n}}$$

has a limiting standard normal distribution.

Example 5.3.7. Let Y_n (or Y for simplicity) be $b(n, p)$. Thus, Y/n is approximately $N[p, p(1-p)/n]$. Statisticians often look for functions of statistics whose variances do not depend upon the parameter. Here the variance of Y/n depends upon p. Can we find a function, say $u(Y/n)$, whose variance is essentially free of p? Since Y/n converges in probability to p, we can approximate $u(Y/n)$ by the first two terms of its Taylor's expansion about p, namely, by

$$u\left(\frac{Y}{n}\right) \doteq v\left(\frac{Y}{n}\right) = u(p) + \left(\frac{Y}{n} - p\right) u'(p).$$

Of course, $v(Y/n)$ is a linear function of Y/n and thus also has an approximate normal distribution; clearly, it has mean $u(p)$ and variance

$$[u'(p)]^2 \frac{p(1-p)}{n}.$$

But it is the latter that we want to be essentially free of p; thus, we set it equal to a constant, obtaining the differential equation

$$u'(p) = \frac{c}{\sqrt{p(1-p)}}.$$

A solution of this is

$$u(p) = (2c) \arcsin \sqrt{p}.$$

If we take $c = \frac{1}{2}$, we have, since $u(Y/n)$ is approximately equal to $v(Y/n)$, that

$$u\left(\frac{Y}{n}\right) = \arcsin\sqrt{\frac{Y}{n}}$$

has an approximate normal distribution with mean $\arcsin\sqrt{p}$ and variance $1/4n$, which is free of p. ∎

EXERCISES

5.3.1. Let $\overline{X}$ denote the mean of a random sample of size 100 from a distribution that is $\chi^2(50)$. Compute an approximate value of $P(49 < \overline{X} < 51)$.

5.3.2. Let $\overline{X}$ denote the mean of a random sample of size 128 from a gamma distribution with $\alpha = 2$ and $\beta = 4$. Approximate $P(7 < \overline{X} < 9)$.

5.3.3. Let Y be $b(72, \frac{1}{3})$. Approximate $P(22 \leq Y \leq 28)$.

5.3.4. Compute an approximate probability that the mean of a random sample of size 15 from a distribution having pdf $f(x) = 3x^2$, $0 < x < 1$, zero elsewhere, is between $\frac{3}{5}$ and $\frac{4}{5}$.

5.3.5. Let Y denote the sum of the observations of a random sample of size 12 from a distribution having pmf $p(x) = \frac{1}{6}$, $x = 1, 2, 3, 4, 5, 6$, zero elsewhere. Compute an approximate value of $P(36 < Y \leq 48)$.
Hint: Since the event of interest is $Y = 36, 37, \ldots, 48$, rewrite the probability as $P(35.5 < Y < 48.5)$.

5.3.6. Let Y be $b(400, \frac{1}{5})$. Compute an approximate value of $P(0.25 < Y/400)$.

5.3.7. If Y is $b(100, \frac{1}{2})$, approximate the value of $P(Y = 50)$.

5.3.8. Let Y be $b(n, 0.55)$. Find the smallest value of n which is such that (approximately) $P(Y/n > \frac{1}{2}) \geq 0.95$.

5.3.9. Let $f(x) = 1/x^2$, $1 < x < \infty$, zero elsewhere, be the pdf of a random variable X. Consider a random sample of size 72 from the distribution having this pdf. Compute approximately the probability that more than 50 of the observations of the random sample are less than 3.

5.3.10. Forty-eight measurements are recorded to several decimal places. Each of these 48 numbers is rounded off to the nearest integer. The sum of the original 48 numbers is approximated by the sum of these integers. If we assume that the errors made by rounding off are iid and have a uniform distribution over the interval $(-\frac{1}{2}, \frac{1}{2})$, compute approximately the probability that the sum of the integers is within two units of the true sum.

5.3.11. We know that $\overline{X}$ is approximately $N(\mu, \sigma^2/n)$ for large n. Find the approximate distribution of $u(\overline{X}) = \overline{X}^3$, provided that $\mu \neq 0$.

5.3.12. Let $X_1, X_2, \ldots, X_n$ be a random sample from a Poisson distribution with mean μ. Thus, $Y = \sum_{i=1}^{n} X_i$ has a Poisson distribution with mean $n\mu$. Moreover, $\overline{X} = Y/n$ is approximately $N(\mu, \mu/n)$ for large n. Show that $u(Y/n) = \sqrt{Y/n}$ is a function of Y/n whose variance is essentially free of μ.

5.3.13. Using the notation of Example 5.3.5, show that equation (5.3.3) is true.

5.4   *Extensions to Multivariate Distributions

In this section, we briefly discuss asymptotic concepts for sequences of random vectors. The concepts introduced for univariate random variables generalize in a straightforward manner to the multivariate case. Our development is brief, and the interested reader can consult more advanced texts for more depth; see Serfling (1980).

We need some notation. For a vector $\mathbf{v} \in R^p$, recall that Euclidean norm of $\mathbf{v}$ is defined to be

$$\|\mathbf{v}\| = \sqrt{\sum_{i=1}^{p} v_i^2}. \qquad (5.4.1)$$

This norm satisfies the usual three properties given by

    (a) For all $\mathbf{v} \in R^p$, $\|\mathbf{v}\| \geq 0$, and $\|\mathbf{v}\| = 0$ if and only if $\mathbf{v} = \mathbf{0}$.
    (b) For all $\mathbf{v} \in R^p$ and $a \in R$, $\|a\mathbf{v}\| = |a|\|\mathbf{v}\|$. $\qquad (5.4.2)$
    (c) For all $\mathbf{v}, \mathbf{u} \in R^p$, $\|\mathbf{u} + \mathbf{v}\| \leq \|\mathbf{u}\| + \|\mathbf{v}\|$.

Denote the standard basis of R^p by the vectors $\mathbf{e}_1, \ldots, \mathbf{e}_p$, where all the components of $\mathbf{e}_i$ are 0 except for the ith component, which is 1. Then we can always write any vector $\mathbf{v}' = (v_1, \ldots, v_p)$ as

$$\mathbf{v} = \sum_{i=1}^{p} v_i \mathbf{e}_i.$$

The following lemma will be useful:

Lemma 5.4.1. *Let $\mathbf{v}' = (v_1, \ldots, v_p)$ be any vector in R^p. Then*

$$|v_j| \leq \|\mathbf{v}\| \leq \sum_{i=1}^{n} |v_i|, \quad \text{for all } j = 1, \ldots, p. \qquad (5.4.3)$$

Proof: Note that for all j,

$$v_j^2 \leq \sum_{i=1}^{p} v_i^2 = \|\mathbf{v}\|^2;$$

hence, taking the square root of this equality leads to the first part of the desired inequality. The second part is

$$\|\mathbf{v}\| = \left\| \sum_{i=1}^{p} v_i \mathbf{e}_i \right\| \leq \sum_{i=1}^{p} |v_i| \|\mathbf{e}_i\| = \sum_{i=1}^{p} |v_i|. \quad \blacksquare$$

Let $\{\mathbf{X}_n\}$ denote a sequence of p-dimensional vectors. Because the absolute value is the Euclidean norm in R^1, the definition of convergence in probability for random vectors is an immediate generalization:

Definition 5.4.1. *Let $\{\mathbf{X}_n\}$ be a sequence of p-dimensional vectors and let $\mathbf{X}$ be a random vector, all defined on the same sample space. We say that $\{\mathbf{X}_n\}$ converges in probability to $\mathbf{X}$ if*

$$\lim_{n \to \infty} P[\|\mathbf{X}_n - \mathbf{X}\| \geq \epsilon] = 0, \tag{5.4.4}$$

for all $\epsilon > 0$. As in the univariate case, we write $\mathbf{X}_n \overset{P}{\to} \mathbf{X}$.

As the next theorem shows, convergence in probability of vectors is equivalent to componentwise convergence in probability.

Theorem 5.4.1. *Let $\{\mathbf{X}_n\}$ be a sequence of p-dimensional vectors and let $\mathbf{X}$ be a random vector, all defined on the same sample space. Then*

$$\mathbf{X}_n \overset{P}{\to} \mathbf{X} \text{ if and only if } X_{nj} \overset{P}{\to} X_j \text{ for all } j = 1, \dots, p.$$

Proof: This follows immediately from Lemma 5.4.1. Suppose $\mathbf{X}_n \overset{P}{\to} \mathbf{X}$. For any j, from the first part of the inequality (5.4.3), we have, for $\epsilon > 0$,

$$\epsilon \leq |X_{nj} - X_j| \leq \|\mathbf{X}_n - \mathbf{X}\|.$$

Hence

$$\overline{\lim}_{n \to \infty} P[|X_{nj} - X_j| \geq \epsilon] < \overline{\lim}_{n \to \infty} P[\|\mathbf{X}_n - \mathbf{X}\| \geq \epsilon] = 0,$$

which is the desired result.

Conversely, if $X_{nj} \overset{P}{\to} X_j$ for all $j = 1, \dots, p$, then by the second part of the inequality (5.4.3),

$$\epsilon \leq \|\mathbf{X}_n - \mathbf{X}\| \leq \sum_{i=1}^{p} |X_{nj} - X_j|,$$

for any $\epsilon > 0$. Hence

$$\overline{\lim}_{n \to \infty} P[\|\mathbf{X}_n - \mathbf{X}\| \geq \epsilon] \leq \overline{\lim}_{n \to \infty} P[\sum_{j=1}^{p} |X_{nj} - X_j| \geq \epsilon]$$

$$\leq \sum_{j=1}^{p} \overline{\lim}_{n \to \infty} P[|X_{nj} - X_j| \geq \epsilon/p] = 0. \quad \blacksquare$$

Based on this result, many of the theorems involving convergence in probability can easily be extended to the multivariate setting. Some of these results are given in the exercises. This is true of statistical results, too. For example, in Section 5.2, we showed that if $X_1, \dots, X_n$ is a random sample from the distribution of a random variable X with mean, μ, and variance, σ^2, then $\overline{X}_n$ and S_n^2 are consistent estimates of μ and σ^2. By the last theorem, we have that $(\overline{X}_n, S_n^2)$ is a consistent estimate of (μ, σ^2).

As another simple application, consider the multivariate analog of the sample mean and sample variance. Let $\{\mathbf{X}_n\}$ be a sequence of iid random vectors with common mean vector $\boldsymbol{\mu}$ and variance-covariance matrix $\boldsymbol{\Sigma}$. Denote the vector of means by

$$\overline{\mathbf{X}}_n = \frac{1}{n} \sum_{i=1}^{n} \mathbf{X}_i. \tag{5.4.5}$$

Of course, $\overline{\mathbf{X}}_n$ is just the vector of sample means, $(\overline{X}_1, \ldots, \overline{X}_p)'$. By the Weak Law of Large Numbers, Theorem 5.1.1, $\overline{X}_j \to \mu_j$, in probability, for each j. Hence, by Theorem 5.4.1, $\overline{\mathbf{X}}_n \to \boldsymbol{\mu}$, in probability.

How about the analog of the sample variances? Let $\mathbf{X}_i = (X_{i1}, \ldots, X_{ip})'$. Define the sample variances and covariances by

$$S_{n,j}^2 = \frac{1}{n-1} \sum_{i=1}^{n} (X_{ij} - \overline{X}_j)^2, \quad \text{for } j = 1, \ldots, p, \tag{5.4.6}$$

$$S_{n,jk} = \frac{1}{n-1} \sum_{i=1}^{n} (X_{ij} - \overline{X}_j)(X_{ik} - \overline{X}_k), \quad \text{for } j \neq k = 1, \ldots, p. \tag{5.4.7}$$

Assuming finite fourth moments, the Weak Law of Large Numbers shows that all these componentwise sample variances and sample covariances converge in probability to distribution variances and covariances, respectively. As in our discussion after the Weak Law of Large Numbers, the Strong Law of Large Numbers implies that this convergence is true under the weaker assumption of the existance of finite second moments. If we define the $p \times p$ matrix $\mathbf{S}$ to be the matrix with the jth diagonal entry $S_{n,j}^2$ and (j, k)th entry $S_{n,jk}$, then $\mathbf{S} \to \boldsymbol{\Sigma}$, in probability.

The definition of convergence in distribution remains the same. We state it here in terms of vector notation.

Definition 5.4.2. *Let $\{\mathbf{X}_n\}$ be a sequence of random vectors with $\mathbf{X}_n$ having distribution function $F_n(\mathbf{x})$ and $\mathbf{X}$ be a random vector with distribution function $F(\mathbf{x})$. Then $\{\mathbf{X}_n\}$ **converges in distribution** to $\mathbf{X}$ if*

$$\lim_{n \to \infty} F_n(\mathbf{x}) = F(\mathbf{x}), \tag{5.4.8}$$

for all points $\mathbf{x}$ at which $F(\mathbf{x})$ is continuous. We write $\mathbf{X}_n \xrightarrow{D} \mathbf{X}$.

In the multivariate case, there are analogs to many of the theorems in Section 5.2. We state two important theorems without proof.

Theorem 5.4.2. *Let $\{\mathbf{X}_n\}$ be a sequence of random vectors which converge in distribution to a random vector $\mathbf{X}$ and let $g(\mathbf{x})$ be a function which is continuous on the support of $\mathbf{X}$. Then $g(\mathbf{X}_n)$ converges in distribution to $g(\mathbf{X})$.*

We can apply this theorem to show that convergence in distribution implies marginal convergence. Simply take $g(\mathbf{x}) = x_j$, where $\mathbf{x} = (x_1, \ldots, x_p)'$. Since g is continuous, the desired result follows.

It is often difficult to determine convergence in distribution by using the definition. As in the univariate case, convergence in distribution is equivalent to convergence of moment generating functions, which we state in the following theorem.

Theorem 5.4.3. *Let $\{\mathbf{X}_n\}$ be a sequence of random vectors with $\mathbf{X}_n$ having distribution function $F_n(\mathbf{x})$ and moment generating function $M_n(\mathbf{t})$. Let $\mathbf{X}$ be a random vector with distribution function $F(\mathbf{x})$ and moment generating function $M(\mathbf{t})$. Then $\{\mathbf{X}_n\}$ converges in distribution to $\mathbf{X}$ if and only if, for some $h > 0$,*

$$\lim_{n \to \infty} M_n(\mathbf{t}) = M(\mathbf{t}), \qquad (5.4.9)$$

for all $\mathbf{t}$ such that $\|\mathbf{t}\| < h$.

The proof of this theorem can be found in more advanced books; see, for instance, Tucker (1967). Also, the usual proof is for characteristic functions instead of moment generating functions. As we mentioned previously, characteristic functions always exist, so convergence in distribution is completely characterized by convergence of corresponding characteristic functions.

The moment generating function of $\mathbf{X}_n$ is $E[\exp\{\mathbf{t}'\mathbf{X}_n\}]$. Note that $\mathbf{t}'\mathbf{X}_n$ is a random variable. We can frequently use this and univariate theory to derive results in the multivariate case. A perfect example of this is the multivariate central limit theorem.

Theorem 5.4.4 (Multivariate Central Limit Theorem). *Let $\{\mathbf{X}_n\}$ be a sequence of iid random vectors with common mean vector $\boldsymbol{\mu}$ and variance-covariance matrix $\boldsymbol{\Sigma}$ which is positive definite. Assume the common moment generating function $M(\mathbf{t})$ exists in an open neighborhood of $\mathbf{0}$. Let*

$$\mathbf{Y}_n = \frac{1}{\sqrt{n}} \sum_{i=1}^{n} (\mathbf{X}_i - \boldsymbol{\mu}) = \sqrt{n}(\overline{\mathbf{X}} - \boldsymbol{\mu}).$$

Then $\mathbf{Y}_n$ converges in distribution to a $N_p(\mathbf{0}, \boldsymbol{\Sigma})$ distribution.

Proof: Let $\mathbf{t} \in R^p$ be a vector in the stipulated neighborhood of $\mathbf{0}$. The moment generating function of $\mathbf{Y}_n$ is

$$
\begin{aligned}
M_n(\mathbf{t}) &= E\left[\exp\left\{\mathbf{t}'\frac{1}{\sqrt{n}}\sum_{i=1}^{n}(\mathbf{X}_i - \boldsymbol{\mu})\right\}\right] \\
&= E\left[\exp\left\{\frac{1}{\sqrt{n}}\sum_{i=1}^{n}\mathbf{t}'(\mathbf{X}_i - \boldsymbol{\mu})\right\}\right] \\
&= E\left[\exp\left\{\frac{1}{\sqrt{n}}\sum_{i=1}^{n}W_i\right\}\right], \qquad (5.4.10)
\end{aligned}
$$

where $W_i = \mathbf{t}'(\mathbf{X}_i - \boldsymbol{\mu})$. Note that $W_1, \ldots, W_n$ are iid with mean 0 and variance $\mathrm{Var}(W_i) = \mathbf{t}'\boldsymbol{\Sigma}\mathbf{t}$. Hence, by the simple Central Limit Theorem,

$$\frac{1}{\sqrt{n}}\sum_{i=1}^{n}W_i \xrightarrow{D} N(0, \mathbf{t}'\boldsymbol{\Sigma}\mathbf{t}). \qquad (5.4.11)$$

Expression (5.4.10), though, is the mgf of $(1/\sqrt{n})\sum_{i=1}^{n} W_i$ evaluated at 1. Therefore, by (5.4.11), we must have

$$M_n(\mathbf{t}) = E\left[\exp\left\{(1)\frac{1}{\sqrt{n}}\sum_{i=1}^{n} W_i\right\}\right] \to e^{1^2 \mathbf{t}' \boldsymbol{\Sigma} \mathbf{t}/2} = e^{\mathbf{t}' \boldsymbol{\Sigma} \mathbf{t}/2}.$$

Because the last quantity is the moment generating function of a $N_p(\mathbf{0}, \boldsymbol{\Sigma})$ distribution, we have the desired result. ∎

Suppose $\mathbf{X}_1, \mathbf{X}_2, \dots, \mathbf{X}_n$ is a random sample from a distribution with mean vector $\boldsymbol{\mu}$ and variance-covariance matrix $\boldsymbol{\Sigma}$. Let $\overline{\mathbf{X}}_n$ be the vector of sample means. Then, from the Central Limit Theorem, we say that

$$\overline{\mathbf{X}}_n \text{ has an approximate } N_p\left(\boldsymbol{\mu}, \tfrac{1}{n}\boldsymbol{\Sigma}\right) \text{ distribution.} \tag{5.4.12}$$

A result that we use frequently concerns linear transformations. Its proof is obtained by using moment generating functions and is left as an exercise.

Theorem 5.4.5. *Let* $\{\mathbf{X}_n\}$ *be a sequence of p-dimensional random vectors. Suppose* $\mathbf{X}_n \overset{D}{\to} N(\boldsymbol{\mu}, \boldsymbol{\Sigma})$. *Let* $\mathbf{A}$ *be an $m \times p$ matrix of constants and let $\mathbf{b}$ be an m-dimensional vector of constants. Then* $\mathbf{A}\mathbf{X}_n + \mathbf{b} \overset{D}{\to} N(\mathbf{A}\boldsymbol{\mu} + \mathbf{b}, \mathbf{A}\boldsymbol{\Sigma}\mathbf{A}')$.

A result that will prove to be quite useful is the extension of the Δ-method; see Theorem 5.2.9. A proof can be found in Chapter 3 of Serfling (1980).

Theorem 5.4.6. *Let* $\{\mathbf{X}_n\}$ *be a sequence of p-dimensional random vectors. Suppose*

$$\sqrt{n}(\mathbf{X}_n - \boldsymbol{\mu}_0) \overset{D}{\to} N_p(\mathbf{0}, \boldsymbol{\Sigma}).$$

Let $\mathbf{g}$ *be a transformation* $\mathbf{g}(\mathbf{x}) = (g_1(\mathbf{x}), \dots, g_k(\mathbf{x}))'$ *such that* $1 \le k \le p$ *and the $k \times p$ matrix of partial derivatives,*

$$\mathbf{B} = \left[\frac{\partial g_i}{\partial \mu_j}\right], \quad i = 1, \dots k; \; j = 1, \dots, p,$$

are continuous and do not vanish in a neighborhood of $\boldsymbol{\mu}_0$. *Let* $\mathbf{B}_0 = \mathbf{B}$ *at* $\boldsymbol{\mu}_0$. *Then*

$$\sqrt{n}(\mathbf{g}(\mathbf{X}_n) - \mathbf{g}(\boldsymbol{\mu}_0)) \overset{D}{\to} N_k(\mathbf{0}, \mathbf{B}_0 \boldsymbol{\Sigma} \mathbf{B}_0'). \tag{5.4.13}$$

EXERCISES

5.4.1. Let $\{\mathbf{X}_n\}$ be a sequence of p-dimensional random vectors. Show that

$$\mathbf{X}_n \overset{D}{\to} N_p(\boldsymbol{\mu}, \boldsymbol{\Sigma}) \text{ if and only if } \mathbf{a}'\mathbf{X}_n \overset{D}{\to} N_1(\mathbf{a}'\boldsymbol{\mu}, \mathbf{a}'\boldsymbol{\Sigma}\mathbf{a}),$$

for all vectors $\mathbf{a} \in R^p$.

5.4.2. Let $X_1, \ldots, X_n$ be a random sample from a uniform(a, b) distribution. Let $Y_1 = \min X_i$ and let $Y_2 = \max X_i$. Show that $(Y_1, Y_2)'$ converges in probability to the vector $(a, b)'$.

5.4.3. Let $\mathbf{X}_n$ and $\mathbf{Y}_n$ be p-dimensional random vectors. Show that if

$$\mathbf{X}_n - \mathbf{Y}_n \xrightarrow{P} \mathbf{0} \text{ and } \mathbf{X}_n \xrightarrow{D} \mathbf{X},$$

where $\mathbf{X}$ is a p-dimensional random vector, then $\mathbf{Y}_n \xrightarrow{D} \mathbf{X}$.

5.4.4. Let $\mathbf{X}_n$ and $\mathbf{Y}_n$ be p-dimensional random vectors such that $\mathbf{X}_n$ and $\mathbf{Y}_n$ are independent for each n and their mgfs exist. Show that if

$$\mathbf{X}_n \xrightarrow{D} \mathbf{X} \text{ and } \mathbf{Y}_n \xrightarrow{D} \mathbf{Y},$$

where $\mathbf{X}$ and $\mathbf{Y}$ are p-dimensional random vectors, then $(\mathbf{X}_n, \mathbf{Y}_n) \xrightarrow{D} (\mathbf{X}, \mathbf{Y})$.

5.4.5. Suppose $\mathbf{X}_n$ has a $N_p(\boldsymbol{\mu}_n, \boldsymbol{\Sigma}_n)$ distribution. Show that

$$\mathbf{X}_n \xrightarrow{D} N_p(\boldsymbol{\mu}, \boldsymbol{\Sigma}) \text{ iff } \boldsymbol{\mu}_n \to \boldsymbol{\mu} \text{ and } \boldsymbol{\Sigma}_n \to \boldsymbol{\Sigma}.$$

Chapter 6

Maximum Likelihood Methods

6.1   Maximum Likelihood Estimation

Recall in Chapter 4 that as a point estimation procedure, we introduced maximum likelihood estimates (mle). In this chapter, we continue this development showing that these likelihood procedures give rise to a formal theory of statistical inference (confidence and testing procedures). Under certain conditions (regularity conditions), these procedures are asymptotically optimal.

As in Section 4.1, consider a random variable X whose pdf $f(x;\theta)$ depends on an unknown parameter θ which is in a set Ω. Our general discussion is for the continuous case, but the results extend to the discrete case also. For information, we have a random sample (iid) $X_1,\ldots,X_n$ on X. Suppose that $X_1,\ldots,X_n$ are iid random variables with common pdf $f(x;\theta), \theta \in \Omega$. For now, we assume that θ is a scalar, but we do extend the results to vectors in Sections 6.4 and 6.5. The parameter θ is unknown. The basis of our inferential procedures is the likelihood function given by

$$L(\theta; \mathbf{x}) = \prod_{i=1}^{n} f(x_i; \theta), \quad \theta \in \Omega, \tag{6.1.1}$$

where $\mathbf{x} = (x_1,\ldots,x_n)'$. Because we treat L as a function of θ in this chapter, we have transposed the x_i and θ in the argument of the likelihood function. In fact, we often write it as $L(\theta)$. Actually, the log of this function is usually more convenient to use and we denote it by

$$l(\theta) = \log L(\theta) = \sum_{i=1}^{n} \log f(x_i; \theta), \quad \theta \in \Omega. \tag{6.1.2}$$

Note that there is no loss of information in using $l(\theta)$ because the log is a one-to-one function. Most of our discussion in this chapter remains the same if X is a random

$\widehat{\theta}$ —— θ 的 mle.

θ_0 —— θ 的 true value.

$X = (X)$.

即1别1维度号。而 vector 是 Y n 维度阵.

vector. Although we generally consider X to be a univariate random variable, for several of our examples it is a random vector. —— $X = (X_1, X_2, \cdots, X_n)$

As in Chapter 4, our point estimator of θ is $\widehat{\theta} = \widehat{\theta}(X_1, \ldots, X_n)$, where $\widehat{\theta}$ maximizes the function $L(\theta)$. We call $\widehat{\theta}$ the maximum likelihood estimator (mle) of θ. In Section 4.1, several motivating examples were given, including the binomial and normal probability models. Later we give several more examples, but first we offer a theoretical justification for considering the mle. Let θ_0 denote the *true value* of θ. Theorem 6.1.1 shows that the maximum of $L(\theta)$ asymptotically separates the true model at θ_0 from models at $\theta \neq \theta_0$. To prove this theorem, we assume certain assumptions, usually called *regularity conditions*.

Assumptions 6.1.1 (Regularity Conditions). *Regularity conditions (R0)–(R1) are given by*

(R0) *The pdfs are distinct; i.e., $\theta \neq \theta' \Rightarrow f(x_i; \theta) \neq f(x_i; \theta')$.*

(R1) *The pdfs have common support for all θ.* —— 即所有的 θ 所服从 $X_1, \cdots, X_n$ 而来的分布, $X_1, \cdots X_n$ 而取值都一样?

support 表示取值范围

意即不管 θ 怎么变,

形状怎么变, X_i 的

取值范围都不变!

(R2) *The point θ_0 is an interior point in Ω.* $\theta_0 \in \Omega$.

—— 即 1. 别 1 而来差.

The first assumption states that the parameter identifies the pdf. The second assumption implies that the support of X_i does not depend on θ. This is restrictive, and some examples and exercises cover models in which (R1) is not true.

Theorem 6.1.1. *Let θ_0 be the true parameter. Under assumptions (R0) and (R1),*

$$\lim_{n \to \infty} P_{\theta_0}[L(\theta_0, \mathbf{X}) > L(\theta, \mathbf{X})] = 1, \quad \text{for all } \theta \neq \theta_0. \quad (6.1.3)$$

意即 $L(\theta_0, X)$ 值 比 $L(\theta, X)$ 而值 大的可能性趋近于 = 1, 当 $n \to \infty$ 时,

Proof: By taking logs, the inequality $L(\theta_0, \mathbf{X}) > L(\theta, \mathbf{X})$ is equivalent to

$L(\theta, X) < L(\theta_0, X)$

$\Rightarrow \frac{L(\theta, X)}{L(\theta_0, X)} < 1 \Rightarrow \log \frac{L(\theta, X)}{L(\theta_0, X)} < \log 1 = 0.$

$\Rightarrow \log \frac{\prod f(x_i, \theta)}{\prod f(x_i, \theta_0)} = \log \left[\frac{f(x_1, \theta)}{f(x_1, \theta_0)} \cdot \frac{f(x_2, \theta)}{f(x_2, \theta_0)} \cdots \right] < 0$

$$\frac{1}{n} \sum_{i=1}^{n} \log \left[\frac{f(X_i; \theta)}{f(X_i; \theta_0)} \right] < 0.$$

$\Rightarrow \sum \left[\log \frac{f(x_i, \theta)}{f(x_i, \theta_0)} \right] < 0$

$\Rightarrow \frac{1}{n} \sum [\log \cdots] < 0.$

Since the summands are iid with finite expectation and the function $\phi(x) = -\log(x)$ is strictly convex, it follows from the Law of Large Numbers (Theorem 5.1.1) and Jensen's inequality (Theorem 1.10.5) that, when θ_0 is the true parameter,

$$\frac{1}{n} \sum_{i=1}^{n} \log \left[\frac{f(X_i; \theta)}{f(X_i; \theta_0)} \right] \xrightarrow{P} E_{\theta_0} \left[\log \frac{f(X_1; \theta)}{f(X_1; \theta_0)} \right] < \log E_{\theta_0} \left[\frac{f(X_1; \theta)}{f(X_1; \theta_0)} \right].$$

But

$$E_{\theta_0} \left[\frac{f(X_1; \theta)}{f(X_1; \theta_0)} \right] = \int \frac{f(x; \theta)}{f(x; \theta_0)} f(x; \theta_0) \, dx = 1.$$

$= \int f(x; \theta) \, dx$

∵ 因 $f(x; \theta)$ 是 pdf.

∴ 在 X 的 support 上积分, = 1.

Because $\log 1 = 0$, the theorem follows. Note that common support is needed to obtain the last equalities. ∎

结果妙!

Theorem 6.1.1 says that asymptotically the likelihood function is maximized at the true value θ_0. So in considering estimates of θ_0, it seems natural to consider the value of θ which maximizes the likelihood.

Definition 6.1.1 (Maximum Likelihood Estimator). *We say that $\widehat{\theta} = \widehat{\theta}(\mathbf{X})$ is a* **maximum likelihood estimator** *(mle) of θ if*

$$\widehat{\theta} = Argmax\, L(\theta; \mathbf{X}). \tag{6.1.4}$$

The notation Argmax means that $L(\theta; \mathbf{X})$ achieves its maximum value at $\widehat{\theta}$.

As in Chapter 4, to determine the mle, we often take the log of the likelihood and determine its critical value; that is, letting $l(\theta) = \log L(\theta)$, the mle solves the equation

$$\frac{\partial l(\theta)}{\partial \theta} = 0. \tag{6.1.5}$$

This is an example of an **estimating equation**, which we often label as an EE. This is the first of several EEs in the text.

Example 6.1.1 (Laplace Distribution). Let $X_1, \ldots, X_n$ be iid with density

$$f(x; \theta) = \frac{1}{2} e^{-|x-\theta|}, \quad -\infty < x < \infty, -\infty < \theta < \infty. \tag{6.1.6}$$

This pdf is referred to as either the *Laplace* or the *double exponential distribution*. The log of the likelihood simplifies to

$$l(\theta) = -n \log 2 - \sum_{i=1}^{n} |x_i - \theta|.$$

The first partial derivative is

$$l'(\theta) = \sum_{i=1}^{n} \text{sgn}(x_i - \theta), \tag{6.1.7}$$

where $\text{sgn}(t) = 1, 0,$ or -1 depending on whether $t > 0, t = 0$, or $t < 0$. Note that we have used $\frac{d}{dt}|t| = \text{sgn}(t)$, which is true unless $t = 0$. Setting equation (6.1.7) to 0, the solution for θ is $\text{med}\{x_1, x_2, \ldots, x_n\}$, because the median makes half the terms of the sum in expression (6.1.7) nonpositive and half nonnegative. Recall that we denote the median of a sample by Q_2 (the second quartile of the sample). Hence, $\widehat{\theta} = Q_2$ is the mle of θ for the Laplace pdf (6.1.6). ∎

There is no guarantee that the mle exists or, if it does, whether it is unique. This is often clear from the application as in the next two examples. Other examples are given in the exercises.

Example 6.1.2 (Logistic Distribution). Let $X_1, \ldots, X_n$ be iid with density

$$f(x; \theta) = \frac{\exp\{-(x-\theta)\}}{(1 + \exp\{-(x-\theta)\})^2}, \quad -\infty < x < \infty, \ -\infty < \theta < \infty. \tag{6.1.8}$$

The log of the likelihood simplifies to

$$l(\theta) = \sum_{i=1}^{n} \log f(x_i; \theta) = n\theta - n\overline{x} - 2 \sum_{i=1}^{n} \log(1 + \exp\{-(x_i - \theta)\}).$$

Using this, the first partial derivative is

$$l'(\theta) = n - 2 \sum_{i=1}^{n} \frac{\exp\{-(x_i - \theta)\}}{1 + \exp\{-(x_i - \theta)\}}. \tag{6.1.9}$$

Setting this equation to 0 and rearranging terms results in the equation

$$\sum_{i=1}^{n} \frac{\exp\{-(x_i - \theta)\}}{1 + \exp\{-(x_i - \theta)\}} = \frac{n}{2}. \tag{6.1.10}$$

Although this does not simplify, we can show that equation (6.1.10) has a unique solution. The derivative of the left side of equation (6.1.10) simplifies to

$$(\partial/\partial\theta) \sum_{i=1}^{n} \frac{\exp\{-(x_i - \theta)\}}{1 + \exp\{-(x_i - \theta)\}} = \sum_{i=1}^{n} \frac{\exp\{-(x_i - \theta)\}}{(1 + \exp\{-(x_i - \theta)\})^2} > 0.$$

Thus the left side of equation (6.1.10) is a strictly increasing function of θ. Finally, the left side of (6.1.10) approaches 0 as $\theta \to -\infty$ and approaches n as $\theta \to \infty$. Thus equation (6.1.10) has a unique solution. Also, the second derivative of $l(\theta)$ is strictly negative for all θ; so the solution is a maximum.

Having shown that the mle exists and is unique, we can use a numerical method to obtain the solution. In this case, Newton's procedure is useful. We discuss this in general in the next section, at which time we reconsider this example. ∎

Example 6.1.3. In Example 4.1.2, we discussed the mle of the probability of success θ for a random sample $X_1, X_2, \ldots, X_n$ from the Bernoulli distribution with pmf

$$p(x) = \begin{cases} \theta^x (1-\theta)^{1-x} & x = 0, 1 \\ 0 & \text{elsewhere}, \end{cases}$$

where $0 \le \theta \le 1$. Recall that the mle is $\overline{X}$, the proportion of sample successes. Now suppose that we know in advance that, instead of $0 \le \theta \le 1$, θ is restricted by the inequalities $0 \le \theta \le 1/3$. If the observations were such that $\overline{x} > 1/3$, then $\overline{x}$ would not be a satisfactory estimate. Since $\frac{\partial l(\theta)}{\partial \theta} > 0$, provided $\theta < \overline{x}$, under the restriction $0 \le \theta \le 1/3$, we can maximize $l(\theta)$ by taking $\widehat{\theta} = \min\left\{\overline{x}, \frac{1}{3}\right\}$. ∎

The following is an appealing property of maximum likelihood estimates.

Theorem 6.1.2. Let $X_1, \ldots, X_n$ be iid with the pdf $f(x; \theta), \theta \in \Omega$. For a specified function g, let $\eta = g(\theta)$ be a parameter of interest. Suppose $\widehat{\theta}$ is the mle of θ. Then $g(\widehat{\theta})$ is the mle of $\eta = g(\theta)$.

Proof: First suppose g is a one-to-one function. The likelihood of interest is $L(g(\theta))$, but because g is one-to-one,

$$\max L(g(\theta)) = \max_{\eta = g(\theta)} L(\eta) = \max_{\eta} L(g^{-1}(\eta)).$$

But the maximum occurs when $g^{-1}(\eta) = \widehat{\theta}$; i.e., take $\widehat{\eta} = g(\widehat{\theta})$.

Suppose g is not one-to-one. For each η in the range of g, define the set (preimage)

$$g^{-1}(\eta) = \{\theta : g(\theta) = \eta\}.$$

The maximum occurs at $\widehat{\theta}$ and the domain of g is Ω, which covers $\widehat{\theta}$. Hence, $\widehat{\theta}$ is in one of these preimages and, in fact, it can only be in one preimage. Hence to maximize $L(\eta)$, choose $\widehat{\eta}$ so that $g^{-1}(\widehat{\eta})$ is that unique preimage containing $\widehat{\theta}$. Then $\widehat{\eta} = g(\widehat{\theta})$. ∎

Consider Example 4.1.2, where $X_1, \ldots, X_n$ are iid Bernoulli random variables with probability of success p. As shown in this example, $\widehat{p} = \overline{X}$ is the mle of p. Recall that in the large sample confidence interval for p, (4.2.7), an estimate of $\sqrt{p(1-p)}$ is required. By Theorem 6.1.2, the mle of this quantity is $\sqrt{\widehat{p}(1-\widehat{p})}$.

We close this section by showing that maximum likelihood estimators, under regularity conditions, are consistent estimators. Recall that $\mathbf{X}' = (X_1, \ldots, X_n)$.

$(p292)$

Theorem 6.1.3. *Assume that $X_1, \ldots, X_n$ satisfy the regularity conditions (R0) through (R2), where θ_0 is the true parameter, and further that $f(x; \theta)$ is differentiable with respect to θ in Ω. Then the likelihood equation,*

$$\frac{\partial}{\partial \theta} L(\theta) = 0,$$

· Likelihood function: $L(\theta)$.

· likelihood equation: $\frac{\partial L(\theta)}{\partial \theta} = 0$.

or equivalently

(∵ log is a one-to-one function.)

· Estimating equation: $\frac{\partial l(\theta)}{\partial \theta} = 0$.

$$\frac{\partial}{\partial \theta} l(\theta) = 0,$$

has a solution $\widehat{\theta}_n$ such that $\widehat{\theta}_n \xrightarrow{P} \theta_0$.

Proof: Because θ_0 is an interior point in Ω, $(\theta_0 - a, \theta_0 + a) \subset \Omega$, for some $a > 0$. Define S_n to be the event

$$S_n = \{\mathbf{X} : l(\theta_0; \mathbf{X}) > l(\theta_0 - a; \mathbf{X})\} \cap \{\mathbf{X} : l(\theta_0; \mathbf{X}) > l(\theta_0 + a; \mathbf{X})\}.$$

By Theorem 6.1.1, $P(S_n) \to 1$. So we can restrict attention to the event S_n. But on S_n, $l(\theta)$ has a local maximum, say, $\widehat{\theta}_n$, such that $\theta_0 - a < \widehat{\theta}_n < \theta_0 + a$ and $l'(\widehat{\theta}_n) = 0$. That is,

$$S_n \subset \left\{\mathbf{X} : |\widehat{\theta}_n(\mathbf{X}) - \theta_0| < a\right\} \cap \left\{\mathbf{X} : l'(\widehat{\theta}_n(\mathbf{X})) = 0\right\}.$$

Therefore,

$$1 = \lim_{n \to \infty} P(S_n) \leq \varlimsup_{n \to \infty} P\left[\left\{\mathbf{X} : |\widehat{\theta}_n(\mathbf{X}) - \theta_0| < a\right\} \cap \left\{\mathbf{X} : l'(\widehat{\theta}_n(\mathbf{X})) = 0\right\}\right] \leq 1;$$

see Remark 5.2.3 for discussion on $\varlimsup$. It follows that for the sequence of solutions $\widehat{\theta}_n$, $P[|\widehat{\theta}_n - \theta_0| < a] \to 1$.

The only contentious point in the proof is that the sequence of solutions might depend on a. But we can always choose a solution "closest" to θ_0 in the following way. For each n, the set of all solutions in the interval is bounded; hence, the infimum over solutions closest to θ_0 exists. ■

Note that this theorem is vague in that it discusses solutions of the equation. If, however, we know that the mle is the unique solution of the equation $l'(\theta) = 0$, then it is consistent. We state this as a corollary:

Corollary 6.1.1. *Assume that $X_1, \ldots, X_n$ satisfy the regularity conditions (R0) through (R2), where θ_0 is the true parameter, and that $f(x; \theta)$ is differentiable with respect to θ in Ω. Suppose the likelihood equation has the unique solution $\widehat{\theta}_n$. Then $\widehat{\theta}_n$ is a consistent estimator of θ_0.*

即如果 $\widehat{\theta}_n$ 是用 mle 方法设计出的 estimator, $\widehat{\theta}_n$ 也一定是 θ_0 的 consistent estimator.

EXERCISES

6.1.1. Let $X_1, X_2, \ldots, X_n$ be a random sample from a $\Gamma(\alpha = 3, \beta = \theta)$ distribution, $0 < \theta < \infty$. Determine the mle of θ.

6.1.2. Let $X_1, X_2, \ldots, X_n$ represent a random sample from each of the distributions having the following pdfs:

(a) $f(x; \theta) = \theta x^{\theta-1}$, $0 < x < 1$, $0 < \theta < \infty$, zero elsewhere.

(b) $f(x; \theta) = e^{-(x-\theta)}$, $\theta \le x < \infty$, $-\infty < \theta < \infty$, zero elsewhere. Note this is a nonregular case.

In each case find the mle $\hat{\theta}$ of θ.

6.1.3. Let $Y_1 < Y_2 < \cdots < Y_n$ be the order statistics of a random sample from a distribution with pdf $f(x; \theta) = 1$, $\theta - \frac{1}{2} \le x \le \theta + \frac{1}{2}$, $-\infty < \theta < \infty$, zero elsewhere. Note this is a nonregular case. Show that every statistic $u(X_1, X_2, \ldots, X_n)$ such that

$$Y_n - \tfrac{1}{2} \le u(X_1, X_2, \ldots, X_n) \le Y_1 + \tfrac{1}{2}$$

is a mle of θ. In particular, $(4Y_1 + 2Y_n + 1)/6$, $(Y_1 + Y_n)/2$, and $(2Y_1 + 4Y_n - 1)/6$ are three such statistics. Thus, uniqueness is not, in general, a property of a mle.

6.1.4. Suppose $X_1, \ldots, X_n$ are iid with pdf $f(x; \theta) = 2x/\theta^2$, $0 < x \le \theta$, zero elsewhere. Note this is a nonregular case. Find:

(a) The mle $\hat{\theta}$ for θ.

(b) The constant c so that $E(c\hat{\theta}) = \theta$.

(c) The mle for the median of the distribution.

6.1.5. Suppose $X_1, X_2, \ldots, X_n$ are iid with pdf $f(x; \theta) = (1/\theta)e^{-x/\theta}$, $0 < x < \infty$, zero elsewhere. Find the mle of $P(X \le 2)$.

6.1.6. Let the table

x	0	1	2	3	4	5
Frequency	6	10	14	13	6	1

represent a summary of a sample of size 50 from a binomial distribution having $n = 5$. Find the mle of $P(X \geq 3)$.

6.1.7. Let X_1, X_2, X_3, X_4, X_5 be a random sample from a Cauchy distribution with median θ, that is, with pdf

$$f(x; \theta) = \frac{1}{\pi} \frac{1}{1 + (x - \theta)^2}, \quad -\infty < x < \infty,$$

where $-\infty < \theta < \infty$. If $x_1 = -1.94$, $x_2 = 0.59$, $x_3 = -5.98$, $x_4 = -0.08$, and $x_5 = -0.77$, find by numerical methods the mle of θ.

6.1.8. Let the table

x	0	1	2	3	4	5
Frequency	7	14	12	13	6	3

represent a summary of a random sample of size 55 from a Poisson distribution. Find the maximum likelihood estimate of $P(X = 2)$.

6.1.9. Let $X_1, X_2, \ldots, X_n$ be a random sample from a Bernoulli distribution with parameter p. If p is restricted so that we know that $\frac{1}{2} \leq p \leq 1$, find the mle of this parameter.

6.1.10. Let $X_1, X_2, \ldots, X_n$ be a random sample from a $N(\theta, \sigma^2)$ distribution, where σ^2 is fixed but $-\infty < \theta < \infty$.

(a) Show that the mle of θ is $\overline{X}$.

(b) If θ is restricted by $0 \leq \theta < \infty$, show that the mle of θ is $\hat{\theta} = \max\{0, \overline{X}\}$.

6.1.11. Let $X_1, X_2, \ldots, X_n$ be a random sample from the Poisson distribution with $0 < \theta \leq 2$. Show that the mle of θ is $\hat{\theta} = \min\{\overline{X}, 2\}$.

6.1.12. Let $X_1, X_2, \ldots, X_n$ be a random sample from a distribution with one of two pdfs. If $\theta = 1$, then $f(x; \theta = 1) = \frac{1}{\sqrt{2\pi}} e^{-x^2/2}$, $-\infty < x < \infty$. If $\theta = 2$, then $f(x; \theta = 2) = 1/[\pi(1 + x^2)]$, $-\infty < x < \infty$. Find the mle of θ.

6.2 Rao–Cramér Lower Bound and Efficiency

In this section, we establish a remarkable inequality called the **Rao–Cramér** lower bound, which gives a lower bound on the variance of any unbiased estimate. We then show that, under regularity conditions, the variances of the maximum likelihood estimates achieve this lower bound asymptotically.

As in the last section, let X be a random variable with pdf $f(x; \theta)$, $\theta \in \Omega$, where the parameter space Ω is an open interval. In addition to the regularity conditions (6.1.1) of Section 6.1, for the following derivations, we require two more regularity conditions, namely,

Assumptions 6.2.1 (Additional Regularity Conditions). *Regularity conditions (R3) and (R4) are given by*

(R3) *The pdf $f(x;\theta)$ is twice differentiable as a function of θ.*

(R4) *The integral $\int f(x;\theta)\,dx$ can be differentiated twice under the integral sign as a function of θ.*

Note that conditions (R1)–(R4) mean that the parameter θ does not appear in the endpoints of the interval in which $f(x;\theta) > 0$ and that we can interchange integration and differentiation with respect to θ. Our derivation is for the continuous case, but the discrete case can be handled in a similar manner. We begin with the identity

$$1 = \int_{-\infty}^{\infty} f(x;\theta)\,dx.$$

Taking the derivative with respect to θ results in

$$0 = \int_{-\infty}^{\infty} \frac{\partial f(x;\theta)}{\partial \theta}\,dx.$$

The latter expression can be rewritten as

$$0 = \int_{-\infty}^{\infty} \frac{\partial f(x;\theta)/\partial \theta}{f(x;\theta)} f(x;\theta)\,dx,$$

or, equivalently,

$$0 = \int_{-\infty}^{\infty} \frac{\partial \log f(x;\theta)}{\partial \theta} f(x;\theta)\,dx. \tag{6.2.1}$$

Writing this last equation as an expectation, we have established

$$E\left[\frac{\partial \log f(X;\theta)}{\partial \theta}\right] = 0; \tag{6.2.2}$$

that is, the mean of the random variable $\frac{\partial \log f(X;\theta)}{\partial \theta}$ is 0. If we differentiate (6.2.1) again, it follows that

$$0 = \int_{-\infty}^{\infty} \frac{\partial^2 \log f(x;\theta)}{\partial \theta^2} f(x;\theta)\,dx + \int_{-\infty}^{\infty} \frac{\partial \log f(x;\theta)}{\partial \theta} \frac{\partial \log f(x;\theta)}{\partial \theta} f(x;\theta)\,dx. \tag{6.2.3}$$

The second term of the right side of this equation can be written as an expectation, which we call **Fisher information** and we denote it by $I(\theta)$; that is,

$$I(\theta) = \int_{-\infty}^{\infty} \frac{\partial \log f(x;\theta)}{\partial \theta} \frac{\partial \log f(x;\theta)}{\partial \theta} f(x;\theta)\,dx = E\left[\left(\frac{\partial \log f(X;\theta)}{\partial \theta}\right)^2\right]. \tag{6.2.4}$$

From equation (6.2.3), we see that $I(\theta)$ can be computed from

$$I(\theta) = -\int_{-\infty}^{\infty} \frac{\partial^2 \log f(x;\theta)}{\partial \theta^2} f(x;\theta)\,dx = -E\left[\frac{\partial^2 \log f(X;\theta)}{\partial \theta^2}\right]. \tag{6.2.5}$$

Using equation (6.2.2), Fisher information is the variance of the random variable $\frac{\partial \log f(X;\theta)}{\partial \theta}$; i.e.,

$$I(\theta) = \text{Var}\left(\frac{\partial \log f(X;\theta)}{\partial \theta}\right) \qquad (6.2.6)$$

[handwritten: $= E(\cdots^2) - (E(\cdots))^2$ $= E(\cdots^2) - 0^2$ $\because E(\frac{\partial \log f(X;\theta)}{\partial \theta}) = 0$ 6.2.2式*]*

Usually, expression (6.2.5) is easier to compute than expression (6.2.4).

Remark 6.2.1. Note that the information is the weighted mean of either

$$\left[\frac{\partial \log f(x;\theta)}{\partial \theta}\right]^2 \quad \text{or} \quad -\frac{\partial^2 \log f(x;\theta)}{\partial \theta^2},$$

where the weights are given by the pdf $f(x;\theta)$. That is, the greater these derivatives are on the average, the more information that we get about θ. Clearly, if they were equal to zero [so that θ would not be in $\log f(x;\theta)$], there would be zero information about θ. The important function

$$\frac{\partial \log f(x;\theta)}{\partial \theta}$$

is called the **score function**. Recall that it determines the estimating equations for the mle; that is, the mle $\hat{\theta}$ solves

$$\sum_{i=1}^{n} \frac{\partial \log f(x_i;\theta)}{\partial \theta} = 0$$

[handwritten: $\frac{\partial \ell}{\partial \theta} = \frac{\partial \log L(\theta)}{\partial \theta} = \frac{\partial \log[f(x_1,\theta)\cdots f(x_n;\theta)]}{\partial \theta} = \frac{\partial \sum \log f(x_i,\theta)}{\partial \theta} = \sum \frac{\partial \log f(x_i;\theta)}{\partial \theta}$*]*

for θ. ∎

Example 6.2.1 (Information for a Bernoulli Random Variable). Let X be Bernoulli $b(1,\theta)$. Thus

$$\log f(x;\theta) = x \log \theta + (1-x)\log(1-\theta)$$
$$\frac{\partial \log f(x;\theta)}{\partial \theta} = \frac{x}{\theta} - \frac{1-x}{1-\theta}$$
$$\frac{\partial^2 \log f(x;\theta)}{\partial \theta^2} = -\frac{x}{\theta^2} - \frac{1-x}{(1-\theta)^2}.$$

[handwritten: $f(x,\theta) = P(x) = \begin{cases} \theta^x(1-\theta)^{1-x}, & x=0,1. \\ 0 & else. \end{cases}$ $\begin{cases} f(0,\theta) = \cdots \\ f(1,\theta) = \cdots \\ 其余 = 0. \end{cases}$*]*

Clearly,

[handwritten: $= E\left[\frac{\partial^2 \log f(x;\theta)}{\partial \theta^2}\right]$*]*

$$I(\theta) = -E\left[\frac{-X}{\theta^2} - \frac{1-X}{(1-\theta)^2}\right]$$

[handwritten: $= -\sum_{x=0,1}\left[\frac{-x}{\theta^2} - \frac{1-x}{(1-\theta)^2}\right]P(x)$ $= -\left\{\left[\frac{-0}{\theta^2} - \frac{1-0}{(1-\theta)^2}\right]\times P(0) + \left[\frac{-1}{\theta^2} - \frac{1-1}{(1-\theta)^2}\right]\times P(1)\right\}$*]*

$$= \frac{\theta}{\theta^2} + \frac{1-\theta}{(1-\theta)^2} = \frac{1}{\theta} + \frac{1}{(1-\theta)} = \frac{1}{\theta(1-\theta)},$$

which is larger for θ values close to zero or one. ∎

[handwritten: $\begin{pmatrix} P(0) = \theta^0(1-\theta)^1 = 1-\theta \\ P(1) = \theta^1(1-\theta)^0 = \theta. \end{pmatrix}$*]*

Example 6.2.2 (Information for a Location Family). Consider a random sample $X_1, \ldots, X_n$ such that

$$X_i = \theta + e_i, \quad i = 1, \ldots, n, \qquad (6.2.7)$$

$x_i = \theta + e_i \Rightarrow e_i = x_i - \theta \Rightarrow \frac{de_i}{dx_i} = (x_i - \theta)' = 1 = \text{Jacobian.}$

$f_x(x) = f(e_i) \cdot |J|$

$= f(x - \theta) \cdot 1$

$= f(x - \theta).$

where $e_1, e_2, \ldots, e_n$ are iid with common pdf $f(x)$ and with support $(-\infty, \infty)$. Then the common pdf of X_i is $f_X(x; \theta) = f(x - \theta)$. We call model (6.2.7) a **location model**. Assume that $f(x)$ satisfies the regularity conditions. Then the information is

$\therefore I(\theta) = E\left[\left(\frac{\partial \log f(x;\theta)}{\partial \theta}\right)^2\right]$

$= \int \left(\frac{\partial \log f(x;\theta)}{\partial \theta}\right)^2 f(x;\theta)\, dx$

$$I(\theta) = \int_{-\infty}^{\infty} \left(\frac{f'(x-\theta)}{f(x-\theta)}\right)^2 f(x-\theta)\, dx$$

$\left(\because \frac{\partial \log f(x;\theta)}{\partial \theta} = \frac{\frac{1}{f(x;\theta)}\frac{\partial f(x;\theta)}{\partial \theta}}{}\right)$

$$= \int_{-\infty}^{\infty} \left(\frac{f'(z)}{f(z)}\right)^2 f(z)\, dz, \tag{6.2.8}$$

$\left(= \frac{\frac{\partial f(x;\theta)}{\partial \theta}}{f(x;\theta)} = \frac{1}{f(x;\theta)} \cdot \frac{\partial f(x;\theta)}{\partial \theta} = f'(x;\theta)/f(x;\theta)\right)$

where the last equality follows from the transformation $z = x - \theta$. Hence, in the location model, the information does not depend on θ.

$= \int \left(\frac{f'(x;\theta)}{f(x;\theta)}\right)^2 f(x;\theta)\, dx$

As an illustration, reconsider Example 6.1.1 concerning the Laplace distribution. Let $X_1, X_2, \ldots, X_n$ be a random sample from this distribution. Then it follows that X_i can be expressed as

$$X_i = \theta + e_i, \tag{6.2.9}$$

where $e_1, \ldots, e_n$ are iid with common pdf $f(z) = 2^{-1}\exp\{-|z|\}$, for $-\infty < z < \infty$.

$\text{sgn}(z) = 1, 0, \text{或} -1.$

As we did in Example 6.1.1, use $\frac{d}{dz}|z| = \text{sgn}(z)$. Then $f'(z) = -2^{-1}\text{sgn}(z)\exp\{-|z|\}$

$\left(\frac{f'(z)}{f(z)}\right)^2 = (-\text{sgn}(z))^2 = \begin{cases} 1, & \text{当} z \neq 0 \\ 0, & \text{当} z = 0 \end{cases}$

and, hence, $[f'(z)/f(z)]^2 = [-\text{sgn}(z)]^2 = 1$, so that

$\because f(z) \text{是pdf}. \therefore z \text{在所}$
有值进行积分
分 必定31.

$I(\theta) = \int_{-\infty}^{\infty} [-\text{sgn}(z)]^2 f(z)\, dz$

$$I(\theta) = \int_{-\infty}^{\infty} \left(\frac{f'(z)}{f(z)}\right)^2 f(z)\, dz = \int_{-\infty}^{\infty} f(z)\, dz = 1. \tag{6.2.10}$$

$= \left(\int_{-\infty}^{0^-} + \int_{0^+}^{+\infty}\right)(\text{sgn}(z))^2 f(z) dz + \int_{z=0}^{0} [\text{sgn}(z)]^2 f(z) dz$

$= \left(\int_{-\infty}^{0^-} + \int_{0^+}^{+\infty}\right) f(z) dz$

$+ \int_0^0 0^2 f(z) dz$

Note that the Laplace pdf does not satisfy the regularity conditions, but this argument can be made rigorous; see Huber (1981) and also Chapter 10. ∎

$= \left(\int_{-\infty}^{0} + \int_{0}^{+\infty}\right) f(z) dz$

$\cong \int_{-\infty}^{+\infty} f(z) dz$

$= 1.$

$(\text{因}\int f(z)dz 连续集$
$\text{点的测度 cdf} = 0.$

$\int f(z)dz \text{是指相对于 cdf 的积率.})$

From (6.2.6), for a sample of size 1, say X_1, Fisher information is the variance of the random variable $\frac{\partial \log f(X_1;\theta)}{\partial \theta}$. What about a sample of size n? Let $X_1, X_2, \ldots, X_n$ be a random sample from a distribution having pdf $f(x; \theta)$. The likelihood $L(\theta)$ is the pdf of the random sample, and the random variable whose variance is the information in the sample is given by

$\therefore$ 不需考虑 $\text{sgn}(z) = 0$ 的情形.

$$\frac{\partial \log L(\theta, \mathbf{X})}{\partial \theta} = \sum_{i=1}^{n} \frac{\partial \log f(X_i; \theta)}{\partial \theta}. = \frac{\partial \ell(\theta)}{\partial \theta}$$

The summands are iid with common variance $I(\theta)$. Hence the information in the sample is

$$\text{Var}\left(\frac{\partial \log L(\theta, \mathbf{X})}{\partial \theta}\right) = nI(\theta). \tag{6.2.11}$$

Thus the information in a random sample of size n is n times the information in a sample of size 1. So, in Example 6.2.1, the Fisher information in a random sample of size n from a Bernoulli $b(1, \theta)$ distribution is $n/[\theta(1 - \theta)]$.

We are now ready to obtain the Rao–Cramér lower bound, which we state as a theorem.

Theorem 6.2.1 (Rao–Cramér Lower Bound). *Let $X_1, \ldots, X_n$ be iid with common pdf $f(x; \theta)$ for $\theta \in \Omega$. Assume that the regularity conditions (R0)-(R4) hold. Let $Y = u(X_1, X_2, \ldots, X_n)$ be a statistic with mean $E(Y) = E[u(X_1, X_2, \ldots, X_n)] = k(\theta)$. Then*

$$Var(Y) \geq \frac{[k'(\theta)]^2}{nI(\theta)}. \qquad (6.2.12)$$

Proof: The proof is for the continuous case, but the proof for the discrete case is quite similar. Write the mean of Y as

$$= E[u(x_1, \cdots, x_n)]$$

$$k(\theta) = \int_{-\infty}^{\infty} \cdots \int_{-\infty}^{\infty} u(x_1, \ldots, x_n) f(x_1; \theta) \cdots f(x_n; \theta) \, dx_1 \cdots dx_n.$$

Differentiating with respect to θ, we obtain

$$\frac{\partial [f(x_1,\theta) \cdots f(x_n;\theta)]}{\partial \theta} = \frac{\partial f(x_1,\theta)}{\partial \theta} f(x_2;\theta) \cdots f(x_n;\theta)$$
$$+ f(x_1;\theta) \frac{\partial f(x_2,\theta)}{\partial \theta} f(x_3;\theta) \cdots f(x_n;\theta) + \cdots$$

$$k'(\theta) = \int_{-\infty}^{\infty} \cdots \int_{-\infty}^{\infty} u(x_1, x_2, \ldots, x_n) \left[\sum_1^n \frac{1}{f(x_i; \theta)} \frac{\partial f(x_i; \theta)}{\partial \theta} \right]$$
$$\times f(x_1; \theta) \cdots f(x_n; \theta) \, dx_1 \cdots dx_n$$

$$= \frac{\partial f(x_1;\theta)}{\partial \theta} \frac{1}{f(x_1;\theta)} f(x_1;\theta) \cdots f(x_n;\theta)$$
$$+ \cdots$$
$$= \left[\sum \frac{\partial f(x_i;\theta)}{\partial \theta} \cdot \frac{1}{f(x_i;\theta)} \right] f(x_1) \cdots f(x_n)$$
$$= \left[\sum \frac{\partial \log f(x_i;\theta)}{\partial \theta} \right] f(x_1,\theta) \cdots f(x_n,\theta)$$

$$= \int_{-\infty}^{\infty} \cdots \int_{-\infty}^{\infty} u(x_1, x_2, \ldots, x_n) \left[\sum_1^n \frac{\partial \log f(x_i; \theta)}{\partial \theta} \right]$$
$$= \partial \ell / \partial \theta$$
$$\times f(x_1; \theta) \cdots f(x_n; \theta) \, dx_1 \cdots dx_n. \qquad = E[YZ] \qquad (6.2.13)$$

$$YZ$$

Define the random variable Z by $Z = \sum_1^n [\partial \log f(X_i; \theta)/\partial \theta]$. We know from (6.2.2) and (6.2.11) that $E(Z) = 0$ and $Var(Z) = nI(\theta)$, respectively. Also, equation (6.2.13) can be expressed in terms of expectation as $k'(\theta) = E(YZ)$. Hence we have

$$k'(\theta) = E(YZ) = E(Y)E(Z) + \rho\sigma_Y \sqrt{nI(\theta)},$$

where ρ is the correlation coefficient between Y and Z. Using $E(Z) = 0$, this simplifies to

$$\rho = \frac{k'(\theta)}{\sigma_Y \sqrt{nI(\theta)}}.$$

$$\because E(YZ) - E(Y)E(Z) = Cov(Y,Z)$$
$$\therefore k'(\theta) = E(YZ) = E(Y)E(Z) + Cov(Y,Z),$$
$$= E(Y)E(Z) + \rho \cdot \sigma_Y \cdot \sigma_Z$$
$$= E(Y)E(Z) + \rho \cdot \sigma_Y \cdot \sqrt{nI(\theta)}$$
$$\left(\because \sigma_Z = \sqrt{Var(Z)} = \sqrt{Var\left(\frac{\partial \log L(\theta)}{\partial \theta}\right)} \underset{(6.2.11)}{=} \sqrt{nI(\theta)}. \right)$$

Because $\rho^2 \leq 1$, we have

$$\frac{[k'(\theta)]^2}{\sigma_Y^2 nI(\theta)} \leq 1,$$

which, upon rearrangement, is the desired result. ∎

$$E(u(x_1 \cdots x_n)) = k(\theta) \quad\Rightarrow k(\theta) = \theta$$
$$E(u(x_1, \cdots x_n)) = E(\hat{\theta}) = \theta \quad\Rightarrow k'(\theta) = \theta'$$
$$= 1.$$

Corollary 6.2.1. *Under the assumptions of Theorem 6.2.1, if $Y = u(X_1, \ldots, X_n)$ is an unbiased estimator of θ, so that $k(\theta) = \theta$, then the Rao–Cramér inequality becomes*

$$\Rightarrow k'(\theta) = \theta' = \frac{\partial \theta}{\partial \theta} = 1.$$

$$Var(Y) \geq \frac{1}{nI(\theta)}.$$

"Rao–Cramér Lower Bound."

$$y = \overline{X} = u(X_1, \cdots, X_n) = \frac{\Sigma X_i}{n}, \quad E(y) = E(\overline{x}) = E\left(\frac{\Sigma X_i}{n}\right) = u = P. \quad \therefore \overline{x} 为 \text{ unbiased } 估$$

$$\text{Var}(y) = \text{var}(\overline{x}) = \text{Var}\left(\frac{\Sigma X_i}{n}\right) = \Sigma \text{Var}(X_i) = \frac{\sigma^2}{n} = \frac{Pq}{n} \quad (\because \sigma^2 = Pq, \text{ 对于 Bernoulli 分布})$$

$$\frac{1}{n I(\theta)} = \frac{\theta(1-\theta)}{n} = \frac{P(1-P)}{n} = \frac{Pq}{n}.$$

$$\therefore y = \overline{x} \text{ 为 efficient 估}.$$

Consider the Bernoulli model with probability of success θ which was treated in Example 6.2.1. In the example we showed that $1/nI(\theta) = \theta(1-\theta)/n$. From Example 4.1.2 of Section 4.1, the mle of θ is $\overline{X}$. The mean and variance of a Bernoulli (θ) distribution are θ and $\theta(1-\theta)$, respectively. Hence the mean and variance of $\overline{X}$ are θ and $\theta(1-\theta)/n$, respectively. That is, in this case the variance of the mle has attained the Rao–Cramér lower bound.

We now make the following definitions.

Definition 6.2.1 (Efficient Estimator). *Let Y be an unbiased estimator of a parameter θ in the case of point estimation. The statistic Y is called an* **efficient estimator** *of θ if and only if the variance of Y attains the Rao–Cramér lower bound.*

Definition 6.2.2 (Efficiency). *In cases in which we can differentiate with respect to a parameter under an integral or summation symbol, the ratio of the Rao–Cramér lower bound to the actual variance of any unbiased estimator of a parameter is called the* **efficiency** *of that estimator.* $= \frac{1}{nI(\theta)} / \text{var}(y)$ (根据 Corollary 6.2.1. 此比例 ≤ 1 所以, $=1$ 为 efficient 的.)

Example 6.2.3 (Poisson(θ) Distribution). Let $X_1, X_2, \ldots, X_n$ denote a random sample from a Poisson distribution that has the mean $\theta > 0$. It is known that $\overline{X}$ is an mle of θ; we shall show that it is also an efficient estimator of θ. We have

$$\frac{\partial \log f(x; \theta)}{\partial \theta} = \frac{\partial}{\partial \theta}(x \log \theta - \theta - \log x!)$$

$$= \frac{x}{\theta} - 1 = \frac{x - \theta}{\theta}.$$

Accordingly,

$$I(\theta) = E\left[\left(\frac{\partial \log f(X; \theta)}{\partial \theta}\right)^2\right] = \frac{E(X - \theta)^2}{\theta^2} = \frac{\sigma^2}{\theta^2} = \frac{\theta}{\theta^2} = \frac{1}{\theta}.$$

(6.2.4) 式 $= \frac{X-\theta}{\theta}$ $= \text{Var}(X)$. Variance 的定义. $= \text{Var}(X)$.

The Rao–Cramér lower bound in this case is $1/[n(1/\theta)] = \theta/n$. But θ/n is the variance of $\overline{X}$. Hence $\overline{X}$ is an efficient estimator of θ. ■ $\text{Var}(\hat{\theta}) = \text{Var}(\overline{X})$

$\because$ Poisson 分布 的 $\sigma^2 = \lambda = \theta$. $= \text{Var}\left(\frac{\Sigma X_i}{n}\right) = \frac{\sigma^2}{n} = \frac{\theta}{n}$

Example 6.2.4 (Beta($\theta, 1$) Distribution). Let $X_1, X_2, \ldots, X_n$ denote a random sample of size $n > 2$ from a distribution with pdf

$$f(x; \theta) = \begin{cases} \theta x^{\theta-1} & \text{for } 0 < x < 1 \\ 0 & \text{elsewhere,} \end{cases} \tag{6.2.14}$$

$\theta \in (0, \infty)$,

where the parameter space is $\Omega = (0, \infty)$. This is the beta distribution, (3.3.5), with parameters θ and 1, which we denote by beta($\theta, 1$). The derivative of the log of f is

$$\frac{\partial \log f}{\partial \theta} = \log x + \frac{1}{\theta}. \tag{6.2.15}$$

用(6.2.5)式

From this we have $\partial^2 \log f / \partial \theta^2 = -\theta^{-2}$. Hence the information is $I(\theta) = \theta^{-2}$.

$$I(\theta) = -E\left(\frac{\partial^2 \log f}{\partial \theta^2}\right)$$

$$= -E\left(-\frac{1}{\theta^2}\right) = \frac{1}{\theta^2}$$

($\because \theta$ 为常数, 与 x 无关.)

Next, we find the mle of θ and investigate its efficiency. The log of the likelihood function is

$$l(\theta) = \theta \sum_{i=1}^{n} \log x_i - \sum_{i=1}^{n} \log x_i + n \log \theta.$$

The first partial of $l(\theta)$ is

$$\frac{\partial l(\theta)}{\partial \theta} = \sum_{i=1}^{n} \log x_i + \frac{n}{\theta}. \tag{6.2.16}$$

Setting this to 0 and solving for θ, the mle is $\widehat{\theta} = -n / \left(\sum_{i=1}^{n} \log X_i \right)$. To obtain the distribution of $\widehat{\theta}$, let $Y_i = -\log X_i$. A straight transformation argument shows that the distribution is $\Gamma(1, 1/\theta)$. Because the X_is are independent, Theorem 3.3.2 shows that $W = \sum_{i=1}^{n} Y_i$ is $\Gamma(n, 1/\theta)$. Theorem 3.3.1 shows that

$$E[W^k] = \frac{(n+k-1)!}{\theta^k (n-1)!}, \tag{6.2.17}$$

for $k > -n$. So, in particular for $k = -1$, we get

$$E[\widehat{\theta}] = nE[W^{-1}] = \theta \frac{n}{n-1}.$$

Hence, $\widehat{\theta}$ is biased, but the bias vanishes as $n \to \infty$. Also, note that the estimator $[(n-1)/n]\widehat{\theta}$ is unbiased. For $k = -2$, we get

$$E[\widehat{\theta}^2] = n^2 E[W^{-2}] = \theta^2 \frac{n^2}{(n-1)(n-2)},$$

and, hence, after simplifying $E(\widehat{\theta}^2) - [E(\widehat{\theta})]^2$, we obtain

$$\text{Var}(\widehat{\theta}) = \theta^2 \frac{n^2}{(n-1)^2(n-2)}.$$

From this, we can obtain the variance of the unbiased estimator $[(n-1)/n]\widehat{\theta}$, i.e.,

$$\text{Var}\left(\frac{n-1}{n} \widehat{\theta} \right) = \frac{\theta^2}{n-2}.$$

由 corollary 6.2.1, $\frac{1}{nI(\theta)} = \frac{1}{n \cdot \theta^{-2}} = \frac{\theta^2}{n}$.

From above, the information is $I(\theta) = \theta^{-2}$ and, hence, the variance of an unbiased efficient estimator is θ^2/n. Because $\frac{\theta^2}{n-2} > \frac{\theta^2}{n}$, the unbiased estimator $[(n-1)/n]\widehat{\theta}$ is not efficient. Notice, though, that its efficiency (as in Definition 6.2.2) converges to 1 as $n \to \infty$. Later in this section, we say that $[(n-1)/n]\widehat{\theta}$ is asymptotically efficient. ∎ 由 $\widehat{\theta}$的 efficiency $= \frac{1}{nI(\theta)} / \text{Var}(\widehat{\theta}) = \frac{\theta^2}{n} / \frac{\theta^2}{n-2} = \frac{n-2}{n} \xrightarrow{n \to \infty} 1$ ∴ 是它为 asymptotically efficient.

In the above examples, we were able to obtain the mles in closed form along with their distributions and, hence, moments. This is often not the case. Maximum likelihood estimators, however, have an asymptotic normal distribution. In fact, mles are asymptotically efficient. To prove these assertions, we need the additional regularity condition given by

Assumptions 6.2.2 (Additional Regularity Condition). *Regularity condition (R5) is*

(R5) *The pdf $f(x;\theta)$ is three times differentiable as a function of θ. Further, for all $\theta \in \Omega$, there exist a constant c and a function $M(x)$ such that*

$$\left| \frac{\partial^3}{\partial \theta^3} \log f(x;\theta) \right| \leq M(x),$$

with $E_{\theta_0}[M(X)] < \infty$, for all $\theta_0 - c < \theta < \theta_0 + c$ and all x in the support of X.

Theorem 6.2.2. *Assume $X_1, \ldots, X_n$ are iid with pdf $f(x;\theta_0)$ for $\theta_0 \in \Omega$ such that the regularity conditions (R0)–(R5) are satisfied. Suppose further that the Fisher information satisfies $0 < I(\theta_0) < \infty$. Then any consistent sequence of solutions of the mle equations satisfies*

$$\sqrt{n}(\widehat{\theta} - \theta_0) \xrightarrow{D} N\left(0, \frac{1}{I(\theta_0)}\right). \tag{6.2.18}$$

Proof: Expanding the function $l'(\theta)$ into a Taylor series of order 2 about θ_0 and evaluating it at $\widehat{\theta}_n$, we get

$$l'(\widehat{\theta}_n) = l'(\theta_0) + (\widehat{\theta}_n - \theta_0)l''(\theta_0) + \frac{1}{2}(\widehat{\theta}_n - \theta_0)^2 l'''(\theta_n^*), \tag{6.2.19}$$

where θ_n^* is between θ_0 and $\widehat{\theta}_n$. But $l'(\widehat{\theta}_n) = 0$. Hence, rearranging terms, we obtain

$$\sqrt{n}(\widehat{\theta}_n - \theta_0) = \frac{n^{-1/2} l'(\theta_0)}{-n^{-1} l''(\theta_0) - (2n)^{-1}(\widehat{\theta}_n - \theta_0)l'''(\theta_n^*)}. \tag{6.2.20}$$

By the Central Limit Theorem,

$$\frac{1}{\sqrt{n}} l'(\theta_0) = \frac{1}{\sqrt{n}} \sum_{i=1}^{n} \frac{\partial \log f(X_i;\theta_0)}{\partial \theta} \xrightarrow{D} N(0, I(\theta_0)), \tag{6.2.21}$$

because the summands are iid with $\text{Var}(\partial \log f(X_i;\theta_0)/\partial \theta) = I(\theta_0) < \infty$. Also, by the Law of Large Numbers,

$$-\frac{1}{n} l''(\theta_0) = -\frac{1}{n} \sum_{i=1}^{n} \frac{\partial^2 \log f(X_i;\theta_0)}{\partial \theta^2} \xrightarrow{P} I(\theta_0). \tag{6.2.22}$$

To complete the proof then, we need only show that the second term in the denominator of expression (6.2.20) goes to zero in probability. Because $\widehat{\theta}_n - \theta_0 \xrightarrow{P} 0$, by Theorem 5.2.7, this follows provided that $n^{-1} l'''(\theta_n^*)$ is bounded in probability. Let c_0 be the constant defined in condition (R5). Note that $|\widehat{\theta}_n - \theta_0| < c_0$ implies that $|\theta_n^* - \theta_0| < c_0$, which in turn by condition (R5) implies the following string of inequalities:

$$\left| -\frac{1}{n} l'''(\theta_n^*) \right| \leq \frac{1}{n} \sum_{i=1}^{n} \left| \frac{\partial^3 \log f(X_i;\theta)}{\partial \theta^3} \right| \leq \frac{1}{n} \sum_{i=1}^{n} M(X_i). \tag{6.2.23}$$

By condition (R5), $E_{\theta_0}[M(X)] < \infty$; hence, $\frac{1}{n}\sum_{i=1}^{n} M(X_i) \xrightarrow{P} E_{\theta_0}[M(X)]$, by the 弟[部分]的
Law of Large Numbers. For the bound, we select $1 + E_{\theta_0}[M(X)]$. Let $\epsilon > 0$ be 没看完!)
given. Choose N_1 and N_2 so that

$$n \geq N_1 \quad \Rightarrow \quad P[|\widehat{\theta}_n - \theta_0| < c_0] \geq 1 - \frac{\epsilon}{2} \tag{6.2.24}$$

$$n \geq N_2 \quad \Rightarrow \quad P\left[\left|\frac{1}{n}\sum_{i=1}^{n} M(X_i) - E_{\theta_0}[M(X)]\right| < 1\right] \geq 1 - \frac{\epsilon}{2}. \tag{6.2.25}$$

It follows from (6.2.23)–(6.2.25) that

$$n \geq \max\{N_1, N_2\} \Rightarrow P\left[\left|-\frac{1}{n}l'''(\theta_n^*)\right| \leq 1 + E_{\theta_0}[M(X)]\right] \geq 1 - \frac{\epsilon}{2};$$

hence, $n^{-1}l'''(\theta_n^*)$ is bounded in probability. ∎

We next generalize Definitions 6.2.1 and 6.2.2 concerning efficiency to the asymptotic case.

Definition 6.2.3. *Let $X_1, \ldots, X_n$ be independent and identically distributed with probability density function $f(x; \theta)$. Suppose $\hat{\theta}_{1n} = \hat{\theta}_{1n}(X_1, \ldots, X_n)$ is an estimator of θ_0 such that $\sqrt{n}(\hat{\theta}_{1n} - \theta_0) \xrightarrow{D} N\left(0, \sigma_{\hat{\theta}_{1n}}^2\right)$. Then*

(a) *The **asymptotic efficiency** of $\hat{\theta}_{1n}$ is defined to be*

$$e(\hat{\theta}_{1n}) = \frac{1/I(\theta_0)}{\sigma_{\hat{\theta}_{1n}}^2}. \tag{6.2.26}$$

(b) *The estimator $\hat{\theta}_{1n}$ is said to be **asymptotically efficient** if the ratio in part (a) is 1.*

(c) *Let $\hat{\theta}_{2n}$ be another estimator such that $\sqrt{n}(\hat{\theta}_{2n} - \theta_0) \xrightarrow{D} N\left(0, \sigma_{\hat{\theta}_{2n}}^2\right)$. Then the* **asymptotic relative efficiency** *(ARE) of $\hat{\theta}_{1n}$ to $\hat{\theta}_{2n}$ is the reciprocal of the ratio of their respective asymptotic variances; i.e.,*

$$\left. N(0, \tfrac{1}{I(\theta_0)}) = N(0, \sigma_{\hat{\theta}}^2). \right.$$
$$e(\hat{\theta}_{1n}, \hat{\theta}_{2n}) = \frac{\sigma_{\hat{\theta}_{2n}}^2}{\sigma_{\hat{\theta}_{1n}}^2}. \tag{6.2.27}$$

:根据 Theorem 6.2.2, $\sqrt{n}(\hat{\theta}-\theta_0) \xrightarrow{D} N(0, \tfrac{1}{I(\theta_0)})$.

∴ $\sigma_{\hat{\theta}}^2 = \frac{1}{I(\theta_0)}$ ∴ $e(\hat{\theta}) = \frac{1/I(\theta_0)}{\sigma_{\hat{\theta}}^2} = \frac{1/I(\theta_0)}{1/I(\theta_0)} = 1$. ∴ 根据(b), $\hat{\theta}$ is asymptotically efficient.

Hence, by Theorem 6.2.2, under regularity conditions, maximum likelihood estimators are asymptotically efficient estimators. This is a nice optimality result. Also, if two estimators are asymptotically normal with the same asymptotic mean, then intuitively the estimator with the smaller asymptotic variance would be selected over the other as a better estimator. In this case, the ARE of the selected estimator to the nonselected one is greater than 1.

由 Theorem 6.2.2, $\sqrt{n}(\hat{\theta}-\theta_0) \xrightarrow{D} N(0, \frac{1}{I(\theta_0)})$, 其例 $\bar{w}$ $\hat{\theta}=Q_2$,

即 $E[\sqrt{n}(\hat{\theta}-\theta_0)]=0 \Rightarrow \sqrt{n}E[\hat{\theta}-\theta_0]=0 \Rightarrow E(\hat{\theta}-\theta_0)=E(\hat{\theta})-E(\theta_0)=0 \Rightarrow E(\hat{\theta})=E(\theta_0)=\theta_0.$

$Var(\sqrt{n}(\hat{\theta}-\theta_0)) = \frac{1}{I(\theta_0)}? \Rightarrow n \, Var(\hat{\theta}-\theta_0) = n(Var(\hat{\theta})+Var(\theta_0)) = \frac{1}{1}=1? \Rightarrow n\,Var(\hat{\theta})=1 \Rightarrow Var(\hat{\theta})=\frac{1}{n}$

$\frac{1}{I(\theta_0)}=1$ $Var(\theta_0)=0.$

$\begin{cases} E(Q_2)=\theta_0 \\ Var(Q_2)=1/n \end{cases}$ $\therefore \sqrt{n}(Q_2-\theta_0)\xrightarrow{D} N(0, 1/I(\theta_0)) \Rightarrow Q_2 \xrightarrow{P} N(\theta_0, \frac{1}{n}) = N(\theta, \frac{1}{n})$

       θ_0 是渐近无偏量, 没有偏差. 无偏.

Example 6.2.5 (ARE of the Sample Median to the Sample Mean). We obtain this ARE under the Laplace and normal distributions. Consider first the Laplace location model as given in expression (6.2.9); i.e.,

$$X_i = \theta + e_i, \quad i = 1, \ldots, n. \tag{6.2.28}$$

(一个 Normal 分布参数估计的效率收敛 + 一×1 正态后特别设计估计成正态 Normal 分布无偏.)   即 $\hat{\theta}=Q_2.$

By Example 6.1.1, we know that the mle of θ is the sample median, Q_2. By (6.2.10), the information $I(\theta_0) = 1$ for this distribution; hence, Q_2 is asymptotically normal with mean θ and variance $1/n$. On the other hand, by the Central Limit Theorem, the sample mean $\overline{X}$ is asymptotically normal with mean θ and variance σ^2/n, where $\sigma^2 = \mathrm{Var}(X_i) = \mathrm{Var}(e_i + \theta) = \mathrm{Var}(e_i) = E(e_i^2)$. But $\overline{X} \sim N(\theta, \frac{\sigma^2}{n})$

$e(Q_2)=\frac{1/I(\theta_0)}{\sigma^2_{Q_2}}$ $E(e_i^2) = \int_{-\infty}^{\infty} z^2 2^{-1} \exp\{-|z|\}\, dz = \int_0^{\infty} z^{3-1} \exp\{-z\}\, dz = \Gamma(3) = 2.$

$= 1/\frac{1}{n} = n.$

$e(\overline{X})=\frac{1/I(\theta_0)}{\sigma^2_{\overline{X}}} = 1/\frac{\sigma^2}{n} = 1/\frac{2}{n} = \frac{n}{2}.$ Therefore, the $\mathrm{ARE}(Q_2, \overline{X}) = \frac{2}{1} = 2$. Thus, if the sample comes from a Laplace

$\therefore ARE(Q_2,\overline{X})$ distribution, then asymptotically the sample median is twice as efficient as the

$= n/\frac{n}{2}$ sample mean.

$= 2.$ Next suppose the location model (6.2.28) holds, except now the pdf of e_i is $N(0,1)$. Under this model, by Theorem 10.2.3, Q_2 is asymptotically normal with mean θ and variance $(\pi/2)/n$. Because the variance of $\overline{X}$ is $1/n$, in this case, the $\mathrm{ARE}(Q_2, \overline{X}) = \frac{1}{\pi/2} = 2/\pi = 0.636$. Since $\pi/2 = 1.57$, asymptotically, $\overline{X}$ is 1.57 times more efficient than Q_2 if the sample arises from the normal distribution. ∎

Theorem 6.2.2 is also a practical result for it gives us a way of doing inference. The asymptotic standard deviation of the mle $\hat{\theta}$ is $[nI(\theta_0)]^{-1/2}$. Because $I(\theta)$ is a continuous function of θ, it follows from Theorems 5.1.4 and 6.1.2 that

$$I(\hat{\theta}_n) \xrightarrow{P} I(\theta_0).$$

Thus we have a consistent estimate of the asymptotic standard deviation of the mle. Based on this result and the discussion of confidence intervals in Chapter 4, for a specified $0 < \alpha < 1$, the following interval is an approximate $(1 - \alpha)100\%$ confidence interval for θ,

$$\left(\hat{\theta}_n - z_{\alpha/2} \frac{1}{\sqrt{nI(\hat{\theta}_n)}}, \hat{\theta}_n + z_{\alpha/2} \frac{1}{\sqrt{nI(\hat{\theta}_n)}} \right). \tag{6.2.29}$$

Remark 6.2.2. If we use the asymptotic distributions to construct confidence intervals for θ, the fact that the $ARE(Q_2, \overline{X}) = 2$ when the underlying distribution is the Laplace means that n would need to be twice as large for $\overline{X}$ to get the same length confidence interval as we would if we used Q_2. ∎

A simple corollary to Theorem 6.2.2 yields the asymptotic distribution of a function $g(\hat{\theta}_n)$ of the mle.

Corollary 6.2.2. *Under the assumptions of Theorem 6.2.2, suppose $g(x)$ is a continuous function of x which is differentiable at θ_0 such that $g'(\theta_0) \neq 0$. Then*

$$\sqrt{n}(g(\widehat{\theta}_n) - g(\theta_0)) \xrightarrow{D} N\left(0, \frac{g'(\theta_0)^2}{I(\theta_0)}\right). \qquad (6.2.30)$$

The proof of this corollary follows immediately from the Δ-method, Theorem 5.2.9, and Theorem 6.2.2.

The proof of Theorem 6.2.2 contains an asymptotic representation of $\widehat{\theta}$ which proves useful; hence, we state it as another corollary.

Corollary 6.2.3. *Under the assumptions of Theorem 6.2.2,*

$$\sqrt{n}(\widehat{\theta}_n - \theta_0) = \frac{1}{I(\theta_0)} \frac{1}{\sqrt{n}} \sum_{i=1}^{n} \frac{\partial \log f(X_i; \theta_0)}{\partial \theta} + R_n, \qquad (6.2.31)$$

where $R_n \xrightarrow{P} 0$.

The proof is just a rearrangement of equation (6.2.20) and the ensuing results in the proof of Theorem 6.2.2.

Example 6.2.6 (Example 6.2.4, Continued). Let $X_1, \ldots, X_n$ be a random sample having the common pdf (6.2.14). Recall that $I(\theta) = \theta^{-2}$ and that the mle is $\widehat{\theta} = -n/\sum_{i=1}^{n} \log X_i$. Hence, $\widehat{\theta}$ is approximately normally distributed with mean θ and variance θ^2/n. Based on this, an approximate $(1 - \alpha)100\%$ confidence interval for θ is

$$\widehat{\theta} \pm z_{\alpha/2} \frac{\widehat{\theta}}{\sqrt{n}}.$$

Recall that we were able to obtain the exact distribution of $\widehat{\theta}$ in this case. As Exercise 6.2.12 shows, based on this distribution of $\widehat{\theta}$, an exact confidence interval for θ can be constructed. ∎

In obtaining the mle of θ, we are often in the situation of Example 6.1.2; that is, we can verify the existence of the mle, but the solution of the equation $l'(\widehat{\theta}) = 0$ cannot be obtained in closed form. In such situations, numerical methods are used. One iterative method that exhibits rapid (quadratic) convergence is Newton's method. The sketch in Figure 6.2.1 helps recall this method. Suppose $\widehat{\theta}^{(0)}$ is an initial guess at the solution. The next guess (one-step estimate) is the point $\widehat{\theta}^{(1)}$, which is the horizontal intercept of the tangent line to the curve $l'(\theta)$ at the point $(\widehat{\theta}^{(0)}, l'(\widehat{\theta}^{(0)}))$. A little algebra finds

$$\widehat{\theta}^{(1)} = \widehat{\theta}^{(0)} - \frac{l'(\widehat{\theta}^{(0)})}{l''(\widehat{\theta}^{(0)})}. \qquad (6.2.32)$$

We then substitute $\widehat{\theta}^{(1)}$ for $\widehat{\theta}^{(0)}$ and repeat the process. On the figure, trace the second step estimate $\widehat{\theta}^{(2)}$; the process is continued until convergence.

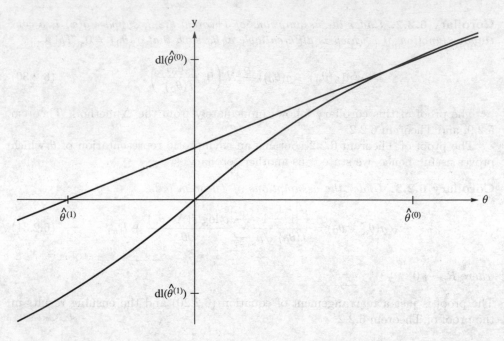

Figure 6.2.1: Beginning with the starting value $\widehat{\theta}^{(0)}$, the one-step estimate is $\widehat{\theta}^{(1)}$, which is the intersection of the tangent line to the curve $l'(\theta)$ at $\widehat{\theta}^{(0)}$ and the horizontal axis. In the figure, $dl(\theta) = l'(\theta)$.

Example 6.2.7 (Example 6.1.2, continued). Recall Example 6.1.2, where the random sample $X_1, \ldots, X_n$ has the common logisitic density

$$f(x; \theta) = \frac{\exp\{-(x - \theta)\}}{(1 + \exp\{-(x - \theta)\})^2}, \quad -\infty < x < \infty, \ -\infty < \theta < \infty. \quad (6.2.33)$$

We showed that the likelihood equation has a unique solution, though it cannot be be obtained in closed form. To use formula (6.2.32), we need the first and second partial derivatives of $l(\theta)$ and an initial guess. Expression (6.1.9) of Example 6.1.2 gives the first partial derivative, from which the second partial is

$$l''(\theta) = -2 \sum_{i=1}^{n} \frac{\exp\{-(x_i - \theta)\}}{(1 + \exp\{-(x_i - \theta)\})^2}.$$

The logistic distribution is similar to the normal distribution; hence, we can use $\overline{X}$ as our initial guess of θ. The subroutine `mlelogistic` in Appendix B is an R routine which obtains the k-step estimates. ∎

We close this section with a remarkable fact. The estimate $\widehat{\theta}^{(1)}$ in equation (6.2.32) is called the **one-step estimator**. As Exercise 6.2.13 shows, this estimator has the same asymptotic distribution as the mle, [i.e., (6.2.18)], provided that the initial guess $\widehat{\theta}^{(0)}$ is a consistent estimator of θ. That is, the one-step estimate is an asymptotically efficient estimate of θ. This is also true of the other iterative steps.

EXERCISES

6.2.1. Prove that $\overline{X}$, the mean of a random sample of size n from a distribution that is $N(\theta, \sigma^2)$, $-\infty < \theta < \infty$, is, for every known $\sigma^2 > 0$, an efficient estimator of θ.

6.2.2. Given $f(x; \theta) = 1/\theta$, $0 < x < \theta$, zero elsewhere, with $\theta > 0$, formally compute the reciprocal of

$$nE\left\{\left[\frac{\partial \log f(X : \theta)}{\partial \theta}\right]^2\right\}.$$

Compare this with the variance of $(n+1)Y_n/n$, where Y_n is the largest observation of a random sample of size n from this distribution. Comment.

6.2.3. Given the pdf

$$f(x; \theta) = \frac{1}{\pi[1 + (x - \theta)^2]}, \quad -\infty < x < \infty, \quad -\infty < \theta < \infty,$$

show that the Rao–Cramér lower bound is $2/n$, where n is the size of a random sample from this Cauchy distribution. What is the asymptotic distribution of $\sqrt{n}(\widehat{\theta} - \theta)$ if $\widehat{\theta}$ is the mle of θ?

6.2.4. Consider Example 6.2.2, where we discussed the location model.

(a) Write the location model when e_i has the logistic pdf given in expression (4.4.9).

(b) Using expression (6.2.8), show that the information $I(\theta) = 1/3$ for the model in part (a). *Hint*: In the integral of expression (6.2.8), use the substitution $u = (1 + e^{-z})^{-1}$. Then $du = f(z)dz$, where $f(z)$ is the pdf (4.4.9).

6.2.5. Using the same location model as in part (a) Exercise 6.2.4, obtain the ARE of the sample median to mle of the model.
Hint: The mle of θ for this model is discussed in Example 6.2.7. Furthermore, as shown in Theorem 10.2.3 of Chapter 10, Q_2 is asymptotically normal with asymptotic mean θ and asymptotic variance $1/(4f^2(0)n)$.

6.2.6. Consider a location model (Example 6.2.2) when the error pdf is the contaminated normal (3.4.14) with ϵ as the proportion of contamination and with σ_c^2 as the variance of the contaminated part. Show that the ARE of the sample median to the sample mean is given by

$$e(Q_2, \overline{X}) = \frac{2[1 + \epsilon(\sigma_c^2 - 1)][1 - \epsilon + (\epsilon/\sigma_c)]^2}{\pi}. \tag{6.2.34}$$

Use the hint in Exercise 6.2.5 for the median.

(a) If $\sigma_c^2 = 9$, use (6.2.34) to fill in the following table:

ϵ	0	0.05	0.10	0.15
$e(Q_2, \overline{X})$				

(b) Notice from the table that the sample median becomes the "better" estimator when ϵ increases from 0.10 to 0.15. Determine the value for ϵ where this occurs [this involves a third-degree polynomial in ϵ, so one way of obtaining the root is to use the Newton algorithm discussed around expression (6.2.32)].

$\sqrt{}$ **6.2.7.** Let X have a gamma distribution with $\alpha = 4$ and $\beta = \theta > 0$.

(a) Find the Fisher information $I(\theta)$.

(b) If $X_1, X_2, \ldots, X_n$ is a random sample from this distribution, show that the mle of θ is an efficient estimator of θ.

(c) What is the asymptotic distribution of $\sqrt{n}(\widehat{\theta} - \theta)$?

6.2.8. Let X be $N(0, \theta)$, $0 < \theta < \infty$.

(a) Find the Fisher information $I(\theta)$.

(b) If $X_1, X_2, \ldots, X_n$ is a random sample from this distribution, show that the mle of θ is an efficient estimator of θ.

(c) What is the asymptotic distribution of $\sqrt{n}(\widehat{\theta} - \theta)$?

6.2.9. If $X_1, X_2, \ldots, X_n$ is a random sample from a distribution with pdf

$$f(x; \theta) = \begin{cases} \frac{3\theta^3}{(x+\theta)^4} & 0 < x < \infty, 0 < \theta < \infty \\ 0 & \text{elsewhere}, \end{cases}$$

show that $Y = 2\overline{X}$ is an unbiased estimator of θ and determine its efficiency.

6.2.10. Let $X_1, X_2, \ldots, X_n$ be a random sample from a $N(0, \theta)$ distribution. We want to estimate the standard deviation $\sqrt{\theta}$. Find the constant c so that $Y = c \sum_{i=1}^n |X_i|$ is an unbiased estimator of $\sqrt{\theta}$ and determine its efficiency.

6.2.11. Let $\overline{X}$ be the mean of a random sample of size n from a $N(\theta, \sigma^2)$ distribution, $-\infty < \theta < \infty, \sigma^2 > 0$. Assume that σ^2 is known. Show that $\overline{X}^2 - \frac{\sigma^2}{n}$ is an unbiased estimator of θ^2 and find its efficiency.

6.2.12. Recall that $\widehat{\theta} = -n / \sum_{i=1}^n \log X_i$ is the mle of θ for a beta$(\theta, 1)$ distribution. Also, $W = - \sum_{i=1}^n \log X_i$ has the gamma distribution $\Gamma(n, 1/\theta)$.

(a) Show that $2\theta W$ has a $\chi^2(2n)$ distribution.

(b) Using part (a), find c_1 and c_2 so that

$$P\left(c_1 < \frac{2\theta n}{\widehat{\theta}} < c_2\right) = 1 - \alpha,$$

for $0 < \alpha < 1$. Next, obtain a $(1 - \alpha)100\%$ confidence interval for θ.

(c) For $\alpha = 0.05$ and $n = 10$, compare the length of this interval with the length of the interval found in Example 6.2.6.

6.2.13. By using expressions (6.2.21) and (6.2.22), obtain the result for the one-step estimate discussed at the end of this section.

6.2.14. Let S^2 be the sample variance of a random sample of size $n > 1$ from $N(\mu, \theta)$, $0 < \theta < \infty$, where μ is known. We know $E(S^2) = \theta$.

  (a) What is the efficiency of S^2?

  (b) Under these conditions, what is the mle $\widehat{\theta}$ of θ?

  (c) What is the asymptotic distribution of $\sqrt{n}(\widehat{\theta} - \theta)$?

6.3 Maximum Likelihood Tests

The last section presented an inference for pointwise estimation and confidence intervals based on likelihood theory. In this section, we present a corresponding inference for testing hypotheses.

As in the last section, let $X_1, \ldots, X_n$ be iid with pdf $f(x; \theta)$ for $\theta \in \Omega$. In this section, θ is a scalar, but in Sections 6.4 and 6.5 extensions to the vector-valued case are discussed. Consider the two-sided hypotheses

$$H_0 : \theta = \theta_0 \text{ versus } H_1 : \theta \neq \theta_0, \tag{6.3.1}$$

where θ_0 is a specified value.

Recall that the likelihood function and its log are given by

$$L(\theta) = \prod_{i=1}^{n} f(X_i; \theta)$$

$$l(\theta) = \sum_{i=1}^{n} \log f(X_i; \theta).$$

Let $\widehat{\theta}$ denote the maximum likelihood estimate of θ.

To motivate the test, consider Theorem 6.1.1, which says that if θ_0 is the true value of θ, then, asymptotically, $L(\theta_0)$ is the maximum value of $L(\theta)$. Consider the ratio of two likelihood functions, namely,

$$\Lambda = \frac{L(\theta_0)}{L(\widehat{\theta})}. \tag{6.3.2}$$

Note that $\Lambda \leq 1$, but if H_0 is true, Λ should be large (close to 1), while if H_1 is true, Λ should be smaller. For a specified significance level α, this leads to the intuitive decision rule

Reject H_0 in favor of H_1 if $\Lambda \leq c$, \qquad (6.3.3)

where c is such that $\alpha = P_{\theta_0}[\Lambda \leq c]$. We call it the **likelihood ratio test** (LRT). Theorem 6.3.1 derives the asymptotic distribution of Λ under H_0, but first we look at two examples.

Example 6.3.1 (Likelihood Ratio Test for the Exponential Distribution). Suppose $X_1, \ldots, X_n$ are iid with pdf $f(x; \theta) = \theta^{-1} \exp\{-x/\theta\}$, for $x, \theta > 0$. Let the hypotheses be given by (6.3.1). The likelihood function simplifies to

$$L(\theta) = \theta^{-n} \exp\{-(n/\theta)\overline{X}\}.$$

From Example 4.1.1, the mle of θ is $\overline{X}$. After some simplification, the likelihood ratio test statistic simplifies to

$$\Lambda = e^n \left(\frac{\overline{X}}{\theta_0}\right)^n \exp\{-n\overline{X}/\theta_0\}. \tag{6.3.4}$$

The decision rule is to reject H_0 if $\Lambda \leq c$. But further simplification of the test is possible. Other than the constant e^n, the test statistic is of the form

$$g(t) = t^n \exp\{-nt\}, \quad t > 0,$$

where $t = \overline{x}/\theta_0$. Using differentiable calculus, it is easy to show that $g(t)$ has a unique critical value at 1, i.e., $g'(1) = 0$, and further that $t = 1$ provides a maximum, because $g''(1) < 0$. As Figure 6.3.1 depicts, $g(t) \leq c$ if and only if $t \leq c_1$ or $t \geq c_2$. This leads to

$$\Lambda \leq c, \text{ if and only if, } \frac{\overline{X}}{\theta_0} \leq c_1 \text{ or } \frac{\overline{X}}{\theta_0} \geq c_2.$$

Note that under the null hypothesis, H_0, the statistic $(2/\theta_0) \sum_{i=1}^{n} X_i$ has a χ^2 distribution with $2n$ degrees of freedom. Based on this, the following decision rule results in a level α test:

Reject H_0 if $(2/\theta_0) \sum_{i=1}^{n} X_i \leq \chi^2_{1-\alpha/2}(2n)$ or $(2/\theta_0) \sum_{i=1}^{n} X_i \geq \chi^2_{\alpha/2}(2n)$, (6.3.5)

where $\chi^2_{1-\alpha/2}(2n)$ is the lower $\alpha/2$ quantile of a χ^2 distribution with $2n$ degrees of freedom and $\chi^2_{\alpha/2}(2n)$ is the upper $\alpha/2$ quantile of a χ^2 distribution with $2n$ degrees of freedom. Other choices of c_1 and c_2 can be made, but these are usually the choices used in practice. Exercise 6.3.1 investigates the power curve for this test. ∎

Example 6.3.2 (Likelihood Ratio Test for the Mean of a Normal pdf). Consider a random sample $X_1, X_2, \ldots, X_n$ from a $N(\theta, \sigma^2)$ distribution where $-\infty < \theta < \infty$ and $\sigma^2 > 0$ is known. Consider the hypotheses

$$H_0 : \theta = \theta_0 \text{ versus } H_1 : \theta \neq \theta_0,$$

where θ_0 is specified. The likelihood function is

$$\begin{aligned} L(\theta) &= \left(\frac{1}{2\pi\sigma^2}\right)^{n/2} \exp\left\{-(2\sigma^2)^{-1} \sum_{i=1}^{n}(x_i - \theta)^2\right\} \\ &= \left(\frac{1}{2\pi\sigma^2}\right)^{n/2} \exp\left\{-(2\sigma^2)^{-1} \sum_{i=1}^{n}(x_i - \overline{x})^2\right\} \exp\{-(2\sigma^2)^{-1}n(\overline{x} - \theta)^2\}. \end{aligned}$$

Figure 6.3.1: Plot for Example 6.3.1, showing that the function $g(t) \leq c$ if and only if $t \leq c_1$ or $t \geq c_2$.

Of course, in $\Omega = \{\theta : -\infty < \theta < \infty\}$, the mle is $\widehat{\theta} = \overline{X}$ and thus

$$\Lambda = \frac{L(\theta_0)}{L(\widehat{\theta})} = \exp\{-(2\sigma^2)^{-1}n(\overline{X} - \theta_0)^2\}.$$

Then $\Lambda \leq c$ is equivalent to $-2\log \Lambda \geq -2\log c$. However,

$$-2\log \Lambda = \left(\frac{\overline{X} - \theta_0}{\sigma/\sqrt{n}}\right)^2,$$

which has a $\chi^2(1)$ distribution under H_0. Thus, the likelihood ratio test with significance level α states that we reject H_0 and accept H_1 when

$$-2\log \Lambda = \left(\frac{\overline{X} - \theta_0}{\sigma/\sqrt{n}}\right)^2 \geq \chi_\alpha^2(1). \tag{6.3.6}$$

In Exercise 6.3.3, the power function of this decision rule is obtained. Note also that this test is the same as the z-test for a normal mean discussed in Chapter 4 with s replaced by σ; see Exercise 6.3.2. ■

Other examples are given in the exercises. In the last two examples the likelihood ratio tests simplify and we are able to get the test in closed form. Often, though, this is impossible. In such cases, similarly to Example 6.2.7, we can obtain the mle by iterative routines and, hence, also the test statistic Λ. In Example 6.3.2, $-2\log \Lambda$ had an exact $\chi^2(1)$ null distribution. While not true in general, as the following theorem shows, under regularity conditions, the asymptotic null distribution of $-2\log \Lambda$ is χ^2 with one degree of freedom. Hence in all cases an asymptotic test can be constructed.

Theorem 6.3.1. *Assume the same regularity conditions as for Theorem 6.2.2. Under the null hypothesis, $H_0 : \theta = \theta_0$,*

$$-2\log \Lambda \xrightarrow{D} \chi^2(1). \tag{6.3.7}$$

Proof: Expand the function $l(\theta)$ into a Taylor series about θ_0 of order 1 and evaluate it at the mle, $\widehat{\theta}$. This results in

$$l(\widehat{\theta}) = l(\theta_0) + (\widehat{\theta} - \theta_0)l'(\theta_0) + \frac{1}{2}(\widehat{\theta} - \theta_0)^2 l''(\theta_n^*), \qquad (6.3.8)$$

where θ_n^* is between $\widehat{\theta}$ and θ_0. Because $\widehat{\theta} \xrightarrow{P} \theta_0$, it follows that $\theta_n^* \xrightarrow{P} \theta_0$. This, in addition to the fact that the function $l''(\theta)$ is continuous, and equation (6.2.22) of Theorem 6.2.2 imply that

$$-\frac{1}{n}l''(\theta_n^*) \xrightarrow{P} I(\theta_0). \qquad (6.3.9)$$

By Corollary 6.2.3,

$$\frac{1}{\sqrt{n}}l'(\theta_0) = \sqrt{n}(\widehat{\theta} - \theta_0)I(\theta_0) + R_n, \qquad (6.3.10)$$

where $R_n \to 0$, in probability. If we substitute (6.3.9) and (6.3.10) into expression (6.3.8) and do some simplification, we have

$$-2\log\Lambda = 2(l(\widehat{\theta}) - l(\theta_0)) = \{\sqrt{nI(\theta_0)}(\widehat{\theta} - \theta_0)\}^2 + R_n^*, \qquad (6.3.11)$$

where $R_n^* \to 0$, in probability. By Theorems 5.2.4 and 6.2.2, the first term on the right side of the above equation converges in distribution to a χ^2-distribution with one degree of freedom. ∎

Define the test statistic $\chi_L^2 = -2\log\Lambda$. For the hypotheses (6.3.1), this theorem suggests the decision rule

$$\text{Reject } H_0 \text{ in favor of } H_1 \text{ if } \chi_L^2 \geq \chi_\alpha^2(1). \qquad (6.3.12)$$

By the last theorem, this test has asymptotic level α. If we cannot obtain the test statistic or its distribution in closed form, we can use this asymptotic test.

Besides the likelihood ratio test, in practice two other likelihood-related tests are employed. A natural test statistic is based on the asymptotic distribution of $\widehat{\theta}$. Consider the statistic

$$\chi_W^2 = \left\{ \sqrt{nI(\widehat{\theta})}(\widehat{\theta} - \theta_0) \right\}^2. \qquad (6.3.13)$$

Because $I(\theta)$ is a continuous function, $I(\widehat{\theta}) \to I(\theta_0)$ in probability under the null hypothesis, (6.3.1). It follows, under H_0, that χ_W^2 has an asymptotic χ^2-distribution with one degree of freedom. This suggests the decision rule

$$\text{Reject } H_0 \text{ in favor of } H_1 \text{ if } \chi_W^2 \geq \chi_\alpha^2(1). \qquad (6.3.14)$$

As with the test based on χ_L^2, this test has asymptotic level α. Actually, the relationship between the two test statistics is strong, because as equation (6.3.11) shows, under H_0,

$$\chi_W^2 - \chi_L^2 \xrightarrow{P} 0. \qquad (6.3.15)$$

The test (6.3.14) is often referred to as a **Wald**-type test, after Abraham Wald, who was a prominent statistician of the 20th century.

The third test is called a **scores**-type test, which is often referred to as Rao's score test, after another prominent statistician, C. R. Rao. The **scores** are the components of the vector

$$\mathbf{S}(\theta) = \left(\frac{\partial \log f(X_1; \theta)}{\partial \theta}, \ldots, \frac{\partial \log f(X_n; \theta)}{\partial \theta} \right)'. \tag{6.3.16}$$

In our notation, we have

$$\frac{1}{\sqrt{n}} l'(\theta_0) = \frac{1}{\sqrt{n}} \sum_{i=1}^{n} \frac{\partial \log f(X_i; \theta_0)}{\partial \theta}. \tag{6.3.17}$$

Define the statistic

$$\chi_R^2 = \left(\frac{l'(\theta_0)}{\sqrt{nI(\theta_0)}} \right)^2. \tag{6.3.18}$$

Under H_0, it follows from expression (6.3.10) that

$$\chi_R^2 = \chi_W^2 + R_{0n}, \tag{6.3.19}$$

where R_{0n} converges to 0 in probability. Hence the following decision rule defines an asymptotic level α test under H_0:

$$\text{Reject } H_0 \text{ in favor of } H_1 \text{ if } \chi_R^2 \geq \chi_\alpha^2(1). \tag{6.3.20}$$

Example 6.3.3 (Example 6.2.6, Continued). As in Example 6.2.6, let $X_1, \ldots, X_n$ be a random sample having the common beta$(\theta, 1)$ pdf (6.2.14). We use this pdf to illustrate the three test statistics discussed above for the hypotheses

$$H_0 : \theta = 1 \text{ versus } H_1 : \theta \neq 1. \tag{6.3.21}$$

Under H_0, $f(x; \theta)$ is the uniform$(0, 1)$ pdf. Recall that $\widehat{\theta} = -n / \sum_{i=1}^{n} \log X_i$ is the mle of θ. After some simplification, the value of the likelihood function at the mle is

$$L(\widehat{\theta}) = \left(-\sum_{i=1}^{n} \log X_i \right)^{-n} \exp \left\{ -\sum_{i=1}^{n} \log X_i \right\} \exp \left\{ n(\log n - 1) \right\}.$$

Also, $L(1) = 1$. Hence the likelihood ratio test statistic is $\Lambda = 1/L(\widehat{\theta})$, so that

$$\chi_L^2 = -2 \log \Lambda = 2 \left\{ -\sum_{i=1}^{n} \log X_i - n \log \left(-\sum_{i=1}^{n} \log X_i \right) - n + n \log n \right\}.$$

Recall that the information for this pdf is $I(\theta) = \theta^{-2}$. For the Wald-type test, we would estimate this consistently by $\widehat{\theta}^{-2}$. The Wald-type test simplifies to

$$\chi_W^2 = \left(\sqrt{\frac{n}{\widehat{\theta}^2}} (\widehat{\theta} - 1) \right)^2 = n \left\{ 1 - \frac{1}{\widehat{\theta}} \right\}^2. \tag{6.3.22}$$

Finally, for the scores-type course, recall from (6.2.15) that the $l'(1)$ is

$$l'(1) = \sum_{i=1}^{n} \log X_i + n.$$

Hence the scores-type test statistic is

$$\chi_R^2 = \left\{ \frac{\sum_{i=1}^{n} \log X_i + n}{\sqrt{n}} \right\}^2. \tag{6.3.23}$$

It is easy to show that expressions (6.3.22) and (6.3.23) are the same. From Example 6.2.4, we know the exact distribution of the maximum likelihood estimate. Exercise 6.3.7 uses this distribution to obtain an exact test. ∎

Example 6.3.4 (Likelihood Tests for the Laplace Location Model). Consider the location model

$$X_i = \theta + e_i, \quad i = 1, \ldots, n,$$

where $-\infty < \theta < \infty$ and the random errors e_is are iid each having the Laplace pdf, (2.2.1). Technically, the Laplace distribution does not satisfy all of the regularity conditions (R0)–(R5), but the results below can be derived rigorously; see, for example, Hettmansperger and McKean (2011). Consider testing the hypotheses

$$H_0 : \theta = \theta_0 \text{ versus } H_1 : \theta \neq \theta_0,$$

where θ_0 is specified. Here $\Omega = (-\infty, \infty)$ and $\omega = \{\theta_0\}$. By Example 6.1.1, we know that the mle of θ under Ω is $Q_2 = \text{med}\{X, \ldots, X_n\}$, the sample median. It follows that

$$L(\widehat{\Omega}) = 2^{-n} \exp \left\{ -\sum_{i=1}^{n} |x_i - Q_2| \right\},$$

while

$$L(\widehat{\omega}) = 2^{-n} \exp \left\{ -\sum_{i=1}^{n} |x_i - \theta_0| \right\}.$$

Hence the negative of twice the log of the likelihood ratio test statistic is

$$-2 \log \Lambda = 2 \left[\sum_{i=1}^{n} |x_i - \theta_0| - \sum_{i=1}^{n} |x_i - Q_2| \right]. \tag{6.3.24}$$

Thus the size α asymptotic likelihood ratio test for H_0 versus H_1 rejects H_0 in favor of H_1 if

$$2 \left[\sum_{i=1}^{n} |x_i - \theta_0| - \sum_{i=1}^{n} |x_i - Q_2| \right] \geq \chi_\alpha^2(1).$$

By (6.2.10), the Fisher information for this model is $I(\theta) = 1$. Thus, the Wald-type test statistic simplifies to

$$\chi_W^2 = [\sqrt{n}(Q_2 - \theta_0)]^2.$$

For the scores test, we have

$$\frac{\partial \log f(x_i - \theta)}{\partial \theta} = \frac{\partial}{\partial \theta}\left[\log \frac{1}{2} - |x_i - \theta|\right] = \text{sgn}(x_i - \theta).$$

Hence the score vector for this model is $\mathbf{S}(\theta) = (\text{sgn}(X_1 - \theta), \ldots, \text{sgn}(X_n - \theta))'$. From the above discussion [see equation (6.3.17)], the scores test statistic can be written as

$$\chi_R^2 = (S^*)^2/n,$$

where

$$S^* = \sum_{i=1}^{n} \text{sgn}(X_i - \theta_0).$$

As Exercise 6.3.4 shows, under H_0, S^* is a linear function of a random variable with a $b(n, 1/2)$ distribution. ∎

Which of the three tests should we use? Based on the above discussion, all three tests are asymptotically equivalent under the null hypothesis. Similarly to the concept of asymptotic relative efficiency (ARE), we can derive an equivalent concept of efficiency for tests; see Chapter 10 and more advanced books such as Hettmansperger and McKean (2011). However, all three tests have the same asymptotic efficiency. Hence, asymptotic theory offers little help in separating the tests. There have been finite sample comparisons in the literature; but, these studies have not selected any of these as a "best" test overall; see Chapter 7 of Lehmann (1999) for more discussion.

EXERCISES

6.3.1. Consider the decision rule (6.3.5) derived in Example 6.3.1. Obtain the distribution of the test statistic under a general alternative and use it to obtain the power function of the test. If computational facilities are available, sketch this power curve for the case when $\theta_0 = 1$, $n = 10$, and $\alpha = 0.05$.

6.3.2. Show that the test with decision rule (6.3.6) is like that of Example 4.6.1 except that here σ^2 is known.

6.3.3. Consider the decision rule (6.3.6) derived in Example 6.3.2. Obtain an equivalent test statistic which has a standard normal distribution under H_0. Next obtain the distribution of this test statistic under a general alternative and use it to obtain the power function of the test. If computational facilities are available, sketch this power curve for the case when $\theta_0 = 0$, $n = 10$, $\sigma^2 = 1$, and $\alpha = 0.05$.

6.3.4. Consider Example 6.3.4.

(a) Show that we can write $S^* = 2T - n$, where $T = \#\{X_i > \theta_0\}$.

(b) Show that the scores test for this model is equivalent to rejecting H_0 if $T < c_1$ or $T > c_2$.

(c) Show that under H_0, T has the binomial distribution $b(n, 1/2)$; hence, determine c_1 and c_2 so the test has size α.

(d) Determine the power function for the test based on T as a function of θ.

6.3.5. Let $X_1, X_2, \ldots, X_n$ be a random sample from a $N(\mu_0, \sigma^2 = \theta)$ distribution, where $0 < \theta < \infty$ and μ_0 is known. Show that the likelihood ratio test of $H_0 : \theta = \theta_0$ versus $H_1 : \theta \neq \theta_0$ can be based upon the statistic $W = \sum_{i=1}^{n}(X_i - \mu_0)^2/\theta_0$. Determine the null distribution of W and give, explicitly, the rejection rule for a level α test.

6.3.6. For the test described in Exercise 6.3.5, obtain the distribution of the test statistic under general alternatives. If computational facilities are available, sketch this power curve for the case when $\theta_0 = 1$, $n = 10$, $\mu = 0$, and $\alpha = 0.05$.

6.3.7. Using the results of Example 6.2.4, find an exact size α test for the hypotheses (6.3.21).

6.3.8. Let $X_1, X_2, \ldots, X_n$ be a random sample from a Poisson distribution with mean $\theta > 0$.

(a) Show that the likelihood ratio test of $H_0 : \theta = \theta_0$ versus $H_1 : \theta \neq \theta_0$ is based upon the statistic $Y = \sum_{i=1}^{n} X_i$. Obtain the null distribution of Y.

(b) For $\theta_0 = 2$ and $n = 5$, find the significance level of the test that rejects H_0 if $Y \leq 4$ or $Y \geq 17$.

6.3.9. Let $X_1, X_2, \ldots, X_n$ be a random sample from a Bernoulli $b(1, \theta)$ distribution, where $0 < \theta < 1$.

(a) Show that the likelihood ratio test of $H_0 : \theta = \theta_0$ versus $H_1 : \theta \neq \theta_0$ is based upon the statistic $Y = \sum_{i=1}^{n} X_i$. Obtain the null distribution of Y.

(b) For $n = 100$ and $\theta_0 = 1/2$, find c_1 so that the test rejects H_0 when $Y \leq c_1$ or $Y \geq c_2 = 100 - c_1$ has the approximate significance level of $\alpha = 0.05$. *Hint:* Use the Central Limit Theorem.

6.3.10. Let $X_1, X_2, \ldots, X_n$ be a random sample from a $\Gamma(\alpha = 3, \beta = \theta)$ distribution, where $0 < \theta < \infty$.

(a) Show that the likelihood ratio test of $H_0 : \theta = \theta_0$ versus $H_1 : \theta \neq \theta_0$ is based upon the statistic $W = \sum_{i=1}^{n} X_i$. Obtain the null distribution of $2W/\theta_0$.

(b) For $\theta_0 = 3$ and $n = 5$, find c_1 and c_2 so that the test that rejects H_0 when $W \leq c_1$ or $W \geq c_2$ has significance level 0.05.

6.3.11. Let $X_1, X_2, \ldots, X_n$ be a random sample from a distribution with pdf $f(x; \theta) = \theta \exp\left\{-|x|^\theta\right\}/2\Gamma(1/\theta)$, $-\infty < x < \infty$, where $\theta > 0$. Suppose $\Omega = \{\theta : \theta = 1, 2\}$. Consider the hypotheses $H_0 : \theta = 2$ (a normal distribution) versus $H_1 : \theta = 1$ (a double exponential distribution). Show that the likelihood ratio test can be based on the statistic $W = \sum_{i=1}^{n}(X_i^2 - |X_i|)$.

6.3.12. Let $X_1, X_2, \ldots, X_n$ be a random sample from the beta distribution with $\alpha = \beta = \theta$ and $\Omega = \{\theta : \theta = 1, 2\}$. Show that the likelihood ratio test statistic Λ for testing $H_0 : \theta = 1$ versus $H_1 : \theta = 2$ is a function of the statistic $W = \sum_{i=1}^{n} \log X_i + \sum_{i=1}^{n} \log(1 - X_i)$.

6.3.13. Consider a location model

$$X_i = \theta + e_i, \quad i = 1, \ldots, n, \tag{6.3.25}$$

where $e_1, e_2, \ldots, e_n$ are iid with pdf $f(z)$. There is a nice geometric interpretation for estimating θ. Let $\mathbf{X} = (X_1, \ldots, X_n)'$ and $\mathbf{e} = (e_1, \ldots, e_n)'$ be the vectors of observations and random error, respectively, and let $\boldsymbol{\mu} = \theta \mathbf{1}$, where $\mathbf{1}$ is a vector with all components equal to 1. Let V be the subspace of vectors of the form $\boldsymbol{\mu}$; i.e., $V = \{\mathbf{v} : \mathbf{v} = a\mathbf{1}, \text{ for some } a \in R\}$. Then in vector notation we can write the model as

$$\mathbf{X} = \boldsymbol{\mu} + \mathbf{e}, \quad \boldsymbol{\mu} \in V. \tag{6.3.26}$$

Then we can summarize the model by saying, "Except for the random error vector $\mathbf{e}$, $\mathbf{X}$ would reside in V." Hence, it makes sense intuitively to estimate $\boldsymbol{\mu}$ by a vector in V which is "closest" to $\mathbf{X}$. That is, given a norm $\|\cdot\|$ in R^n, choose

$$\widehat{\boldsymbol{\mu}} = \text{Argmin}\|\mathbf{X} - \mathbf{v}\|, \quad \mathbf{v} \in V. \tag{6.3.27}$$

(a) If the error pdf is the Laplace, (2.2.1), show that the minimization in (6.3.27) is equivalent to maximizing the likelihood when the norm is the l_1 norm given by

$$\|\mathbf{v}\|_1 = \sum_{i=1}^{n} |v_i|. \tag{6.3.28}$$

(b) If the error pdf is the $N(0, 1)$, show that the minimization in (6.3.27) is equivalent to maximizing the likelihood when the norm is given by the square of the l_2 norm

$$\|\mathbf{v}\|_2^2 = \sum_{i=1}^{n} v_i^2. \tag{6.3.29}$$

6.3.14. Continuing with the last exercise, besides estimation there is also a nice geometric interpretation for testing. For the model (6.3.26), consider the hypotheses

$$H_0 : \theta = \theta_0 \text{ versus } H_1 : \theta \neq \theta_0, \tag{6.3.30}$$

where θ_0 is specified. Given a norm $\|\cdot\|$ on R^n, denote by $d(\mathbf{X}, V)$ the distance between $\mathbf{X}$ and the subspace V; i.e., $d(\mathbf{X}, V) = \|\mathbf{X} - \widehat{\boldsymbol{\mu}}\|$, where $\widehat{\boldsymbol{\mu}}$ is defined in equation (6.3.27). If H_0 is true, then $\widehat{\boldsymbol{\mu}}$ should be close to $\boldsymbol{\mu} = \theta_0 \mathbf{1}$ and, hence, $\|\mathbf{X} - \theta_0 \mathbf{1}\|$ should be close to $d(\mathbf{X}, V)$. Denote the difference by

$$RD = \|\mathbf{X} - \theta_0 \mathbf{1}\| - \|\mathbf{X} - \widehat{\boldsymbol{\mu}}\|. \tag{6.3.31}$$

Small values of RD indicate that the null hypothesis is true, while large values indicate H_1. So our rejection rule when using RD is

$$\text{Reject } H_0 \text{ in favor of } H_1 \text{ if } RD > c. \tag{6.3.32}$$

(a) If the error pdf is the Laplace, (6.1.6), show that expression (6.3.31) is equivalent to the likelihood ratio test when the norm is given by (6.3.28).

(b) If the error pdf is the $N(0,1)$, show that expression (6.3.31) is equivalent to the likelihood ratio test when the norm is given by the square of the l_2 norm, (6.3.29).

6.3.15. Let $X_1, X_2, \ldots, X_n$ be a random sample from a distribution with pmf $p(x; \theta) = \theta^x (1 - \theta)^{1-x}$, $x = 0, 1$, where $0 < \theta < 1$. We wish to test $H_0 : \theta = 1/3$ versus $H_1 : \theta \neq 1/3$.

(a) Find Λ and $-2 \log \Lambda$.

(b) Determine the Wald-type test.

(c) What is Rao's score statistic?

6.3.16. Let $X_1, X_2, \ldots, X_n$ be a random sample from a Poisson distribution with mean $\theta > 0$. Test $H_0 : \theta = 2$ against $H_1 : \theta \neq 2$ using

(a) $-2 \log \Lambda$.

(b) A Wald-type statistic.

(c) Rao's score statistic.

6.3.17. Let $X_1, X_2, \ldots, X_n$ be a random sample from a $\Gamma(\alpha, \beta)$ distribution where α is known and $\beta > 0$. Determine the likelihood ratio test for $H_0 : \beta = \beta_0$ against $H_1 : \beta \neq \beta_0$.

6.3.18. Let $Y_1 < Y_2 < \cdots < Y_n$ be the order statistics of a random sample from a uniform distribution on $(0, \theta)$, where $\theta > 0$.

(a) Show that Λ for testing $H_0 : \theta = \theta_0$ against $H_1 : \theta \neq \theta_0$ is $\Lambda = (Y_n/\theta_0)^n$, $Y_n \leq \theta_0$, and $\Lambda = 0$ if $Y_n > \theta_0$.

(b) When H_0 is true, show that $-2 \log \Lambda$ has an exact $\chi^2(2)$ distribution, not $\chi^2(1)$. Note that the regularity conditions are not satisfied.

6.4   Multiparameter Case: Estimation

In this section, we discuss the case where $\boldsymbol{\theta}$ is a vector of p parameters. There are analogs to the theorems in the previous sections in which θ is a scalar, and we present their results but, for the most part, without proofs. The interested reader can find additional information in more advanced books; see, for instance, Lehmann and Casella (1998) and Rao (1973).

Let $X_1, \ldots, X_n$ be iid with common pdf $f(x; \boldsymbol{\theta})$, where $\boldsymbol{\theta} \in \Omega \subset R^p$. As before, the likelihood function and its log are given by

$$L(\boldsymbol{\theta}) = \prod_{i=1}^{n} f(x_i; \boldsymbol{\theta})$$

$$l(\boldsymbol{\theta}) = \log L(\boldsymbol{\theta}) = \sum_{i=1}^{n} \log f(x_i; \boldsymbol{\theta}), \tag{6.4.1}$$

for $\boldsymbol{\theta} \in \Omega$. The theory requires additional regularity conditions, which are listed in Appendix A, (A.1.1). In keeping with our number scheme in the last three sections, we have labeled these (R6)–(R9). In this section, when we say "under regularity conditions," we mean all of the conditions of (6.1.1), (6.2.1), (6.2.2), and (A.1.1) which are relevant to the argument. The discrete case follows in the same way as the continuous case, so in general we state material in terms of the continuous case.

Note that the proof of Theorem 6.1.1 does not depend on whether the parameter is a scalar or a vector. Therefore, with probability going to 1, $L(\boldsymbol{\theta})$ is maximized at the true value of $\boldsymbol{\theta}$. Hence, as an estimate of $\boldsymbol{\theta}$ we consider the value which maximizes $L(\boldsymbol{\theta})$ or equivalently solves the vector equation $(\partial/\partial\boldsymbol{\theta})l(\boldsymbol{\theta}) = \mathbf{0}$. If it exists, this value is called the **maximum likelihood estimator** (mle) and we denote it by $\widehat{\boldsymbol{\theta}}$. Often we are interested in a function of $\boldsymbol{\theta}$, say, the parameter $\eta = g(\boldsymbol{\theta})$. Because the second part of the proof of Theorem 6.1.2 remains true for $\boldsymbol{\theta}$ as a vector, $\widehat{\eta} = g(\widehat{\boldsymbol{\theta}})$ is the mle of η.

Example 6.4.1 (Maximum Likelihood Estimates Under the Normal Model). Suppose $X_1, \ldots, X_n$ are iid $N(\mu, \sigma^2)$. In this case, $\boldsymbol{\theta} = (\mu, \sigma^2)'$ and Ω is the product space $(-\infty, \infty) \times (0, \infty)$. The log of the likelihood simplifies to

$$l(\mu, \sigma^2) = -\frac{n}{2} \log 2\pi - n \log \sigma - \frac{1}{2\sigma^2} \sum_{i=1}^{n} (x_i - \mu)^2. \tag{6.4.2}$$

Taking partial derivatives of (6.4.2) with respect to μ and σ and setting them to 0, we get the simultaneous equations

$$\frac{\partial l}{\partial \mu} = \frac{1}{\sigma^2} \sum_{i=1}^{n} (x_i - \mu) = 0$$

$$\frac{\partial l}{\partial \sigma} = -\frac{n}{\sigma} + \frac{1}{\sigma^3} \sum_{i=1}^{n} (x_i - \mu)^2 = 0.$$

Solving these equations, we obtain $\widehat{\mu} = \overline{X}$ and $\widehat{\sigma} = \sqrt{(1/n) \sum_{i=1}^{n} (X_i - \overline{X})^2}$ as solutions. A check of the second partials shows that these maximize $l(\mu, \sigma^2)$, so these are the mles. Also, by Theorem 6.1.2, $(1/n) \sum_{i=1}^{n} (X_i - \overline{X})^2$ is the mle of σ^2. We know from our discussion in Section 5.1 that these are consistent estimates of μ and σ^2, respectively, that $\widehat{\mu}$ is an unbiased estimate of μ, and that $\widehat{\sigma^2}$ is a biased estimate of σ^2 whose bias vanishes as $n \to \infty$. ∎

Example 6.4.2 (General Laplace pdf). Let $X_1, X_2, \ldots, X_n$ be a random sample from the Laplace pdf $f_X(x) = (2b)^{-1} \exp\{-|x-a|/b\}$, $-\infty < x < \infty$, where the parameters (a, b) are in the space $\Omega = \{(a, b) : -\infty < a < \infty, b > 0\}$. Recall in the last sections we looked at the special case where $b = 1$. As we now show, the mle of a is the sample median, regardless of the value of b. The log of the likelihood function is

$$l(a, b) = -n \log 2 - n \log b - \sum_{i=1}^{n} \left| \frac{x_i - a}{b} \right|.$$

The partial of $l(a, b)$ with respect to a is

$$\frac{\partial l(a, b)}{\partial a} = \frac{1}{b} \sum_{i=1}^{n} \mathrm{sgn}\left\{ \frac{x_i - a}{b} \right\} = \frac{1}{b} \sum_{i=1}^{n} \mathrm{sgn}\{x_i - a\},$$

where the second equality follows because $b > 0$. Setting this partial to 0, we obtain the mle of a to be $Q_2 = \mathrm{med}\{X_1, X_2, \ldots, X_n\}$, just as in Example 6.1.1. Hence the mle of a is invariant to the parameter b. Taking the partial of $l(a, b)$ with respect to b, we obtain

$$\frac{\partial l(a, b)}{\partial b} = -\frac{n}{b} + \frac{1}{b^2} \sum_{i=1}^{n} |x_i - a|.$$

Setting to 0 and solving the two equations simultaneously, we obtain, as the mle of b, the statistic

$$\widehat{b} = \frac{1}{n} \sum_{i=1}^{n} |X_i - Q_2|. \quad \blacksquare$$

Recall that the Fisher information in the scalar case was the variance of the random variable $(\partial/\partial\theta) \log f(X; \theta)$. The analog in the multiparameter case is the variance-covariance matrix of the gradient of $\log f(X; \boldsymbol{\theta})$, that is, the variance-covariance matrix of the random vector given by

$$\bigtriangledown \log f(X; \boldsymbol{\theta}) = \left(\frac{\partial \log f(X; \boldsymbol{\theta})}{\partial \theta_1}, \ldots, \frac{\partial \log f(X; \boldsymbol{\theta})}{\partial \theta_p} \right)'. \tag{6.4.3}$$

Fisher information is then defined by the $p \times p$ matrix

$$\mathbf{I}(\boldsymbol{\theta}) = \mathrm{Cov}\left(\bigtriangledown \log f(X; \boldsymbol{\theta}) \right). \tag{6.4.4}$$

The (j, k)th entry of $\mathbf{I}(\boldsymbol{\theta})$ is given by

$$I_{jk} = \mathrm{cov}\left(\frac{\partial}{\partial \theta_j} \log f(X; \boldsymbol{\theta}), \frac{\partial}{\partial \theta_k} \log f(X; \boldsymbol{\theta}) \right); \quad j, k = 1, \ldots, p. \tag{6.4.5}$$

As in the scalar case, we can simplify this by using the identity $1 = \int f(x; \boldsymbol{\theta}) \, dx$. Under the regularity conditions, as discussed in the second paragraph of this section, the partial derivative of this identity with respect to θ_j results in

$$0 = \int \frac{\partial}{\partial \theta_j} f(x; \boldsymbol{\theta}) \, dx = \int \left[\frac{\partial}{\partial \theta_j} \log f(x; \boldsymbol{\theta}) \right] f(x; \boldsymbol{\theta}) \, dx$$

$$= E\left[\frac{\partial}{\partial \theta_j} \log f(X; \boldsymbol{\theta}) \right]. \tag{6.4.6}$$

Next, on both sides of the first equality above, take the partial derivative with respect to θ_k. After simplification, this results in

$$
\begin{aligned}
0 \;=\; & \int \left(\frac{\partial^2}{\partial\theta_j \partial\theta_k} \log f(x; \boldsymbol{\theta}) \right) f(x; \boldsymbol{\theta})\, dx \\
& + \int \left(\frac{\partial}{\partial\theta_j} \log f(x; \boldsymbol{\theta}) \frac{\partial}{\partial\theta_k} \log f(x; \boldsymbol{\theta}) \right) f(x; \boldsymbol{\theta})\, dx;
\end{aligned}
$$

that is,

$$
E\left[\frac{\partial}{\partial\theta_j} \log f(X; \boldsymbol{\theta}) \frac{\partial}{\partial\theta_k} \log f(X; \boldsymbol{\theta}) \right] = -E\left[\frac{\partial^2}{\partial\theta_j \partial\theta_k} \log f(X; \boldsymbol{\theta}) \right]. \tag{6.4.7}
$$

Using (6.4.6) and (6.4.7) together, we obtain

$$
I_{jk} = -E\left[\frac{\partial^2}{\partial\theta_j \partial\theta_k} \log f(X; \boldsymbol{\theta}) \right]. \tag{6.4.8}
$$

Information for a random sample follows in the same way as the scalar case. The pdf of the sample is the likelihood function $L(\boldsymbol{\theta}; \mathbf{X})$. Replace $f(X; \boldsymbol{\theta})$ by $L(\boldsymbol{\theta}; \mathbf{X})$ in the vector given in expression (6.4.3). Because $\log L$ is a sum, this results in the random vector

$$
\triangledown \log L(\boldsymbol{\theta}; \mathbf{X}) = \sum_{i=1}^{n} \triangledown \log f(X_i; \boldsymbol{\theta}). \tag{6.4.9}
$$

Because the summands are iid with common covariance matrix $\mathbf{I}(\boldsymbol{\theta})$, we have

$$
\mathrm{Cov}(\triangledown \log L(\boldsymbol{\theta}; \mathbf{X})) = n\mathbf{I}(\boldsymbol{\theta}). \tag{6.4.10}
$$

As in the scalar case, the information in a random sample of size n is n times the information in a sample of size 1.

The diagonal entries of $\mathbf{I}(\boldsymbol{\theta})$ are

$$
I_{ii}(\boldsymbol{\theta}) = \mathrm{Var}\left[\frac{\partial \log f(X; \boldsymbol{\theta})}{\partial\theta_i} \right] = -E\left[\frac{\partial^2}{\partial\theta_i^2} \log f(X_i; \boldsymbol{\theta}) \right].
$$

This is similar to the case when θ is a scalar, except now $I_{ii}(\boldsymbol{\theta})$ is a function of the vector $\boldsymbol{\theta}$. Recall in the scalar case that $(nI(\theta))^{-1}$ was the Rao-Cramér lower bound for an unbiased estimate of θ. There is an analog to this in the multiparameter case. In particular, if $Y_j = u_j(X_1, \ldots, X_n)$ is an unbiased estimate of θ_j, then it can be shown that

$$
\mathrm{Var}(Y_j) \geq \frac{1}{n} \left[\mathbf{I}^{-1}(\boldsymbol{\theta}) \right]_{jj}; \tag{6.4.11}
$$

see, for example, Lehmann (1983). As in the scalar case, we shall call an unbiased estimate **efficient** if its variance attains this lower bound.

Example 6.4.3 (Information Matrix for the Normal pdf). The log of a $N(\mu, \sigma^2)$ pdf is given by

$$
\log f(x; \mu, \sigma^2) = -\frac{1}{2} \log 2\pi - \log \sigma - \frac{1}{2\sigma^2}(x - \mu)^2. \tag{6.4.12}
$$

The first and second partial derivatives are

$$\frac{\partial \log f}{\partial \mu} = \frac{1}{\sigma^2}(x - \mu)$$

$$\frac{\partial^2 \log f}{\partial \mu^2} = -\frac{1}{\sigma^2}$$

$$\frac{\partial \log f}{\partial \sigma} = -\frac{1}{\sigma} + \frac{1}{\sigma^3}(x - \mu)^2$$

$$\frac{\partial^2 \log f}{\partial \sigma^2} = \frac{1}{\sigma^2} - \frac{3}{\sigma^4}(x - \mu)^2$$

$$\frac{\partial^2 \log f}{\partial \mu \partial \sigma} = -\frac{2}{\sigma^3}(x - \mu).$$

Upon taking the negative of the expectations of the second partial derivatives, the information matrix for a normal density is

$$\mathbf{I}(\mu, \sigma) = \begin{bmatrix} \frac{1}{\sigma^2} & 0 \\ 0 & \frac{2}{\sigma^2} \end{bmatrix}. \tag{6.4.13}$$

We may want the information matrix for (μ, σ^2). This can be obtained by taking partial derivatives with respect to σ^2 instead of σ; however, in Example 6.4.6, we obtain it via a transformation. From Example 6.4.1, the maximum likelihood estimates of μ and σ^2 are $\widehat{\mu} = \overline{X}$ and $\widehat{\sigma}^2 = (1/n)\sum_{i=1}^{n}(X_i - \overline{X})^2$, respectively. Based on the information matrix, we note that $\overline{X}$ is an efficient estimate of μ for finite samples. In Example 6.4.6, we consider the sample variance. ∎

Example 6.4.4 (Information Matrix for a Location and Scale Family). Suppose $X_1, X_2, \ldots, X_n$ is a random sample with common pdf $f_X(x) = b^{-1}f\left(\frac{x-a}{b}\right)$, $-\infty < x < \infty$, where (a, b) is in the space $\Omega = \{(a, b) : -\infty < a < \infty, b > 0\}$ and $f(z)$ is a pdf such that $f(z) > 0$ for $-\infty < z < \infty$. As Exercise 6.4.8 shows, we can model X_i as

$$X_i = a + be_i, \tag{6.4.14}$$

where the e_is are iid with pdf $f(z)$. This is called a *location and scale model* (LASP). Example 6.4.2 illustrated this model when $f(z)$ had the Laplace pdf. In Exercise 6.4.9, the reader is asked to show that the partial derivatives are

$$\frac{\partial}{\partial a}\left\{\log\left[\frac{1}{b}f\left(\frac{x-a}{b}\right)\right]\right\} = -\frac{1}{b}\frac{f'\left(\frac{x-a}{b}\right)}{f\left(\frac{x-a}{b}\right)}$$

$$\frac{\partial}{\partial b}\left\{\log\left[\frac{1}{b}f\left(\frac{x-a}{b}\right)\right]\right\} = -\frac{1}{b}\left[1 + \frac{\frac{x-a}{b}f'\left(\frac{x-a}{b}\right)}{f\left(\frac{x-a}{b}\right)}\right].$$

Using (6.4.5) and (6.4.6), we then obtain

$$I_{11} = \int_{-\infty}^{\infty} \frac{1}{b^2}\left[\frac{f'\left(\frac{x-a}{b}\right)}{f\left(\frac{x-a}{b}\right)}\right]^2 \frac{1}{b}f\left(\frac{x-a}{b}\right)\, dx.$$

Now make the substitution $z = (x - a)/b$, $dz = (1/b)dx$. Then we have

$$I_{11} = \frac{1}{b^2} \int_{-\infty}^{\infty} \left[\frac{f'(z)}{f(z)} \right]^2 f(z)\, dz; \tag{6.4.15}$$

hence, information on the location parameter a does not depend on a. As Exercise 6.4.9 shows, upon making this substitution, the other entries in the information matrix are

$$I_{22} = \frac{1}{b^2} \int_{-\infty}^{\infty} \left[1 + \frac{z f'(z)}{f(z)} \right]^2 f(z)\, dz \tag{6.4.16}$$

$$I_{12} = \frac{1}{b^2} \int_{-\infty}^{\infty} z \left[\frac{f'(z)}{f(z)} \right]^2 f(z)\, dz. \tag{6.4.17}$$

Thus, the information matrix can be written as $(1/b)^2$ times a matrix whose entries are free of the parameters a and b. As Exercise 6.4.10 shows, the off-diagonal entries of the information matrix are 0 if the pdf $f(z)$ is symmetric about 0. ∎

Example 6.4.5 (Multinomial Distribution). Consider a random trial which can result in one, and only one, of k outcomes or categories. Let X_j be 1 or 0 depending on whether the jth outcome occurs or does not, for $j = 1, \ldots, k$. Suppose the probability that outcome j occurs is p_j; hence, $\sum_{j=1}^{k} p_j = 1$. Let $\mathbf{X} = (X_1, \ldots, X_{k-1})'$ and $\mathbf{p} = (p_1, \ldots, p_{k-1})'$. The distribution of $\mathbf{X}$ is multinomial; see Section 3.1. Recall that the pmf is given by

$$f(\mathbf{x}, \mathbf{p}) = \left(\prod_{j=1}^{k-1} p_j^{x_j} \right) \left(1 - \sum_{j=1}^{k-1} p_j \right)^{1 - \sum_{j=1}^{k-1} x_j}, \tag{6.4.18}$$

where the parameter space is $\Omega = \{ \mathbf{p} : 0 < p_j < 1, j = 1, \ldots, k-1; \sum_{j=1}^{k-1} p_j < 1 \}$.

We first obtain the information matrix. The first partial of the log of f with respect to p_i simplifies to

$$\frac{\partial \log f}{\partial p_i} = \frac{x_i}{p_i} - \frac{1 - \sum_{j=1}^{k-1} x_j}{1 - \sum_{j=1}^{k-1} p_j}.$$

The second partial derivatives are given by

$$\frac{\partial^2 \log f}{\partial p_i^2} = -\frac{x_i}{p_i^2} - \frac{1 - \sum_{j=1}^{k-1} x_j}{(1 - \sum_{j=1}^{k-1} p_j)^2}$$

$$\frac{\partial^2 \log f}{\partial p_i \partial p_h} = -\frac{1 - \sum_{j=1}^{k-1} x_j}{(1 - \sum_{j=1}^{k-1} p_j)^2}, \quad i \neq h < k.$$

Recall for this distribution that marginally each random variable X_j has a Bernoulli distribution with mean p_j. Recalling that $p_k = 1 - (p_1 + \cdots + p_{k-1})$, the expectations of the negatives of the second partial derivatives are straightforward and result in the information matrix

$$
\mathbf{I(p)} = \begin{bmatrix} \frac{1}{p_1} + \frac{1}{p_k} & \frac{1}{p_k} & \cdots & \frac{1}{p_k} \\ \frac{1}{p_k} & \frac{1}{p_2} + \frac{1}{p_k} & \cdots & \frac{1}{p_k} \\ \vdots & \vdots & & \vdots \\ \frac{1}{p_k} & \frac{1}{p_k} & \cdots & \frac{1}{p_{k-1}} + \frac{1}{p_k} \end{bmatrix}. \tag{6.4.19}
$$

This is a patterned matrix with inverse [see page 170 of Graybill (1969)],

$$
\mathbf{I}^{-1}(\mathbf{p}) = \begin{bmatrix} p_1(1 - p_1) & -p_1 p_2 & \cdots & -p_1 p_{k-1} \\ -p_1 p_2 & p_2(1 - p_2) & \cdots & -p_2 p_{k-1} \\ \vdots & \vdots & & \vdots \\ -p_1 p_{k-1} & -p_2 p_{k-1} & \cdots & p_{k-1}(1 - p_{k-1}) \end{bmatrix}. \tag{6.4.20}
$$

Next, we obtain the mles for a random sample $\mathbf{X}_1, \mathbf{X}_2, \ldots, \mathbf{X}_n$. The likelihood function is given by

$$
L(\mathbf{p}) = \prod_{i=1}^{n} \prod_{j=1}^{k-1} p_j^{x_{ji}} \left(1 - \sum_{j=1}^{k-1} p_j\right)^{1 - \sum_{j=1}^{k-1} x_{ji}}. \tag{6.4.21}
$$

Let $t_j = \sum_{i=1}^{n} x_{ji}$, for $j = 1, \ldots, k-1$. With simplification, the log of L reduces to

$$
l(\mathbf{p}) = \sum_{j=1}^{k-1} t_j \log p_j + \left(n - \sum_{j=1}^{k-1} t_j\right) \log\left(1 - \sum_{j=1}^{k-1} p_j\right).
$$

The first partial of $l(\mathbf{p})$ with respect to p_h leads to the system of equations

$$
\frac{\partial l(\mathbf{p})}{\partial p_h} = \frac{t_h}{p_h} - \frac{n - \sum_{j=1}^{k-1} t_j}{1 - \sum_{j=1}^{k-1} p_j} = 0, \quad h = 1, \ldots, k-1.
$$

It is easily seen that $p_h = t_h/n$ satisfies these equations. Hence the maximum likelihood estimates are

$$
\widehat{p_h} = \frac{\sum_{i=1}^{n} X_{ih}}{n}, \quad h = 1, \ldots, k-1. \tag{6.4.22}
$$

Each random variable $\sum_{i=1}^{n} X_{ih}$ is binomial(n, p_h) with variance $np_h(1-p_h)$. Therefore, the maximum likelihood estimates are efficient estimates. ∎

As a final note on information, suppose the information matrix is diagonal. Then the lower bound of the variance of the jth estimator (6.4.11) is $1/(n\mathbf{I}_{jj}(\boldsymbol{\theta}))$. Because $\mathbf{I}_{jj}(\boldsymbol{\theta})$ is defined in terms of partial derivatives, [see (6.4.5)], this is the information in treating all θ_i, except θ_j, as known. For instance, in Example 6.4.3, for the normal pdf the information matrix is diagonal; hence, the information for

μ could have been obtained by treating σ^2 as known. Example 6.4.4 discusses the information for a general location and scale family. For this general family, of which the normal is a member, the information matrix is diagonal provided the underlying pdf is symmetric.

In the next theorem, we summarize the asymptotic behavior of the maximum likelihood estimator of the vector $\boldsymbol{\theta}$. It shows that the mles are asymptotically efficient estimates.

Theorem 6.4.1. *Let $X_1, \ldots, X_n$ be iid with pdf $f(x; \boldsymbol{\theta})$ for $\boldsymbol{\theta} \in \Omega$. Assume the regularity conditions hold. Then*

1. *The likelihood equation,*

$$\frac{\partial}{\partial \boldsymbol{\theta}} l(\boldsymbol{\theta}) = \mathbf{0},$$

has a solution $\widehat{\boldsymbol{\theta}}_n$ such that $\widehat{\boldsymbol{\theta}}_n \xrightarrow{P} \boldsymbol{\theta}$.

2. *For any sequence which satisfies (1),*

$$\sqrt{n}(\widehat{\boldsymbol{\theta}}_n - \boldsymbol{\theta}) \xrightarrow{D} N_p(\mathbf{0}, \mathbf{I}^{-1}(\boldsymbol{\theta})).$$

The proof of this theorem can be found in more advanced books; see, for example, Lehmann and Casella (1998). As in the scalar case, the theorem does not assure that the maximum likelihood estimates are unique. But if the sequence of solutions are unique, then they are both consistent and asymptotically normal. In applications, we can often verify uniqueness.

We immediately have the following corollary,

Corollary 6.4.1. *Let $X_1, \ldots, X_n$ be iid with pdf $f(x; \boldsymbol{\theta})$ for $\boldsymbol{\theta} \in \Omega$. Assume the regularity conditions hold. Let $\widehat{\boldsymbol{\theta}}_n$ be a sequence of consistent solutions of the likelihood equation. Then $\widehat{\boldsymbol{\theta}}_n$ are asymptotically efficient estimates; that is, for $j = 1, \ldots, p$,*

$$\sqrt{n}(\widehat{\theta}_{n,j} - \theta_j) \xrightarrow{D} N(0, [\mathbf{I}^{-1}(\boldsymbol{\theta})]_{jj}).$$

Let $\mathbf{g}$ be a transformation $\mathbf{g}(\boldsymbol{\theta}) = (g_1(\boldsymbol{\theta}), \ldots, g_k(\boldsymbol{\theta}))'$ such that $1 \leq k \leq p$ and that the $k \times p$ matrix of partial derivatives

$$\mathbf{B} = \left[\frac{\partial g_i}{\partial \theta_j} \right], \quad i = 1, \ldots k, \ j = 1, \ldots, p,$$

has continuous elements and does not vanish in a neighborhood of $\boldsymbol{\theta}$. Let $\widehat{\boldsymbol{\eta}} = \mathbf{g}(\widehat{\boldsymbol{\theta}})$. Then $\widehat{\boldsymbol{\eta}}$ is the mle of $\boldsymbol{\eta} = \mathbf{g}(\boldsymbol{\theta})$. By Theorem 5.4.6,

$$\sqrt{n}(\widehat{\boldsymbol{\eta}} - \boldsymbol{\eta}) \xrightarrow{D} N_k(\mathbf{0}, \mathbf{B}\mathbf{I}^{-1}(\boldsymbol{\theta})\mathbf{B}'). \tag{6.4.23}$$

Hence the information matrix for $\sqrt{n}(\widehat{\boldsymbol{\eta}} - \boldsymbol{\eta})$ is

$$\mathbf{I}(\boldsymbol{\eta}) = \left[\mathbf{B}\mathbf{I}^{-1}(\boldsymbol{\theta})\mathbf{B}' \right]^{-1}, \tag{6.4.24}$$

provided the inverse exists.

For a simple example of this result, reconsider Example 6.4.3.

Example 6.4.6 (Information for the Variance of a Normal Distribution). Suppose $X_1, \ldots, X_n$ are iid $N(\mu, \sigma^2)$. Recall from Example 6.4.3 that the information matrix was $\mathbf{I}(\mu, \sigma) = \text{diag}\{\sigma^{-2}, 2\sigma^{-2}\}$. Consider the transformation $g(\mu, \sigma) = \sigma^2$. Hence the matrix of partials $\mathbf{B}$ is the row vector $[0 \; 2\sigma]$. Thus the information for σ^2 is

$$I(\sigma^2) = \left\{ \begin{bmatrix} 0 & 2\sigma \end{bmatrix} \begin{bmatrix} \frac{1}{\sigma^2} & 0 \\ 0 & \frac{2}{\sigma^2} \end{bmatrix}^{-1} \begin{bmatrix} 0 \\ 2\sigma \end{bmatrix} \right\}^{-1} = \frac{1}{2\sigma^4}.$$

The Rao-Cramér lower bound for the variance of an estimator of σ^2 is $(2\sigma^4)/n$. Recall that the sample variance is unbiased for σ^2, but its variance is $(2\sigma^4)/(n-1)$. Hence, it is not efficient for finite samples, but it is asymptotically efficient. ∎

EXERCISES

6.4.1. Let X_1, X_2, and X_3 have a multinomial distribution in which $n = 25$, $k = 4$, and the unknown probabilities are θ_1, θ_2, and θ_3, respectively. Here we can, for convenience, let $X_4 = 25 - X_1 - X_2 - X_3$ and $\theta_4 = 1 - \theta_1 - \theta_2 - \theta_3$. If the observed values of the random variables are $x_1 = 4$, $x_2 = 11$, and $x_3 = 7$, find the maximum likelihood estimates of θ_1, θ_2, and θ_3.

6.4.2. Let $X_1, X_2, \ldots, X_n$ and $Y_1, Y_2, \ldots, Y_m$ be independent random samples from $N(\theta_1, \theta_3)$ and $N(\theta_2, \theta_4)$ distributions, respectively.

 (a) If $\Omega \subset R^3$ is defined by

$$\Omega = \{(\theta_1, \theta_2, \theta_3) : -\infty < \theta_i < \infty, i = 1, 2; 0 < \theta_3 = \theta_4 < \infty\},$$

find the mles of θ_1, θ_2, and θ_3.

 (b) If $\Omega \subset R^2$ is defined by

$$\Omega = \{(\theta_1, \theta_3) : -\infty < \theta_1 = \theta_2 < \infty; 0 < \theta_3 = \theta_4 < \infty\},$$

find the mles of θ_1 and θ_3.

6.4.3. Let $X_1, X_2, \ldots, X_n$ be iid, each with the distribution having pdf $f(x; \theta_1, \theta_2) = (1/\theta_2)e^{-(x-\theta_1)/\theta_2}$, $\theta_1 \le x < \infty$, $-\infty < \theta_2 < \infty$, zero elsewhere. Find the maximum likelihood estimators of θ_1 and θ_2.

6.4.4. The *Pareto distribution* is a frequently used model in the study of incomes and has the distribution function

$$F(x; \theta_1, \theta_2) = \begin{cases} 1 - (\theta_1/x)^{\theta_2} & \theta_1 \le x \\ 0 & \text{elsewhere}, \end{cases}$$

where $\theta_1 > 0$ and $\theta_2 > 0$. If $X_1, X_2, \ldots, X_n$ is a random sample from this distribution, find the maximum likelihood estimators of θ_1 and θ_2. (*Hint:* This exercise deals with a nonregular case.)

6.4.5. Let $Y_1 < Y_2 < \cdots < Y_n$ be the order statistics of a random sample of size n from the uniform distribution of the continuous type over the closed interval $[\theta - \rho, \theta + \rho]$. Find the maximum likelihood estimators for θ and ρ. Are these two unbiased estimators?

6.4.6. Let $X_1, X_2, \ldots, X_n$ be a random sample from $N(\mu, \sigma^2)$.

    (a) If the constant b is defined by the equation $P(X \leq b) = 0.90$, find the mle of b.

    (b) If c is given constant, find the mle of $P(X \leq c)$.

6.4.7. Consider two Bernoulli distributions with unknown parameters p_1 and p_2. If Y and Z equal the numbers of successes in two independent random samples, each of size n, from the respective distributions, determine the mles of p_1 and p_2 if we know that $0 \leq p_1 \leq p_2 \leq 1$.

6.4.8. Show that if X_i follows the model (6.4.14), then its pdf is $b^{-1} f((x-a)/b)$.

6.4.9. Verify the partial derivatives and the entries of the information matrix for the location and scale family as given in Example 6.4.4.

6.4.10. Suppose the pdf of X is of a location and scale family as defined in Example 6.4.4. Show that if $f(z) = f(-z)$, then the entry I_{12} of the information matrix is 0. Then argue that in this case the mles of a and b are asymptotically independent.

6.4.11. Suppose $X_1, X_2, \ldots, X_n$ are iid $N(\mu, \sigma^2)$. Show that X_i follows a location and scale family as given in Example 6.4.4. Obtain the entries of the information matrix as given in this example and show that they agree with the information matrix determined in Example 6.4.3.

6.5   Multiparameter Case: Testing

In the multiparameter case, hypotheses of interest often specify $\boldsymbol{\theta}$ to be in a subregion of the space. For example, suppose X has a $N(\mu, \sigma^2)$ distribution. The full space is $\Omega = \{(\mu, \sigma^2) : \sigma^2 > 0, -\infty < \mu < \infty\}$. This is a two-dimensional space. We may be interested though in testing that $\mu = \mu_0$, where μ_0 is a specified value. Here we are not concerned about the parameter σ^2. Under H_0, the parameter space is the one-dimensional space $\omega = \{(\mu_0, \sigma^2) : \sigma^2 > 0\}$. We say that H_0 is defined in terms of one constraint on the space Ω.

    In general, let $X_1, \ldots, X_n$ be iid with pdf $f(x; \boldsymbol{\theta})$ for $\boldsymbol{\theta} \in \Omega \subset R^p$. As in the last section, we assume that the regularity conditions listed in (6.1.1), (6.2.1), (6.2.2), and (A.1.1) are satisfied. In this section, we invoke these by the phrase *under regularity conditions.* The hypotheses of interest are

$$H_0 : \boldsymbol{\theta} \in \omega \text{ versus } H_1 : \boldsymbol{\theta} \in \Omega \cap \omega^c, \tag{6.5.1}$$

where $\omega \subset \Omega$ is defined in terms of q, $0 < q \leq p$, independent constraints of the form $g_1(\boldsymbol{\theta}) = a_1, \ldots, g_q(\boldsymbol{\theta}) = a_q$. The functions $g_1, \ldots, g_q$ must be continuously differentiable. This implies that ω is a $(p-q)$-dimensional space. Based on Theorem 6.1.1, the true parameter maximizes the likelihood function, so an intuitive test statistic is given by the likelihood ratio

$$\Lambda = \frac{\max_{\boldsymbol{\theta} \in \omega} L(\boldsymbol{\theta})}{\max_{\boldsymbol{\theta} \in \Omega} L(\boldsymbol{\theta})}. \tag{6.5.2}$$

Large values (close to 1) of Λ suggest that H_0 is true, while small values indicate H_1 is true. For a specified level α, $0 < \alpha < 1$, this suggests the decision rule

$$\text{Reject } H_0 \text{ in favor of } H_1 \text{ if } \Lambda \le c, \tag{6.5.3}$$

where c is such that $\alpha = \max_{\boldsymbol{\theta} \in \omega} P_{\boldsymbol{\theta}}[\Lambda \le c]$. As in the scalar case, this test often has optimal properties; see Section 6.3. To determine c, we need to determine the distribution of Λ or a function of Λ when H_0 is true.

Let $\widehat{\boldsymbol{\theta}}$ denote the maximum likelihood estimator when the parameter space is the full space Ω and let $\widehat{\boldsymbol{\theta}}_0$ denote the maximum likelihood estimator when the parameter space is the reduced space ω. For convenience, define $L(\widehat{\Omega}) = L\left(\widehat{\boldsymbol{\theta}}\right)$ and $L(\widehat{\omega}) = L\left(\widehat{\boldsymbol{\theta}}_0\right)$. Then we can write the **likelihood ratio test (LRT)** statistic as

$$\Lambda = \frac{L(\widehat{\omega})}{L(\widehat{\Omega})}. \tag{6.5.4}$$

Example 6.5.1 (LRT for the Mean of a Normal pdf). Let $X_1, \ldots, X_n$ be a random sample from a normal distribution with mean μ and variance σ^2. Suppose we are interested in testing

$$H_0 : \mu = \mu_0 \text{ versus } H_1 : \mu \ne \mu_0, \tag{6.5.5}$$

where μ_0 is specified. Let $\Omega = \{(\mu, \sigma^2) : -\infty < \mu < \infty, \sigma^2 > 0\}$ denote the full model parameter space. The reduced model parameter space is the one-dimensional subspace $\omega = \{(\mu_0, \sigma^2) : \sigma^2 > 0\}$. By Example 6.4.1, the mles of μ and σ^2 under Ω are $\widehat{\mu} = \overline{X}$ and $\widehat{\sigma}^2 = (1/n) \sum_{i=1}^{n} (X_i - \overline{X})^2$, respectively. Under Ω, the maximum value of the likelihood function is

$$L(\widehat{\Omega}) = \frac{1}{(2\pi)^{n/2}} \frac{1}{(\widehat{\sigma}^2)^{n/2}} \exp\{-(n/2)\}. \tag{6.5.6}$$

Following Example 6.4.1, it is easy to show that under the reduced parameter space ω, $\widehat{\sigma}_0^2 = (1/n) \sum_{i=1}^{n} (X_i - \mu_0)^2$. Thus the maximum value of the likelihood function under ω is

$$L(\widehat{\omega}) = \frac{1}{(2\pi)^{n/2}} \frac{1}{(\widehat{\sigma}_0^2)^{n/2}} \exp\{-(n/2)\}. \tag{6.5.7}$$

The likelihood ratio test statistic is the ratio of $L(\widehat{\omega})$ to $L(\widehat{\Omega})$; i.e,

$$\Lambda = \left(\frac{\sum_{i=1}^{n} (X_i - \overline{X})^2}{\sum_{i=1}^{n} (X_i - \mu_0)^2} \right)^{n/2}. \tag{6.5.8}$$

The likelihood ratio test rejects H_0 if $\Lambda \leq c$, but this is equivalent to rejecting H_0 if $\Lambda^{-2/n} \geq c'$. Next, consider the identity

$$\sum_{i=1}^{n}(X_i - \mu_0)^2 = \sum_{i=1}^{n}(X_i - \overline{X})^2 + n(\overline{X} - \mu_0)^2. \qquad (6.5.9)$$

Substituting (6.5.9) for $\sum_{i=1}^{n}(X_i - \mu_0)^2$, after simplification, the test becomes reject H_0 if

$$1 + \frac{n(\overline{X} - \mu_0)^2}{\sum_{i=1}^{n}(X_i - \overline{X})^2} \geq c',$$

or equivalently, reject H_0 if

$$\left\{ \frac{\sqrt{n}(\overline{X} - \mu_0)}{\sqrt{\sum_{i=1}^{n}(X_i - \overline{X})^2/(n-1)}} \right\}^2 \geq c'' = (c'-1)(n-1).$$

Let T denote the expression within braces on the left side of this inequality. Then the decision rule is equivalent to

$$\text{Reject } H_0 \text{ in favor of } H_1 \text{ if } |T| \geq c^*, \qquad (6.5.10)$$

where $\alpha = P_{H_0}[|T| \geq c^*]$. Of course, this is the two-sided version of the t-test presented in Example 4.5.4. If we take c to be $t_{\alpha/2, n-1}$, the upper $\alpha/2$-critical value of a t-distribution with $n-1$ degrees of freedom, then our test has exact level α. ■

Other examples of likelihood ratio tests for normal distributions can be found in the exercises.

We are not always as fortunate as in Example 6.5.1 to obtain the likelihood ratio test in a simple form. Often it is difficult or perhaps impossible to obtain its finite sample distribution. But, as the next theorem shows, we can always obtain an asymptotic test based on it.

Theorem 6.5.1. *Let $X_1, \ldots, X_n$ be iid with pdf $f(x; \boldsymbol{\theta})$ for $\boldsymbol{\theta} \in \Omega \subset R^p$. Assume the regularity conditions hold. Let $\widehat{\boldsymbol{\theta}}_n$ be a sequence of consistent solutions of the likelihood equation when the parameter space is the full space Ω. Let $\widehat{\boldsymbol{\theta}}_{0,n}$ be a sequence of consistent solutions of the likelihood equation when the parameter space is the reduced space ω, which has dimension $p - q$. Let Λ denote the likelihood ratio test statistic given in (6.5.4). Under H_0, (6.5.1),*

$$-2\log\Lambda \xrightarrow{D} \chi^2(q). \qquad (6.5.11)$$

A proof of this theorem can be found in Rao (1973).

There are analogs of the Wald-type and scores-type tests, also. The Wald-type test statistic is formulated in terms of the constraints, which define H_0, evaluated at the mle under Ω. We do not formally state it here, but as the following example shows, it is often a straightforward formulation. The interested reader can find a discussion of these tests in Lehmann (1999).

A careful reading of the development of this chapter shows that much of it remains the same if X is a random vector. The next example demonstrates this.

Example 6.5.2 (Application of a Multinomial Distribution). As an example, consider a poll for a presidential race with k candidates. Those polled are asked to select the person for which they would vote if the election were held tomorrow. Assuming that those polled are selected independently of one another and that each can select one and only one candidate, the multinomial model seems appropriate. In this problem, suppose we are interested in comparing how the two "leaders" are doing. In fact, say the null hypothesis of interest is that they are equally favorable. This can be modeled with a multinomial model which has the three categories: (1) and (2) for the two leading candidates and (3) for all other candidates. Our observation is a vector (X_1, X_2), where X_i is 1 or 0 depending on whether category i is selected or not. If both are 0, then category (3) has been selected. Let p_i denote the probability that category i is selected. Then the pmf of (X_1, X_2) is the trinomial density,

$$f(x_1, x_2; p_1, p_2) = p_1^{x_1} p_2^{x_2} (1 - p_1 - p_2)^{1 - x_1 - x_2}, \qquad (6.5.12)$$

for $x_i = 0, 1, i = 1, 2; x_1 + x_2 \leq 1$, where the parameter space is $\Omega = \{(p_1, p_2) : 0 < p_i < 1, \ p_1 + p_2 < 1\}$. Suppose $(X_{11}, X_{21}), \ldots, (X_{1n}, X_{2n})$ is a random sample from this distribution. We shall consider the hypotheses

$$H_0 : \ p_1 = p_2 \text{ versus } H_1 : \ p_1 \neq p_2. \qquad (6.5.13)$$

We first derive the likelihood ratio test. Let $T_j = \sum_{i=1}^{n} X_{ji}$ for $j = 1, 2$. From Example 6.4.5, we know that the maximum likelihood estimates are $\widehat{p}_j = T_j / n$, for $j = 1, 2$. The value of the likelihood function (6.4.21) at the mles under Ω is

$$L\left(\hat{\Omega}\right) = \hat{p}_1^{n\hat{p}_1} \hat{p}_2^{n\hat{p}_2} (1 - \hat{p}_1 - \hat{p}_2)^{n(1 - \hat{p}_1 - \hat{p}_2)}.$$

Under the null hypothesis, let p be the common value of p_1 and p_2. The pmf of (X_1, X_2) is

$$f(x_1, x_2; p) = p^{x_1 + x_2} (1 - 2p)^{1 - x_1 - x_2}; \quad x_1, x_2 = 0, 1; x_1 + x_2 \leq 1, \qquad (6.5.14)$$

where the parameter space is $\omega = \{p : 0 < p < 1/2\}$. The likelihood under ω is

$$L(p) = p^{t_1 + t_2} (1 - 2p)^{n - t_1 - t_2}. \qquad (6.5.15)$$

Differentiating $\log L(p)$ with respect to p and setting the derivative to 0 results in the following maximum likelihood estimate, under ω:

$$\widehat{p}_0 = \frac{t_1 + t_2}{2n} = \frac{\widehat{p}_1 + \widehat{p}_2}{2}, \qquad (6.5.16)$$

where $\widehat{p}_1$ and $\widehat{p}_2$ are the mles under Ω. The likelihood function evaluated at the mle under ω simplifies to

$$L\left(\hat{\omega}\right) = \left(\frac{\hat{p}_1 + \hat{p}_2}{2}\right)^{n(\hat{p}_1 + \hat{p}_2)} (1 - \hat{p}_1 - \hat{p}_2)^{n(1 - \hat{p}_1 - \hat{p}_2)}. \qquad (6.5.17)$$

The reciprocal of the likelihood ratio test statistic then simplifies to

$$\Lambda^{-1} = \left(\frac{2\widehat{p_1}}{\widehat{p_1} + \widehat{p_2}} \right)^{n\widehat{p_1}} \left(\frac{2\widehat{p_2}}{\widehat{p_1} + \widehat{p_2}} \right)^{n\widehat{p_2}}. \tag{6.5.18}$$

Based on Theorem 6.5.11, an asymptotic level α test rejects H_0 if $2\log\Lambda^{-1} > \chi_\alpha^2(1)$.

This is an example where the Wald's test can easily be formulated. The constraint under H_0 is $p_1 - p_2 = 0$. Hence, the Wald-type statistic is $W = \widehat{p_1} - \widehat{p_2}$, which can be expressed as $W = [1,-1][\widehat{p_1} ; \widehat{p_2}]'$. Recall that the information matrix and its inverse were found for k categories in Example 6.4.5. From Theorem 6.4.1, we then have

$$\left[\begin{array}{c} \widehat{p_1} \\ \widehat{p_2} \end{array} \right] \text{ is approximately } N_2\left(\left(\begin{array}{c} p_1 \\ p_2 \end{array} \right), \frac{1}{n} \left[\begin{array}{cc} p_1(1-p_1) & -p_1p_2 \\ -p_1p_2 & p_2(1-p_2) \end{array} \right] \right). \tag{6.5.19}$$

As shown in Example 6.4.5, the finite sample moments are the same as the asymptotic moments. Hence the variance of W is

$$\begin{aligned} \text{Var}(W) &= [1,-1]\frac{1}{n} \left[\begin{array}{cc} p_1(1-p_1) & -p_1p_2 \\ -p_1p_2 & p_2(1-p_2) \end{array} \right] \left[\begin{array}{c} 1 \\ -1 \end{array} \right] \\ &= \frac{p_1 + p_2 - (p_1 - p_2)^2}{n}. \end{aligned}$$

Because W is asymptotically normal, an asymptotic level α test for the hypotheses (6.5.13) is to reject H_0 if $\chi_W^2 \geq \chi_\alpha^2(1)$, where

$$\chi_W^2 = \frac{(\widehat{p_1} - \widehat{p_2})^2}{(\widehat{p_1} + \widehat{p_2} - (\widehat{p_1} - \widehat{p_2})^2)/n}.$$

It also follows that an asymptotic $(1-\alpha)100\%$ confidence interval for the difference $p_1 - p_2$ is

$$\widehat{p_1} - \widehat{p_2} \pm z_{\alpha/2} \left(\frac{\widehat{p_1} + \widehat{p_2} - (\widehat{p_1} - \widehat{p_2})^2}{n} \right)^{1/2}.$$

Returning to the polling situation discussed at the beginning of this example, we would say the race is too close to call if 0 is in this confidence interval. ∎

Example 6.5.3 (Two-Sample Binomial Proportions). In Example 6.5.2, we developed tests for $p_1 = p_2$ based on a single sample from a multinomial distribution. Now consider the situation where $X_1, X_2, \ldots, X_{n_1}$ is a random sample from a $b(1, p_1)$ distribution, $Y_1, Y_2, \ldots, Y_{n_2}$ is a random sample from a $b(1, p_2)$ distribution, and the X_is and Y_js are mutually independent. The hypotheses of interest are

$$H_0 : p_1 = p_2 \text{ versus } H_1 : p_1 \neq p_2. \tag{6.5.20}$$

This situation occurs in practice when, for instance, we are comparing the president's rating from one month to the next. The full and reduced model parameter spaces are given respectively by $\Omega = \{(p_1, p_2) : 0 < p_i < 1, i = 1, 2\}$ and $\omega = \{(p, p) : 0 < p < 1\}$. The likelihood function for the full model simplifies to

$$L(p_1, p_2) = p_1^{n_1 \overline{x}} (1 - p_1)^{n_1 - n_1 \overline{x}} p_2^{n_2 \overline{y}} (1 - p_2)^{n_2 - n_2 \overline{y}}. \tag{6.5.21}$$

It follows immediately that the mles of p_1 and p_2 are $\overline{x}$ and $\overline{y}$, respectively. Note, for the reduced model, that we can combine the samples into one large sample from a $b(n, p)$ distribution, where $n = n_1 + n_2$ is the combined sample size. Hence, for the reduced model, the mle of p is

$$\widehat{p} = \frac{\sum_{i=1}^{n_1} x_i + \sum_{i=1}^{n_2} y_i}{n_1 + n_2} = \frac{n_1 \overline{x} + n_2 \overline{y}}{n}, \qquad (6.5.22)$$

i.e., a weighted average of the individual sample proportions. Using this, the reader is asked to derive the LRT for the hypotheses (6.5.20) in Exercise 6.5.9. We next derive the Wald-type test. Let $\widehat{p}_1 = \overline{x}$ and $\widehat{p}_2 = \overline{y}$. From the Central Limit Theorem, we have

$$\frac{\sqrt{n_i}(\widehat{p}_i - p_i)}{\sqrt{p_i(1 - p_i)}} \overset{D}{\to} Z_i, \quad i = 1, 2,$$

where Z_1 and Z_2 are iid $N(0, 1)$ random variables. Assume for $i = 1, 2$ that, as $n \to \infty$, $n_i/n \to \lambda_i$, where $0 < \lambda_i < 1$ and $\lambda_1 + \lambda_2 = 1$. As Exercise 6.5.10 shows,

$$\sqrt{n}[(\widehat{p}_1 - \widehat{p}_2) - (p_1 - p_2)] \overset{D}{\to} N\left(0, \frac{1}{\lambda_1} p_1(1 - p_1) + \frac{1}{\lambda_2} p_2(1 - p_2)\right). \qquad (6.5.23)$$

It follows that the random variable

$$Z = \frac{(\widehat{p}_1 - \widehat{p}_2) - (p_1 - p_2)}{\sqrt{\frac{p_1(1-p_1)}{n_1} + \frac{p_2(1-p_2)}{n_2}}} \qquad (6.5.24)$$

has an approximate $N(0, 1)$ distribution. Under H_0, $p_1 - p_2 = 0$. We could use Z as a test statistic, provided we replace the parameters $p_1(1 - p_1)$ and $p_2(1 - p_2)$ in its denominator with a consistent estimate. Recall that $\widehat{p}_i \to p_i$, $i = 1, 2$, in probability. Thus under H_0, the statistic

$$Z^* = \frac{\widehat{p}_1 - \widehat{p}_2}{\sqrt{\frac{\widehat{p}_1(1-\widehat{p}_1)}{n_1} + \frac{\widehat{p}_2(1-\widehat{p}_2)}{n_2}}} \qquad (6.5.25)$$

has an approximate $N(0, 1)$ distribution. Hence an approximate level α test is to reject H_0 if $|z^*| \geq z_{\alpha/2}$. Another consistent estimator of the denominator is discussed in Exercise 6.5.11. ∎

EXERCISES

6.5.1. In Example 6.5.1 let $n = 10$, and let the experimental value of the random variables yield $\overline{x} = 0.6$ and $\sum_1^{10}(x_i - \overline{x})^2 = 3.6$. If the test derived in that example is used, do we accept or reject $H_0 : \theta_1 = 0$ at the 5% significance level?

6.5.2. Let $X_1, X_2, \ldots, X_n$ be a random sample from the distribution $N(\theta_1, \theta_2)$. Show that the likelihood ratio principle for testing $H_0 : \theta_2 = \theta_2'$ specified, and θ_1 unspecified against $H_1 : \theta_2 \neq \theta_2'$, θ_1 unspecified, leads to a test that rejects when $\sum_1^n(x_i - \overline{x})^2 \leq c_1$ or $\sum_1^n(x_i - \overline{x})^2 \geq c_2$, where $c_1 < c_2$ are selected appropriately.

6.5.3. Let $X_1, \ldots, X_n$ and $Y_1, \ldots, Y_m$ be independent random samples from the distributions $N(\theta_1, \theta_3)$ and $N(\theta_2, \theta_4)$, respectively.

(a) Show that the likelihood ratio for testing $H_0 : \theta_1 = \theta_2$, $\theta_3 = \theta_4$ against all alternatives is given by

$$\frac{\left[\sum_1^n (x_i - \bar{x})^2 / n\right]^{n/2} \cdot \left[\sum_1^m (y_i - \bar{y})^2 / m\right]^{m/2}}{\left\{\left[\sum_1^n (x_i - u)^2 + \sum_1^m (y_i - u)^2\right] \middle/ (m + n)\right\}^{(n+m)/2}},$$

where $u = (n\bar{x} + m\bar{y})/(n + m)$.

(b) Show that the likelihood ratio test for testing $H_0 : \theta_3 = \theta_4$, θ_1 and θ_2 unspecified, against $H_1 : \theta_3 \neq \theta_4$, θ_1 and θ_2 unspecified, can be based on the random variable

$$F = \frac{\sum_1^n (X_i - \bar{X})^2 / (n - 1)}{\sum_1^m (Y_i - \bar{Y})^2 / (m - 1)}.$$

6.5.4. Let $X_1, X_2, \ldots, X_n$ and $Y_1, Y_2, \ldots, Y_m$ be independent random samples from the two normal distributions $N(0, \theta_1)$ and $N(0, \theta_2)$.

(a) Find the likelihood ratio Λ for testing the composite hypothesis $H_0 : \theta_1 = \theta_2$ against the composite alternative $H_1 : \theta_1 \neq \theta_2$.

(b) This Λ is a function of what F-statistic that would actually be used in this test?

6.5.5. Let X and Y be two independent random variables with respective pdfs

$$f(x; \theta_i) = \begin{cases} \left(\frac{1}{\theta_i}\right) e^{-x/\theta_i} & 0 < x < \infty, 0 < \theta_i < \infty \\ 0 & \text{elsewhere,} \end{cases}$$

for $i = 1, 2$. To test $H_0 : \theta_1 = \theta_2$ against $H_1 : \theta_1 \neq \theta_2$, two independent samples of sizes n_1 and n_2, respectively, were taken from these distributions. Find the likelihood ratio Λ and show that Λ can be written as a function of a statistic having an F-distribution, under H_0.

6.5.6. Consider the two uniform distributions with respective pdfs

$$f(x; \theta_i) = \begin{cases} \frac{1}{2\theta_i} & -\theta_i < x < \theta_i, -\infty < \theta_i < \infty \\ 0 & \text{elsewhere,} \end{cases}$$

for $i = 1, 2$. The null hypothesis is $H_0 : \theta_1 = \theta_2$, while the alternative is $H_1 : \theta_1 \neq \theta_2$. Let $X_1 < X_2 < \cdots < X_{n_1}$ and $Y_1 < Y_2 < \cdots < Y_{n_2}$ be the order statistics of two independent random samples from the respective distributions. Using the likelihood ratio Λ, find the statistic used to test H_0 against H_1. Find the distribution of $-2\log\Lambda$ when H_0 is true. Note that in this nonregular case, the number of degrees of freedom is two times the difference of the dimensions of Ω and ω.

6.5.7. Let $(X_1, Y_1), (X_2, Y_2), \ldots, (X_n, Y_n)$ be a random sample from a bivariate normal distribution with $\mu_1, \mu_2, \sigma_1^2 = \sigma_2^2 = \sigma^2, \rho = \frac{1}{2}$, where μ_1, μ_2, and $\sigma^2 > 0$ are unknown real numbers. Find the likelihood ratio Λ for testing $H_0 : \mu_1 = \mu_2 = 0$, σ^2 unknown against all alternatives. The likelihood ratio Λ is a function of what statistic that has a well-known distribution?

6.5.8. Let n independent trials of an experiment be such that $x_1, x_2, \ldots, x_k$ are the respective numbers of times that the experiment ends in the mutually exclusive and exhaustive events $C_1, C_2, \ldots, C_k$. If $p_i = P(C_i)$ is constant throughout the n trials, then the probability of that particular sequence of trials is $L = p_1^{x_1} p_2^{x_2} \cdots p_k^{x_k}$.

(a) Recalling that $p_1 + p_2 + \cdots + p_k = 1$, show that the likelihood ratio for testing $H_0 : p_i = p_{i0} > 0$, $i = 1, 2, \ldots, k$, against all alternatives is given by

$$\Lambda = \prod_{i=1}^{k} \left(\frac{(p_{i0})^{x_i}}{(x_i/n)^{x_i}} \right).$$

(b) Show that

$$-2\log\Lambda = \sum_{i=1}^{k} \frac{x_i(x_i - np_{i0})^2}{(np_i')^2},$$

where p_i' is between p_{i0} and x_i/n.
Hint: Expand $\log p_{i0}$ in a Taylor's series with the remainder in the term involving $(p_{i0} - x_i/n)^2$.

(c) For large n, argue that $x_i/(np_i')^2$ is approximated by $1/(np_{i0})$ and hence

$$-2\log\Lambda \approx \sum_{i=1}^{k} \frac{(x_i - np_{i0})^2}{np_{i0}} \quad \text{when } H_0 \text{ is true.}$$

Theorem 6.5.1 says that the right-hand member of this last equation defines a statistic that has an approximate chi-square distribution with $k - 1$ degrees of freedom. Note that

$$\text{dimension of } \Omega - \text{dimension of } \omega = (k - 1) - 0 = k - 1.$$

6.5.9. Finish the derivation of the LRT found in Example 6.5.3. Simplify as much as possible.

6.5.10. Show that expression (6.5.23) of Example 6.5.3 is true.

6.5.11. As discussed in Example 6.5.3, Z, (6.5.25), can be used as a test statistic provided we have a consistent estimator of $p_1(1-p_1)$ and $p_2(1-p_2)$ when H_0 is true. In the example, we discussed an estimator which is consistent under both H_0 and H_1. Under H_0, though, $p_1(1-p_1) = p_2(1-p_2) = p(1-p)$, where $p = p_1 = p_2$. Show that the statistic (6.5.22) is a consistent estimator of p, under H_0. Thus determine another test of H_0.

6.5.12. A machine shop that manufactures toggle levers has both a day and a night shift. A toggle lever is defective if a standard nut cannot be screwed onto the threads. Let p_1 and p_2 be the proportion of defective levers among those manufactured by the day and night shifts, respectively. We shall test the null hypothesis, $H_0 : p_1 = p_2$, against a two-sided alternative hypothesis based on two random samples, each of 1000 levers taken from the production of the respective shifts. Use the test statistic Z^* given in Example 6.5.3.

(a) Sketch a standard normal pdf illustrating the critical region having $\alpha = 0.05$.

(b) If $y_1 = 37$ and $y_2 = 53$ defectives were observed for the day and night shifts, respectively, calculate the value of the test statistic and the approximate p-value (note that this is a two-sided test). Locate the calculated test statistic on your figure in part (a) and state your conclusion. Obtain the approximate p-value of the test.

6.5.13. For the situation given in part (b) of Exercise 6.5.12, calculate the tests defined in Exercises 6.5.9 and 6.5.11. Obtain the approximate p-values of all three tests. Discuss the results.

6.6 The EM Algorithm

In practice, we are often in the situation where part of the data is missing. For example, we may be observing lifetimes of mechanical parts which have been put on test and some of these parts are still functioning when the statistical analysis is carried out. In this section, we introduce the EM algorithm, which frequently can be used in these situations to obtain maximum likelihood estimates. Our presentation is brief. For further information, the interested reader can consult the literature in this area, including the monograph by McLachlan and Krishnan (1997). Although, for convenience, we write in terms of continuous random variables, the theory in this section holds for the discrete case as well.

Suppose we consider a sample of n items, where n_1 of the items are observed, while $n_2 = n - n_1$ items are not observable. Denote the observed items by $\mathbf{X}' = (X_1, X_2, \ldots, X_{n_1})$ and unobserved items by $\mathbf{Z}' = (Z_1, Z_2, \ldots, Z_{n_2})$. Assume that the X_is are iid with pdf $f(x|\theta)$, where $\theta \in \Omega$. Assume that Z_js and the X_is are mutually independent. The conditional notation will prove useful here. Let $g(\mathbf{x}|\theta)$ denote the joint pdf of $\mathbf{X}$. Let $h(\mathbf{x}, \mathbf{z}|\theta)$ denote the joint pdf of the observed and unobserved items. Let $k(\mathbf{z}|\theta, \mathbf{x})$ denote the conditional pdf of the missing data given the observed data. By the definition of a conditional pdf, we have the identity

$$k(\mathbf{z}|\theta, \mathbf{x}) = \frac{h(\mathbf{x}, \mathbf{z}|\theta)}{g(\mathbf{x}|\theta)}. \tag{6.6.1}$$

The **observed likelihood** function is $L(\theta|\mathbf{x}) = g(\mathbf{x}|\theta)$. The **complete likelihood** function is defined by

$$L^c(\theta|\mathbf{x}, \mathbf{z}) = h(\mathbf{x}, \mathbf{z}|\theta). \tag{6.6.2}$$

Our goal is maximize the likelihood function $L(\theta|\mathbf{x})$ by using the complete likelihood $L^c(\theta|\mathbf{x}, \mathbf{z})$ in this process.

Using (6.6.1), we derive the following basic identity for an arbitrary but fixed $\theta_0 \in \Omega$:

$$
\begin{aligned}
\log L(\theta|\mathbf{x}) &= \int \log L(\theta|\mathbf{x}) k(\mathbf{z}|\theta_0, \mathbf{x}) \, d\mathbf{z} \\[2mm]
&= \int \log g(\mathbf{x}|\theta) k(\mathbf{z}|\theta_0, \mathbf{x}) \, d\mathbf{z} \\[2mm]
&= \int [\log h(\mathbf{x}, \mathbf{z}|\theta) - \log k(\mathbf{z}|\theta, \mathbf{x})] k(\mathbf{z}|\theta_0, \mathbf{x}) \, d\mathbf{z} \\[2mm]
&= \int \log[h(\mathbf{x}, \mathbf{z}|\theta)] k(\mathbf{z}|\theta_0, \mathbf{x}) \, d\mathbf{z} - \int \log[k(\mathbf{z}|\theta, \mathbf{x})] k(\mathbf{z}|\theta_0, \mathbf{x}) \, d\mathbf{z} \\[2mm]
&= E_{\theta_0}[\log L^c(\theta|\mathbf{x}, \mathbf{Z})|\theta_0, \mathbf{x}] - E_{\theta_0}[\log k(\mathbf{Z}|\theta, \mathbf{x})|\theta_0, \mathbf{x}], \tag{6.6.3}
\end{aligned}
$$

where the expectations are taken under the conditional pdf $k(\mathbf{z}|\theta_0, \mathbf{x})$. Define the first term on the right side of (6.6.3) to be the function

$$Q(\theta|\theta_0, \mathbf{x}) = E_{\theta_0}[\log L^c(\theta|\mathbf{x}, \mathbf{Z})|\theta_0, \mathbf{x}]. \tag{6.6.4}$$

The expectation which defines the function Q is called the E step of the EM algorithm. Recall that we want to maximize $\log L(\theta|\mathbf{x})$. As discussed below, we need only maximize $Q(\theta|\theta_0, \mathbf{x})$. This maximization is called the M step of the EM algorithm.

Denote by $\widehat{\theta}^{(0)}$ an initial estimate of θ, perhaps based on the observed likelihood. Let $\widehat{\theta}^{(1)}$ be the argument which maximizes $Q(\theta|\widehat{\theta}^{(0)}, \mathbf{x})$. This is the first-step estimate of θ. Proceeding this way, we obtain a sequence of estimates $\widehat{\theta}^{(m)}$. We formally define this algorithm as follows:

Algorithm 6.6.1 (EM Algorithm). *Let $\widehat{\theta}^{(m)}$ denote the estimate on the mth step. To compute the estimate on the $(m+1)$st step, do*

1. *Expectation Step: Compute*

$$Q(\theta|\widehat{\theta}^{(m)}, \mathbf{x}) = E_{\widehat{\theta}^{(m)}}[\log L^c(\theta|\mathbf{x}, \mathbf{Z})|\widehat{\theta}_m, \mathbf{x}], \tag{6.6.5}$$

   where the expectation is taken under the conditional pdf $k(\mathbf{z}|\widehat{\theta}^{(m)}, \mathbf{x})$.

2. *Maximization Step: Let*

$$\widehat{\theta}^{(m+1)} = Argmax \, Q(\theta|\widehat{\theta}^{(m)}, \mathbf{x}). \tag{6.6.6}$$

Under strong assumptions, it can be shown that $\widehat{\theta}^{(m)}$ converges in probability to the maximum likelihood estimate, as $m \to \infty$. We will not show these results, but as the next theorem shows, $\widehat{\theta}^{(m+1)}$ always increases the likelihood over $\widehat{\theta}^{(m)}$.

Theorem 6.6.1. *The sequence of estimates $\widehat{\theta}^{(m)}$, defined by Algorithm 6.6.1, satisfies*

$$L(\widehat{\theta}^{(m+1)}|\mathbf{x}) \geq L(\widehat{\theta}^{(m)}|\mathbf{x}). \tag{6.6.7}$$

Proof: Because $\widehat{\theta}^{(m+1)}$ maximizes $Q(\theta|\widehat{\theta}^{(m)}, \mathbf{x})$, we have

$$Q(\widehat{\theta}^{(m+1)}|\widehat{\theta}^{(m)}, \mathbf{x}) \geq Q(\widehat{\theta}^{(m)}|\widehat{\theta}^{(m)}, \mathbf{x});$$

that is,

$$E_{\widehat{\theta}^{(m)}}[\log L^c(\widehat{\theta}^{(m+1)}|\mathbf{x}, \mathbf{Z})] \geq E_{\widehat{\theta}^{(m)}}[\log L^c(\widehat{\theta}^{(m)}|\mathbf{x}, \mathbf{Z})], \tag{6.6.8}$$

where the expectation is taken under the pdf $k(\mathbf{z}|\widehat{\theta}^{(m)}, \mathbf{x})$. By expression (6.6.3), we can complete the proof by showing that

$$E_{\widehat{\theta}^{(m)}}[\log k(\mathbf{Z}|\widehat{\theta}^{(m+1)}, \mathbf{x})] \leq E_{\widehat{\theta}^{(m)}}[\log k(\mathbf{Z}|\widehat{\theta}^{(m)}, \mathbf{x})]. \tag{6.6.9}$$

Keep in mind that these expectations are taken under the conditional pdf of $\mathbf{Z}$ given $\widehat{\theta}^{(m)}$ and $\mathbf{x}$. An application of Jensen's inequality, (1.10.5), yields

$$
\begin{aligned}
E_{\widehat{\theta}^{(m)}}\left\{\log\left[\frac{k(\mathbf{Z}|\widehat{\theta}^{(m+1)}, \mathbf{x})}{k(\mathbf{Z}|\widehat{\theta}^{(m)}, \mathbf{x})}\right]\right\} &\leq \log E_{\widehat{\theta}^{(m)}}\left[\frac{k(\mathbf{Z}|\widehat{\theta}^{(m+1)}, \mathbf{x})}{k(\mathbf{Z}|\widehat{\theta}^{(m)}, \mathbf{x})}\right] \\
&= \log \int \frac{k(\mathbf{z}|\widehat{\theta}^{(m+1)}, \mathbf{x})}{k(\mathbf{z}|\widehat{\theta}^{(m)}, \mathbf{x})} k(\mathbf{z}|\widehat{\theta}^{(m)}, \mathbf{x})\, d\mathbf{z} \\
&= \log(1) = 0. \tag{6.6.10}
\end{aligned}
$$

This last result establishes (6.6.9) and, hence, finishes the proof. ∎

As an example, suppose $X_1, X_2, \ldots, X_{n_1}$ are iid with pdf $f(x - \theta)$, for $-\infty < x < \infty$, where $-\infty < \theta < \infty$. Denote the cdf of X_i by $F(x - \theta)$. Let $Z_1, Z_2, \ldots, Z_{n_2}$ denote the censored observations. For these observations, we only know that $Z_j > a$, for some a which is known, and that the Z_js are independent of the X_is. Then the observed and complete likelihoods are given by

$$L(\theta|\mathbf{x}) = [1 - F(a - \theta)]^{n_2} \prod_{i=1}^{n_1} f(x_i - \theta) \tag{6.6.11}$$

$$L^c(\theta|\mathbf{x}, \mathbf{z}) = \prod_{i=1}^{n_1} f(x_i - \theta) \prod_{i=1}^{n_2} f(z_i - \theta). \tag{6.6.12}$$

By expression (6.6.1), the conditional distribution $\mathbf{Z}$ given $\mathbf{X}$ is the ratio of (6.6.12) to (6.6.11); that is,

$$
\begin{aligned}
k(\mathbf{z}|\theta, \mathbf{x}) &= \frac{\prod_{i=1}^{n_1} f(x_i - \theta) \prod_{i=1}^{n_2} f(z_i - \theta)}{[1 - F(a - \theta)]^{n_2} \prod_{i=1}^{n_1} f(x_i - \theta)} \\
&= [1 - F(a - \theta)]^{-n_2} \prod_{i=1}^{n_2} f(z_i - \theta), \quad a < z_i, i = 1, \ldots, n_2. \tag{6.6.13}
\end{aligned}
$$

Thus, $\mathbf{Z}$ and $\mathbf{X}$ are independent, and $Z_1, \ldots, Z_{n_2}$ are iid with the common pdf $f(z - \theta)/[1 - F(a - \theta)]$, for $z > a$. Based on these observations and expression (6.6.13), we have the following derivation:

$$
\begin{aligned}
Q(\theta|\theta_0, \mathbf{x}) &= E_{\theta_0}[\log L^c(\theta|\mathbf{x}, \mathbf{Z})] \\
&= E_{\theta_0}\left[\sum_{i=1}^{n_1} \log f(x_i - \theta) + \sum_{i=1}^{n_2} \log f(Z_i - \theta)\right] \\
&= \sum_{i=1}^{n_1} \log f(x_i - \theta) + n_2 E_{\theta_0}[\log f(Z - \theta)] \\
&= \sum_{i=1}^{n_1} \log f(x_i - \theta) \\
&\quad + n_2 \int_a^\infty \log f(z - \theta) \frac{f(z - \theta_0)}{1 - F(a - \theta_0)} \, dz.
\end{aligned} \tag{6.6.14}
$$

This last result is the E step of the EM algorithm. For the M step, we need the partial derivative of $Q(\theta|\theta_0, \mathbf{x})$ with respect to θ. This is easily found to be

$$
\frac{\partial Q}{\partial \theta} = -\left\{\sum_{i=1}^{n_1} \frac{f'(x_i - \theta)}{f(x_i - \theta)} + n_2 \int_a^\infty \frac{f'(z - \theta)}{f(z - \theta)} \frac{f(z - \theta_0)}{1 - F(a - \theta_0)} \, dz\right\}. \tag{6.6.15}
$$

Assuming that $\theta_0 = \widehat{\theta}_0$, the first-step EM estimate would be the value of θ, say $\widehat{\theta}^{(1)}$, which solves $\frac{\partial Q}{\partial \theta} = 0$. In the next example, we obtain the solution for a normal model.

Example 6.6.1. Assume the censoring model given above, but now assume that X has a $N(\theta, 1)$ distribution. Then $f(x) = \phi(x) = (2\pi)^{-1/2} \exp\{-x^2/2\}$. It is easy to show that $f'(x)/f(x) = -x$. Letting $\Phi(z)$ denote, as usual, the cdf of a standard normal random variable, by (6.6.15) the partial derivative of $Q(\theta|\theta_0, \mathbf{x})$ with respect to θ for this model simplifies to

$$
\begin{aligned}
\frac{\partial Q}{\partial \theta} &= \sum_{i=1}^{n_1}(x_i - \theta) + n_2 \int_a^\infty (z - \theta) \frac{1}{\sqrt{2\pi}} \frac{\exp\{-(z - \theta_0)^2/2\}}{1 - \Phi(a - \theta_0)} \, dz \\
&= n_1(\bar{x} - \theta) + n_2 \int_a^\infty (z - \theta_0) \frac{1}{\sqrt{2\pi}} \frac{\exp\{-(z - \theta_0)^2/2\}}{1 - \Phi(a - \theta_0)} \, dz - n_2(\theta - \theta_0) \\
&= n_1(\bar{x} - \theta) + \frac{n_2}{1 - \Phi(a - \theta_0)} \phi(a - \theta_0) - n_2(\theta - \theta_0).
\end{aligned}
$$

Solving $\partial Q/\partial \theta = 0$ for θ determines the EM step estimates. In particular, given that $\widehat{\theta}^{(m)}$ is the EM estimate on the mth step, the $(m+1)$st step estimate is

$$
\widehat{\theta}^{(m+1)} = \frac{n_1}{n}\bar{x} + \frac{n_2}{n}\widehat{\theta}^{(m)} + \frac{n_2}{n}\frac{\phi(a - \widehat{\theta}^{(m)})}{1 - \Phi(a - \widehat{\theta}^{(m)})}, \tag{6.6.16}
$$

where $n = n_1 + n_2$. ∎

For our second example, consider a mixture problem involving normal distributions. Suppose Y_1 has a $N(\mu_1, \sigma_1^2)$ distribution and Y_2 has a $N(\mu_2, \sigma_2^2)$ distribution. Let W be a Bernoulli random variable independent of Y_1 and Y_2 and with probability of success $\epsilon = P(W = 1)$. Suppose the random variable we observe is $X = (1 - W)Y_1 + WY_2$. In this case, the vector of parameters is given by $\boldsymbol{\theta}' = (\mu_1, \mu_2, \sigma_1, \sigma_2, \epsilon)$. As shown in Section 3.4, the pdf of the mixture random variable X is

$$f(x) = (1 - \epsilon)f_1(x) + \epsilon f_2(x), \quad -\infty < x < \infty, \tag{6.6.17}$$

where $f_j(x) = \sigma_j^{-1}\phi[(x - \mu_j)/\sigma_j]$, $j = 1, 2$, and $\phi(z)$ is the pdf of a standard normal random variable. Suppose we observe a random sample $\mathbf{X}' = (X_1, X_2, \ldots, X_n)$ from this mixture distribution with pdf $f(x)$. Then the log of the likelihood function is

$$l(\boldsymbol{\theta}|\mathbf{x}) = \sum_{i=1}^{n} \log[(1 - \epsilon)f_1(x_i) + \epsilon f_2(x_i)]. \tag{6.6.18}$$

In this mixture problem, the unobserved data are the random variables which identify the distribution membership. For $i = 1, 2, \ldots, n$, define the random variables

$$W_i = \begin{cases} 0 & \text{if } X_i \text{ has pdf } f_1(x) \\ 1 & \text{if } X_i \text{ has pdf } f_2(x). \end{cases}$$

These variables, of course, constitute the random sample on the Bernoulli random variable W. Accordingly, assume that $W_1, W_2, \ldots, W_n$ are iid Bernoulli random variables with probability of success ϵ. The complete likelihood function is

$$L^c(\boldsymbol{\theta}|\mathbf{x}, \mathbf{w}) = \prod_{W_i=0} f_1(x_i) \prod_{W_i=1} f_2(x_i).$$

Hence the log of the complete likelihood function is

$$\begin{aligned} l^c(\boldsymbol{\theta}|\mathbf{x}, \mathbf{w}) &= \sum_{W_i=0} \log f_1(x_i) + \sum_{W_i=1} \log f_2(x_i) \\ &= \sum_{i=1}^{n}[(1 - w_i) \log f_1(x_i) + w_i \log f_2(x_i)]. \tag{6.6.19} \end{aligned}$$

For the E step of the algorithm, we need the conditional expectation of W_i given $\mathbf{x}$ under $\boldsymbol{\theta}_0$; that is,

$$E_{\boldsymbol{\theta}_0}[W_i|\boldsymbol{\theta}_0, \mathbf{x}] = P[W_i = 1|\boldsymbol{\theta}_0, \mathbf{x}].$$

An estimate of this expectation is the likelihood of x_i being drawn from distribution $f_2(x)$, which is given by

$$\gamma_i = \frac{\widehat{\epsilon}f_{2,0}(x_i)}{(1 - \widehat{\epsilon})f_{1,0}(x_i) + \widehat{\epsilon}f_{2,0}(x_i)}, \tag{6.6.20}$$

where the subscript 0 signifies that the parameters at $\boldsymbol{\theta}_0$ are being used. Expression (6.6.20) is intuitively evident; see McLachlan and Krishnan (1997) for more discussion. Replacing w_i by γ_i in expression (6.6.19), the M step of the algorithm is to maximize

$$Q(\boldsymbol{\theta}|\boldsymbol{\theta}_0, \mathbf{x}) = \sum_{i=1}^{n}[(1 - \gamma_i)\log f_1(x_i) + \gamma_i \log f_2(x_i)]. \tag{6.6.21}$$

This maximization is easy to obtain by taking partial derivatives of $Q(\boldsymbol{\theta}|\boldsymbol{\theta}_0, \mathbf{x})$ with respect to the parameters. For example,

$$\frac{\partial Q}{\partial \mu_1} = \sum_{i=1}^{n}(1 - \gamma_i)(-1/2\sigma_1^2)(-2)(x_i - \mu_1).$$

Setting this to 0 and solving for μ_1 yields the estimate of μ_1. The estimates of the other mean and the variances can be obtained similarly. These estimates are

$$\begin{aligned}
\widehat{\mu}_1 &= \frac{\sum_{i=1}^{n}(1 - \gamma_i)x_i}{\sum_{i=1}^{n}(1 - \gamma_i)} \\
\widehat{\sigma}_1^2 &= \frac{\sum_{i=1}^{n}(1 - \gamma_i)(x_i - \widehat{\mu}_1)^2}{\sum_{i=1}^{n}(1 - \gamma_i)} \\
\widehat{\mu}_2 &= \frac{\sum_{i=1}^{n}\gamma_i x_i}{\sum_{i=1}^{n}\gamma_i} \\
\widehat{\sigma}_2^2 &= \frac{\sum_{i=1}^{n}\gamma_i(x_i - \widehat{\mu}_2)^2}{\sum_{i=1}^{n}\gamma_i}.
\end{aligned}$$

Since γ_i is an estimate of $P[W_i = 1|\boldsymbol{\theta}_0, \mathbf{x}]$, the average $n^{-1}\sum_{i=1}^{n}\gamma_i$ is an estimate of $\epsilon = P[W_i = 1]$. This average is our estimate of $\widehat{\epsilon}$.

EXERCISES

6.6.1. Rao (page 368, 1973) considers a problem in the estimation of linkages in genetics. McLachlan and Krishnan (1997) also discuss this problem and we present their model. For our purposes, it can be described as a multinomial model with the four categories C_1, C_2, C_3, and C_4. For a sample of size n, let $\mathbf{X} = (X_1, X_2, X_3, X_4)'$ denote the observed frequencies of the four categories. Hence, $n = \sum_{i=1}^{4} X_i$. The probability model is

C_1	C_2	C_3	C_4
$\frac{1}{2} + \frac{1}{4}\theta$	$\frac{1}{4} - \frac{1}{4}\theta$	$\frac{1}{4} - \frac{1}{4}\theta$	$\frac{1}{4}\theta$

where the parameter θ satisfies $0 \le \theta \le 1$. In this exercise, we obtain the mle of θ.

(a) Show that likelihood function is given by

$$L(\theta|\mathbf{x}) = \frac{n!}{x_1! x_2! x_3! x_4!}\left[\frac{1}{2} + \frac{1}{4}\theta\right]^{x_1}\left[\frac{1}{4} - \frac{1}{4}\theta\right]^{x_2 + x_3}\left[\frac{1}{4}\theta\right]^{x_4}. \tag{6.6.22}$$

(b) Show that the log of the likelihood function can be expressed as a constant (not involving parameters) plus the term

$$x_1 \log[2 + \theta] + [x_2 + x_3] \log[1 - \theta] + x_4 \log \theta.$$

(c) Obtain the partial derivative with respect to θ of the last expression, set the result to 0, and solve for the mle. (This will result in a quadratic equation which has one positive and one negative root.)

6.6.2. In this exercise, we set up an EM algorithm to determine the mle for the situation described in Exercise 6.6.1. Split category C_1 into the two subcategories C_{11} and C_{12} with probabilities $1/2$ and $\theta/4$, respectively. Let Z_{11} and Z_{12} denote the respective "frequencies." Then $X_1 = Z_{11} + Z_{12}$. Of course, we cannot observe Z_{11} and Z_{12}. Let $\mathbf{Z} = (Z_{11}, Z_{12})'$.

(a) Obtain the complete likelihood $L^c(\theta | \mathbf{x}, \mathbf{z})$.

(b) Using the last result and (6.6.22), show that the conditional pmf $k(\mathbf{z} | \theta, \mathbf{x})$ is binomial with parameters x_1 and probability of success $\theta/(2 + \theta)$.

(c) Obtain the E step of the EM algorithm given an initial estimate $\widehat{\theta}^{(0)}$ of θ. That is, obtain

$$Q(\theta | \widehat{\theta}^{(0)}, \mathbf{x}) = E_{\widehat{\theta}^{(0)}}[\log L^c(\theta | \mathbf{x}, \mathbf{Z}) | \widehat{\theta}^{(0)}, \mathbf{x}].$$

Recall that this expectation is taken using the conditional pmf $k(\mathbf{z} | \widehat{\theta}^{(0)}, \mathbf{x})$. Keep in mind the next step; i.e., we need only terms that involve θ.

(d) For the M step of the EM algorithm, solve the equation $\partial Q(\theta | \widehat{\theta}^{(0)}, \mathbf{x})/\partial\theta = 0$. Show that the solution is

$$\widehat{\theta}^{(1)} = \frac{x_1 \widehat{\theta}^{(0)} + 2x_4 + x_4 \widehat{\theta}^{(0)}}{n \widehat{\theta}^{(0)} + 2(x_2 + x_3 + x_4)}. \tag{6.6.23}$$

6.6.3. For the setup of Exercise 6.6.2, show that the following estimator of θ is unbiased:

$$\widetilde{\theta} = n^{-1}(X_1 - X_2 - X_3 + X_4). \tag{6.6.24}$$

6.6.4. Rao (page 368, 1973) presents data for the situation described in Exercise 6.6.1. The observed frequencies are $\mathbf{x} = (125, 18, 20, 34)'$.

(a) Using computational packages (for example, R), with (6.6.24) as the initial estimate, write a program that obtains the stepwise EM estimates $\widehat{\theta}^{(k)}$.

(b) Using the data from Rao, compute the EM estimate of θ with your program. List the sequence of EM estimates, $\{\widehat{\theta}^k\}$, that you obtained. Did your sequence of estimates converge?

(c) Show that the mle using the likelihood approach in Exercise 6.6.1 is the positive root of the equation $197\theta^2 - 15\theta - 68 = 0$. Compare it with your EM solution. They should be the same within roundoff error.

6.6.5. Suppose $X_1, X_2, \ldots, X_{n_1}$ is a random sample from a $N(\theta, 1)$ distribution. Besides these n_1 observable items, suppose there are n_2 missing items, which we denote by $Z_1, Z_2, \ldots, Z_{n_2}$. Show that the first-step EM estimate is

$$\widehat{\theta}^{(1)} = \frac{n_1 \overline{x} + n_2 \widehat{\theta}^{(0)}}{n},$$

where $\widehat{\theta}^{(0)}$ is an initial estimate of θ and $n = n_1 + n_2$. Note that if $\widehat{\theta}^{(0)} = \overline{x}$, then $\widehat{\theta}^{(k)} = \overline{x}$ for all k.

6.6.6. Consider the situation described in Example 6.6.1. But suppose we have left censoring. That is, if $Z_1, Z_2, \ldots, Z_{n_2}$ are the censored items, then all we know is that each $Z_j < a$. Obtain the EM algorithm estimate of θ.

6.6.7. Suppose the following data follow the model of Example 6.6.1.

2.01	0.74	0.68	1.50^+	1.47	1.50^+	1.50^+	1.52
0.07	-0.04	-0.21	0.05	-0.09	0.67	0.14	

where the superscript $^+$ denotes that the observation was censored at 1.50. Write a computer program to obtain the EM algorithm estimate of θ.

6.6.8. The following data are observations of the random variable $X = (1-W)Y_1 + WY_2$, where W has a Bernoulli distribution with probability of success 0.70; Y_1 has a $N(100, 20^2)$ distribution; Y_2 has a $N(120, 25^2)$ distribution; W and Y_1 are independent; and W and Y_2 are independent.

119.0	96.0	146.2	138.6	143.4	98.2	124.5
114.1	136.2	136.4	184.8	79.8	151.9	114.2
145.7	95.9	97.3	136.4	109.2	103.2	

Program the EM algorithm for this mixing problem as discussed at the end of the section. Use a dotplot to obtain initial estimates of the parameters. Compute the estimates. How close are they to the true parameters?

Chapter 7

Sufficiency

7.1 Measures of Quality of Estimators

In Chapters 4 and 6 we presented procedures for finding point estimates, interval estimates, and tests of statistical hypotheses based on likelihood theory. In this and the next chapter, we present some optimal point estimates and tests for certain situations. We first consider point estimation.

In this chapter, as in Chapters 4 and 6, we find it convenient to use the letter f to denote a pmf as well as a pdf. It is clear from the context whether we are discussing the distributions of discrete or continuous random variables.

Suppose $f(x;\theta)$ for $\theta \in \Omega$ is the pdf (pmf) of a continuous (discrete) random variable X. Consider a point estimator $Y_n = u(X_1,\ldots,X_n)$ based on a sample $X_1,\ldots,X_n$. In Chapters 4 and 5, we discussed several properties of point estimators. Recall that Y_n is a consistent estimator (Definition 5.1.2) of θ if Y_n converges to θ in probability; i.e., Y_n is close to θ for large sample sizes. This is definitely a desirable property of a point estimator. Under suitable conditions, Theorem 6.1.3 shows that the maximum likelihood estimator is consistent. Another property was unbiasedness (Definition 4.1.3), which says that Y_n is an unbiased estimator of θ if $E(Y_n) = \theta$. Recall that maximum likelihood estimators may not be unbiased, although generally they are asymptotically unbiased (see Theorem 6.2.2).

If two estimators of θ are unbiased, it would seem that we would choose the one with the smaller variance. This would be especially true if they were both approximately normal because the one with the smaller asymptotic variance (and hence asymptotic standard error) would tend to produce shorter asymptotic confidence intervals for θ. This leads to the following definition:

Definition 7.1.1. *For a given positive integer n, $Y = u(X_1, X_2,\ldots,X_n)$ is called a* **minimum variance unbiased estimator** *(MVUE) of the parameter θ if Y is unbiased, that is, $E(Y) = \theta$, and if the variance of Y is less than or equal to the variance of every other unbiased estimator of θ.*

Example 7.1.1. As an illustration, let $X_1, X_2,\ldots,X_9$ denote a random sample from a distribution that is $N(\theta,\sigma^2)$, where $-\infty < \theta < \infty$. Because the statistic

$\overline{X} = (X_1+X_2+\cdots+X_9)/9$ is $N(\theta, \frac{\sigma^2}{9})$, $\overline{X}$ is an unbiased estimator of θ. The statistic X_1 is $N(\theta, \sigma^2)$, so X_1 is also an unbiased estimator of θ. Although the variance $\frac{\sigma^2}{9}$ of $\overline{X}$ is less than the variance σ^2 of X_1, we cannot say, with $n = 9$, that $\overline{X}$ is the minimum variance unbiased estimator (MVUE) of θ; that definition requires that the comparison be made with every unbiased estimator of θ. To be sure, it is quite impossible to tabulate all other unbiased estimators of this parameter θ, so other methods must be developed for making the comparisons of the variances. A beginning on this problem is made in this chapter. ■

Let us now discuss the problem of point estimation of a parameter from a slightly different standpoint. Let $X_1, X_2, \ldots, X_n$ denote a random sample of size n from a distribution that has the pdf $f(x; \theta)$, $\theta \in \Omega$. The distribution may be of either the continuous or the discrete type. Let $Y = u(X_1, X_2, \ldots, X_n)$ be a statistic on which we wish to base a point estimate of the parameter θ. Let $\delta(y)$ be that function of the observed value of the statistic Y which is the point estimate of θ. Thus the function δ *decides* the value of our point estimate of θ and δ is called a **decision function** or a **decision rule**. One value of the decision function, say $\delta(y)$, is called a *decision*. Thus a numerically determined point estimate of a parameter θ is a decision. Now a decision may be correct or it may be wrong. It would be useful to have a measure of the seriousness of the difference, if any, between the true value of θ and the point estimate $\delta(y)$. Accordingly, with each pair, $[\theta, \delta(y)]$, $\theta \in \Omega$, we associate a nonnegative number $\mathcal{L}[\theta, \delta(y)]$ that reflects this seriousness. We call the function $\mathcal{L}$ the **loss function**. The expected (mean) value of the loss function is called the **risk function**. If $f_Y(y; \theta)$, $\theta \in \Omega$, is the pdf of Y, the risk function $R(\theta, \delta)$ is given by

$$R(\theta, \delta) = E\{\mathcal{L}[\theta, \delta(y)]\} = \int_{-\infty}^{\infty} \mathcal{L}[\theta, \delta(y)] f_Y(y; \theta)\, dy$$

if Y is a random variable of the continuous type. It would be desirable to select a decision function that minimizes the risk $R(\theta, \delta)$ for all values of θ, $\theta \in \Omega$. But this is usually impossible because the decision function δ that minimizes $R(\theta, \delta)$ for one value of θ may not minimize $R(\theta, \delta)$ for another value of θ. Accordingly, we need either to restrict our decision function to a certain class or to consider methods of ordering the risk functions. The following example, while very simple, dramatizes these difficulties.

Example 7.1.2. Let $X_1, X_2, \ldots, X_{25}$ be a random sample from a distribution that is $N(\theta, 1)$, for $-\infty < \theta < \infty$. Let $Y = \overline{X}$, the mean of the random sample, and let $\mathcal{L}[\theta, \delta(y)] = [\theta - \delta(y)]^2$. We shall compare the two decision functions given by $\delta_1(y) = y$ and $\delta_2(y) = 0$ for $-\infty < y < \infty$. The corresponding risk functions are

$$R(\theta, \delta_1) = E[(\theta - Y)^2] = \tfrac{1}{25}$$

and

$$R(\theta, \delta_2) = E[(\theta - 0)^2] = \theta^2.$$

If, in fact, $\theta = 0$, then $\delta_2(y) = 0$ is an excellent decision and we have $R(0, \delta_2) = 0$. However, if θ differs from zero by very much, it is equally clear that $\delta_2 = 0$ is a poor decision. For example, if, in fact, $\theta = 2$, $R(2, \delta_2) = 4 > R(2, \delta_1) = \frac{1}{25}$. In general, we see that $R(\theta, \delta_2) < R(\theta, \delta_1)$, provided that $-\frac{1}{5} < \theta < \frac{1}{5}$, and that otherwise $R(\theta, \delta_2) \geq R(\theta, \delta_1)$. That is, one of these decision functions is better than the other for some values of θ, while the other decision function is better for other values of θ. If, however, we had restricted our consideration to decision functions δ such that $E[\delta(Y)] = \theta$ for all values of θ, $\theta \in \Omega$, then the decision function $\delta_2(y) = 0$ is not allowed. Under this restriction and with the given $\mathcal{L}[\theta, \delta(y)]$, the risk function is the variance of the unbiased estimator $\delta(Y)$, and we are confronted with the problem of finding the MVUE. Later in this chapter we show that the solution is $\delta(y) = y = \overline{x}$.

Suppose, however, that we do not want to restrict ourselves to decision functions δ, such that $E[\delta(Y)] = \theta$ for all values of θ, $\theta \in \Omega$. Instead, let us say that the decision function that minimizes the maximum of the risk function is the best decision function. Because, in this example, $R(\theta, \delta_2) = \theta^2$ is unbounded, $\delta_2(y) = 0$ is not, in accordance with this criterion, a good decision function. On the other hand, with $-\infty < \theta < \infty$, we have

$$\max_{\theta} R(\theta, \delta_1) = \max_{\theta}(\tfrac{1}{25}) = \tfrac{1}{25}.$$

Accordingly, $\delta_1(y) = y = \overline{x}$ seems to be a very good decision in accordance with this criterion because $\frac{1}{25}$ is small. As a matter of fact, it can be proved that δ_1 is the best decision function, as measured by the **minimax criterion**, when the loss function is $\mathcal{L}[\theta, \delta(y)] = [\theta - \delta(y)]^2$. ∎

In this example we illustrated the following:

1. Without some restriction on the decision function, it is difficult to find a decision function that has a risk function which is uniformly less than the risk function of another decision.

2. One principle of selecting a best decision function is called the **minimax principle**. This principle may be stated as follows: If the decision function given by $\delta_0(y)$ is such that, for all $\theta \in \Omega$,

$$\max_{\theta} R[\theta, \delta_0(y)] \leq \max_{\theta} R[\theta, \delta(y)]$$

for every other decision function $\delta(y)$, then $\delta_0(y)$ is called a **minimax decision function**.

With the restriction $E[\delta(Y)] = \theta$ and the loss function $\mathcal{L}[\theta, \delta(y)] = [\theta - \delta(y)]^2$, the decision function that minimizes the risk function yields an unbiased estimator with minimum variance. If, however, the restriction $E[\delta(Y)] = \theta$ is replaced by some other condition, the decision function $\delta(Y)$, if it exists, which minimizes $E\{[\theta - \delta(Y)]^2\}$ uniformly in θ is sometimes called the **minimum mean-squared-error estimator**. Exercises 7.1.6–7.1.8 provide examples of this type of estimator.

There are two additional observations about decision rules and loss functions that should be made at this point. First, since Y is a statistic, the decision rule

$\delta(Y)$ is also a statistic, and we could have started directly with a decision rule based on the observations in a random sample, say, $\delta_1(X_1, X_2, \ldots, X_n)$. The risk function is then given by

$$
\begin{aligned}
R(\theta, \delta_1) &= E\{\mathcal{L}[\theta, \delta_1(X_1, \ldots, X_n)]\} \\
&= \int_{-\infty}^{\infty} \cdots \int_{-\infty}^{\infty} \mathcal{L}[\theta, \delta_1(x_1, \ldots, x_n)] f(x_1; \theta) \cdots f(x_n; \theta) \, dx_1 \cdots dx_n
\end{aligned}
$$

if the random sample arises from a continuous-type distribution. We do not do this, because, as we show in this chapter, it is rather easy to find a good statistic, say Y, upon which to base all of the statistical inferences associated with a particular model. Thus we thought it more appropriate to start with a statistic that would be familiar, like the mle $Y = \overline{X}$ in Example 7.1.2. The second decision rule of that example could be written $\delta_2(X_1, X_2, \ldots, X_n) = 0$, a constant no matter what values of $X_1, X_2, \ldots, X_n$ are observed.

The second observation is that we have only used one loss function, namely, the **squared-error loss function** $\mathcal{L}(\theta, \delta) = (\theta - \delta)^2$. The **absolute-error loss function** $\mathcal{L}(\theta, \delta) = |\theta - \delta|$ is another popular one. The loss function defined by

$$
\begin{aligned}
\mathcal{L}(\theta, \delta) &= 0, \quad |\theta - \delta| \le a, \\
&= b, \quad |\theta - \delta| > a,
\end{aligned}
$$

where a and b are positive constants, is sometimes referred to as the *goalpost loss function*. The reason for this terminology is that football fans recognize that it is similar to kicking a field goal: There is no loss (actually a three-point gain) if within a units of the middle but b units of loss (zero points awarded) if outside that restriction. In addition, loss functions can be asymmetric as well as symmetric, as the three previous ones have been. That is, for example, it might be more costly to underestimate the value of θ than to overestimate it. (Many of us think about this type of loss function when estimating the time it takes us to reach an airport to catch a plane.) Some of these loss functions are considered when studying Bayesian estimates in Chapter 11.

Let us close this section with an interesting illustration that raises a question leading to the likelihood principle, which many statisticians believe is a quality characteristic that estimators should enjoy. Suppose that two statisticians, A and B, observe 10 independent trials of a random experiment ending in success or failure. Let the probability of success on each trial be θ, where $0 < \theta < 1$. Let us say that each statistician observes one success in these 10 trials. Suppose, however, that A had decided to take $n = 10$ such observations in advance and found only one success, while B had decided to take as many observations as needed to get the first success, which happened on the 10th trial. The model of A is that Y is $b(n = 10, \theta)$ and $y = 1$ is observed. On the other hand, B is considering the random variable Z that has a geometric pmf $g(z) = (1-\theta)^{z-1}\theta$, $z = 1, 2, 3, \ldots$, and $z = 10$ is observed. In either case, an estimate of θ could be the relative frequency of success given by

$$
\frac{y}{n} = \frac{1}{z} = \frac{1}{10}.
$$

Let us observe, however, that one of the corresponding estimators, Y/n and $1/Z$, is biased. We have

$$E\left(\frac{Y}{10}\right) = \frac{1}{10}E(Y) = \frac{1}{10}(10\theta) = \theta,$$

while

$$
\begin{aligned}
E\left(\frac{1}{Z}\right) &= \sum_{z=1}^{\infty} \frac{1}{z}(1-\theta)^{z-1}\theta \\
&= \theta + \tfrac{1}{2}(1-\theta)\theta + \tfrac{1}{3}(1-\theta)^2\theta + \cdots > \theta.
\end{aligned}
$$

That is, $1/Z$ is a biased estimator while $Y/10$ is unbiased. Thus A is using an unbiased estimator while B is not. Should we adjust B's estimator so that it, too, is unbiased?

It is interesting to note that if we maximize the two respective likelihood functions, namely,

$$L_1(\theta) = \binom{10}{y}\theta^y(1-\theta)^{10-y}$$

and

$$L_2(\theta) = (1-\theta)^{z-1}\theta,$$

with $n = 10$, $y = 1$, and $z = 10$, we get exactly the same answer, $\hat{\theta} = \frac{1}{10}$. This must be the case, because in each situation we are maximizing $(1-\theta)^9\theta$. Many statisticians believe that this is the way it should be and accordingly adopt the *likelihood principle*:

Suppose two different sets of data from possibly two different random experiments lead to respective likelihood ratios, $L_1(\theta)$ and $L_2(\theta)$, that are proportional to each other. These two data sets provide the same information about the parameter θ and a statistician should obtain the same estimate of θ from either.

In our special illustration, we note that $L_1(\theta) \propto L_2(\theta)$, and the likelihood principle states that statisticians A and B should make the same inference. Thus believers in the likelihood principle would not adjust the second estimator to make it unbiased.

EXERCISES

7.1.1. Show that the mean $\overline{X}$ of a random sample of size n from a distribution having pdf $f(x;\theta) = (1/\theta)e^{-(x/\theta)}$, $0 < x < \infty$, $0 < \theta < \infty$, zero elsewhere, is an unbiased estimator of θ and has variance θ^2/n.

7.1.2. Let $X_1, X_2, \ldots, X_n$ denote a random sample from a normal distribution with mean zero and variance θ, $0 < \theta < \infty$. Show that $\sum_1^n X_i^2/n$ is an unbiased estimator of θ and has variance $2\theta^2/n$.

7.1.3. Let $Y_1 < Y_2 < Y_3$ be the order statistics of a random sample of size 3 from the uniform distribution having pdf $f(x; \theta) = 1/\theta$, $0 < x < \theta$, $0 < \theta < \infty$, zero elsewhere. Show that $4Y_1$, $2Y_2$, and $\frac{4}{3}Y_3$ are all unbiased estimators of θ. Find the variance of each of these unbiased estimators.

7.1.4. Let Y_1 and Y_2 be two independent unbiased estimators of θ. Assume that the variance of Y_1 is twice the variance of Y_2. Find the constants k_1 and k_2 so that $k_1 Y_1 + k_2 Y_2$ is an unbiased estimator with the smallest possible variance for such a linear combination.

7.1.5. In Example 7.1.2 of this section, take $\mathcal{L}[\theta, \delta(y)] = |\theta - \delta(y)|$. Show that $R(\theta, \delta_1) = \frac{1}{5}\sqrt{2/\pi}$ and $R(\theta, \delta_2) = |\theta|$. Of these two decision functions δ_1 and δ_2, which yields the smaller maximum risk?

7.1.6. Let $X_1, X_2, \ldots, X_n$ denote a random sample from a Poisson distribution with parameter θ, $0 < \theta < \infty$. Let $Y = \sum_1^n X_i$ and let $\mathcal{L}[\theta, \delta(y)] = [\theta - \delta(y)]^2$. If we restrict our considerations to decision functions of the form $\delta(y) = b + y/n$, where b does not depend on y, show that $R(\theta, \delta) = b^2 + \theta/n$. What decision function of this form yields a uniformly smaller risk than every other decision function of this form? With this solution, say δ, and $0 < \theta < \infty$, determine $\max_\theta R(\theta, \delta)$ if it exists.

7.1.7. Let $X_1, X_2, \ldots, X_n$ denote a random sample from a distribution that is $N(\mu, \theta)$, $0 < \theta < \infty$, where μ is unknown. Let $Y = \sum_1^n (X_i - \overline{X})^2/n$ and let $\mathcal{L}[\theta, \delta(y)] = [\theta - \delta(y)]^2$. If we consider decision functions of the form $\delta(y) = by$, where b does not depend upon y, show that $R(\theta, \delta) = (\theta^2/n^2)[(n^2 - 1)b^2 - 2n(n-1)b + n^2]$. Show that $b = n/(n+1)$ yields a minimum risk decision function of this form. Note that $nY/(n+1)$ is not an unbiased estimator of θ. With $\delta(y) = ny/(n+1)$ and $0 < \theta < \infty$, determine $\max_\theta R(\theta, \delta)$ if it exists.

7.1.8. Let $X_1, X_2, \ldots, X_n$ denote a random sample from a distribution that is $b(1, \theta)$, $0 \leq \theta \leq 1$. Let $Y = \sum_1^n X_i$ and let $\mathcal{L}[\theta, \delta(y)] = [\theta - \delta(y)]^2$. Consider decision functions of the form $\delta(y) = by$, where b does not depend upon y. Prove that $R(\theta, \delta) = b^2 n\theta(1 - \theta) + (bn - 1)^2\theta^2$. Show that

$$\max_\theta R(\theta, \delta) = \frac{b^4 n^2}{4[b^2 n - (bn - 1)^2]},$$

provided that the value b is such that $b^2 n > (bn - 1)^2$. Prove that $b = 1/n$ does not minimize $\max_\theta R(\theta, \delta)$.

7.1.9. Let $X_1, X_2, \ldots, X_n$ be a random sample from a Poisson distribution with mean $\theta > 0$.

(a) Statistician A observes the sample to be the values $x_1, x_2, \ldots, x_n$ with sum $y = \sum x_i$. Find the mle of θ.

(b) Statistician B loses the sample values $x_1, x_2, \ldots, x_n$ but remembers the sum y_1 and the fact that the sample arose from a Poisson distribution. Thus

B decides to create some fake observations, which he calls $z_1, z_2, \ldots, z_n$ (as he knows they will probably not equal the original x-values) as follows. He notes that the conditional probability of independent Poisson random variables $Z_1, Z_2, \ldots, Z_n$ being equal to $z_1, z_2, \ldots, z_n$, given $\sum z_i = y_1$, is

$$\frac{\frac{\theta^{z_1} e^{-\theta}}{z_1!} \frac{\theta^{z_2} e^{-\theta}}{z_2!} \cdots \frac{\theta^{z_n} e^{-\theta}}{z_n!}}{\frac{(n\theta)^{y_1} e^{-n\theta}}{y_1!}} = \frac{y_1!}{z_1! z_2! \cdots z_n!} \left(\frac{1}{n}\right)^{z_1} \left(\frac{1}{n}\right)^{z_2} \cdots \left(\frac{1}{n}\right)^{z_n}$$

since $Y_1 = \sum Z_i$ has a Poisson distribution with mean $n\theta$. The latter distribution is multinomial with y_1 independent trials, each terminating in one of n mutually exclusive and exhaustive ways, each of which has the same probability $1/n$. Accordingly, B runs such a multinomial experiment y_1 independent trials and obtains $z_1, z_2, \ldots, z_n$. Find the likelihood function using these z-values. Is it proportional to that of statistician A?

Hint: Here the likelihood function is the product of this conditional pdf and the pdf of $Y_1 = \sum Z_i$.

7.2 A Sufficient Statistic for a Parameter

Suppose that $X_1, X_2, \ldots, X_n$ is a random sample from a distribution that has pdf $f(x; \theta)$, $\theta \in \Omega$. In Chapters 4 and 6, we constructed statistics to make statistical inferences as illustrated by point and interval estimation and tests of statistical hypotheses. We note that a statistic, for example, $Y = u(X_1, X_2, \ldots, X_n)$, is a form of data reduction. To illustrate, instead of listing all of the individual observations $X_1, X_2, \ldots, X_n$, we might prefer to give only the sample mean $\overline{X}$ or the sample variance S^2. Thus statisticians look for ways of reducing a set of data so that these data can be more easily understood without losing the meaning associated with the entire set of observations.

It is interesting to note that a statistic $Y = u(X_1, X_2, \ldots, X_n)$ really partitions the sample space of $X_1, X_2, \ldots, X_n$. For illustration, suppose we say that the sample was observed and $\overline{x} = 8.32$. There are many points in the sample space which have that same mean of 8.32, and we can consider them as belonging to the set $\{(x_1, x_2, \ldots, x_n) : \overline{x} = 8.32\}$. As a matter of fact, all points on the hyperplane

$$x_1 + x_2 + \cdots + x_n = (8.32)n$$

yield the mean of $\overline{x} = 8.32$, so this hyperplane is the set. However, there are many values that $\overline{X}$ can take, and thus there are many such sets. So, in this sense, the sample mean $\overline{X}$, or any statistic $Y = u(X_1, X_2, \ldots, X_n)$, partitions the sample space into a collection of sets.

Often in the study of statistics the parameter θ of the model is unknown; thus, we need to make some statistical inference about it. In this section we consider a statistic denoted by $Y_1 = u_1(X_1, X_2, \ldots, X_n)$, which we call a **sufficient statistic** and which we find is good for making those inferences. This sufficient statistic partitions the sample space in such a way that, given

$$(X_1, X_2, \ldots, X_n) \in \{(x_1, x_2, \ldots, x_n) : u_1(x_1, x_2, \ldots, x_n) = y_1\},$$

the conditional probability of $X_1, X_2, \ldots, X_n$ does not depend upon θ. Intuitively, this means that once the set determined by $Y_1 = y_1$ is fixed, the distribution of another statistic, say $Y_2 = u_2(X_1, X_2, \ldots, X_n)$, does not depend upon the parameter θ because the conditional distribution of $X_1, X_2, \ldots, X_n$ does not depend upon θ. Hence it is impossible to use Y_2, given $Y_1 = y_1$, to make a statistical inference about θ. So, in a sense, Y_1 *exhausts* all the information about θ that is contained in the sample. This is why we call $Y_1 = u_1(X_1, X_2, \ldots, X_n)$ a sufficient statistic.

To understand clearly the definition of a sufficient statistic for a parameter θ, we start with an illustration.

Example 7.2.1. Let $X_1, X_2, \ldots, X_n$ denote a random sample from the distribution that has pmf

$$f(x; \theta) = \begin{cases} \theta^x (1-\theta)^{1-x} & x = 0, 1; \quad 0 < \theta < 1 \\ 0 & \text{elsewhere.} \end{cases}$$

The statistic $Y_1 = X_1 + X_2 + \cdots + X_n$ has the pmf

$$f_{Y_1}(y_1; \theta) = \begin{cases} \binom{n}{y_1} \theta^{y_1} (1-\theta)^{n-y_1} & y_1 = 0, 1, \ldots, n \\ 0 & \text{elsewhere.} \end{cases}$$

What is the conditional probability

$$P(X_1 = x_1, \ X_2 = x_2, \ldots, X_n = x_n | Y_1 = y_1) = P(A|B),$$

say, where $y_1 = 0, 1, 2, \ldots, n$? Unless the sum of the integers $x_1, x_2, \ldots, x_n$ (each of which equals zero or 1) is equal to y_1, the conditional probability obviously equals zero because $A \cap B = \phi$. But in the case $y_1 = \sum x_i$, we have that $A \subset B$, so that $A \cap B = A$ and $P(A|B) = P(A)/P(B)$; thus, the conditional probability equals

$$\frac{\theta^{x_1}(1-\theta)^{1-x_1}\theta^{x_2}(1-\theta)^{1-x_2}\cdots\theta^{x_n}(1-\theta)^{1-x_n}}{\binom{n}{y_1}\theta^{y_1}(1-\theta)^{n-y_1}} = \frac{\theta^{\sum x_i}(1-\theta)^{n-\sum x_i}}{\binom{n}{\sum x_i}\theta^{\sum x_i}(1-\theta)^{n-\sum x_i}}$$

$$= \frac{1}{\binom{n}{\sum x_i}}.$$

Since $y_1 = x_1 + x_2 + \cdots + x_n$ equals the number of ones in the n independent trials, this is the conditional probability of selecting a particular arrangement of y_1 ones and $(n - y_1)$ zeros. Note that this conditional probability does *not* depend upon the value of the parameter θ. ■

In general, let $f_{Y_1}(y_1; \theta)$ be the pmf of the statistic $Y_1 = u_1(X_1, X_2, \ldots, X_n)$, where $X_1, X_2, \ldots, X_n$ is a random sample arising from a distribution of the discrete type having pmf $f(x; \theta)$, $\theta \in \Omega$. The conditional probability of $X_1 = x_1$, $X_2 = x_2, \ldots, X_n = x_n$, given $Y_1 = y_1$, equals

$$\frac{f(x_1; \theta)f(x_2; \theta)\cdots f(x_n; \theta)}{f_{Y_1}[u_1(x_1, x_2, \ldots, x_n); \theta]},$$

provided that $x_1, x_2, \ldots, x_n$ are such that the fixed $y_1 = u_1(x_1, x_2, \ldots, x_n)$, and equals zero otherwise. We say that $Y_1 = u_1(X_1, X_2, \ldots, X_n)$ is a *sufficient statistic* for θ if and only if this ratio does not depend upon θ. While, with distributions of the continuous type, we cannot use the same argument, we do, in this case, accept the fact that if this ratio does not depend upon θ, then the conditional distribution of $X_1, X_2, \ldots, X_n$, given $Y_1 = y_1$, does not depend upon θ. Thus, in both cases, we use the same definition of a sufficient statistic for θ.

Definition 7.2.1. *Let $X_1, X_2, \ldots, X_n$ denote a random sample of size n from a distribution that has pdf or pmf $f(x; \theta)$, $\theta \in \Omega$. Let $Y_1 = u_1(X_1, X_2, \ldots, X_n)$ be a statistic whose pdf or pmf is $f_{Y_1}(y_1; \theta)$. Then Y_1 is a **sufficient statistic** for θ if and only if*

$$\frac{f(x_1; \theta) f(x_2; \theta) \cdots f(x_n; \theta)}{f_{Y_1}[u_1(x_1, x_2, \ldots, x_n); \theta]} = H(x_1, x_2, \ldots, x_n),$$

where $H(x_1, x_2, \ldots, x_n)$ does not depend upon $\theta \in \Omega$.

Remark 7.2.1. In most cases in this book, $X_1, X_2, \ldots, X_n$ represent the observations of a random sample; that is, they are iid. It is not necessary, however, in more general situations, that these random variables be independent; as a matter of fact, they do not need to be identically distributed. Thus, more generally, the definition of sufficiency of a statistic $Y_1 = u_1(X_1, X_2, \ldots, X_n)$ would be extended to read that

$$\frac{f(x_1, x_2, \ldots, x_n; \theta)}{f_{Y_1}[u_1(x_1, x_2, \ldots, x_n); \theta)]} = H(x_1, x_2, \ldots, x_n)$$

does not depend upon $\theta \in \Omega$, where $f(x_1, x_2, \ldots, x_n; \theta)$ is the joint pdf or pmf of $X_1, X_2, \ldots, X_n$. There are even a few situations in which we need an extension like this one in this book. ∎

We now give two examples that are illustrative of the definition.

Example 7.2.2. Let $X_1, X_2, \ldots, X_n$ be a random sample from a gamma distribution with $\alpha = 2$ and $\beta = \theta > 0$. Because the mgf associated with this distribution is given by $M(t) = (1 - \theta t)^{-2}$, $t < 1/\theta$, the mgf of $Y_1 = \sum_{i=1}^{n} X_i$ is

$$
\begin{aligned}
E[e^{t(X_1 + X_2 + \cdots + X_n)}] &= E(e^{tX_1}) E(e^{tX_2}) \cdots E(e^{tX_n}) \\
&= [(1 - \theta t)^{-2}]^n = (1 - \theta t)^{-2n}.
\end{aligned}
$$

Thus Y_1 has a gamma distribution with $\alpha = 2n$ and $\beta = \theta$, so that its pdf is

$$f_{Y_1}(y_1; \theta) = \begin{cases} \frac{1}{\Gamma(2n)\theta^{2n}} y_1^{2n-1} e^{-y_1/\theta} & 0 < y_1 < \infty \\ 0 & \text{elsewhere.} \end{cases}$$

Thus we have

$$\frac{\left[\dfrac{x_1^{2-1} e^{-x_1/\theta}}{\Gamma(2)\theta^2}\right] \left[\dfrac{x_2^{2-1} e^{-x_2/\theta}}{\Gamma(2)\theta^2}\right] \cdots \left[\dfrac{x_n^{2-1} e^{-x_n/\theta}}{\Gamma(2)\theta^2}\right]}{\dfrac{(x_1 + x_2 + \cdots + x_n)^{2n-1} e^{-(x_1 + x_2 + \cdots + x_n)/\theta}}{\Gamma(2n)\theta^{2n}}} = \frac{\Gamma(2n)}{[\Gamma(2)]^n} \frac{x_1 x_2 \cdots x_n}{(x_1 + x_2 + \cdots + x_n)^{2n-1}},$$

where $0 < x_i < \infty$, $i = 1, 2, \ldots, n$. Since this ratio does not depend upon θ, the sum Y_1 is a sufficient statistic for θ. ∎

Example 7.2.3. Let $Y_1 < Y_2 < \cdots < Y_n$ denote the order statistics of a random sample of size n from the distribution with pdf

$$f(x; \theta) = e^{-(x-\theta)} I_{(\theta, \infty)}(x).$$

Here we use the indicator function of a set A defined by

$$I_A(x) = \begin{cases} 1 & x \in A \\ 0 & x \notin A. \end{cases}$$

This means, of course, that $f(x; \theta) = e^{-(x-\theta)}$, $\theta < x < \infty$, zero elsewhere. The pdf of $Y_1 = \min(X_i)$ is

$$f_{Y_1}(y_1; \theta) = ne^{-n(y_1-\theta)} I_{(\theta, \infty)}(y_1).$$

Note that $\theta < \min\{x_i\}$ if and only if $\theta < x_i$, for all $i = 1, \ldots, n$. Notationally this can be expressed as $I_{(\theta,\infty)}(\min x_i) = \prod_{i=1}^{n} I_{(\theta,\infty)}(x_i)$. Thus we have that

$$\frac{\prod_{i=1}^{n} e^{-(x_i-\theta)} I_{(\theta,\infty)}(x_i)}{ne^{-n(\min x_i - \theta)} I_{(\theta,\infty)}(\min x_i)} = \frac{e^{-x_1 - x_2 - \cdots - x_n}}{ne^{-n \min x_i}}.$$

Since this ratio does not depend upon θ, the first order statistic Y_1 is a sufficient statistic for θ. ∎

If we are to show by means of the definition that a certain statistic Y_1 is or is not a sufficient statistic for a parameter θ, we must first of all know the pdf of Y_1, say $f_{Y_1}(y_1; \theta)$. In many instances it may be quite difficult to find this pdf. Fortunately, this problem can be avoided if we prove the following **factorization theorem** of Neyman.

Theorem 7.2.1 (Neyman). *Let* $X_1, X_2, \ldots, X_n$ *denote a random sample from a distribution that has pdf or pmf* $f(x; \theta)$, $\theta \in \Omega$. *The statistic* $Y_1 = u_1(X_1, \ldots, X_n)$ *is a sufficient statistic for* θ *if and only if we can find two nonnegative functions,* k_1 *and* k_2, *such that*

$$f(x_1; \theta) f(x_2; \theta) \cdots f(x_n; \theta) = k_1[u_1(x_1, x_2, \ldots, x_n); \theta] k_2(x_1, x_2, \ldots, x_n), \quad (7.2.1)$$

where $k_2(x_1, x_2, \ldots, x_n)$ *does not depend upon* θ.

Proof. We shall prove the theorem when the random variables are of the continuous type. Assume that the factorization is as stated in the theorem. In our proof we shall make the one-to-one transformation $y_1 = u_1(x_1, x_2, \ldots, x_n)$, $y_2 = u_2(x_1, x_2, \ldots, x_n), \ldots, y_n = u_n(x_1, x_2, \ldots, x_n)$ having the inverse functions $x_1 = w_1(y_1, y_2, \ldots, y_n)$, $x_2' = w_2(y_1, y_2, \ldots, y_n), \ldots, x_n = w_n(y_1, y_2, \ldots, y_n)$ and Jacobian J; see the note after the proof. The pdf of the statistic $Y_1, Y_2, \ldots, Y_n$ is then given by

$$g(y_1, y_2, \ldots, y_n; \theta) = k_1(y_1; \theta) k_2(w_1, w_2, \ldots, w_n)|J|,$$

where $w_i = w_i(y_1, y_2, \ldots, y_n)$, $i = 1, 2, \ldots, n$. The pdf of Y_1, say $f_{Y_1}(y_1; \theta)$, is given by

$$
\begin{aligned}
f_{Y_1}(y_1; \theta) &= \int_{-\infty}^{\infty} \cdots \int_{-\infty}^{\infty} g(y_1, y_2, \ldots, y_n; \theta)\, dy_2 \cdots dy_n \\
&= k_1(y_1; \theta) \int_{-\infty}^{\infty} \cdots \int_{-\infty}^{\infty} |J| k_2(w_1, w_2, \ldots, w_n)\, dy_2 \cdots dy_n.
\end{aligned}
$$

Now the function k_2 does not depend upon θ, nor is θ involved in either the Jacobian J or the limits of integration. Hence the $(n-1)$-fold integral in the right-hand member of the preceding equation is a function of y_1 alone, for example, $m(y_1)$. Thus

$$
f_{Y_1}(y_1; \theta) = k_1(y_1; \theta) m(y_1).
$$

If $m(y_1) = 0$, then $f_{Y_1}(y_1; \theta) = 0$. If $m(y_1) > 0$, we can write

$$
k_1[u_1(x_1, x_2, \ldots, x_n); \theta] = \frac{f_{Y_1}[u_1(x_1, \ldots, x_n); \theta]}{m[u_1(x_1, \ldots, x_n)]},
$$

and the assumed factorization becomes

$$
f(x_1; \theta) \cdots f(x_n; \theta) = f_{Y_1}[u_1(x_1, \ldots, x_n); \theta] \frac{k_2(x_1, \ldots, x_n)}{m[u_1(x_1, \ldots, x_n)]}.
$$

Since neither the function k_2 nor the function m depends upon θ, then in accordance with the definition, Y_1 is a sufficient statistic for the parameter θ.

Conversely, if Y_1 is a sufficient statistic for θ, the factorization can be realized by taking the function k_1 to be the pdf of Y_1, namely, the function f_{Y_1}. This completes the proof of the theorem. ■

Note that the assumption of a one-to-one transformation made in the proof is not needed; see Lehmann (1986) for a more rigorous prrof. This theorem characterizes sufficiency and, as the following examples show, is usually much easier to work with than the definition of sufficiency.

Example 7.2.4. Let $X_1, X_2, \ldots, X_n$ denote a random sample from a distribution that is $N(\theta, \sigma^2)$, $-\infty < \theta < \infty$, where the variance $\sigma^2 > 0$ is known. If $\bar{x} = \sum_1^n x_i / n$, then

$$
\sum_{i=1}^{n}(x_i - \theta)^2 = \sum_{i=1}^{n}[(x_i - \bar{x}) + (\bar{x} - \theta)]^2 = \sum_{i=1}^{n}(x_i - \bar{x})^2 + n(\bar{x} - \theta)^2
$$

because

$$
2\sum_{i=1}^{n}(x_i - \bar{x})(\bar{x} - \theta) = 2(\bar{x} - \theta)\sum_{i=1}^{n}(x_i - \bar{x}) = 0.
$$

Thus the joint pdf of $X_1, X_2, \ldots, X_n$ may be written

$$\left(\frac{1}{\sigma\sqrt{2\pi}}\right)^n \exp\left[-\sum_{i=1}^{n}(x_i-\theta)^2/2\sigma^2\right]$$

$$= \{\exp[-n(\bar{x}-\theta)^2/2\sigma^2]\}\left\{\frac{\exp\left[-\sum_{i=1}^{n}(x_i-\bar{x})^2/2\sigma^2\right]}{(\sigma\sqrt{2\pi})^n}\right\}.$$

Because the first factor of the right-hand member of this equation depends upon $x_1, x_2, \ldots, x_n$ only through $\bar{x}$, and the second factor does not depend upon θ, the factorization theorem implies that the mean $\overline{X}$ of the sample is, for any particular value of σ^2, a sufficient statistic for θ, the mean of the normal distribution. ∎

We could have used the definition in the preceding example because we know that $\overline{X}$ is $N(\theta, \sigma^2/n)$. Let us now consider an example in which the use of the definition is inappropriate.

Example 7.2.5. Let $X_1, X_2, \ldots, X_n$ denote a random sample from a distribution with pdf

$$f(x;\theta) = \begin{cases} \theta x^{\theta-1} & 0 < x < 1 \\ 0 & \text{elsewhere,} \end{cases}$$

where $0 < \theta$. By the factorization theorem, $u_1(X_1, X_2, \ldots, X_n) = \prod_{i=1}^{n} X_i$ is a sufficient statistic for θ. The joint pdf of $X_1, X_2, \ldots, X_n$ is

$$\theta^n\left(\prod_{i=1}^{n} x_i\right)^{\theta-1} = \left[\theta^n\left(\prod_{i=1}^{n} x_i\right)^{\theta}\right]\left(\frac{1}{\prod_{i=1}^{n} x_i}\right),$$

where $0 < x_i < 1$, $i = 1, 2, \ldots, n$. In the factorization theorem, let

$$k_1[u_1(x_1, x_2, \ldots, x_n); \theta] = \theta^n\left(\prod_{i=1}^{n} x_i\right)^{\theta}$$

and

$$k_2(x_1, x_2, \ldots, x_n) = \frac{1}{\prod_{i=1}^{n} x_i}.$$

Since $k_2(x_1, x_2, \ldots, x_n)$ does not depend upon θ, the product $\prod_{i=1}^{n} X_i$ is a sufficient statistic for θ. ∎

There is a tendency for some readers to apply incorrectly the factorization theorem in those instances in which the domain of positive probability density depends upon the parameter θ. This is due to the fact that they do not give proper consideration to the domain of the function $k_2(x_1, x_2, \ldots, x_n)$. This is illustrated in the next example.

Example 7.2.6. In Example 7.2.3 with $f(x; \theta) = e^{-(x-\theta)} I_{(\theta,\infty)}(x)$, it was found that the first order statistic Y_1 is a sufficient statistic for θ. To illustrate our point about not considering the domain of the function, take $n = 3$ and note that

$$e^{-(x_1-\theta)} e^{-(x_2-\theta)} e^{-(x_3-\theta)} = [e^{-3\max x_i + 3\theta}][e^{-x_1-x_2-x_3+3\max x_i}]$$

or a similar expression. Certainly, in the latter formula, there is no θ in the second factor and it might be assumed that $Y_3 = \max X_i$ is a sufficient statistic for θ. Of course, this is incorrect because we should have written the joint pdf of X_1, X_2, X_3 as

$$\prod_{i=1}^{3} [e^{-(x_i-\theta)} I_{(\theta,\infty)}(x_i)] = [e^{3\theta} I_{(\theta,\infty)}(\min x_i)] \left[\exp\left\{ -\sum_{i=1}^{3} x_i \right\} \right]$$

because $I_{(\theta,\infty)}(\min x_i) = I_{(\theta,\infty)}(x_1) I_{(\theta,\infty)}(x_2) I_{(\theta,\infty)}(x_3)$. A similar statement cannot be made with $\max x_i$. Thus $Y_1 = \min X_i$ is the sufficient statistic for θ, not $Y_3 = \max X_i$. ∎

EXERCISES

7.2.1. Let $X_1, X_2, \ldots, X_n$ be iid $N(0, \theta)$, $0 < \theta < \infty$. Show that $\sum_1^n X_i^2$ is a sufficient statistic for θ.

7.2.2. Prove that the sum of the observations of a random sample of size n from a Poisson distribution having parameter θ, $0 < \theta < \infty$, is a sufficient statistic for θ.

7.2.3. Show that the nth order statistic of a random sample of size n from the uniform distribution having pdf $f(x; \theta) = 1/\theta$, $0 < x < \theta$, $0 < \theta < \infty$, zero elsewhere, is a sufficient statistic for θ. Generalize this result by considering the pdf $f(x; \theta) = Q(\theta) M(x)$, $0 < x < \theta$, $0 < \theta < \infty$, zero elsewhere. Here, of course,

$$\int_0^\theta M(x)\, dx = \frac{1}{Q(\theta)}.$$

7.2.4. Let $X_1, X_2, \ldots, X_n$ be a random sample of size n from a geometric distribution that has pmf $f(x; \theta) = (1-\theta)^x \theta$, $x = 0, 1, 2, \ldots$, $0 < \theta < 1$, zero elsewhere. Show that $\sum_1^n X_i$ is a sufficient statistic for θ.

7.2.5. Show that the sum of the observations of a random sample of size n from a gamma distribution that has pdf $f(x; \theta) = (1/\theta) e^{-x/\theta}$, $0 < x < \infty$, $0 < \theta < \infty$, zero elsewhere, is a sufficient statistic for θ.

7.2.6. Let $X_1, X_2, \ldots, X_n$ be a random sample of size n from a beta distribution with parameters $\alpha = \theta$ and $\beta = 5$. Show that the product $X_1 X_2 \cdots X_n$ is a sufficient statistic for θ.

7.2.7. Show that the product of the sample observations is a sufficient statistic for $\theta > 0$ if the random sample is taken from a gamma distribution with parameters $\alpha = \theta$ and $\beta = 6$.

7.2.8. What is the sufficient statistic for θ if the sample arises from a beta distribution in which $\alpha = \beta = \theta > 0$?

7.2.9. We consider a random sample $X_1, X_2, \ldots, X_n$ from a distribution with pdf $f(x; \theta) = (1/\theta) \exp(-x/\theta)$, $0 < x < \infty$, zero elsewhere, where $0 < \theta$. Possibly, in a life-testing situation, however, we only observe the first r order statistics $Y_1 < Y_2 < \cdots < Y_r$.

  (a) Record the joint pdf of these order statistics and denote it by $L(\theta)$.

  (b) Under these conditions, find the mle, $\hat{\theta}$, by maximizing $L(\theta)$.

  (c) Find the mgf and pdf of $\hat{\theta}$.

  (d) With a slight extension of the definition of sufficiency, is $\hat{\theta}$ a sufficient statistic?

7.3   Properties of a Sufficient Statistic

Suppose $X_1, X_2, \ldots, X_n$ is a random sample on a random variable with pdf or pmf $f(x; \theta)$, where $\theta \in \Omega$. In this section we discuss how sufficiency is used to determine MVUEs. First note that a sufficient estimate is not unique in any sense. For if $Y_1 = u_1(X_1, X_2, \ldots, X_n)$ is a sufficient statistic and $Y_2 = g(Y_1)$, where $g(x)$ is a one-to-one function, is a statistic, then

$$
\begin{aligned}
f(x_1; \theta)f(x_2; \theta) \cdots f(x_n; \theta) &= k_1[u_1(y_1); \theta]k_2(x_1, x_2, \ldots, x_n) \\
&= k_1[u_1(g^{-1}(y_2)); \theta]k_2(x_1, x_2, \ldots, x_n);
\end{aligned}
$$

hence, by the factorization theorem, Y_2 is also sufficient. However, as the theorem below shows, sufficiency can lead to a best point estimate.

We first refer back to Theorem 2.3.1 of Section 2.3: If X_1 and X_2 are random variables such that the variance of X_2 exists, then

$$
E[X_2] = E[E(X_2|X_1)]
$$

and

$$
\mathrm{Var}(X_2) \geq \mathrm{Var}[E(X_2|X_1)].
$$

For the adaptation in the context of sufficient statistics, we let the sufficient statistic Y_1 be X_1 and Y_2, an unbiased statistic of θ, be X_2. Thus, with $E(Y_2|y_1) = \varphi(y_1)$, we have

$$
\theta = E(Y_2) = E[\varphi(Y_1)]
$$

and

$$
\mathrm{Var}(Y_2) \geq \mathrm{Var}[\varphi(Y_1)].
$$

That is, through this conditioning, the function $\varphi(Y_1)$ of the sufficient statistic Y_1 is an unbiased estimator of θ having a smaller variance than that of the unbiased estimator Y_2. We summarize this discussion more formally in the following theorem, which can be attributed to Rao and Blackwell.

Theorem 7.3.1 (Rao–Blackwell). *Let $X_1, X_2, \ldots, X_n$, n a fixed positive integer, denote a random sample from a distribution (continuous or discrete) that has pdf or pmf $f(x; \theta)$, $\theta \in \Omega$. Let $Y_1 = u_1(X_1, X_2, \ldots, X_n)$ be a sufficient statistic for θ, and let $Y_2 = u_2(X_1, X_2, \ldots, X_n)$, not a function of Y_1 alone, be an unbiased estimator of θ. Then $E(Y_2|y_1) = \varphi(y_1)$ defines a statistic $\varphi(Y_1)$. This statistic $\varphi(Y_1)$ is a function of the sufficient statistic for θ; it is an unbiased estimator of θ; and its variance is less than or equal to that of Y_2.*

This theorem tells us that in our search for an MVUE of a parameter, we may, if a sufficient statistic for the parameter exists, restrict that search to functions of the sufficient statistic. For if we begin with an unbiased estimator Y_2 alone, then we can always improve on this by computing $E(Y_2|y_1) = \varphi(y_1)$ so that $\varphi(Y_1)$ is an unbiased estimator with a smaller variance than that of Y_2.

After Theorem 7.3.1, many students believe that it is necessary to find first some unbiased estimator Y_2 in their search for $\varphi(Y_1)$, an unbiased estimator of θ based upon the sufficient statistic Y_1. This is not the case at all, and Theorem 7.3.1 simply convinces us that we can restrict our search for a best estimator to functions of Y_1. Furthermore, there is a connection between sufficient statistics and maximum likelihood estimates, as shown in the following theorem:

Theorem 7.3.2. *Let $X_1, X_2, \ldots, X_n$ denote a random sample from a distribution that has pdf or pmf $f(x; \theta)$, $\theta \in \Omega$. If a sufficient statistic $Y_1 = u_1(X_1, X_2, \ldots, X_n)$ for θ exists and if a maximum likelihood estimator $\hat{\theta}$ of θ also exists uniquely, then $\hat{\theta}$ is a function of $Y_1 = u_1(X_1, X_2, \ldots, X_n)$.*

Proof. Let $f_{Y_1}(y_1; \theta)$ be the pdf or pmf of Y_1. Then by the definition of sufficiency, the likelihood function

$$
\begin{aligned}
L(\theta; x_1, x_2, \ldots, x_n) &= f(x_1; \theta) f(x_2; \theta) \cdots f(x_n; \theta) \\
&= f_{Y_1}[u_1(x_1, x_2, \ldots, x_n); \theta] H(x_1, x_2, \ldots, x_n),
\end{aligned}
$$

where $H(x_1, x_2, \ldots, x_n)$ does not depend upon θ. Thus L and f_{Y_1}, as functions of θ, are maximized simultaneously. Since there is one and only one value of θ that maximizes L and hence $f_{Y_1}[u_1(x_1, x_2, \ldots, x_n); \theta]$, that value of θ must be a function of $u_1(x_1, x_2, \ldots, x_n)$. Thus the mle $\hat{\theta}$ is a function of the sufficient statistic $Y_1 = u_1(X_1, X_2, \ldots, X_n)$. ∎

We know from Chapters 4 and 6 that, generally, mles are asymptotically unbiased estimators of θ. Hence, one way to proceed is to find a sufficient statistic and then find the mle. Based on this, we can often obtain an unbiased estimator which is a function of the sufficient statistic. This process is illustrated in the following example.

Example 7.3.1. Let $X_1, \ldots, X_n$ be iid with pdf

$$f(x; \theta) = \begin{cases} \theta e^{-\theta x} & 0 < x < \infty, \ \theta > 0 \\ 0 & \text{elsewhere.} \end{cases}$$

Suppose we want an MVUE of θ. The joint pdf (likelihood function) is

$$L(\theta; x_1, \ldots, x_n) = \theta^n e^{-\theta \sum_{i=1}^n x_i}, \quad \text{for } x_i > 0, \ i = 1, \ldots, n.$$

Hence, by the factorization theorem, the statistic $Y_1 = \sum_{i=1}^n X_i$ is sufficient. The log of the likelihood function is

$$l(\theta) = n \log \theta - \theta \sum_{i=1}^n x_i.$$

Taking the partial with respect to θ of $l(\theta)$ and setting it to 0 results in the mle of θ, which is given by

$$Y_2 = \frac{1}{\overline{X}}.$$

Note that $Y_2 = n/Y_1$ is a function of the sufficient statistic Y_1. Also, since Y_2 is the mle of θ, it is asymptotically unbiased. Hence, as a first step, we shall determine its expectation. In this problem, X_i are iid $\Gamma(1, 1/\theta)$ random variables; hence, $Y_1 = \sum_{i=1}^n X_i$ is $\Gamma(n, 1/\theta)$. Therefore,

$$E(Y_2) = E\left[\frac{1}{\overline{X}}\right] = nE\left[\frac{1}{\sum_{i=1}^n X_i}\right] = n \int_0^\infty \frac{\theta^n}{\Gamma(n)} t^{-1} t^{n-1} e^{-\theta t} \, dt;$$

making the change of variable $z = \theta t$ and simplifying results in

$$E(Y_2) = E\left[\frac{1}{\overline{X}}\right] = \theta \frac{n}{(n-1)!} \Gamma(n-1) = \theta \frac{n}{n-1}.$$

Thus the statistic $[(n-1)Y_2]/n = (n-1)/\sum_{i=1}^n X_i$ is an MVUE of θ. ∎

In the next two sections, we discover that, in most instances, if there is one function $\varphi(Y_1)$ that is unbiased, $\varphi(Y_1)$ is the only unbiased estimator based on the sufficient statistic Y_1.

Remark 7.3.1. Since the unbiased estimator $\varphi(Y_1)$, where $\varphi(Y_1) = E(Y_2|y_1)$, has a variance smaller than that of the unbiased estimator Y_2 of θ, students sometimes reason as follows. Let the function $\Upsilon(y_3) = E[\varphi(Y_1)|Y_3 = y_3]$, where Y_3 is another statistic, which is not sufficient for θ. By the Rao–Blackwell theorem, we have $E[\Upsilon(Y_3)] = \theta$ and $\Upsilon(Y_3)$ has a smaller variance than does $\varphi(Y_1)$. Accordingly, $\Upsilon(Y_3)$ must be better than $\varphi(Y_1)$ as an unbiased estimator of θ. But this is *not* true, because Y_3 is not sufficient; thus, θ is present in the conditional distribution of Y_1, given $Y_3 = y_3$, and the conditional mean $\Upsilon(y_3)$. So although indeed $E[\Upsilon(Y_3)] = \theta$, $\Upsilon(Y_3)$ is not even a statistic because it involves the unknown parameter θ and hence cannot be used as an estimate. ∎

Example 7.3.2. Let X_1, X_2, X_3 be a random sample from an exponential distribution with mean $\theta > 0$, so that the joint pdf is

$$\left(\frac{1}{\theta}\right)^3 e^{-(x_1+x_2+x_3)/\theta}, \quad 0 < x_i < \infty,$$

$i = 1, 2, 3$, zero elsewhere. From the factorization theorem, we see that $Y_1 = X_1 + X_2 + X_3$ is a sufficient statistic for θ. Of course,

$$E(Y_1) = E(X_1 + X_2 + X_3) = 3\theta,$$

and thus $Y_1/3 = \overline{X}$ is a function of the sufficient statistic that is an unbiased estimator of θ.

In addition, let $Y_2 = X_2 + X_3$ and $Y_3 = X_3$. The one-to-one transformation defined by

$$x_1 = y_1 - y_2, \quad x_2 = y_2 - y_3, \quad x_3 = y_3$$

has Jacobian equal to 1 and the joint pdf of Y_1, Y_2, Y_3 is

$$g(y_1, y_2, y_3; \theta) = \left(\frac{1}{\theta}\right)^3 e^{-y_1/\theta}, \quad 0 < y_3 < y_2 < y_1 < \infty,$$

zero elsewhere. The marginal pdf of Y_1 and Y_3 is found by integrating out y_2 to obtain

$$g_{13}(y_1, y_3; \theta) = \left(\frac{1}{\theta}\right)^3 (y_1 - y_3)e^{-y_1/\theta}, \quad 0 < y_3 < y_1 < \infty,$$

zero elsewhere. The pdf of Y_3 alone is

$$g_3(y_3; \theta) = \frac{1}{\theta}e^{-y_3/\theta}, \quad 0 < y_3 < \infty,$$

zero elsewhere, since $Y_3 = X_3$ is an observation of a random sample from this exponential distribution.

Accordingly, the conditional pdf of Y_1, given $Y_3 = y_3$, is

$$
\begin{aligned}
g_{1|3}(y_1|y_3) &= \frac{g_{13}(y_1, y_3; \theta)}{g_3(y_3; \theta)} \\
&= \left(\frac{1}{\theta}\right)^2 (y_1 - y_3)e^{-(y_1-y_3)/\theta}, \quad 0 < y_3 < y_1 < \infty,
\end{aligned}
$$

zero elsewhere. Thus

$$
\begin{aligned}
E\left(\frac{Y_1}{3}\middle| y_3\right) &= E\left(\frac{Y_1 - Y_3}{3}\middle| y_3\right) + E\left(\frac{Y_3}{3}\middle| y_3\right) \\
&= \left(\frac{1}{3}\right)\int_{y_3}^{\infty} \left(\frac{1}{\theta}\right)^2 (y_1 - y_3)^2 e^{-(y_1-y_3)/\theta}\, dy_1 + \frac{y_3}{3} \\
&= \left(\frac{1}{3}\right)\frac{\Gamma(3)\theta^3}{\theta^2} + \frac{y_3}{3} = \frac{2\theta}{3} + \frac{y_3}{3} = \Upsilon(y_3).
\end{aligned}
$$

Of course, $E[\Upsilon(Y_3)] = \theta$ and $\text{var}[\Upsilon(Y_3)] \leq \text{var}(Y_1/3)$, but $\Upsilon(Y_3)$ is not a statistic, as it involves θ and cannot be used as an estimator of θ. This illustrates the preceding remark. ∎

EXERCISES

7.3.1. In each of Exercises 7.2.1–7.2.4, show that the mle of θ is a function of the sufficient statistic for θ.

7.3.2. Let $Y_1 < Y_2 < Y_3 < Y_4 < Y_5$ be the order statistics of a random sample of size 5 from the uniform distribution having pdf $f(x; \theta) = 1/\theta$, $0 < x < \theta$, $0 < \theta < \infty$, zero elsewhere. Show that $2Y_3$ is an unbiased estimator of θ. Determine the joint pdf of Y_3 and the sufficient statistic Y_5 for θ. Find the conditional expectation $E(2Y_3|y_5) = \varphi(y_5)$. Compare the variances of $2Y_3$ and $\varphi(Y_5)$.

7.3.3. If X_1, X_2 is a random sample of size 2 from a distribution having pdf $f(x; \theta) = (1/\theta)e^{-x/\theta}$, $0 < x < \infty$, $0 < \theta < \infty$, zero elsewhere, find the joint pdf of the sufficient statistic $Y_1 = X_1 + X_2$ for θ and $Y_2 = X_2$. Show that Y_2 is an unbiased estimator of θ with variance θ^2. Find $E(Y_2|y_1) = \varphi(y_1)$ and the variance of $\varphi(Y_1)$.

7.3.4. Let $f(x, y) = (2/\theta^2)e^{-(x+y)/\theta}$, $0 < x < y < \infty$, zero elsewhere, be the joint pdf of the random variables X and Y.

 (a) Show that the mean and the variance of Y are, respectively, $3\theta/2$ and $5\theta^2/4$.

 (b) Show that $E(Y|x) = x + \theta$. In accordance with the theory, the expected value of $X + \theta$ is that of Y, namely, $3\theta/2$, and the variance of $X + \theta$ is less than that of Y. Show that the variance of $X + \theta$ is in fact $\theta^2/4$.

7.3.5. In each of Exercises 7.2.1–7.2.3, compute the expected value of the given sufficient statistic and, in each case, determine an unbiased estimator of θ that is a function of that sufficient statistic alone.

7.3.6. Let $X_1, X_2, \ldots, X_n$ be a random sample from a Poisson distribution with mean θ. Find the conditional expectation $E(X_1 + 2X_2 + 3X_3 \mid \sum_1^n X_i)$.

7.4 Completeness and Uniqueness

Let $X_1, X_2, \ldots, X_n$ be a random sample from the Poisson distribution that has pmf

$$f(x; \theta) = \begin{cases} \frac{\theta^x e^{-\theta}}{x!} & x = 0, 1, 2, \ldots; \ \theta > 0 \\ 0 & \text{elsewhere.} \end{cases}$$

From Exercise 7.2.2, we know that $Y_1 = \sum_{i=1}^{n} X_i$ is a sufficient statistic for θ and its pmf is

$$g_1(y_1; \theta) = \begin{cases} \frac{(n\theta)^{y_1} e^{-n\theta}}{y_1!} & y_1 = 0, 1, 2, \ldots \\ 0 & \text{elsewhere.} \end{cases}$$

Let us consider the family $\{g_1(y_1; \theta) : \theta > 0\}$ of probability mass functions. Suppose that the function $u(Y_1)$ of Y_1 is such that $E[u(Y_1)] = 0$ for every $\theta > 0$. We shall show that this requires $u(y_1)$ to be zero at every point $y_1 = 0, 1, 2, \ldots$. That is, $E[u(Y_1)] = 0$ for $\theta > 0$ requires

$$0 = u(0) = u(1) = u(2) = u(3) = \cdots.$$

We have for all $\theta > 0$ that

$$\begin{aligned} 0 = E[u(Y_1)] &= \sum_{y_1=0}^{\infty} u(y_1) \frac{(n\theta)^{y_1} e^{-n\theta}}{y_1!} \\ &= e^{-n\theta} \left[u(0) + u(1)\frac{n\theta}{1!} + u(2)\frac{(n\theta)^2}{2!} + \cdots \right]. \end{aligned}$$

Since $e^{-n\theta}$ does not equal zero, we have shown that

$$0 = u(0) + [nu(1)]\theta + \left[\frac{n^2 u(2)}{2} \right] \theta^2 + \cdots.$$

However, if such an infinite (power) series converges to zero for all $\theta > 0$, then each of the coefficients must equal zero. That is,

$$u(0) = 0, \quad nu(1) = 0, \quad \frac{n^2 u(2)}{2} = 0, \ldots,$$

and thus $0 = u(0) = u(1) = u(2) = \cdots$, as we wanted to show. Of course, the condition $E[u(Y_1)] = 0$ for all $\theta > 0$ does not place any restriction on $u(y_1)$ when y_1 is not a nonnegative integer. So we see that, in this illustration, $E[u(Y_1)] = 0$ for all $\theta > 0$ requires that $u(y_1)$ equals zero except on a set of points that has probability zero for each pmf $g_1(y_1; \theta)$, $0 < \theta$. From the following definition we observe that the family $\{g_1(y_1; \theta) : 0 < \theta\}$ is complete.

Definition 7.4.1. *Let the random variable Z of either the continuous type or the discrete type have a pdf or pmf that is one member of the family $\{h(z; \theta) : \theta \in \Omega\}$. If the condition $E[u(Z)] = 0$, for every $\theta \in \Omega$, requires that $u(z)$ be zero except on a set of points that has probability zero for each $h(z; \theta)$, $\theta \in \Omega$, then the family $\{h(z; \theta) : \theta \in \Omega\}$ is called a* **complete family** *of probability density or mass functions.*

Remark 7.4.1. In Section 1.8, it was noted that the existence of $E[u(X)]$ implies that the integral (or sum) converges absolutely. This absolute convergence was tacitly assumed in our definition of completeness and it is needed to prove that certain families of probability density functions are complete. ∎

In order to show that certain families of probability density functions of the continuous type are complete, we must appeal to the same type of theorem in analysis that we used when we claimed that the moment generating function uniquely determines a distribution. This is illustrated in the next example.

Example 7.4.1. Consider the family of pdfs $\{h(z; \theta) : 0 < \theta < \infty\}$. Suppose Z has a pdf in this family given by

$$h(z; \theta) = \begin{cases} \frac{1}{\theta} e^{-z/\theta} & 0 < z < \infty \\ 0 & \text{elsewhere.} \end{cases}$$

Let us say that $E[u(Z)] = 0$ for every $\theta > 0$. That is,

$$\frac{1}{\theta} \int_0^\infty u(z) e^{-z/\theta} \, dz = 0, \quad \theta > 0.$$

Readers acquainted with the theory of transformations recognize the integral in the left-hand member as being essentially the Laplace transform of $u(z)$. In that theory we learn that the only function $u(z)$ transforming to a function of θ which is identically equal to zero is $u(z) = 0$, except (in our terminology) on a set of points that has probability zero for each $h(z; \theta)$, $\theta > 0$. That is, the family $\{h(z; \theta) : 0 < \theta < \infty\}$ is complete. ∎

Let the parameter θ in the pdf or pmf $f(x; \theta)$, $\theta \in \Omega$, have a sufficient statistic $Y_1 = u_1(X_1, X_2, \ldots, X_n)$, where $X_1, X_2, \ldots, X_n$ is a random sample from this distribution. Let the pdf or pmf of Y_1 be $f_{Y_1}(y_1; \theta)$, $\theta \in \Omega$. It has been seen that if there is any unbiased estimator Y_2 (not a function of Y_1 alone) of θ, then there is at least one function of Y_1 that is an unbiased estimator of θ, and our search for a best estimator of θ may be restricted to functions of Y_1. Suppose it has been verified that a certain function $\varphi(Y_1)$, not a function of θ, is such that $E[\varphi(Y_1)] = \theta$ for all values of θ, $\theta \in \Omega$. Let $\psi(Y_1)$ be another function of the sufficient statistic Y_1 alone, so that we also have $E[\psi(Y_1)] = \theta$ for all values of θ, $\theta \in \Omega$. Hence

$$E[\varphi(Y_1) - \psi(Y_1)] = 0, \quad \theta \in \Omega.$$

If the family $\{f_{Y_1}(y_1; \theta) : \theta \in \Omega\}$ is complete, the function of $\varphi(y_1) - \psi(y_1) = 0$, except on a set of points that has probability zero. That is, for every other unbiased estimator $\psi(Y_1)$ of θ, we have

$$\varphi(y_1) = \psi(y_1)$$

except possibly at certain special points. Thus, in this sense [namely $\varphi(y_1) = \psi(y_1)$, except on a set of points with probability zero], $\varphi(Y_1)$ is the unique function of Y_1, which is an unbiased estimator of θ. In accordance with the Rao–Blackwell theorem, $\varphi(Y_1)$ has a smaller variance than every other unbiased estimator of θ. That is, the statistic $\varphi(Y_1)$ is the MVUE of θ. This fact is stated in the following theorem of Lehmann and Scheffé.

Theorem 7.4.1 (Lehmann and Scheffé). *Let $X_1, X_2, \ldots, X_n$, n a fixed positive integer, denote a random sample from a distribution that has pdf or pmf $f(x; \theta)$, $\theta \in \Omega$, let $Y_1 = u_1(X_1, X_2, \ldots, X_n)$ be a sufficient statistic for θ, and let the family $\{f_{Y_1}(y_1; \theta) : \theta \in \Omega\}$ be complete. If there is a function of Y_1 that is an unbiased estimator of θ, then this function of Y_1 is the unique MVUE of θ. Here "unique" is used in the sense described in the preceding paragraph.*

The statement that Y_1 is a sufficient statistic for a parameter θ, $\theta \in \Omega$, and that the family $\{f_{Y_1}(y_1; \theta) : \theta \in \Omega\}$ of probability density functions is complete is lengthy and somewhat awkward. We shall adopt the less descriptive, but more convenient, terminology that Y_1 is a **complete sufficient statistic** for θ. In the next section, we study a fairly large class of probability density functions for which a complete sufficient statistic Y_1 for θ can be determined by inspection.

Example 7.4.2 (Uniform Distribution). Let $X_1, X_2, \ldots, X_n$ be a random sample from the uniform distribution with pdf $f(x; \theta) = 1/\theta$, $0 < x < \theta$, $\theta > 0$, and zero elsewhere. As Exercise 7.2.3 shows, $Y_n = \max\{X_1, X_2, \ldots, X_n\}$ is a sufficient statistic for θ. It is easy to show that the pdf of Y_n is

$$g(y_n; \theta) = \begin{cases} \frac{n y_n^{n-1}}{\theta^n} & 0 < y_n < \theta \\ 0 & \text{elsewhere.} \end{cases} \qquad (7.4.1)$$

To show that Y_n is complete, suppose for any function $u(t)$ and any θ that $E[u(Y_n)] = 0$; i.e.,

$$0 = \int_0^\theta u(t) \frac{n t^{n-1}}{\theta^n}\, dt.$$

Since $\theta > 0$, this equation is equivalent to

$$0 = \int_0^\theta u(t) t^{n-1}\, dt.$$

Taking partial derivatives of both sides with respect to θ and using the Fundamental Theorem of Calculus, we have

$$0 = u(\theta)\theta^{n-1}.$$

Since $\theta > 0$, $u(\theta) = 0$, for all $\theta > 0$. Thus Y_n is a complete and sufficient statistic for θ. It is easy to show that

$$E(Y_n) = \int_0^\theta y \frac{n y^{n-1}}{\theta^n}\, dy = \frac{n}{n+1}\theta.$$

Therefore, the MVUE of θ is $((n+1)/n)Y_n$. ■

EXERCISES

7.4.1. If $az^2 + bz + c = 0$ for more than two values of z, then $a = b = c = 0$. Use this result to show that the family $\{b(2, \theta) : 0 < \theta < 1\}$ is complete.

7.4.2. Show that each of the following families is not complete by finding at least one nonzero function $u(x)$ such that $E[u(X)] = 0$, for all $\theta > 0$.

(a)

$$f(x; \theta) = \begin{cases} \frac{1}{2\theta} & -\theta < x < \theta, \quad \text{where } 0 < \theta < \infty \\ 0 & \text{elsewhere.} \end{cases}$$

(b) $N(0, \theta)$, where $0 < \theta < \infty$.

7.4.3. Let $X_1, X_2, \ldots, X_n$ represent a random sample from the discrete distribution having the pmf

$$f(x; \theta) = \begin{cases} \theta^x (1 - \theta)^{1-x} & x = 0, 1, \quad 0 < \theta < 1 \\ 0 & \text{elsewhere.} \end{cases}$$

Show that $Y_1 = \sum_1^n X_i$ is a complete sufficient statistic for θ. Find the unique function of Y_1 that is the MVUE of θ.
Hint: Display $E[u(Y_1)] = 0$, show that the constant term $u(0)$ is equal to zero, divide both members of the equation by $\theta \neq 0$, and repeat the argument.

7.4.4. Consider the family of probability density functions $\{h(z; \theta) : \theta \in \Omega\}$, where $h(z; \theta) = 1/\theta$, $0 < z < \theta$, zero elsewhere.

(a) Show that the family is complete provided that $\Omega = \{\theta : 0 < \theta < \infty\}$.
Hint: For convenience, assume that $u(z)$ is continuous and note that the derivative of $E[u(Z)]$ with respect to θ is equal to zero also.

(b) Show that this family is not complete if $\Omega = \{\theta : 1 < \theta < \infty\}$.
Hint: Concentrate on the interval $0 < z < 1$ and find a nonzero function $u(z)$ on that interval such that $E[u(Z)] = 0$ for all $\theta > 1$.

7.4.5. Show that the first order statistic Y_1 of a random sample of size n from the distribution having pdf $f(x; \theta) = e^{-(x-\theta)}$, $\theta < x < \infty$, $-\infty < \theta < \infty$, zero elsewhere, is a complete sufficient statistic for θ. Find the unique function of this statistic which is the MVUE of θ.

7.4.6. Let a random sample of size n be taken from a distribution of the discrete type with pmf $f(x; \theta) = 1/\theta$, $x = 1, 2, \ldots, \theta$, zero elsewhere, where θ is an unknown positive integer.

(a) Show that the largest observation, say Y, of the sample is a complete sufficient statistic for θ.

(b) Prove that

$$[Y^{n+1} - (Y - 1)^{n+1}]/[Y^n - (Y - 1)^n]$$

is the unique MVUE of θ.

7.4.7. Let X have the pdf $f_X(x; \theta) = 1/(2\theta)$, for $-\theta < x < \theta$, zero elsewhere, where $\theta > 0$.

(a) Is the statistic $Y = |X|$ a sufficient statistic for θ? Why?

(b) Let $f_Y(y; \theta)$ be the pdf of Y. Is the family $\{f_Y(y; \theta) : \theta > 0\}$ complete? Why?

7.4.8. Let X have the pmf $p(x; \theta) = \frac{1}{2}\binom{n}{|x|}\theta^{|x|}(1 - \theta)^{n-|x|}$, for $x = \pm 1, \pm 2, \ldots, \pm n$, $p(0, \theta) = (1 - \theta)^n$, and zero elsewhere, where $0 < \theta < 1$.

(a) Show that this family $\{p(x; \theta) : 0 < \theta < 1\}$ is not complete.

(b) Let $Y = |X|$. Show that Y is a complete and sufficient statistic for θ.

7.4.9. Let $X_1, \ldots, X_n$ be iid with pdf $f(x; \theta) = 1/(3\theta)$, $-\theta < x < 2\theta$, zero elsewhere, where $\theta > 0$.

(a) Find the mle $\widehat{\theta}$ of θ.

(b) Is $\widehat{\theta}$ a sufficient statistic for θ? Why?

(c) Is $(n+1)\widehat{\theta}/n$ the unique MVUE of θ? Why?

7.4.10. Let $Y_1 < Y_2 < \cdots < Y_n$ be the order statistics of a random sample of size n from a distribution with pdf $f(x; \theta) = 1/\theta$, $0 < x < \theta$, zero elsewhere. By Example 7.4.2, the statistic Y_n is a complete sufficient statistic for θ and it has pdf

$$g(y_n; \theta) = \frac{ny_n^{n-1}}{\theta^n}, \quad 0 < y_n < \theta,$$

and zero elsewhere.

(a) Find the distribution function $H_n(z; \theta)$ of $Z = n(\theta - Y_n)$.

(b) Find the $\lim_{n \to \infty} H_n(z; \theta)$ and thus the limiting distribution of Z.

7.5 The Exponential Class of Distributions

In this section we discuss an important class of distributions, called the *exponential class*. As we show, this class possesses complete and sufficient statistics which are readily determined from the distribution.

Consider a family $\{f(x; \theta) : \theta \in \Omega\}$ of probability density or mass functions, where Ω is the interval set $\Omega = \{\theta : \gamma < \theta < \delta\}$, where γ and δ are known constants (they may be $\pm\infty$), and where

$$f(x; \theta) = \begin{cases} \exp[p(\theta)K(x) + H(x) + q(\theta)] & x \in \mathcal{S} \\ 0 & \text{elsewhere,} \end{cases} \qquad (7.5.1)$$

where $\mathcal{S}$ is the support of X. In this section we are concerned with a particular class of the family called the regular exponential class.

Definition 7.5.1 (Regular Exponential Class). *A pdf of the form (7.5.1) is said to be a member of the **regular exponential class** of probability density or mass functions if*

1. *$\mathcal{S}$, the support of X, does not depend upon θ*

2. *$p(\theta)$ is a nontrivial continuous function of $\theta \in \Omega$*

3. *Finally,*

   (a) if X is a continuous random variable, then each of $K'(x) \not\equiv 0$ and $H(x)$ is a continuous function of $x \in \mathcal{S}$,

(b) *if X is a discrete random variable, then $K(x)$ is a nontrivial function of $x \in S$.*

For example, each member of the family $\{f(x; \theta) : 0 < \theta < \infty\}$, where $f(x; \theta)$ is $N(0, \theta)$, represents a regular case of the exponential class of the continuous type because

$$
\begin{aligned}
f(x; \theta) &= \frac{1}{\sqrt{2\pi\theta}} e^{-x^2/2\theta} \\
&= \exp\left(-\frac{1}{2\theta} x^2 - \log\sqrt{2\pi\theta}\right), \quad -\infty < x < \infty.
\end{aligned}
$$

On the other hand, consider the uniform density function given by

$$
f(x; \theta) = \begin{cases} \exp\{-\log\theta\} & x \in (0, \theta) \\ 0 & \text{elsewhere.} \end{cases}
$$

This can be written in the form (7.5.1), but the support is the interval $(0, \theta)$, which depends on θ. Hence the uniform family is not a regular exponential family.

Let $X_1, X_2, \ldots, X_n$ denote a random sample from a distribution that represents a regular case of the exponential class. The joint pdf or pmf of $X_1, X_2, \ldots, X_n$ is

$$
\exp\left[p(\theta) \sum_1^n K(x_i) + \sum_1^n H(x_i) + nq(\theta)\right]
$$

for $x_i \in S$, $i = 1, 2, \ldots, n$ and zero elsewhere. At points in the S of X, this joint pdf or pmf may be written as the product of the two nonnegative functions

$$
\exp\left[p(\theta) \sum_1^n K(x_i) + nq(\theta)\right] \exp\left[\sum_1^n H(x_i)\right].
$$

In accordance with the factorization theorem, Theorem 7.2.1, $Y_1 = \sum_1^n K(X_i)$ is a sufficient statistic for the parameter θ.

Besides the fact that Y_1 is a sufficient statistic, we can obtain the general form of the distribution of Y_1 and its mean and variance. We summarize these results in a theorem. The details of the proof are given in Exercises 7.5.5 and 7.5.8. Exercise 7.5.6 obtains the mgf of Y_1 in the case that $p(\theta) = \theta$.

Theorem 7.5.1. *Let $X_1, X_2, \ldots, X_n$ denote a random sample from a distribution that represents a regular case of the exponential class, with pdf or pmf given by (7.5.1). Consider the statistic $Y_1 = \sum_{i=1}^n K(X_i)$. Then*

1. *The pdf or pmf of Y_1 has the form*

$$
f_{Y_1}(y_1; \theta) = R(y_1) \exp[p(\theta)y_1 + nq(\theta)], \tag{7.5.2}
$$

   for $y_1 \in S_{Y_1}$ and some function $R(y_1)$. Neither S_{Y_1} nor $R(y_1)$ depends on θ.

2. $E(Y_1) = -n\frac{q'(\theta)}{p'(\theta)}.$

3. $Var(Y_1) = n\frac{1}{p'(\theta)^3}\left\{p''(\theta)q'(\theta) - q''(\theta)p'(\theta)\right\}$.

Example 7.5.1. Let X have a Poisson distribution with parameter $\theta \in (0, \infty)$. Then the support of X is the set $\mathcal{S} = \{0, 1, 2, \ldots\}$, which does not depend on θ. Further, the pmf of X on its support is

$$f(x, \theta) = e^{-\theta}\frac{\theta^x}{x!} = \exp\{(\log\theta)x + \log(1/x!) + (-\theta)\}.$$

Hence the Poisson distribution is a member of the regular exponential class, with $p(\theta) = \log(\theta)$, $q(\theta) = -\theta$, and $K(x) = x$. Therefore, if $X_1, X_2, \ldots, X_n$ denotes a random sample on X, then the statistic $Y_1 = \sum_{i=1}^{n} X_i$ is sufficient. But since $p'(\theta) = 1/\theta$ and $q'(\theta) = -1$, Theorem 7.5.1 verifies that the mean of Y_1 is $n\theta$. It is easy to verify that the variance of Y_1 is $n\theta$ also. Finally, we can show that the function $R(y_1)$ in Theorem 7.5.1 is given by $R(y_1) = n^{y_1}(1/y_1!)$. ∎

For the regular case of the exponential class, we have shown that the statistic $Y_1 = \sum_{1}^{n} K(X_i)$ is sufficient for θ. We now use the form of the pdf of Y_1 given in Theorem 7.5.1 to establish the completeness of Y_1.

Theorem 7.5.2. *Let $f(x; \theta)$, $\gamma < \theta < \delta$, be a pdf or pmf of a random variable X whose distribution is a regular case of the exponential class. Then if $X_1, X_2, \ldots, X_n$ (where n is a fixed positive integer) is a random sample from the distribution of X, the statistic $Y_1 = \sum_{1}^{n} K(X_i)$ is a sufficient statistic for θ and the family $\{f_{Y_1}(y_1; \theta) : \gamma < \theta < \delta\}$ of probability density functions of Y_1 is complete. That is, Y_1 is a complete sufficient statistic for θ.*

Proof: We have shown above that Y_1 is sufficient. For completeness, suppose that $E[u(Y_1)] = 0$. Expression (7.5.2) of Theorem 7.5.1 gives the pdf of Y_1. Hence we have the equation

$$\int_{\mathcal{S}_{Y_1}} u(y_1)R(y_1)\exp\{p(\theta)y_1 + nq(\theta)\}\,dy_1 = 0$$

or equivalently since $\exp\{nq(\theta)\} \neq 0$,

$$\int_{\mathcal{S}_{Y_1}} u(y_1)R(y_1)\exp\{p(\theta)y_1\}\,dy_1 = 0$$

for all θ. However, $p(\theta)$ is a nontrivial continuous function of θ, and thus this integral is essentially a type of Laplace transform of $u(y_1)R(y_1)$. The only function of y_1 transforming to the 0 function is the zero function (except for a set of points with probability zero in our context). That is,

$$u(y_1)R(y_1) \equiv 0.$$

However, $R(y_1) \neq 0$ for all $y_1 \in \mathcal{S}_{Y_1}$ because it is factor in the pdf of Y_1. Hence $u(y_1) \equiv 0$ (except for a set of points with probability zero). Therefore, Y_1 is a complete sufficient statistic for θ. ∎

This theorem has useful implications. In a regular case of form (7.5.1), we can see by inspection that the sufficient statistic is $Y_1 = \sum_1^n K(X_i)$. If we can see how to form a function of Y_1, say $\varphi(Y_1)$, so that $E[\varphi(Y_1)] = \theta$, then the statistic $\varphi(Y_1)$ is unique and is the MVUE of θ.

Example 7.5.2. Let $X_1, X_2, \ldots, X_n$ denote a random sample from a normal distribution that has pdf

$$f(x; \theta) = \frac{1}{\sigma\sqrt{2\pi}} \exp\left[-\frac{(x-\theta)^2}{2\sigma^2}\right], \quad -\infty < x < \infty, \quad -\infty < \theta < \infty,$$

or

$$f(x; \theta) = \exp\left(\frac{\theta}{\sigma^2}x - \frac{x^2}{2\sigma^2} - \log\sqrt{2\pi\sigma^2} - \frac{\theta^2}{2\sigma^2}\right).$$

Here σ^2 is any fixed positive number. This is a regular case of the exponential class with

$$p(\theta) = \frac{\theta}{\sigma^2}, \quad K(x) = x,$$

$$H(x) = -\frac{x^2}{2\sigma^2} - \log\sqrt{2\pi\sigma^2}, \quad q(\theta) = -\frac{\theta^2}{2\sigma^2}.$$

Accordingly, $Y_1 = X_1 + X_2 + \cdots + X_n = n\overline{X}$ is a complete sufficient statistic for the mean θ of a normal distribution for every fixed value of the variance σ^2. Since $E(Y_1) = n\theta$, then $\varphi(Y_1) = Y_1/n = \overline{X}$ is the only function of Y_1 that is an unbiased estimator of θ; and being a function of the sufficient statistic Y_1, it has a minimum variance. That is, $\overline{X}$ is the unique MVUE of θ. Incidentally, since Y_1 is a one-to-one function of $\overline{X}$, $\overline{X}$ itself is also a complete sufficient statistic for θ. ∎

Example 7.5.3 (Example 7.5.1, Continued). Reconsider the discussion concerning the Poisson distribution with parameter θ found in Example 7.5.1. Based on this discussion, the statistic $Y_1 = \sum_{i=1}^n X_i$ was sufficient. It follows from Theorem 7.5.2 that its family of distributions is complete. Since $E(Y_1) = n\theta$, it follows that $\overline{X} = n^{-1}Y_1$ is the unique MVUE of θ. ∎

EXERCISES

7.5.1. Write the pdf

$$f(x; \theta) = \frac{1}{6\theta^4}x^3 e^{-x/\theta}, \quad 0 < x < \infty, \quad 0 < \theta < \infty,$$

zero elsewhere, in the exponential form. If $X_1, X_2, \ldots, X_n$ is a random sample from this distribution, find a complete sufficient statistic Y_1 for θ and the unique function $\varphi(Y_1)$ of this statistic that is the MVUE of θ. Is $\varphi(Y_1)$ itself a complete sufficient statistic?

7.5.2. Let $X_1, X_2, \ldots, X_n$ denote a random sample of size $n > 1$ from a distribution with pdf $f(x; \theta) = \theta e^{-\theta x}$, $0 < x < \infty$, zero elsewhere, and $\theta > 0$. Then $Y = \sum_1^n X_i$ is a sufficient statistic for θ. Prove that $(n-1)/Y$ is the MVUE of θ.

7.5.3. Let $X_1, X_2, \ldots, X_n$ denote a random sample of size n from a distribution with pdf $f(x; \theta) = \theta x^{\theta - 1}$, $0 < x < 1$, zero elsewhere, and $\theta > 0$.

(a) Show that the *geometric mean* $(X_1 X_2 \cdots X_n)^{1/n}$ of the sample is a complete sufficient statistic for θ.

(b) Find the maximum likelihood estimator of θ, and observe that it is a function of this geometric mean.

7.5.4. Let $\overline{X}$ denote the mean of the random sample $X_1, X_2, \ldots, X_n$ from a gamma-type distribution with parameters $\alpha > 0$ and $\beta = \theta > 0$. Compute $E[X_1 | \overline{x}]$.
Hint: Can you find directly a function $\psi(\overline{X})$ of $\overline{X}$ such that $E[\psi(\overline{X})] = \theta$? Is $E(X_1 | \overline{x}) = \psi(\overline{x})$? Why?

7.5.5. Let X be a random variable with the pdf of a regular case of the exponential class, given by $f(x; \theta) = \exp[\theta K(x) + H(x) + q(\theta)]$, $a < x < b$, $\gamma < \theta < \delta$. Show that $E[K(X)] = -q'(\theta)/p'(\theta)$, provided these derivatives exist, by differentiating both members of the equality

$$\int_a^b \exp[p(\theta)K(x) + H(x) + q(\theta)]\, dx = 1$$

with respect to θ. By a second differentiation, find the variance of $K(X)$.

7.5.6. Given that $f(x; \theta) = \exp[\theta K(x) + H(x) + q(\theta)]$, $a < x < b$, $\gamma < \theta < \delta$, represents a regular case of the exponential class, show that the moment-generating function $M(t)$ of $Y = K(X)$ is $M(t) = \exp[q(\theta) - q(\theta + t)]$, $\gamma < \theta + t < \delta$.

7.5.7. In the preceding exercise, given that $E(Y) = E[K(X)] = \theta$, prove that Y is $N(\theta, 1)$.
Hint: Consider $M'(0) = \theta$ and solve the resulting differential equation.

7.5.8. If $X_1, X_2, \ldots, X_n$ is a random sample from a distribution that has a pdf which is a regular case of the exponential class, show that the pdf of $Y_1 = \sum_1^n K(X_i)$ is of the form $f_{Y_1}(y_1; \theta) = R(y_1) \exp[p(\theta) y_1 + n q(\theta)]$.
Hint: Let $Y_2 = X_2, \ldots, Y_n = X_n$ be $n - 1$ auxiliary random variables. Find the joint pdf of $Y_1, Y_2, \ldots, Y_n$ and then the marginal pdf of Y_1.

7.5.9. Let Y denote the median and let $\overline{X}$ denote the mean of a random sample of size $n = 2k + 1$ from a distribution that is $N(\mu, \sigma^2)$. Compute $E(Y | \overline{X} = \overline{x})$.
Hint: See Exercise 7.5.4.

7.5.10. Let $X_1, X_2, \ldots, X_n$ be a random sample from a distribution with pdf $f(x; \theta) = \theta^2 x e^{-\theta x}$, $0 < x < \infty$, where $\theta > 0$.

(a) Argue that $Y = \sum_1^n X_i$ is a complete sufficient statistic for θ.

(b) Compute $E(1/Y)$ and find the function of Y which is the unique MVUE of θ.

7.5.11. Let $X_1, X_2, \ldots, X_n$, $n > 2$, be a random sample from the binomial distribution $b(1, \theta)$.

(a) Show that $Y_1 = X_1 + X_2 + \cdots + X_n$ is a complete sufficient statistic for θ.

(b) Find the function $\varphi(Y_1)$ which is the MVUE of θ.

(c) Let $Y_2 = (X_1 + X_2)/2$ and compute $E(Y_2)$.

(d) Determine $E(Y_2 | Y_1 = y_1)$.

7.5.12. Let $X_1, X_2, \ldots, X_n$ be a random sample from a distribution with pmf $p(x; \theta) = \theta^x (1 - \theta)$, $x = 0, 1, 2, \ldots$, zero elsewhere, where $0 \le \theta \le 1$.

(a) Find the mle, $\hat{\theta}$, of θ.

(b) Show that $\sum_1^n X_i$ is a complete sufficient statistic for θ.

(c) Determine the MVUE of θ.

7.6   Functions of a Parameter

Up to this point we have sought an MVUE of a parameter θ. Not always, however, are we interested in θ but rather in a function of θ. There are several techniques we can use to the find the MVUE. One is by inspection of the expected value of a sufficient statistic. This is how we found the MVUEs in Examples 7.5.2 and 7.5.3 of the last section. In this section and its exercises, we offer more examples of the inspection technique. The second technique is based on the conditional expectation of an unbiased estimate given a sufficient statistic. The third example illustrates this technique.

Recall in Chapter 6, that under regularity conditions we obtained the asymptotic distribution theory for maximum likelihood estimators (mles). This allows certain asymptotic inferences (confidence intervals and tests) for these estimators. Such a simple theory is not available for MVUEs. As Theorem 7.3.2 shows, though, sometimes we can determine the relationship between the mle and the MVUE. In these situations, we can often obtain the asymptotic distribution for the MVUE based on the asymptotic distribution of the mle. We illustrate this for some of the following examples.

Example 7.6.1. Let $X_1, X_2, \ldots, X_n$ denote the observations of a random sample of size $n > 1$ from a distribution that is $b(1, \theta)$, $0 < \theta < 1$. We know that if $Y = \sum_1^n X_i$, then Y/n is the unique minimum variance unbiased estimator of θ. Now suppose we want to estimate the variance of Y/n, which is $\theta(1 - \theta)/n$. Let $\delta = \theta(1 - \theta)$. Because Y is a sufficient statistic for θ, it is known that we can restrict our search to functions of Y. The maximum likelihood estimate of δ, which is given by $\tilde{\delta} = (Y/n)(1 - Y/n)$, is a function of the sufficient statistic and seems to be a reasonable starting point. The expectation of this statistic is given by

$$E[\tilde{\delta}] = E\left[\frac{Y}{n}\left(1 - \frac{Y}{n}\right)\right] = \frac{1}{n}E(Y) - \frac{1}{n^2}E(Y^2).$$

Now $E(Y) = n\theta$ and $E(Y^2) = n\theta(1-\theta) + n^2\theta^2$. Hence

$$E\left[\frac{Y}{n}\left(1 - \frac{Y}{n}\right)\right] = (n-1)\frac{\theta(1-\theta)}{n}.$$

If we multiply both members of this equation by $n/(n-1)$, we find that the statistic $\hat{\delta} = (n/(n-1))(Y/n)(1 - Y/n) = (n/(n-1))\tilde{\delta}$ is the unique MVUE of δ. Hence the MVUE of δ/n, the variance of Y/n, is $\hat{\delta}/n$.

It is interesting to compare the mle $\tilde{\delta}$ with $\hat{\delta}$. Recall from Chapter 6 that the mle $\tilde{\delta}$ is a consistent estimate of δ and that $\sqrt{n}(\tilde{\delta} - \delta)$ is asymptotically normal. Because

$$\hat{\delta} - \tilde{\delta} = \tilde{\delta}\frac{1}{n-1} \xrightarrow{P} \delta \cdot 0 = 0,$$

it follows that $\hat{\delta}$ is also a consistent estimator of δ. Further,

$$\sqrt{n}(\hat{\delta} - \delta) - \sqrt{n}(\tilde{\delta} - \delta) = \frac{\sqrt{n}}{n-1}\tilde{\delta} \xrightarrow{P} 0. \tag{7.6.1}$$

Hence $\sqrt{n}(\hat{\delta} - \delta)$ has the same asymptotic distribution as $\sqrt{n}(\tilde{\delta} - \delta)$. Using the Δ-method, Theorem 5.2.9, we can obtain the asymptotic distribution of $\sqrt{n}(\tilde{\delta} - \delta)$. Let $g(\theta) = \theta(1-\theta)$. Then $g'(\theta) = 1 - 2\theta$. Hence, by Theorem 5.2.9 and (7.6.1), the asymptotic distribution of $\sqrt{n}(\tilde{\delta} - \delta)$ is given by

$$\sqrt{n}(\hat{\delta} - \delta) \xrightarrow{D} N(0, \theta(1-\theta)(1-2\theta)^2),$$

provided $\theta \neq 1/2$; see Exercise 7.6.11 for the case $\theta = 1/2$. ∎

In the next example, we consider the uniform $(0, \theta)$ distribution and obtain the MVUE for all differentiable functions of θ. This example was sent to us by Professor Bradford Crain of Portland State University.

Example 7.6.2. Suppose $X_1, X_2, \ldots, X_n$ are iid random variables with the common uniform $(0, \theta)$ distribution. Let $Y_n = \max\{X_1, X_2, \ldots, X_n\}$. In Example 7.4.2, we showed that Y_n is a complete and sufficient statistic of θ and the pdf of Y_n is given by (7.4.1). Let $g(\theta)$ be any differentiable function of θ. Then the MVUE of $g(\theta)$ is the statistic $u(Y_n)$, which satisfies the equation

$$g(\theta) = \int_0^\theta u(y)\frac{ny^{n-1}}{\theta^n}\,dy, \quad \theta > 0,$$

or equivalently,

$$g(\theta)\theta^n = \int_0^\theta u(y)ny^{n-1}\,dy, \quad \theta > 0.$$

Differentiating both sides of this equation with respect to θ, we obtain

$$n\theta^{n-1}g(\theta) + \theta^n g'(\theta) = u(\theta)n\theta^{n-1}.$$

Solving for $u(\theta)$, we obtain

$$u(\theta) = g(\theta) + \frac{\theta g'(\theta)}{n}.$$

Therefore, the MVUE of $g(\theta)$ is

$$u(Y_n) = g(Y_n) + \frac{Y_n}{n} g'(Y_n). \tag{7.6.2}$$

For example, if $g(\theta) = \theta$, then

$$u(Y_n) = Y_n + \frac{Y_n}{n} = \frac{n+1}{n} Y_n,$$

which agrees with the result obtained in Example 7.4.2. Other examples are given in Exercise 7.6.4. ∎

A somewhat different but also very important problem in point estimation is considered in the next example. In the example the distribution of a random variable X is described by a pdf $f(x; \theta)$ that depends upon $\theta \in \Omega$. The problem is to estimate the fractional part of the probability for this distribution, which is at, or to the left of, a fixed point c. Thus we seek an MVUE of $F(c; \theta)$, where $F(x; \theta)$ is the cdf of X.

Example 7.6.3. Let $X_1, X_2, \ldots, X_n$ be a random sample of size $n > 1$ from a distribution that is $N(\theta, 1)$. Suppose that we wish to find an MVUE of the function of θ defined by

$$P(X \le c) = \int_{-\infty}^{c} \frac{1}{\sqrt{2\pi}} e^{-(x-\theta)^2/2}\, dx = \Phi(c - \theta),$$

where c is a fixed constant. There are many unbiased estimators of $\Phi(c - \theta)$. We first exhibit one of these, say $u(X_1)$, a function of X_1 alone. We shall then compute the conditional expectation, $E[u(X_1) | \overline{X} = \overline{x}] = \varphi(\overline{x})$, of this unbiased statistic, given the sufficient statistic $\overline{X}$, the mean of the sample. In accordance with the theorems of Rao–Blackwell and Lehmann–Scheffé, $\varphi(\overline{X})$ is the unique MVUE of $\Phi(c - \theta)$.

Consider the function $u(x_1)$, where

$$u(x_1) = \begin{cases} 1 & x_1 \le c \\ 0 & x_1 > c. \end{cases}$$

The expected value of the random variable $u(X_1)$ is given by

$$E[u(X_1)] = 1 \cdot P[X_1 - \theta \le c - \theta] = \Phi(c - \theta).$$

That is, $u(X_1)$ is an unbiased estimator of $\Phi(c - \theta)$.

We shall next discuss the joint distribution of X_1 and $\overline{X}$ and the conditional distribution of X_1, given $\overline{X} = \overline{x}$. This conditional distribution enables us to compute the conditional expectation $E[u(X_1)|\overline{X} = \overline{x}] = \varphi(\overline{x})$. In accordance with Exercise 7.6.7, the joint distribution of X_1 and $\overline{X}$ is bivariate normal with mean vector (θ, θ), variances $\sigma_1^2 = 1$ and $\sigma_2^2 = 1/n$, and correlation coefficient $\rho = 1/\sqrt{n}$. Thus the conditional pdf of X_1, given $\overline{X} = \overline{x}$, is normal with linear conditional mean

$$\theta + \frac{\rho\sigma_1}{\sigma_2}(\overline{x} - \theta) = \overline{x}$$

and with variance

$$\sigma_1^2(1 - \rho^2) = \frac{n-1}{n}.$$

The conditional expectation of $u(X_1)$, given $\overline{X} = \overline{x}$, is then

$$
\begin{aligned}
\varphi(\overline{x}) &= \int_{-\infty}^{\infty} u(x_1)\sqrt{\frac{n}{n-1}}\frac{1}{\sqrt{2\pi}}\exp\left[-\frac{n(x_1 - \overline{x})^2}{2(n-1)}\right]dx_1 \\
&= \int_{-\infty}^{c}\sqrt{\frac{n}{n-1}}\frac{1}{\sqrt{2\pi}}\exp\left[-\frac{n(x_1 - \overline{x})^2}{2(n-1)}\right]dx_1.
\end{aligned}
$$

The change of variable $z = \sqrt{n}(x_1 - \overline{x})/\sqrt{n-1}$ enables us to write this conditional expectation as

$$\varphi(\overline{x}) = \int_{-\infty}^{c'}\frac{1}{\sqrt{2\pi}}e^{-z^2/2}\,dz = \Phi(c') = \Phi\left[\frac{\sqrt{n}(c - \overline{x})}{\sqrt{n-1}}\right],$$

where $c' = \sqrt{n}(c - \overline{x})/\sqrt{n-1}$. Thus the unique MVUE of $\Phi(c - \theta)$ is, for every fixed constant c, given by $\varphi(\overline{X}) = \Phi[\sqrt{n}(c - \overline{X})/\sqrt{n-1}]$.

In this example the mle of $\Phi(c - \theta)$ is $\Phi(c - \overline{X})$. These two estimators are close because $\sqrt{n/(n-1)} \to 1$, as $n \to \infty$. ∎

Remark 7.6.1. We should like to draw the attention of the reader to a rather important fact. This has to do with the adoption of a *principle*, such as the principle of unbiasedness and minimum variance. A principle is not a theorem; and seldom does a principle yield satisfactory results in all cases. So far, this principle has provided quite satisfactory results. To see that this is not always the case, let X have a Poisson distribution with parameter θ, $0 < \theta < \infty$. We may look upon X as a random sample of size 1 from this distribution. Thus X is a complete sufficient statistic for θ. We seek the estimator of $e^{-2\theta}$ that is unbiased and has minimum variance. Consider $Y = (-1)^X$. We have

$$E(Y) = E[(-1)^X] = \sum_{x=0}^{\infty}\frac{(-\theta)^x e^{-\theta}}{x!} = e^{-2\theta}.$$

Accordingly, $(-1)^X$ is the MVUE of $e^{-2\theta}$. Here this estimator leaves much to be desired. We are endeavoring to elicit some information about the number $e^{-2\theta}$, where $0 < e^{-2\theta} < 1$; yet our point estimate is either -1 or $+1$, each of which is a very poor estimate of a number between 0 and 1. We do not wish to leave the reader with the impression that an MVUE is *bad*. That is not the case at all. We merely wish to point out that if one tries hard enough, one can find instances where such a statistic is *not good*. Incidentally, the maximum likelihood estimator of $e^{-2\theta}$ is, in the case where the sample size equals 1, e^{-2X}, which is probably a much better estimator in practice than is the unbiased estimator $(-1)^X$. ∎

EXERCISES

7.6.1. Let $X_1, X_2, \ldots, X_n$ denote a random sample from a distribution that is $N(\theta, 1)$, $-\infty < \theta < \infty$. Find the MVUE of θ^2.
Hint: First determine $E(\overline{X}^2)$.

7.6.2. Let $X_1, X_2, \ldots, X_n$ denote a random sample from a distribution that is $N(0, \theta)$. Then $Y = \sum X_i^2$ is a complete sufficient statistic for θ. Find the MVUE of θ^2.

7.6.3. In the notation of Example 7.6.3 of this section, does $P(-c \leq X \leq c)$ have an MVUE? Here $c > 0$.

7.6.4. Let $X_1, X_2, \ldots, X_n$ be a random sample from a uniform $(0, \theta)$ distribution. Continuing with Example 7.6.2, find the MVUEs for the following functions of θ.

  (a) $g(\theta) = \frac{\theta^2}{12}$, i.e., the variance of the distribution.

  (b) $g(\theta) = \frac{1}{\theta}$, i.e., the pdf of the distribution.

  (c) For t real, $g(\theta) = \frac{e^{t\theta}-1}{t\theta}$, i.e., the mgf of the distribution.

7.6.5. Let $X_1, X_2, \ldots, X_n$ be a random sample from a Poisson distribution with parameter $\theta > 0$.

  (a) Find the MVUE of $P(X \leq 1) = (1 + \theta)e^{-\theta}$.
  Hint: Let $u(x_1) = 1$, $x_1 \leq 1$, zero elsewhere, and find $E[u(X_1)|Y = y]$, where $Y = \sum_1^n X_i$.

  (b) Express the MVUE as a function of the mle of θ.

  (c) Determine the asymptotic distribution of the mle of θ.

  (d) Obtain the mle of $P(X \leq 1)$. Then use Theorem 5.2.9 to determine its asymptotic distribution.

7.6.6. Let $X_1, X_2, \ldots, X_n$ denote a random sample from a Poisson distribution with parameter $\theta > 0$. From Remark 7.6.1, we know that $E[(-1)^{X_1}] = e^{-2\theta}$.

  (a) Show that $E[(-1)^{X_1}|Y_1 = y_1] = (1 - 2/n)^{y_1}$, where $Y_1 = X_1 + X_2 + \cdots + X_n$.
  Hint: First show that the conditional pdf of $X_1, X_2, \ldots, X_{n-1}$, given $Y_1 = y_1$, is multinomial, and hence that of X_1, given $Y_1 = y_1$, is $b(y_1, 1/n)$.

  (b) Show that the mle of $e^{-2\theta}$ is $e^{-2\overline{X}}$.

(c) Since $y_1 = n\bar{x}$, show that $(1 - 2/n)^{y_1}$ is approximately equal to $e^{-2\bar{x}}$ when n is large.

7.6.7. As in Example 7.6.3, let $X_1, X_2, \ldots, X_n$ be a random sample of size $n > 1$ from a distribution that is $N(\theta, 1)$. Show that the joint distribution of X_1 and $\overline{X}$ is bivariate normal with mean vector (θ, θ), variances $\sigma_1^2 = 1$ and $\sigma_2^2 = 1/n$, and correlation coefficient $\rho = 1/\sqrt{n}$.

7.6.8. Let a random sample of size n be taken from a distribution that has the pdf $f(x; \theta) = (1/\theta) \exp(-x/\theta) I_{(0,\infty)}(x)$. Find the mle and MVUE of $P(X \leq 2)$.

7.6.9. Let $X_1, X_2, \ldots, X_n$ be a random sample with the common pdf $f(x) = \theta^{-1} e^{-x/\theta}$, for $x > 0$, zero elsewhere; that is, $f(x)$ is a $\Gamma(1, \theta)$ pdf.

(a) Show that the statistic $\overline{X} = n^{-1} \sum_{i=1}^{n} X_i$ is a complete and sufficient statistic for θ.

(b) Determine the MVUE of θ.

(c) Determine the mle of θ.

(d) Often, though, this pdf is written as $f(x) = \tau e^{-\tau x}$, for $x > 0$, zero elsewhere. Thus $\tau = 1/\theta$. Use Theorem 6.1.2 to determine the mle of τ.

(e) Show that the statistic $\overline{X} = n^{-1} \sum_{i=1}^{n} X_i$ is a complete and sufficient statistic for τ. Show that $(n-1)/(n\overline{X})$ is the MVUE of $\tau = 1/\theta$. Hence, as usual, the reciprocal of the mle of θ is the mle of $1/\theta$, but, in this situation, the reciprocal of the MVUE of θ is not the MVUE of $1/\theta$.

(f) Compute the variances of each of the unbiased estimators in parts (b) and (e).

7.6.10. Consider the situation of the last exercise, but suppose we have the following two independent random samples: (1) $X_1, X_2, \ldots, X_n$ is a random sample with the common pdf $f_X(x) = \theta^{-1} e^{-x/\theta}$, for $x > 0$, zero elsewhere, and (2) $Y_1, Y_2, \ldots, Y_n$ is a random sample with common pdf $f_Y(y) = \tau e^{-\tau y}$, for $y > 0$, zero elsewhere. Assume that $\tau = 1/\theta$. The last exercise suggests that, for some constant c, $Z = c\overline{X}/\overline{Y}$ might be an unbiased estimator of θ^2. Find this constant c and the variance of Z. *Hint:* Show that $\overline{X}/(\theta^2 \overline{Y})$ has an F-distribution.

7.6.11. Obtain the asymptotic distribution of the MVUE in Example 7.6.1 for the case $\theta = 1/2$.

7.7 The Case of Several Parameters

In many of the interesting problems we encounter, the pdf or pmf may not depend upon a single parameter θ, but perhaps upon two (or more) parameters. In general, our parameter space Ω is a subset of R^p, but in many of our examples p is 2.

Definition 7.7.1. *Let* $X_1, X_2, \ldots, X_n$ *denote a random sample from a distribution that has pdf or pmf* $f(x; \boldsymbol{\theta})$, *where* $\boldsymbol{\theta} \in \Omega \subset R^p$. *Let* $\mathcal{S}$ *denote the support of* X. *Let* $\mathbf{Y}$ *be an* m-*dimensional random vector of statistics* $\mathbf{Y} = (Y_1, \ldots, Y_m)'$, *where* $Y_i = u_i(X_1, X_2, \ldots, X_n)$, *for* $i = 1, \ldots, m$. *Denote the pdf or pmf of* $\mathbf{Y}$ *by* $f_{\mathbf{Y}}(\mathbf{y}; \boldsymbol{\theta})$ *for* $\mathbf{y} \in R^m$. *The random vector of statistics* $\mathbf{Y}$ *is* **jointly sufficient** *for* $\boldsymbol{\theta}$ *if and only if*

$$\frac{\prod_{i=1}^{n} f(x_i; \boldsymbol{\theta})}{f_{\mathbf{Y}}(\mathbf{y}; \boldsymbol{\theta})} = H(x_1, x_2, \ldots, x_n), \quad \textit{for all } x_i \in \mathcal{S},$$

where $H(x_1, x_2, \ldots, x_n)$ *does not depend upon* $\boldsymbol{\theta}$.

In general, $m \neq p$, i.e., the number of sufficient statistics does not have to be the same as the number of parameters, but in most of our examples this is the case.

As may be anticipated, the factorization theorem can be extended. In our notation it can be stated in the following manner. The vector of statistics $\mathbf{Y}$ is jointly sufficient for the parameter $\boldsymbol{\theta} \in \Omega$ if and only if we can find two nonnegative functions k_1 and k_2 such that

$$\prod_{i=1}^{n} f(x_i; \boldsymbol{\theta}) = k_1(\mathbf{y}; \boldsymbol{\theta}) k_2(x_1, \ldots, x_n), \quad \text{for all } x_i \in \mathcal{S}, \qquad (7.7.1)$$

where the function $k_2(x_1, x_2, \ldots, x_n)$ does not depend upon $\boldsymbol{\theta}$.

Example 7.7.1. Let $X_1, X_2, \ldots, X_n$ be a random sample from a distribution having pdf

$$f(x; \theta_1, \theta_2) = \begin{cases} \frac{1}{2\theta_2} & \theta_1 - \theta_2 < x < \theta_1 + \theta_2 \\ 0 & \text{elsewhere}, \end{cases}$$

where $-\infty < \theta_1 < \infty$, $0 < \theta_2 < \infty$. Let $Y_1 < Y_2 < \cdots < Y_n$ be the order statistics. The joint pdf of Y_1 and Y_n is given by

$$f_{Y_1, Y_2}(y_1, y_n; \theta_1, \theta_2) = \frac{n(n-1)}{(2\theta_2)^n}(y_n - y_1)^{n-2}, \quad \theta_1 - \theta_2 < y_1 < y_n < \theta_1 + \theta_2,$$

and equals zero elsewhere. Accordingly, the joint pdf of $X_1, X_2, \ldots, X_n$ can be written, for all points in its support (all x_i such that $\theta_1 - \theta_2 < x_i < \theta_1 + \theta_2$),

$$\left(\frac{1}{2\theta_2}\right)^n = \frac{n(n-1)[\max(x_i) - \min(x_i)]^{n-2}}{(2\theta_2)^n} \left(\frac{1}{n(n-1)[\max(x_i) - \min(x_i)]^{n-2}}\right).$$

Since $\min(x_i) \leq x_j \leq \max(x_i)$, $j = 1, 2, \ldots, n$, the last factor does not depend upon the parameters. Either the definition or the factorization theorem assures us that Y_1 and Y_n are joint sufficient statistics for θ_1 and θ_2. ∎

The concept of a complete family of probability density functions is generalized as follows: Let

$$\{f(v_1, v_2, \ldots, v_k; \boldsymbol{\theta}) : \boldsymbol{\theta} \in \Omega\}$$

denote a family of pdfs of k random variables $V_1, V_2, \ldots, V_k$ that depends upon the p-dimensional vector of parameters $\boldsymbol{\theta} \in \Omega$. Let $u(v_1, v_2, \ldots, v_k)$ be a function of $v_1, v_2, \ldots, v_k$ (but not a function of any or all of the parameters). If

$$E[u(V_1, V_2, \ldots, V_k)] = 0$$

for all $\boldsymbol{\theta} \in \Omega$ implies that $u(v_1, v_2, \ldots, v_k) = 0$ at all points $(v_1, v_2, \ldots, v_k)$, except on a set of points that has probability zero for all members of the family of probability density functions, we shall say that the family of probability density functions is a complete family.

In the case where $\boldsymbol{\theta}$ is a vector, we generally consider best estimators of functions of $\boldsymbol{\theta}$, that is, parameters δ, where $\delta = g(\boldsymbol{\theta})$ for a specified function g. For example, suppose we are sampling from a $N(\theta_1, \theta_2)$ distribution, where θ_2 is the variance. Let $\boldsymbol{\theta} = (\theta_1, \theta_2)'$ and consider the two parameters $\delta_1 = g_1(\boldsymbol{\theta}) = \theta_1$ and $\delta_2 = g_2(\boldsymbol{\theta}) = \sqrt{\theta_2}$. Hence we are interested in best estimates of δ_1 and δ_2.

The Rao–Blackwell, Lehmann–Scheffé theory outlined in Sections 7.3 and 7.4 extends naturally to this vector case. Briefly, suppose $\delta = g(\boldsymbol{\theta})$ is the parameter of interest and $\mathbf{Y}$ is a vector of sufficient and complete statistics for $\boldsymbol{\theta}$. Let T be a statistic which is a function of $\mathbf{Y}$, such as $T = T(\mathbf{Y})$. If $E(T) = \delta$, then T is the unique MVUE of δ.

The remainder of our treatment of the case of several parameters is restricted to probability density functions that represent what we shall call regular cases of the exponential class. Here $m = p$.

Definition 7.7.2. *Let X be a random variable with pdf or pmf $f(x; \boldsymbol{\theta})$, where the vector of parameters $\boldsymbol{\theta} \in \Omega \subset R^m$. Let $\mathcal{S}$ denote the support of X. If X is continuous, assume that $\mathcal{S} = (a, b)$, where a or b may be $-\infty$ or ∞, respectively. If X is discrete, assume that $\mathcal{S} = \{a_1, a_2, \ldots\}$. Suppose $f(x; \boldsymbol{\theta})$ is of the form*

$$f(x; \boldsymbol{\theta}) = \begin{cases} \exp\left[\sum_{j=1}^m p_j(\boldsymbol{\theta}) K_j(x) + H(x) + q(\theta_1, \theta_2, \ldots, \theta_m)\right] & \text{for all } x \in \mathcal{S} \\ 0 & \text{elsewhere.} \end{cases}$$

$$(7.7.2)$$

*Then we say this pdf or pmf is a member of the **exponential class**. We say it is a **regular case** of the exponential family if, in addition,*

1. *the support does not depend on the vector of parameters $\boldsymbol{\theta}$,*

2. *the space Ω contains a nonempty, m-dimensional open rectangle,*

3. *the $p_j(\boldsymbol{\theta})$, $j = 1, \ldots, m$, are nontrivial, functionally independent, continuous functions of $\boldsymbol{\theta}$,*

4. *and, depending on whether X is continuous or discrete, one of the following holds, respectively:*

    (a) *if X is a continuous random variable, then the m derivatives $K_j'(x)$, for $j = 1, 2, \ldots, m$, are continuous for $a < x < b$ and no one is a linear homogeneous function of the others, and $H(x)$ is a continuous function of x, $a < x < b$.*

(b) *if X is discrete, the $K_j(x)$, $j = 1, 2, \ldots, m$, are nontrivial functions of x on the support $\mathcal{S}$ and no one is a linear homogeneous function of the others.*

Let $X_1, \ldots, X_n$ be a random sample on X where the pdf or pmf of X is a regular case of the exponential class with the same notation as in Definition 7.7.2. It follows from (7.7.2) that the joint pdf or pmf of the sample is given by

$$\prod_{i=1}^{n} f(x_i; \boldsymbol{\theta}) = \exp\left[\sum_{j=1}^{m} p_j(\boldsymbol{\theta}) \sum_{i=1}^{n} K_j(x_i) + nq(\boldsymbol{\theta})\right] \exp\left[\sum_{i=1}^{n} H(x_i)\right], \qquad (7.7.3)$$

for all $x_i \in \mathcal{S}$. In accordance with the factorization theorem, the statistics

$$Y_1 = \sum_{i=1}^{n} K_1(x_i), \quad Y_2 = \sum_{i=1}^{n} K_2(x_i), \ldots, Y_m = \sum_{i=1}^{n} K_m(x_i)$$

are joint sufficient statistics for the m-dimensional vector of parameters $\boldsymbol{\theta}$. It is left as an exercise to prove that the joint pdf of $\mathbf{Y} = (Y_1, \ldots, Y_m)'$ is of the form

$$R(\mathbf{y}) \exp\left[\sum_{j=1}^{m} p_j(\boldsymbol{\theta}) y_j + nq(\boldsymbol{\theta})\right], \qquad (7.7.4)$$

at points of positive probability density. These points of positive probability density and the function $R(\mathbf{y})$ do not depend upon the vector of parameters $\boldsymbol{\theta}$. Moreover, in accordance with a theorem in analysis, it can be asserted that in a regular case of the exponential class, the family of probability density functions of these joint sufficient statistics $Y_1, Y_2, \ldots, Y_m$ is complete when $n > m$. In accordance with a convention previously adopted, we shall refer to $Y_1, Y_2, \ldots, Y_m$ as **joint complete sufficient statistics** for the vector of parameters $\boldsymbol{\theta}$.

Example 7.7.2. Let $X_1, X_2, \ldots, X_n$ denote a random sample from a distribution that is $N(\theta_1, \theta_2)$, $-\infty < \theta_1 < \infty$, $0 < \theta_2 < \infty$. Thus the pdf $f(x; \theta_1, \theta_2)$ of the distribution may be written as

$$f(x; \theta_1, \theta_2) = \exp\left(\frac{-1}{2\theta_2}x^2 + \frac{\theta_1}{\theta_2}x - \frac{\theta_1^2}{2\theta_2} - \ln\sqrt{2\pi\theta_2}\right).$$

Therefore, we can take $K_1(x) = x^2$ and $K_2(x) = x$. Consequently, the statistics

$$Y_1 = \sum_{1}^{n} X_i^2 \quad \text{and} \quad Y_2 = \sum_{1}^{n} X_i$$

are joint complete sufficient statistics for θ_1 and θ_2. Since the relations

$$Z_1 = \frac{Y_2}{n} = \overline{X}, \quad Z_2 = \frac{Y_1 - Y_2^2/n}{n-1} = \frac{\sum(X_i - \overline{X})^2}{n-1}$$

define a one-to-one transformation, Z_1 and Z_2 are also joint complete sufficient statistics for θ_1 and θ_2. Moreover,

$$E(Z_1) = \theta_1 \quad \text{and} \quad E(Z_2) = \theta_2.$$

From completeness, we have that Z_1 and Z_2 are the only functions of Y_1 and Y_2 that are unbiased estimators of θ_1 and θ_2, respectively. Hence Z_1 and Z_2 are the unique minimum variance estimators of θ_1 and θ_2, respectively. The MVUE of the standard deviation $\sqrt{\theta_2}$ is derived in Exercise 7.7.5. ∎

In this section we have extended the concepts of sufficiency and completeness to the case where $\boldsymbol{\theta}$ is a p-dimensional vector. We now extend these concepts to the case where $\mathbf{X}$ is a k-dimensional random vector. We only consider the regular exponential class.

Suppose $\mathbf{X}$ is a k-dimensional random vector with pdf or pmf $f(\mathbf{x}; \boldsymbol{\theta})$, where $\boldsymbol{\theta} \in \Omega \subset R^p$. Let $\mathcal{S} \subset R^k$ denote the support of $\mathbf{X}$. Suppose $f(\mathbf{x}; \boldsymbol{\theta})$ is of the form

$$f(\mathbf{x}; \boldsymbol{\theta}) = \begin{cases} \exp\left[\sum_{j=1}^{m} p_j(\boldsymbol{\theta}) K_j(\mathbf{x}) + H(\mathbf{x}) + q(\boldsymbol{\theta})\right] & \text{for all } \mathbf{x} \in \mathcal{S} \\ 0 & \text{elsewhere.} \end{cases} \tag{7.7.5}$$

Then we say this pdf or pmf is a member of the **exponential class**. If, in addition, $p = m$, the support does not depend on the vector of parameters $\boldsymbol{\theta}$, and conditions similar to those of Definition 7.7.2 hold, then we say this pdf is a **regular case** of the exponential class.

Suppose that $\mathbf{X}_1, \ldots, \mathbf{X}_n$ constitute a random sample on $\mathbf{X}$. Then the statistics,

$$Y_j = \sum_{i=1}^{n} K_j(\mathbf{X}_i), \quad \text{for } j = 1, \ldots, m, \tag{7.7.6}$$

are sufficient and complete statistics for $\boldsymbol{\theta}$. Let $\mathbf{Y} = (Y_1, \ldots, Y_m)'$. Suppose $\delta = g(\boldsymbol{\theta})$ is a parameter of interest. If $T = h(\mathbf{Y})$ for some function h and $E(T) = \delta$ then T is the unique minimum variance unbiased estimator of δ.

Example 7.7.3 (Multinomial). In Example 6.4.5, we consider the mles of the multinomial distribution. In this example we determine the MVUEs of several of the parameters. As in Example 6.4.5, consider a random trial which can result in one, and only one, of k outcomes or categories. Let X_j be 1 or 0 depending on whether the jth outcome does or does not occur, for $j = 1, \ldots, k$. Suppose the probability that outcome j occurs is p_j; hence, $\sum_{j=1}^{k} p_j = 1$. Let $\mathbf{X} = (X_1, \ldots, X_{k-1})'$ and $\mathbf{p} = (p_1, \ldots, p_{k-1})'$. The distribution of $\mathbf{X}$ is multinomial and can be found in expression (6.4.18), which can be reexpressed as

$$f(\mathbf{x}, \mathbf{p}) = \exp\left\{\sum_{j=1}^{k-1}\left(\log\left[\frac{p_j}{1 - \sum_{i \neq k} p_i}\right]\right) x_j + \log\left(1 - \sum_{i \neq k} p_i\right)\right\}.$$

Because this a regular case of the exponential family, the following statistics, resulting from a random sample $\mathbf{X}_1, \ldots, \mathbf{X}_n$ from the distribution of $\mathbf{X}$, are jointly sufficient and complete for the parameters $\mathbf{p} = (p_1, \ldots, p_{k-1})'$:

$$Y_j = \sum_{i=1}^{n} X_{ij}, \quad \text{for } j = 1, \ldots, k-1.$$

Each random variable X_{ij} is Bernoulli with parameter p_j and the variables X_{ij} are independent for $i = 1, \ldots, n$. Hence the variables Y_j are binomial(n, p_j) for $j = 1, \ldots, k$. Thus the MVUE of p_j is the statistic $n^{-1}Y_j$.

Next, we shall find the MVUE of $p_j p_l$, for $j \neq l$. Exercise 7.7.8 shows that the mle of $p_j p_l$ is $n^{-2}Y_j Y_l$. Recall from Section 3.1 that the conditional distribution of Y_j, given Y_l, is $b[n - Y_l, p_j/(1-p_l)]$. As an initial guess at the MVUE, consider the mle, which, as shown by Exercise 7.7.8, is $n^{-2}Y_j Y_l$. Hence

$$
\begin{aligned}
E[n^{-2}Y_j Y_l] &= \frac{1}{n^2} E[E(Y_j Y_l | Y_l)] = \frac{1}{n^2} E[Y_l E(Y_j | Y_l)] \\
&= \frac{1}{n^2} E\left[Y_l(n - Y_l)\frac{p_j}{1-p_l}\right] = \frac{1}{n^2}\frac{p_j}{1-p_l}\{E[nY_l] - E[Y_l^2]\} \\
&= \frac{1}{n^2}\frac{p_j}{1-p_l}\{n^2 p_l - n p_l(1-p_l) - n^2 p_l^2\} \\
&= \frac{1}{n^2}\frac{p_j}{1-p_l} n p_l(n-1)(1-p_l) = \frac{(n-1)}{n} p_j p_l.
\end{aligned}
$$

Hence the MVUE of $p_j p_l$ is $\frac{1}{n(n-1)}Y_j Y_l$. ∎

Example 7.7.4 (Multivariate Normal). Let $\mathbf{X}$ have the multivariate normal distribution $N_k(\boldsymbol{\mu}, \boldsymbol{\Sigma})$, where $\boldsymbol{\Sigma}$ is a positive definite $k \times k$ matrix. The pdf of $\mathbf{X}$ is given in expression (3.5.12). In this case $\boldsymbol{\theta}$ is a $\{k + [k(k+1)/2]\}$-dimensional vector whose first k components consist of the mean vector $\boldsymbol{\mu}$ and whose last $\frac{k(k+1)}{2}$ components consist of the componentwise variances σ_i^2 and the covariances σ_{ij}, for $j \geq i$. The density of $\mathbf{X}$ can be written as

$$f_{\mathbf{X}}(\mathbf{x}) = \exp\left\{-\frac{1}{2}\mathbf{x}'\boldsymbol{\Sigma}^{-1}\mathbf{x} + \boldsymbol{\mu}'\boldsymbol{\Sigma}^{-1}\mathbf{x} - \frac{1}{2}\boldsymbol{\mu}'\boldsymbol{\Sigma}^{-1}\boldsymbol{\mu} - \frac{1}{2}\log|\boldsymbol{\Sigma}| - \frac{k}{2}\log 2\pi\right\},$$

(7.7.7)

for $\mathbf{x} \in R^k$. Hence, by (7.7.5), the multivariate normal pdf is a regular case of the exponential class of distributions. We need only identify the functions $K(\mathbf{x})$. The second term in the exponent on the right side of (7.7.7) can be written as $(\boldsymbol{\mu}'\boldsymbol{\Sigma}^{-1})\mathbf{x}$; hence, $K_1(\mathbf{x}) = \mathbf{x}$. The first term is easily seen to be a linear combination of the products $x_i x_j$, $i, j = 1, 2, \ldots, k$, which are the entries of the matrix $\mathbf{x}\mathbf{x}'$. Hence we can take $K_2(\mathbf{x}) = \mathbf{x}\mathbf{x}'$. Now, let $\mathbf{X}_1, \ldots, \mathbf{X}_n$ be a random sample on $\mathbf{X}$. Based on (7.7.7) then, a set of sufficient and complete statistics is given by

$$\mathbf{Y}_1 = \sum_{i=1}^{n} \mathbf{X}_i \quad \text{and} \quad \mathbf{Y}_2 = \sum_{i=1}^{n} \mathbf{X}_i \mathbf{X}_i'.$$

(7.7.8)

Note that $\mathbf{Y}_1$ is a vector of k statistics and that $\mathbf{Y}_2$ is a $k \times k$ symmetric matrix. Because the matrix is symmetric, we can eliminate the bottom-half [elements (i, j)

with $i > j$] of the matrix, which results in $\{k + [k(k + 1)]\}$ complete sufficient statistics, i.e., as many complete sufficient statistics as there are parameters.

Based on marginal distributions, it is easy to show that $\overline{X}_j = n^{-1} \sum_{i=1}^{n} X_{ij}$ is the MVUE of μ_j and that $(n-1)^{-1} \sum_{i=1}^{n} (X_{ij} - \overline{X}_j)^2$ is the MVUE of σ_j^2. The MVUEs of the covariance parameters are obtained in Exercise 7.7.9. ∎

For our last example, we consider a case where the set of parameters is the cdf.

Example 7.7.5. Let $X_1, X_2, \ldots, X_n$ be a random sample having the common continuous cdf $F(x)$. Let $Y_1 < Y_2 < \cdots < Y_n$ denote the corresponding order statistics. Note that given $Y_1 = y_1, Y_2 = y_2, \ldots, Y_n = y_n$, the conditional distribution of $X_1, X_2, \ldots, X_n$ is discrete with probability $\frac{1}{n!}$ on each of the $n!$ permutations of the vector $(y_1, y_2, \ldots, y_n)$, [because $F(x)$ is continuous, we can assume that each of the values $y_1, y_2, \ldots, y_n$ is distinct]. That is, the conditional distribution does not depend on $F(x)$. Hence, by the definition of sufficiency, the order statistics are sufficient for $F(x)$. Furthermore, while the proof is beyond the scope of this book, it can be shown that the order statistics are also complete; see page 72 of Lehmann and Casella (1998).

Let $T = T(x_1, x_2, \ldots, x_n)$ be any statistic which is *symmetric in its arguments*; i.e., $T(x_1, x_2, \ldots, x_n) = T(x_{i_1}, x_{i_2}, \ldots, x_{i_n})$ for any permutation $(x_{i_1}, x_{i_2}, \ldots, x_{i_n})$ of $(x_1, x_2, \ldots, x_n)$. Then T is a function of the order statistics. This is useful in determining MVUEs for this situation; see Exercises 7.7.12 and 7.7.13. ∎

EXERCISES

7.7.1. Let $Y_1 < Y_2 < Y_3$ be the order statistics of a random sample of size 3 from the distribution with pdf

$$f(x; \theta_1, \theta_2) = \begin{cases} \frac{1}{\theta_2} \exp\left(-\frac{x - \theta_1}{\theta_2}\right) & \theta_1 < x < \infty, \ -\infty < \theta_1 < \infty, \ 0 < \theta_2 < \infty \\ 0 & \text{elsewhere.} \end{cases}$$

Find the joint pdf of $Z_1 = Y_1, Z_2 = Y_2$, and $Z_3 = Y_1 + Y_2 + Y_3$. The corresponding transformation maps the space $\{(y_1, y_2, y_3) : \theta_1 < y_1 < y_2 < y_3 < \infty\}$ onto the space

$$\{(z_1, z_2, z_3) : \theta_1 < z_1 < z_2 < (z_3 - z_1)/2 < \infty\}.$$

Show that Z_1 and Z_3 are joint sufficient statistics for θ_1 and θ_2.

7.7.2. Let $X_1, X_2, \ldots, X_n$ be a random sample from a distribution that has a pdf of the form (7.7.2) of this section. Show that $Y_1 = \sum_{i=1}^{n} K_1(X_i), \ldots, Y_m = \sum_{i=1}^{m} K_m(X_i)$ have a joint pdf of the form (7.7.4) of this section.

7.7.3. Let $(X_1, Y_1), (X_2, Y_2), \ldots, (X_n, Y_n)$ denote a random sample of size n from a bivariate normal distribution with means μ_1 and μ_2, positive variances σ_1^2 and σ_2^2, and correlation coefficient ρ. Show that $\sum_1^n X_i, \sum_1^n Y_i, \sum_1^n X_i^2, \sum_1^n Y_i^2$, and $\sum_1^n X_i Y_i$ are joint complete sufficient statistics for the five parameters. Are $\overline{X} = \sum_1^n X_i/n$, $\overline{Y} = \sum_1^n Y_i/n$, $S_1^2 = \sum_1^n (X_i - \overline{X})^2/(n-1)$, $S_2^2 = \sum_1^n (Y_i - \overline{Y})^2/(n-1)$, and $\sum_1^n (X_i - \overline{X})(Y_i - \overline{Y})/(n-1)S_1 S_2$ also joint complete sufficient statistics for these parameters?

7.7.4. Let the pdf $f(x; \theta_1, \theta_2)$ be of the form

$$\exp[p_1(\theta_1, \theta_2)K_1(x) + p_2(\theta_1, \theta_2)K_2(x) + H(x) + q_1(\theta_1, \theta_2)], \quad a < x < b,$$

zero elsewhere. Suppose that $K_1'(x) = cK_2'(x)$. Show that $f(x; \theta_1, \theta_2)$ can be written in the form

$$\exp[p(\theta_1, \theta_2)K_2(x) + H(x) + q(\theta_1, \theta_2)], \quad a < x < b,$$

zero elsewhere. This is the reason why it is required that no one $K_j'(x)$ be a linear homogeneous function of the others, that is, so that the number of sufficient statistics equals the number of parameters.

7.7.5. In Example 7.7.2, find the MVUE of the standard deviation $\sqrt{\theta_2}$.

7.7.6. Let $X_1, X_2, \ldots, X_n$ be a random sample from the uniform distribution with pdf $f(x; \theta_1, \theta_2) = 1/(2\theta_2)$, $\theta_1 - \theta_2 < x < \theta_1 + \theta_2$, where $-\infty < \theta_1 < \infty$ and $\theta_2 > 0$, and the pdf is equal to zero elsewhere.

(a) Show that $Y_1 = \min(X_i)$ and $Y_n = \max(X_i)$, the joint sufficient statistics for θ_1 and θ_2, are complete.

(b) Find the MVUEs of θ_1 and θ_2.

7.7.7. Let $X_1, X_2, \ldots, X_n$ be a random sample from $N(\theta_1, \theta_2)$.

(a) If the constant b is defined by the equation $P(X \leq b) = 0.90$, find the mle and the MVUE of b.

(b) If c is a given constant, find the mle and the MVUE of $P(X \leq c)$.

7.7.8. In the notation of Example 7.7.3, show that the mle of $p_j p_l$ is $n^{-2} Y_j Y_l$.

7.7.9. Refer to Example 7.7.4 on sufficiency for the multivariate normal model.

(a) Determine the MVUE of the covariance parameters σ_{ij}.

(b) Let $g = \sum_{i=1}^{k} a_i \mu_i$, where $a_1, \ldots, a_k$ are specified constants. Find the MVUE for g.

7.7.10. In a personal communication, LeRoy Folks noted that the inverse Gaussian pdf

$$f(x; \theta_1, \theta_2) = \left(\frac{\theta_2}{2\pi x^3}\right)^{1/2} \exp\left[\frac{-\theta_2(x - \theta_1)^2}{2\theta_1^2 x}\right], \quad 0 < x < \infty, \qquad (7.7.9)$$

where $\theta_1 > 0$ and $\theta_2 > 0$, is often used to model lifetimes. Find the complete sufficient statistics for (θ_1, θ_2) if $X_1, X_2, \ldots, X_n$ is a random sample from the distribution having this pdf.

7.7.11. Let $X_1, X_2, \ldots, X_n$ be a random sample from a $N(\theta_1, \theta_2)$ distribution.

(a) Show that $E[(X_1 - \theta_1)^4] = 3\theta_2^2$.

(b) Find the MVUE of $3\theta_2^2$.

7.7.12. Let $X_1, \ldots, X_n$ be a random sample from a distribution of the continuous type with cdf $F(x)$. Suppose the mean, $\mu = E(X_1)$, exists. Using Example 7.7.5, show that the sample mean, $\overline{X} = n^{-1} \sum_{i=1}^{n} X_i$, is the MVUE of μ.

7.7.13. Let $X_1, \ldots, X_n$ be a random sample from a distribution of the continuous type with cdf $F(x)$. Let $\theta = P(X_1 \leq a) = F(a)$, where a is known. Show that the proportion $n^{-1} \#\{X_i \leq a\}$ is the MVUE of θ.

7.8 Minimal Sufficiency and Ancillary Statistics

In the study of statistics, it is clear that we want to reduce the data contained in the entire sample as much as possible without losing relevant information about the important characteristics of the underlying distribution. That is, a large collection of numbers in the sample is not as meaningful as a few good summary statistics of those data. Sufficient statistics, if they exist, are valuable because we know that the statisticians with those summary measures have as much information as the statistician with the entire sample. Sometimes, however, there are several sets of joint sufficient statistics, and thus we would like to find the simplest one of these sets. For illustration, in a sense, the observations $X_1, X_2, \ldots, X_n$, $n > 2$, of a random sample from $N(\theta_1, \theta_2)$ could be thought of as joint sufficient statistics for θ_1 and θ_2. We know, however, that we can use $\overline{X}$ and S^2 as joint sufficient statistics for those parameters, which is a great simplification over using $X_1, X_2, \ldots, X_n$, particularly if n is large.

In most instances in this chapter, we have been able to find a single sufficient statistic for one parameter or two joint sufficient statistics for two parameters. Possibly the most complicated cases considered so far are given in Example 7.7.3, in which we find $k + k(k+1)/2$ joint sufficient statistics for $k + k(k+1)/2$ parameters; or the multivariate normal distribution given in Example 7.7.4; or the use the order statistics of a random sample for some completely unknown distribution of the continuous type as in Example 7.7.5.

What we would like to do is to change from one set of joint sufficient statistics to another, always reducing the number of statistics involved until we cannot go any further without losing the sufficiency of the resulting statistics. Those statistics that are there at the end of this reduction are called **minimal sufficient statistics**. These are sufficient for the parameters and are functions of every other set of sufficient statistics for those same parameters. Often, if there are k parameters, we can find k joint sufficient statistics that are minimal. In particular, if there is one parameter, we can often find a single sufficient statistic which is minimal. Most of the earlier examples that we have considered illustrate this point, but this is not always the case, as shown by the following example.

Example 7.8.1. Let $X_1, X_2, \ldots, X_n$ be a random sample from the uniform distribution over the interval $(\theta - 1, \theta + 1)$ having pdf

$$f(x; \theta) = (\tfrac{1}{2}) I_{(\theta-1, \theta+1)}(x), \quad \text{where} - \infty < \theta < \infty.$$

The joint pdf of $X_1, X_2, \ldots, X_n$ equals the product of $(\frac{1}{2})^n$ and certain indicator functions, namely,

$$\left(\frac{1}{2}\right)^n \prod_{i=1}^n I_{(\theta-1,\theta+1)}(x_i) = \left(\frac{1}{2}\right)^n \{I_{(\theta-1,\theta+1)}[\min(x_i)]\}\{I_{(\theta-1,\theta+1)}[\max(x_i)]\},$$

because $\theta - 1 < \min(x_i) \le x_j \le \max(x_i) < \theta + 1$, $j = 1, 2, \ldots, n$. Thus the order statistics $Y_1 = \min(X_i)$ and $Y_n = \max(X_i)$ are the sufficient statistics for θ. These two statistics actually are minimal for this one parameter, as we cannot reduce the number of them to less than two and still have sufficiency. ∎

There is an observation that helps us see that almost all the sufficient statistics that we have studied thus far are minimal. We have noted that the mle $\hat{\theta}$ of θ is a function of one or more sufficient statistics, when the latter exists. Suppose that this mle $\hat{\theta}$ is also sufficient. Since this sufficient statistic $\hat{\theta}$ is a function of the other sufficient statistics, by Theorem 7.3.2, it must be minimal. For example, we have

1. The mle $\hat{\theta} = \overline{X}$ of θ in $N(\theta, \sigma^2)$, σ^2 known, is a minimal sufficient statistic for θ.

2. The mle $\hat{\theta} = \overline{X}$ of θ in a Poisson distribution with mean θ is a minimal sufficient statistic for θ.

3. The mle $\hat{\theta} = Y_n = \max(X_i)$ of θ in the uniform distribution over $(0, \theta)$ is a minimal sufficient statistic for θ.

4. The maximum likelihood estimators $\hat{\theta}_1 = \overline{X}$ and $\hat{\theta}_2 = [(n-1)/n]S^2$ of θ_1 and θ_2 in $N(\theta_1, \theta_2)$ are joint minimal sufficient statistics for θ_1 and θ_2.

From these examples we see that the minimal sufficient statistics do not need to be unique, for any one-to-one transformation of them also provides minimal sufficient statistics. The linkage between minimal sufficient statistics and the mle, however, does not hold in many interesting instances. We illustrate this in the next two examples.

Example 7.8.2. Consider the model given in Example 7.8.1. There we noted that $Y_1 = \min(X_i)$ and $Y_n = \max(X_i)$ are joint sufficient statistics. Also, we have

$$\theta - 1 < Y_1 < Y_n < \theta + 1$$

or, equivalently,

$$Y_n - 1 < \theta < Y_1 + 1.$$

Hence, to maximize the likelihood function so that it equals $(\frac{1}{2})^n$, θ can be any value between $Y_n - 1$ and $Y_1 + 1$. For example, many statisticians take the mle to be the mean of these two endpoints, namely,

$$\hat{\theta} = \frac{Y_n - 1 + Y_1 + 1}{2} = \frac{Y_1 + Y_n}{2},$$

which is the midrange. We recognize, however, that this mle is not unique. Some might argue that since $\hat{\theta}$ is an mle of θ and since it is a function of the joint sufficient statistics, Y_1 and Y_n, for θ, it is a minimal sufficient statistic. This is not the case at all, for $\hat{\theta}$ is not even sufficient. Note that the mle must itself be a sufficient statistic for the parameter before it can be considered the minimal sufficient statistic. ∎

Note that we can model the situation in the last example by

$$X_i = \theta + W_i, \qquad (7.8.1)$$

where $W_1, W_2, \ldots, W_n$ are iid with the common uniform$(-1, 1)$ pdf. Hence this is an example of a location model. We discuss these models in general next.

Example 7.8.3. Consider a location model given by

$$X_i = \theta + W_i, \qquad (7.8.2)$$

where $W_1, W_2, \ldots, W_n$ are iid with the common pdf $f(w)$ and common continuous cdf $F(w)$. From Example 7.7.5, we know that the order statistics $Y_1 < Y_2 < \cdots < Y_n$ are a set of complete and sufficient statistics for this situation. Can we obtain a smaller set of minimal sufficient statistics? Consider the following four situations:

(a) Suppose $f(w)$ is the $N(0, 1)$ pdf. Then we know that $\overline{X}$ is both the MVUE and mle of θ. Also, $\overline{X} = n^{-1} \sum_{i=1}^{n} Y_i$, i.e., a function of the order statistics. Hence $\overline{X}$ is minimal sufficient.

(b) Suppose $f(w) = \exp\{-w\}$, for $w > 0$, zero elsewhere. Then the statistic Y_1 is a sufficient statistic as well as the mle, and thus is minimal sufficient.

(c) Suppose $f(w)$ is the logistic pdf. As discussed in Example 6.1.2, the mle of θ exists and it is easy to compute. As shown on page 38 of Lehmann and Casella (1998), though, the order statistics are minimal sufficient for this situation. That is, no reduction is possible.

(d) Suppose $f(w)$ is the Laplace pdf. It was shown in Example 6.1.1 that the median, Q_2 is the mle of θ, but it is not a sufficient statistic. Further, similar to the logistic pdf, it can be shown that the order statistics are minimal sufficient for this situation. ∎

In general, the situation described in parts (c) and (d), where the mle is obtained rather easily while the set of minimal sufficient statistics is the set of order statistics and no reduction is possible, is the norm for location models.

There is also a relationship between a minimal sufficient statistic and completeness that is explained more fully in Lehmann and Scheffé (1950). Let us say simply and without explanation that for the cases in this book, complete sufficient statistics are minimal sufficient statistics. The converse is not true, however, by noting that in Example 7.8.1, we have

$$E\left[\frac{Y_n - Y_1}{2} - \frac{n-1}{n+1}\right] = 0, \quad \text{for all } \theta.$$

That is, there is a nonzero function of those minimal sufficient statistics, Y_1 and Y_n, whose expectation is zero for all θ.

There are other statistics that almost seem opposites of sufficient statistics. That is, while sufficient statistics contain all the information about the parameters, these other statistics, called **ancillary statistics**, have distributions free of the parameters and seemingly contain no information about those parameters. As an illustration, we know that the variance S^2 of a random sample from $N(\theta, 1)$ has a distribution that does not depend upon θ and hence is an ancillary statistic. Another example is the ratio $Z = X_1/(X_1 + X_2)$, where X_1, X_2 is a random sample from a gamma distribution with known parameter $\alpha > 0$ and unknown parameter $\beta = \theta$, because Z has a beta distribution that is free of θ. There are many examples of ancillary statistics, and we provide some rules that make them rather easy to find with certain models, which we present in the next three examples.

Example 7.8.4 (Location-Invariant Statistics). In Example 7.8.3, we introduced the location model. Recall that a random sample $X_1, X_2, \ldots, X_n$ follows this model if

$$X_i = \theta + W_i, \quad i = 1, \ldots, n, \tag{7.8.3}$$

where $-\infty < \theta < \infty$ is a parameter and $W_1, W_2, \ldots, W_n$ are iid random variables with the pdf $f(w)$, which does not depend on θ. Then the common pdf of X_i is $f(x - \theta)$.

Let $Z = u(X_1, X_2, \ldots, X_n)$ be a statistic such that

$$u(x_1 + d, x_2 + d, \ldots, x_n + d) = u(x_1, x_2, \ldots, x_n),$$

for all real d. Hence

$$Z = u(W_1 + \theta, W_2 + \theta, \ldots, W_n + \theta) = u(W_1, W_2, \ldots, W_n)$$

is a function of $W_1, W_2, \ldots, W_n$ alone (not of θ). Hence Z must have a distribution that does not depend upon θ. We call $Z = u(X_1, X_2, \ldots, X_n)$ a **location-invariant statistic**.

Assuming a location model, the following are some examples of location-invariant statistics: the sample variance $= S^2$, the sample range $= \max\{X_i\} - \min\{X_i\}$, the mean deviation from the sample median $= (1/n) \sum |X_i - \text{median}(X_i)|$, $X_1 + X_2 - X_3 - X_4$, $X_1 + X_3 - 2X_2$, $(1/n) \sum [X_i - \min(X_i)]$, and so on. To see that the range is location-invariant, note that

$$\max\{X_i\} - \theta = \max\{X_i - \theta\} = \max\{W_i\}$$
$$\min\{X_i\} - \theta = \min\{X_i - \theta\} = \min\{W_i\}.$$

So,

$$\text{range} = \max\{X_i\} - \min\{X_i\} = \max\{X_i\} - \theta - (\min\{X_i\} - \theta) = \max\{W_i\} - \min\{W_i\}.$$

Hence the distribution of the range only depends on the distribution of the W_is and, thus, it is location-invariant. For the location invariance of other statistics, see Exercise 7.8.4. ■

Example 7.8.5 (Scale-Invariant Statistics). Consider a random sample $X_1, \ldots, X_n$ which follows a **scale model**, i.e., a model of the form

$$X_i = \theta W_i, \quad i = 1, \ldots, n, \tag{7.8.4}$$

where $\theta > 0$ and $W_1, W_2, \ldots, W_n$ are iid random variables with pdf $f(w)$, which does not depend on θ. Then the common pdf of X_i is $\theta^{-1} f(x/\theta)$. We call θ a scale parameter. Suppose that $Z = u(X_1, X_2, \ldots, X_n)$ is a statistic such that

$$u(cx_1, cx_2, \ldots, cx_n) = u(x_1, x_2, \ldots, x_n)$$

for all $c > 0$. Then

$$Z = u(X_1, X_2, \ldots, X_n) = u(\theta W_1, \theta W_2, \ldots, \theta W_n) = u(W_1, W_2, \ldots, W_n).$$

Since neither the joint pdf of $W_1, W_2, \ldots, W_n$ nor Z contains θ, the distribution of Z must not depend upon θ. We say that Z is a **scale-invariant statistic**.

The following are some examples of scale-invariant statistics: $X_1/(X_1 + X_2)$, $X_1^2/\sum_1^n X_i^2$, $\min(X_i)/\max(X_i)$, and so on. The scale invariance of the first statistic follows from

$$\frac{X_1}{X_1 + X_2} = \frac{(\theta X_1)/\theta}{[(\theta X_1) + (\theta X_2)]/\theta} = \frac{W_1}{W_1 + W_2}.$$

The scale invariance of the other statistics is asked for in Exercise 7.8.5. ∎

Example 7.8.6 (Location- and Scale-Invariant Statistics). Finally, consider a random sample $X_1, X_2, \ldots, X_n$ which follows a location and scale model as in Example 7.7.5. That is,

$$X_i = \theta_1 + \theta_2 W_i, \quad i = 1, \ldots, n, \tag{7.8.5}$$

where W_i are iid with the common pdf $f(t)$ which is free of θ_1 and θ_2. In this case, the pdf of X_i is $\theta_2^{-1} f((x - \theta_1)/\theta_2)$. Consider the statistic $Z = u(X_1, X_2, \ldots, X_n)$, where

$$u(cx_1 + d, \ldots, cx_n + d) = u(x_1, \ldots, x_n).$$

Then

$$Z = u(X_1, \ldots, X_n) = u(\theta_1 + \theta_2 W_1, \ldots, \theta_1 + \theta_2 W_n) = u(W_1, \ldots, W_n).$$

Since neither the joint pdf of $W_1, \ldots, W_n$ nor Z contains θ_1 and θ_2, the distribution of Z must not depend upon θ_1 nor θ_2. Statistics such as $Z = u(X_1, X_2, \ldots, X_n)$ are called **location- and scale-invariant statistics**. The following are four examples of such statistics:

(a) $T_1 = [\max(X_i) - \min(X_i)]/S$;

(b) $T_2 = \sum_{i=1}^{n-1} (X_{i+1} - X_i)^2/S^2$;

(c) $T_3 = (X_i - \overline{X})/S$;

(d) $T_4 = |X_i - X_j|/S,, \; ; i \neq j$.

Let $\overline{X} - \theta_1 = n^{-1}\sum_{i=1}^{n}(X_i - \theta_1)$. Then the location and scale invariance of the statistic in (d) follows from the two identities

$$S^2 = \theta_2^2 \sum_{i=1}^{n}\left[\frac{X_i - \theta_1}{\theta_2} - \frac{\overline{X} - \theta_1}{\theta_2}\right]^2 = \theta_2^2 \sum_{i=1}^{n}(W_i - \overline{W})^2$$

$$X_i - X_j = \theta_2\left[\frac{X_i - \theta_1}{\theta_2} - \frac{X_j - \theta_1}{\theta_2}\right] = \theta_2(W_i - W_j).$$

See Exercise 7.8.6 for the other statistics. ∎

Thus, these location-invariant, scale-invariant, and location- and scale-invariant statistics provide good illustrations, with the appropriate model for the pdf, of ancillary statistics. Since an ancillary statistic and a complete (minimal) sufficient statistic are such opposites, we might believe that there is, in some sense, no relationship between the two. This is true, and in the next section we show that they are independent statistics.

EXERCISES

7.8.1. Let $X_1, X_2, \ldots, X_n$ be a random sample from each of the following distributions involving the parameter θ. In each case find the mle of θ and show that it is a sufficient statistic for θ and hence a minimal sufficient statistic.

(a) $b(1, \theta)$, where $0 \le \theta \le 1$.

(b) Poisson with mean $\theta > 0$.

(c) Gamma with $\alpha = 3$ and $\beta = \theta > 0$.

(d) $N(\theta, 1)$, where $-\infty < \theta < \infty$.

(e) $N(0, \theta)$, where $0 < \theta < \infty$.

7.8.2. Let $Y_1 < Y_2 < \cdots < Y_n$ be the order statistics of a random sample of size n from the uniform distribution over the closed interval $[-\theta, \theta]$ having pdf $f(x; \theta) = (1/2\theta)I_{[-\theta,\theta]}(x)$.

(a) Show that Y_1 and Y_n are joint sufficient statistics for θ.

(b) Argue that the mle of θ is $\hat{\theta} = \max(-Y_1, Y_n)$.

(c) Demonstrate that the mle $\hat{\theta}$ is a sufficient statistic for θ and thus is a minimal sufficient statistic for θ.

7.8.3. Let $Y_1 < Y_2 < \cdots < Y_n$ be the order statistics of a random sample of size n from a distribution with pdf

$$f(x; \theta_1, \theta_2) = \left(\frac{1}{\theta_2}\right)e^{-(x-\theta_1)/\theta_2}I_{(\theta_1,\infty)}(x),$$

where $-\infty < \theta_1 < \infty$ and $0 < \theta_2 < \infty$. Find the joint minimal sufficient statistics for θ_1 and θ_2.

7.8.4. Continuing with Example 7.8.4, show that the following statistics are location-invariant:

(a) The sample variance $= S^2$.

(b) The mean deviation from the sample median $= (1/n) \sum |X_i - \text{median}(X_i)|$.

(c) $(1/n) \sum [X_i - \min(X_i)]$.

7.8.5. In Example 7.8.5, a scale model was presented and scale invariance was defined. Using the notation of this example, show that the following statistics are scale-invariant:

(a) $X_1^2 / \sum_{1}^{n} X_i^2$.

(b) $\min\{X_i\} / \max\{X_i\}$.

7.8.6. Obtain the location and scale invariance of the other statistics listed in Example 7.8.6, i.e., the statistics

(a) $T_1 = [\max(X_i) - \min(X_i)]/S$.

(b) $T_2 = \sum_{i=1}^{n-1} (X_{i+1} - X_i)^2 / S^2$.

(c) $T_3 = (X_i - \overline{X})/S$.

7.8.7. With random samples from each of the distributions given in Exercises 7.8.1(d), 7.8.2, and 7.8.3, define at least two ancillary statistics that are different from the examples given in the text. These examples illustrate, respectively, location-invariant, scale invariant, and location- and scale-invariant statistics.

7.9 Sufficiency, Completeness, and Independence

We have noted that if we have a sufficient statistic Y_1 for a parameter θ, $\theta \in \Omega$, then $h(z|y_1)$, the conditional pdf of another statistic Z, given $Y_1 = y_1$, does not depend upon θ. If, moreover, Y_1 and Z are independent, the pdf $g_2(z)$ of Z is such that $g_2(z) = h(z|y_1)$, and hence $g_2(z)$ must not depend upon θ either. So the independence of a statistic Z and the sufficient statistic Y_1 for a parameter θ mean that the distribution of Z does not depend upon $\theta \in \Omega$. That is, Z is an ancillary statistic.

It is interesting to investigate a converse of that property. Suppose that the distribution of an ancillary statistic Z does not depend upon θ; then are Z and the sufficient statistic Y_1 for θ independent? To begin our search for the answer, we know that the joint pdf of Y_1 and Z is $g_1(y_1; \theta) h(z|y_1)$, where $g_1(y_1; \theta)$ and $h(z|y_1)$ represent the marginal pdf of Y_1 and the conditional pdf of Z given $Y_1 = y_1$, respectively. Thus the marginal pdf of Z is

$$\int_{-\infty}^{\infty} g_1(y_1; \theta) h(z|y_1) \, dy_1 = g_2(z),$$

which, by hypothesis, does not depend upon θ. Because

$$\int_{-\infty}^{\infty} g_2(z)g_1(y_1;\theta)\,dy_1 = g_2(z),$$

if follows, by taking the difference of the last two integrals, that

$$\int_{-\infty}^{\infty} [g_2(z) - h(z|y_1)]g_1(y_1;\theta)\,dy_1 = 0 \qquad (7.9.1)$$

for all $\theta \in \Omega$. Since Y_1 is sufficient statistic for θ, $h(z|y_1)$ does not depend upon θ. By assumption, $g_2(z)$ and hence $g_2(z) - h(z|y_1)$ do not depend upon θ. Now if the family $\{g_1(y_1;\theta) : \theta \in \Omega\}$ is complete, Equation (7.9.1) would require that

$$g_2(z) - h(z|y_1) = 0 \quad \text{or} \quad g_2(z) = h(z|y_1).$$

That is, the joint pdf of Y_1 and Z must be equal to

$$g_1(y_1;\theta)h(z|y_1) = g_1(y_1;\theta)g_2(z).$$

Accordingly, Y_1 and Z are independent, and we have proved the following theorem, which was considered in special cases by Neyman and Hogg and proved in general by Basu.

Theorem 7.9.1. *Let $X_1, X_2, \ldots, X_n$ denote a random sample from a distribution having a pdf $f(x;\theta)$, $\theta \in \Omega$, where Ω is an interval set. Suppose that the statistic Y_1 is a complete and sufficient statistic for θ. Let $Z = u(X_1, X_2, \ldots, X_n)$ be any other statistic (not a function of Y_1 alone). If the distribution of Z does not depend upon θ, then Z is independent of the sufficient statistic Y_1.*

In the discussion above, it is interesting to observe that if Y_1 is a sufficient statistic for θ, then the independence of Y_1 and Z implies that the distribution of Z does not depend upon θ whether $\{g_1(y_1;\theta) : \theta \in \Omega\}$ is or is not complete. Conversely, to prove the independence from the fact that $g_2(z)$ does not depend upon θ, we definitely need the completeness. Accordingly, if we are dealing with situations in which we know that family $\{g_1(y_1;\theta) : \theta \in \Omega\}$ is complete (such as a regular case of the exponential class), we can say that the statistic Z is independent of the sufficient statistic Y_1 if and only if the distribution of Z does not depend upon θ(i.e., Z is an ancillary statistic).

It should be remarked that the theorem (including the special formulation of it for regular cases of the exponential class) extends immediately to probability density functions that involve m parameters for which there exist m joint sufficient statistics. For example, let $X_1, X_2, \ldots, X_n$ be a random sample from a distribution having the pdf $f(x;\theta_1,\theta_2)$ that represents a regular case of the exponential class so that there are two joint complete sufficient statistics for θ_1 and θ_2. Then any other statistic $Z = u(X_1, X_2, \ldots, X_n)$ is independent of the joint complete sufficient statistics if and only if the distribution of Z does not depend upon θ_1 or θ_2.

We present an example of the theorem that provides an alternative proof of the independence of $\overline{X}$ and S^2, the mean and the variance of a random sample of size n

from a distribution that is $N(\mu, \sigma^2)$. This proof is given as if we were unaware that $(n-1)S^2/\sigma^2$ is $\chi^2(n-1)$, because that fact and the independence were established in Theorem 3.6.1.

Example 7.9.1. Let $X_1, X_2, \ldots, X_n$ denote a random sample of size n from a distribution that is $N(\mu, \sigma^2)$. We know that the mean $\overline{X}$ of the sample is, for every known σ^2, a complete sufficient statistic for the parameter μ, $-\infty < \mu < \infty$. Consider the statistic

$$S^2 = \frac{1}{n-1} \sum_{i=1}^{n} (X_i - \overline{X})^2,$$

which is location-invariant. Thus S^2 must have a distribution that does not depend upon μ; and hence, by the theorem, S^2 and $\overline{X}$, the complete sufficient statistic for μ, are independent. ∎

Example 7.9.2. Let $X_1, X_2, \ldots, X_n$ be a random sample of size n from the distribution having pdf

$$\begin{aligned} f(x; \theta) &= e^{-(x-\theta)}, \quad \theta < x < \infty, \quad -\infty < \theta < \infty, \\ &= 0 \quad \text{elsewhere.} \end{aligned}$$

Here the pdf is of the form $f(x - \theta)$, where $f(w) = e^{-w}$, $0 < w < \infty$, zero elsewhere. Moreover, we know (Exercise 7.4.5) that the first order statistic $Y_1 = \min(X_i)$ is a complete sufficient statistic for θ. Hence Y_1 must be independent of each location-invariant statistic $u(X_1, X_2, \ldots, X_n)$, enjoying the property that

$$u(x_1 + d, x_2 + d, \ldots, x_n + d) = u(x_1, x_2, \ldots, x_n)$$

for all real d. Illustrations of such statistics are S^2, the sample range, and

$$\frac{1}{n} \sum_{i=1}^{n} [X_i - \min(X_i)]. \quad \blacksquare$$

Example 7.9.3. Let X_1, X_2 denote a random sample of size $n = 2$ from a distribution with pdf

$$\begin{aligned} f(x; \theta) &= \frac{1}{\theta} e^{-x/\theta}, \quad 0 < x < \infty, \quad 0 < \theta < \infty, \\ &= 0 \quad \text{elsewhere.} \end{aligned}$$

The pdf is of the form $(1/\theta) f(x/\theta)$, where $f(w) = e^{-w}$, $0 < w < \infty$, zero elsewhere. We know that $Y_1 = X_1 + X_2$ is a complete sufficient statistic for θ. Hence, Y_1 is independent of every scale-invariant statistic $u(X_1, X_2)$ with the property $u(cx_1, cx_2) = u(x_1, x_2)$. Illustrations of these are X_1/X_2 and $X_1/(X_1 + X_2)$, statistics that have F- and beta distributions, respectively. ∎

Example 7.9.4. Let $X_1, X_2, \ldots, X_n$ denote a random sample from a distribution that is $N(\theta_1, \theta_2)$, $-\infty < \theta_1 < \infty$, $0 < \theta_2 < \infty$. In Example 7.7.2 it was proved that the mean $\overline{X}$ and the variance S^2 of the sample are joint complete sufficient statistics for θ_1 and θ_2. Consider the statistic

$$Z = \frac{\sum_1^{n-1}(X_{i+1} - X_i)^2}{\sum_1^n (X_i - \overline{X})^2} = u(X_1, X_2, \ldots, X_n),$$

which satisfies the property that $u(cx_1 + d, \ldots, cx_n + d) = u(x_1, \ldots, x_n)$. That is, the ancillary statistic Z is independent of both $\overline{X}$ and S^2. ∎

In this section we have given several examples in which the complete sufficient statistics are independent of ancillary statistics. Thus, in those cases, the ancillary statistics provide no information about the parameters. However, if the sufficient statistics are not complete, the ancillary statistics could provide some information as the following example demonstrates.

Example 7.9.5. We refer back to Examples 7.8.1 and 7.8.2. There the first and nth order statistics, Y_1 and Y_n, were minimal sufficient statistics for θ, where the sample arose from an underlying distribution having pdf $(\frac{1}{2})I_{(\theta-1,\theta+1)}(x)$. Often $T_1 = (Y_1 + Y_n)/2$ is used as an estimator of θ, as it is a function of those sufficient statistics which is unbiased. Let us find a relationship between T_1 and the ancillary statistic $T_2 = Y_n - Y_1$.

The joint pdf of Y_1 and Y_n is

$$g(y_1, y_n; \theta) = n(n-1)(y_n - y_1)^{n-2}/2^n, \quad \theta - 1 < y_1 < y_n < \theta + 1,$$

zero elsewhere. Accordingly, the joint pdf of T_1 and T_2 is, since the absolute value of the Jacobian equals 1,

$$h(t_1, t_2; \theta) = n(n-1)t_2^{n-2}/2^n, \quad \theta - 1 + \frac{t_2}{2} < t_1 < \theta + 1 - \frac{t_2}{2}, \quad 0 < t_2 < 2,$$

zero elsewhere. Thus the pdf of T_2 is

$$h_2(t_2; \theta) = n(n-1)t_2^{n-2}(2 - t_2)/2^n, \quad 0 < t_2 < 2,$$

zero elsewhere, which, of course, is free of θ as T_2 is an ancillary statistic. Thus, the conditional pdf of T_1, given $T_2 = t_2$, is

$$h_{1|2}(t_1|t_2; \theta) = \frac{1}{2 - t_2}, \quad \theta - 1 + \frac{t_2}{2} < t_1 < \theta + 1 - \frac{t_2}{2}, \quad 0 < t_2 < 2,$$

zero elsewhere. Note that this is uniform on the interval $(\theta - 1 + t_2/2, \theta + 1 - t_2/2)$; so the conditional mean and variance of T_1 are, respectively,

$$E(T_1|t_2) = \theta \quad \text{and} \quad \text{var}(T_1|t_2) = \frac{(2 - t_2)^2}{12}.$$

Given $T_2 = t_2$, we know something about the conditional variance of T_1. In particular, if that observed value of T_2 is large (close to 2), then that variance is small and we can place more reliance on the estimator T_1. On the other hand, a small value of t_2 means that we have less confidence in T_1 as an estimator of θ. It is extremely interesting to note that this conditional variance does not depend upon the sample size n but only on the given value of $T_2 = t_2$. As the sample size increases, T_2 tends to becomes larger and, in those cases, T_1 has smaller conditional variance. ∎

While Example 7.9.5 is a special one demonstrating mathematically that an ancillary statistic can provide some help in point estimation, this does actually happen in practice, too. For illustration, we know that if the sample size is large enough, then

$$T = \frac{\overline{X} - \mu}{S/\sqrt{n}}$$

has an approximate standard normal distribution. Of course, if the sample arises from a normal distribution, $\overline{X}$ and S are independent and T has a t-distribution with $n - 1$ degrees of freedom. Even if the sample arises from a symmetric distribution, $\overline{X}$ and S are uncorrelated and T has an approximate t-distribution and certainly an approximate standard normal distribution with sample sizes around 30 or 40. On the other hand, if the sample arises from a highly skewed distribution (say to the right), then $\overline{X}$ and S are highly correlated and the probability $P(-1.96 < T < 1.96)$ is not necessarily close to 0.95 unless the sample size is extremely large (certainly much greater than 30). Intuitively, one can understand why this correlation exists if the underlying distribution is highly skewed to the right. While S has a distribution free of μ (and hence is an ancillary), a large value of S implies a large value of $\overline{X}$, since the underlying pdf is like the one depicted in Figure 7.9.1. Of course, a small value of $\overline{X}$ (say less than the mode) requires a relatively small value of S. This means that unless n is extremely large, it is risky to say that

$$\overline{x} - \frac{1.96s}{\sqrt{n}}, \quad \overline{x} + \frac{1.96s}{\sqrt{n}}$$

provides an approximate 95% confidence interval with data from a very skewed distribution. As a matter of fact, the authors have seen situations in which this confidence coefficient is closer to 80%, rather than 95%, with sample sizes of 30 to 40.

EXERCISES

7.9.1. Let $Y_1 < Y_2 < Y_3 < Y_4$ denote the order statistics of a random sample of size $n = 4$ from a distribution having pdf $f(x; \theta) = 1/\theta$, $0 < x < \theta$, zero elsewhere, where $0 < \theta < \infty$. Argue that the complete sufficient statistic Y_4 for θ is independent of each of the statistics Y_1/Y_4 and $(Y_1 + Y_2)/(Y_3 + Y_4)$.
Hint: Show that the pdf is of the form $(1/\theta)f(x/\theta)$, where $f(w) = 1$, $0 < w < 1$, zero elsewhere.

Figure 7.9.1: Graph of a right skewed distribution; see also Exercise 7.9.14.

7.9.2. Let $Y_1 < Y_2 < \cdots < Y_n$ be the order statistics of a random sample from a $N(\theta, \sigma^2)$, $-\infty < \theta < \infty$, distribution. Show that the distribution of $Z = Y_n - \overline{X}$ does not depend upon θ. Thus $\overline{Y} = \sum_1^n Y_i/n$, a complete sufficient statistic for θ is independent of Z.

7.9.3. Let $X_1, X_2, \ldots, X_n$ be iid with the distribution $N(\theta, \sigma^2)$, $-\infty < \theta < \infty$. Prove that a necessary and sufficient condition that the statistics $Z = \sum_1^n a_i X_i$ and $Y = \sum_1^n X_i$, a complete sufficient statistic for θ, are independent is that $\sum_1^n a_i = 0$.

7.9.4. Let X and Y be random variables such that $E(X^k)$ and $E(Y^k) \neq 0$ exist for $k = 1, 2, 3, \ldots$. If the ratio X/Y and its denominator Y are independent, prove that $E[(X/Y)^k] = E(X^k)/E(Y^k), k = 1, 2, 3, \ldots$.
Hint: Write $E(X^k) = E[Y^k(X/Y)^k]$.

7.9.5. Let $Y_1 < Y_2 < \cdots < Y_n$ be the order statistics of a random sample of size n from a distribution that has pdf $f(x; \theta) = (1/\theta)e^{-x/\theta}$, $0 < x < \infty$, $0 < \theta < \infty$, zero elsewhere. Show that the ratio $R = nY_1 / \sum_1^n Y_i$ and its denominator (a complete sufficient statistic for θ) are independent. Use the result of the preceding exercise to determine $E(R^k)$, $k = 1, 2, 3, \ldots$.

7.9.6. Let $X_1, X_2, \ldots, X_5$ be iid with pdf $f(x) = e^{-x}$, $0 < x < \infty$, zero elsewhere. Show that $(X_1 + X_2)/(X_1 + X_2 + \cdots + X_5)$ and its denominator are independent.
Hint: The pdf $f(x)$ is a member of $\{f(x; \theta) : 0 < \theta < \infty\}$, where $f(x; \theta) = (1/\theta)e^{-x/\theta}$, $0 < x < \infty$, zero elsewhere.

7.9.7. Let $Y_1 < Y_2 < \cdots < Y_n$ be the order statistics of a random sample from the normal distribution $N(\theta_1, \theta_2)$, $-\infty < \theta_1 < \infty$, $0 < \theta_2 < \infty$. Show that the joint complete sufficient statistics $\overline{X} = \overline{Y}$ and S^2 for θ_1 and θ_2 are independent of each of $(Y_n - \overline{Y})/S$ and $(Y_n - Y_1)/S$.

7.9.8. Let $Y_1 < Y_2 < \cdots < Y_n$ be the order statistics of a random sample from a distribution with the pdf

$$f(x; \theta_1, \theta_2) = \frac{1}{\theta_2} \exp\left(-\frac{x - \theta_1}{\theta_2}\right),$$

$\theta_1 < x < \infty$, zero elsewhere, where $-\infty < \theta_1 < \infty$, $0 < \theta_2 < \infty$. Show that the joint complete sufficient statistics Y_1 and $\overline{X} = \overline{Y}$ for the parameters θ_1 and θ_2 are independent of $(Y_2 - Y_1)/\sum_1^n (Y_i - Y_1)$.

7.9.9. Let $X_1, X_2, \ldots, X_5$ be a random sample of size $n = 5$ from the normal distribution $N(0, \theta)$.

(a) Argue that the ratio $R = (X_1^2 + X_2^2)/(X_1^2 + \cdots + X_5^2)$ and its denominator $(X_1^2 + \cdots + X_5^2)$ are independent.

(b) Does $5R/2$ have an F-distribution with 2 and 5 degrees of freedom? Explain your answer.

(c) Compute $E(R)$ using Exercise 7.9.4.

7.9.10. Referring to Example 7.9.5 of this section, determine c so that

$$P(-c < T_1 - \theta < c | T_2 = t_2) = 0.95.$$

Use this result to find a 95% confidence interval for θ, given $T_2 = t_2$; and note how its length is smaller when the range of t_2 is larger.

7.9.11. Show that $Y = |X|$ is a complete sufficient statistic for $\theta > 0$, where X has the pdf $f_X(x; \theta) = 1/(2\theta)$, for $-\theta < x < \theta$, zero elsewhere. Show that $Y = |X|$ and $Z = \text{sgn}(X)$ are independent.

7.9.12. Let $Y_1 < Y_2 < \cdots < Y_n$ be the order statistics of a random sample from a $N(\theta, \sigma^2)$ distribution, where σ^2 is fixed but arbitrary. Then $\overline{Y} = \overline{X}$ is a complete sufficient statistic for θ. Consider another estimator T of θ, such as $T = (Y_i + Y_{n+1-i})/2$, for $i = 1, 2, \ldots, [n/2]$, or T could be any weighted average of these latter statistics.

(a) Argue that $T - \overline{X}$ and $\overline{X}$ are independent random variables.

(b) Show that $\text{Var}(T) = \text{Var}(\overline{X}) + \text{Var}(T - \overline{X})$.

(c) Since we know $\text{Var}(\overline{X}) = \sigma^2/n$, it might be more efficient to estimate $\text{Var}(T)$ by estimating the $\text{Var}(T - \overline{X})$ by Monte Carlo methods rather than doing that with $\text{Var}(T)$ directly, because $\text{Var}(T) \geq \text{Var}(T - \overline{X})$. This is often called the *Monte Carlo Swindle*.

7.9.13. Suppose $X_1, X_2, \ldots, X_n$ is a random sample from a distribution with pdf $f(x; \theta) = (1/2)\theta^3 x^2 e^{-\theta x}$, $0 < x < \infty$, zero elsewhere, where $0 < \theta < \infty$:

(a) Find the mle, $\hat{\theta}$, of θ. Is $\hat{\theta}$ unbiased?
   Hint: Find the pdf of $Y = \sum_1^n X_i$ and then compute $E(\hat{\theta})$.

(b) Argue that Y is a complete sufficient statistic for θ.

(c) Find the MVUE of θ.

(d) Show that X_1/Y and Y are independent.

(e) What is the distribution of X_1/Y?

7.9.14. The pdf depicted in Figure 7.9.1 is given by

$$f_{m_2}(x) = e^{-x}(1 + m_2^{-1}e^{-x})^{-(m_2+1)}, \quad -\infty < x < \infty, \tag{7.9.2}$$

where $m_2 > 0$ (the pdf graphed is for $m_2 = 0.1$). This is a member of a large family of pdfs, $\log F$-family, which are useful in survival (lifetime) analysis; see Chapter 3 of Hettmansperger and McKean (2011).

(a) Let W be a random variable with pdf (7.9.2). Show that $W = \log Y$, where Y has an F-distribution with 2 and $2m_2$ degrees of freedom.

(b) Show that the pdf becomes the logistic (6.1.8) if $m_2 = 1$.

(c) Consider the location model where

$$X_i = \theta + W_i \quad i = 1, \ldots, n,$$

where $W_1, \ldots, W_n$ are iid with pdf (7.9.2). Similar to the logistic location model, the order statistics are minimal sufficient for this model. Show, similar to Example 6.1.2, that the mle of θ exists.

Chapter 8

Optimal Tests of Hypotheses

8.1 Most Powerful Tests

In Section 4.5, we introduced the concept of hypotheses testing and followed it with the introduction of likelihood ratio tests in Chapter 6. In this chapter, we discuss certain best tests.

For convenience to the reader, in the next several paragraphs we quickly review concepts of testing which were presented in Section 4.5. We are interested in a random variable X which has pdf or pmf $f(x; \theta)$, where $\theta \in \Omega$. We assume that $\theta \in \omega_0$ or $\theta \in \omega_1$, where ω_0 and ω_1 are disjoint subsets of Ω and $\omega_0 \cup \omega_1 = \Omega$. We label the hypotheses as

$$H_0 : \theta \in \omega_0 \text{ versus } H_1 : \theta \in \omega_1. \tag{8.1.1}$$

The hypothesis H_0 is referred to as the **null hypothesis**, while H_1 is referred to as the **alternative hypothesis**. The test of H_0 versus H_1 is based on a sample $X_1, \ldots, X_n$ from the distribution of X. In this chapter, we often use the vector $\mathbf{X}' = (X_1, \ldots, X_n)$ to denote the random sample and $\mathbf{x}' = (x_1, \ldots, x_n)$ to denote the values of the sample. Let $\mathcal{S}$ denote the support of the random sample $\mathbf{X}' = (X_1, \ldots, X_n)$.

A **test** of H_0 versus H_1 is based on a subset C of $\mathcal{S}$. This set C is called the **critical region** and its corresponding decision rule is

$$
\begin{aligned}
&\text{Reject } H_0 \text{ (Accept } H_1) && \text{if } \mathbf{X} \in C \\
&\text{Retain } H_0 \text{ (Reject } H_1) && \text{if } \mathbf{X} \in C^c.
\end{aligned}
\tag{8.1.2}
$$

Note that a test is defined by its critical region. Conversely, a critical region defines a test.

Recall that the 2×2 decision table, Table 4.5.1, summarizes the results of the hypothesis test in terms of the true state of nature. Besides the correct decisions, two errors can occur. A **Type I** error occurs if H_0 is rejected when it is true, while a **Type II** error occurs if H_0 is accepted when H_1 is true. The **size** or **significance**

level of the test is the probability of a Type I error; i.e.,

$$\alpha = \max_{\theta \in \omega_0} P_\theta(\mathbf{X} \in C). \tag{8.1.3}$$

Note that $P_\theta(\mathbf{X} \in C)$ should be read as the probability that $\mathbf{X} \in C$ when θ is the true parameter. Subject to tests having size α, we select tests that minimize Type II error or equivalently maximize the probability of rejecting H_0 when $\theta \in \omega_1$. Recall that the **power function** of a test is given by

$$\gamma_C(\theta) = P_\theta(\mathbf{X} \in C); \quad \theta \in \omega_1. \tag{8.1.4}$$

In Chapter 4, we gave examples of tests of hypotheses, while in Sections 6.3 and 6.4, we discussed tests based on maximum likelihood theory. In this chapter, we want to construct best tests for certain situations.

We begin with testing a simple hypothesis H_0 against a simple alternative H_1. Let $f(x; \theta)$ denote the pdf or pmf of a random variable X, where $\theta \in \Omega = \{\theta', \theta''\}$. Let $\omega_0 = \{\theta'\}$ and $\omega_1 = \{\theta''\}$. Let $\mathbf{X}' = (X_1, \ldots, X_n)$ be a random sample from the distribution of X. We now define a best critical region (and hence a best test) for testing the simple hypothesis H_0 against the alternative simple hypothesis H_1.

Definition 8.1.1. *Let C denote a subset of the sample space. Then we say that C is a **best critical region** of size α for testing the simple hypothesis $H_0 : \theta = \theta'$ against the alternative simple hypothesis $H_1 : \theta = \theta''$ if*

(a) *$P_{\theta'}[\mathbf{X} \in C] = \alpha$.*

(b) *And for every subset A of the sample space,*

$$P_{\theta'}[\mathbf{X} \in A] = \alpha \Rightarrow P_{\theta''}[\mathbf{X} \in C] \geq P_{\theta''}[\mathbf{X} \in A].$$

This definition states, in effect, the following: In general, there is a multiplicity of subsets A of the sample space such that $P_{\theta'}[\mathbf{X} \in A] = \alpha$. Suppose that there is one of these subsets, say C, such that when H_1 is true, the power of the test associated with C is at least as great as the power of the test associated with every other A. Then C is defined as a best critical region of size α for testing H_0 against H_1.

As Theorem 8.1.1 shows, there is a best test for this simple versus simple case. But first, we offer a simple example examining this definition in some detail.

Example 8.1.1. Consider the one random variable X that has a binomial distribution with $n = 5$ and $p = \theta$. Let $f(x; \theta)$ denote the pmf of X and let $H_0 : \theta = \frac{1}{2}$ and $H_1 : \theta = \frac{3}{4}$. The following tabulation gives, at points of positive probability density, the values of $f(x; \frac{1}{2})$, $f(x; \frac{3}{4})$, and the ratio $f(x; \frac{1}{2})/f(x; \frac{3}{4})$.

x	0	1	2
$f(x; 1/2)$	1/32	5/32	10/32
$f(x; 3/4)$	1/1024	15/1024	90/1024
$f(x; 1/2)/f(x; 3/4)$	32/1	32/3	32/9

x	3	4	5
$f(x; 1/2)$	10/32	5/32	1/32
$f(x; 3/4)$	270/1024	405/1024	243/1024
$f(x; 1/2)/f(x; 3/4)$	32/27	32/81	32/243

We shall use one random value of X to test the simple hypothesis $H_0 : \theta = \frac{1}{2}$ against the alternative simple hypothesis $H_1 : \theta = \frac{3}{4}$, and we shall first assign the significance level of the test to be $\alpha = \frac{1}{32}$. We seek a best critical region of size $\alpha = \frac{1}{32}$. If $A_1 = \{x : x = 0\}$ or $A_2 = \{x : x = 5\}$, then $P_{\{\theta=1/2\}}(X \in A_1) = P_{\{\theta=1/2\}}(X \in A_2) = \frac{1}{32}$ and there is no other subset A_3 of the space $\{x : x = 0, 1, 2, 3, 4, 5\}$ such that $P_{\{\theta=1/2\}}(X \in A_3) = \frac{1}{32}$. Then either A_1 or A_2 is the best critical region C of size $\alpha = \frac{1}{32}$ for testing H_0 against H_1. We note that $P_{\{\theta=1/2\}}(X \in A_1) = \frac{1}{32}$ and $P_{\{\theta=3/4\}}(X \in A_1) = \frac{1}{1024}$. Thus, if the set A_1 is used as a critical region of size $\alpha = \frac{1}{32}$, we have the intolerable situation that the probability of rejecting H_0 when H_1 is true (H_0 is false) is much less than the probability of rejecting H_0 when H_0 is true.

On the other hand, if the set A_2 is used as a critical region, then $P_{\{\theta=1/2\}}(X \in A_2) = \frac{1}{32}$ and $P_{\{\theta=3/4\}}(X \in A_2) = \frac{243}{1024}$. That is, the probability of rejecting H_0 when H_1 is true is much greater than the probability of rejecting H_0 when H_0 is true. Certainly, this is a more desirable state of affairs, and actually A_2 is the best critical region of size $\alpha = \frac{1}{32}$. The latter statement follows from the fact that when H_0 is true, there are but two subsets, A_1 and A_2, of the sample space, each of whose probability measure is $\frac{1}{32}$ and the fact that

$$\frac{243}{1024} = P_{\{\theta=3/4\}}(X \in A_2) > P_{\{\theta=3/4\}}(X \in A_1) = \frac{1}{1024}.$$

It should be noted in this problem that the best critical region $C = A_2$ of size $\alpha = \frac{1}{32}$ is found by including in C the point (or points) at which $f(x; \frac{1}{2})$ is *small* in comparison with $f(x; \frac{3}{4})$. This is seen to be true once it is observed that the ratio $f(x; \frac{1}{2})/f(x; \frac{3}{4})$ is a minimum at $x = 5$. Accordingly, the ratio $f(x; \frac{1}{2})/f(x; \frac{3}{4})$, which is given in the last line of the above tabulation, provides us with a precise tool by which to find a best critical region C for certain given values of α. To illustrate this, take $\alpha = \frac{6}{32}$. When H_0 is true, each of the subsets $\{x : x = 0, 1\}$, $\{x : x = 0, 4\}$, $\{x : x = 1, 5\}$, $\{x : x = 4, 5\}$ has probability measure $\frac{6}{32}$. By direct computation it is found that the best critical region of this size is $\{x : x = 4, 5\}$. This reflects the fact that the ratio $f(x; \frac{1}{2})/f(x; \frac{3}{4})$ has its two smallest values for $x = 4$ and $x = 5$. The power of this test, which has $\alpha = \frac{6}{32}$, is

$$P_{\{\theta=3/4\}}(X = 4, 5) = \frac{405}{1024} + \frac{243}{1024} = \frac{648}{1024}. \quad \blacksquare$$

The preceding example should make the following theorem, due to Neyman and Pearson, easier to understand. It is an important theorem because it provides a systematic method of determining a best critical region.

Theorem 8.1.1. Neyman–Pearson Theorem. *Let* $X_1, X_2, \ldots, X_n$, *where* n *is a fixed positive integer, denote a random sample from a distribution that has pdf or pmf* $f(x; \theta)$. *Then the likelihood of* $X_1, X_2, \ldots, X_n$ *is*

$$L(\theta; \mathbf{x}) = \prod_{i=1}^{n} f(x_i; \theta), \quad \text{for } \mathbf{x}' = (x_1, \ldots, x_n).$$

Let θ' *and* θ'' *be distinct fixed values of* θ *so that* $\Omega = \{\theta : \theta = \theta', \theta''\}$, *and let* k *be a positive number. Let* C *be a subset of the sample space such that*

(a) $\dfrac{L(\theta'; \mathbf{x})}{L(\theta''; \mathbf{x})} \leq k$, *for each point* $\mathbf{x} \in C$.

(b) $\dfrac{L(\theta'; \mathbf{x})}{L(\theta''; \mathbf{x})} \geq k$, *for each point* $\mathbf{x} \in C^c$.

(c) $\alpha = P_{H_0}[\mathbf{X} \in C]$.

Then C *is a best critical region of size* α *for testing the simple hypothesis* $H_0 : \theta = \theta'$ *against the alternative simple hypothesis* $H_1 : \theta = \theta''$.

Proof: We shall give the proof when the random variables are of the continuous type. If C is the only critical region of size α, the theorem is proved. If there is another critical region of size α, denote it by A. For convenience, we shall let $\int \cdots \int_R L(\theta; x_1, \ldots, x_n) \, dx_1 \cdots dx_n$ be denoted by $\int_R L(\theta)$. In this notation we wish to show that

$$\int_C L(\theta'') - \int_A L(\theta'') \geq 0.$$

Since C is the union of the disjoint sets $C \cap A$ and $C \cap A^c$ and A is the union of the disjoint sets $A \cap C$ and $A \cap C^c$, we have

$$\int_C L(\theta'') - \int_A L(\theta'') = \int_{C \cap A} L(\theta'') + \int_{C \cap A^c} L(\theta'') - \int_{A \cap C} L(\theta'') - \int_{A \cap C^c} L(\theta'')$$

$$= \int_{C \cap A^c} L(\theta'') - \int_{A \cap C^c} L(\theta''). \tag{8.1.5}$$

However, by the hypothesis of the theorem, $L(\theta'') \geq (1/k)L(\theta')$ at each point of C, and hence at each point of $C \cap A^c$; thus,

$$\int_{C \cap A^c} L(\theta'') \geq \frac{1}{k} \int_{C \cap A^c} L(\theta').$$

But $L(\theta'') \leq (1/k)L(\theta')$ at each point of C^c, and hence at each point of $A \cap C^c$; accordingly,

$$\int_{A \cap C^c} L(\theta'') \leq \frac{1}{k} \int_{A \cap C^c} L(\theta').$$

These inequalities imply that

$$\int_{C \cap A^c} L(\theta'') - \int_{A \cap C^c} L(\theta'') \geq \frac{1}{k} \int_{C \cap A^c} L(\theta') - \frac{1}{k} \int_{A \cap C^c} L(\theta');$$

and, from Equation (8.1.5), we obtain

$$\int_C L(\theta'') - \int_A L(\theta'') \geq \frac{1}{k}\left[\int_{C \cap A^c} L(\theta') - \int_{A \cap C^c} L(\theta')\right]. \qquad (8.1.6)$$

However,

$$\int_{C \cap A^c} L(\theta') - \int_{A \cap C^c} L(\theta') = \int_{C \cap A^c} L(\theta') + \int_{C \cap A} L(\theta')$$
$$- \int_{A \cap C} L(\theta') - \int_{A \cap C^c} L(\theta')$$
$$= \int_C L(\theta') - \int_A L(\theta') = \alpha - \alpha = 0.$$

If this result is substituted in inequality (8.1.6), we obtain the desired result,

$$\int_C L(\theta'') - \int_A L(\theta'') \geq 0.$$

If the random variables are of the discrete type, the proof is the same with integration replaced by summation. ∎

Remark 8.1.1. As stated in the theorem, conditions (a), (b), and (c) are sufficient ones for region C to be a best critical region of size α. However, they are also necessary. We discuss this briefly. Suppose there is a region A of size α that does not satisfy (a) and (b) and that is as powerful at $\theta = \theta''$ as C, which satisfies (a), (b), and (c). Then expression (8.1.5) would be zero, since the power at θ'' using A is equal to that using C. It can be proved that to have expression (8.1.5) equal zero, A must be of the same form as C. As a matter of fact, in the continuous case, A and C would essentially be the same region; that is, they could differ only by a set having probability zero. However, in the discrete case, if $P_{H_0}[L(\theta') = kL(\theta'')]$ is positive, A and C could be different sets, but each would necessarily enjoy conditions (a), (b), and (c) to be a best critical region of size α. ∎

It would seem that a test should have the property that its power should never fall below its significance level; otherwise, the probability of falsely rejecting H_0 (level) is higher than the probability of correctly rejecting H_0 (power). We say a test having this property is **unbiased**, which we now formally define:

Definition 8.1.2. *Let X be a random variable which has pdf or pmf $f(x; \theta)$, where $\theta \in \Omega$. Consider the hypotheses given in expression (8.1.1). Let $\mathbf{X}' = (X_1, \ldots, X_n)$ denote a random sample on X. Consider a test with critical region C and level α. We say that this test is* **unbiased** *if*

$$P_\theta(\mathbf{X} \in C) \geq \alpha,$$

for all $\theta \in \omega_1$.

As the next corollary shows, the best test given in Theorem 8.1.1 is an unbiased test.

Corollary 8.1.1. *As in Theorem 8.1.1, let C be the critical region of the best test of $H_0 : \theta = \theta'$ versus $H_1 : \theta = \theta''$. Suppose the significance level of the test is α. Let $\gamma_C(\theta'') = P_{\theta''}[\mathbf{X} \in C]$ denote the power of the test. Then $\alpha \leq \gamma_C(\theta'')$.*

Proof: Consider the "unreasonable" test in which the data are ignored, but a Bernoulli trial is performed which has probability α of success. If the trial ends in success, we reject H_0. The level of this test is α. Because the power of a test is the probability of rejecting H_0 when H_1 is true, the power of this unreasonable test is α also. But C is the best critical region of size α and thus has power greater than or equal to the power of the unreasonable test. That is, $\gamma_C(\theta'') \geq \alpha$, which is the desired result. ∎

Another aspect of Theorem 8.1.1 to be emphasized is that if we take C to be the set of all points $\mathbf{x}$ which satisfy

$$\frac{L(\theta'; \mathbf{x})}{L(\theta''; \mathbf{x})} \leq k, \quad k > 0,$$

then, in accordance with the theorem, C is a best critical region. This inequality can frequently be expressed in one of the forms (where c_1 and c_2 are constants)

$$u_1(\mathbf{x}; \theta', \theta'') \leq c_1$$

or

$$u_2(\mathbf{x}; \theta', \theta'') \geq c_2.$$

Suppose that it is the first form, $u_1 \leq c_1$. Since θ' and θ'' are given constants, $u_1(\mathbf{X}; \theta', \theta'')$ is a statistic; and if the pdf or pmf of this statistic can be found when H_0 is true, then the significance level of the test of H_0 against H_1 can be determined from this distribution. That is,

$$\alpha = P_{H_0}[u_1(\mathbf{X}; \theta', \theta'') \leq c_1].$$

Moreover, the test may be based on this statistic; for if the observed vector value of $\mathbf{X}$ is $\mathbf{x}$, we reject H_0 (accept H_1) if $u_1(\mathbf{x}) \leq c_1$.

A positive number k determines a best critical region C whose size is $\alpha = P_{H_0}[\mathbf{X} \in C]$ for that particular k. It may be that this value of α is unsuitable for the purpose at hand; that is, it is too large or too small. However, if there is a statistic $u_1(\mathbf{X})$ as in the preceding paragraph, whose pdf or pmf can be determined when H_0 is true, we need not experiment with various values of k to obtain a desirable significance level. For if the distribution of the statistic is known, or can be found, we may determine c_1 such that $P_{H_0}[u_1(\mathbf{X}) \leq c_1]$ is a desirable significance level.

An illustrative example follows.

Example 8.1.2. Let $\mathbf{X}' = (X_1, \ldots, X_n)$ denote a random sample from the distribution that has the pdf

$$f(x; \theta) = \frac{1}{\sqrt{2\pi}} \exp\left(-\frac{(x-\theta)^2}{2}\right), \quad -\infty < x < \infty.$$

It is desired to test the simple hypothesis $H_0 : \theta = \theta' = 0$ against the alternative simple hypothesis $H_1 : \theta = \theta'' = 1$. Now

$$\frac{L(\theta'; \mathbf{x})}{L(\theta''; \mathbf{x})} = \frac{(1/\sqrt{2\pi})^n \exp\left[-\sum_1^n x_i^2 / 2\right]}{(1/\sqrt{2\pi})^n \exp\left[-\sum_1^n (x_i - 1)^2 \Big/ 2\right]}$$

$$= \exp\left(-\sum_1^n x_i + \frac{n}{2}\right).$$

If $k > 0$, the set of all points $(x_1, x_2, \ldots, x_n)$ such that

$$\exp\left(-\sum_1^n x_i + \frac{n}{2}\right) \le k$$

is a best critical region. This inequality holds if and only if

$$-\sum_1^n x_i + \frac{n}{2} \le \log k$$

or, equivalently,

$$\sum_1^n x_i \ge \frac{n}{2} - \log k = c.$$

In this case, a best critical region is the set $C = \{(x_1, x_2, \ldots, x_n) : \sum_1^n x_i \ge c\}$, where c is a constant that can be determined so that the size of the critical region is a desired number α. The event $\sum_1^n X_i \ge c$ is equivalent to the event $\overline{X} \ge c/n = c_1$, for example, so the test may be based upon the statistic $\overline{X}$. If H_0 is true, that is, $\theta = \theta' = 0$, then $\overline{X}$ has a distribution that is $N(0, 1/n)$. For a given positive integer n, the size of the sample and a given significance level α, the number c_1 can be found from Table III in Appendix C, so that $P_{H_0}(\overline{X} \ge c_1) = \alpha$. Hence, if the experimental values of $X_1, X_2, \ldots, X_n$ were, respectively, $x_1, x_2, \ldots, x_n$, we would compute $\overline{x} = \sum_1^n x_i/n$. If $\overline{x} \ge c_1$, the simple hypothesis $H_0 : \theta = \theta' = 0$ would be rejected at the significance level α; if $\overline{x} < c_1$, the hypothesis H_0 would be accepted. The probability of rejecting H_0 when H_0 is true is α; the probability of rejecting H_0, when H_0 is false, is the value of the power of the test at $\theta = \theta'' = 1$. That is,

$$P_{H_1}(\overline{X} \ge c_1) = \int_{c_1}^{\infty} \frac{1}{\sqrt{2\pi}\sqrt{1/n}} \exp\left[-\frac{(\overline{x}-1)^2}{2(1/n)}\right] d\overline{x}.$$

For example, if $n = 25$ and if α is selected to be 0.05, then from Table III we find $c_1 = 1.645/\sqrt{25} = 0.329$. Thus the power of this best test of H_0 against H_1 is 0.05 when H_0 is true, and is

$$\int_{0.329}^{\infty} \frac{1}{\sqrt{2\pi}\sqrt{\frac{1}{25}}} \exp\left[-\frac{(\overline{x}-1)^2}{2(\frac{1}{25})}\right] d\overline{x} = \int_{-3.355}^{\infty} \frac{1}{\sqrt{2\pi}} e^{-w^2/2} \, dw = 0.9996,$$

when H_1 is true. ■

There is another aspect of this theorem that warrants special mention. It has to do with the number of parameters that appear in the pdf. Our notation suggests that there is but one parameter. However, a careful review of the proof reveals that nowhere was this needed or assumed. The pdf or pmf may depend upon any finite number of parameters. What is essential is that the hypothesis H_0 and the alternative hypothesis H_1 be simple, namely, that they completely specify the distributions. With this in mind, we see that the simple hypotheses H_0 and H_1 do not need to be hypotheses about the parameters of a distribution, nor, as a matter of fact, do the random variables $X_1, X_2, \ldots, X_n$ need to be independent. That is, if H_0 is the simple hypothesis that the joint pdf or pmf is $g(x_1, x_2, \ldots, x_n)$, and if H_1 is the alternative simple hypothesis that the joint pdf or pmf is $h(x_1, x_2, \ldots, x_n)$, then C is a best critical region of size α for testing H_0 against H_1 if, for $k > 0$,

1. $\dfrac{g(x_1, x_2, \ldots, x_n)}{h(x_1, x_2, \ldots, x_n)} \leq k$ for $(x_1, x_2, \ldots, x_n) \in C$.

2. $\dfrac{g(x_1, x_2, \ldots, x_n)}{h(x_1, x_2, \ldots, x_n)} \geq k$ for $(x_1, x_2, \ldots, x_n) \in C^c$.

3. $\alpha = P_{H_0}[(X_1, X_2, \ldots, X_n) \in C]$.

An illustrative example follows.

Example 8.1.3. Let $X_1, \ldots, X_n$ denote a random sample from a distribution which has a pmf $f(x)$ that is positive on and only on the nonnegative integers. It is desired to test the simple hypothesis

$$H_0 : f(x) = \begin{cases} \frac{e^{-1}}{x!} & x = 0, 1, 2, \ldots \\ 0 & \text{elsewhere}, \end{cases}$$

against the alternative simple hypothesis

$$H_1 : f(x) = \begin{cases} (\frac{1}{2})^{x+1} & x = 0, 1, 2, \ldots \\ 0 & \text{elsewhere}. \end{cases}$$

Here

$$\frac{g(x_1, \ldots, x_n)}{h(x_1, \ldots, x_n)} = \frac{e^{-n}/(x_1! x_2! \cdots x_n!)}{(\frac{1}{2})^n (\frac{1}{2})^{x_1 + x_2 + \cdots + x_n}}$$

$$= \frac{(2e^{-1})^n 2^{\sum x_i}}{\prod_1^n (x_i!)}.$$

If $k > 0$, the set of points $(x_1, x_2, \ldots, x_n)$ such that

$$\left(\sum_1^n x_i\right) \log 2 - \log \left[\prod_1^n (x_i!)\right] \leq \log k - n \log(2e^{-1}) = c$$

is a best critical region C. Consider the case of $k = 1$ and $n = 1$. The preceding inequality may be written $2^{x_1}/x_1! \leq e/2$. This inequality is satisfied by all points in the set $C = \{x_1 : x_1 = 0, 3, 4, 5, \ldots\}$. Thus the power of the test when H_0 is true is

$$P_{H_0}(X_1 \in C) = 1 - P_{H_0}(X_1 = 1, 2) = 0.448,$$

approximately, in accordance with Table I of Appendix C; i.e., the significance level of this test is 0.448. The power of the test when H_1 is true is given by

$$P_{H_1}(X_1 \in C) = 1 - P_{H_1}(X_1 = 1, 2) = 1 - (\tfrac{1}{4} + \tfrac{1}{8}) = 0.625. \quad \blacksquare$$

Note that these results are consistent with Corollary 8.1.1.

Remark 8.1.2. In the notation of this section, say C is a critical region such that

$$\alpha = \int_C L(\theta') \quad \text{and} \quad \beta = \int_{C^c} L(\theta''),$$

where α and β equal the respective probabilities of the Type I and Type II errors associated with C. Let d_1 and d_2 be two given positive constants. Consider a certain linear function of α and β, namely,

$$d_1 \int_C L(\theta') + d_2 \int_{C^c} L(\theta'') = d_1 \int_C L(\theta') + d_2 \left[1 - \int_C L(\theta'')\right]$$

$$= d_2 + \int_C [d_1 L(\theta') - d_2 L(\theta'')].$$

If we wished to minimize this expression, we would select C to be the set of all $(x_1, x_2, \ldots, x_n)$ such that

$$d_1 L(\theta') - d_2 L(\theta'') < 0$$

or, equivalently,

$$\frac{L(\theta')}{L(\theta'')} < \frac{d_2}{d_1}, \quad \text{for all } (x_1, x_2, \ldots, x_n) \in C,$$

which according to the Neyman–Pearson theorem provides a best critical region with $k = d_2/d_1$. That is, this critical region C is one that minimizes $d_1\alpha + d_2\beta$. There could be others, including points on which $L(\theta')/L(\theta'') = d_2/d_1$, but these would still be best critical regions according to the Neyman–Pearson theorem. $\quad \blacksquare$

EXERCISES

8.1.1. In Example 8.1.2 of this section, let the simple hypotheses read $H_0 : \theta = \theta' = 0$ and $H_1 : \theta = \theta'' = -1$. Show that the best test of H_0 against H_1 may be carried out by use of the statistic $\overline{X}$, and that if $n = 25$ and $\alpha = 0.05$, the power of the test is 0.9996 when H_1 is true.

8.1.2. Let the random variable X have the pdf $f(x; \theta) = (1/\theta)e^{-x/\theta}$, $0 < x < \infty$, zero elsewhere. Consider the simple hypothesis $H_0 : \theta = \theta' = 2$ and the alternative hypothesis $H_1 : \theta = \theta'' = 4$. Let X_1, X_2 denote a random sample of size 2 from this distribution. Show that the best test of H_0 against H_1 may be carried out by use of the statistic $X_1 + X_2$.

8.1.3. Repeat Exercise 8.1.2 when $H_1 : \theta = \theta'' = 6$. Generalize this for every $\theta'' > 2$.

8.1.4. Let $X_1, X_2, \ldots, X_{10}$ be a random sample of size 10 from a normal distribution $N(0, \sigma^2)$. Find a best critical region of size $\alpha = 0.05$ for testing $H_0 : \sigma^2 = 1$ against $H_1 : \sigma^2 = 2$. Is this a best critical region of size 0.05 for testing $H_0 : \sigma^2 = 1$ against $H_1 : \sigma^2 = 4$? Against $H_1 : \sigma^2 = \sigma_1^2 > 1$?

8.1.5. If $X_1, X_2, \ldots, X_n$ is a random sample from a distribution having pdf of the form $f(x; \theta) = \theta x^{\theta - 1}$, $0 < x < 1$, zero elsewhere, show that a best critical region for testing $H_0 : \theta = 1$ against $H_1 : \theta = 2$ is $C = \{(x_1, x_2, \ldots, x_n) : c \leq \prod_{i=1}^{n} x_i\}$.

8.1.6. Let $X_1, X_2, \ldots, X_{10}$ be a random sample from a distribution that is $N(\theta_1, \theta_2)$. Find a best test of the simple hypothesis $H_0 : \theta_1 = \theta_1' = 0$, $\theta_2 = \theta_2' = 1$ against the alternative simple hypothesis $H_1 : \theta_1 = \theta_1'' = 1$, $\theta_2 = \theta_2'' = 4$.

8.1.7. Let $X_1, X_2, \ldots, X_n$ denote a random sample from a normal distribution $N(\theta, 100)$. Show that $C = \{(x_1, x_2, \ldots, x_n) : c \leq \overline{x} = \sum_1^n x_i/n\}$ is a best critical region for testing $H_0 : \theta = 75$ against $H_1 : \theta = 78$. Find n and c so that

$$P_{H_0}[(X_1, X_2, \ldots, X_n) \in C] = P_{H_0}(\overline{X} \geq c) = 0.05$$

and

$$P_{H_1}[(X_1, X_2, \ldots, X_n) \in C] = P_{H_1}(\overline{X} \geq c) = 0.90,$$

approximately.

8.1.8. If $X_1, X_2, \ldots, X_n$ is a random sample from a beta distribution with parameters $\alpha = \beta = \theta > 0$, find a best critical region for testing $H_0 : \theta = 1$ against $H_1 : \theta = 2$.

8.1.9. Let $X_1, X_2, \ldots, X_n$ be iid with pmf $f(x; p) = p^x(1 - p)^{1-x}$, $x = 0, 1$, zero elsewhere. Show that $C = \{(x_1, \ldots, x_n) : \sum_1^n x_i \leq c\}$ is a best critical region for testing $H_0 : p = \frac{1}{2}$ against $H_1 : p = \frac{1}{3}$. Use the Central Limit Theorem to find n and c so that approximately $P_{H_0}(\sum_1^n X_i \leq c) = 0.10$ and $P_{H_1}(\sum_1^n X_i \leq c) = 0.80$.

8.1.10. Let $X_1, X_2, \ldots, X_{10}$ denote a random sample of size 10 from a Poisson distribution with mean θ. Show that the critical region C defined by $\sum_1^{10} x_i \geq 3$ is a best critical region for testing $H_0 : \theta = 0.1$ against $H_1 : \theta = 0.5$. Determine, for this test, the significance level α and the power at $\theta = 0.5$.

8.2 Uniformly Most Powerful Tests

This section takes up the problem of a test of a simple hypothesis H_0 against an alternative composite hypothesis H_1. We begin with an example.

Example 8.2.1. Consider the pdf

$$f(x;\theta) = \begin{cases} \frac{1}{\theta}e^{-x/\theta} & 0 < x < \infty \\ 0 & \text{elsewhere} \end{cases}$$

of Exercises 8.1.2 and 8.1.3. It is desired to test the simple hypothesis $H_0 : \theta = 2$ against the alternative composite hypothesis $H_1 : \theta > 2$. Thus $\Omega = \{\theta : \theta \geq 2\}$. A random sample, X_1, X_2, of size $n = 2$ is used, and the critical region is $C = \{(x_1, x_2) : 9.5 \leq x_1 + x_2 < \infty\}$. It was shown in the exercises cited that the significance level of the test is approximately 0.05 and the power of the test when $\theta = 4$ is approximately 0.31. The power function $\gamma(\theta)$ of the test for all $\theta \geq 2$ is

$$\begin{aligned}
\gamma(\theta) &= 1 - \int_0^{9.5} \int_0^{9.5-x_2} \frac{1}{\theta^2} \exp\left(-\frac{x_1 + x_2}{\theta}\right) dx_1 dx_2 \\
&= \left(\frac{\theta + 9.5}{\theta}\right) e^{-9.5/\theta}, \quad 2 \leq \theta.
\end{aligned}$$

For example, $\gamma(2) = 0.05$, $\gamma(4) = 0.31$, and $\gamma(9.5) = 2/e \approx 0.74$. It is shown (Exercise 8.1.3) that the set $C = \{(x_1, x_2) : 9.5 \leq x_1 + x_2 < \infty\}$ is a best critical region of size 0.05 for testing the simple hypothesis $H_0 : \theta = 2$ against each simple hypothesis in the composite hypothesis $H_1 : \theta > 2$. ∎

The preceding example affords an illustration of a test of a simple hypothesis H_0 that is a best test of H_0 against every simple hypothesis in the alternative composite hypothesis H_1. We now define a critical region, when it exists, which is a best critical region for testing a simple hypothesis H_0 against an alternative composite hypothesis H_1. It seems desirable that this critical region should be a best critical region for testing H_0 against each simple hypothesis in H_1. That is, the power function of the test that corresponds to this critical region should be at least as great as the power function of any other test with the same significance level for every simple hypothesis in H_1.

Definition 8.2.1. *The critical region C is a* **uniformly most powerful (UMP) critical region** *of size α for testing the simple hypothesis H_0 against an alternative composite hypothesis H_1 if the set C is a best critical region of size α for testing H_0 against each simple hypothesis in H_1. A test defined by this critical region C is called a* **uniformly most powerful (UMP) test**, *with significance level α, for testing the simple hypothesis H_0 against the alternative composite hypothesis H_1.*

As will be seen presently, uniformly most powerful tests do not always exist. However, when they do exist, the Neyman–Pearson theorem provides a technique for finding them. Some illustrative examples are given here.

Example 8.2.2. Let $X_1, X_2, \ldots, X_n$ denote a random sample from a distribution that is $N(0, \theta)$, where the variance θ is an unknown positive number. It will be shown that there exists a uniformly most powerful test with significance level α for testing the simple hypothesis $H_0 : \theta = \theta'$, where θ' is a fixed positive number, against the alternative composite hypothesis $H_1 : \theta > \theta'$. Thus $\Omega = \{\theta : \theta \geq \theta'\}$. The joint pdf of $X_1, X_2, \ldots, X_n$ is

$$L(\theta; x_1, x_2, \ldots, x_n) = \left(\frac{1}{2\pi\theta} \right)^{n/2} \exp \left\{ -\frac{1}{2\theta} \sum_{i=1}^{n} x_i^2 \right\}.$$

Let θ'' represent a number greater than θ', and let k denote a positive number. Let C be the set of points where

$$\frac{L(\theta'; x_1, x_2, \ldots, x_n)}{L(\theta''; x_1, x_2, \ldots, x_n)} \leq k,$$

that is, the set of points where

$$\left(\frac{\theta''}{\theta'} \right)^{n/2} \exp \left[-\left(\frac{\theta'' - \theta'}{2\theta'\theta''} \right) \sum_{1}^{n} x_i^2 \right] \leq k$$

or, equivalently,

$$\sum_{1}^{n} x_i^2 \geq \frac{2\theta'\theta''}{\theta'' - \theta'} \left[\frac{n}{2} \log \left(\frac{\theta''}{\theta'} \right) - \log k \right] = c.$$

The set $C = \{(x_1, x_2, \ldots, x_n) : \sum_{1}^{n} x_i^2 \geq c\}$ is then a best critical region for testing the simple hypothesis $H_0 : \theta = \theta'$ against the simple hypothesis $\theta = \theta''$. It remains to determine c, so that this critical region has the desired size α. If H_0 is true, the random variable $\sum_{1}^{n} X_i^2 / \theta'$ has a chi-square distribution with n degrees of freedom. Since $\alpha = P_{\theta'}(\sum_{1}^{n} X_i^2 / \theta' \geq c/\theta')$, c/θ' may be read from Table II in Appendix C and c determined. Then $C = \{(x_1, x_2, \ldots, x_n) : \sum_{1}^{n} x_i^2 \geq c\}$ is a best critical region of size α for testing $H_0 : \theta = \theta'$ against the hypothesis $\theta = \theta''$. Moreover, for each number θ'' greater than θ', the foregoing argument holds. That is, $C = \{(x_1, \ldots, x_n) : \sum_{1}^{n} x_i^2 \geq c\}$ is a uniformly most powerful critical region of size α for testing $H_0 : \theta = \theta'$ against $H_1 : \theta > \theta'$. If $x_1, x_2, \ldots, x_n$ denote the experimental values of $X_1, X_2, \ldots, X_n$, then $H_0 : \theta = \theta'$ is rejected at the significance level α, and $H_1 : \theta > \theta'$ is accepted if $\sum_{1}^{n} x_i^2 \geq c$; otherwise, $H_0 : \theta = \theta'$ is accepted.

If, in the preceding discussion, we take $n = 15$, $\alpha = 0.05$, and $\theta' = 3$, then here the two hypotheses are $H_0 : \theta = 3$ and $H_1 : \theta > 3$. From Table II, $c/3 = 25$ and hence $c = 75$. ■

Example 8.2.3. Let $X_1, X_2, \ldots, X_n$ denote a random sample from a distribution that is $N(\theta, 1)$, where θ is unknown. It will be shown that there is no uniformly most powerful test of the simple hypothesis $H_0 : \theta = \theta'$, where θ' is a fixed number against the alternative composite hypothesis $H_1 : \theta \neq \theta'$. Thus $\Omega = \{\theta : -\infty < \theta < \infty\}$.

Let θ'' be a number not equal to θ'. Let k be a positive number and consider

$$\frac{(1/2\pi)^{n/2}\exp\left[-\sum_1^n (x_i - \theta')^2/2\right]}{(1/2\pi)^{n/2}\exp\left[-\sum_1^n (x_i - \theta'')^2/2\right]} \le k.$$

The preceding inequality may be written as

$$\exp\left\{-(\theta'' - \theta')\sum_1^n x_i + \frac{n}{2}[(\theta'')^2 - (\theta')^2]\right\} \le k$$

or

$$(\theta'' - \theta')\sum_1^n x_i \ge \frac{n}{2}[(\theta'')^2 - (\theta')^2] - \log k.$$

This last inequality is equivalent to

$$\sum_1^n x_i \ge \frac{n}{2}(\theta'' + \theta') - \frac{\log k}{\theta'' - \theta'},$$

provided that $\theta'' > \theta'$, and it is equivalent to

$$\sum_1^n x_i \le \frac{n}{2}(\theta'' + \theta') - \frac{\log k}{\theta'' - \theta'}$$

if $\theta'' < \theta'$. The first of these two expressions defines a best critical region for testing $H_0 : \theta = \theta'$ against the hypothesis $\theta = \theta''$ provided that $\theta'' > \theta'$, while the second expression defines a best critical region for testing $H_0 : \theta = \theta'$ against the hypothesis $\theta = \theta''$ provided that $\theta'' < \theta'$. That is, a best critical region for testing the simple hypothesis against an alternative simple hypothesis, say $\theta = \theta' + 1$, does not serve as a best critical region for testing $H_0 : \theta = \theta'$ against the alternative simple hypothesis $\theta = \theta' - 1$. By definition, then, there is no uniformly most powerful test in the case under consideration.

It should be noted that had the alternative composite hypothesis been one-sided, either $H_1 : \theta > \theta'$ or $H_1 : \theta < \theta'$, a uniformly most powerful test would exist in each instance. ∎

Example 8.2.4. In Exercise 8.1.10, the reader was asked to show that if a random sample of size $n = 10$ is taken from a Poisson distribution with mean θ, the critical region defined by $\sum_1^n x_i \ge 3$ is a best critical region for testing $H_0 : \theta = 0.1$ against $H_1 : \theta = 0.5$. This critical region is also a uniformly most powerful one for testing $H_0 : \theta = 0.1$ against $H_1 : \theta > 0.1$ because, with $\theta'' > 0.1$,

$$\frac{(0.1)^{\sum x_i} e^{-10(0.1)}/(x_1! x_2! \cdots x_n!)}{(\theta'')^{\sum x_i} e^{-10(\theta'')}/(x_1! x_2! \cdots x_n!)} \le k$$

is equivalent to

$$\left(\frac{0.1}{\theta''}\right)^{\sum x_i} e^{-10(0.1-\theta'')} \le k.$$

The preceding inequality may be written as

$$\left(\sum_1^n x_i\right)(\log 0.1 - \log \theta'') \le \log k + 10(1 - \theta'')$$

or, since $\theta'' > 0.1$, equivalently as

$$\sum_1^n x_i \ge \frac{\log k + 10 - 10\theta''}{\log 0.1 - \log \theta''}.$$

Of course, $\sum_1^n x_i \ge 3$ is of the latter form. ∎

Let us make an important observation, although obvious when pointed out. Let $X_1, X_2, \ldots, X_n$ denote a random sample from a distribution that has pdf $f(x; \theta)$, $\theta \in \Omega$. Suppose that $Y = u(X_1, X_2, \ldots, X_n)$ is a sufficient statistic for θ. In accordance with the factorization theorem, the joint pdf of $X_1, X_2, \ldots, X_n$ may be written

$$L(\theta; x_1, x_2, \ldots, x_n) = k_1[u(x_1, x_2, \ldots, x_n); \theta]k_2(x_1, x_2, \ldots, x_n),$$

where $k_2(x_1, x_2, \ldots, x_n)$ does not depend upon θ. Consequently, the ratio

$$\frac{L(\theta'; x_1, x_2, \ldots, x_n)}{L(\theta''; x_1, x_2, \ldots, x_n)} = \frac{k_1[u(x_1, x_2, \ldots, x_n); \theta']}{k_1[u(x_1, x_2, \ldots, x_n); \theta'']}$$

depends upon $x_1, x_2, \ldots, x_n$ only through $u(x_1, x_2, \ldots, x_n)$. Accordingly, if there is a sufficient statistic $Y = u(X_1, X_2, \ldots, X_n)$ for θ and if a best test or a uniformly most powerful test is desired, there is no need to consider tests which are based upon any statistic other than the sufficient statistic. This result supports the importance of sufficiency.

In the above examples, we have presented uniformly most powerful tests. For some families of pdfs and hypotheses, we can obtain general forms of such tests. We sketch these results for the general one-sided hypotheses of the form

$$H_0 : \theta \le \theta' \text{ versus } H_1 : \theta > \theta'. \tag{8.2.1}$$

The other one-sided hypotheses with the null hypothesis $H_0 : \theta \ge \theta'$, is completely analogous. Note that the null hypothesis of (8.2.1) is a composite hypothesis. Recall from Chapter 4 that the level of a test for the hypotheses (8.2.1) is defined by $\max_{\theta \le \theta'} \gamma(\theta)$, where $\gamma(\theta)$ is the power function of the test. That is, the significance level is the maximum probability of Type I error.

Let $\mathbf{X}' = (X_1, \ldots, X_n)$ be a random sample with common pdf (or pmf) $f(x; \theta)$, $\theta \in \Omega$, and, hence with the likelihood function

$$L(\theta, \mathbf{x}) = \prod_{i=1}^n f(x_i; \theta), \quad \mathbf{x}' = (x_1, \ldots, x_n).$$

We consider the family of pdfs which has monotone likelihood ratio as defined next.

Definition 8.2.2. *We say that the likelihood* $L(\theta, \mathbf{x})$ *has* **monotone likelihood ratio** *(***mlr***) in the statistic* $y = u(\mathbf{x})$ *if, for* $\theta_1 < \theta_2$, *the ratio*

$$\frac{L(\theta_1, \mathbf{x})}{L(\theta_2, \mathbf{x})} \tag{8.2.2}$$

is a monotone function of $y = u(\mathbf{x})$.

Assume then that our likelihood function $L(\theta, \mathbf{x})$ has a monotone decreasing likelihood ratio in the statistic $y = u(\mathbf{x})$. Then the ratio in (8.2.2) is equal to $g(y)$, where g is a decreasing function. The case where the likelihood function has a monotone increasing likelihood ratio (i.e., g is an increasing function) follows similarly by changing the sense of the inequalities below. Let α denote the significance level. Then we claim that the following test is UMP level α for the hypotheses (8.2.1):

$$\text{Reject } H_0 \text{ if } Y \geq c_Y, \tag{8.2.3}$$

where c_Y is determined by $\alpha = P_{\theta'}[Y \geq c_Y]$. To show this claim, first consider the simple null hypothesis $H_0' : \theta = \theta'$. Let $\theta'' > \theta'$ be arbitrary but fixed. Let C denote the most powerful critical region for θ' versus θ''. By the Neyman–Pearson Theorem, C is defined by

$$\frac{L(\theta', \mathbf{X})}{L(\theta'', \mathbf{X})} \leq k \text{ if and only if } \mathbf{X} \in C,$$

where k is determined by $\alpha = P_{\theta'}[\mathbf{X} \in C]$. But by Definition 8.2.2, because $\theta'' > \theta'$,

$$\frac{L(\theta', \mathbf{X})}{L(\theta'', \mathbf{X})} = g(Y) \leq k \Leftrightarrow Y \geq g^{-1}(k),$$

where $g^{-1}(k)$ satisfies $\alpha = P_{\theta'}[Y \geq g^{-1}(k)]$; i.e., $c_Y = g^{-1}(k)$. Hence the Neyman–Pearson test is equivalent to the test defined by (8.2.3). Furthermore, the test is UMP for θ' versus $\theta'' > \theta'$ because the test only depends on $\theta'' > \theta'$ and $g^{-1}(k)$ is uniquely determined under θ'.

Let $\gamma_Y(\theta)$ denote the power function of the test (8.2.3). To finish, we need to show that $\max_{\theta \leq \theta'} \gamma_Y(\theta) = \alpha$. But this follows immediately if we can show that $\gamma_Y(\theta)$ is a nondecreasing function. To see this, let $\theta_1 < \theta_2$. Note that since $\theta_1 < \theta_2$, the test (8.2.3) is the most powerful test for testing θ_1 versus θ_2 with the level $\gamma_Y(\theta_1)$. By Corollary 8.1.1, the power of the test at θ_2 must not be below the level; i.e., $\gamma_Y(\theta_2) \geq \gamma_Y(\theta_1)$. Hence $\gamma_Y(\theta)$ is a nondecreasing function. Since the power function is nondecreasing, it follows from Definition 8.1.2 that the mlr tests are unbiased tests for the hypotheses (8.2.1); see Exercise 8.2.14.

Example 8.2.5. Let $X_1, X_2, \ldots, X_n$ be a random sample from a Bernoulli distribution with parameter $p = \theta$, where $0 < \theta < 1$. Let $\theta' < \theta''$. Consider the ratio of likelihoods

$$\frac{L(\theta'; x_1, x_2, \ldots, x_n)}{L(\theta''; x_1, x_2, \ldots, x_n)} = \frac{(\theta')^{\sum x_i}(1-\theta')^{n-\sum x_i}}{(\theta'')^{\sum x_i}(1-\theta'')^{n-\sum x_i}} = \left[\frac{\theta'(1-\theta'')}{\theta''(1-\theta')}\right]^{\sum x_i} \left(\frac{1-\theta'}{1-\theta''}\right)^n.$$

Since $\theta'/\theta'' < 1$ and $(1 - \theta'')/(1 - \theta') < 1$, so that $\theta'(1 - \theta'')/\theta''(1 - \theta') < 1$, the ratio is a decreasing function of $y = \sum x_i$. Thus we have a monotone likelihood ratio in the statistic $Y = \sum X_i$.

Consider the hypotheses

$$H_0 : \theta \leq \theta' \text{ versus } H_1 : \theta > \theta'. \tag{8.2.4}$$

By our discussion above, the UMP level α decision rule for testing H_0 versus H_1 is given by

$$\text{Reject } H_0 \text{ if } Y = \sum_{i=1}^{n} X_i \geq c,$$

where c is such that $\alpha = P_{\theta'}[Y \geq c]$. ∎

In the last example concerning a Bernoulli pmf, we obtained a UMP test by showing that its likelihood possesses mlr. The Bernoulli distribution is a regular case of the exponential family and our argument, under the one assumption below, can be generalized to the entire regular exponential family. To show this, suppose that the random sample $X_1, X_2, \ldots, X_n$ arises from a pdf or pmf representing a regular case of the exponential class, namely,

$$f(x; \theta) = \begin{cases} \exp[p(\theta)K(x) + H(x) + q(\theta)] & x \in \mathcal{S} \\ 0 & \text{elsewhere,} \end{cases}$$

where the support of X, $\mathcal{S}$, is free of θ. Further assume that $p(\theta)$ is an increasing function of θ. Then

$$\frac{L(\theta')}{L(\theta'')} = \frac{\exp\left[p(\theta')\sum_1^n K(x_i) + \sum_1^n H(x_i) + nq(\theta')\right]}{\exp\left[p(\theta'')\sum_1^n K(x_i) + \sum_1^n H(x_i) + nq(\theta'')\right]}$$

$$= \exp\left\{[p(\theta') - p(\theta'')]\sum_1^n K(x_i) + n[q(\theta') - q(\theta'')]\right\}.$$

If $\theta' < \theta''$, $p(\theta)$ being an increasing function, requires this ratio to be a decreasing function of $y = \sum_1^n K(x_i)$. Thus, we have a monotone likelihood ratio in the statistic $Y = \sum_1^n K(X_i)$. Hence consider the hypotheses

$$H_0 : \theta \leq \theta' \text{ versus } H_1 : \theta > \theta'. \tag{8.2.5}$$

By our discussion above concerning mlr, the UMP level α decision rule for testing H_0 versus H_1 is given by

$$\text{Reject } H_0 \text{ if } Y = \sum_{i=1}^{n} K(X_i) \geq c,$$

where c is such that $\alpha = P_{\theta'}[Y \geq c]$. Furthermore, the power function of this test is an increasing function in θ.

For the record, consider the other one-sided alternative hypotheses,

$$H_0 : \ \theta \geq \theta' \text{ versus } H_1 : \ \theta < \theta'. \tag{8.2.6}$$

The UMP level α decision rule is, for $p(\theta)$ an increasing function,

$$\text{Reject } H_0 \text{ if } Y = \sum_{i=1}^{n} K(X_i) \leq c,$$

where c is such that $\alpha = P_{\theta'}[Y \leq c]$.

If in the preceding situation with monotone likelihood ratio we test $H_0 : \theta = \theta'$ against $H_1 : \theta > \theta'$, then $\sum K(x_i) \geq c$ would be a uniformly most powerful critical region. From the likelihood ratios displayed in Examples 8.2.2–8.2.5, we see immediately that the respective critical regions

$$\sum_{i=1}^{n} x_i^2 \geq c, \quad \sum_{i=1}^{n} x_i \geq c, \quad \sum_{i=1}^{n} x_i \geq c, \quad \sum_{i=1}^{n} x_i \geq c$$

are uniformly most powerful for testing $H_0 : \theta = \theta'$ against $H_1 : \theta > \theta'$.

There is a final remark that should be made about uniformly most powerful tests. Of course, in Definition 8.2.1, the word *uniformly* is associated with θ; that is, C is a best critical region of size α for testing $H_0 : \theta = \theta_0$ against all θ values given by the composite alternative H_1. However, suppose that the form of such a region is

$$u(x_1, x_2, \ldots, x_n) \leq c.$$

Then this form provides uniformly most powerful critical regions for all attainable α values by, of course, appropriately changing the value of c. That is, there is a certain uniformity property, also associated with α, that is not always noted in statistics texts.

EXERCISES

8.2.1. Let X have the pmf $f(x; \theta) = \theta^x (1 - \theta)^{1-x}$, $x = 0, 1$, zero elsewhere. We test the simple hypothesis $H_0 : \theta = \frac{1}{4}$ against the alternative composite hypothesis $H_1 : \theta < \frac{1}{4}$ by taking a random sample of size 10 and rejecting $H_0 : \theta = \frac{1}{4}$ if and only if the observed values $x_1, x_2, \ldots, x_{10}$ of the sample observations are such that $\sum_1^{10} x_i \leq 1$. Find the power function $\gamma(\theta)$, $0 < \theta \leq \frac{1}{4}$, of this test.

8.2.2. Let X have a pdf of the form $f(x; \theta) = 1/\theta$, $0 < x < \theta$, zero elsewhere. Let $Y_1 < Y_2 < Y_3 < Y_4$ denote the order statistics of a random sample of size 4 from this distribution. Let the observed value of Y_4 be y_4. We reject $H_0 : \theta = 1$ and accept $H_1 : \theta \neq 1$ if either $y_4 \leq \frac{1}{2}$ or $y_4 > 1$. Find the power function $\gamma(\theta)$, $0 < \theta$, of the test.

8.2.3. Consider a normal distribution of the form $N(\theta, 4)$. The simple hypothesis $H_0 : \theta = 0$ is rejected, and the alternative composite hypothesis $H_1 : \theta > 0$ is accepted if and only if the observed mean $\bar{x}$ of a random sample of size 25 is greater than or equal to $\frac{3}{5}$. Find the power function $\gamma(\theta)$, $0 \leq \theta$, of this test.

8.2.4. Consider the distributions $N(\mu_1, 400)$ and $N(\mu_2, 225)$. Let $\theta = \mu_1 - \mu_2$. Let $\overline{x}$ and $\overline{y}$ denote the observed means of two independent random samples, each of size n, from these two distributions. We reject $H_0 : \theta = 0$ and accept $H_1 : \theta > 0$ if and only if $\overline{x} - \overline{y} \geq c$. If $\gamma(\theta)$ is the power function of this test, find n and c so that $\gamma(0) = 0.05$ and $\gamma(10) = 0.90$, approximately.

8.2.5. Consider Example 8.2.2. Show that $L(\theta)$ has a monotone likelihood ratio in the statistic $\sum_{i=1}^{n} X_i^2$. Use this to determine the UMP test for $H_0 : \theta = \theta'$, where θ' is a fixed positive number, versus $H_1 : \theta < \theta'$.

8.2.6. If, in Example 8.2.2 of this section, $H_0 : \theta = \theta'$, where θ' is a fixed positive number, and $H_1 : \theta \neq \theta'$, show that there is no uniformly most powerful test for testing H_0 against H_1.

8.2.7. Let $X_1, X_2, \ldots, X_{25}$ denote a random sample of size 25 from a normal distribution $N(\theta, 100)$. Find a uniformly most powerful critical region of size $\alpha = 0.10$ for testing $H_0 : \theta = 75$ against $H_1 : \theta > 75$.

8.2.8. Let $X_1, X_2, \ldots, X_n$ denote a random sample from a normal distribution $N(\theta, 16)$. Find the sample size n and a uniformly most powerful test of $H_0 : \theta = 25$ against $H_1 : \theta < 25$ with power function $\gamma(\theta)$ so that approximately $\gamma(25) = 0.10$ and $\gamma(23) = 0.90$.

8.2.9. Consider a distribution having a pmf of the form $f(x; \theta) = \theta^x (1 - \theta)^{1-x}$, $x = 0, 1$, zero elsewhere. Let $H_0 : \theta = \frac{1}{20}$ and $H_1 : \theta > \frac{1}{20}$. Use the Central Limit Theorem to determine the sample size n of a random sample so that a uniformly most powerful test of H_0 against H_1 has a power function $\gamma(\theta)$, with approximately $\gamma(\frac{1}{20}) = 0.05$ and $\gamma(\frac{1}{10}) = 0.90$.

8.2.10. Illustrative Example 8.2.1 of this section dealt with a random sample of size $n = 2$ from a gamma distribution with $\alpha = 1$, $\beta = \theta$. Thus the mgf of the distribution is $(1 - \theta t)^{-1}$, $t < 1/\theta$, $\theta \geq 2$. Let $Z = X_1 + X_2$. Show that Z has a gamma distribution with $\alpha = 2$, $\beta = \theta$. Express the power function $\gamma(\theta)$ of Example 8.2.1 in terms of a single integral. Generalize this for a random sample of size n.

8.2.11. Let $X_1, X_2, \ldots, X_n$ be a random sample from a distribution with pdf $f(x; \theta) = \theta x^{\theta-1}$, $0 < x < 1$, zero elsewhere, where $\theta > 0$. Show the likelihood has mlr in the statistic $\prod_{i=1}^{n} X_i$. Use this to determine the UMP test for $H_0 : \theta = \theta'$ against $H_1 : \theta < \theta'$, for fixed $\theta' > 0$.

8.2.12. Let X have the pdf $f(x; \theta) = \theta^x (1 - \theta)^{1-x}$, $x = 0, 1$, zero elsewhere. We test $H_0 : \theta = \frac{1}{2}$ against $H_1 : \theta < \frac{1}{2}$ by taking a random sample $X_1, X_2, \ldots, X_5$ of size $n = 5$ and rejecting H_0 if $Y = \sum_1^n X_i$ is observed to be less than or equal to a constant c.

(a) Show that this is a uniformly most powerful test.

(b) Find the significance level when $c = 1$.

(c) Find the significance level when $c = 0$.

(d) By using a *randomized test*, as discussed in Example 4.6.4, modify the tests given in parts (b) and (c) to find a test with significance level $\alpha = \frac{2}{32}$.

8.2.13. Let $X_1, \ldots, X_n$ denote a random sample from a gamma-type distribution with $\alpha = 2$ and $\beta = \theta$. Let $H_0 : \theta = 1$ and $H_1 : \theta > 1$.

(a) Show that there exists a uniformly most powerful test for H_0 against H_1, determine the statistic Y upon which the test may be based, and indicate the nature of the best critical region.

(b) Find the pdf of the statistic Y in part (a). If we want a significance level of 0.05, write an equation which can be used to determine the critical region. Let $\gamma(\theta)$, $\theta \geq 1$, be the power function of the test. Express the power function as an integral.

8.2.14. Show that the mlr test defined by expression (8.2.3) is an unbiased test for the hypotheses (8.2.1).

8.3 Likelihood Ratio Tests

In the first section of this chapter, we presented the most powerful tests for simple versus simple hypotheses. In the second section, we extended this theory to uniformly most powerful tests for essentially one-sided alternative hypotheses and families of distributions which have a monotone likelihood ratio. What about the general case? That is, suppose the random variable X has pdf or pmf $f(x; \boldsymbol{\theta})$, where $\boldsymbol{\theta}$ is a vector of parameters in Ω. Let $\omega \subset \Omega$ and consider the hypotheses

$$H_0 : \boldsymbol{\theta} \in \omega \text{ versus } H_1 : \boldsymbol{\theta} \in \Omega \cap \omega^c. \tag{8.3.1}$$

There are complications in extending the optimal theory to this general situation, which are addressed in more advanced books; see, in particular, Lehmann (1986). We illustrate some of these complications with an example. Suppose X has a $N(\theta_1, \theta_2)$ distribution and that we want to test $\theta_1 = \theta_1'$, where θ_1' is specified. In the notation of (8.3.1), $\boldsymbol{\theta} = (\theta_1, \theta_2)$, $\Omega = \{\boldsymbol{\theta} : -\infty < \theta_1 < \infty, \theta_2 > 0\}$, and $\omega = \{\boldsymbol{\theta} : \theta_1 = \theta_1', \theta_2 > 0\}$. Notice that $H_0 : \boldsymbol{\theta} \in \omega$ is a composite null hypothesis. Let $X_1, \ldots, X_n$ be a random sample on X.

Assume for the moment that θ_2 is known. Then H_0 becomes the simple hypothesis $\theta_1 = \theta_1'$. This is essentially the situation discussed in Example 8.2.3. There it was shown that no UMP test exists for this situation. If we restrict attention to the class of unbiased tests (Definition 8.1.2), then a theory of best tests can be constructed; see Lehmann (1986). For our illustrative example, as Exercise 8.3.18 shows, the test based on the critical region

$$C_2 = \left\{ |\overline{X} - \theta_1'| > \sqrt{\frac{\theta_2}{n}} z_{\alpha/2} \right\}$$

is unbiased. Then it follows from Lehmann that it is an UMP unbiased level α test.

In practice, though, the variance θ_2 is unknown. In this case, theory for optimal tests can be constructed using the concept of what are called conditional tests. We do not pursue this any further in this text, but refer the interested reader to Lehmann (1986).

Recall from Chapter 6 that the likelihood ratio tests (6.3.3) can be used to test general hypotheses such as (8.3.1). There is no guarantee that they are optimal. However, as are tests based on the Neyman–Pearson Theorem, they are based on a ratio of likelihood functions. In many situations, the likelihood ratio test statistics are optimal. In the example above on testing for the mean of a normal distribution, with known variance, the likelihood ratio test is the same as the UMP unbiased test. When the variance is unknown, the likelihood ratio test results in the one-sample t-test as shown in Example 6.5.1 of Chapter 6. This is the same as the conditional test discussed in Lehmann (1986).

In Chapter 6, we presented likelihood ratio tests for several situations. For example, the one-sample t-test to test for the mean of a normal distribution with unknown variance was derived in Example 6.5.1. In the remainder of this section, we present likelihood ratio tests for other situations when sampling from normal distributions.

Example 8.3.1. Let the independent random variables X and Y have distributions that are $N(\theta_1, \theta_3)$ and $N(\theta_2, \theta_3)$, where the means θ_1 and θ_2 and common variance θ_3 are unknown. Then $\Omega = \{(\theta_1, \theta_2, \theta_3) : -\infty < \theta_1 < \infty, -\infty < \theta_2 < \infty, 0 < \theta_3 < \infty\}$. Let $X_1, X_2, \ldots, X_n$ and $Y_1, Y_2, \ldots, Y_m$ denote independent random samples from these distributions. The hypothesis $H_0 : \theta_1 = \theta_2$, unspecified, and θ_3 unspecified, is to be tested against all alternatives. Then $\omega = \{(\theta_1, \theta_2, \theta_3) : -\infty < \theta_1 = \theta_2 < \infty, 0 < \theta_3 < \infty\}$. Here $X_1, X_2, \ldots, X_n, Y_1, Y_2, \ldots, Y_m$ are $n + m > 2$ mutually independent random variables having the likelihood functions

$$L(\omega) = \left(\frac{1}{2\pi\theta_3}\right)^{(n+m)/2} \exp\left\{-\frac{1}{2\theta_3}\left[\sum_1^n (x_i - \theta_1)^2 + \sum_1^m (y_i - \theta_1)^2\right]\right\}$$

and

$$L(\Omega) = \left(\frac{1}{2\pi\theta_3}\right)^{(n+m)/2} \exp\left\{-\frac{1}{2\theta_3}\left[\sum_1^n (x_i - \theta_1)^2 + \sum_1^m (y_i - \theta_2)^2\right]\right\}.$$

If $\partial \log L(\omega)/\partial \theta_1$ and $\partial \log L(\omega)/\partial \theta_3$ are equated to zero, then (Exercise 8.3.2)

$$\sum_1^n (x_i - \theta_1) + \sum_1^m (y_i - \theta_1) = 0$$

$$\frac{1}{\theta_3}\left[\sum_1^n (x_i - \theta_1)^2 + \sum_1^m (y_i - \theta_1)^2\right] = n + m. \qquad (8.3.2)$$

The solutions for θ_1 and θ_3 are, respectively,

$$u = (n+m)^{-1}\left\{\sum_1^n x_i + \sum_1^m y_i\right\}$$

$$w = (n+m)^{-1}\left\{\sum_1^n (x_i - u)^2 + \sum_1^m (y_i - u)^2\right\}.$$

Further, u and w maximize $L(\omega)$. The maximum is

$$L(\hat{\omega}) = \left(\frac{e^{-1}}{2\pi w}\right)^{(n+m)/2}.$$

In a like manner, if

$$\frac{\partial \log L(\Omega)}{\partial \theta_1}, \quad \frac{\partial \log L(\Omega)}{\partial \theta_2}, \quad \frac{\partial \log L(\Omega)}{\partial \theta_3}$$

are equated to zero, then (Exercise 8.3.3)

$$\sum_1^n (x_i - \theta_1) = 0$$

$$\sum_1^m (y_i - \theta_2) = 0 \qquad\qquad (8.3.3)$$

$$-(n+m) + \frac{1}{\theta_3}\left[\sum_1^n (x_i - \theta_1)^2 + \sum_1^m (y_i - \theta_2)^2\right] = 0.$$

The solutions for θ_1, θ_2, and θ_3 are, respectively,

$$u_1 = n^{-1}\sum_1^n x_i$$

$$u_2 = m^{-1}\sum_1^m y_i$$

$$w' = (n+m)^{-1}\left[\sum_1^n (x_i - u_1)^2 + \sum_1^m (y_i - u_2)^2\right],$$

and, further, u_1, u_2, and w' maximize $L(\Omega)$. The maximum is

$$L(\hat{\Omega}) = \left(\frac{e^{-1}}{2\pi w'}\right)^{(n+m)/2},$$

so that

$$\Lambda(x_1, \ldots, x_n, y_1, \ldots, y_m) = \Lambda = \frac{L(\hat{\omega})}{L(\hat{\Omega})} = \left(\frac{w'}{w}\right)^{(n+m)/2}.$$

The random variable defined by $\Lambda^{2/(n+m)}$ is

$$\frac{\sum_1^n (X_i - \overline{X})^2 + \sum_1^m (Y_i - \overline{Y})^2}{\sum_1^n \{X_i - [(n\overline{X} + m\overline{Y})/(n+m)]\}^2 + \sum_1^n \{Y_i - [(n\overline{X} + m\overline{Y})/(n+m)]\}^2}.$$

Now

$$\sum_1^n \left(X_i - \frac{n\overline{X} + m\overline{Y}}{n+m}\right)^2 = \sum_1^n \left[(X_i - \overline{X}) + \left(\overline{X} - \frac{n\overline{X} + m\overline{Y}}{n+m}\right)\right]^2$$

$$= \sum_1^n (X_i - \overline{X})^2 + n\left(\overline{X} - \frac{n\overline{X} + m\overline{Y}}{n+m}\right)^2$$

and

$$\sum_1^m \left(Y_i - \frac{n\overline{X} + m\overline{Y}}{n+m}\right)^2 = \sum_1^m \left[(Y_i - \overline{Y}) + \left(\overline{Y} - \frac{n\overline{X} + m\overline{Y}}{n+m}\right)\right]^2$$

$$= \sum_1^m (Y_i - \overline{Y})^2 + m\left(\overline{Y} - \frac{n\overline{X} + m\overline{Y}}{n+m}\right)^2.$$

But

$$n\left(\overline{X} - \frac{n\overline{X} + m\overline{Y}}{n+m}\right)^2 = \frac{m^2 n}{(n+m)^2}(\overline{X} - \overline{Y})^2$$

and

$$m\left(\overline{Y} - \frac{n\overline{X} + m\overline{Y}}{n+m}\right)^2 = \frac{n^2 m}{(n+m)^2}(\overline{X} - \overline{Y})^2.$$

Hence the random variable defined by $\Lambda^{2/(n+m)}$ may be written

$$\frac{\sum_1^n (X_i - \overline{X})^2 + \sum_1^m (Y_i - \overline{Y})^2}{\sum_1^n (X_i - \overline{X})^2 + \sum_1^m (Y_i - \overline{Y})^2 + [nm/(n+m)](\overline{X} - \overline{Y})^2}$$

$$= \frac{1}{1 + \dfrac{[nm/(n+m)](\overline{X} - \overline{Y})^2}{\sum_1^n (X_i - \overline{X})^2 + \sum_1^m (Y_i - \overline{Y})^2}}.$$

If the hypothesis $H_0 : \theta_1 = \theta_2$ is true, the random variable

$$T = \sqrt{\frac{nm}{n+m}}(\overline{X} - \overline{Y})\left\{(n+m-2)^{-1}\left[\sum_1^n(X_i - \overline{X})^2 + \sum_1^m(Y_i - \overline{Y})^2\right]\right\}^{-1/2}$$
(8.3.4)

has, in accordance with Section 3.6, a t-distribution with $n+m-2$ degrees of freedom. Thus the random variable defined by $\Lambda^{2/(n+m)}$ is

$$\frac{n+m-2}{(n+m-2)+T^2}.$$

The test of H_0 against all alternatives may then be based on a t-distribution with $n+m-2$ degrees of freedom.

The likelihood ratio principle calls for the rejection of H_0 if and only if $\Lambda \leq \lambda_0 < 1$. Thus the significance level of the test is

$$\alpha = P_{H_0}[\Lambda(X_1, \ldots, X_n, Y_1, \ldots, Y_m) \leq \lambda_0].$$

However, $\Lambda(X_1, \ldots, X_n, Y_1, \ldots, Y_m) \leq \lambda_0$ is equivalent to $|T| \geq c$, and so

$$\alpha = P(|T| \geq c; H_0).$$

For given values of n and m, the number c is determined from Table IV in Appendix C (with $n+m-2$ degrees of freedom) to yield a desired α. Then H_0 is rejected at a significance level α if and only if $|t| \geq c$, where t is the observed value of T. If, for instance, $n = 10$, $m = 6$, and $\alpha = 0.05$, then $c = 2.124$. ∎

For this last example as well as the one-sample t-test derived in Example 6.5.1, it was found that the likelihood ratio test could be based on a statistic which, when the hypothesis H_0 is true, has a t-distribution. To help us compute the powers of these tests at parameter points other than those described by the hypothesis H_0, we turn to the following definition.

Definition 8.3.1. *Let the random variable W be $N(\delta, 1)$; let the random variable V be $\chi^2(r)$, and let W and V be independent. The quotient*

$$T = \frac{W}{\sqrt{V/r}}$$

is said to have a noncentral t-distribution *with r degrees of freedom and noncentrality parameter δ. If $\delta = 0$, we say that T has a central t-distribution.*

In the light of this definition, let us reexamine the t-statistics of Examples 6.5.1

and 8.3.1. In Example 6.5.1 we had

$$t(X_1, \ldots, X_n) = \frac{\sqrt{n}\overline{X}}{\sqrt{\sum_1^n (X_i - \overline{X})^2/(n-1)}}$$

$$= \frac{\sqrt{n}\overline{X}/\sigma}{\sqrt{\sum_1^n (X_i - \overline{X})^2/[\sigma^2(n-1)]}}.$$

Here, where θ_1 is the mean of the normal distribution, $W_1 = \sqrt{n}\overline{X}/\sigma$ is $N(\sqrt{n}\theta_1/\sigma, 1)$, $V_1 = \sum_1^n (X_i - \overline{X})^2/\sigma^2$ is $\chi^2(n-1)$, and W_1 and V_1 are independent. Thus, if $\theta_1 \neq 0$, we see, in accordance with the definition, that $t(X_1, \ldots, X_n)$ has a noncentral t-distribution with $n-1$ degrees of freedom and noncentrality parameter $\delta_1 = \sqrt{n}\theta_1/\sigma$. In Example 8.3.1 we had

$$T = \frac{W_2}{\sqrt{V_2/(n+m-2)}},$$

where

$$W_2 = \sqrt{\frac{nm}{n+m}}(\overline{X} - \overline{Y}) \Big/ \sigma$$

and

$$V_2 = \frac{\sum_1^n (X_i - \overline{X})^2 + \sum_1^m (Y_i - \overline{Y})^2}{\sigma^2}.$$

Here W_2 is $N[\sqrt{nm/(n+m)}(\theta_1 - \theta_2)/\sigma, 1]$, V_2 is $\chi^2(n+m-2)$, and W_2 and V_2 are independent. Accordingly, if $\theta_1 \neq \theta_2$, T has a noncentral t-distribution with $n+m-2$ degrees of freedom and noncentrality parameter $\delta_2 = \sqrt{nm/(n+m)}(\theta_1 - \theta_2)/\sigma$. It is interesting to note that $\delta_1 = \sqrt{n}\theta_1/\sigma$ measures the deviation of θ_1 from $\theta_1 = 0$ in units of the standard deviation $\sigma/\sqrt{n}$ of $\overline{X}$. The noncentrality parameter $\delta_2 = \sqrt{nm/(n+m)}(\theta_1 - \theta_2)/\sigma$ is equal to the deviation of $\theta_1 - \theta_2$ from $\theta_1 - \theta_2 = 0$ in units of the standard deviation $\sigma/\sqrt{(n+m)/mn}$ of $\overline{X} - \overline{Y}$.

The package R contains functions which evaluate noncentral t-distributional quantities. For example, to obtain the value $P(T \leq t)$ when T has a t-distribution with a degrees of freedom and noncentrality parameter b, use the command pt(t, a, ncp=b). For the value of the associated pdf at t, use the command dt(t, a, ncp=b). There are also various tables of the noncentral t-distribution, but they are much too cumbersome to be included in this book.

Remark 8.3.1. The one- and two-sample tests for normal means, presented in Examples 6.5.1 and 8.3.1, are the tests for normal means presented in most elementary statistics books. They are based on the assumption of normality. What if the underlying distributions are not normal? In that case, with finite variances, the t-test statistics for these situations are asymptotically correct. For example, consider the one-sample t-test. Suppose $X_1, \ldots, X_n$ are iid with a common nonnormal pdf which has mean θ_1 and finite variance σ^2. The hypotheses remain the same, i.e., $H_0 : \theta_1 = \theta_1'$ versus $H_1 : \theta_1 \neq \theta_1'$. The t-test statistic, T_n, is given by

$$T_n = \frac{\sqrt{n}(\overline{X} - \theta_1')}{S_n}, \tag{8.3.5}$$

where S_n is the sample standard deviation. Our critical region is $C_1 = \{|T_n| \geq t_{\alpha/2, n-1}\}$. Recall that $S_n \to \sigma$ in probability. Hence, by the Central Limit Theorem, under H_0,

$$T_n = \frac{\sigma}{S_n} \frac{\sqrt{n}(\overline{X} - \theta_1')}{\sigma} \xrightarrow{D} Z, \tag{8.3.6}$$

where Z has a standard normal distribution. Hence the asymptotic test would use the critical region $C_2 = \{|T_n| \geq z_{\alpha/2}\}$. By (8.3.6) the critical region C_2 would have approximate size α. In practice, we would use C_1. Because t critical values are generally larger than z critical values, the use of C_1 would be conservative; i.e., the size of C_1 would be slightly smaller than that of C_2. For nonnormal situations where the distribution is "close" to the normal distribution, the t-test is essentially valid; i,e., the true level of significance is close to the nominal α. In terms of robustness, we would say that for these situations the t-test possesses **robustness of validity**. But the t-test may not possess **robustness of power**. For nonnormal situations, there are more powerful tests than the t-test; see Chapter 10 for discussion. For distributions which are decidedly not normal, very skewed for instance, the validity of the t-test may be questionable. Example 8.3.2 shows that the t-test may be quite liberal (empirical α levels much larger than the nominal α level) for such situations. In this case, the tests discussed in Chapter 10 could be used.

As Exercise 8.3.4 shows, the two-sample t-test is also asymptotically correct, provided the underlying distributions have the *same* variance. ∎

Example 8.3.2 (Skewed Contaminated Normal Distribution). Consider the random variable X given by

$$X = (1 - I_\epsilon)Z + (1 - I_\epsilon)Y, \tag{8.3.7}$$

where Z has a $N(0, 1)$ distribution, Y has a $N(\mu_c, \sigma_c^2)$ distribution, I_ϵ has a $bin(1, \epsilon)$ distribution, and Z, Y, and I_ϵ are mutually independent. Assume that $\epsilon < 0.5$ and $\sigma_c > 1$, so that Y is the contaminating random variable in the mixture. Note that if $\mu_c = 0$, then X has the contaminated normal distribution discussed in Section 3.4.1, which is symmetrically distributed about 0. For $\mu_c \neq 0$, the distribution of X, (8.3.7), is skewed and we call it the **skewed contaminated normal distribution**, $SCN(\epsilon, \sigma_c, \mu_C)$. Note that $E(X) = \epsilon\mu_c$ and in Exercise 8.3.15 the cdf and pdf of X are derived. In this example, we show the results of a small simulation study on the validity of the t-test for random samples from the distribution of X. Consider the one-sided hypotheses

$$H_0 : \mu = \mu_X \text{ versus } H_0 : \mu < \mu_X.$$

Table 8.3.1: Empirical α Levels for the Nominal 0.05 t-Test of Example 8.3.2

	Empirical α				
μ_c	0	5	10	15	20
$\widehat{\alpha}$	0.0458	0.0961	0.1238	0.1294	0.1301

Let $X_1, X_2, \ldots, X_n$ be a random sample from the distribution of X. As a test statistic we consider the t-test discussed in Example 4.5.4, which is also given in expression (8.3.5); that is, the test statistic is $T_n = (\overline{X} - \mu_X)/(S_n/\sqrt{n})$, where $\overline{X}$ and S_n are the sample mean and standard deviation of $X_1, X_2, \ldots, X_n$, respectively. We set the level of significance at $\alpha = 0.05$ and used the decision rule: Reject H_0 if $T_n \leq t_{0.05,n-1}$. For the study, we set $n = 30$, $\epsilon = 0.20$, and $\sigma_c = 25$. We chose the five values of $0, 5, 10, 15$, and 20 for μ_c, as shown in Table 8.3.1. For each of these five situations, we ran 10,000 simulations and recorded $\widehat{\alpha}$, which is the number of rejections of H_0 divided by the number of simulations, i.e., the empirical α level. For the test to be valid, $\widehat{\alpha}$ should be close to the nominal value of 0.05. As Table 8.3.1 shows, though, for all cases other than $\mu_c = 0$, the t-test is quite liberal; that is, its empirical significance level far exceeds the nominal 0.05 level (as Exercise 8.3.16 shows, the sampling error in the table is about 0.004). Note that when $\mu_c = 0$ the distribution of X is symmetric about 0 and in this case the empirical level is close to the nominal value of 0.05. ∎

In Example 8.3.1, in testing the equality of the means of two normal distributions, it was assumed that the unknown variances of the distributions were equal. Let us now consider the problem of testing the equality of these two unknown variances.

Example 8.3.3. We are given the independent random samples $X_1, \ldots, X_n$ and $Y_1, \ldots, Y_m$ from the distributions, which are $N(\theta_1, \theta_3)$ and $N(\theta_2, \theta_4)$, respectively. We have

$$\Omega = \{(\theta_1, \theta_2, \theta_3, \theta_4) : -\infty < \theta_1, \theta_2 < \infty, 0 < \theta_3, \theta_4 < \infty\}.$$

The hypothesis $H_0 : \theta_3 = \theta_4$, unspecified, with θ_1 and θ_2 also unspecified, is to be tested against all alternatives. Then

$$\omega = \{(\theta_1, \theta_2, \theta_3, \theta_4) : -\infty < \theta_1, \theta_2 < \infty, 0 < \theta_3 = \theta_4 < \infty\}.$$

It is easy to show (see Exercise 8.3.8) that the statistic defined by $\Lambda = L(\hat{\omega})/L(\hat{\Omega})$ is a function of the statistic

$$F = \frac{\sum_1^n (X_i - \overline{X})^2/(n-1)}{\sum_1^m (Y_i - \overline{Y})^2/(m-1)}. \tag{8.3.8}$$

If $\theta_3 = \theta_4$, this statistic F has an F-distribution with $n-1$ and $m-1$ degrees of freedom. The hypothesis that $(\theta_1, \theta_2, \theta_3, \theta_4) \in \omega$ is rejected if the computed $F \leq c_1$

or if the computed $F \geq c_2$. The constants c_1 and c_2 are usually selected so that, if $\theta_3 = \theta_4$,

$$P(F \leq c_1) = P(F \geq c_2) = \frac{\alpha_1}{2},$$

where α_1 is the desired significance level of this test. ∎

Example 8.3.4. Let the independent random variables X and Y have distributions that are $N(\theta_1, \theta_3)$ and $N(\theta_2, \theta_4)$. In Example 8.3.1, we derived the likelihood ratio test statistic T of the hypothesis $\theta_1 = \theta_2$ when $\theta_3 = \theta_4$, while in Example 8.3.3 we obtained the likelihood ratio test statistic F of the hypothesis $\theta_3 = \theta_4$. The hypothesis that $\theta_1 = \theta_2$ is rejected if the computed $|T| \geq c$, where the constant c is selected so that $\alpha_2 = P(|T| \geq c; \theta_1 = \theta_2, \theta_3 = \theta_4)$ is the assigned significance level of the test. We shall show that, if $\theta_3 = \theta_4$, the likelihood ratio test statistics for equality of variances and equality of means, respectively F and T, are independent. Among other things, this means that if these two tests based on F and T, respectively, are performed sequentially with significance levels α_1 and α_2, the probability of accepting both these hypotheses, when they are true, is $(1 - \alpha_1)(1 - \alpha_2)$. Thus the significance level of this joint test is $\alpha = 1 - (1 - \alpha_1)(1 - \alpha_2)$.

Independence of F and T, when $\theta_3 = \theta_4$, can be established using sufficiency and completeness. The statistics $\overline{X}$, $\overline{Y}$, and $\sum_1^n (X_i - \overline{X})^2 + \sum_1^n (Y_i - \overline{Y})^2$ are joint complete sufficient statistics for the three parameters θ_1, θ_2, and $\theta_3 = \theta_4$. Obviously, the distribution of F does not depend upon θ_1, θ_2, or $\theta_3 = \theta_4$, and hence F is independent of the three joint complete sufficient statistics. However, T is a function of these three joint complete sufficient statistics alone, and, accordingly, T is independent of F. It is important to note that these two statistics are independent whether $\theta_1 = \theta_2$ or $\theta_1 \neq \theta_2$. This permits us to calculate probabilities other than the significance level of the test. For example, if $\theta_3 = \theta_4$ and $\theta_1 \neq \theta_2$, then

$$P(c_1 < F < c_2, \ |T| \geq c) = P(c_1 < F < c_2)P(|T| \geq c).$$

The second factor in the right-hand member is evaluated by using the probabilities of a noncentral t-distribution. Of course, if $\theta_3 = \theta_4$ and the difference $\theta_1 - \theta_2$ is large, we would want the preceding probability to be close to 1 because the event $\{c_1 < F < c_2, \ |T| \geq c\}$ leads to a correct decision, namely, accept $\theta_3 = \theta_4$ and reject $\theta_1 = \theta_2$. ∎

Remark 8.3.2. We caution the reader on this last test for the equality of two variances. In Remark 8.3.1, we discussed that the one- and two-sample t-tests for means are asymptotically correct. The two-sample variance test of the last example is not, however; see, for example, page 143 of Hettmansperger and McKean (2011). If the underlying distributions are not normal, then the F-critical values may be far from valid critical values (unlike the t-critical values for the means tests as discussed in Remark 8.3.1). In a large simulation study, Conover, Johnson, and Johnson (1981) showed that instead of having the nominal size of $\alpha = 0.05$, the F-test for variances using the F-critical values could have significance levels as high as 0.80, in certain nonnormal situations. Thus the two-sample F-test for variances does not possess robustness of validity. It should only be used in situations where the assumption of normality can be justified. See Exercise 8.3.14 for an illustrative data set. ■

In the above examples, we were able to determine the null distribution of the test statistic. This is often impossible in practice. As discussed in Chapter 6, though, minus twice the log of the likelihood ratio test statistic is asymptotically χ^2 under H_0. Hence we can obtain an approximate test in most situations.

EXERCISES

8.3.1. In Example 8.3.1, suppose $n = m = 8$, $\overline{x} = 75.2$, $\overline{y} = 78.6$, $\sum_1^8 (x_i - \overline{x})^2 = 71.2$, and $\sum_1^8 (y_i - \overline{y})^2 = 54.8$. If we use the test derived in that example, do we accept or reject $H_0 : \theta_1 = \theta_2$ at the 5% significance level? Obtain the p-value of the test; see Remark (4.6.1).

8.3.2. Verify Equations (8.3.2) of Example 8.3.1 of this section.

8.3.3. Verify Equations (8.3.3) of Example 8.3.1 of this section.

8.3.4. Let $X_1, \ldots, X_n$ and $Y_1, \ldots, Y_m$ follow the location model

$$
\begin{aligned}
X_i &= \theta_1 + Z_i, \quad i = 1, \ldots, n \\
Y_i &= \theta_2 + Z_{n+i}, \quad i = 1, \ldots, m,
\end{aligned}
$$

where $Z_1, \ldots, Z_{n+m}$ are iid random variables with common pdf $f(z)$. Assume that $E(Z_i) = 0$ and $\mathrm{Var}(Z_i) = \theta_3 < \infty$.

(a) Show that $E(X_i) = \theta_1$, $E(Y_i) = \theta_2$, and $\mathrm{Var}(X_i) = \mathrm{Var}(Y_i) = \theta_3$.

(b) Consider the hypotheses of Example 8.3.1, i.e.,

$$
H_0 : \theta_1 = \theta_2 \text{ versus } H_1 : \theta_1 \neq \theta_2.
$$

Show that under H_0, the test statistic T given in expression (8.3.4) has a limiting $N(0, 1)$ distribution.

(c) Using part (b), determine the corresponding large sample test (decision rule) of H_0 versus H_1. (This shows that the test in Example 8.3.1 is asymptotically correct.)

8.3.5. Show that the likelihood ratio principle leads to the same test when testing a simple hypothesis H_0 against an alternative simple hypothesis H_1, as that given by the Neyman–Pearson theorem. Note that there are only two points in Ω.

8.3.6. Let $X_1, X_2, \ldots, X_n$ be a random sample from the normal distribution $N(\theta, 1)$. Show that the likelihood ratio principle for testing $H_0 : \theta = \theta'$, where θ' is specified, against $H_1 : \theta \neq \theta'$ leads to the inequality $|\overline{x} - \theta'| \geq c$.

(a) Is this a uniformly most powerful test of H_0 against H_1?

(b) Is this a uniformly most powerful unbiased test of H_0 against H_1?

8.3.7. Let $X_1, X_2, \ldots, X_n$ be iid $N(\theta_1, \theta_2)$. Show that the likelihood ratio principle for testing $H_0 : \theta_2 = \theta_2'$ specified, and θ_1 unspecified, against $H_1 : \theta_2 \neq \theta_2'$, θ_1 unspecified, leads to a test that rejects when $\sum_1^n (x_i - \overline{x})^2 \leq c_1$ or $\sum_1^n (x_i - \overline{x})^2 \geq c_2$, where $c_1 < c_2$ are selected appropriately.

8.3.8. Let $X_1, \ldots, X_n$ and $Y_1, \ldots, Y_m$ be independent random samples from the distributions $N(\theta_1, \theta_3)$ and $N(\theta_2, \theta_4)$, respectively.

(a) Show that the likelihood ratio for testing $H_0 : \theta_1 = \theta_2, \theta_3 = \theta_4$ against all alternatives is given by

$$\frac{\left[\sum_1^n (x_i - \overline{x})^2 / n\right]^{n/2} \left[\sum_1^m (y_i - \overline{y})^2 / m\right]^{m/2}}{\left\{\left[\sum_1^n (x_i - u)^2 + \sum_1^m (y_i - u)^2\right] \Big/ (m + n)\right\}^{(n+m)/2}},$$

where $u = (n\overline{x} + m\overline{y}) / (n + m)$.

(b) Show that the likelihood ratio for testing $H_0 : \theta_3 = \theta_4$ with θ_1 and θ_2 unspecified can be based on the test statistic F given in expression (8.3.8).

8.3.9. Let $Y_1 < Y_2 < \cdots < Y_5$ be the order statistics of a random sample of size $n = 5$ from a distribution with pdf $f(x; \theta) = \frac{1}{2} e^{-|x-\theta|}$, $-\infty < x < \infty$, for all real θ. Find the likelihood ratio test Λ for testing $H_0 : \theta = \theta_0$ against $H_1 : \theta \neq \theta_0$.

8.3.10. A random sample $X_1, X_2, \ldots, X_n$ arises from a distribution given by

$$H_0 : f(x; \theta) = \frac{1}{\theta}, \quad 0 < x < \theta, \quad \text{zero elsewhere,}$$

or

$$H_1 : f(x; \theta) = \frac{1}{\theta} e^{-x/\theta}, \quad 0 < x < \infty, \quad \text{zero elsewhere.}$$

Determine the likelihood ratio (Λ) test associated with the test of H_0 against H_1.

8.3.11. Consider a random sample $X_1, X_2, \ldots, X_n$ from a distribution with pdf $f(x; \theta) = \theta(1 - x)^{\theta-1}$, $0 < x < 1$, zero elsewhere, where $\theta > 0$.

(a) Find the form of the uniformly most powerful test of $H_0 : \theta = 1$ against $H_1 : \theta > 1$.

(b) What is the likelihood ratio Λ for testing $H_0 : \theta = 1$ against $H_1 : \theta \neq 1$?

8.3.12. Let $X_1, X_2, \ldots, X_n$ and $Y_1, Y_2, \ldots, Y_n$ be independent random samples from two normal distributions $N(\mu_1, \sigma^2)$ and $N(\mu_2, \sigma^2)$, respectively, where σ^2 is the common but unknown variance.

(a) Find the likelihood ratio Λ for testing $H_0 : \mu_1 = \mu_2 = 0$ against all alternatives.

(b) Rewrite Λ so that it is a function of a statistic Z which has a well-known distribution.

(c) Give the distribution of Z under both null and alternative hypotheses.

8.3.13. Let $(X_1, Y_1), (X_2, Y_2), \ldots, (X_n, Y_n)$ be a random sample from a bivariate normal distribution with $\mu_1, \mu_2, \sigma_1^2 = \sigma_2^2 = \sigma^2, \rho = \frac{1}{2}$, where μ_1, μ_2, and $\sigma^2 > 0$ are unknown real numbers. Find the likelihood ratio Λ for testing $H_0 : \mu_1 = \mu_2 = 0$, σ^2 unknown against all alternatives. The likelihood ratio Λ is a function of what statistic that has a well-known distribution?

8.3.14. Let X be a random variable with pdf $f_X(x) = (2b_X)^{-1} \exp\{-|x|/b_X\}$, for $-\infty < x < \infty$ and $b_X > 0$. First, show that the variance of X is $\sigma_X^2 = 2b_X^2$. Next, let Y, independent of X, have pdf $f_Y(y) = (2b_Y)^{-1} \exp\{-|y|/b_Y\}$, for $-\infty < x < \infty$ and $b_Y > 0$. Consider the hypotheses

$$H_0 : \sigma_X^2 = \sigma_Y^2 \text{ versus } H_1 : \sigma_X^2 > \sigma_Y^2.$$

To illustrate Remark 8.3.2 for testing these hypotheses, consider the following data set. Sample 1 represents the values of a sample drawn on X with $b_X = 1$, while Sample 2 represents the values of a sample drawn on Y with $b_Y = 1$. Hence, in this case H_0 is true.

Sample	-0.389	-2.177	0.813	-0.001
1	-0.110	-0.709	0.456	0.135
Sample	0.763	-0.570	-2.565	-1.733
1	0.403	0.778	-0.115	
Sample	-1.067	-0.577	0.361	-0.680
2	-0.634	-0.996	-0.181	0.239
Sample	-0.775	-1.421	-0.818	0.328
2	0.213	1.425	-0.165	

(a) Obtain *comparison boxplots* of these two samples. Comparison boxplots consist of boxplots of both samples drawn on the same scale. Based on these plots, in particular the interquartile ranges, what do you conclude about H_0?

(b) Obtain the F-test (for a one-sided hypothesis) as discussed in Remark 8.3.2 at level $\alpha = 0.10$. What is your conclusion?

(c) The test in part (b) is not exact. Why?

8.3.15. For the skewed contaminated normal random variable X of Example 8.3.2, derive the cdf, pdf, mean, and variance of X.

8.3.16. For Table 8.3.1 of Example 8.3.2, show that the half-width of the 95% confidence interval for a binomial proportion as given in Chapter 4 is 0.004 at the nominal value of 0.05.

8.3.17. If computational facilities are available, perform a Monte Carlo study of the two-sided t-test for the skewed contaminated normal situation of Example 8.3.2. The R function `rscn` of Appendix B generates variates from the distribution of X.

8.3.18. Suppose $X_1, \ldots, X_n$ is a random sample on X which has a $N(\mu, \sigma_0^2)$ distribution, where σ_0^2 is known. Consider the two-sided hypotheses

$$H_0: \ \mu = 0 \text{ versus } H_1: \ \mu \neq 0.$$

Show that the test based on the critical region $C = \{|\overline{X}| > \sqrt{\sigma_0^2/n} z_{\alpha/2}\}$ is an unbiased level α test.

8.3.19. Assume that same situation as in the last exercise but consider the test with critical region $C^* = \{\overline{X} > \sqrt{\sigma_0^2/n} z_\alpha\}$. Show that the test based on C^* has significance level α but that it is not an unbiased test.

8.4 The Sequential Probability Ratio Test

Theorem 8.1.1 provides us with a method for determining a best critical region for testing a simple hypothesis against an alternative simple hypothesis. Recall its statement: Let $X_1, X_2, \ldots, X_n$ be a random sample with fixed sample size n from a distribution that has pdf or pmf $f(x; \theta)$, where $\theta = \{\theta : \theta - \theta', \theta''\}$ and θ' and θ'' are known numbers. For this section, we denote the likelihood of $X_1, X_2, \ldots, X_n$ by

$$L(\theta; n) = f(x_1; \theta) f(x_2; \theta) \cdots f(x_n; \theta),$$

a notation that reveals both the parameter θ and the sample size n. If we reject $H_0: \theta = \theta'$ and accept $H_1: \theta = \theta''$ when and only when

$$\frac{L(\theta'; n)}{L(\theta''; n)} \leq k,$$

where $k > 0$, then by Theorem 8.1.1 this is a best test of H_0 against H_1.

Let us now suppose that the sample size n is *not* fixed in advance. In fact, let the sample size be a random variable N with sample space $\{1, 2, , 3, \ldots\}$. An interesting procedure for testing the simple hypothesis $H_0: \theta = \theta'$ against the simple hypothesis $H_1: \theta = \theta''$ is the following: Let k_0 and k_1 be two positive constants with $k_0 < k_1$. Observe the independent outcomes $X_1, X_2, X_3, \ldots$ in a sequence, for example, $x_1, x_2, x_3, \ldots$, and compute

$$\frac{L(\theta'; 1)}{L(\theta''; 1)}, \frac{L(\theta'; 2)}{L(\theta''; 2)}, \frac{L(\theta'; 3)}{L(\theta''; 3)}, \ldots.$$

The hypothesis $H_0: \theta = \theta'$ is rejected (and $H_1: \theta = \theta''$ is accepted) if and only if there exists a positive integer n so that $\mathbf{x}_n = (x_1, x_2, \ldots, x_n)$ belongs to the set

$$C_n = \left\{ \mathbf{x}_n : k_0 < \frac{L(\theta', j)}{L(\theta'', j)} < k_1, \ j = 1, \ldots, n-1, \text{ and } \frac{L(\theta', n)}{L(\theta'', n)} \leq k_0 \right\}. \quad (8.4.1)$$

On the other hand, the hypothesis $H_0 : \theta = \theta'$ is accepted (and $H_1 : \theta = \theta''$ is rejected) if and only if there exists a positive integer n so that $(x_1, x_2, \ldots, x_n)$ belongs to the set

$$B_n = \left\{ \mathbf{x}_n : k_0 < \frac{L(\theta', j)}{L(\theta'', j)} < k_1, \ j = 1, \ldots, n-1, \ \text{and} \ \frac{L(\theta', n)}{L(\theta'', n)} \geq k_1 \right\}. \quad (8.4.2)$$

That is, we continue to observe sample observations as long as

$$k_0 < \frac{L(\theta', n)}{L(\theta'', n)} < k_1. \quad (8.4.3)$$

We stop these observations in one of two ways:

1. With rejection of $H_0 : \theta = \theta'$ as soon as

$$\frac{L(\theta', n)}{L(\theta'', n)} \leq k_0$$

   or

2. With acceptance of $H_0 : \theta = \theta'$ as soon as

$$\frac{L(\theta', n)}{L(\theta'', n)} \geq k_1,$$

A test of this kind is called Wald's **sequential probability ratio test**. Frequently, inequality (8.4.3) can be conveniently expressed in an equivalent form:

$$c_0(n) < u(x_1, x_2, \ldots, x_n) < c_1(n), \quad (8.4.4)$$

where $u(X_1, X_2, \ldots, X_n)$ is a statistic and $c_0(n)$ and $c_1(n)$ depend on the constants $k_0, k_1, \theta', \theta''$, and on n. Then the observations are stopped and a decision is reached as soon as

$$u(x_1, x_2, \ldots, x_n) \leq c_0(n) \quad \text{or} \quad u(x_1, x_2, \ldots, x_n) \geq c_1(n).$$

We now give an illustrative example.

Example 8.4.1. Let X have a pmf

$$f(x; \theta) = \begin{cases} \theta^x (1-\theta)^{1-x} & x = 0, 1 \\ 0 & \text{elsewhere.} \end{cases}$$

In the preceding discussion of a sequential probability ratio test, let $H_0 : \theta = \frac{1}{3}$ and $H_1 : \theta = \frac{2}{3}$; then, with $\sum x_i = \sum_{i=1}^{n} x_i$,

$$\frac{L(\frac{1}{3}, n)}{L(\frac{2}{3}, n)} = \frac{(\frac{1}{3})^{\sum x_i}(\frac{2}{3})^{n-\sum x_i}}{(\frac{2}{3})^{\sum x_i}(\frac{1}{3})^{n-\sum x_i}} = 2^{n-2\sum x_i}.$$

If we take logarithms to the base 2, the inequality

$$k_0 < \frac{L(\frac{1}{3}, n)}{L(\frac{2}{3}, n)} < k_1,$$

with $0 < k_0 < k_1$, becomes

$$\log_2 k_0 < n - 2\sum_1^n x_i < \log_2 k_1,$$

or, equivalently, in the notation of expression (8.4.4),

$$c_0(n) = \frac{n}{2} - \frac{1}{2}\log_2 k_1 < \sum_1^n x_i < \frac{n}{2} - \frac{1}{2}\log_2 k_0 = c_1(n).$$

Note that $L(\frac{1}{3}, n)/L(\frac{2}{3}, n) \leq k_0$ if and only if $c_1(n) \leq \sum_1^n x_i$; and $L(\frac{1}{3}, n)/L(\frac{2}{3}, n) \geq k_1$ if and only if $c_0(n) \geq \sum_1^n x_i$. Thus we continue to observe outcomes as long as $c_0(n) < \sum_1^n x_i < c_1(n)$. The observation of outcomes is discontinued with the first value of n of N for which either $c_1(n) \leq \sum_1^n x_i$ or $c_0(n) \geq \sum_1^n x_i$. The inequality $c_1(n) \leq \sum_1^n x_i$ leads to rejection of $H_0 : \theta = \frac{1}{3}$ (the acceptance of H_1), and the inequality $c_0(n) \geq \sum_1^n x_i$ leads to the acceptance of $H_0 : \theta = \frac{1}{3}$ (the rejection of H_1). ∎

Remark 8.4.1. At this point, the reader undoubtedly sees that there are many questions that should be raised in connection with the sequential probability ratio test. Some of these questions are possibly among the following:

1. What is the probability of the procedure continuing indefinitely?

2. What is the value of the power function of this test at each of the points $\theta = \theta'$ and $\theta = \theta''$?

3. If θ'' is one of several values of θ specified by an alternative composite hypothesis, say $H_1 : \theta > \theta'$, what is the power function at each point $\theta \geq \theta'$?

4. Since the sample size N is a random variable, what are some of the properties of the distribution of N? In particular, what is the expected value $E(N)$ of N?

5. How does this test compare with tests that have a fixed sample size n? ∎

A course in sequential analysis would investigate these and many other problems. However, in this book our objective is largely that of acquainting the reader with this kind of test procedure. Accordingly, we assert that the answer to question 1 is zero. Moreover, it can be proved that if $\theta = \theta'$ or if $\theta = \theta''$, $E(N)$ is smaller for this sequential procedure than the sample size of a fixed-sample-size test which has the same values of the power function at those points. We now consider question 2 in some detail.

In this section we shall denote the power of the test when H_0 is true by the symbol α and the power of the test when H_1 is true by the symbol $1 - \beta$. Thus α is the probability of committing a Type I error (the rejection of H_0 when H_0 is true), and β is the probability of committing a Type II error (the acceptance of H_0 when H_0 is false). With the sets C_n and B_n as previously defined, and with random variables of the continuous type, we then have

$$\alpha = \sum_{n=1}^{\infty} \int_{C_n} L(\theta', n), \quad 1 - \beta = \sum_{n=1}^{\infty} \int_{C_n} L(\theta'', n).$$

Since the probability is 1 that the procedure terminates, we also have

$$1 - \alpha = \sum_{n=1}^{\infty} \int_{B_n} L(\theta', n), \quad \beta = \sum_{n=1}^{\infty} \int_{B_n} L(\theta'', n).$$

If $(x_1, x_2, \ldots, x_n) \in C_n$, we have $L(\theta', n) \le k_0 L(\theta'', n)$; hence, it is clear that

$$\alpha = \sum_{n=1}^{\infty} \int_{C_n} L(\theta', n) \le \sum_{n=1}^{\infty} \int_{C_n} k_0 L(\theta'', n) = k_0 (1 - \beta).$$

Because $L(\theta', n) \ge k_1 L(\theta'', n)$ at each point of the set B_n, we have

$$1 - \alpha = \sum_{n=1}^{\infty} \int_{B_n} L(\theta', n) \ge \sum_{n=1}^{\infty} \int_{B_n} k_1 L(\theta'', n) = k_1 \beta.$$

Accordingly, it follows that

$$\frac{\alpha}{1 - \beta} \le k_0, \quad k_1 \le \frac{1 - \alpha}{\beta}, \tag{8.4.5}$$

provided that β is not equal to 0 or 1.

Now let α_a and β_a be preassigned proper fractions; some typical values in the applications are 0.01, 0.05, and 0.10. If we take

$$k_0 = \frac{\alpha_a}{1 - \beta_a}, \quad k_1 = \frac{1 - \alpha_a}{\beta_a},$$

then inequalities (8.4.5) become

$$\frac{\alpha}{1 - \beta} \le \frac{\alpha_a}{1 - \beta_a}, \quad \frac{1 - \alpha_a}{\beta_a} \le \frac{1 - \alpha}{\beta}; \tag{8.4.6}$$

or, equivalently,

$$\alpha(1 - \beta_a) \le (1 - \beta)\alpha_a, \quad \beta(1 - \alpha_a) \le (1 - \alpha)\beta_a.$$

If we add corresponding members of the immediately preceding inequalities, we find that

$$\alpha + \beta - \alpha\beta_a - \beta\alpha_a \le \alpha_a + \beta_a - \beta\alpha_a - \alpha\beta_a$$

and hence

$$\alpha + \beta \le \alpha_a + \beta_a;$$

that is, the sum $\alpha + \beta$ of the probabilities of the two kinds of errors is bounded above by the sum $\alpha_a + \beta_a$ of the preassigned numbers. Moreover, since α and β are positive proper fractions, inequalities (8.4.6) imply that

$$\alpha \le \frac{\alpha_a}{1 - \beta_a}, \quad \beta \le \frac{\beta_a}{1 - \alpha_a};$$

consequently, we have an upper bound on each of α and β. Various investigations of the sequential probability ratio test seem to indicate that in most practical cases, the values of α and β are quite close to α_a and β_a. This prompts us to approximate the power function at the points $\theta = \theta'$ and $\theta = \theta''$ by α_a and $1 - \beta_a$, respectively.

Example 8.4.2. Let X be $N(\theta, 100)$. To find the sequential probability ratio test for testing $H_0 : \theta = 75$ against $H_1 : \theta = 78$ such that each of α and β is approximately equal to 0.10, take

$$k_0 = \frac{0.10}{1 - 0.10} = \frac{1}{9}, \quad k_1 = \frac{1 - 0.10}{0.10} = 9.$$

Since

$$\frac{L(75, n)}{L(78, n)} = \frac{\exp\left[-\sum(x_i - 75)^2 / 2(100)\right]}{\exp\left[-\sum(x_i - 78)^2 / 2(100)\right]} = \exp\left(-\frac{6\sum x_i - 459n}{200}\right),$$

the inequality

$$k_0 = \frac{1}{9} < \frac{L(75, n)}{L(78, n)} < 9 = k_1$$

can be rewritten, by taking logarithms, as

$$-\log 9 < \frac{6\sum x_i - 459n}{200} < \log 9.$$

This inequality is equivalent to the inequality

$$c_0(n) = \frac{153}{2}n - \frac{100}{3}\log 9 < \sum_1^n x_i < \frac{153}{2}n + \frac{100}{3}\log 9 = c_1(n).$$

Moreover, $L(75, n)/L(78, n) \le k_0$ and $L(75, n)/L(78, n) \ge k_1$ are equivalent to the inequalities $\sum_1^n x_i \ge c_1(n)$ and $\sum_1^n x_i \le c_0(n)$, respectively. Thus the observation of outcomes is discontinued with the first value of n of N for which either $\sum_1^n x_i \ge c_1(n)$ or $\sum_1^n x_i \le c_0(n)$. The inequality $\sum_1^n x_i \ge c_1(n)$ leads to the rejection of $H_0 : \theta = 75$, and the inequality $\sum_1^n x_i \le c_0(n)$ leads to the acceptance of $H_0 : \theta = 75$. The power of the test is approximately 0.10 when H_0 is true, and approximately 0.90 when H_1 is true. ∎

Remark 8.4.2. It is interesting to note that a sequential probability ratio test can be thought of as a *random-walk procedure*. To illustrate, the final inequalities of Examples 8.4.1 and 8.4.2 can be written as

$$-\log_2 k_1 < \sum_1^n 2(x_i - 0.5) < -\log_2 k_0$$

and

$$-\frac{100}{3}\log 9 < \sum_1^n (x_i - 76.5) < \frac{100}{3}\log 9,$$

respectively. In each instance, think of starting at the point zero and taking random steps until one of the boundaries is reached. In the first situation the random steps are $2(X_1 - 0.5), 2(X_2 - 0.5), 2(X_3 - 0.5), \ldots$, which have the same length, 1, but with random directions. In the second instance, both the length and the direction of the steps are random variables, $X_1 - 76.5, X_2 - 76.5, X_3 - 76.5, \ldots$. ∎

In recent years, there has been much attention devoted to improving quality of products using statistical methods. One such simple method was developed by Walter Shewhart in which a sample of size n of the items being produced is taken and they are measured, resulting in n values. The mean $\overline{X}$ of these n measurements has an approximate normal distribution with mean μ and variance σ^2/n. In practice, μ and σ^2 must be estimated, but in this discussion, we assume that they are known. From theory we know that the probability is 0.997 that $\overline{x}$ is between

$$\text{LCL} = \mu - \frac{3\sigma}{\sqrt{n}} \quad \text{and} \quad \text{UCL} = \mu + \frac{3\sigma}{\sqrt{n}}.$$

These two values are called the lower (LCL) and upper (UCL) control limits, respectively. Samples like these are taken periodically, resulting in a sequence of means, say $\overline{x}_1, \overline{x}_2, \overline{x}_3, \ldots$. These are usually plotted; and if they are between the LCL and UCL, we say that the process is **in control**. If one falls outside the limits, this would suggest that the mean μ has shifted, and the process would be investigated.

It was recognized by some that there could be a shift in the mean, say from μ to $\mu + (\sigma/\sqrt{n})$; and it would still be difficult to detect that shift with a single sample mean, for now the probability of a single $\overline{x}$ exceeding UCL is only about 0.023. This means that we would need about $1/0.023 \approx 43$ samples, each of size n, on the average before detecting such a shift. This seems too long; so statisticians recognized that they should be cumulating experience as the sequence $\overline{X}_1, \overline{X}_2, \overline{X}_3, \ldots$ is observed in order to help them detect the shift sooner. It is the practice to compute the standardized variable $Z = (\overline{X} - \mu)/(\sigma/\sqrt{n})$; thus, we state the problem in these terms and provide the solution given by a sequential probability ratio test.

Here Z is $N(\theta, 1)$, and we wish to test $H_0 : \theta = 0$ against $H_1 : \theta = 1$ using the sequence of iid random variables $Z_1, Z_2, \ldots, Z_m, \ldots$. We use m rather than n, as the latter is the size of the samples taken periodically. We have

$$\frac{L(0,m)}{L(1,m)} = \frac{\exp\left[-\sum z_i^2/2\right]}{\exp\left[-\sum(z_i - 1)^2/2\right]} = \exp\left[-\sum_{i=1}^m (z_i - 0.5)\right].$$

Thus

$$k_0 < \exp\left[-\sum_{i=1}^{m}(z_i - 0.5)\right] < k_1$$

can be written as

$$h = -\log k_0 > \sum_{i=1}^{m}(z_i - 0.5) > -\log k_1 = -h.$$

It is true that $-\log k_0 = \log k_1$ when $\alpha_a = \beta_a$. Often, $h = -\log k_0$ is taken to be about 4 or 5, suggesting that $\alpha_a = \beta_a$ is small, like 0.01. As $\sum(z_i - 0.5)$ is cumulating the sum of $z_i - 0.5$, $i = 1, 2, 3, \ldots$, these procedures are often called CUSUMS. If the CUSUM $= \sum(z_i - 0.5)$ exceeds h, we would investigate the process, as it seems that the mean has shifted upward. If this shift is to $\theta = 1$, the theory associated with these procedures shows that we need only eight or nine samples on the average, rather than 43, to detect this shift. For more information about these methods, the reader is referred to one of the many books on quality improvement through statistical methods. What we would like to emphasize here is that through sequential methods (not only the sequential probability ratio test), we should take advantage of all past experience that we can gather in making inferences.

EXERCISES

8.4.1. Let X be $N(0, \theta)$ and, in the notation of this section, let $\theta' = 4$, $\theta'' = 9$, $\alpha_a = 0.05$, and $\beta_a = 0.10$. Show that the sequential probability ratio test can be based upon the statistic $\sum_1^n X_i^2$. Determine $c_0(n)$ and $c_1(n)$.

8.4.2. Let X have a Poisson distribution with mean θ. Find the sequential probability ratio test for testing $H_0 : \theta = 0.02$ against $H_1 : \theta = 0.07$. Show that this test can be based upon the statistic $\sum_1^n X_i$. If $\alpha_a = 0.20$ and $\beta_a = 0.10$, find $c_0(n)$ and $c_1(n)$.

8.4.3. Let the independent random variables Y and Z be $N(\mu_1, 1)$ and $N(\mu_2, 1)$, respectively. Let $\theta = \mu_1 - \mu_2$. Let us observe independent observations from each distribution, say $Y_1, Y_2, \ldots$ and $Z_1, Z_2, \ldots$. To test sequentially the hypothesis $H_0 : \theta = 0$ against $H_1 : \theta = \frac{1}{2}$, use the sequence $X_i = Y_i - Z_i$, $i = 1, 2, \ldots$. If $\alpha_a = \beta_a = 0.05$, show that the test can be based upon $\overline{X} = \overline{Y} - \overline{Z}$. Find $c_0(n)$ and $c_1(n)$.

8.4.4. Suppose that a manufacturing process makes about 3% defective items, which is considered satisfactory for this particular product. The managers would like to decrease this to about 1% and clearly want to guard against a substantial increase, say to 5%. To monitor the process, periodically $n = 100$ items are taken and the number X of defectives counted. Assume that X is $b(n = 100, p = \theta)$. Based on a sequence $X_1, X_2, \ldots, X_m, \ldots$, determine a sequential probability ratio test that tests $H_0 : \theta = 0.01$ against $H_1 : \theta = 0.05$. (Note that $\theta = 0.03$, the present level, is in between these two values.) Write this test in the form

$$h_0 > \sum_{i=1}^{m} (x_i - nd) > h_1$$

and determine d, h_0, and h_1 if $\alpha_a = \beta_a = 0.02$.

8.4.5. Let $X_1, X_2, \ldots, X_n$ be a random sample from a distribution with pdf $f(x; \theta) = \theta x^{\theta-1}$, $0 < x < 1$, zero elsewhere.

(a) Find a complete sufficient statistic for θ.

(b) If $\alpha_a = \beta_a = \frac{1}{10}$, find the sequential probability ratio test of $H_0 : \theta = 2$ against $H_1 : \theta = 3$.

8.5   Minimax and Classification Procedures

We have considered several procedures which may be used in problems of point estimation. Among these were decision function procedures (in particular, minimax decisions). In this section, we apply minimax procedures to the problem of testing a simple hypothesis H_0 against an alternative simple hypothesis H_1. It is important to observe that these procedures yield, in accordance with the Neyman–Pearson theorem, a best test of H_0 against H_1. We end this section with a discussion on an application of these procedures to a classification problem.

8.5.1   Minimax Procedures

We first investigate the decision function approach to the problem of testing a simple null hypothesis against a simple alternative hypothesis. Let the joint pdf of the n random variables $X_1, X_2, \ldots, X_n$ depend upon the parameter θ. Here n is a fixed positive integer. This pdf is denoted by $L(\theta; x_1, x_2, \ldots, x_n)$ or, for brevity, by $L(\theta)$. Let θ' and θ'' be distinct and fixed values of θ. We wish to test the simple hypothesis $H_0 : \theta = \theta'$ against the simple hypothesis $H_1 : \theta = \theta''$. Thus the parameter space is $\Omega = \{\theta : \theta = \theta', \theta''\}$. In accordance with the decision function procedure, we need a function δ of the observed values of $X_1, \ldots, X_n$ (or, of the observed value of a statistic Y) that decides which of the two values of θ, θ' or θ'', to accept. That is, the function δ selects either $H_0 : \theta = \theta'$ or $H_1 : \theta = \theta''$. We denote these decisions by $\delta = \theta'$ and $\delta = \theta''$, respectively. Let $\mathcal{L}(\theta, \delta)$ represent the loss function associated with this decision problem. Because the pairs $(\theta = \theta', \delta = \theta')$ and $(\theta = \theta'', \delta = \theta'')$ represent correct decisions, we shall always take $\mathcal{L}(\theta', \theta') = \mathcal{L}(\theta'', \theta'') = 0$. On the other hand, if either $\delta = \theta''$ when $\theta = \theta'$ or $\delta = \theta'$ when $\theta = \theta''$, then a positive value should be assigned to the loss function; that is, $\mathcal{L}(\theta', \theta'') > 0$ and $\mathcal{L}(\theta'', \theta') > 0$.

It has previously been emphasized that a test of $H_0 : \theta = \theta'$ against $H_1 : \theta = \theta''$ can be described in terms of a critical region in the sample space. We can do the same kind of thing with the decision function. That is, we can choose a subset of C of the sample space and if $(x_1, x_2, \ldots, x_n) \in C$, we can make the decision $\delta = \theta''$; whereas if $(x_1, x_2, \ldots, x_n) \in C^c$, the complement of C, we make the decision $\delta = \theta'$.

Thus a given critical region C determines the decision function. In this sense, we may denote the risk function by $R(\theta, C)$ instead of $R(\theta, \delta)$. That is, in a notation used in Section 7.1,

$$R(\theta, C) = R(\theta, \delta) = \int_{C \cup C^c} \mathcal{L}(\theta, \delta) L(\theta).$$

Since $\delta = \theta''$ if $(x_1, \ldots, x_n) \in C$ and $\delta = \theta'$ if $(x_1, \ldots, x_n) \in C^c$, we have

$$R(\theta, C) = \int_C \mathcal{L}(\theta, \theta'') L(\theta) + \int_{C^c} \mathcal{L}(\theta, \theta') L(\theta). \qquad (8.5.1)$$

If, in Equation (8.5.1), we take $\theta = \theta'$, then $\mathcal{L}(\theta', \theta') = 0$ and hence

$$R(\theta', C) = \int_C \mathcal{L}(\theta', \theta'') L(\theta') = \mathcal{L}(\theta', \theta'') \int_C L(\theta').$$

On the other hand, if in Equation (8.5.1) we let $\theta = \theta''$, then $\mathcal{L}(\theta'', \theta'') = 0$ and, accordingly,

$$R(\theta'', C) = \int_{C^c} \mathcal{L}(\theta'', \theta') L(\theta'') = \mathcal{L}(\theta'', \theta') \int_{C^c} L(\theta'').$$

It is enlightening to note that if $\gamma(\theta)$ is the power function of the test associated with the critical region C, then

$$R(\theta', C) = \mathcal{L}(\theta', 0'') \gamma(\theta') = \mathcal{L}(\theta', \theta'') \alpha,$$

where $\alpha = \gamma(\theta')$ is the significance level; and

$$R(\theta'', C) = \mathcal{L}(\theta'', \theta')[1 - \gamma(\theta'')] = \mathcal{L}(\theta'', \theta') \beta,$$

where $\beta = 1 - \gamma(\theta'')$ is the probability of the type II error.

Let us now see if we can find a minimax solution to our problem. That is, we want to find a critical region C so that

$$\max[R(\theta', C), R(\theta'', C)]$$

is minimized. We shall show that the solution is the region

$$C = \left\{ (x_1, \ldots, x_n) : \frac{L(\theta'; x_1, \ldots, x_n)}{L(\theta''; x_1, \ldots, x_n)} \le k \right\},$$

provided the positive constant k is selected so that $R(\theta', C) = R(\theta'', C)$. That is, if k is chosen so that

$$\mathcal{L}(\theta', \theta'') \int_C L(\theta') = \mathcal{L}(\theta'', \theta') \int_{C^c} L(\theta''),$$

then the critical region C provides a minimax solution. In the case of random variables of the continuous type, k can always be selected so that $R(\theta', C) = R(\theta'', C)$.

However, with random variables of the discrete type, we may need to consider an auxiliary random experiment when $L(\theta')/L(\theta'') = k$ in order to achieve the exact equality $R(\theta', C) = R(\theta'', C)$.

To see that C is the minimax solution, consider every other region A for which $R(\theta', C) \geq R(\theta', A)$. A region A for which $R(\theta', C) < R(\theta', A)$ is not a candidate for a minimax solution, for then $R(\theta', C) = R(\theta'', C) < \max[R(\theta', A), R(\theta'', A)]$. Since $R(\theta', C) \geq R(\theta', A)$ means that

$$\mathcal{L}(\theta', \theta'') \int_C L(\theta') \geq \mathcal{L}(\theta', \theta'') \int_A L(\theta'),$$

we have

$$\alpha = \int_C L(\theta') \geq \int_A L(\theta');$$

that is, the significance level of the test associated with the critical region A is less than or equal to α. But C, in accordance with the Neyman–Pearson theorem, is a best critical region of size α. Thus

$$\int_C L(\theta'') \geq \int_A L(\theta'')$$

and

$$\int_{C^c} L(\theta'') \leq \int_{A^c} L(\theta'').$$

Accordingly,

$$\mathcal{L}(\theta'', \theta') \int_{C^c} L(\theta'') \leq \mathcal{L}(\theta'', \theta') \int_{A^c} L(\theta''),$$

or, equivalently,

$$R(\theta'', C) \leq R(\theta'', A).$$

That is,

$$R(\theta', C) = R(\theta'', C) \leq R(\theta'', A).$$

This means that

$$\max[R(\theta', C), R(\theta'', C)] \leq R(\theta'', A).$$

Then certainly,

$$\max[R(\theta', C), R(\theta'', C)] \leq \max[R(\theta', A), R(\theta'', A)],$$

and the critical region C provides a minimax solution, as we wanted to show.

Example 8.5.1. Let $X_1, X_2, \ldots, X_{100}$ denote a random sample of size 100 from a distribution that is $N(\theta, 100)$. We again consider the problem of testing $H_0 : \theta = 75$ against $H_1 : \theta = 78$. We seek a minimax solution with $\mathcal{L}(75, 78) = 3$ and $\mathcal{L}(78, 75) = 1$. Since $L(75)/L(78) \leq k$ is equivalent to $\overline{x} \geq c$, we want to determine c, and thus k, so that

$$3P(\overline{X} \geq c; \theta = 75) = P(\overline{X} < c; \theta = 78). \tag{8.5.2}$$

Because $\overline{X}$ is $N(\theta, 1)$, the preceding equation can be rewritten as

$$3[1 - \Phi(c - 75)] = \Phi(c - 78).$$

As requested in Exercise 8.5.4, the reader can show by using Newton's algorithm that the solution to one place is $c = 76.8$. The significance level of the test is $1 - \Phi(1.8) = 0.036$, approximately, and the power of the test when H_1 is true is $1 - \Phi(-1.2) = 0.885$, approximately. ∎

8.5.2 Classification

The summary above has an interesting application to the problem of **classification**, which can be described as follows. An investigator makes a number of measurements on an item and wants to place it into one of several categories (or classify it). For convenience in our discussion, we assume that only two measurements, say X and Y, are made on the item to be classified. Moreover, let X and Y have a joint pdf $f(x, y; \theta)$, where the parameter θ represents one or more parameters. In our simplification, suppose that there are only two possible joint distributions (categories) for X and Y, which are indexed by the parameter values θ' and θ'', respectively. In this case, the problem then reduces to one of observing $X = x$ and $Y = y$ and then testing the hypothesis $\theta = \theta'$ against the hypothesis $\theta = \theta''$, with the classification of X and Y being in accord with which hypothesis is accepted. From the Neyman–Pearson theorem, we know that a best decision of this sort is of the following form: If

$$\frac{f(x, y; \theta')}{f(x, y; \theta'')} \leq k,$$

choose the distribution indexed by θ''; that is, we classify (x, y) as coming from the distribution indexed by θ''. Otherwise, choose the distribution indexed by θ'; that is, we classify (x, y) as coming from the distribution indexed by θ'. Some discussion on the choice of k follows in the next remark.

Remark 8.5.1 (On the Choice of k). Consider the following probabilities:

$$\pi' = P[(X, Y) \text{ is drawn from the distribution with pdf } f(x, y; \theta')]$$
$$\pi'' = P[(X, Y) \text{ is drawn from the distribution with pdf } f(x, y; \theta'')].$$

Note that $\pi' + \pi'' = 1$. Then it can be shown that the optimal classification rule is determined by taking $k = \pi''/\pi'$; see, for instance, Seber (1984). Hence, if we have prior information on how likely the item is drawn from the distribution with parameter θ', then we can obtain the classification rule. In practice, it is common for each distribution to be equilikely, in which case, $\pi' = \pi'' = 1/2$ and, hence, $k = 1$. ∎

Example 8.5.2. Let (x, y) be an observation of the random pair (X, Y), which has a bivariate normal distribution with parameters $\mu_1, \mu_2, \sigma_1^2, \sigma_2^2$, and ρ. In Section 3.5 that joint pdf is given by

$$f(x, y; \mu_1, \mu_2, \sigma_1^2, \sigma_2^2) = \frac{1}{2\pi\sigma_1\sigma_2\sqrt{1 - \rho^2}} e^{-q(x, y; \mu_1, \mu_2)/2},$$

for $-\infty < x < \infty$ and $-\infty < y < \infty$, where $\sigma_1 > 0$, $\sigma_2 > 0$, $-1 < \rho < 1$, and

$$q(x, y; \mu_1, \mu_2) = \frac{1}{1 - \rho^2} \left[\left(\frac{x - \mu_1}{\sigma_1} \right)^2 - 2\rho \left(\frac{x - \mu_1}{\sigma_1} \right) \left(\frac{y - \mu_2}{\sigma_2} \right) + \left(\frac{y - \mu_2}{\sigma_2} \right)^2 \right].$$

Assume that σ_1^2, σ_2^2, and ρ are known but that we do not know whether the respective means of (X, Y) are (μ_1', μ_2') or (μ_1'', μ_2''). The inequality

$$\frac{f(x, y; \mu_1', \mu_2', \sigma_1^2, \sigma_2^2, \rho)}{f(x, y; \mu_1'', \mu_2'', \sigma_1^2, \sigma_2^2, \rho)} \leq k$$

is equivalent to

$$\tfrac{1}{2}[q(x, y; \mu_1'', \mu_2'') - q(x, y; \mu_1', \mu_2')] \leq \log k.$$

Moreover, it is clear that the difference in the left-hand member of this inequality does not contain terms involving x^2, xy, and y^2. In particular, this inequality is the same as

$$\frac{1}{1 - \rho^2} \left\{ \left[\frac{\mu_1' - \mu_1''}{\sigma_1^2} - \frac{\rho(\mu_2' - \mu_2'')}{\sigma_1 \sigma_2} \right] x + \left[\frac{\mu_2' - \mu_2''}{\sigma_2^2} - \frac{\rho(\mu_1' - \mu_1'')}{\sigma_1 \sigma_2} \right] y \right\}$$
$$\leq \log k + \tfrac{1}{2}[q(0, 0; \mu_1', \mu_2') - q(0, 0; \mu_1'', \mu_2'')],$$

or, for brevity,

$$ax + by \leq c. \qquad (8.5.3)$$

That is, if this linear function of x and y in the left-hand member of inequality (8.5.3) is less than or equal to a constant, we classify (x, y) as coming from the bivariate normal distribution with means μ_1'' and μ_2''. Otherwise, we classify (x, y) as arising from the bivariate normal distribution with means μ_1' and μ_2'. Of course, if the prior probabilities can be assigned as discussed in Remark 8.5.1 then k and thus c can be found easily; see Exercise 8.5.3. ∎

Once the rule for classification is established, the statistician might be interested in the two probabilities of misclassifications using that rule. The first of these two is associated with the classification of (x, y) as arising from the distribution indexed by θ'' if, in fact, it comes from that index by θ'. The second misclassification is similar, but with the interchange of θ' and θ''. In the preceding example, the probabilities of these respective misclassifications are

$$P(aX + bY \leq c; \mu_1', \mu_2') \quad \text{and} \quad P(aX + bY > c; \mu_1'', \mu_2'').$$

The distribution of $Z = aX + bY$ is obtained from Theorem 3.5.1. It follows that the distribution of $Z = aX + bY$ is given by

$$N(a\mu_1 + b\mu_2, a^2\sigma_1^2 + 2ab\rho\sigma_1\sigma_2 + b^2\sigma_2^2).$$

With this information, it is easy to compute the probabilities of misclassifications; see Exercise 8.5.3.

One final remark must be made with respect to the use of the important classification rule established in Example 8.5.2. In most instances the parameter values μ_1', μ_2' and μ_1'', μ_2'' as well as σ_1^2, σ_2^2, and ρ are unknown. In such cases the statistician has usually observed a random sample (frequently called a *training sample*) from each of the two distributions. Let us say the samples have sizes n' and n'', respectively, with sample characteristics

$$\overline{x}', \overline{y}', (s_x')^2, (s_y')^2, r' \quad \text{and} \quad \overline{x}'', \overline{y}'', (s_x'')^2, (s_y'')^2, r''.$$

The statistics r' and r'' are the sample correlation coefficients, as defined in expression (9.7.1) of Section 9.7. The sample correlation coefficient is the mle for the correlation parameter ρ of a bivariate normal distribution; see Section 9.7. If in inequality (8.5.3) the parameters $\mu_1', \mu_2', \mu_1'', \mu_2'', \sigma_1^2, \sigma_2^2$, and $\rho\sigma_1\sigma_2$ are replaced by the unbiased estimates

$$\overline{x}', \overline{y}', \overline{x}'', \overline{y}'', \frac{(n'-1)(s_x')^2 + (n''-1)(s_x'')^2}{n'+n''-2}, \frac{(n'-1)(s_y')^2 + (n''-1)(s_y'')^2}{n'+n''-2},$$
$$\frac{(n'-1)r's_x's_y' + (n''-1)r''s_x''s_y''}{n'+n''-2},$$

the resulting expression in the left-hand member is frequently called Fisher's **linear discriminant function**. Since those parameters have been estimated, the distribution theory associated with $aX + bY$ does provide an approximation.

Although we have considered only bivariate distributions in this section, the results can easily be extended to multivariate normal distributions using the results of Section 3.5; see also Chapter 6 of Seber (1984).

EXERCISES

8.5.1. Let $X_1, X_2, \ldots, X_{20}$ be a random sample of size 20 from a distribution which is $N(\theta, 5)$. Let $L(\theta)$ represent the joint pdf of $X_1, X_2, \ldots, X_{20}$. The problem is to test $H_0 : \theta = 1$ against $H_1 : \theta = 0$. Thus $\Omega = \{\theta : \theta = 0, 1\}$.

(a) Show that $L(1)/L(0) \leq k$ is equivalent to $\overline{x} \leq c$.

(b) Find c so that the significance level is $\alpha = 0.05$. Compute the power of this test if H_1 is true.

(c) If the loss function is such that $\mathcal{L}(1,1) = \mathcal{L}(0,0) = 0$ and $\mathcal{L}(1,0) = \mathcal{L}(0,1) > 0$, find the minimax test. Evaluate the power function of this test at the points $\theta = 1$ and $\theta = 0$.

8.5.2. Let $X_1, X_2, \ldots, X_{10}$ be a random sample of size 10 from a Poisson distribution with parameter θ. Let $L(\theta)$ be the joint pdf of $X_1, X_2, \ldots, X_{10}$. The problem is to test $H_0 : \theta = \frac{1}{2}$ against $H_1 : \theta = 1$.

(a) Show that $L(\frac{1}{2})/L(1) \leq k$ is equivalent to $y = \sum_1^n x_i \geq c$.

(b) In order to make $\alpha = 0.05$, show that H_0 is rejected if $y > 9$ and, if $y = 9$, reject H_0 with probability $\frac{1}{2}$ (using some auxiliary random experiment).

(c) If the loss function is such that $\mathcal{L}(\frac{1}{2}, \frac{1}{2}) = \mathcal{L}(1,1) = 0$ and $\mathcal{L}(\frac{1}{2},1) = 1$ and $\mathcal{L}(1,\frac{1}{2}) = 2$, show that the minimax procedure is to reject H_0 if $y > 6$ and, if $y = 6$, reject H_0 with probability 0.08 (using some auxiliary random experiment).

8.5.3. In Example 8.5.2 let $\mu_1' = \mu_2' = 0$, $\mu_1'' = \mu_2'' = 1$, $\sigma_1^2 = 1$, $\sigma_2^2 = 1$, and $\rho = \frac{1}{2}$.

(a) Find the distribution of the linear function $aX + bY$.

(b) With $k = 1$, compute $P(aX + bY \leq c; \mu_1' = \mu_2' = 0)$ and $P(aX + bY > c; \mu_1'' = \mu_2'' = 1)$.

8.5.4. Determine Newton's algorithm to find the solution of Equation (8.5.2). If software is available, write a program which performs your algorithm and then show that the solution is $c = 76.8$. If software is not available, solve (8.5.2) by "trial and error."

8.5.5. Let X and Y have the joint pdf

$$f(x, y; \theta_1, \theta_2) = \frac{1}{\theta_1 \theta_2} \exp\left(-\frac{x}{\theta_1} - \frac{y}{\theta_2}\right), \quad 0 < x < \infty, \ 0 < y < \infty,$$

zero elsewhere, where $0 < \theta_1$, $0 < \theta_2$. An observation (x, y) arises from the joint distribution with parameters equal to either $(\theta_1' = 1, \theta_2' = 5)$ or $(\theta_1'' = 3, \theta_2'' = 2)$. Determine the form of the classification rule.

8.5.6. Let X and Y have a joint bivariate normal distribution. An observation (x, y) arises from the joint distribution with parameters equal to either

$$\mu_1' = \mu_2' = 0, \quad (\sigma_1^2)' = (\sigma_2^2)' = 1, \quad \rho' = \frac{1}{2}$$

or

$$\mu_1'' = \mu_2'' = 1, \quad (\sigma_1^2)'' = 4, \quad (\sigma_2^2)'' = 9, \quad \rho'' = \frac{1}{2}.$$

Show that the classification rule involves a second-degree polynomial in x and y.

8.5.7. Let $W' = (W_1, W_2)$ be an observation from one of two bivariate normal distributions, I and II, each with $\mu_1 = \mu_2 = 0$ but with the respective variance-covariance matrices

$$V_1 = \begin{pmatrix} 1 & 0 \\ 0 & 4 \end{pmatrix} \quad \text{and} \quad V_2 = \begin{pmatrix} 3 & 0 \\ 0 & 12 \end{pmatrix}.$$

How would you classify W into I or II?

Chapter 9

Inferences About Normal Models

9.1 Quadratic Forms

A homogeneous polynomial of degree 2 in n variables is called a **quadratic** form in those variables. If both the variables and the coefficients are real, the form is called a **real quadratic** form. Only real quadratic forms are considered in this book. To illustrate, the form $X_1^2 + X_1 X_2 + X_2^2$ is a quadratic form in the two variables X_1 and X_2; the form $X_1^2 + X_2^2 + X_3^2 - 2X_1 X_2$ is a quadratic form in the three variables X_1, X_2, and X_3; but the form $(X_1 - 1)^2 + (X_2 - 2)^2 = X_1^2 + X_2^2 - 2X_1 - 4X_2 + 5$ is not a quadratic form in X_1 and X_2, although it is a quadratic form in the variables $X_1 - 1$ and $X_2 - 2$.

Let $\overline{X}$ and S^2 denote, respectively, the mean and variance of a random sample $X_1, X_2, \ldots, X_n$ from an arbitrary distribution. Thus

$$
\begin{aligned}
(n-1)S^2 &= \sum_1^n (X_i - \overline{X})^2 = \sum_1^n \left(X_i - \frac{X_1 + X_2 + \cdots + X_n}{n} \right)^2 \\
&= \frac{n-1}{n}(X_1^2 + X_2^2 + \cdots + X_n^2) \\
&\quad - \frac{2}{n}(X_1 X_2 + \cdots + X_1 X_n + \cdots + X_{n-1} X_n)
\end{aligned}
$$

is a quadratic form in the n variables $X_1, X_2, \ldots, X_n$. If the sample arises from a distribution that is $N(\mu, \sigma^2)$, we know that the random variable $(n-1)S^2/\sigma^2$ is $\chi^2(n-1)$ regardless of the value of μ. This fact proved useful in our search for a confidence interval for σ^2 when μ is unknown.

It has been seen that tests of certain statistical hypotheses require a statistic that is a quadratic form. For instance, Example 8.2.2 made use of the statistic $\sum_1^n X_i^2$, which is a quadratic form in the variables $X_1, X_2, \ldots, X_n$. Later in this chapter, tests of other statistical hypotheses are investigated, showing that statistics composed of functions of quadratic forms are necessary to conduct the tests in an expeditious manner. But first we shall make a study of the distribution of certain quadratic forms in normal and independent random variables.

The following theorem is proved in Section 9.9.

Theorem 9.1.1. *Let* $Q = Q_1 + Q_2 + \cdots + Q_{k-1} + Q_k$, *where* $Q, Q_1, \ldots, Q_k$ *are* $k+1$ *random variables that are real quadratic forms in* n *independent random variables which are normally distributed with common mean and variance* μ *and* σ^2, *respectively. Let* $Q/\sigma^2, Q_1/\sigma^2, \ldots, Q_{k-1}/\sigma^2$ *have chi-square distributions with degrees of freedom* $r, r_1, \ldots, r_{k-1}$, *respectively. Let* Q_k *be nonnegative. Then*

(a) $Q_1, \ldots, Q_k$ *are independent, and hence*

(b) Q_k/σ^2 *has a chi-square distribution with* $r - (r_1 + \cdots + r_{k-1}) = r_k$ *degrees of freedom.*

Three examples illustrative of the theorem follow, each of which deals with a distribution problem that is based on the remarks made in the subsequent paragraph.

Let the random variable X have a distribution that is $N(\mu, \sigma^2)$. Let a and b denote positive integers greater than 1 and let $n = ab$. Consider a random sample of size $n = ab$ from this normal distribution. The observations of the random sample are denoted by the symbols

$$
\begin{array}{ccccccc}
X_{11}, & X_{12}, & \ldots, & X_{1j}, & \ldots, & X_{1b} \\
X_{21}, & X_{22}, & \ldots, & X_{2j}, & \ldots, & X_{2b} \\
& & \vdots & & & \\
X_{i1}, & X_{i2}, & \ldots, & X_{ij}, & \ldots, & X_{ib} \\
& & \vdots & & & \\
X_{a1}, & X_{a2}, & \ldots, & X_{aj}, & \ldots, & X_{ab}.
\end{array}
$$

By assumption, these $n = ab$ random variables are independent, and each has the same normal distribution with mean μ and variance σ^2. Thus, if we wish, we may consider each row as being a random sample of size b from the given distribution; and we may consider each column as being a random sample of size a from the given distribution. We now define $a + b + 1$ statistics. They are

$$
\overline{X}_{..} = \frac{X_{11} + \cdots + X_{1b} + \cdots + X_{a1} + \cdots + X_{ab}}{ab} = \frac{\sum_{i=1}^{a}\sum_{j=1}^{b} X_{ij}}{ab}
$$

$$
\overline{X}_{i.} = \frac{X_{i1} + X_{i2} + \cdots + X_{ib}}{b} = \frac{\sum_{j=1}^{b} X_{ij}}{b}, \quad i = 1, 2, \ldots, a,
$$

$$
\overline{X}_{.j} = \frac{X_{1j} + X_{2j} + \cdots + X_{aj}}{a} = \frac{\sum_{i=1}^{a} X_{ij}}{a}, \quad j = 1, 2, \ldots, b.
$$

Thus the statistic $\overline{X}_{..}$ is the mean of the random sample of size $n = ab$; the statistics $\overline{X}_{1.}, \overline{X}_{2.}, \ldots, \overline{X}_{a.}$ are, respectively, the means of the rows; and the statistics $\overline{X}_{.1}, \overline{X}_{.2}, \ldots, \overline{X}_{.b}$ are, respectively, the means of the columns. Examples illustrative of the theorem follow.

Example 9.1.1. Consider the variance S^2 of the random sample of size $n = ab$. We have the algebraic identity

$$\begin{aligned}
(ab-1)S^2 &= \sum_{i=1}^{a}\sum_{j=1}^{b}(X_{ij} - \overline{X}_{..})^2 \\
&= \sum_{i=1}^{a}\sum_{j=1}^{b}[(X_{ij} - \overline{X}_{i.}) + (\overline{X}_{i.} - \overline{X}_{..})]^2 \\
&= \sum_{i=1}^{a}\sum_{j=1}^{b}(X_{ij} - \overline{X}_{i.})^2 + \sum_{i=1}^{a}\sum_{j=1}^{b}(\overline{X}_{i.} - \overline{X}_{..})^2 \\
&\quad + 2\sum_{i=1}^{a}\sum_{j=1}^{b}(X_{ij} - \overline{X}_{i.})(\overline{X}_{i.} - \overline{X}_{..}).
\end{aligned}$$

The last term of the right-hand member of this identity may be written

$$2\sum_{i=1}^{a}\left[(\overline{X}_{i.} - \overline{X}_{..})\sum_{j=1}^{b}(X_{ij} - \overline{X}_{i.})\right] = 2\sum_{i=1}^{a}[(\overline{X}_{i.} - \overline{X}_{..})(b\overline{X}_{i.} - b\overline{X}_{i.})] = 0,$$

and the term

$$\sum_{i=1}^{a}\sum_{j=1}^{b}(\overline{X}_{i.} - \overline{X}_{..})^2$$

may be written

$$b\sum_{i=1}^{a}(\overline{X}_{i.} - \overline{X}_{..})^2.$$

Thus,

$$(ab-1)S^2 = \sum_{i=1}^{a}\sum_{j=1}^{b}(X_{ij} - \overline{X}_{i.})^2 + b\sum_{i=1}^{a}(\overline{X}_{i.} - \overline{X}_{..})^2,$$

or, for brevity,

$$Q = Q_1 + Q_2.$$

We shall use Theorem 9.1.1 with $k = 2$ to show that Q_1 and Q_2 are independent. Since S^2 is the variance of a random variable of size $n = ab$ from the given normal distribution, then $(ab-1)S^2/\sigma^2$ has a chi-square distribution with $ab - 1$ degrees of freedom. Now

$$\frac{Q_1}{\sigma^2} = \sum_{i=1}^{a}\left[\sum_{j=1}^{b}(X_{ij} - \overline{X}_{i.})^2/\sigma^2\right].$$

For each fixed value of i, $\sum_{j=1}^{b}(X_{ij} - \overline{X}_{i.})^2$ is the product of $(b-1)$ and the variance of a random sample of size b from the given normal distribution, and accordingly, $\sum_{j=1}^{b}(X_{ij} - \overline{X}_{i.})^2/\sigma^2$ has a chi-square distribution with $b-1$ degrees of freedom. Because the X_{ij}s are independent, Q_1/σ^2 is the sum of a independent random variables, each having a chi-square distribution with $b-1$ degrees of freedom. Hence Q_1/σ^2 has a chi-square distribution with $a(b-1)$ degrees of freedom. Now $Q_2 = b\sum_{i=1}^{a}(\overline{X}_{i.} - \overline{X}_{..})^2 \geq 0$. In accordance with the theorem, Q_1 and Q_2 are independent, and Q_2/σ^2 has a chi-square distribution with $ab - 1 - a(b-1) = a-1$ degrees of freedom. ∎

Example 9.1.2. In $(ab-1)S^2$, replace $X_{ij} - \overline{X}_{..}$ by $(X_{ij} - \overline{X}_{.j}) + (\overline{X}_{.j} - \overline{X}_{..})$ to obtain

$$(ab-1)S^2 = \sum_{j=1}^{b}\sum_{i=1}^{a}[(X_{ij} - \overline{X}_{.j}) + (\overline{X}_{.j} - \overline{X}_{..})]^2,$$

or

$$(ab-1)S^2 = \sum_{j=1}^{b}\sum_{i=1}^{a}(X_{ij} - \overline{X}_{.j})^2 + a\sum_{j=1}^{b}(\overline{X}_{.j} - \overline{X}_{..})^2,$$

or, for brevity,

$$Q = Q_3 + Q_4.$$

It is easy to show (Exercise 9.1.1) that Q_3/σ^2 has a chi-square distribution with $b(a-1)$ degrees of freedom. Since $Q_4 = a\sum_{j=1}^{b}(\overline{X}_{.j} - \overline{X}_{..})^2 \geq 0$, the theorem enables us to assert that Q_3 and Q_4 are independent and that Q_4/σ^2 has a chi-square distribution with $ab - 1 - b(a-1) = b-1$ degrees of freedom. ∎

Example 9.1.3. In $(ab-1)S^2$, replace $X_{ij} - \overline{X}_{..}$ by $(\overline{X}_{i.} - \overline{X}_{..}) + (\overline{X}_{.j} - \overline{X}_{..}) + (X_{ij} - \overline{X}_{i.} - \overline{X}_{.j} + \overline{X}_{..})$ to obtain (Exercise 9.1.2)

$$(ab-1)S^2 = b\sum_{i=1}^{a}(\overline{X}_{i.} - \overline{X}_{..})^2 + a\sum_{j=1}^{b}(\overline{X}_{.j} - \overline{X}_{..})^2 + \sum_{j=1}^{b}\sum_{i=1}^{a}(X_{ij} - \overline{X}_{i.} - \overline{X}_{.j} + \overline{X}_{..})^2,$$

or, for brevity,

$$Q = Q_2 + Q_4 + Q_5,$$

where Q_2 and Q_4 are defined in Examples 9.1.1 and 9.1.2. From Examples 9.1.1 and 9.1.2, Q/σ^2, Q_2/σ^2, and Q_4/σ^2 have chi-square distributions with $ab-1$, $a-1$, and $b-1$ degrees of freedom, respectively. Since $Q_5 \geq 0$, the theorem asserts that Q_2, Q_4, and Q_5 are independent and that Q_5/σ^2 has a chi-square distribution with $ab - 1 - (a-1) - (b-1) = (a-1)(b-1)$ degrees of freedom. ∎

Once these quadratic form statistics have been shown to be independent, a multiplicity of F-statistics can be defined. For instance,

$$\frac{Q_4/[\sigma^2(b-1)]}{Q_3/[\sigma^2 b(a-1)]} = \frac{Q_4/(b-1)}{Q_3/[b(a-1)]}$$

has an F-distribution with $b-1$ and $b(a-1)$ degrees of freedom; and

$$\frac{Q_4/[\sigma^2(b-1)]}{Q_5/[\sigma^2(a-1)(b-1)]} = \frac{Q_4/(b-1)}{Q_5/(a-1)(b-1)}$$

has an F-distribution with $b-1$ and $(a-1)(b-1)$ degrees of freedom. The subsequent sections show that likelihood ratio tests of certain statistical hypotheses can be based on these F-statistics.

EXERCISES

9.1.1. In Example 9.1.2, verify that $Q = Q_3 + Q_4$ and that Q_3/σ^2 has a chi-square distribution with $b(a-1)$ degrees of freedom.

9.1.2. In Example 9.1.3, verify that $Q = Q_2 + Q_4 + Q_5$.

9.1.3. Let $X_1, X_2, \ldots, X_n$ be a random sample from a normal distribution $N(\mu, \sigma^2)$. Show that

$$\sum_{i=1}^{n}(X_i - \overline{X})^2 = \sum_{i=2}^{n}(X_i - \overline{X}')^2 + \frac{n-1}{n}(X_1 - \overline{X}')^2,$$

where $\overline{X} = \sum_{i=1}^{n} X_i/n$ and $\overline{X}' = \sum_{i=2}^{n} X_i/(n-1)$.
Hint: Replace $X_i - \overline{X}$ by $(X_i - \overline{X}') - (X_1 - \overline{X}')/n$. Show that $\sum_{i=2}^{n}(X_i - \overline{X}')^2/\sigma^2$ has a chi-square distribution with $n-2$ degrees of freedom. Prove that the two terms in the right-hand member are independent. What then is the distribution of

$$\frac{[(n-1)/n](X_1 - \overline{X}')^2}{\sigma^2}?$$

9.1.4. Let $X_{ijk}, i = 1, \ldots, a; j = 1, \ldots, b; k = 1, \ldots, c$, be a random sample of size $n = abc$ from a normal distribution $N(\mu, \sigma^2)$. Let $\overline{X}_{...} = \sum_{k=1}^{c}\sum_{j=1}^{b}\sum_{i=1}^{a} X_{ijk}/n$ and $\overline{X}_{i..} = \sum_{k=1}^{c}\sum_{j=1}^{b} X_{ijk}/bc$. Prove that

$$\sum_{i=1}^{a}\sum_{j=1}^{b}\sum_{k=1}^{c}(X_{ijk} - \overline{X}_{...})^2 = \sum_{i=1}^{a}\sum_{j=1}^{b}\sum_{k=1}^{c}(X_{ijk} - \overline{X}_{i..})^2 + bc\sum_{i=1}^{a}(\overline{X}_{i..} - \overline{X}_{...})^2.$$

Show that $\sum_{i=1}^{a}\sum_{j=1}^{b}\sum_{k=1}^{c}(X_{ijk} - \overline{X}_{i..})^2/\sigma^2$ has a chi-square distribution with $a(bc-1)$ degrees of freedom. Prove that the two terms in the right-hand member are independent. What, then, is the distribution of $bc\sum_{i=1}^{a}(\overline{X}_{i..} - \overline{X}_{...})^2/\sigma^2$?

Furthermore, let $\overline{X}_{.j.} = \sum_{k=1}^{c} \sum_{i=1}^{a} X_{ijk}/ac$ and $\overline{X}_{ij.} = \sum_{k=1}^{c} X_{ijk}/c$. Show that

$$\sum_{i=1}^{a} \sum_{j=1}^{b} \sum_{k=1}^{c} (X_{ijk} - \overline{X}_{...})^2 = \sum_{i=1}^{a} \sum_{j=1}^{b} \sum_{k=1}^{c} (X_{ijk} - \overline{X}_{ij.})^2$$

$$+ bc \sum_{i=1}^{a} (\overline{X}_{i..} - \overline{X}_{...})^2 + ac \sum_{j=1}^{b} (\overline{X}_{.j.} - \overline{X}_{...})^2$$

$$+ c \sum_{i=1}^{a} \sum_{j=1}^{b} (\overline{X}_{ij.} - \overline{X}_{i..} - \overline{X}_{.j.} + \overline{X}_{...}).$$

Prove that the four terms in the right-hand member, when divided by σ^2, are independent chi-square variables with $ab(c-1)$, $a-1$, $b-1$, and $(a-1)(b-1)$ degrees of freedom, respectively.

9.1.5. Let X_1, X_2, X_3, X_4 be a random sample of size $n = 4$ from the normal distribution $N(0,1)$. Show that $\sum_{i=1}^{4} (X_i - \overline{X})^2$ equals

$$\frac{(X_1 - X_2)^2}{2} + \frac{[X_3 - (X_1 + X_2)/2]^2}{3/2} + \frac{[X_4 - (X_1 + X_2 + X_3)/3]^2}{4/3}$$

and argue that these three terms are independent, each with a chi-square distribution with 1 degree of freedom.

9.2 One-Way ANOVA

Consider b independent random variables that have normal distributions with unknown means $\mu_1, \mu_2, \ldots, \mu_b$, respectively, and unknown but common variance σ^2. For each $j = 1, 2, \ldots, b$, let $X_{1j}, X_{2j}, \ldots, X_{aj}$ represent a random sample of size a from the normal distribution with mean μ_j and variance σ^2. The appropriate model for the observations is

$$X_{ij} = \mu_j + e_{ij} ; \quad i = 1, \ldots, a, j = 1, \ldots, b, \tag{9.2.1}$$

where e_{ij} are iid $N(0, \sigma^2)$. Suppose that it is desired to test the composite hypothesis $H_0 : \mu_1 = \mu_2 = \cdots = \mu_b = \mu$, μ unspecified, against all possible alternative hypotheses H_1. A likelihood ratio test is used.

Such problems often arise in practice. For example, suppose for a certain type of disease there are b drugs which can be used to treat it and we are interested in determining which drug is best in terms of a certain response. Let X_j denote this response when drug j is applied and let $\mu_j = E(X_j)$. If we assume that X_j is $N(\mu_j, \sigma^2)$, then the above null hypothesis says that all the drugs are equally effective. We often summarize this problem by saying that we have one factor at b levels. In this case the factor is the treatment of the disease and each level corresponds to one of the treatment drugs. Model (9.2.1) is called a **one-way** model. As shown, the likelihood ratio test can be thought of in terms of estimates of variance. Hence this is an example of an **analysis of variance (ANOVA)**. In short, we say that this example is a one-way ANOVA problem.

Here the total parameter space is

$$\Omega = \{(\mu_1, \mu_2, \ldots, \mu_b, \sigma^2) : -\infty < \mu_j < \infty, \ 0 < \sigma^2 < \infty\}$$

and

$$\omega = \{(\mu_1, \mu_2, \ldots, \mu_b, \sigma^2) : -\infty < \mu_1 = \mu_2 = \cdots = \mu_b = \mu < \infty, \ 0 < \sigma^2 < \infty\}.$$

The likelihood functions, denoted by $L(\omega)$ and $L(\Omega)$ are, respectively,

$$L(\omega) = \left(\frac{1}{2\pi\sigma^2}\right)^{ab/2} \exp\left[-\frac{1}{2\sigma^2} \sum_{j=1}^{b} \sum_{i=1}^{a} (x_{ij} - \mu)^2\right]$$

and

$$L(\Omega) = \left(\frac{1}{2\pi\sigma^2}\right)^{ab/2} \exp\left[-\frac{1}{2\sigma^2} \sum_{j=1}^{b} \sum_{i=1}^{a} (x_{ij} - \mu_j)^2\right].$$

Now

$$\frac{\partial \log L(\omega)}{\partial \mu} = \sigma^{-2} \sum_{j=1}^{b} \sum_{i=1}^{a} (x_{ij} - \mu)$$

and

$$\frac{\partial \log L(\omega)}{\partial(\sigma^2)} = -\frac{ab}{2\sigma^2} + \frac{1}{2\sigma^4} \sum_{j=1}^{b} \sum_{i=1}^{a} (x_{ij} - \mu_j)^2.$$

If we equate these partial derivatives to zero, the solutions for μ and σ^2 are, respectively, in ω,

$$(ab)^{-1} \sum_{j=1}^{b} \sum_{i=1}^{a} x_{ij} = \overline{x}_{..}$$

$$(ab)^{-1} \sum_{j=1}^{b} \sum_{i=1}^{a} (x_{ij} - \overline{x}_{..})^2 = v, \tag{9.2.2}$$

and these values maximize $L(\omega)$. Furthermore,

$$\frac{\partial \log L(\Omega)}{\partial \mu_j} = \sigma^{-2} \sum_{i=1}^{a} (x_{ij} - \mu_j), \quad j = 1, 2, \ldots, b,$$

and

$$\frac{\partial \log L(\Omega)}{\partial(\sigma^2)} = -\frac{ab}{2\sigma^2} + \frac{1}{2\sigma^4} \sum_{j=1}^{b} \sum_{i=1}^{a} (x_{ij} - \mu_j)^2.$$

If we equate these partial derivatives to zero, the solutions for $\mu_1, \mu_2, \ldots, \mu_b$ and σ^2 are, respectively, in Ω,

$$a^{-1} \sum_{i=1}^{a} x_{ij} = \overline{x}_{.j}, \quad j = 1, 2, \ldots, b,$$

$$(ab)^{-1} \sum_{j=1}^{b} \sum_{i=1}^{a} (x_{ij} - \overline{x}_{.j})^2 = w, \qquad (9.2.3)$$

and these values maximize $L(\Omega)$. These maxima are, respectively,

$$L(\hat{\omega}) = \left[\frac{ab}{2\pi \sum_{j=1}^{b} \sum_{i=1}^{a} (x_{ij} - \overline{x}_{..})^2} \right]^{ab/2} \exp\left[-\frac{ab \sum_{j=1}^{b} \sum_{i=1}^{a} (x_{ij} - \overline{x}_{..})^2}{2 \sum_{j=1}^{b} \sum_{i=1}^{a} (x_{ij} - \overline{x}_{..})^2} \right]$$

$$= \left[\frac{ab}{2\pi \sum_{j=1}^{b} \sum_{i=1}^{a} (x_{ij} - \overline{x}_{..})^2} \right]^{ab/2} e^{-ab/2}$$

and

$$L(\hat{\Omega}) = \left[\frac{ab}{2\pi \sum_{j=1}^{b} \sum_{i=1}^{a} (x_{ij} - \overline{x}_{.j})^2} \right]^{ab/2} e^{-ab/2}.$$

Finally,

$$\Lambda = \frac{L(\hat{\omega})}{L(\hat{\Omega})} = \left[\frac{\sum_{j=1}^{b} \sum_{i=1}^{a} (x_{ij} - \overline{x}_{.j})^2}{\sum_{j=1}^{b} \sum_{i=1}^{a} (x_{ij} - \overline{x}_{..})^2} \right]^{ab/2}.$$

In the notation of Section 9.1, the statistics defined by the functions $\overline{x}_{..}$ and v given by the equations in expression (9.2.2) of this section are

$$\overline{X}_{..} = \frac{1}{ab}\sum_{j=1}^{b}\sum_{i=1}^{a}X_{ij} \quad \text{and} \quad V = \frac{1}{ab}\sum_{j=1}^{b}\sum_{i=1}^{a}(X_{ij} - \overline{X}_{..})^2 = \frac{Q}{ab}, \qquad (9.2.4)$$

while the statistics defined by the functions $\overline{x}_{.1}, \overline{x}_{.2}, \ldots, \overline{x}_{.b}$ and w given by Equations (9.2.3) in this section are, respectively, given by the formulas $\overline{X}_{.j} = \sum_{i=1}^{a} X_{ij}/a$, $j = 1, 2, \ldots, b$, and $Q_3/ab = \sum_{j=1}^{b}\sum_{i=1}^{a}(X_{ij} - \overline{X}_{.j})^2/ab$. Thus, in the notation of Section 9.1, $\Lambda^{2/ab}$ defines the statistic Q_3/Q.

We reject the hypothesis H_0 if $\Lambda \leq \lambda_0$. To find λ_0 so that we have a desired significance level α, we must assume that the hypothesis H_0 is true. If the hypothesis H_0 is true, the random variables X_{ij} constitute a random sample of size $n = ab$ from a distribution that is normal with mean μ and variance σ^2. Thus, by Example 9.1.2, we have that $Q = Q_3 + Q_4$, where $Q_4 = a\sum_{j=1}^{b}(\overline{X}_{.j} - \overline{X}_{..})^2$; that Q_3 and Q_4 are independent; and that Q_3/σ^2 and Q_4/σ^2 have chi-square distributions with $b(a-1)$ and $b-1$ degrees of freedom, respectively. Thus, the statistic defined by $\lambda^{2/ab}$ may be written

$$\frac{Q_3}{Q_3 + Q_4} = \frac{1}{1 + Q_4/Q_3}.$$

The significance level of the test of H_0 is

$$\alpha = P_{H_0}\left[\frac{1}{1 + Q_4/Q_3} \leq \lambda_0^{2/ab}\right]$$

$$= P_{H_0}\left[\frac{Q_4/(b-1)}{Q_3/([b(a-1)]} \geq c\right],$$

where

$$c = \frac{b(a-1)}{b-1}(\lambda_0^{-2/ab} - 1).$$

But

$$F = \frac{Q_4/[\sigma^2(b-1)]}{Q_3/[\sigma^2 b(a-1)]} = \frac{Q_4/(b-1)}{Q_3/[b(a-1)]}$$

has an F-distribution with $b-1$ and $b(a-1)$ degrees of freedom. Hence the test of the composite hypothesis $H_0 : \mu_1 = \mu_2 = \cdots = \mu_b = \mu$, μ unspecified, against all possible alternatives may be tested with an F-statistic. Setting the constant c to the upper α F-critical point with $b-1$ and $b(a-1)$ degress of freedom, denoted by $F(\alpha, b-1, b(a-1))$, yields a test of level α.

Remark 9.2.1. It should be pointed out that a test of the equality of the b means μ_j, $j = 1, 2, \ldots, b$, does not require that we take a random sample of size a from each of the b normal distributions. That is, the samples may be of different sizes, for instance, $a_1, a_2, \ldots, a_b$; see Exercise 9.2.1. ∎

Suppose now that we wish to compute the power of the test of H_0 against H_1 when H_0 is false, that is, when we do not have $\mu_1 = \mu_2 = \cdots = \mu_b = \mu$. In Section 9.3 we show that under H_1, Q_4/σ^2 no longer has a $\chi^2(b-1)$ distribution. Thus we cannot use an F-statistic to compute the power of the test when H_1 is true. The problem is discussed in Section 9.3.

An observation should be made in connection with maximizing a likelihood function with respect to certain parameters. Sometimes it is easier to avoid the use of the calculus. For example, $L(\Omega)$ of this section can be maximized with respect to μ_j, for every fixed positive σ^2, by minimizing

$$z = \sum_{j=1}^{b} \sum_{i=1}^{a} (x_{ij} - \mu_j)^2$$

with respect to μ_j, $j = 1, 2, \ldots, b$. Now z can be written as

$$z = \sum_{j=1}^{b} \sum_{i=1}^{a} [(x_{ij} - \overline{x}_{.j}) + (\overline{x}_{.j} - \mu_j)]^2$$

$$= \sum_{j=1}^{b} \sum_{i=1}^{a} (x_{ij} - \overline{x}_{.j})^2 + a \sum_{j=1}^{b} (\overline{x}_{.j} - \mu_j)^2.$$

Since each term in the right-hand member of the preceding equation is nonnegative, clearly z is a minimum, with respect to μ_j, if we take $\mu_j = \overline{x}_{.j}$, $j = 1, 2, \ldots, b$.

EXERCISES

9.2.1. Let $X_{1j}, X_{2j}, \ldots, X_{a_j j}$ represent independent random samples of sizes a_j from a normal distribution with means μ_j and variances σ^2, $j = 1, 2, \ldots, b$. Show that

$$\sum_{j=1}^{b} \sum_{i=1}^{a_j} (X_{ij} - \overline{X}_{..})^2 = \sum_{j=1}^{b} \sum_{i=1}^{a_j} (X_{ij} - \overline{X}_{.j})^2 + \sum_{j=1}^{b} a_j (\overline{X}_{.j} - \overline{X}_{..})^2,$$

or $Q' = Q'_3 + Q'_4$. Here $\overline{X}_{..} = \sum_{j=1}^{b} \sum_{i=1}^{a_j} X_{ij} / \sum_{j=1}^{b} a_j$ and $\overline{X}_{.j} = \sum_{i=1}^{a_j} X_{ij}/a_j$. If $\mu_1 = \mu_2 = \cdots = \mu_b$, show that Q'/σ^2 and Q'_3/σ^2 have chi-square distributions. Prove that Q'_3 and Q'_4 are independent, and hence Q'_4/σ^2 also has a chi-square distribution. If the likelihood ratio Λ is used to test $H_0 : \mu_1 = \mu_2 = \cdots = \mu_b = \mu$, μ unspecified and σ^2 unknown against all possible alternatives, show that $\Lambda \leq \lambda_0$ is equivalent to the computed $F \geq c$, where

$$F = \frac{\left(\sum_{j=1}^{b} a_j - b\right) Q'_4}{(b-1)Q'_3}.$$

Determine the distribution of F when H_0 is true and, hence, determine c so that the test has level α.

9.2.2. Consider the T-statistic that was derived through a likelihood ratio for testing the equality of the means of two normal distributions having common variance in Example 8.3.1. Show that T^2 is exactly the F-statistic of Exercise 9.2.1 with $a_1 = n$, $a_2 = m$, and $b = 2$. Of course, $X_1, \ldots, X_n, \overline{X}$ are replaced with $X_{11}, \ldots, X_{1n}, \overline{X}_{1.}$ and $Y_1, \ldots, Y_m, \overline{Y}$ by $X_{21} \ldots, X_{2m}, \overline{X}_{2.}$.

9.2.3. In Exercise 9.2.1, show that the linear functions $X_{ij} - \overline{X}_{.j}$ and $\overline{X}_{.j} - \overline{X}_{..}$ are uncorrelated.
Hint: Recall the definition of $\overline{X}_{.j}$ and $\overline{X}_{..}$ and, without loss of generality, we can let $E(X_{ij}) = 0$ for all i, j.

9.2.4. The following are observations associated with independent random samples from three normal distributions having equal variances and respective means μ_1, μ_2, μ_3.

I	II	III
0.5	2.1	3.0
1.3	3.3	5.1
−1.0	0.0	1.9
1.8	2.3	2.4
	2.5	4.2
		4.1

Compute the F-statistic that is used to test $H_0 : \mu_1 = \mu_2 = \mu_3$.

9.2.5. Using the notation of this section, assume that the means satisfy the condition that $\mu = \mu_1 + (b-1)d = \mu_2 - d = \mu_3 - d = \cdots = \mu_b - d$. That is, the last $b - 1$ means are equal but differ from the first mean μ_1, provided that $d \neq 0$. Let independent random samples of size a be taken from the b normal distributions with common unknown variance σ^2.

(a) Show that the maximum likelihood estimators of μ and d are $\hat{\mu} = \overline{X}_{..}$ and

$$\hat{d} = \frac{\sum\limits_{j=2}^{b} \overline{X}_{.j}/(b-1) - \overline{X}_{.1}}{b}.$$

(b) Using Exercise 9.1.3, find Q_6 and $Q_7 = c\hat{d}^2$ so that, when $d = 0$, Q_7/σ^2 is $\chi^2(1)$ and

$$\sum_{i=1}^{a}\sum_{j=1}^{b}(X_{ij} - \overline{X}_{..})^2 = Q_3 + Q_6 + Q_7.$$

(c) Argue that the three terms in the right-hand member of part (b), once divided by σ^2, are independent random variables with chi-square distributions, provided that $d = 0$.

(d) The ratio $Q_7/(Q_3 + Q_6)$ times what constant has an F-distribution, provided that $d = 0$? Note that this F is really the square of the two-sample T used to test the equality of the mean of the first distribution and the common mean of the other distributions, in which the last $b - 1$ samples are combined into one.

9.2.6. Let μ_1, μ_2, μ_3 be, respectively, the means of three normal distributions with a common but unknown variance σ^2. In order to test, at the $\alpha = 5\%$ significance level, the hypothesis $H_0 : \mu_1 = \mu_2 = \mu_3$ against all possible alternative hypotheses, we take an independent random sample of size 4 from each of these distributions. Determine whether we accept or reject H_0 if the observed values from these three distributions are, respectively,

$$
\begin{array}{lcccc}
X_1 : & 5 & 9 & 6 & 8 \\
X_2 : & 11 & 13 & 10 & 12 \\
X_3 : & 10 & 6 & 9 & 9
\end{array}
$$

9.2.7. The driver of a diesel-powered automobile decided to test the quality of three types of diesel fuel sold in the area based on mpg. Test the null hypothesis that the three means are equal using the following data. Make the usual assumptions and take $\alpha = 0.05$.

$$
\begin{array}{lccccc}
\text{Brand A:} & 38.7 & 39.2 & 40.1 & 38.9 & \\
\text{Brand B:} & 41.9 & 42.3 & 41.3 & & \\
\text{Brand C:} & 40.8 & 41.2 & 39.5 & 38.9 & 40.3
\end{array}
$$

9.3   Noncentral χ^2 and F-Distributions

Let $X_1, X_2, \ldots, X_n$ denote independent random variables that are $N(\mu_i, \sigma^2)$, $i = 1, 2, \ldots, n$, and consider the quadratic form $Y = \sum_1^n X_i^2/\sigma^2$. If each μ_i is zero, we know that Y is $\chi^2(n)$. We shall now investigate the distribution of Y when each μ_i is not zero. The mgf of Y is given by

$$
M(t) = E\left[\exp\left(t \sum_{i=1}^n \frac{X_i^2}{\sigma^2}\right)\right]
$$

$$
= \prod_{i=1}^n E\left[\exp\left(t \frac{X_i^2}{\sigma^2}\right)\right].
$$

Consider

$$
E\left[\exp\left(\frac{tX_i^2}{\sigma^2}\right)\right] = \int_{-\infty}^{\infty} \frac{1}{\sigma\sqrt{2\pi}} \exp\left[\frac{tx_i^2}{\sigma^2} - \frac{(x_i - \mu_i)^2}{2\sigma^2}\right] dx_i.
$$

The integral exists if $t < \frac{1}{2}$. To evaluate the integral, note that

$$
\frac{tx_i^2}{\sigma^2} - \frac{(x_i - \mu_i)^2}{2\sigma^2} = -\frac{x_i^2(1 - 2t)}{2\sigma^2} + \frac{2\mu_i x_i}{2\sigma^2} - \frac{\mu_i^2}{2\sigma^2}
$$

$$
= \frac{t\mu_i^2}{\sigma^2(1 - 2t)} - \frac{1 - 2t}{2\sigma^2}\left(x_i - \frac{\mu_i}{1 - 2t}\right)^2.
$$

Accordingly, with $t < \frac{1}{2}$, we have

$$E\left[\exp\left(\frac{tX_i^2}{\sigma^2}\right)\right] = \exp\left[\frac{t\mu_i^2}{\sigma^2(1-2t)}\right]\int_{-\infty}^{\infty}\frac{1}{\sigma\sqrt{2\pi}}\exp\left[-\frac{1-2t}{2\sigma^2}\left(x_i-\frac{\mu_i}{1-2t}\right)^2\right]dx_i.$$

If we multiply the integrand by $\sqrt{1-2t}$, $t < \frac{1}{2}$, we have the integral of a normal pdf with mean $\mu_i/(1-2t)$ and variance $\sigma^2/(1-2t)$. Thus

$$E\left[\exp\left(\frac{tX_i^2}{\sigma^2}\right)\right] = \frac{1}{\sqrt{1-2t}}\exp\left[\frac{t\mu_i^2}{\sigma^2(1-2t)}\right],$$

and the mgf of $Y = \sum_1^n X_i^2/\sigma^2$ is given by

$$M(t) = \frac{1}{(1-2t)^{n/2}}\exp\left[\frac{t\sum_1^n\mu_i^2}{\sigma^2(1-2t)}\right], \quad t < \frac{1}{2}. \tag{9.3.1}$$

A random variable that has an mgf of the functional form

$$M(t) = \frac{1}{(1-2t)^{r/2}}e^{t\theta/(1-2t)}, \tag{9.3.2}$$

where $t < \frac{1}{2}$, $0 < \theta$, and r is a positive integer, is said to have a **noncentral chi-square distribution** with r degrees of freedom and noncentrality parameter θ. If one sets the noncentrality parameter $\theta = 0$, one has $M(t) = (1-2t)^{-r/2}$, which is the mgf of a random variable that is $\chi^2(r)$. Such a random variable can appropriately be called a **central chi-square variable**. We shall use the symbol $\chi^2(r,\theta)$ to denote a noncentral chi-square distribution that has the parameters r and θ; and we shall say that a random variable is $\chi^2(r,\theta)$ when that random variable has this kind of distribution. The symbol $\chi^2(r,0)$ is equivalent to $\chi^2(r)$. Thus our random variable $Y = \sum_1^n X_i^2/\sigma^2$ of this section is $\chi^2\left(n, \sum_1^n\mu_i^2/\sigma^2\right)$. If each μ_i is equal to zero, then Y is $\chi^2(n,0)$ or, more simply, Y is $\chi^2(n)$.

The noncentral chi-square variables in which we have interest are certain quadratic forms in normally distributed variables divided by a variance σ^2. In our example it is worth noting that the noncentrality parameter of $\sum_1^n X_i^2/\sigma^2$, which is $\sum_1^n\mu_i^2/\sigma^2$, may be computed by replacing each X_i in the quadratic form by its mean μ_i, $i = 1, 2, \ldots, n$. This is no fortuitous circumstance; any quadratic form $Q = Q(X_1, \ldots, X_n)$ in normally distributed variables, which is such that Q/σ^2 is $\chi^2(r,\theta)$, has $\theta = Q(\mu_1, \mu_2, \ldots, \mu_n)/\sigma^2$; and if Q/σ^2 is a chi-square variable (central or noncentral) for certain real values of $\mu_1, \mu_2, \ldots, \mu_n$, it is chi-square (central or noncentral) for *all* real values of these means.

It should be pointed out that Theorem 9.1.1, Section 9.1, is valid whether the random variables are central or noncentral chi-square variables.

We next discuss the noncentral F-distribution. If U and V are independent and are, respectively, $\chi^2(r_1)$ and $\chi^2(r_2)$, the random variable F has been defined by $F = r_2U/r_1V$. Now suppose, in particular, that U is $\chi^2(r_1,\theta)$, V is $\chi^2(r_2)$, and U and V are independent. The distribution of the random variable r_2U/r_1V is called a **noncentral F-distribution** with r_1 and r_2 degrees of freedom with noncentrality parameter θ. Note that the noncentrality parameter of F is precisely the noncentrality parameter of the random variable U, which is $\chi^2(r_1, \theta)$.

There are R commands which compute the cdf of noncentral χ^2 and F random variables. For example, suppose we want to compute $P(Y \le y)$, where Y has a χ^2-distribution with d degrees of freedom and noncentrality parameter b. This probability is returned with the command pchisq(y,d,b). The corresponding value of the pdf at y is computed by the command dchisq(y,d,b). As another example, suppose we want $P(W \ge w)$, where W has an F-distribution with n1 and n2 degrees of freedom and noncentrality parameter b. This is computed by the command 1-pf(w,n1,n2,b), while the command df(w,n1,n2,b) computes the value of the density of W at w. Tables of the noncentral chi-square and noncentral F-distributions are available in the literature also.

EXERCISES

9.3.1. Let Y_i, $i = 1, 2, \ldots, n$, denote independent random variables that are, respectively, $\chi^2(r_i, \theta_i)$, $i = 1, 2, \ldots, n$. Prove that $Z = \sum_1^n Y_i$ is $\chi^2 \left(\sum_1^n r_i, \sum_1^n \theta_i \right)$.

9.3.2. Compute the mean and variance of a random variable that is $\chi^2(r, \theta)$.

9.3.3. Compute the mean of a random variable that has a noncentral F-distribution with degrees of freedom r_1 and $r_2 > 2$ and noncentrality parameter θ.

9.3.4. Show that the square of a noncentral T random variable is a noncentral F random variable.

9.3.5. Let X_1 and X_2 be two independent random variables. Let X_1 and $Y = X_1 + X_2$ be $\chi^2(r_1, \theta_1)$ and $\chi^2(r, \theta)$, respectively. Here $r_1 < r$ and $\theta_1 \le \theta$. Show that X_2 is $\chi^2(r - r_1, \theta - \theta_1)$.

9.3.6. In Exercise 9.2.1, if $\mu_1, \mu_2, \ldots, \mu_b$ are not equal, what are the distributions of Q_3'/σ^2, Q_4'/σ^2, and F?

9.4   Multiple Comparisons

Consider b independent random variables that have normal distributions with unknown means $\mu_1, \mu_2, \ldots, \mu_b$, respectively, and with unknown but common variance σ^2. Let $k_1, \ldots, k_b$ represent b known real constants that are not all zero. We want to find a confidence interval of $\sum_{j=1}^b k_j \mu_j$, a linear function of the means $\mu_1, \mu_2, \ldots, \mu_b$. To do this, we take a random sample $X_{1j}, X_{2j}, \ldots, X_{aj}$ of size a from the distribution $N(\mu_j, \sigma^2)$, $j = 1, 2, \ldots, b$. If we denote $\sum_{i=1}^a X_{ij}/a$ by $\overline{X}_{.j}$, then we know that $\overline{X}_{.j}$ is $N(\mu_j, \sigma^2/a)$, that $\sum_{i=1}^a (X_{ij} - \overline{X}_{.j})^2/\sigma^2$ is $\chi^2(a - 1)$, and that the two random variables are independent. Since the independent random samples are taken from the b distributions, the $2b$ random variables $\overline{X}_{.j}$, $\sum_{i=1}^a (X_{ij} - \overline{X}_{.j})^2/\sigma^2$, $j = 1, 2, \ldots, b$, are independent. Moreover, $\overline{X}_{.1}, \overline{X}_{.2}, \ldots, \overline{X}_{.b}$ and

$$\sum_{j=1}^b \sum_{i=1}^a \frac{(X_{ij} - \overline{X}_{.j})^2}{\sigma^2}$$

are independent and the latter is $\chi^2[b(a-1)]$. Let $Z = \sum_1^b k_j \overline{X}_{\cdot j}$. Then Z is normal with mean $\sum_1^b k_j \mu_j$ and variance $\left(\sum_1^b k_j^2\right) \sigma^2/a$, and Z is independent of

$$V = \frac{1}{b(a-1)} \sum_{j=1}^b \sum_{i=1}^a (X_{ij} - \overline{X}_{\cdot j})^2.$$

Hence the random variable

$$T = \frac{\left(\sum_1^b k_j \overline{X}_{\cdot j} - \sum_1^b k_j \mu_j\right)/\sqrt{(\sigma^2/a)\sum_1^b k_i^2}}{\sqrt{V/\sigma^2}} = \frac{\sum_1^b k_j \overline{X}_{\cdot j} - \sum_1^b k_j \mu_j}{\sqrt{(V/a)\sum_1^b k_j^2}}$$

has a t-distribution with $b(a-1)$ degrees of freedom. For $0 < \alpha < 1$, let $c = t_{\alpha/2, b(a-1)}$. It follows that the probability is $1 - \alpha$ that

$$\sum_1^b k_j \overline{X}_{\cdot j} - c\sqrt{\left(\sum_1^b k_j^2\right)\frac{V}{a}} \le \sum_1^b k_j \mu_j \le \sum_1^b k_j \overline{X}_{\cdot j} + c\sqrt{\left(\sum_1^b k_j^2\right)\frac{V}{a}}.$$

The observed values of $\overline{X}_{\cdot j}$, $j = 1, 2, \ldots, b$, and V provide a $100(1-\alpha)\%$ confidence interval for $\sum_1^b k_j \mu_j$.

It should be observed that the confidence interval for $\sum_1^b k_j \mu_j$ depends upon the particular choice of $k_1, k_2, \ldots, k_b$. It is conceivable that we may be interested in more than one linear function of $\mu_1, \mu_2, \ldots, \mu_b$, such as $\mu_2 - \mu_1$, $\mu_3 - (\mu_1 + \mu_2)/2$, or $\mu_1 + \cdots + \mu_b$. We can, of course, find for each $\sum_1^b k_j \mu_j$ a random interval that has a preassigned probability of including that particular $\sum_1^b k_j \mu_j$. But how can we compute the probability that **simultaneously** these random intervals include their respective linear functions of $\mu_1, \mu_2, \ldots, \mu_b$? The following procedure of **multiple comparisons**, due to Scheffé, is one solution to this problem.

The random variable

$$\frac{\sum_{j=1}^b (\overline{X}_{\cdot j} - \mu_j)^2}{\sigma^2/a}$$

is $\chi^2(b)$ and, because it is a function of $\overline{X}_{\cdot 1}, \ldots, \overline{X}_{\cdot b}$ alone, it is independent of the random variable

$$V = \frac{1}{b(a-1)} \sum_{j=1}^b \sum_{i=1}^a (X_{ij} - \overline{X}_{\cdot j})^2.$$

Hence, the random variable

$$F = \frac{a\sum_{j=1}^b (\overline{X}_{\cdot j} - \mu_j)^2/b}{V}$$

has an F-distribution with b and $b(a-1)$ degrees of freedom. For $0 < \alpha < 1$, let $d = F(\alpha, b, b(a-1))$. Then $P(F \le d) = 1 - \alpha$ or

$$P\left[\sum_{j=1}^{b}(\overline{X}_{.j} - \mu_j)^2 \le bd\frac{V}{a}\right] = 1 - \alpha.$$

Note that $\sum_{j=1}^{b}(\overline{X}_{.j} - \mu_j)^2$ is the square of the distance, in b-dimensional space, from the point $(\mu_1, \mu_2, \ldots, \mu_b)$ to the random point $(\overline{X}_{.1}, \overline{X}_{.2}, \ldots, \overline{X}_{.b})$. Consider a space of dimension b and let $(t_1, t_2, \ldots, t_b)$ denote the coordinates of a point in that space. An equation of a hyperplane that passes through the point $(\mu_1, \mu_2, \ldots, \mu_b)$ is given by

$$k_1(t_1 - \mu_1) + k_2(t_2 - \mu_2) + \cdots + k_b(t_b - \mu_b) = 0, \qquad (9.4.1)$$

where not all the real numbers k_j, $j = 1, 2, \ldots, b$, are equal to zero. The square of the distance from this hyperplane to the point $(t_1 = \overline{X}_{.1}, t_2 = \overline{X}_{.2}, \ldots, t_b = \overline{X}_{.b})$ is

$$\frac{[k_1(\overline{X}_{.1} - \mu_1) + k_2(\overline{X}_{.2} - \mu_2) + \cdots + k_b(\overline{X}_{.b} - \mu_b)]^2}{k_1^2 + k_2^2 + \cdots + k_b^2}. \qquad (9.4.2)$$

From the geometry of the situation it follows that $\sum_{1}^{b}(\overline{X}_{.j} - \mu_j)^2$ is equal to the maximum of expression (9.4.2) with respect to $k_1, k_2, \ldots, k_b$. Thus the inequality $\sum_{1}^{b}(\overline{X}_{.j} - \mu_j)^2 \le (bd)(V/a)$ holds if and only if

$$\frac{\left[\sum_{1}^{b}k_j(\overline{X}_{.j} - \mu_j)\right]^2}{\sum_{j=1}^{b}k_j^2} \le bd\frac{V}{a}, \qquad (9.4.3)$$

for every real $k_1, k_2, \ldots, k_b$, not all zero. Accordingly, these two equivalent events have the same probability, $1 - \alpha$. However, inequality (9.4.3) may be written in the form

$$\left|\sum_{1}^{b}k_j\overline{X}_{.j} - \sum_{1}^{b}k_j\mu_j\right| \le \sqrt{bd\left(\sum_{1}^{b}k_j^2\right)\frac{V}{a}}.$$

Thus the probability is $1 - \alpha$ that simultaneously, for *all* real $k_1, k_2, \ldots, k_b$, not all zero,

$$\sum_{1}^{b}k_j\overline{X}_{.j} - \sqrt{bd\left(\sum_{1}^{b}k_j^2\right)\frac{V}{a}} \le \sum_{1}^{b}k_j\mu_j \le \sum_{1}^{b}k_j\overline{X}_{.j} + \sqrt{bd\left(\sum_{1}^{b}k_j^2\right)\frac{V}{a}}. \qquad (9.4.4)$$

Denote by A the event where inequality (9.4.4) is true for all real $k_1, \ldots, k_b$, and denote by B the event where that inequality is true for a finite number of b-tuples $(k_1, \ldots, k_b)$. If A occurs, then B occurs; hence, $P(A) \le P(B)$. In the applications, one is often interested only in a finite number of linear functions $\sum_1^b k_j \mu_j$. Once the observed values are available, we obtain from (9.4.4) a confidence interval for each of these linear functions. Since $P(B) \geq P(A) = 1 - \alpha$, we have a confidence coefficient of at least $100(1 - \alpha)\%$ that the linear functions are in these respective confidence intervals.

Remark 9.4.1. If the sample sizes, say $a_1, a_2, \ldots, a_b$, are unequal, inequality (9.4.4) becomes

$$\sum_1^b k_j \overline{X}_{.j} - \sqrt{bd \left(\sum_1^b \frac{k_j^2}{a_j} \right) V} \leq \sum_1^b k_j \mu_j \leq \sum_1^b k_j \overline{X}_{.j} + \sqrt{bd \left(\sum_1^b \frac{k_j^2}{a_j} \right) V}, \quad (9.4.5)$$

where

$$\overline{X}_{.j} = \frac{\sum_{i=1}^{a_j} X_{ij}}{a_j}, \quad V = \frac{\sum_{j=1}^{b} \sum_{i=1}^{a_j} (X_{ij} - \overline{X}_{.j})^2}{\sum_1^b (a_j - 1)},$$

and d is selected from Table V with b and $\sum_1^b (a_j - 1)$ degrees of freedom. Inequality (9.4.5) reduces to inequality (9.4.4) when $a_1 = a_2 = \cdots = a_b$.

Moreover, if we restrict our attention to linear functions of the form $\sum_1^b k_j \mu_j$ with $\sum_1^b k_j = 0$ (such linear functions are called **contrasts**), the radical in inequality (9.4.5) is replaced by

$$\sqrt{d(b-1) \sum_1^b \frac{k_j^2}{a_j} V},$$

where d is now found in Table V with $b - 1$ and $\sum_1^b (a_j - 1)$ degrees of freedom. ∎

In multiple comparisons based on the Scheffé procedure, one often finds that the length of a confidence interval is much greater than the length of a $100(1 - \alpha)\%$ confidence interval for a particular linear function $\sum_1^b k_j \mu_j$. But this is to be expected because in one case the probability $1 - \alpha$ applies to just one event, and in the other it applies to the simultaneous occurrence of many events. One reasonable way to reduce the length of these intervals is to take a larger value of α, say 0.25, instead of 0.05. After all, it is still a very strong statement to say that the probability is 0.75 that *all* these events occur. There are, however, other multiple comparison procedures which are often used in practice. One of these is the Bonferroni procedure described in Exercise 9.4.2. This procedure can be used for a finite number of confidence intervals and, as Exercise 9.4.3 shows, the concept is easily extended to tests of hypotheses. In the case of the $\binom{b}{2}$ pairwise comparisons of means, i.e., comparisons of the form $\mu_i - \mu_j$, the procedure most often used is the Tukey–Kramer procedure; see Miller (1981) and Hsu (1996) for discussion.

EXERCISES

9.4.1. If $A_1, A_2, \ldots, A_k$ are events, prove, by induction, Boole's inequality

$$P(A_1 \cup A_2 \cup \cdots \cup A_k) \leq \sum_1^k P(A_i).$$

Then show that

$$P(A_1^c \cap A_2^c \cap \cdots \cap A_k^c) \geq 1 - \sum_1^b P(A_i).$$

9.4.2 (Bonferroni Multiple Comparison Procedure). In the notation of this section, let $(k_{i1}, k_{i2}, \ldots, k_{ib})$, $i = 1, 2, \ldots, m$, represent a finite number of b-tuples. The problem is to find simultaneous confidence intervals for $\sum_{j=1}^b k_{ij}\mu_j$, $i = 1, 2, \ldots, m$, by a method different from that of Scheffé. Define the random variable T_i by

$$\left(\sum_{j=1}^b k_{ij}\overline{X}_{.j} - \sum_{j=1}^b k_{ij}\mu_j \right) \Bigg/ \sqrt{\left(\sum_{j=1}^b k_{ij}^2 \right) V/a}, \quad i = 1, 2, \ldots, m.$$

(a) Let the event A_i^c be given by $-c_i \leq T_i \leq c_i$, $i = 1, 2, \ldots, m$. Find the random variables U_i and W_i such that $U_i \leq \sum_1^b k_{ij}\mu_j \leq W_j$ is equivalent to A_i^c.

(b) Select $c_i = t_{\alpha/(2m), b(a-1)}$. Then $P(A_i^c) = 1 - \alpha/m$; i.e., $P(A_i) = \alpha/m$. Determine a lower bound on the probability that simultaneously the random intervals $(U_1, W_1), \ldots, (U_m, W_m)$ include $\sum_{j=1}^b k_{1j}\mu_j, \ldots, \sum_{j=1}^b k_{mj}\mu_j$. *Hint:* Use Exercise 9.4.1.

(c) Let $a = 3$, $b = 6$, and $\alpha = 0.05$. Consider the linear functions $\mu_1 - \mu_2$, $\mu_2 - \mu_3$, $\mu_3 - \mu_4$, $\mu_4 - (\mu_5 + \mu_6)/2$, and $(\mu_1 + \mu_2 + \cdots + \mu_6)/6$. Here $m = 5$. Show that the lengths of the confidence intervals given by the results of part (b) are shorter than the corresponding ones given by the method of Scheffé as described in the text. If m becomes sufficiently large, however, this is not the case.

9.4.3. Extend the Bonferroni procedure described in the last problem to simultaneous testing. That is, suppose we have m hypotheses of interest: H_{0i} versus H_{1i}, $i = 1, \ldots, m$. For testing H_{0i} versus H_{1i}, let $C_{i,\alpha}$ be a critical region of size α and assume H_{0i} is rejected if $\mathbf{X}_i \in C_{i,\alpha}$, for a sample $\mathbf{X}_i$. Determine a rule so that we can simultaneously test these m hypotheses with a Type I error rate less than or equal to α.

9.5   The Analysis of Variance

Recall the one-way analysis of variance (ANOVA) problem considered in Section 9.2 which was concerned with one factor at b levels. In this section, we are concerned with the situation where we have two factors A and B with levels a and

b, respectively. This is called a **two-way** analysis of variance (ANOVA). Let X_{ij}, $i = 1, 2, \ldots, a$ and $j = 1, 2, \ldots, b$, denote the response for factor A at level i and factor B at level j. Denote the total sample size by $n = ab$. We shall assume that the X_{ij}s are independent normally distributed random variables with common variance σ^2. Denote the mean of X_{ij} by μ_{ij}. The mean μ_{ij} is often referred to as the mean of the (i, j)th cell. For our first model, we consider the **additive model** where

$$\mu_{ij} = \overline{\mu} + (\overline{\mu}_{i\cdot} - \overline{\mu}) + (\overline{\mu}_{\cdot j} - \overline{\mu}) ; \qquad (9.5.1)$$

that is, the mean in the (i, j)th cell is due to additive effects of the levels, i of factor A and j of factor B, over the average (constant) $\overline{\mu}$. Let $\alpha_i = \overline{\mu}_{i\cdot} - \overline{\mu}$, $i = 1, \ldots, a$; $\beta_j = \overline{\mu}_{\cdot j} - \overline{\mu}$, $j = 1, \ldots, b$; and $\mu = \overline{\mu}$. Then the model can be written more simply as

$$\mu_{ij} = \mu + \alpha_i + \beta_j, \qquad (9.5.2)$$

where $\sum_{i=1}^{a} \alpha_i = 0$ and $\sum_{j=1}^{b} \beta_j = 0$. We refer to this model as being a **two-way** ANOVA model.

For example, take $a = 2$, $b = 3$, $\mu = 5$, $\alpha_1 = 1$, $\alpha_2 = -1$, $\beta_1 = 1$, $\beta_2 = 0$, and $\beta_3 = -1$. Then the cell means are

		Factor B		
		1	2	3
Factor A	1	$\mu_{11} = 7$	$\mu_{12} = 6$	$\mu_{13} = 5$
	2	$\mu_{21} = 5$	$\mu_{22} = 4$	$\mu_{23} = 3$

Note that for each i, the plots of μ_{ij} versus j are parallel. This is true for additive models in general; see Exercise 9.5.8. We call these plots **mean profile plots**.

Had we taken $\beta_1 = \beta_2 = \beta_3 = 0$, then the cell means would be

		Factor B		
		1	2	3
Factor A	1	$\mu_{11} = 6$	$\mu_{12} = 6$	$\mu_{13} = 6$
	2	$\mu_{21} = 4$	$\mu_{22} = 4$	$\mu_{23} = 4$

The hypotheses of interest are

$$H_{0A} : \alpha_1 = \cdots = \alpha_a = 0 \text{ versus } H_{1A} : \alpha_i \neq 0, \text{ for some } i, \qquad (9.5.3)$$

and

$$H_{0B} : \beta_1 = \cdots = \beta_b = 0 \text{ versus } H_{1B} : \beta_j \neq 0, \text{ for some } j. \qquad (9.5.4)$$

If H_{0A} is true, then by (9.5.2) the mean of the (i, j)th cell does not depend on the level of A. The second example above is under H_{0B}. The cell means remain the same from column to column for a specified row. We call these hypotheses **main effect** hypotheses.

Remark 9.5.1. The model just described, and others similar to it, are widely used in statistical applications. Consider a situation in which it is desirable to investigate the effects of two factors that influence an outcome. Thus the variety of a grain and the type of fertilizer used influence the yield; or the teacher and the size of the class may influence the score on a standardized test. Let X_{ij} denote the yield from the use of variety i of a grain and type j of fertilizer. A test of the hypothesis that $\beta_1 = \beta_2 = \cdots = \beta_b = 0$ would then be a test of the hypothesis that the mean yield of each variety of grain is the same regardless of the type of fertilizer used. ∎

To construct a test of the composite hypothesis H_{0B} versus H_{1B}, we could obtain the corresponding likelihood ratio. However, to gain more insight into such a test, let us reconsider the likelihood ratio test of Section 9.2, namely, that of the equality of the means of b distributions. There the important quadratic forms are Q, Q_3, and Q_4, which are related through the equation $Q = Q_4 + Q_3$. That is,

$$(ab - 1)S^2 = \sum_{j=1}^{b} \sum_{i=1}^{a} (\overline{X}_{\cdot j} - \overline{X}_{\cdot \cdot})^2 + \sum_{j=1}^{b} \sum_{i=1}^{a} (X_{ij} - \overline{X}_{\cdot j})^2,$$

so we see that the total sum of squares, $(ab - 1)S^2$, is decomposed into a sum of squares, Q_4, *among* column means and a sum of squares, Q_3, *within* columns. The latter sum of squares, divided by $n = ab$, is the mle of σ^2, provided that the parameters are in Ω; and we denote it by $\hat{\sigma}_\Omega^2$. Of course, $(ab - 1)S^2/ab$ is the mle of σ^2 under ω, here denoted by $\hat{\sigma}_\omega^2$. So the likelihood ratio $\Lambda = (\hat{\sigma}_\Omega^2/\hat{\sigma}_\omega^2)^{ab/2}$ is a monotone function of the statistic

$$F = \frac{Q_4/(b - 1)}{Q_3/[b(a - 1)]}$$

upon which the test of the equality of means is based.

To help find a test for H_{0B} versus H_{1B}, (9.5.4), return to the decomposition of Example 9.1.3, Section 9.1, namely, $Q = Q_2 + Q_4 + Q_5$. That is,

$$(ab-1)S^2 = \sum_{i=1}^{a} \sum_{j=1}^{b} (\overline{X}_{i\cdot} - \overline{X}_{\cdot\cdot})^2 + \sum_{i=1}^{a} \sum_{j=1}^{b} (\overline{X}_{\cdot j} - \overline{X}_{\cdot\cdot})^2 + \sum_{i=1}^{a} \sum_{j=1}^{b} (X_{ij} - \overline{X}_{i\cdot} - \overline{X}_{\cdot j} + \overline{X}_{\cdot\cdot})^2.$$

Thus the total sum of squares is decomposed into that among *rows* (Q_2), that among *columns* (Q_4), and that *remaining* (Q_5). It is interesting to observe that $\hat{\sigma}_\Omega^2 = Q_5/ab$ is the mle of σ^2 under Ω and

$$\hat{\sigma}_\omega^2 = \frac{(Q_4 + Q_5)}{ab} = \sum_{i=1}^{a} \sum_{j=1}^{b} \frac{(X_{ij} - \overline{X}_{i\cdot})^2}{ab}$$

is that estimator under ω. A useful monotone function of the likelihood ratio $\Lambda = (\hat{\sigma}_\Omega^2/\hat{\sigma}_\omega^2)^{ab/2}$ is

$$F = \frac{Q_4/(b - 1)}{Q_5/[(a - 1)(b - 1)]},$$

which has, under H_{0B}, an F-distribution with $b - 1$ and $(a - 1)(b - 1)$ degrees of freedom. The hypothesis H_{0B} is rejected if $F \geq F(\alpha, b - 1, (a - 1)(b - 1))$, at significance level α. This is the likelihood ratio test for H_{0B} versus H_{1B}.

If we are to compute the power function of the test, we need the distribution of F when H_{0B} is not true. From Section 9.3 we know, when H_{1B} is true, that Q_4/σ^2 and Q_5/σ^2 are independent (central or noncentral) chi-square variables. We shall compute the noncentrality parameters of Q_4/σ^2 and Q_5/σ^2 when H_{1B} is true. We have $E(X_{ij}) = \mu + \alpha_i + \beta_j$, $E(\overline{X}_{i.}) = \mu + \alpha_i$, $E(\overline{X}_{.j}) = \mu + \beta_j$, and $E(\overline{X}_{..}) = \mu$. Accordingly, the noncentrality parameter Q_4/σ^2 is

$$\frac{a}{\sigma^2} \sum_{j=1}^{b} (\mu + \beta_j - \mu)^2 = \frac{a}{\sigma^2} \sum_{j=1}^{b} \beta_j^2$$

and that of Q_5/σ^2 is

$$\sigma^{-2} \sum_{j=1}^{b} \sum_{i=1}^{a} (\mu + \alpha_i + \beta_j - \mu - \alpha_i - \mu - \beta_j + \mu)^2 = 0.$$

Thus, if the hypothesis H_{0B} is not true, F has a noncentral F-distribution with $b-1$ and $(a-1)(b-1)$ degrees of freedom and noncentrality parameter $a \sum_{j=1}^{b} \beta_j^2/\sigma^2$. The desired probabilities can then be found in tables of the noncentral F-distribution.

A similar argument can be used to construct the F needed to test the equality of row means; that is, H_{0A} versus H_{1A}, (9.5.3). The F test statistic is essentially the ratio of the sum of squares among rows and Q_5. In particular, this F is defined by

$$F = \frac{Q_2/(a-1)}{Q_5/[(a-1)(b-1)]}$$

and under $H_{0A} : \alpha_1 = \alpha_2 = \cdots = \alpha_a = 0$ has an F-distribution with $a-1$ and $(a-1)(b-1)$ degrees of freedom.

The analysis of variance problem that has just been discussed is usually referred to as a *two-way classification with one observation per cell*. Each combination of i and j determines a cell; thus, there is a total of ab cells in this model. Let us now investigate another two-way classification problem, but in this case we take $c > 1$ independent observations per cell.

Let X_{ijk}, $i = 1, 2, \ldots, a$, $j = 1, 2, \ldots, b$, and $k = 1, 2, \ldots, c$, denote $n = abc$ random variables which are independent and which have normal distributions with common, but unknown, variance σ^2. Denote the mean of each X_{ijk}, $k = 1, 2, \ldots, c$, by μ_{ij}. Under the additive model, (9.5.1), the mean of each cell depended on its row and column, but often the mean is cell-specific. To allow this, consider the parameters

$$\begin{aligned} \gamma_{ij} &= \mu_{ij} - \{\mu + (\overline{\mu}_{i.} - \mu) + (\overline{\mu}_{.j} - \mu)\} \\ &= \mu_{ij} - \overline{\mu}_{i.} - \overline{\mu}_{.j} + \mu, \end{aligned}$$

for $i = 1, \ldots a, j = 1, \ldots, b$. Hence γ_{ij} reflects the specific contribution to the cell mean over and above the additive model. These parameters are called **interaction parameters**. Using the second form (9.5.2), we can write the cell means as

$$\mu_{ij} = \mu + \alpha_i + \beta_j + \gamma_{ij}, \tag{9.5.5}$$

where $\sum_{i=1}^{a} \alpha_i = 0$, $\sum_{j=1}^{b} \beta_j = 0$, and $\sum_{i=1}^{a} \gamma_{ij} = \sum_{j=1}^{b} \gamma_{ij} = 0$. This model is called a **two-way** model with interaction.

For example, take $a = 2$, $b = 3$, $\mu = 5$, $\alpha_1 = 1$, $\alpha_2 = -1$, $\beta_1 = 1$, $\beta_2 = 0$, $\beta_3 = -1$, $\gamma_{11} = 1$, $\gamma_{12} = 1$, $\gamma_{13} = -2$, $\gamma_{21} = -1$, $\gamma_{22} = -1$, and $\gamma_{23} = 2$. Then the cell means are

		Factor B		
		1	2	3
Factor A	1	$\mu_{11} = 8$	$\mu_{12} = 7$	$\mu_{13} = 3$
	2	$\mu_{21} = 4$	$\mu_{22} = 3$	$\mu_{23} = 5$

Note that, if each $\gamma_{ij} = 0$, then the cell means are

		Factor B		
		1	2	3
Factor A	1	$\mu_{11} = 7$	$\mu_{12} = 6$	$\mu_{13} = 5$
	2	$\mu_{21} = 5$	$\mu_{22} = 4$	$\mu_{23} = 3$

Note that the mean profile plots for this second example are parallel, but those in the first example (where interaction is present) are not.

The major hypotheses of interest for the interaction model are

$$H_{0AB} : \gamma_{ij} = 0 \text{ for all } i,j \text{ versus } H_{1AB} : \gamma_{ij} \neq 0, \text{ for some } i,j. \qquad (9.5.6)$$

From Exercise 9.1.4 of Section 9.1, we have that

$$\sum_{i=1}^{a}\sum_{j=1}^{b}\sum_{k=1}^{c}(X_{ijk} - \overline{X}_{...})^2 = bc\sum_{i=1}^{a}(\overline{X}_{i..} - \overline{X}_{...})^2 + ac\sum_{j=1}^{b}(\overline{X}_{.j.} - \overline{X}_{...})^2$$
$$+ c\sum_{i=1}^{a}\sum_{j=1}^{b}(\overline{X}_{ij.} - \overline{X}_{i..} - \overline{X}_{.j.} + \overline{X}_{...})^2$$
$$+ \sum_{i=1}^{a}\sum_{j=1}^{b}\sum_{k=1}^{c}(X_{ijk} - \overline{X}_{ij.})^2;$$

that is, the total sum of squares is decomposed into that due to *row* differences, that due to *column* differences, that due to *interaction*, and that *within cells*. The test of H_{0AB} versus H_{1AB} is based upon an F with $(a-1)(b-1)$ and $ab(c-1)$ degrees of freedom given by

$$F = \frac{\left[c\sum_{i=1}^{a}\sum_{j=1}^{b}(\overline{X}_{ij.} - \overline{X}_{i..} - \overline{X}_{.j.} + \overline{X}_{...})^2\right] \Big/ [(a-1)(b-1)]}{\left[\sum\sum\sum(X_{ijk} - \overline{X}_{ij.})^2\right] \Big/ [ab(c-1)]}.$$

The reader should verify that the noncentrality parameter of this F-distribution is equal to $c\sum_{j=1}^{b}\sum_{i=1}^{a}\gamma_{ij}^2/\sigma^2$. Thus F is central when $H_{0AB} : \gamma_{ij} = 0$, $i = 1, 2, \ldots, a$, $j = 1, 2, \ldots, b$, is true.

If $H_{0AB} : \gamma_{ij} = 0$ is accepted, then one usually continues to test $\alpha_i = 0$, $i = 1, 2, \ldots, a$, by using the test statistic

$$F = \frac{bc \displaystyle\sum_{i=1}^{a} (\overline{X}_{i..} - \overline{X}_{...})^2 / (a-1)}{\displaystyle\sum_{i=1}^{a} \sum_{j=1}^{b} \sum_{k=1}^{c} (X_{ijk} - \overline{X}_{ij.})^2 / [ab(c-1)]},$$

which has a null F-distribution with $a-1$ and $ab(c-1)$ degrees of freedom. Similarly, the test of $\beta_j = 0$, $j = 1, 2, \ldots, b$, proceeds by using the test statistic

$$F = \frac{ac \displaystyle\sum_{j=1}^{b} (\overline{X}_{.j.} - \overline{X}_{...})^2 / (b-1)}{\displaystyle\sum_{i=1}^{a} \sum_{j=1}^{b} \sum_{k=1}^{c} (X_{ijk} - \overline{X}_{ij.})^2 / [ab(c-1)]},$$

which has a null F-distribution with $b-1$ and $ab(c-1)$ degrees of freedom.

EXERCISES

9.5.1. Show that

$$\sum_{j=1}^{b} \sum_{i=1}^{a} (X_{ij} - \overline{X}_{i.})^2 = \sum_{j=1}^{b} \sum_{i=1}^{a} (X_{ij} - \overline{X}_{i.} - \overline{X}_{.j} + \overline{X}_{..})^2 + a \sum_{j=1}^{b} (\overline{X}_{.j} - \overline{X}_{..})^2.$$

9.5.2. If at least one $\gamma_{ij} \neq 0$, show that the F', which is used to test that each interaction is equal to zero, has noncentrality parameter equal to $c \sum_{j=1}^{b} \sum_{i=1}^{a} \gamma_{ij}^2 / \sigma^2$.

9.5.3. Using the background of the two-way classification with one observation per cell, show that the maximum likelihood estimator of α_i, β_j, and μ are $\hat{\alpha}_i = \overline{X}_{i.} - \overline{X}_{..}$, $\hat{\beta}_j = \overline{X}_{.j} - \overline{X}_{..}$, and $\hat{\mu} = \overline{X}_{..}$, respectively. Show that these are unbiased estimators of their respective parameters and compute $\mathrm{var}(\hat{\alpha}_i)$, $\mathrm{var}(\hat{\beta}_j)$, and $\mathrm{var}(\hat{\mu})$.

9.5.4. Prove that the linear functions $X_{ij} - \overline{X}_{i.} - \overline{X}_{.j} + \overline{X}_{..}$ and $\overline{X}_{.j} - \overline{X}_{..}$ are uncorrelated, under the assumptions of this section.

9.5.5. Given the following observations associated with a two-way classification with $a = 3$ and $b = 4$, compute the F-statistic used to test the equality of the column means ($\beta_1 = \beta_2 = \beta_3 = \beta_4 = 0$) and the equality of the row means ($\alpha_1 = \alpha_2 = \alpha_3 = 0$), respectively.

Row/Column	1	2	3	4
1	3.1	4.2	2.7	4.9
2	2.7	2.9	1.8	3.0
3	4.0	4.6	3.0	3.9

9.5.6. With the background of the two-way classification with $c > 1$ observations per cell, show that the maximum likelihood estimators of the parameters are

$$\hat{\alpha}_i = \overline{X}_{i..} - \overline{X}_{...}$$
$$\hat{\beta}_j = \overline{X}_{.j.} - \overline{X}_{...}$$
$$\hat{\gamma}_{ij} = \overline{X}_{ij.} - \overline{X}_{i..} - \overline{X}_{.j.} + \overline{X}_{...}$$
$$\hat{\mu} = \overline{X}_{...}.$$

Show that these are unbiased estimators of the respective parameters. Compute the variance of each estimator.

9.5.7. Given the following observations in a two-way classification with $a = 3$, $b = 4$, and $c = 2$, compute the F-statistics used to test that all interactions are equal to zero ($\gamma_{ij} = 0$), all column means are equal ($\beta_j = 0$), and all row means are equal ($\alpha_i = 0$), respectively.

Row/Column	1	2	3	4
1	3.1	4.2	2.7	4.9
	2.9	4.9	3.2	4.5
2	2.7	2.9	1.8	3.0
	2.9	2.3	2.4	3.7
3	4.0	4.6	3.0	3.9
	4.4	5.0	2.5	4.2

9.5.8. For the additive model (9.5.1), show that the mean profile plots are parallel. The sample mean profile plots are given by plotting $\overline{X}_{ij.}$ versus j, for each i. These offer a graphical diagnostic for interaction detection. Obtain these plots for the last exercise.

9.5.9. We wish to compare compressive strengths of concrete corresponding to $a = 3$ different drying methods (treatments). Concrete is mixed in batches that are just large enough to produce three cylinders. Although care is taken to achieve uniformity, we expect some variability among the $b = 5$ batches used to obtain the following compressive strengths. (There is little reason to suspect interaction, and hence only one observation is taken in each cell.)

Treatment	Batch				
	B_1	B_2	B_3	B_4	B_5
A_1	52	47	44	51	42
A_2	60	55	49	52	43
A_3	56	48	45	44	38

(a) Use the 5% significance level and test $H_A : \alpha_1 = \alpha_2 = \alpha_3 = 0$ against all alternatives.

(b) Use the 5% significance level and test $H_B : \beta_1 = \beta_2 = \beta_3 = \beta_4 = \beta_5 = 0$ against all alternatives.

9.5.10. With $a = 3$ and $b = 4$, find μ, α_i, β_j and γ_{ij} if μ_{ij}, for $i = 1, 2, 3$ and $j = 1, 2, 3, 4$, are given by

$$
\begin{array}{cccc}
6 & 7 & 7 & 12 \\
10 & 3 & 11 & 8 \\
8 & 5 & 9 & 10
\end{array}
$$

9.6   A Regression Problem

There is often interest in the relationship between two variables, for example, a student's scholastic aptitude test score in mathematics and this same student's grade in calculus. Frequently, one of these variables, say x, is known in advance of the other, and hence there is interest in predicting a future random variable Y. Since Y is a random variable, we cannot predict its future observed value $Y = y$ with certainty. Thus let us first concentrate on the problem of estimating the mean of Y, that is, $E(Y)$. Now $E(Y)$ is usually a function of x; for example, in our illustration with the calculus grade, say Y, we would expect $E(Y)$ to increase with increasing mathematics aptitude score x. Sometimes $E(Y) = \mu(x)$ is assumed to be of a given form, such as a linear or quadratic or exponential function; that is, $\mu(x)$ could be assumed to be equal to $\alpha + \beta x$ or $\alpha + \beta x + \gamma x^2$ or $\alpha e^{\beta x}$. To estimate $E(Y) = \mu(x)$, or equivalently the parameters α, β, and γ, we observe the random variable Y for each of n possible different values of x, say $x_1, x_2, \ldots, x_n$, which are not all equal. Once the n independent experiments have been performed, we have n pairs of known numbers $(x_1, y_1), (x_2, y_2), \ldots, (x_n, y_n)$. These pairs are then used to estimate the mean $E(Y)$. Problems like this are often classified under *regression* because $E(Y) = \mu(x)$ is frequently called a regression curve.

Remark 9.6.1. A model for the mean such as $\alpha + \beta x + \gamma x^2$ is called a **linear model** because it is linear in the parameters α, β, and γ. Thus $\alpha e^{\beta x}$ is not a linear model because it is not linear in α and β. Note that, in Sections 9.1 to 9.4, all the means were linear in the parameters and hence are linear models. ∎

Let us begin with the case in which $E(Y) = \mu(x)$ is a linear function. Denote by Y_i the response at x_i and consider the model

$$Y_i = \alpha + \beta(x_i - \overline{x}) + e_i, \quad i = 1, \ldots, n, \tag{9.6.1}$$

where $\overline{x} = n^{-1} \sum_{i=1}^n x_i$ and $e_1, \ldots, e_n$ are iid random variables with a common $N(0, \sigma^2)$ distribution. Hence $E(Y_i) = \alpha + \beta(x_i - \overline{x})$, $\text{Var}(Y_i) = \sigma^2$, and Y_i has $N(\alpha + \beta(x_i - \overline{x}), \sigma^2)$ distribution. The n points are $(x_1, y_1), (x_2, y_2), \ldots, (x_n, y_n)$; so the first problem is that of fitting a straight line to the set of points. Figure 9.6.1 shows a **scatterplot** of 60 observations $(x_1, y_1), \ldots, (x_{60}, y_{60})$ drawn from a linear model of the form (9.6.1).

The joint pdf of $Y_1, \ldots, Y_n$ is the product of the individual probability density functions; that is, the likelihood function equals

$$L(\alpha, \beta, \sigma^2) = \prod_{i=1}^{n} \frac{1}{\sqrt{2\pi\sigma^2}} \exp\left\{ -\frac{[y_i - \alpha - \beta(x_i - \overline{x})]^2}{2\sigma^2} \right\}$$

$$= \left(\frac{1}{2\pi\sigma^2}\right)^{n/2} \exp\left\{ -\frac{1}{2\sigma^2} \sum_{i=1}^{n} [y_i - \alpha - \beta(x_i - \overline{x})]^2 \right\}.$$

Figure 9.6.1: The plot shows the least squares fitted line (solid line) to a set of data. The dashed-line segment from $(x_i, \hat{y}_i)$ to (x_i, y_i) shows the deviation of (x_i, y_i) from its fit.

To maximize $L(\alpha, \beta, \sigma^2)$, or, equivalently, to minimize

$$-\log L(\alpha, \beta, \sigma^2) = \frac{n}{2} \log(2\pi\sigma^2) + \frac{\sum_{i=1}^{n} [y_i - \alpha - \beta(x_i - \overline{x})]^2}{2\sigma^2},$$

we must select α and β to minimize

$$H(\alpha, \beta) = \sum_{i=1}^{n} [y_i - \alpha - \beta(x_i - \overline{x})]^2.$$

Since $|y_i - \alpha - \beta(x_i - \overline{x})| = |y_i - \mu(x_i)|$ is the vertical distance from the point (x_i, y_i) to the line $y = \mu(x)$ (see the dashed-line segment in Figure 9.6.1), we note that $H(\alpha, \beta)$ represents the sum of the squares of those distances. Thus, selecting α and β so that the sum of the squares is minimized means that we are fitting the straight line to the data by the **method of least squares** (LS).

To minimize $H(\alpha, \beta)$, we find the two first partial derivatives,

$$\frac{\partial H(\alpha, \beta)}{\partial \alpha} = 2 \sum_{i=1}^{n} [y_i - \alpha - \beta(x_i - \overline{x})](-1)$$

and

$$\frac{\partial H(\alpha, \beta)}{\partial \beta} = 2 \sum_{i=1}^{n} [y_i - \alpha - \beta(x_i - \overline{x})][-(x_i - \overline{x})].$$

Setting $\partial H(\alpha, \beta)/\partial \alpha = 0$, we obtain

$$\sum_{i=1}^{n} y_i - n\alpha - \beta \sum_{i=1}^{n} (x_i - \overline{x}) = 0. \tag{9.6.2}$$

Since

$$\sum_{i=1}^{n} (x_i - \overline{x}) = 0,$$

we have that

$$\sum_{i=1}^{n} y_i - n\alpha = 0$$

and, thus, the mle of α is

$$\hat{\alpha} = \overline{Y}.$$

The equation $\partial H(\alpha, \beta)/\partial \beta = 0$ yields, with α replaced by $\overline{y}$,

$$\sum_{i=1}^{n} (y_i - \overline{y})(x_i - \overline{x}) - \beta \sum_{i=1}^{n} (x_i - \overline{x})^2 = 0 \tag{9.6.3}$$

and, hence, the mle of β is

$$\hat{\beta} = \frac{\sum_{i=1}^{n} (Y_i - \overline{Y})(x_i - \overline{x})}{\sum_{i=1}^{n} (x_i - \overline{x})^2} = \frac{\sum_{i=1}^{n} Y_i(x_i - \overline{x})}{\sum_{i=1}^{n} (x_i - \overline{x})^2}.$$

Equations (9.6.2) and (9.6.3) are the estimating equations for the LS solutions for this simple linear model. The **fitted value** at the point (x_i, y_i) is given by

$$\hat{y}_i = \hat{\alpha} + \hat{\beta}(x_i - \overline{x}), \tag{9.6.4}$$

which is shown on Figure 9.6.1. The fitted value $\hat{y}_i$ is also called the **predicted value** of y_i at x_i. The **residual** at the point (x_i, y_i) is given by

$$\hat{e}_i = y_i - \hat{y}_i, \tag{9.6.5}$$

which is also shown on Figure 9.6.1. Residual means "what is left" and the residual in regression is exactly that, i.e., what is left over after the fit. The relationship between the fitted values and the residuals is explored in Exercise 9.6.11.

To find the maximum likelihood estimator of σ^2, consider the partial derivative

$$\frac{\partial[-\log L(\alpha, \beta, \sigma^2)]}{\partial(\sigma^2)} = \frac{n}{2\sigma^2} - \frac{\sum_{i=1}^{n}[y_i - \alpha - \beta(x_i - \overline{x})]^2}{2(\sigma^2)^2}.$$

Setting this equal to zero and replacing α and β by their solutions $\hat{\alpha}$ and $\hat{\beta}$, we obtain

$$\hat{\sigma}^2 = \frac{1}{n} \sum_{i=1}^{n} [Y_i - \hat{\alpha} - \hat{\beta}(x_i - \overline{x})]^2.$$

Of course, due to the invariance of mles, $\hat{\sigma} = \sqrt{\hat{\sigma}^2}$. Note that in terms of the residuals, $\hat{\sigma}^2 = n^{-1} \sum_{i=1}^{n} \hat{e}_i^2$. As shown in Exercise 9.6.11, the average of the residuals is 0.

Since $\hat{\alpha}$ is a linear function of independent and normally distributed random variables, $\hat{\alpha}$ has a normal distribution with mean

$$E(\hat{\alpha}) = E\left(\frac{1}{n} \sum_{i=1}^{n} Y_i\right) = \frac{1}{n} \sum_{i=1}^{n} E(Y_i)$$

$$= \frac{1}{n} \sum_{i=1}^{n} [\alpha + \beta(x_i - \overline{x})] = \alpha$$

and variance

$$\text{var}(\hat{\alpha}) = \sum_{i=1}^{n} \left(\frac{1}{n}\right)^2 \text{var}(Y_i) = \frac{\sigma^2}{n}.$$

The estimator $\hat{\beta}$ is also a linear function of $Y_1, Y_2, \ldots, Y_n$ and hence has a normal distribution with mean

$$E(\hat{\beta}) = \frac{\sum_{i=1}^{n}(x_i - \overline{x})[\alpha + \beta(x_i - \overline{x})]}{\sum_{i=1}^{n}(x_i - \overline{x})^2}$$

$$= \frac{\alpha \sum_{i=1}^{n}(x_i - \overline{x}) + \beta \sum_{i=1}^{n}(x_i - \overline{x})^2}{\sum_{i=1}^{n}(x_i - \overline{x})^2} = \beta$$

and variance

$$\text{var}(\hat{\beta}) = \sum_{i=1}^{n} \left[\frac{x_i - \overline{x}}{\sum_{i=1}^{n}(x_i - \overline{x})^2}\right]^2 \text{var}(Y_i)$$

$$= \frac{\sum_{i=1}^{n}(x_i - \overline{x})^2}{\left[\sum_{i=1}^{n}(x_i - \overline{x})^2\right]^2} \sigma^2 = \frac{\sigma^2}{\sum_{i=1}^{n}(x_i - \overline{x})^2}.$$

In summary, the estimators $\hat{\alpha}$ and $\hat{\beta}$ are linear functions of the independent normal random variables $Y_1, \ldots, Y_n$. In Exercise 9.6.10 it is further shown that the covariance between $\hat{\alpha}$ and $\hat{\beta}$ is zero. It follows that $\hat{\alpha}$ and $\hat{\beta}$ are independent random variables with a bivariate normal distribution; that is,

$$\begin{pmatrix} \hat{\alpha} \\ \hat{\beta} \end{pmatrix} \text{ has a } N_2 \left(\begin{pmatrix} \alpha \\ \beta \end{pmatrix}, \sigma^2 \begin{bmatrix} \frac{1}{n} & 0 \\ 0 & \frac{1}{\sum_{i=1}^{n}(x_i - \overline{x})^2} \end{bmatrix} \right) \text{ distribution.} \qquad (9.6.6)$$

Next, we consider the estimator of σ^2. It can be shown (Exercise 9.6.6) that

$$\begin{aligned} \sum_{i=1}^{n}[Y_i - \alpha - \beta(x_i - \overline{x})]^2 &= \sum_{i=1}^{n}\{(\hat{\alpha} - \alpha) + (\hat{\beta} - \beta)(x_i - \overline{x}) \\ &\quad + [Y_i - \hat{\alpha} - \hat{\beta}(x_i - \overline{x})]\}^2 \\ &= n(\hat{\alpha} - \alpha)^2 + (\hat{\beta} - \beta)^2 \sum_{i=1}^{n}(x_i - \overline{x})^2 + n\hat{\sigma}^2, \end{aligned}$$

or for brevity,

$$Q = Q_1 + Q_2 + Q_3.$$

Here Q, Q_1, Q_2, and Q_3 are real quadratic forms in the variables

$$Y_i - \alpha - \beta(x_i - \overline{x}), \quad i = 1, 2, \ldots, n.$$

In this equation, Q represents the sum of the squares of n independent random variables that have normal distributions with means zero and variances σ^2. Thus Q/σ^2 has a χ^2 distribution with n degrees of freedom. Each of the random variables $\sqrt{n}(\hat{\alpha} - \alpha)/\sigma$ and $\sqrt{\sum_{i=1}^{n}(x_i - \overline{x})^2}(\hat{\beta} - \beta)/\sigma$ has a normal distribution with zero mean and unit variance; thus, each of Q_1/σ^2 and Q_2/σ^2 has a χ^2 distribution with 1 degree of freedom. Since Q_3 is nonnegative, we have, in accordance with Theorem 9.1.1, that Q_1, Q_2, and Q_3 are independent, so that Q_3/σ^2 has a χ^2 distribution with $n - 1 - 1 = n - 2$ degrees of freedom. That is, $n\hat{\sigma}^2/\sigma^2$ has a χ^2 distribution with $n - 2$ degrees of freedom.

We now extend this discussion to obtain inference for the parameters α and β. It follows from the above derivations that both the random variable T_1

$$T_1 = \frac{[\sqrt{n}(\hat{\alpha} - \alpha)]/\sigma}{\sqrt{Q_3/[\sigma^2(n-2)]}} = \frac{\hat{\alpha} - \alpha}{\sqrt{\hat{\sigma}^2/(n-2)}}$$

and the random variable T_2

$$T_2 = \frac{\left[\sqrt{\sum_{i=1}^{n}(x_i - \overline{x})^2}(\hat{\beta} - \beta)\right]/\sigma}{\sqrt{Q_3/[\sigma^2(n-2)]}} = \frac{\hat{\beta} - \beta}{\sqrt{n\hat{\sigma}^2/[(n-2)\sum_{1}^{n}(x_i - \overline{x})^2]}}$$

have a t-distribution with $n - 2$ degrees of freedom. These facts enable us to obtain confidence intervals for α and β; see Exercise 9.6.3. The fact that $n\hat{\sigma}^2/\sigma^2$ has a χ^2 distribution with $n - 2$ degrees of freedom provides a means of determining a confidence interval for σ^2. These are some of the statistical inferences about the parameters to which reference was made in the introductory remarks of this section.

Remark 9.6.2. The more discerning reader should quite properly question our construction of T_1 and T_2 immediately above. We know that the *squares* of the linear forms are independent of $Q_3 = n\hat{\sigma}^2$, but we do not know, at this time, that the linear forms themselves enjoy this independence. A more general result is obtained in Theorem 9.9.1 of Section 9.9 and the present case is a special instance. ∎

Example 9.6.1 (Geometry of the Least Squares Fit). In the modern literature, linear models are usually expressed in terms of matrices and vectors, which we briefly introduce in this example. Furthermore, this allows us to discuss the simple geometry behind the least squares fit. Consider then Model (9.6.1). Write the vectors $\mathbf{Y} = (Y_1, \ldots, Y_n)'$, $\mathbf{e} = (e_1, \ldots, e_n)'$, and $\mathbf{x}_c = (x_1 - \overline{x}, \ldots, x_n - \overline{x})'$. Let $\mathbf{1}$ denote the $n \times 1$ vector whose components are all 1. Then Model (9.6.1) can be expressed equivalently as

$$
\begin{aligned}
\mathbf{Y} &= \alpha\mathbf{1} + \beta\mathbf{x}_c + \mathbf{e} \\
&= [\mathbf{1}\ \mathbf{x}_c]\begin{pmatrix} \alpha \\ \beta \end{pmatrix} + \mathbf{e} \\
&= \mathbf{X}\boldsymbol{\beta} + \mathbf{e},
\end{aligned}
\tag{9.6.7}
$$

where $\mathbf{X}$ is the $n \times 2$ matrix with columns $\mathbf{1}$ and $\mathbf{x}_c$ and $\boldsymbol{\beta} = (\alpha, \beta)'$. Next, let $\boldsymbol{\theta} = E(\mathbf{Y}) = \mathbf{X}\boldsymbol{\beta}$. Finally, let V be the two-dimensional subspace of R^n spanned by the columns of $\mathbf{X}$; i.e., V is the range of the matrix $\mathbf{X}$. Hence we can also express the model succinctly as

$$
\mathbf{Y} = \boldsymbol{\theta} + \mathbf{e}, \quad \boldsymbol{\theta} \in V.
\tag{9.6.8}
$$

Hence, except for the random error vector $\mathbf{e}$, $\mathbf{Y}$ would lie in V. It makes sense intuitively then, as suggested by Figure 9.6.2, to estimate $\boldsymbol{\theta}$ by the vector in V which is "closest" (in Euclidean distance) to $\mathbf{Y}$, that is, by $\hat{\boldsymbol{\theta}}$, where

$$
\hat{\boldsymbol{\theta}} = \text{Argmin}_{\boldsymbol{\theta} \in V} \|\mathbf{Y} - \boldsymbol{\theta}\|^2,
\tag{9.6.9}
$$

where the square of the **Euclidean norm** is given by $\|\mathbf{u}\|^2 = \sum_{i=1}^n u_i^2$, for $\mathbf{u} \in R^n$. As shown in Exercise 9.6.11 and depicted on the plot in Figure 9.6.2, $\hat{\boldsymbol{\theta}} = \hat{\alpha}\mathbf{1} + \hat{\beta}\mathbf{x}_c$, where $\hat{\alpha}$ and $\hat{\beta}$ are the least squares estimates given above. Also, the vector $\hat{\mathbf{e}} = \mathbf{Y} - \hat{\boldsymbol{\theta}}$ is the vector of residuals and $n\hat{\sigma}^2 = \|\hat{\mathbf{e}}\|^2$. Also, just as depicted in Figure 9.6.2, the angle between the vectors $\hat{\boldsymbol{\theta}}$ and $\hat{\mathbf{e}}$ is a right angle. In linear models, we say that $\hat{\boldsymbol{\theta}}$ is the projection of $\mathbf{Y}$ onto the subspace V. ∎

EXERCISES

9.6.1. Students' scores on the mathematics portion of the ACT examination, x, and on the final examination in the first-semester calculus (200 points possible), y, are given.

   (a) Calculate the least squares regression line for these data.

Figure 9.6.2: The sketch shows the geometry of least squares. The vector of responses is **Y**, the fit is $\widehat{\boldsymbol{\theta}}$, and the vector of residuals is $\widehat{\mathbf{e}}$.

(b) Plot the points and the least squares regression line on the same graph.

(c) Find point estimates for α, β, and σ^2.

(d) Find 95% confidence intervals for α and β under the usual assumptions.

x	y	x	y
25	138	20	100
20	84	25	143
26	104	26	141
26	112	28	161
28	88	25	124
28	132	31	118
29	90	30	168
32	183		

9.6.2 (Telephone Data). Consider the data presented below. The responses (y) for this data set are the numbers of telephone calls (tens of millions) made in Belgium for the years 1950 through 1973. Time, the years, serves as the predictor variable (x). The data are discussed on page 172 of Hettmansperger and McKean (2011).

Year	50	51	52	53	54	55
No. Calls	0.44	0.47	0.47	0.59	0.66	0.73
Year	56	57	58	59	60	61
No. Calls	0.81	0.88	1.06	1.20	1.35	1.49
Year	62	63	64	65	66	67
No. Calls	1.61	2.12	11.90	12.40	14.20	15.90
Year	68	69	70	71	72	73
No. Calls	18.20	21.20	4.30	2.40	2.70	2.90

(a) Calculate the least squares regression line for these data.

(b) Plot the points and the least squares regression line on the same graph.

(c) What is the reason for the poor least squares fit?

9.6.3. Find $(1 - \alpha)100\%$ confidence intervals for the parameters α and β in Model (9.6.1).

9.6.4. Consider Model (9.6.1). Let $\eta_0 = E(Y|x = x_0 - \overline{x})$. The least squares estimator of η_0 is $\hat{\eta}_0 = \hat{\alpha} + \hat{\beta}(x_0 - \overline{x})$.

(a) Using (9.6.6), determine the distribution of $\hat{\eta}_0$.

(b) Obtain a $(1 - \alpha)100\%$ confidence interval for η_0.

9.6.5. Assume that the sample $(x_1, Y_1), \ldots, (x_n, Y_n)$ follows the linear model (9.6.1). Suppose Y_0 is a future observation at $x = x_0 - \overline{x}$ and we want to determine a predictive interval for it. Assume that the model (9.6.1) holds for Y_0; i.e., Y_0 has a $N(\alpha + \beta(x_0 - \overline{x}), \sigma^2)$ distribution. We use $\hat{\eta}_0$ of Exercise 9.6.4 as our prediction of Y_0.

(a) Obtain the distribution of $Y_0 - \hat{\eta}_0$. Use the fact that the future observation Y_0 is independent of the sample $(x_1, Y_1), \ldots, (x_n, Y_n)$.

(b) Determine a t-statistic with numerator $Y_0 - \hat{\eta}_0$.

(c) Now beginning with $1 - \alpha = P[-t_{\alpha/2, n-2} < T < t_{\alpha/2, n-2}]$, where $0 < \alpha < 1$, determine a $(1 - \alpha)100\%$ predictive interval for Y_0.

(d) Compare this predictive interval with the confidence interval obtained in Exercise 9.6.4. Intuitively, why is the predictive interval larger?

9.6.6. Show that

$$\sum_{i=1}^{n}[Y_i - \alpha - \beta(x_i - \overline{x})]^2 = n(\hat{\alpha} - \alpha)^2 + (\hat{\beta} - \beta)^2 \sum_{i=1}^{n}(x_i - \overline{x})^2 + \sum_{i=1}^{n}[Y_i - \hat{\alpha} - \hat{\beta}(x_i - \overline{x})]^2.$$

9.6.7. Let the independent random variables $Y_1, Y_2, \ldots, Y_n$ have, respectively, the probability density functions $N(\beta x_i, \gamma^2 x_i^2)$, $i = 1, 2, \ldots, n$, where the given numbers $x_1, x_2, \ldots, x_n$ are not all equal and no one is zero. Find the maximum likelihood estimators of β and γ^2.

9.6.8. Let the independent random variables $Y_1, \ldots, Y_n$ have the joint pdf

$$L(\alpha, \beta, \sigma^2) = \left(\frac{1}{2\pi\sigma^2}\right)^{n/2} \exp\left\{-\frac{1}{2\sigma^2}\sum_{1}^{n}[y_i - \alpha - \beta(x_i - \overline{x})]^2\right\},$$

where the given numbers $x_1, x_2, \ldots, x_n$ are not all equal. Let $H_0 : \beta = 0$ (α and σ^2 unspecified). It is desired to use a likelihood ratio test to test H_0 against all possible alternatives. Find Λ and see whether the test can be based on a familiar statistic.

Hint: In the notation of this section, show that

$$\sum_{1}^{n}(Y_i - \hat{\alpha})^2 = Q_3 + \widehat{\beta}^2 \sum_{1}^{n}(x_i - \overline{x})^2.$$

9.6.9. Using the notation of Section 9.2, assume that the means μ_j satisfy a linear function of j, namely, $\mu_j = c + d[j - (b+1)/2]$. Let independent random samples of size a be taken from the b normal distributions having means $\mu_1, \mu_2, \ldots, \mu_b$, respectively, and common unknown variance σ^2.

(a) Show that the maximum likelihood estimators of c and d are, respectively, $\hat{c} = \overline{X}_{..}$ and

$$\hat{d} = \frac{\sum_{j=1}^{b}[j - (b-1)/2](\overline{X}_{.j} - \overline{X}_{..})}{\sum_{j=1}^{b}[j - (b+1)/2]^2}.$$

(b) Show that

$$\sum_{i=1}^{a}\sum_{j=1}^{b}(X_{ij} - \overline{X}_{..})^2 = \sum_{i=1}^{a}\sum_{j=1}^{b}\left[X_{ij} - \overline{X}_{..} - \hat{d}\left(j - \frac{b+1}{2}\right)\right]^2$$

$$+ \hat{d}^2 \sum_{j=1}^{b} a\left(j - \frac{b+1}{2}\right)^2.$$

(c) Argue that the two terms in the right-hand member of part (b), once divided by σ^2, are independent random variables with χ^2 distributions provided that $d = 0$.

(d) What F-statistic would be used to test the equality of the means, that is, $H_0 : d = 0$?

9.6.10. Show that the covariance between $\hat{\alpha}$ and $\hat{\beta}$ is zero.

9.6.11. Reconsider Example 9.6.1.

(a) Show that $\hat{\boldsymbol{\theta}} = \hat{\alpha}\mathbf{1} + \hat{\beta}\mathbf{x}_c$, where $\hat{\alpha}$ and $\hat{\beta}$ are the least squares estimators derived in this section.

(b) Show that the vector $\hat{\mathbf{e}} = \mathbf{Y} - \hat{\boldsymbol{\theta}}$ is the vector of residuals; i.e., its ith entry is $\hat{e}_i$, (9.6.5).

(c) As depicted in Figure 9.6.2, show that the angle between the vectors $\hat{\theta}$ and $\hat{e}$ is a right angle.

(d) Show that the residuals sum to zero; i.e., $1'\hat{e} = 0$.

9.6.12. Fit $y = a + x$ to the data

x	0	1	2
y	1	3	4

by the method of least squares.

9.6.13. Fit by the method of least squares the plane $z = a + bx + cy$ to the five points $(x, y, z) : (-1, -2, 5), (0, -2, 4), (0, 0, 4), (1, 0, 2), (2, 1, 0)$.

9.6.14. Let the 4×1 matrix Y be multivariate normal $N(X\beta, \sigma^2 I)$, where the 4×3 matrix X equals

$$X = \begin{bmatrix} 1 & 1 & 2 \\ 1 & -1 & 2 \\ 1 & 0 & -3 \\ 1 & 0 & -1 \end{bmatrix}$$

and β is the 3×1 regression coefficient matrix.

(a) Find the mean matrix and the covariance matrix of $\hat{\beta} = (X'X)^{-1}X'Y$.

(b) If we observe Y' to be equal to $(6, 1, 11, 3)$, compute $\hat{\beta}$.

9.6.15. Suppose Y is an $n \times 1$ random vector, X is an $n \times p$ matrix of known constants of rank p, and β is a $p \times 1$ vector of regression coefficients. Let Y have a $N(X\beta, \sigma^2 I)$ distribution. Discuss the joint pdf of $\hat{\beta} = (X'X)^{-1}X'Y$ and $Y'[I - X(X'X)^{-1}X']Y/\sigma^2$.

9.6.16. Let the independent normal random variables $Y_1, Y_2, \ldots, Y_n$ have, respectively, the probability density functions $N(\mu, \gamma^2 x_i^2)$, $i = 1, 2, \ldots, n$, where the given $x_1, x_2, \ldots, x_n$ are not all equal and no one of which is zero. Discuss the test of the hypothesis $H_0 : \gamma = 1$, μ unspecified, against all alternatives $H_1 : \gamma \neq 1$, μ unspecified.

9.6.17. Let $Y_1, Y_2, \ldots, Y_n$ be n independent normal variables with common unknown variance σ^2. Let Y_i have mean βx_i, $i = 1, 2, \ldots, n$, where $x_1, x_2, \ldots, x_n$ are known but not all the same and β is an unknown constant. Find the likelihood ratio test for $H_0 : \beta = 0$ against all alternatives. Show that this likelihood ratio test can be based on a statistic that has a well-known distribution.

9.7   A Test of Independence

Let X and Y have a bivariate normal distribution with means μ_1 and μ_2, positive variances σ_1^2 and σ_2^2, and correlation coefficient ρ. We wish to test the hypothesis that X and Y are independent. Because two jointly normally distributed random variables are independent if and only if $\rho = 0$, we test the hypothesis $H_0 : \rho = 0$ against the hypothesis $H_1 : \rho \neq 0$. A likelihood ratio test is used. Let $(X_1, Y_1), (X_2, Y_2), \ldots, (X_n, Y_n)$ denote a random sample of size $n > 2$ from the bivariate normal distribution; that is, the joint pdf of these $2n$ random variables is given by

$$f(x_1, y_1)f(x_2, y_2) \cdots f(x_n, y_n).$$

Although it is fairly difficult to show, the statistic that is defined by the likelihood ratio Λ is a function of the statistic, which is the mle of ρ, namely,

$$R = \frac{\sum_{i=1}^{n}(X_i - \overline{X})(Y_i - \overline{Y})}{\sqrt{\sum_{i=1}^{n}(X_i - \overline{X})^2 \sum_{i=1}^{n}(Y_i - \overline{Y})^2}}. \tag{9.7.1}$$

This statistic R is called the sample **correlation coefficient** of the random sample. Following the discussion after expression (5.4.5), the statistic R is a consistent estimate of ρ; see Exercise 9.7.5. The likelihood ratio principle, which calls for the rejection of H_0 if $\Lambda \leq \lambda_0$, is equivalent to the computed value of $|R| \geq c$. That is, if the absolute value of the correlation coefficient of the sample is too large, we reject the hypothesis that the correlation coefficient of the distribution is equal to zero. To determine a value of c for a satisfactory significance level, it is necessary to obtain the distribution of R, or a function of R, when H_0 is true, as we outline next.

Let $X_1 = x_1, X_2 = x_2, \ldots, X_n = x_n$, $n > 2$, where $x_1, x_2, \ldots, x_n$ and $\overline{x} = \sum_1^n x_i/n$ are fixed numbers such that $\sum_1^n (x_i - \overline{x})^2 > 0$. Consider the conditional pdf of $Y_1, Y_2, \ldots, Y_n$ given that $X_1 = x_1, X_2 = x_2, \ldots, X_n = x_n$. Because $Y_1, Y_2, \ldots, Y_n$ are independent and, with $\rho = 0$, are also independent of $X_1, X_2, \ldots, X_n$, this conditional pdf is given by

$$\left(\frac{1}{\sqrt{2\pi}\sigma_2}\right)^n \exp\left\{-\frac{1}{2\sigma_2^2} \sum_1^n (y_i - \mu_2)^2\right\}.$$

Let R_c be the correlation coefficient, given $X_1 = x_1, X_2 = x_2, \ldots, X_n = x_n$, so that

$$\frac{R_c\sqrt{\sum_{i=1}^{n}(Y_i - \overline{Y})^2}}{\sqrt{\sum_{i=1}^{n}(x_i - \overline{x})^2}} = \frac{\sum_{i=1}^{n}(x_i - \overline{x})(Y_i - \overline{Y})}{\sum_{i=1}^{n}(x_i - \overline{x})^2} = \frac{\sum_{i=1}^{n}(x_i - \overline{x})Y_i}{\sum_{i=1}^{n}(x_i - \overline{x})^2}$$

is like $\hat{\beta}$ of Section 9.6 and has mean zero when $\rho = 0$. Thus, referring to T_2 of Section 9.6, we see that

$$\frac{R_c\sqrt{\sum(Y_i - \overline{Y})^2}/\sqrt{\sum(x_i - \overline{x})^2}}{\sqrt{\frac{\sum_{i=1}^{n}\left\{Y_i - \overline{Y} - \left[R_c\sqrt{\sum_{j=1}^{n}(Y_j - \overline{Y})^2}/\sqrt{\sum_{j=1}^{n}(x_j - \overline{x})^2}\right](x_i - \overline{x})\right\}^2}{(n-2)\sum_{j=1}^{n}(x_j - \overline{x})^2}}} = \frac{R_c\sqrt{n - 2}}{\sqrt{1 - R_c^2}} \tag{9.7.2}$$

has, given $X_1 = x_1, \ldots, X_n = x_n$, a conditional t-distribution with $n - 2$ degrees of freedom. Note that the pdf, say $g(t)$, of this t-distribution does not depend upon $x_1, x_2, \ldots, x_n$. Now the joint pdf of $X_1, X_2, \ldots, X_n$ and $R\sqrt{n-2}/\sqrt{1-R^2}$, where

$$R = \frac{\sum_1^n (X_i - \overline{X})(Y_i - \overline{Y})}{\sqrt{\sum_1^n (X_i - \overline{X})^2 \sum_1^n (Y_i - \overline{Y})^2}},$$

is the product of $g(t)$ and the joint pdf of $X_1, \ldots, X_n$. Integration on $x_1, x_2, \ldots, x_n$ yields the marginal pdf of $R\sqrt{n-2}/\sqrt{1-R^2}$; because $g(t)$ does not depend upon $x_1, x_2, \ldots, x_n$, it is obvious that this marginal pdf is $g(t)$, the conditional pdf of $R\sqrt{n-2}/\sqrt{1-R^2}$. The change-of-variable technique can now be used to find the pdf of R.

Remark 9.7.1. Since R has, when $\rho = 0$, a conditional distribution that does not depend upon $x_1, x_2, \ldots, x_n$ (and hence that conditional distribution is, in fact, the marginal distribution of R), we have the remarkable fact that R is independent of $X_1, X_2, \ldots, X_n$. It follows that R is independent of *every function* of $X_1, X_2, \ldots, X_n$ alone, that is, a function that does not depend upon any Y_i. In like manner, R is independent of every function of $Y_1, Y_2, \ldots, Y_n$ alone. Moreover, a careful review of the argument reveals that nowhere did we use the fact that X has a normal marginal distribution. Thus, if X and Y are independent, and if Y has a normal distribution, then R has the same conditional distribution whatever is the distribution of X, subject to the condition $\sum_1^n (x_i - \overline{x})^2 > 0$. Moreover, if $P[\sum_1^n (X_i - \overline{X})^2 > 0] = 1$, then R has the same marginal distribution whatever is the distribution of X. ∎

If we write $T = R\sqrt{n-2}/\sqrt{1-R^2}$, where T has a t-distribution with $n - 2 > 0$ degrees of freedom, it is easy to show by the change-of-variable technique (Exercise 9.7.4) that the pdf of R is given by

$$h(r) = \begin{cases} \frac{\Gamma[(n-1)/2]}{\Gamma(\frac{1}{2})\Gamma[(n-2)/2]}(1-r^2)^{(n-4)/2} & -1 < r < 1 \\ 0 & \text{elsewhere.} \end{cases} \tag{9.7.3}$$

We have now solved the problem of the distribution of R, when $\rho = 0$ and $n > 2$, or perhaps more conveniently, that of $R\sqrt{n-2}/\sqrt{1-R^2}$. The likelihood ratio test of the hypothesis $H_0 : \rho = 0$ against all alternatives $H_1 : \rho \neq 0$ may be based either on the statistic R or on the statistic $R\sqrt{n-2}/\sqrt{1-R^2} = T$, although the latter is easier to use. Therefore, a level α test is to reject $H_0 : \rho = 0$ if $|T| \geq t_{\alpha/2, n-2}$.

Remark 9.7.2. It is possible to obtain an approximate test of size α by using the fact that

$$W = \frac{1}{2} \log \left(\frac{1+R}{1-R} \right)$$

has an approximate normal distribution with mean $\frac{1}{2}\log[(1+\rho)/(1-\rho)]$ and with variance $1/(n-3)$. We accept this statement without proof. Thus a test of $H_0 : \rho = 0$ can be based on the statistic

$$Z = \frac{\frac{1}{2}\log[(1+R)/(1-R)] - \frac{1}{2}\log[(1+\rho)/(1-\rho)]}{\sqrt{1/(n-3)}},$$

with $\rho = 0$ so that $\frac{1}{2}\log[(1+\rho)/(1-\rho)] = 0$. However, using W, we can also test a hypothesis like $H_0 : \rho = \rho_0$ against $H_1 : \rho \neq \rho_0$, where ρ_0 is not necessarily zero. In that case, the hypothesized mean of W is

$$\frac{1}{2}\log\left(\frac{1+\rho_0}{1-\rho_0}\right). \quad \blacksquare$$

EXERCISES

9.7.1. Show that

$$R = \frac{\displaystyle\sum_1^n (X_i - \overline{X})(Y_i - \overline{Y})}{\sqrt{\displaystyle\sum_1^n (X_i - \overline{X})^2 \sum_1^n (Y_i - \overline{Y})^2}} = \frac{\displaystyle\sum_1^n X_i Y_i - n\overline{X}\overline{Y}}{\sqrt{\left(\displaystyle\sum_1^n X_i^2 - n\overline{X}^2\right)\left(\displaystyle\sum_1^n Y_i^2 - n\overline{Y}^2\right)}}.$$

9.7.2. A random sample of size $n = 6$ from a bivariate normal distribution yields a value of the correlation coefficient of 0.89. Would we accept or reject, at the 5% significance level, the hypothesis that $\rho = 0$?

9.7.3. Verify Equation (9.7.2) of this section.

9.7.4. Verify the pdf (9.7.3) of this section.

9.7.5. Using the results of Section 4.5, show that R, (9.7.1), is a consistent estimate of ρ.

9.7.6. Two experiments gave the following results:

n	$\overline{x}$	$\overline{y}$	s_x	s_y	r
100	10	20	5	8	0.70
200	12	22	6	10	0.80

Calculate r for the combined sample.

9.8 The Distributions of Certain Quadratic Forms

Remark 9.8.1. It is essential that the reader have the background of the multivariate normal distribution as given in Section 3.5 to understand Sections 9.8 and 9.9. $\blacksquare$

Remark 9.8.2. We make use of the **trace** of a square matrix. If $\mathbf{A} = [a_{ij}]$ is an $n \times n$ matrix, then we define the trace of $\mathbf{A}$, $(\operatorname{tr} \mathbf{A})$, to be the sum of its diagonal entries; i.e.,

$$\operatorname{tr} \mathbf{A} = \sum_{i=1}^{n} a_{ii}. \tag{9.8.1}$$

The trace of a matrix has several interesting properties. One is that it is a linear operator; that is,

$$\operatorname{tr}(a\mathbf{A} + b\mathbf{B}) = a \operatorname{tr} \mathbf{A} + b \operatorname{tr} \mathbf{B}. \tag{9.8.2}$$

A second useful property is: If $\mathbf{A}$ is an $n \times m$ matrix, $\mathbf{B}$ is an $m \times k$ matrix, and $\mathbf{C}$ is a $k \times n$ matrix, then

$$\operatorname{tr}(\mathbf{ABC}) = \operatorname{tr}(\mathbf{BCA}) = \operatorname{tr}(\mathbf{CAB}). \tag{9.8.3}$$

The reader is asked to prove these facts in Exercise 9.8.7. Finally, a simple but useful property is that $\operatorname{tr} a = a$, for any scalar a. ■

We begin this section with a more formal but equivalent definition of a quadratic form. Let $\mathbf{X} = (X_1, \ldots, X_n)$ be an n-dimensional random vector and let $\mathbf{A}$ be a real $n \times n$ symmetric matrix. Then the random variable $Q = \mathbf{X}'\mathbf{AX}$ is called a **quadratic form** in $\mathbf{X}$. Due to the symmetry of $\mathbf{A}$, there are several ways we can write Q:

$$Q = \mathbf{X}'\mathbf{AX} = \sum_{i=1}^{n}\sum_{j=1}^{n} a_{ij}X_iX_j = \sum_{i=1}^{n} a_{ii}X_i^2 + \sum\sum_{i\neq j} a_{ij}X_iX_j \tag{9.8.4}$$

$$= \sum_{i=1}^{n} a_{ii}X_i^2 + 2\sum\sum_{i<j} a_{ij}X_iX_j. \tag{9.8.5}$$

These are very useful random variables in analysis of variance models. As the following theorem shows, the mean of a quadratic form is easily obtained.

Theorem 9.8.1. *Suppose the n-dimensional random vector* $\mathbf{X}$ *has mean* $\boldsymbol{\mu}$ *and variance–covariance matrix* $\boldsymbol{\Sigma}$. *Let* $Q = \mathbf{X}'\mathbf{AX}$, *where* $\mathbf{A}$ *is a real* $n \times n$ *symmetric matrix. Then*

$$E(Q) = \operatorname{tr} \mathbf{A}\boldsymbol{\Sigma} + \boldsymbol{\mu}'\mathbf{A}\boldsymbol{\mu}. \tag{9.8.6}$$

Proof: Using the trace operator and property (9.8.3), we have

$$
\begin{aligned}
E(Q) = E(\operatorname{tr} \mathbf{X}'\mathbf{AX}) &= E(\operatorname{tr} \mathbf{AXX}') \\
&= \operatorname{tr} \mathbf{A}E(\mathbf{XX}') \\
&= \operatorname{tr} \mathbf{A}(\boldsymbol{\Sigma} + \boldsymbol{\mu}\boldsymbol{\mu}') \\
&= \operatorname{tr} \mathbf{A}\boldsymbol{\Sigma} + \boldsymbol{\mu}'\mathbf{A}\boldsymbol{\mu},
\end{aligned}
$$

where the third line follows from Theorem 2.6.3. ■

Example 9.8.1 (Sample Variance). Let $\mathbf{X}' = (X_1, \ldots, X_n)$ be an n-dimensional vector of random variables. Let $\mathbf{1}' = (1, \ldots, 1)$ be the n-dimensional vector whose components are 1. Let $\mathbf{I}$ be the $n \times n$ identity matrix. Consider the quadratic form $Q = \mathbf{X}'(\mathbf{I} - \frac{1}{n}\mathbf{J})\mathbf{X}$, where $\mathbf{J} = \mathbf{11}'$; i.e., $\mathbf{J}$ is an $n \times n$ matrix with all entries equal to 1. Note that the off-diagonal entries of $(\mathbf{I} - \frac{1}{n}\mathbf{J})$ are $-n^{-1}$ while the diagonal entries are $1 - n^{-1}$; hence, by (9.8.4), Q simplifies to

$$
\begin{aligned}
Q &= \sum_{i=1}^{n} X_i^2 \left(1 - \frac{1}{n}\right) + \sum\sum_{i \neq j} \left(-\frac{1}{n}\right) X_i X_j \\
&= \sum_{i=1}^{n} X_i^2 \left(1 - \frac{1}{n}\right) - \frac{1}{n}\sum_{i=1}^{n} X_i \sum_{j=1}^{n} X_j + \frac{1}{n}\sum_{i=1}^{n} X_i^2 \\
&= \sum_{i=1}^{n} X_i^2 - n\overline{X}^2 = (n-1)S^2,
\end{aligned}
\tag{9.8.7}
$$

where $\overline{X}$ and S^2 denote the sample mean and variance of $X_1, \ldots, X_n$.

Suppose we further assume that $X_1, \ldots, X_n$ are iid random variables with common mean μ and variance σ^2. Using Theorem 9.8.1, we can obtain yet another proof that S^2 is an unbiased estimate of σ^2. Note that the mean of the random vector $\mathbf{X}$ is $\mu\mathbf{1}$ and that its variance–covariance matrix is $\sigma^2\mathbf{I}$. Based on Theorem 9.8.1, we find immediately that

$$
E(S^2) = \frac{1}{n-1}\left\{\mathrm{tr}\left(\mathbf{I} - \frac{1}{n}\mathbf{J}\right)\sigma^2\mathbf{I} + \mu^2\left(\mathbf{1}'\mathbf{1} - \frac{1}{n}\mathbf{1}'\mathbf{11}'\mathbf{1}\right)\right\} = \sigma^2 . \quad \blacksquare
$$

The spectral decomposition of symmetric matrices proves quite useful in this part of the chapter. As discussed around expression (3.5.4), a real symmetric matrix $\mathbf{A}$ can be diagonalized as

$$
\mathbf{A} = \mathbf{\Gamma}'\mathbf{\Lambda}\mathbf{\Gamma}, \tag{9.8.8}
$$

where $\mathbf{\Lambda}$ is the diagonal matrix $\mathbf{\Lambda} = \mathrm{diag}(\lambda_1, \ldots, \lambda_n)$, $\lambda_1 \geq \cdots \geq \lambda_n$ are the eigenvalues of $\mathbf{A}$, and the columns of $\mathbf{\Gamma}' = [\mathbf{v}_1 \cdots \mathbf{v}_n]$ are the corresponding orthonormal eigenvectors (i.e., $\mathbf{\Gamma}$ is an orthogonal matrix). Recall from linear algebra that the rank of $\mathbf{A}$ is the number of nonzero eigenvalues. Further, because $\mathbf{\Lambda}$ is diagonal, we can write this expression as

$$
\mathbf{A} = \sum_{i=1}^{n} \lambda_i \mathbf{v}_i \mathbf{v}_i'. \tag{9.8.9}
$$

For normal random variables, we can use this last equation to obtain the mgf of the quadratic form Q.

Theorem 9.8.2. Let $\mathbf{X}' = (X_1, \ldots, X_n)$, where $X_1, \ldots, X_n$ are iid $N(0, \sigma^2)$. Consider the quadratic form $Q = \sigma^{-2}\mathbf{X}'\mathbf{A}\mathbf{X}$ for a symmetric matrix $\mathbf{A}$ of rank $r \leq n$. Then Q has the moment generating function

$$
M(t) = \prod_{i=1}^{r}(1 - 2t\lambda_i)^{-1/2} = |\mathbf{I} - 2t\mathbf{A}|^{-1/2}, \tag{9.8.10}
$$

where $\lambda_1, \ldots, \lambda_r$ are the nonzero eigenvalues of $\mathbf{A}$, $|t| < 1/(2\lambda^*)$, and the value of λ^* is given by $\lambda^* = \max_{1 \le i \le r} |\lambda_i|$.

Proof: Write the spectral decomposition of $\mathbf{A}$ as in expression (9.8.9). Since the rank of $\mathbf{A}$ is r, exactly r of the eigenvalues are not 0. Denote the nonzero eigenvalues by $\lambda_1, \ldots, \lambda_r$. Then we can write Q as

$$Q = \sum_{i=1}^{r} \lambda_i (\sigma^{-1} \mathbf{v}_i' \mathbf{X})^2. \tag{9.8.11}$$

Let $\mathbf{\Gamma}_1' = [\mathbf{v}_1 \cdots \mathbf{v}_r]$ and define the r-dimensional random vector $\mathbf{W}$ by $\mathbf{W} = \sigma^{-1} \mathbf{\Gamma}_1 \mathbf{X}$. Since $\mathbf{X}$ is $N_n(\mathbf{0}, \sigma^2 \mathbf{I}_n)$ and $\mathbf{\Gamma}_1' \mathbf{\Gamma}_1 = \mathbf{I}_r$, Theorem 3.5.1 shows that $\mathbf{W}$ has a $N_r(\mathbf{0}, \mathbf{I}_r)$ distribution. In terms of the W_i, we can write (9.8.11) as

$$Q = \sum_{i=1}^{r} \lambda_i W_i^2. \tag{9.8.12}$$

Because $W_1, \ldots, W_r$ are independent $N(0,1)$ random variables, $W_1^2, \ldots, W_r^2$ are independent $\chi^2(1)$ random variables. Thus the mgf of Q is

$$
\begin{aligned}
E[\exp\{tQ\}] &= E\left[\exp\left\{\sum_{i=1}^{r} t\lambda_i W_i^2\right\}\right] \\
&= \prod_{i=1}^{r} E[\exp\{t\lambda_i W_i^2\}] = \prod_{i=1}^{r} (1 - 2t\lambda_i)^{-1/2}. \tag{9.8.13}
\end{aligned}
$$

The last equality holds if we assume that $|t| < 1/(2\lambda^*)$, where $\lambda^* = \max_{1 \le i \le r} |\lambda_i|$; see Exercise 9.8.6. To obtain the second form in (9.8.10), recall that the determinant of an orthogonal matrix is 1. The result then follows from

$$
\begin{aligned}
|\mathbf{I} - 2t\mathbf{A}| = |\mathbf{\Gamma}'\mathbf{\Gamma} - 2t\mathbf{\Gamma}'\mathbf{\Lambda}\mathbf{\Gamma}| &= |\mathbf{\Gamma}'(\mathbf{I} - 2t\mathbf{\Lambda})\mathbf{\Gamma}| \\
&= |\mathbf{I} - 2t\mathbf{\Lambda}| = \left\{\prod_{i=1}^{r} (1 - 2t\lambda_i)^{-1/2}\right\}^{-2}. \quad \blacksquare
\end{aligned}
$$

Example 9.8.2. To illustrate this theorem, suppose X_i, $i = 1, 2, \ldots, n$, are independent random variables with X_i distributed as $N(\mu_i, \sigma_i^2)$, $i = 1, 2, \ldots, n$, respectively. Let $Z_i = (X_i - \mu_i)/\sigma_i$. We know that $\sum_{i=1}^{n} Z_i^2$ has a χ^2 distribution with n degrees of freedom. To illustrate Theorem 9.8.2, let $\mathbf{Z}' = (Z_1, \ldots, Z_n)$. Let $Q = \mathbf{Z}'\mathbf{I}\mathbf{Z}$. Hence the symmetric matrix associated with Q is the identity matrix $\mathbf{I}$, which has n eigenvalues, all of value 1; i.e., $\lambda_i \equiv 1$. By Theorem 9.8.2, the mgf of Q is $(1 - 2t)^{-n/2}$; i.e., Q is distributed χ^2 with n degrees of freedom. $\blacksquare$

In general, from Theorem 9.8.2, note how close the mgf of the quadratic form Q is to the mgf of a χ^2 distribution. The next two theorems give conditions where this is true.

Theorem 9.8.3. *Let* $\mathbf{X}' = (X_1, X_2, \ldots, X_n)$ *have a* $N_n(\boldsymbol{\mu}, \boldsymbol{\Sigma})$ *distribution, where* $\boldsymbol{\Sigma}$ *is positive definite. Then* $Q = (\mathbf{X} - \boldsymbol{\mu})'\boldsymbol{\Sigma}^{-1}(\mathbf{X} - \boldsymbol{\mu})$ *has a* $\chi^2(n)$ *distribution.*

Proof: Write the spectral decomposition of $\boldsymbol{\Sigma}$ as $\boldsymbol{\Sigma} = \boldsymbol{\Gamma}'\boldsymbol{\Lambda}\boldsymbol{\Gamma}$, where $\boldsymbol{\Gamma}$ is an orthogonal matrix and $\boldsymbol{\Lambda} = \text{diag}\{\lambda_1, \ldots, \lambda_n\}$ is a diagonal matrix whose diagonal entries are the eigenvalues of $\boldsymbol{\Sigma}$. Because $\boldsymbol{\Sigma}$ is positive definite, all $\lambda_i > 0$. Hence we can write

$$\boldsymbol{\Sigma}^{-1} = \boldsymbol{\Gamma}'\boldsymbol{\Lambda}^{-1}\boldsymbol{\Gamma} = \boldsymbol{\Gamma}'\boldsymbol{\Lambda}^{-1/2}\boldsymbol{\Gamma}\boldsymbol{\Gamma}'\boldsymbol{\Lambda}^{-1/2}\boldsymbol{\Gamma},$$

where $\boldsymbol{\Lambda}^{-1/2} = \text{diag}\{\lambda_1^{-1/2}, \ldots, \lambda_n^{-1/2}\}$. Thus we have

$$Q = \left\{\boldsymbol{\Lambda}^{-1/2}\boldsymbol{\Gamma}(\mathbf{X} - \boldsymbol{\mu})\right\}' \mathbf{I} \left\{\boldsymbol{\Lambda}^{-1/2}\boldsymbol{\Gamma}(\mathbf{X} - \boldsymbol{\mu})\right\}.$$

But by Theorem 3.5.1, it is easy to show that the random vector $\boldsymbol{\Lambda}^{-1/2}\boldsymbol{\Gamma}(\mathbf{X} - \boldsymbol{\mu})$ has a $N_n(\mathbf{0}, \mathbf{I})$ distribution; hence, Q has a $\chi^2(n)$ distribution. ∎

The remarkable fact that the random variable Q in the last theorem is $\chi^2(n)$ stimulates a number of questions about quadratic forms in normally distributed variables. We would like to treat this problem generally, but limitations of space forbid this, and we find it necessary to restrict ourselves to some special cases; see, for instance, Stapleton (1995) for discussion.

Recall from linear algebra that a symmetric matrix $\mathbf{A}$ is **idempotent** if $\mathbf{A}^2 = \mathbf{A}$. In Section 9.1, we have already met some idempotent matrices. For example, the matrix $\mathbf{I} - \frac{1}{n}\mathbf{J}$ of Example 9.8.1 is idempotent. Idempotent matrices possess some important characteristics. Suppose λ is an eigenvalue of an idempotent matrix $\mathbf{A}$ with corresponding eigenvector $\mathbf{v}$. Then the following identity is true:

$$\lambda\mathbf{v} = \mathbf{A}\mathbf{v} = \mathbf{A}^2\mathbf{v} = \lambda\mathbf{A}\mathbf{v} = \lambda^2\mathbf{v}.$$

Hence $\lambda(\lambda - 1)\mathbf{v} = \mathbf{0}$. Since $\mathbf{v} \neq \mathbf{0}$, $\lambda = 0$ or 1. Conversely, if the eigenvalues of a real symmetric matrix are only 0s and 1s then it is idempotent; see Exercise 9.8.10. Thus the rank of an idempotent matrix $\mathbf{A}$ is the number of its eigenvalues which are 1. Denote the spectral decomposition of $\mathbf{A}$ by $\mathbf{A} = \boldsymbol{\Gamma}'\boldsymbol{\Lambda}\boldsymbol{\Gamma}$, where $\boldsymbol{\Lambda}$ is a diagonal matrix of eigenvalues and $\boldsymbol{\Gamma}$ is an orthogonal matrix whose columns are the corresponding orthonormal eigenvectors. Because the diagonal entries of $\boldsymbol{\Lambda}$ are 0 or 1 and $\boldsymbol{\Gamma}$ is orthogonal, we have

$$\text{tr}\,\mathbf{A} = \text{tr}\,\boldsymbol{\Lambda}\boldsymbol{\Gamma}\boldsymbol{\Gamma}' = \text{tr}\,\boldsymbol{\Lambda} = \text{rank}(\mathbf{A});$$

i.e., the rank of an idempotent matrix is equal to its trace.

Theorem 9.8.4. *Let* $\mathbf{X}' = (X_1, \ldots, X_n)$, *where* $X_1, \ldots, X_n$ *are iid* $N(0, \sigma^2)$. *Let* $Q = \sigma^{-2}\mathbf{X}'\mathbf{A}\mathbf{X}$ *for a symmetric matrix* $\mathbf{A}$ *with rank* r. *Then* Q *has a* $\chi^2(r)$ *distribution if and only if* $\mathbf{A}$ *is idempotent.*

Proof: By Theorem 9.8.2, the mgf of Q is

$$M_Q(t) = \prod_{i=1}^{r}(1 - 2t\lambda_i)^{-1/2}, \tag{9.8.14}$$

where $\lambda_1, \ldots, \lambda_r$ are the r nonzero eigenvalues of $\mathbf{A}$. Suppose, first, that $\mathbf{A}$ is idempotent. Then $\lambda_1 = \cdots = \lambda_r = 1$ and the mgf of Q is $M_Q(t) = (1 - 2t)^{-r/2}$; i.e., Q has a $\chi^2(r)$ distribution. Next, suppose Q has a $\chi^2(r)$ distribution. Then for t in a neighborhood of 0, we have the identity

$$\prod_{i=1}^{r}(1 - 2t\lambda_i)^{-1/2} = (1 - 2t)^{-r/2},$$

which, upon squaring both sides, leads to

$$\prod_{i=1}^{r}(1 - 2t\lambda_i) = (1 - 2t)^{r},$$

By the uniqueness of the factorization of polynomials, $\lambda_1 = \cdots = \lambda_r = 1$. Hence $\mathbf{A}$ is idempotent. ∎

Example 9.8.3. Based on this last theorem, we can obtain quickly the distribution of the sample variance when sampling from a normal distribution. Suppose $X_1, X_2, \ldots, X_n$ are iid $N(\mu, \sigma^2)$. Let $\mathbf{X} = (X_1, X_2, \ldots, X_n)'$. Then $\mathbf{X}$ has a $N_n(\mu\mathbf{1}, \sigma^2\mathbf{I})$ distribution, where $\mathbf{1}$ denotes a $n \times 1$ vector with all components equal to 1. Let $S^2 = (n - 1)^{-1} \sum_{i=1}^{n}(X_i - \overline{X})^2$. Then by Example 9.8.1, we can write

$$\frac{(n-1)S^2}{\sigma^2} = \sigma^{-2}\mathbf{X}'\left(\mathbf{I} - \frac{1}{n}\mathbf{J}\right)\mathbf{X} = \sigma^{-2}(\mathbf{X} - \mu\mathbf{1})'\left(\mathbf{I} - \frac{1}{n}\mathbf{J}\right)(\mathbf{X} - \mu\mathbf{1}),$$

where the last equality holds because $\left(\mathbf{I} - \frac{1}{n}\mathbf{J}\right)\mathbf{1} = \mathbf{0}$. Because the matrix $\mathbf{I} - \frac{1}{n}\mathbf{J}$ is idempotent, $\mathrm{tr}\left(\mathbf{I} - \frac{1}{n}\mathbf{J}\right) = n - 1$, and $\mathbf{X} - \mu\mathbf{1}$ is $N_n(\mathbf{0}, \sigma^2\mathbf{I})$, it follows from Theorem 9.8.4 that $(n - 1)S^2/\sigma^2$ has a $\chi^2(n - 1)$ distribution. ∎

Remark 9.8.3. If the normal distribution in Theorem 9.8.4 is $N_n(\boldsymbol{\mu}, \sigma^2\mathbf{I})$, the condition $\mathbf{A}^2 = \mathbf{A}$ remains a necessary and sufficient condition that Q/σ^2 have a chi-square distribution. In general, however, Q/σ^2 is not central $\chi^2(r)$ but instead, Q/σ^2 has a noncentral chi-square distribution if $\mathbf{A}^2 = \mathbf{A}$. The number of degrees of freedom is r, the rank of $\mathbf{A}$, and the noncentrality parameter is $\boldsymbol{\mu}'\mathbf{A}\boldsymbol{\mu}/\sigma^2$. If $\boldsymbol{\mu} = \mu\mathbf{1}$, then $\boldsymbol{\mu}'\mathbf{A}\boldsymbol{\mu} = \mu^2 \sum_{i,j} a_{ij}$, where $\mathbf{A} = [a_{ij}]$. Then, if $\mu \neq 0$, the conditions $\mathbf{A}^2 = \mathbf{A}$ and $\sum_{i,j} a_{ij} = 0$ are necessary and sufficient conditions that Q/σ^2 be central $\chi^2(r)$. Moreover, the theorem may be extended to a quadratic form in random variables which have a multivariate normal distribution with positive definite covariance matrix $\boldsymbol{\Sigma}$; here the necessary and sufficient condition that Q have a chi-square distribution is $\mathbf{A}\boldsymbol{\Sigma}\mathbf{A} = \mathbf{A}$. See Exercise 9.8.9. ∎

EXERCISES

9.8.1. Let $Q = X_1X_2 - X_3X_4$, where X_1, X_2, X_3, X_4 is a random sample of size 4 from a distribution which is $N(0, \sigma^2)$. Show that Q/σ^2 does not have a chi-square distribution. Find the mgf of Q/σ^2.

9.8.2. Let $\mathbf{X}' = [X_1, X_2]$ be bivariate normal with matrix of means $\boldsymbol{\mu}' = [\mu_1, \mu_2]$ and positive definite covariance matrix Σ. Let

$$Q_1 = \frac{X_1^2}{\sigma_1^2(1 - \rho^2)} - 2\rho \frac{X_1 X_2}{\sigma_1 \sigma_2 (1 - \rho^2)} + \frac{X_2^2}{\sigma_2^2 (1 - \rho^2)}.$$

Show that Q_1 is $\chi^2(r, \theta)$ and find r and θ. When and only when does Q_1 have a central chi-square distribution?

9.8.3. Let $\mathbf{X}' = [X_1, X_2, X_3]$ denote a random sample of size 3 from a distribution that is $N(4, 8)$ and let

$$\mathbf{A} = \begin{pmatrix} \frac{1}{2} & 0 & \frac{1}{2} \\ 0 & 1 & 0 \\ \frac{1}{2} & 0 & \frac{1}{2} \end{pmatrix}.$$

Let $Q = \mathbf{X}'\mathbf{A}\mathbf{X}/\sigma^2$.

(a) Use Theorem 9.8.1 to find the $E(Q)$.

(b) Justify the assertion that Q is $\chi^2(2, 6)$.

9.8.4. Suppose $X_1, \ldots, X_n$ are independent random variables with the common mean μ but with unequal variances $\sigma_i^2 = \text{Var}(X_i)$.

(a) Determine the variance of X.

(b) Determine the constant K so that $Q = K \sum_{i=1}^{n} (X_i - \overline{X})^2$ is an unbiased estimate of the variance of $\overline{X}$. (*Hint:* Proceed as in Example 9.8.3.)

9.8.5. Suppose $X_1, \ldots, X_n$ are correlated random variables, with common mean μ and variance σ^2 but with correlations ρ (all correlations are the same).

(a) Determine the variance of $\overline{X}$.

(b) Determine the constant K so that $Q = K \sum_{i=1}^{n} (X_i - \overline{X})^2$ is an unbiased estimate of the variance of $\overline{X}$. (*Hint:* Proceed as in Example 9.8.3.)

9.8.6. Fill in the details for expression (9.8.13).

9.8.7. For the trace operator defined in expression (9.8.1), prove the following properties are true.

(a) If $\mathbf{A}$ and $\mathbf{B}$ are $n \times n$ matrices and a and b are scalars, then

$$\text{tr}\,(a\mathbf{A} + b\mathbf{B}) = a\,\text{tr}\,\mathbf{A} + b\,\text{tr}\,\mathbf{B}.$$

(b) If $\mathbf{A}$ is an $n \times m$ matrix, $\mathbf{B}$ is an $m \times k$ matrix, and $\mathbf{C}$ is a $k \times n$ matrix, then

$$\text{tr}\,(\mathbf{ABC}) = \text{tr}\,(\mathbf{BCA}) = \text{tr}\,(\mathbf{CAB}).$$

(c) If $\mathbf{A}$ is a square matrix and $\boldsymbol{\Gamma}$ is an orthogonal matrix, use the result of part (a) to show that $\text{tr}(\boldsymbol{\Gamma}'\mathbf{A}\boldsymbol{\Gamma}) = \text{tr}\mathbf{A}$.

(d) If $\mathbf{A}$ is a real symmetric idempotent matrix, use the result of part (b) to prove that the rank of $\mathbf{A}$ is equal to tr$\mathbf{A}$.

9.8.8. Let $\mathbf{A} = [a_{ij}]$ be a real symmetric matrix. Prove that $\sum_i \sum_j a_{ij}^2$ is equal to the sum of the squares of the eigenvalues of $\mathbf{A}$.
Hint: If $\mathbf{\Gamma}$ is an orthogonal matrix, show that $\sum_j \sum_i a_{ij}^2 = \text{tr}(\mathbf{A}^2) = \text{tr}(\mathbf{\Gamma}'\mathbf{A}^2\mathbf{\Gamma}) = \text{tr}[(\mathbf{\Gamma}'\mathbf{A}\mathbf{\Gamma})(\mathbf{\Gamma}'\mathbf{A}\mathbf{\Gamma})]$.

9.8.9. Suppose $\mathbf{X}$ has a $N_n(0, \mathbf{\Sigma})$ distribution, where $\mathbf{\Sigma}$ is positive definite. Let $Q = \mathbf{X}'\mathbf{A}\mathbf{X}$ for a symmetric matrix $\mathbf{A}$ with rank r. Prove Q has a $\chi^2(r)$ distribution if and only if $\mathbf{A}\mathbf{\Sigma}\mathbf{A} = \mathbf{A}$.
Hint: Write Q as

$$Q = (\mathbf{\Sigma}^{-1/2}\mathbf{X})'\mathbf{\Sigma}^{1/2}\mathbf{A}\mathbf{\Sigma}^{1/2}(\mathbf{\Sigma}^{-1/2}\mathbf{X}),$$

where $\mathbf{\Sigma}^{1/2} = \mathbf{\Gamma}'\mathbf{\Lambda}^{1/2}\mathbf{\Gamma}$ and $\mathbf{\Sigma} = \mathbf{\Gamma}'\mathbf{\Lambda}\mathbf{\Gamma}$ is the spectral decomposition of $\mathbf{\Sigma}$. Then use Theorem 9.8.4.

9.8.10. Suppose $\mathbf{A}$ is a real symmetric matrix. If the eigenvalues of $\mathbf{A}$ are only 0s and 1s then prove that $\mathbf{A}$ is idempotent.

9.9   The Independence of Certain Quadratic Forms

We have previously investigated the independence of linear functions of normally distributed variables. In this section we shall prove some theorems about the independence of quadratic forms. We shall confine our attention to normally distributed variables that constitute a random sample of size n from a distribution that is $N(0, \sigma^2)$.

Remark 9.9.1. In the proof of the next theorem, we use the fact that if $\mathbf{A}$ is an $m \times n$ matrix of rank n (i.e., $\mathbf{A}$ has full column rank), then the matrix $\mathbf{A}'\mathbf{A}$ is nonsingular. A proof of this linear algebra fact is sketched in Exercises 9.9.12 and 9.9.13. ■

Theorem 9.9.1 (Craig). *Let $\mathbf{X}' = (X_1, \ldots, X_n)$, where $X_1, \ldots, X_n$ are iid $N(0, \sigma^2)$ random variables. For real symmetric matrices $\mathbf{A}$ and $\mathbf{B}$, let $Q_1 = \sigma^{-2}\mathbf{X}'\mathbf{A}\mathbf{X}$ and $Q_2 = \sigma^{-2}\mathbf{X}'\mathbf{B}\mathbf{X}$ denote quadratic forms in $\mathbf{X}$. The random variables Q_1 and Q_2 are independent if and only if $\mathbf{A}\mathbf{B} = \mathbf{0}$.*

Proof: First, we obtain some preliminary results. Based on these results, the proof follows immediately. Assume the ranks of the matrices $\mathbf{A}$ and $\mathbf{B}$ are r and s, respectively. Let $\mathbf{\Gamma}_1'\mathbf{\Lambda}_1\mathbf{\Gamma}_1$ denote the spectral decomposition of $\mathbf{A}$. Denote the r nonzero eigenvalues of $\mathbf{A}$ by $\lambda_1, \ldots, \lambda_r$. Without loss of generality, assume that these nonzero eigenvalues of $\mathbf{A}$ are the first r elements on the main diagonal of $\mathbf{\Lambda}_1$ and let $\mathbf{\Gamma}_{11}'$ be the $n \times r$ matrix whose columns are the corresponding eigenvectors. Finally, let $\mathbf{\Lambda}_{11} = \text{diag}\{\lambda_1, \ldots, \lambda_r\}$. Then we can write the spectral decomposition of $\mathbf{A}$ in either of the two ways

$$\mathbf{A} = \mathbf{\Gamma}_1'\mathbf{\Lambda}_1\mathbf{\Gamma}_1 = \mathbf{\Gamma}_{11}'\mathbf{\Lambda}_{11}\mathbf{\Gamma}_{11}. \tag{9.9.1}$$

Note that we can write Q_1 as

$$Q_1 = \sigma^{-2}\mathbf{X}'\mathbf{\Gamma}_{11}'\mathbf{\Lambda}_{11}\mathbf{\Gamma}_{11}\mathbf{X} = \sigma^{-2}(\mathbf{\Gamma}_{11}\mathbf{X})'\mathbf{\Lambda}_{11}(\mathbf{\Gamma}_{11}\mathbf{X}) = \mathbf{W}_1'\mathbf{\Lambda}_{11}\mathbf{W}_1, \qquad (9.9.2)$$

where $\mathbf{W}_1 = \sigma^{-1}\mathbf{\Gamma}_{11}\mathbf{X}$. Next, obtain a similar representation based on the s nonzero eigenvalues $\gamma_1, \ldots, \gamma_s$ of $\mathbf{B}$. Let $\mathbf{\Lambda}_{22} = \mathrm{diag}\{\gamma_1, \ldots, \gamma_s\}$ denote the $s \times s$ diagonal matrix of nonzero eigenvalues and form the $n \times s$ matrix $\mathbf{\Gamma}_{21}' = [\mathbf{u}_1 \cdots \mathbf{u}_s]$ of corresponding eigenvectors. Then we can write the spectral decomposition of $\mathbf{B}$ as

$$\mathbf{B} = \mathbf{\Gamma}_{21}'\mathbf{\Lambda}_{22}\mathbf{\Gamma}_{21}. \qquad (9.9.3)$$

Also, we can write Q_2 as

$$Q_2 = \mathbf{W}_2'\mathbf{\Lambda}_{22}\mathbf{W}_2, \qquad (9.9.4)$$

where $\mathbf{W}_2 = \sigma^{-1}\mathbf{\Gamma}_{21}\mathbf{X}$. Letting $\mathbf{W}' = (\mathbf{W}_1', \mathbf{W}_2')$, we have

$$\mathbf{W} = \sigma^{-1}\begin{bmatrix} \mathbf{\Gamma}_{11} \\ \mathbf{\Gamma}_{21} \end{bmatrix}\mathbf{X}.$$

Because $\mathbf{X}$ has a $N_n(\mathbf{0}, \sigma^2\mathbf{I})$ distribution, Theorem 3.5.1 shows that $\mathbf{W}$ has an $(r+s)$–dimensional multivariate normal distribution with mean $\mathbf{0}$ and variance–covariance matrix

$$\mathrm{Var}\,(\mathbf{W}) = \begin{bmatrix} \mathbf{I}_r & \mathbf{\Gamma}_{11}\mathbf{\Gamma}_{21}' \\ \mathbf{\Gamma}_{21}\mathbf{\Gamma}_{11}' & \mathbf{I}_s \end{bmatrix}. \qquad (9.9.5)$$

Finally, using (9.9.1) and (9.9.3), we have the identity

$$\mathbf{AB} = \{\mathbf{\Gamma}_{11}'\mathbf{\Lambda}_{11}\}\mathbf{\Gamma}_{11}\mathbf{\Gamma}_{21}'\{\mathbf{\Lambda}_{22}\mathbf{\Gamma}_{21}\}. \qquad (9.9.6)$$

Let $\mathbf{U}$ denote the matrix in the first set of braces. Note that $\mathbf{U}$ has full column rank, so in particular $(\mathbf{U}'\mathbf{U})^{-1}$ exists. Let $\mathbf{V}$ denote the matrix in the second set of braces. Note that $\mathbf{V}$ has full row rank, so in particular $(\mathbf{VV}')^{-1}$ exists. Hence we can express this identity as

$$(\mathbf{U}'\mathbf{U})^{-1}\mathbf{AB}(\mathbf{VV}')^{-1} = \mathbf{\Gamma}_{11}\mathbf{\Gamma}_{21}'. \qquad (9.9.7)$$

For the proof then, suppose $\mathbf{AB} = \mathbf{0}$. Then, by (9.9.7), $\mathbf{\Gamma}_{11}\mathbf{\Gamma}_{21}' = \mathbf{0}$ and, hence, by (9.9.5), the random vectors $\mathbf{W}_1$ and $\mathbf{W}_2$ are independent. Therefore, by (9.9.2) and (9.9.4), Q_1 and Q_2 are independent.

Conversely, if Q_1 and Q_2 are independent, then

$$\{E[\exp\{t_1Q_1 + t_2Q_2\}]\}^{-2} = \{E[\exp\{t_1Q_1\}]\}^{-2}\{E[\exp\{t_2Q_2\}]\}^{-2}, \qquad (9.9.8)$$

for (t_1, t_2) in an open neighborhood of $(0, 0)$. Note that $t_1Q_1 + t_2Q_2$ is a quadratic form in $\mathbf{X}$ with symmetric matrix $t_1\mathbf{A} + t_2\mathbf{B}$. Recall that the matrix $\mathbf{\Gamma}_1$ is orthogonal and hence has determinant ± 1. Using this and Theorem 9.8.2, we can write the left side of (9.9.8) as

$$\begin{aligned} E^{-2}[\exp\{t_1Q_1 + t_2Q_2\}] &= |\mathbf{I}_n - 2t_1\mathbf{A} - 2t_2\mathbf{B}| \\ &= |\mathbf{\Gamma}_1'\mathbf{\Gamma}_1 - 2t_1\mathbf{\Gamma}_1'\mathbf{\Lambda}_1\mathbf{\Gamma}_1 - 2t_2\mathbf{\Gamma}_1'(\mathbf{\Gamma}_1\mathbf{B}\mathbf{\Gamma}_1')\mathbf{\Gamma}_1| \\ &= |\mathbf{I}_n - 2t_1\mathbf{\Lambda}_1 - 2t_2\mathbf{D}|, \qquad (9.9.9) \end{aligned}$$

where the matrix $\mathbf{D}$ is given by

$$\mathbf{D} = \boldsymbol{\Gamma}_1 \mathbf{B} \boldsymbol{\Gamma}_1' = \begin{bmatrix} \mathbf{D}_{11} & \mathbf{D}_{12} \\ \mathbf{D}_{21} & \mathbf{D}_{22} \end{bmatrix}, \qquad (9.9.10)$$

and $\mathbf{D}_{11}$ is $r \times r$. By (9.9.2), (9.9.3), and Theorem 9.8.2, the right side of (9.9.8) can be written as

$$\{E[\exp\{t_1 Q_1\}]\}^{-2} \{E[\exp\{t_2 Q_2\}]\}^{-2} = \left\{ \prod_{i=1}^{r} (1 - 2t_1 \lambda_i) \right\} |\mathbf{I}_n - 2t_2 \mathbf{D}|. \quad (9.9.11)$$

This leads to the identity

$$|\mathbf{I}_n - 2t_1 \boldsymbol{\Lambda}_1 - 2t_2 \mathbf{D}| = \left\{ \prod_{i=1}^{r} (1 - 2t_1 \lambda_i) \right\} |\mathbf{I}_n - 2t_2 \mathbf{D}|, \qquad (9.9.12)$$

for (t_1, t_2) in an open neighborhood of $(0,0)$.

The coefficient of $(-2t_1)^r$ on the right side of (9.9.12) is $\lambda_1 \cdots \lambda_r |\mathbf{I} - 2t_2 \mathbf{D}|$. It is not so easy to find the coefficient of $(-2t_1)^r$ in the left side of the equation (9.9.12). Conceive of expanding this determinant in terms of minors of order r formed from the first r columns. One term in this expansion is the product of the minor of order r in the upper left-hand corner, namely, $|\mathbf{I}_r - 2t_1 \boldsymbol{\Lambda}_{11} - 2t_2 \mathbf{D}_{11}|$, and the minor of order $n - r$ in the lower right-hand corner, namely, $|\mathbf{I}_{n-r} - 2t_2 \mathbf{D}_{22}|$. Moreover, this product is the only term in the expansion of the determinant that involves $(-2t_1)^r$. Thus the coefficient of $(-2t_1)^r$ in the left-hand member of Equation (9.9.12) is $\lambda_1 \cdots \lambda_r |\mathbf{I}_{n-r} - 2t_2 \mathbf{D}_{22}|$. If we equate these coefficients of $(-2t_1)^r$, we have

$$|\mathbf{I} - 2t_2 \mathbf{D}| = |\mathbf{I}_{n-r} - 2t_2 \mathbf{D}_{22}|, \qquad (9.9.13)$$

for t_2 in an open neighborhood of 0. Equation (9.9.13) implies that the nonzero eigenvalues of the matrices $\mathbf{D}$ and $\mathbf{D}_{22}$ are the same (see Exercise 9.9.8). Recall that the sum of the squares of the eigenvalues of a symmetric matrix is equal to the sum of the squares of the elements of that matrix (see Exercise 9.8.8). Thus the sum of the squares of the elements of matrix $\mathbf{D}$ is equal to the sum of the squares of the elements of $\mathbf{D}_{22}$. Since the elements of the matrix $\mathbf{D}$ are real, it follows that each of the elements of $\mathbf{D}_{11}, \mathbf{D}_{12}$, and $\mathbf{D}_{21}$ is zero. Hence we can write

$$\mathbf{0} = \boldsymbol{\Lambda}_1 \mathbf{D} = \boldsymbol{\Gamma}_1 \mathbf{A} \boldsymbol{\Gamma}_1' \boldsymbol{\Gamma}_1 \mathbf{B} \boldsymbol{\Gamma}_1'$$

because $\boldsymbol{\Gamma}_1$ is an orthogonal matrix, $\mathbf{AB} = \mathbf{0}$. ∎

Remark 9.9.2. Theorem 9.9.1 remains valid if the random sample is from a distribution which is $N(\mu, \sigma^2)$, whatever is the real value of μ. Moreover, Theorem 9.9.1 may be extended to quadratic forms in random variables that have a joint multivariate normal distribution with a positive definite covariance matrix $\boldsymbol{\Sigma}$. The necessary and sufficient condition for the independence of two such quadratic forms with symmetric matrices $\boldsymbol{A}$ and $\boldsymbol{B}$ then becomes $\boldsymbol{A} \boldsymbol{\Sigma} \boldsymbol{B} = \mathbf{0}$. In our Theorem 9.9.1, we have $\boldsymbol{\Sigma} = \sigma^2 \boldsymbol{I}$, so that $\boldsymbol{A} \boldsymbol{\Sigma} \boldsymbol{B} = \boldsymbol{A} \sigma^2 \boldsymbol{I} \boldsymbol{B} = \sigma^2 \boldsymbol{A} \boldsymbol{B} = \mathbf{0}$. ∎

The following theorem is from Hogg and Craig (1958).

Theorem 9.9.2 (Hogg and Craig). *Define the sum $Q = Q_1 + \cdots + Q_{k-1} + Q_k$, where $Q, Q_1, \ldots, Q_{k-1}, Q_k$ are $k+1$ random variables that are quadratic forms in the observations of a random sample of size n from a distribution which is $N(0, \sigma^2)$. Let Q/σ^2 be $\chi^2(r)$, let Q_i/σ^2 be $\chi^2(r_i)$, $i = 1, 2, \ldots, k-1$, and let Q_k be nonnegative. Then the random variables $Q_1, Q_2, \ldots, Q_k$ are independent and, hence, Q_k/σ^2 is $\chi^2(r_k = r - r_1 - \cdots - r_{k-1})$.*

Proof: Take first the case of $k = 2$ and let the real symmetric matrices Q, Q_1, and Q_2 be denoted, respectively, by $\boldsymbol{A}, \boldsymbol{A}_1, \boldsymbol{A}_2$. We are given that $Q = Q_1 + Q_2$ or, equivalently, that $\boldsymbol{A} = \boldsymbol{A}_1 + \boldsymbol{A}_2$. We are also given that Q/σ^2 is $\chi^2(r)$ and that Q_1/σ^2 is $\chi^2(r_1)$. In accordance with Theorem 9.8.4, we have $\boldsymbol{A}^2 = \boldsymbol{A}$ and $\boldsymbol{A}_1^2 = \boldsymbol{A}$. Since $Q_2 \geq 0$, each of the matrices $\boldsymbol{A}, \boldsymbol{A}_1$, and $\boldsymbol{A}_2$ is positive semidefinite. Because $\boldsymbol{A}^2 = \boldsymbol{A}$, we can find an orthogonal matrix $\boldsymbol{\Gamma}$ such that

$$\boldsymbol{\Gamma}'\boldsymbol{A}\boldsymbol{\Gamma} = \begin{bmatrix} \boldsymbol{I}_r & \boldsymbol{O} \\ \boldsymbol{O} & \boldsymbol{O} \end{bmatrix}.$$

If we multiply both members of $\boldsymbol{A} = \boldsymbol{A}_1 + \boldsymbol{A}_2$ on the left by $\boldsymbol{\Gamma}'$ and on the right by $\boldsymbol{\Gamma}$, we have

$$\begin{bmatrix} \boldsymbol{I}_r & \boldsymbol{0} \\ \boldsymbol{0} & \boldsymbol{0} \end{bmatrix} = \boldsymbol{\Gamma}'\boldsymbol{A}_1\boldsymbol{\Gamma} + \boldsymbol{\Gamma}'\boldsymbol{A}_2\boldsymbol{\Gamma}.$$

Now each of $\boldsymbol{A}_1$ and $\boldsymbol{A}_2$, and hence each of $\boldsymbol{\Gamma}'\boldsymbol{A}_1\boldsymbol{\Gamma}$ and $\boldsymbol{\Gamma}'\boldsymbol{A}_2\boldsymbol{\Gamma}$ is positive semidefinite. Recall that if a real symmetric matrix is positive semidefinite, each element on the principal diagonal is positive or zero. Moreover, if an element on the principal diagonal is zero, then all elements in that row and all elements in that column are zero. Thus $\boldsymbol{\Gamma}'\boldsymbol{A}\boldsymbol{\Gamma} = \boldsymbol{\Gamma}'\boldsymbol{A}_1\boldsymbol{\Gamma} + \boldsymbol{\Gamma}'\boldsymbol{A}_2\boldsymbol{\Gamma}$ can be written as

$$\begin{bmatrix} \boldsymbol{I}_r & \boldsymbol{0} \\ \boldsymbol{0} & \boldsymbol{0} \end{bmatrix} = \begin{bmatrix} \boldsymbol{G}_r & \boldsymbol{0} \\ \boldsymbol{0} & \boldsymbol{0} \end{bmatrix} + \begin{bmatrix} \boldsymbol{H}_r & \boldsymbol{0} \\ \boldsymbol{0} & \boldsymbol{0} \end{bmatrix}. \tag{9.9.14}$$

Since $\boldsymbol{A}_1^2 = \boldsymbol{A}_1$, we have

$$(\boldsymbol{\Gamma}'\boldsymbol{A}_1\boldsymbol{\Gamma})^2 = \boldsymbol{\Gamma}'\boldsymbol{A}_1\boldsymbol{\Gamma} = \begin{bmatrix} \boldsymbol{G}_r & \boldsymbol{0} \\ \boldsymbol{0} & \boldsymbol{0} \end{bmatrix}.$$

If we multiply both members of Equation (9.9.14) on the left by the matrix $\boldsymbol{\Gamma}'\boldsymbol{A}_1\boldsymbol{\Gamma}$, we see that

$$\begin{bmatrix} \boldsymbol{G}_r & \boldsymbol{0} \\ \boldsymbol{0} & \boldsymbol{0} \end{bmatrix} = \begin{bmatrix} \boldsymbol{G}_r & \boldsymbol{0} \\ \boldsymbol{0} & \boldsymbol{0} \end{bmatrix} + \begin{bmatrix} \boldsymbol{G}_r\boldsymbol{H}_r & \boldsymbol{0} \\ \boldsymbol{0} & \boldsymbol{0} \end{bmatrix}$$

or, equivalently, $\boldsymbol{\Gamma}'\boldsymbol{A}_1\boldsymbol{\Gamma} = \boldsymbol{\Gamma}'\boldsymbol{A}_1\boldsymbol{\Gamma} + (\boldsymbol{\Gamma}'\boldsymbol{A}_1\boldsymbol{\Gamma})(\boldsymbol{\Gamma}'\boldsymbol{A}_2\boldsymbol{\Gamma})$. Thus $(\boldsymbol{\Gamma}'\boldsymbol{A}_1\boldsymbol{\Gamma}) \times (\boldsymbol{\Gamma}'\boldsymbol{A}_2\boldsymbol{\Gamma}) = \boldsymbol{0}$ and $\boldsymbol{A}_1\boldsymbol{A}_2 = \boldsymbol{0}$. In accordance with Theorem 9.9.1, Q_1 and Q_2 are independent. This independence immediately implies that Q_2/σ^2 is $\chi^2(r_2 = r - r_1)$. This completes the proof when $k = 2$. For $k > 2$, the proof may be made by induction. We shall merely indicate how this can be done by using $k = 3$. Take $\boldsymbol{A} = \boldsymbol{A}_1 + \boldsymbol{A}_2 + \boldsymbol{A}_3$, where $\boldsymbol{A}^2 = \boldsymbol{A}$, $\boldsymbol{A}_1^2 = \boldsymbol{A}_1$, $\boldsymbol{A}_2^2 = \boldsymbol{A}_2$, and $\boldsymbol{A}_3$ is positive semidefinite. Write

$A = A_1 + (A_2 + A_3) = A_1 + B_1$, say. Now $A^2 = A$, $A_1^2 = A_1$, and B_1 is positive semidefinite. In accordance with the case of $k = 2$, we have $A_1 B_1 = 0$, so that $B_1^2 = B_1$. With $B_1 = A_2 + A_3$, where $B_1^2 = B_1$, $A_2^2 = A_2$, it follows from the case of $k = 2$ that $A_2 A_3 = 0$ and $A_3^2 = A_3$. If we regroup by writing $A = A_2 + (A_1 + A_3)$, we obtain $A_1 A_3 = 0$, and so on. ∎

Remark 9.9.3. In our statement of Theorem 9.9.2, we took $X_1, X_2, \ldots, X_n$ to be observations of a random sample from a distribution which is $N(0, \sigma^2)$. We did this because our proof of Theorem 9.9.1 was restricted to that case. In fact, if $Q', Q_1', \ldots, Q_k'$ are quadratic forms in any normal variables (including multivariate normal variables), if $Q' = Q_1' + \cdots + Q_k'$, if $Q', Q_1', \ldots, Q_{k-1}'$ are central or noncentral chi-square, and if Q_k' is nonnegative, then $Q_1', \ldots, Q_k'$ are independent and Q_k' is either central or noncentral chi-square. ∎

This section concludes with a proof of a frequently quoted theorem due to Cochran.

Theorem 9.9.3 (Cochran). *Let $X_1, X_2, \ldots, X_n$ denote a random sample from a distribution which is $N(0, \sigma^2)$. Let the sum of the squares of these observations be written in the form*

$$\sum_1^n X_i^2 = Q_1 + Q_2 + \cdots + Q_k,$$

where Q_j is a quadratic form in $X_1, X_2, \ldots, X_n$, with matrix A_j which has rank r_j, $j = 1, 2, \ldots, k$. The random variables $Q_1, Q_2, \ldots, Q_k$ are independent and Q_j/σ^2 is $\chi^2(r_j)$, $j = 1, 2, \ldots, k$, if and only if $\sum_1^k r_j = n$.

Proof. First assume the two conditions $\sum_1^k r_j = n$ and $\sum_1^n X_i^2 = \sum_1^k Q_j$ to be satisfied. The latter equation implies that $I = A_1 + A_2 + \cdots + A_k$. Let $B_i = I - A_i$; that is, B_i is the sum of the matrices $A_1, \ldots, A_k$ exclusive of A_i. Let R_i denote the rank of B_i. Since the rank of the sum of several matrices is less than or equal to the sum of the ranks, we have $R_i \le \sum_1^k r_j - r_i = n - r_i$. However, $I = A_i + B_i$, so that $n \le r_i + R_i$ and $n - r_i \le R_i$. Hence $R_i = n - r_i$. The eigenvalues of B_i are the roots of the equation $|B_i - \lambda I| = 0$. Since $B_i = I - A_i$, this equation can be written as $|I - A_i - \lambda I| = 0$. Thus we have $|A_i - (1 - \lambda)I| = 0$. But each root of the last equation is 1 minus an eigenvalue of A_i. Since B_i has exactly $n - R_i = r_i$ eigenvalues that are zero, then A_i has exactly r_i eigenvalues that are equal to 1. However, r_i is the rank of A_i. Thus each of the r_i nonzero eigenvalues of A_i is 1. That is, $A_i^2 = A_i$ and thus $Q_i/\sigma^2(r_i)$, $i = 1, 2, \ldots, k$. In accordance with Theorem 9.9.2, the random variables $Q_1, Q_2, \ldots, Q_k$ are independent.

To complete the proof of Theorem 9.9.3, take

$$\sum_1^n X_i^2 = Q_1 + Q_2 + \cdots + Q_k,$$

let $Q_1, Q_2, \ldots, Q_k$ be independent, and let Q_j/σ^2 be $\chi^2(r_j)$, $j = 1, 2, \ldots, k$. Then $\sum_1^k Q_j/\sigma^2$ is $\chi^2(\sum_1^k r_j)$. But $\sum_1^k Q_j/\sigma^2 = \sum_1^n X_i^2/\sigma^2$ is $\chi^2(n)$. Thus $\sum_1^k r_j = n$ and the proof is complete. ∎

EXERCISES

9.9.1. Let X_1, X_2, X_3 be a random sample from the normal distribution $N(0, \sigma^2)$. Are the quadratic forms $X_1^2 + 3X_1X_2 + X_2^2 + X_1X_3 + X_3^2$ and $X_1^2 - 2X_1X_2 + \frac{2}{3}X_2^2 - 2X_1X_2 - X_3^2$ independent or dependent?

9.9.2. Let $X_1, X_2, \ldots, X_n$ denote a random sample of size n from a distribution which is $N(0, \sigma^2)$. Prove that $\sum_1^n X_i^2$ and every quadratic form, which is nonidentically zero in $X_1, X_2, \ldots, X_n$, are dependent.

9.9.3. Let X_1, X_2, X_3, X_4 denote a random sample of size 4 from a distribution which is $N(0, \sigma^2)$. Let $Y = \sum_1^4 a_i X_i$, where a_1, a_2, a_3, and a_4 are real constants. If Y^2 and $Q = X_1X_2 - X_3X_4$ are independent, determine a_1, a_2, a_3, and a_4.

9.9.4. Let A be the real symmetric matrix of a quadratic form Q in the observations of a random sample of size n from a distribution which is $N(0, \sigma^2)$. Given that Q and the mean $\overline{X}$ of the sample are independent, what can be said of the elements of each row (column) of A?

Hint: Are Q and $\overline{X}^2$ independent?

9.9.5. Let $A_1, A_2, \ldots, A_k$ be the matrices of $k > 2$ quadratic forms $Q_1, Q_2, \ldots, Q_k$ in the observations of a random sample of size n from a distribution which is $N(0, \sigma^2)$. Prove that the pairwise independence of these forms implies that they are mutually independent.

Hint: Show that $A_iA_j = 0$, $i \neq j$, permits $E[\exp(t_1Q_1 + t_2Q_2 + \cdots + t_kQ_k)]$ to be written as a product of the mgfs of $Q_1, Q_2, \ldots, Q_k$.

9.9.6. Let $X' = [X_1, X_2, \ldots, X_n]$, where $X_1, X_2, \ldots, X_n$ are observations of a random sample from a distribution which is $N(0, \sigma^2)$. Let $b' = [b_1, b_2, \ldots, b_n]$ be a real nonzero vector, and let A be a real symmetric matrix of order n. Prove that the linear form $b'X$ and the quadratic form $X'AX$ are independent if and only if $b'A = 0$. Use this fact to prove that $b'X$ and $X'AX$ are independent if and only if the two quadratic forms $(b'X)^2 = X'bb'X$ and $X'AX$ are independent.

9.9.7. Let Q_1 and Q_2 be two nonnegative quadratic forms in the observations of a random sample from a distribution which is $N(0, \sigma^2)$. Show that another quadratic form Q is independent of $Q_1 + Q_2$ if and only if Q is independent of each of Q_1 and Q_2.

Hint: Consider the orthogonal transformation that diagonalizes the matrix of $Q_1 + Q_2$. After this transformation, what are the forms of the matrices Q, Q_1 and Q_2 if Q and $Q_1 + Q_2$ are independent?

9.9.8. Prove that Equation (9.9.13) of this section implies that the nonzero eigenvalues of the matrices D and D_{22} are the same.

Hint: Let $\lambda = 1/(2t_2)$, $t_2 \neq 0$, and show that Equation (9.9.13) is equivalent to $|D - \lambda I| = (-\lambda)^r |D_{22} - \lambda I_{n-r}|$.

9.9.9. Here Q_1 and Q_2 are quadratic forms in observations of a random sample from $N(0, 1)$. If Q_1 and Q_2 are independent and if $Q_1 + Q_2$ has a chi-square distribution, prove that Q_1 and Q_2 are chi-square variables.

9.9.10. Often in regression the mean of the random variable Y is a linear function of p-values $x_1, x_2, \ldots, x_p$, say $\beta_1 x_1 + \beta_2 x_2 + \cdots + \beta_p x_p$, where $\boldsymbol{\beta}' = (\beta_1, \beta_2, \ldots, \beta_p)$ are the *regression coefficients*. Suppose that n values, $\boldsymbol{Y}' = (Y_1, Y_2, \ldots, Y_n)$, are observed for the x-values in $\boldsymbol{X} = [x_{ij}]$, where $\boldsymbol{X}$ is an $n \times p$ *design matrix* and its ith row is associated with Y_i, $i = 1, 2, \ldots, n$. Assume that $\boldsymbol{Y}$ is multivariate normal with mean $\boldsymbol{X}\boldsymbol{\beta}$ and variance–covariance matrix $\sigma^2 \boldsymbol{I}$, where $\boldsymbol{I}$ is the $n \times n$ identity matrix.

(a) Note that $Y_1, Y_2, \ldots, Y_n$ are independent. Why?

(b) Since $\boldsymbol{Y}$ should approximately equal its mean $\boldsymbol{X}\boldsymbol{\beta}$, we estimate $\boldsymbol{\beta}$ by solving the *normal equations* $\boldsymbol{X}'\boldsymbol{Y} = \boldsymbol{X}'\boldsymbol{X}\boldsymbol{\beta}$ for $\boldsymbol{\beta}$. Assuming that $\boldsymbol{X}'\boldsymbol{X}$ is non-singular, solve the equations to get $\hat{\boldsymbol{\beta}} = (\boldsymbol{X}'\boldsymbol{X})^{-1}\boldsymbol{X}'\boldsymbol{Y}$. Show that $\hat{\boldsymbol{\beta}}$ has a multivariate normal distribution with mean $\boldsymbol{\beta}$ and variance–covariance matrix $\sigma^2(\boldsymbol{X}'\boldsymbol{X})^{-1}$.

(c) Show that

$$(\boldsymbol{Y} - \boldsymbol{X}\boldsymbol{\beta})'(\boldsymbol{Y} - \boldsymbol{X}\boldsymbol{\beta}) = (\hat{\boldsymbol{\beta}} - \boldsymbol{\beta})'(\boldsymbol{X}'\boldsymbol{X})(\hat{\boldsymbol{\beta}} - \boldsymbol{\beta}) + (\boldsymbol{Y} - \boldsymbol{X}\hat{\boldsymbol{\beta}})'(\boldsymbol{Y} - \boldsymbol{X}\hat{\boldsymbol{\beta}}),$$

say $Q = Q_1 + Q_2$ for convenience.

(d) Show that Q_1/σ^2 is $\chi^2(p)$.

(e) Show that Q_1 and Q_2 are independent.

(f) Argue that Q_2/σ^2 is $\chi^2(n - p)$.

(g) Find c so that cQ_1/Q_2 has an F-distribution.

(h) The fact that a value d can be found so that $P(cQ_1/Q_2 \le d) = 1 - \alpha$ could be used to find a $100(1 - \alpha)\%$ confidence ellipsoid for $\boldsymbol{\beta}$. Explain.

9.9.11. Say that G.P.A. (Y) is thought to be a linear function of a "coded" high school rank (x_2) and a "coded" American College Testing score (x_3), namely, $\beta_1 + \beta_2 x_2 + \beta_3 x_3$. Note that all x_1 values equal 1. We observe the following five points:

x_1	x_2	x_3	Y
1	1	2	3
1	4	3	6
1	2	2	4
1	4	2	4
1	3	2	4

(a) Compute $\boldsymbol{X}'\boldsymbol{X}$ and $\hat{\boldsymbol{\beta}} = (\boldsymbol{X}'\boldsymbol{X})^{-1}\boldsymbol{X}'\boldsymbol{Y}$.

(b) Compute a 95% confidence ellipsoid for $\boldsymbol{\beta}' = (\beta_1, \beta_2, \beta_3)$. See part (h) of Exercise 9.9.10.

9.9.12. Assume that $\boldsymbol{X}$ is an $n \times p$ matrix. Then the kernel of $\boldsymbol{X}$ is defined to be the space $\ker(\boldsymbol{X}) = \{\mathbf{b} : \boldsymbol{X}\mathbf{b} = \mathbf{0}\}$.

(a) Show that $\ker(\mathbf{X})$ is a subspace of R^p.

(b) The dimension of $\ker(\mathbf{X})$ is called the **nullity** of $\mathbf{X}$ and is denoted by $\nu(\mathbf{X})$. Let $\rho(\mathbf{X})$ denote the rank of $\mathbf{X}$. A fundamental theorem of linear algebra says that $\rho(\mathbf{X}) + \nu(\mathbf{X}) = p$. Use this to show that if $\mathbf{X}$ has full column rank, then $\ker(\mathbf{X}) = \{\mathbf{0}\}$.

9.9.13. Suppose $\mathbf{X}$ is an $n \times p$ matrix with rank p.

(a) Show that $\ker(\mathbf{X}'\mathbf{X}) = \ker(\mathbf{X})$.

(b) Use part (a) and the last exercise to show that if $\mathbf{X}$ has full column rank, then $\mathbf{X}'\mathbf{X}$ is nonsingular.

Chapter 10

Nonparametric and Robust Statistics

10.1 Location Models

In this chapter, we present some nonparametric procedures for the simple location problems. As we shall show, the test procedures associated with these methods are distribution-free under null hypotheses. We also obtain point estimators and confidence intervals associated with these tests. The distributions of the estimators are not distribution-free; hence, we use the term **rank-based** to refer collectively to these procedures. The asymptotic relative efficiencies of these procedures are easily obtained, thus facilitating comparisons among them and procedures that we have discussed in earlier chapters. We also obtain estimators that are asymptotically efficient; that is, they achieve asymptotically the Rao–Cramér bound.

Our purpose is not a rigorous development of these concepts, and at times we simply sketch the theory. A rigorous treatment can be found in several advanced texts, such as Randles and Wolfe (1979) or Hettmansperger and McKean (2011).

In this and the following section, we consider the one-sample problem. For the most part, we consider continuous random variables X with cdf and pdf $F_X(x)$ and $f_X(x)$, respectively. In this and the succeeding chapters, we want to identify classes of parameters. Think of a parameter as a function of the cdf (or pdf) of a given random variable. For example, consider the mean μ of X. We can write it as $\mu_X = T(F_X)$ if T is defined as

$$T(F_X) = \int_{-\infty}^{\infty} x f_X(x)\, dx.$$

As another example, recall that the median of a random variable X is a parameter ξ such that $F_X(\xi) = 1/2$; i.e., $\xi = F_X^{-1}(1/2)$. Hence, in this notation, we say that the parameter ξ is defined by the function $T(F_X) = F_X^{-1}(1/2)$. Note that these Ts are functions of the cdfs (or pdfs). We shall call them **functionals**.

Functionals induce nonparametric estimators naturally. Let $X_1, X_2, \ldots, X_n$ denote a random sample from some distribution with cdf $F(x)$ and let $T(F)$ be a functional. Recall that the empirical distribution function of the sample is given by

$$\widehat{F}_n(x) = n^{-1}[\#\{X_i \leq x\}], \quad -\infty < x < \infty. \tag{10.1.1}$$

Because $\widehat{F}_n(x)$ is a cdf, $T(\widehat{F}_n)$ is well defined. Furthermore, $T(\widehat{F}_n)$ depends only on the sample; hence, it is a statistic. We call $T(\widehat{F}_n)$ the **induced estimator** of $T(F)$. For example, if $T(F)$ is the mean of the distribution, then it is easy to see that $T(\widehat{F}_n) = \overline{X}$; see Exercise 10.1.3. Likewise, if $T(F) = F^{-1}(1/2)$ is the median of the distribution, then $T(\widehat{F}_n) = Q_2$, the sample median.

We begin with the definition of a location functional.

Definition 10.1.1. *Let X be a continuous random variable with cdf $F_X(x)$ and pdf $f_X(x)$. We say that $T(F_X)$ is a **location functional** if it satisfies*

$$\text{If } Y = X + a, \text{ then } T(F_Y) = T(F_X) + a, \text{ for all } a \in R, \tag{10.1.2}$$

$$\text{If } Y = aX; \text{ then } T(F_Y) = aT(F_X), \text{ for all } a \neq 0. \tag{10.1.3}$$

For example, suppose T is the mean functional; i.e., $T(F_X) = E(X)$. Let $Y = X + a$; then $E(Y) = E(X + a) = E(X) + a$. Secondly, if $Y = aX$, then $E(Y) = aE(X)$. Hence the mean is a location functional. The next example shows that the median is a location functional.

Example 10.1.1. Let $F(x)$ be the cdf of X and let $T(F_X) = F_X^{-1}(1/2)$ be the median functional of X. Note that another way to state this is $F_X(T(F_X)) = 1/2$. Let $Y = X + a$. It then follows that the cdf of Y is $F_Y(y) = F_X(y - a)$. The following identity shows that $T(F_Y) = T(F_X) + a$:

$$F_Y(T(F_X) + a) = F_X(T(F_X) + a - a) = F_X(T(F_X)) = 1/2.$$

Next, suppose $Y = aX$. If $a > 0$, then $F_Y(y) = F_X(y/a)$ and, hence,

$$F_Y(aT(F_X)) = F_X(aT(F_X)/a) = F_X(T(F_X)) = 1/2.$$

Thus $T(F_Y) = aT(F_X)$ when $a > 0$. On the other hand, if $a < 0$, then $F_Y(y) = 1 - F_X(y/a)$. Hence

$$F_Y(aT(F_X)) = 1 - F_X(aT(F_X)/a) = 1 - F_X(T(F_X)) = 1 - \frac{1}{2} = \frac{1}{2}.$$

Therefore, (10.1.3) holds for all $a \neq 0$. Thus the median is a location parameter. Recall that the median is a percentile, namely, the 50th percentile of a distribution. As Exercise 10.1.1 shows, the median is the only percentile which is a location functional. ∎

We often continue to use parameter notation to denote functionals. For example, $\theta_X = T(F_X)$.

In Chapters 4 and 6, we wrote the location model for specified pdfs. In this chapter, we write it for a general pdf in terms of a specified location functional. Let X be a random variable with cdf $F_X(x)$ and pdf $f_X(x)$. Let $\theta_X = T(F_X)$ be a location functional. Define the random variable ε to be $\varepsilon = X - T(F_X)$. Then by (10.1.2), $T(F_\varepsilon) = 0$; i.e., ε has location 0, according to T. Further, the pdf of X can be written as $f_X(x) = f(x - T(F_X))$, where $f(x)$ is the pdf of ε.

Definition 10.1.2 (Location Model). *Let $\theta_X = T(F_X)$ be a location functional. We say that the observations $X_1, X_2, \ldots, X_n$ follow a **location model** with functional $\theta_X = T(F_X)$ if*

$$X_i = \theta_X + \varepsilon_i, \qquad (10.1.4)$$

where $\varepsilon_1, \varepsilon_2, \ldots, \varepsilon_n$ are iid random variables with pdf $f(x)$ and $T(F_\varepsilon) = 0$. Hence, from the above discussion, $X_1, X_2, \ldots, X_n$ are iid with pdf $f_X(x) = f(x - T(F_X))$.

Example 10.1.2. Let ε be a random variable with cdf $F(x)$, such that $F(0) = 1/2$. Assume that $\varepsilon_1, \varepsilon_2, \ldots, \varepsilon_n$ are iid with cdf $F(x)$. Let $\theta \in R$ and define

$$X_i = \theta + \varepsilon_i, \quad i = 1, 2, \ldots, n.$$

Then $X_1, X_2, \ldots, X_n$ follow the location model with the locational functional θ, which is the median of X_i. ∎

Note that the location model very much depends on the functional. It forces one to state clearly which location functional is being used in order to write the model statement. For the class of symmetric densities, though, all location functionals are the same.

Theorem 10.1.1. *Let X be a random variable with cdf $F_X(x)$ and pdf $f_X(x)$ such that the distribution of X is symmetric about a. Let $T(F_X)$ be any location functional. Then $T(F_X) = a$.*

Proof: By (10.1.2), we have

$$T(F_{X-a}) = T(F_X) - a. \qquad (10.1.5)$$

Since the distribution of X is symmetric about a, it is easy to show that $X - a$ and $-(X - a)$ have the same distribution; see Exercise 10.1.2. Hence, using (10.1.2) and (10.1.3), we have

$$T(F_{X-a}) = T(F_{-(X-a)}) = -(T(F_X) - a) = -T(F_X) + a. \qquad (10.1.6)$$

Putting (10.1.5) and (10.1.6) together gives the result. ∎

The assumption of symmetry is very appealing, because the concept of "center" is unique when it is true.

EXERCISES

10.1.1. Let X be a continuous random variable with cdf $F(x)$. For $0 < p < 1$, let ξ_p be the pth quantile; i.e., $F(\xi_p) = p$. If $p \neq 1/2$, show that while property (10.1.2) holds, property (10.1.3) does not. Thus ξ_p is not a location parameter.

10.1.2. Let X be a continuous random variable with pdf $f(x)$. Suppose $f(x)$ is symmetric about a; i.e., $f(x - a) = f(-(x - a))$. Show that the random variables $X - a$ and $-(X - a)$ have the same pdf.

10.1.3. Let $\widehat{F}_n(x)$ denote the empirical cdf of the sample $X_1, X_2, \ldots, X_n$. The distribution of $\widehat{F}_n(x)$ puts mass $1/n$ at each sample item X_i. Show that its mean is $\overline{X}$. If $T(F) = F^{-1}(1/2)$ is the median, show that $T(\widehat{F}_n) = Q_2$, the sample median.

10.1.4. Let X be a random variable with cdf $F(x)$ and let $T(F)$ be a functional. We say that $T(F)$ is a **scale functional** if it satisfies the three properties

$$
\begin{aligned}
(i) & \quad T(F_{aX}) & = & \quad aT(F_X), & \text{for } a > 0 \\
(ii) & \quad T(F_{X+b}) & = & \quad T(F_X), & \text{for all } b \\
(iii) & \quad T(F_{-X}) & = & \quad T(F_X).
\end{aligned}
$$

Show that the following functionals are scale functionals.

(a) The standard deviation, $T(F_X) = (\text{Var}(X))^{1/2}$.

(b) The interquartile range, $T(F_X) = F_X^{-1}(3/4) - F_X^{-1}(1/4)$.

10.2 Sample Median and the Sign Test

In this section, we consider inference for the median of a distribution using the sample median. Fundamental to this discussion is the sign test statistic, which we present first.

Let $X_1, X_2, \ldots, X_n$ be a random sample which follows the location model

$$ X_i = \theta + \varepsilon_i, \tag{10.2.1} $$

where $\varepsilon_1, \varepsilon_2, \ldots, \varepsilon_n$ are iid with cdf $F(x)$, pdf $f(x)$, and median 0. Note that in terms of Section 10.1, the location functional is the median and, hence, θ is the median of X_i. We begin with a test for the one-sided hypotheses

$$ H_0 : \theta = \theta_0 \text{ versus } H_1 : \theta > \theta_0. \tag{10.2.2} $$

Consider the statistic

$$ S(\theta_0) = \#\{X_i > \theta_0\}, \tag{10.2.3} $$

which is called the **sign statistic** because it counts the number of positive signs in the differences $X_i - \theta_0$, $i = 1, 2, \ldots, n$. If we define $I(x > a)$ to be 1 or 0 depending on whether $x > a$ or $x \leq a$, then we can express $S(\theta_0)$ as

$$ S(\theta_0) = \sum_{i=1}^{n} I(X_i > \theta_0). \tag{10.2.4} $$

Note that if H_0 is true, then we expect about half of the observations to exceed θ_0, while if H_1 is true, we expect more than half of the observations to exceed θ_0. Consider then the test of the hypotheses (10.2.2) given by

$$\text{Reject } H_0 \text{ in favor of } H_1 \text{ if } S(\theta_0) \geq c. \qquad (10.2.5)$$

Under the null hypothesis, the random variables $I(X_i > \theta_0)$ are iid with a Bernoulli $b(1, 1/2)$ distribution. Hence the null distribution of $S(\theta_0)$ is $b(n, 1/2)$ with mean $n/2$ and variance $n/4$. Note that under H_0, the sign test does not depend on the distribution of X_i. We call such a test a **distribution free** test.

For a level α test, select c to be c_α, where c_α is the upper α critical point of a binomial $b(n, 1/2)$ distribution. Then $P_{H_0}(S(\theta_0) \geq c_\alpha) = \alpha$. The test statistic, though, has a discrete distribution, so for an exact test there are only a finite number of levels α available. The values of c_α can be found in tables; see, for instance, Hollander and Wolfe (1999). If the computer package R is available, then these critical values are easily obtained. For instance, the command pbinom(0:15,15,.5) returns the cdf of a binomial distribution with $n = 15$ and $p = 0.5$, from which all possible levels can be seen.

For a given data set, the p-value associated with the sign test is given by $\widehat{p} = P_{H_0}(S(\theta_0) \geq s)$, where s is the realized value of $S(\theta_0)$ based on the sample. Tables are available to find these p-values. If the reader has access to the R statistical package, then the command 1 - pbinom(s-1,n,.5) computes $\widehat{p} = P_{H_0}(S(\theta_0) \geq s)$.

It is convenient at times to use a large sample test based on the asymptotic distribution of the test statistic. By the Central Limit Theorem, under H_0 the standardized statistic $[S(\theta_0) - (n/2)]/\sqrt{n}/2$ is asymptotically normal, $N(0,1)$. Hence the large sample test rejects H_0 if

$$\frac{S(\theta_0) - (n/2)}{\sqrt{n}/2} \geq z_\alpha; \qquad (10.2.6)$$

see Exercise 10.2.2.

We briefly touch on the two-sided hypotheses given by

$$H_0 : \theta = \theta_0 \text{ versus } H_1 : \theta \neq \theta_0. \qquad (10.2.7)$$

The following symmetric decision rule seems appropriate:

$$\text{Reject } H_0 \text{ in favor of } H_1 \text{ if } S(\theta_0) \leq c_1 \text{ or if } S(\theta_0) \geq n - c_1. \qquad (10.2.8)$$

For a level α test, c_1 would be chosen such that $\alpha/2 = P_{H_0}(S(\theta_0) \leq c_1)$. The critical point could be found by a statistics package or tables. Recall that the p-value is given by $\widehat{p} = 2\min\{P_{H_0}(S(\theta_0) \leq s), P_{H_0}(S(\theta_0) \geq s)\}$, where s is the realized value of $S(\theta_0)$ based on the sample.

Example 10.2.1 (Shoshoni Rectangles). A golden rectangle is a rectangle in which the ratio of the width (w) to the length (l) is the golden ratio, which is approximately 0.618. It can be characterized in various ways. For example, $w/l = l/(w + l)$ characterizes the golden rectangle. It is considered to be an aesthetic standard in

Western civilization and appears in art and architecture going back to the ancient Greeks. It now appears in such items as credit and business cards. In a cultural anthropology study, DuBois (1960) reports on a study of the Shoshoni beaded baskets. These baskets contain beaded rectangles, and the question was whether the Shoshonis use the same aesthetic standard as the West. Let X denote the ratio of the width to the length of a Shoshoni beaded basket. Let θ be the median of X. The hypotheses of interest are

$$H_0 : \theta = 0.618 \text{ versus } H_1 : \theta \neq 0.618.$$

These are two-sided hypotheses. It follows from the above discussion that the sign test rejects H_0 in favor of H_1 if $S(0.618) \leq c$ or $S(0.618) \geq n - c$.

A sample of 20 width to length (ordered) ratios from Shoshoni baskets resulted in the data

Width-to-Length Ratios of Rectangles

0.553	0.570	0.576	0.601	0.606	0.606	0.609	0.611	0.615	0.628
0.654	0.662	0.668	0.670	0.672	0.690	0.693	0.749	0.844	0.933

For these data, $S(0.618) = 11$, with $2P(\mathrm{b}(20, 0.5) \geq 11) = 0.8238$ as the p-value. Thus there is no evidence to reject H_0 based on these data.

A boxplot and a normal $q-q$ plot of the data are given in Figure 10.2.1. Notice that the data contain two, possibly three, potential outliers. The data do not appear to be drawn from a normal distribution. ■

We next obtain several useful results concerning the power function of the sign test for the hypotheses (10.2.2). Because we can always subtract θ_0 from each X_i, we can assume without loss of generality that $\theta_0 = 0$. The following function proves useful here and in the associated estimation and confidence intervals described below. Define

$$S(\theta) = \#\{X_i > \theta\}. \tag{10.2.9}$$

The sign test statistic is given by $S(\theta_0)$. We can easily describe the function $S(\theta)$. First, note that we can write it in terms of the order statistics $Y_1 < \cdots < Y_n$ of $X_1, \ldots, X_n$ because $\#\{Y_i > \theta\} = \#\{X_i > \theta\}$. Now if $\theta < Y_1$, then all the Y_is are larger than θ and, hence $S(\theta) = n$. Next, if $Y_1 \leq \theta < Y_2$ then $S(\theta) = n - 1$. Continuing this way, we see that $S(\theta)$ is a decreasing step function of θ, which steps down one unit at each order statistic Y_i, attaining its maximum and minimum values n and 0 at Y_1 and Y_n, respectively. Figure 10.2.2 depicts this function. We need the following translation property.

Lemma 10.2.1. *For every k,*

$$P_\theta[S(0) \geq k] = P_0[S(-\theta) \geq k]. \tag{10.2.10}$$

Proof: Note that the left side of equation (10.2.10) concerns the probability of the event $\#\{X_i > 0\}$, where X_i has median θ. The right side concerns the probability of the event $\#\{(X_i + \theta) > 0\}$, where the random variable $X_i + \theta$ has median θ

Figure 10.2.1: Boxplot (Panel A) and normal $q-q$ plot (Panel B) of the Shoshoni data.

(because under $\theta = 0$, X_i has median 0). Hence the left and right sides give the same probability. ∎

Based on this lemma, it is easy to show that the power function of the sign test is monotone for one-sided tests.

Theorem 10.2.1. *Suppose Model (10.2.1) is true. Let $\gamma(\theta)$ be the power function of the sign test of level α for the one-sided hypotheses (10.2.2). Then $\gamma(\theta)$ is a nondecreasing function of θ.*

Proof: Let c_α denote the $b(n, 1/2)$ upper critical value as defined after expression (10.2.8). Without loss of generality, assume that $\theta_0 = 0$. The power function of the sign test is

$$\gamma(\theta) = P_\theta[S(0) \geq c_\alpha], \quad \text{for } -\infty < \theta < \infty.$$

Figure 10.2.2: The sketch shows the graph of the decreasing step function $S(\theta)$. The function drops one unit at each order statistic Y_i.

Suppose $\theta_1 < \theta_2$. Then $-\theta_1 > -\theta_2$ and hence, since $S(\theta)$ is nonincreasing, $S(-\theta_1) \leq S(-\theta_2)$. This and Lemma 10.2.1 yield the desired result; i.e.,

$$\begin{aligned}
\gamma(\theta_1) &= P_{\theta_1}[S(0) \geq c_\alpha] \\
&= P_0[S(-\theta_1) \geq c_\alpha] \\
&\leq P_0[S(-\theta_2) \geq c_\alpha] \\
&= P_{\theta_2}[S(0) \geq c_\alpha] \\
&= \gamma(\theta_2). \quad \blacksquare
\end{aligned}$$

This is a very desirable property for any test. Because the monotonicity of the power function of the sign test holds for all θ, $-\infty < \theta < \infty$, we can extend the simple null hypothesis of (10.2.2) to the composite null hypothesis

$$H_0 : \theta \leq \theta_0 \text{ versus } H_1 : \theta > \theta_0. \tag{10.2.11}$$

Recall from Definition 4.5.4 of Chapter 4 that the size of the test for a composite null hypothesis is given by $\max_{\theta \leq \theta_0} \gamma(\theta)$. Because $\gamma(\theta)$ is nondecreasing, the size of the sign test is α for this extended null hypothesis. As a second result, it follows immediately that the sign test is an unbiased test; see Section 8.3. As Exercise 10.2.7 shows, the power function of the sign test for the other one-sided alternative, $H_1 : \theta < \theta_0$, is nonincreasing.

Under an alternative, say $\theta = \theta_1$, the test statistic $S(\theta_0)$ has the binomial distribution $b(n, p_1)$, where p_1 is given by

$$p_1 = P_{\theta_1}(X > 0) = 1 - F(-\theta_1), \tag{10.2.12}$$

where $F(x)$ is the cdf of ε in Model (10.2.1). Hence $S(\theta_0)$ is not distribution free under alternative hypotheses. As in Exercise 10.2.3, we can determine the power of the test for specified θ_1 and $F(x)$. We want to compare the power of the sign test to other size α tests, in particular the test based on the sample mean. However, for these comparison purposes, we need more general results, some of which are obtained in the next subsection.

10.2.1   Asymptotic Relative Efficiency

One solution to this problem is to consider the behavior of a test under a sequence of local alternatives. In this section, we often take $\theta_0 = 0$ in hypotheses (10.2.2). As noted before expression (10.2.9), this is without loss of generality. For the hypotheses (10.2.2), consider the sequence of alternatives

$$H_0 : \theta = 0 \text{ versus } H_{1n} : \theta_n = \frac{\delta}{\sqrt{n}}, \qquad (10.2.13)$$

where $\delta > 0$. Note that this sequence of alternatives converges to the null hypothesis as $n \to \infty$. We often call such a sequence of alternatives **local alternatives**. The idea is to consider how the power function of a test behaves relative to the power functions of other tests under this sequence of alternatives. We only sketch this development. For more details, the reader can consult the more advanced books cited in Section 10.1. As a first step in that direction, we obtain the asymptotic power lemma for the sign test.

Consider the large sample size α test given by (10.2.6). Under the alternative θ_n, we can approximate the mean of this test as follows:

$$
\begin{aligned}
E_{\theta_n}\left[\frac{1}{\sqrt{n}}\left(S(0) - \frac{n}{2}\right)\right] &= E_0\left[\frac{1}{\sqrt{n}}\left(S(-\theta_n) - \frac{n}{2}\right)\right] \\
&= \frac{1}{\sqrt{n}}\sum_{i=1}^{n} E_0[I(X_i > -\theta_n)] - \frac{\sqrt{n}}{2} \\
&= \frac{1}{\sqrt{n}}\sum_{i=1}^{n} P_0(X_i > -\theta_n) - \frac{\sqrt{n}}{2} \\
&= \sqrt{n}\left(1 - F(-\theta_n) - \frac{1}{2}\right) \\
&= \sqrt{n}\left(\frac{1}{2} - F(-\theta_n)\right) \\
&\approx \sqrt{n}\theta_n f(0) = \delta f(0), \qquad (10.2.14)
\end{aligned}
$$

where the step to the last line is due to the mean value theorem. It can be shown in more advanced texts that the variance of $[S(0) - (n/2)]/(\sqrt{n}/2)$ converges to 1 under θ_n, just as under H_0, and that, furthermore, $[S(0)-(n/2)-\sqrt{n}\delta f(0)]/(\sqrt{n}/2)$ has a limiting standard normal distribution. This leads to the **asymptotic power lemma**, which we state in the form of a theorem.

Theorem 10.2.2 (Asymptotic Power Lemma). *Consider the sequence of hypotheses (10.2.13). The limit of the power function of the large sample, size α, sign test is*

$$\lim_{n\to\infty} \gamma(\theta_n) = 1 - \Phi(z_\alpha - \delta\tau_S^{-1}), \qquad (10.2.15)$$

where $\tau_S = 1/[2f(0)]$ and $\Phi(z)$ is the cdf of a standard normal random variable.

Proof: Using expression (10.2.14) and the discussion which followed its derivation, we have

$$
\begin{aligned}
\gamma(\theta_n) &= P_{\theta_n}\left[\frac{n^{-1/2}[S(0)-(n/2)]}{1/2} \geq z_\alpha \right] \\
&= P_{\theta_n}\left[\frac{n^{-1/2}[S(0)-(n/2)] - \sqrt{n}\delta f(0)}{1/2} \geq z_\alpha - \delta 2f(0) \right] \\
&\to 1 - \Phi(z_\alpha - \delta 2 f(0)),
\end{aligned}
$$

which was to be shown. ∎

As shown in Exercise 10.2.4, the parameter $\tau_S = 1/[2f(0)]$ is a scale parameter (functional) as defined in Exercise 10.1.4 of the last section. We later show that $\tau_S/\sqrt{n}$ is the asymptotic standard deviation of the sample median.

There were several approximations used in the proof of Theorem 10.2.2. A rigorous proof can be found in more advanced texts, such as those cited in Section 10.1. It is quite helpful for the next sections to reconsider the approximation of the mean given in (10.2.14) in terms of another concept called **efficacy**. Consider another standardization of the test statistic given by

$$\overline{S}(0) = \frac{1}{n}\sum_{i=1}^{n} I(X_i > 0), \qquad (10.2.16)$$

where the bar notation is used to signify that $\overline{S}(0)$ is an average of $I(X_i > 0)$ and, in this case under H_0, converges in probability to $\frac{1}{2}$. Let $\mu(\theta) = E_\theta(\overline{S}(0) - \frac{1}{2})$. Then, by expression (10.2.14), we have

$$\mu(\theta_n) = E_{\theta_n}\left(\overline{S}(0) - \frac{1}{2}\right) = \frac{1}{2} - F(-\theta_n). \qquad (10.2.17)$$

Let $\sigma_{\overline{S}}^2 = \mathrm{Var}(\overline{S}(0)) = \frac{1}{4n}$. Finally, define the **efficacy** of the sign test to be

$$c_S = \lim_{n\to\infty} \frac{\mu'(0)}{\sqrt{n}\sigma_{\overline{S}}}. \qquad (10.2.18)$$

That is, the efficacy is the rate of change of the mean of the test statistic at the null divided by the product of $\sqrt{n}$ and the standard deviation of the test statistic at the null. So the efficacy increases with an increase in this rate, as it should. We use this formulation of efficacy throughout this chapter.

Hence, by expression (10.2.14), the efficacy of the sign test is

$$c_S = \frac{f(0)}{1/2} = 2f(0) = \tau_S^{-1}, \tag{10.2.19}$$

the reciprocal of the scale parameter τ_S. In terms of efficacy, we can write the conclusion of the Asymptotic Power Lemma as

$$\lim_{n \to \infty} \gamma(\theta_n) = 1 - \Phi(z_\alpha - \delta c_S). \tag{10.2.20}$$

This is not a coincidence, and it is true for the procedures we consider in the next section.

Remark 10.2.1. In this chapter, we compare nonparametric procedures with traditional parametric procedures. For instance, we compare the sign test with the test based on the sample mean. Traditionally, tests based on sample means are referred to as t-tests. Even though our comparisons are asymptotic and we could use the terminology of z-tests, we instead use the traditional terminology of t-tests. ∎

As a second illustration of efficacy, we determine the efficacy of the t-test for the mean. Assume that the random variables ε_i in Model (10.2.1) are symmetrically distributed about 0 and their mean exists. Hence the parameter θ is the location parameter. In particular, $\theta = E(X_i) = \mathrm{med}(X_i)$. Denote the variance of X_i by σ^2. This allows us to easily compare the sign and t-tests. Recall for hypotheses (10.2.2) that the t-test rejects H_0 in favor of H_1 if $\overline{X} \geq c$. The form of the test statistic is then $\overline{X}$. Furthermore, we have

$$\mu_{\overline{X}}(\theta) = E_\theta(\overline{X}) = \theta \tag{10.2.21}$$

and

$$\sigma_{\overline{X}}^2(0) = V_0(\overline{X}) = \frac{\sigma^2}{n}. \tag{10.2.22}$$

Thus, by (10.2.21) and (10.2.22), the efficacy of the t-test is

$$c_t = \lim_{n \to \infty} \frac{\mu_{\overline{X}}'(0)}{\sqrt{n}(\sigma/\sqrt{n})} = \frac{1}{\sigma}. \tag{10.2.23}$$

As confirmed in Exercise 10.2.8, the asymptotic power of the large sample level α, t-test under the sequence of alternatives (10.2.13) is $1 - \Phi(z_\alpha - \delta c_t)$. Thus we can compare the sign and t-tests by comparing their efficacies. We do this from the perspective of sample size determination.

Assume without loss of generality that $H_0 : \theta = 0$. Now suppose we want to determine the sample size so that a level α sign test can detect the alternative $\theta^* > 0$ with (approximate) probability γ^*. That is, find n so that

$$\gamma^* = \gamma(\theta^*) = P_{\theta^*}\left[\frac{S(0) - (n/2)}{\sqrt{n}/2} \geq z_\alpha\right]. \tag{10.2.24}$$

Write $\theta^* = \sqrt{n}\theta^*/\sqrt{n}$. Then, using the asymptotic power lemma, we have

$$\gamma^* = \gamma(\sqrt{n}\theta^*/\sqrt{n}) \approx 1 - \Phi(z_\alpha - \sqrt{n}\theta^* \tau_S^{-1}).$$

Now denote z_{γ^*} to be the upper $1 - \gamma^*$ quantile of the standard normal distribution. Then, from this last equation, we have

$$z_{\gamma^*} = z_\alpha - \sqrt{n}\theta^* \tau_S^{-1}.$$

Solving for n, we get

$$n_S = \left(\frac{(z_\alpha - z_{\gamma^*})\tau_S}{\theta^*} \right)^2. \tag{10.2.25}$$

As outlined in Exercise 10.2.8, for this situation the sample size determination for the test based on the sample mean is

$$n_{\overline{X}} = \left(\frac{(z_\alpha - z_{\gamma^*})\sigma}{\theta^*} \right)^2, \tag{10.2.26}$$

where $\sigma^2 = \text{Var}(\varepsilon)$.

Suppose we have two tests of the same level for which the asymptotic power lemma holds and for each we determine the sample size necessary to achieve power γ^* at the alternative θ^*. Then the ratio of these sample sizes is called the **asymptotic relative efficiency** (ARE) between the tests. We show later that this is the same as the ARE defined in Chapter 6 between estimators. Hence the ARE of the sign test to the t-test is

$$\text{ARE}(S, t) = \frac{n_{\overline{X}}}{n_S} = \frac{\sigma^2}{\tau_S^2} = \frac{c_S^2}{c_t^2}. \tag{10.2.27}$$

Note that this is the same relative efficiency that was discussed in Example 6.2.5 when the sample median was compared to the sample mean. In the next two examples we revisit this discussion by examining the AREs when X_i has a normal distribution and then a Laplace (double exponential) distribution.

Example 10.2.2 (ARE(S, t): normal distribution). Suppose $X_1, X_2, \ldots, X_n$ follow the location model (10.1.4), where $f(x)$ is a $N(0, \sigma^2)$ pdf. Then $\tau_S = (2f(0))^{-1} = \sigma\sqrt{\pi/2}$. Hence the ARE($S, t$) is given by

$$\text{ARE}(S, t) = \frac{\sigma^2}{\tau_S^2} = \frac{\sigma^2}{(\pi/2)\sigma^2} = \frac{2}{\pi} \approx 0.637. \tag{10.2.28}$$

Hence at the normal distribution the sign test is only 64% as efficient as the t-test. In terms of sample size at the normal distribution, the t-test requires a smaller sample, $0.64n_s$, where n_s is the sample size of the sign test, to achieve the same power as the sign test. A cautionary note is needed here because this is asymptotic efficiency. There have been ample empirical (simulation) studies which give credence to these numbers. ∎

Example 10.2.3 (ARE(S,t) at the Laplace distribution). For this example, consider Model (10.1.4), where $f(x)$ is the Laplace pdf $f(x) = (2b)^{-1}\exp\{-|x|/b\}$ for $-\infty < x < \infty$ and $b > 0$. Then $\tau_S = (2f(0))^{-1} = b$, while $\sigma^2 = E(X^2) = 2b^2$. Hence the ARE(S,t) is given by

$$\text{ARE}(S,t) = \frac{\sigma^2}{\tau_S^2} = \frac{2b^2}{b^2} = 2. \tag{10.2.29}$$

So, at the Laplace distribution, the sign test is (asymptotically) twice as efficient as the t-test. In terms of sample size at the Laplace distribution, the t-test requires twice as large a sample as the sign test to achieve the same asymptotic power as the sign test. ■

The normal distribution has much lighter tails than the Laplace distribution, because the two pdfs are proportional to $\exp\{-t^2/2\sigma^2\}$ and $\exp\{-|t|/b\}$, respectively. Based on the last two examples, it seems that the t-test is more efficient for light-tailed distributions while the sign test is more efficient for heavier-tailed distributions. This is true in general and we illustrate this in the next example where we can easily vary the tail weight from light to heavy.

Example 10.2.4 (ARE(S,t) at a family of contaminated normals). Consider the location Model (10.1.4), where the cdf of ε_i is the contaminated normal cdf given in expression (3.4.16). Assume that $\theta_0 = 0$. Recall that for this distribution, $(1-\epsilon)$ proportion of the time the sample is drawn from a $N(0, b^2)$ distribution, while ϵ proportion of the time the sample is drawn from a $N(0, b^2\sigma_c^2)$ distribution. The corresponding pdf is given by

$$f(x) = \frac{1-\epsilon}{b}\phi\left(\frac{x}{b}\right) + \frac{\epsilon}{b\sigma_c}\phi\left(\frac{x}{b\sigma_c}\right), \tag{10.2.30}$$

where $\phi(z)$ is the pdf of a standard normal random variable. As shown in Section 3.4, the variance of ε_i is $b^2(1 + \epsilon(\sigma_c^2 - 1))$. Also, $\tau_s = (b\sqrt{\pi/2})/[1 - \epsilon + (\epsilon/\sigma_c)]$. Thus the ARE is

$$\text{ARE}(S,t) = \frac{2}{\pi}[(1 + \epsilon(\sigma_c^2 - 1)][1 - \epsilon + (\epsilon/\sigma_c)]^2. \tag{10.2.31}$$

For example, the following table (see Exercise 6.2.6) shows the AREs for various values of ϵ when σ_c is set at 3.0:

ϵ	0	0.01	0.02	0.03	0.05	0.10	0.15	0.25
ARE(S,t)	0.636	0.678	0.718	0.758	0.832	0.998	1.134	1.326

Note: if ϵ increases over the range of values in the table, then the contamination effect becomes larger (generally resulting in a heavier-tailed distribution) and as the table shows, the sign test becomes more efficient relative to the t-test. Increasing σ_c has the same effect. It does take, however, with $\sigma_c = 3$, over 10% contamination before the sign test becomes more efficient than the t-test. ■

10.2.2   Estimating Equations Based on the Sign Test

In practice, we often want to estimate θ, the median of X_i, in Model (10.2.1). The associated point estimate based on the sign test can be described with a simple geometry, which is analogous to the geometry of the sample mean. As Exercise 10.2.5 shows, the sample mean $\overline{X}$ is such that

$$\overline{X} = \text{Argmin}\sqrt{\sum_{i=1}^{n}(X_i - \theta)^2}. \qquad (10.2.32)$$

The quantity $\sqrt{\sum_{i=1}^{n}(X_i - \theta)^2}$ is the Euclidean distance between the vector of observations $\mathbf{X} = (X_1, X_2, \ldots, X_n)'$ and the vector $\theta\mathbf{1}$. If we simply interchange the square root and the summation symbols, we go from the Euclidean distance to the L_1 distance. Let

$$\widehat{\theta} = \text{Argmin}\sum_{i=1}^{n}|X_i - \theta|. \qquad (10.2.33)$$

To determine $\widehat{\theta}$, simply differentiate the quantity on the right side with respect to θ (as in Chapter 6, define the derivative of $|x|$ to be 0 at $x = 0$). We then obtain

$$\frac{\partial}{\partial\theta}\sum_{i=1}^{n}|X_i - \theta| = -\sum_{i=1}^{n}\text{sgn}(X_i - \theta).$$

Setting this to 0, we obtain the estimating equations (EE)

$$\sum_{i=1}^{n}\text{sgn}(X_i - \theta) = 0, \qquad (10.2.34)$$

whose solution is the sample median Q_2.

Because our observations are continuous random variables, we have the identity

$$\sum_{i=1}^{n}\text{sgn}(X_i - \theta) = 2S(\theta) - n.$$

Hence the sample median also solves $S(\theta) \approx n/2$. Consider again Figure 10.2.2. Imagine $n/2$ on the vertical axis. This is halfway in the total drop of $S(\theta)$, from n to 0. The order statistic on the horizontal axis corresponding to $n/2$ is essentially the sample median (middle order statistic). In terms of testing, this last equation says that, based on the data, the sample median is the "most acceptable" hypothesis, because $n/2$ is the null expected value of the test statistic. We often think of this as estimation by the inversion of a test.

We now sketch the asymptotic distribution of the sample median. Assume without loss of generality that the true median of X_i is 0. Suppose $-\infty < x < \infty$. Using the fact that $S(\theta)$ is nonincreasing and the identity $S(\theta) \approx n/2$, we have the following equivalences:

$$\{\sqrt{n}Q_2 \leq x\} \Leftrightarrow \left\{Q_2 \leq \frac{x}{\sqrt{n}}\right\} \Leftrightarrow \left\{S\left(\frac{x}{\sqrt{n}}\right) \leq \frac{n}{2}\right\}.$$

Hence we have

$$
\begin{aligned}
P_0(\sqrt{n}Q_2 \le x) &= P_0\left[S\left(\frac{x}{\sqrt{n}}\right) \le \frac{n}{2}\right] \\
&= P_{-x/\sqrt{n}}\left[S(0) \le \frac{n}{2}\right] \\
&= P_{-x/\sqrt{n}}\left[\frac{S(0) - (n/2)}{\sqrt{n}/2} \le 0\right] \\
&\rightarrow \Phi(0 - x\tau_S^{-1}) = P(\tau_S Z \le x),
\end{aligned}
$$

where Z has a standard normal distribution. Notice that the limit was obtained by invoking the Asymptotic Power Lemma with $\alpha = 0.5$ and hence $z_\alpha = 0$. Rearranging the last term earlier, we obtain the asymptotic distribution of the sample median, which we state as a theorem:

Theorem 10.2.3. *For the random sample $X_1, X_2, \ldots, X_n$, assume that Model (10.2.1) holds. Suppose that $f(0) > 0$. Let Q_2 denote the sample median. Then*

$$\sqrt{n}(Q_2 - \theta) \rightarrow N(0, \tau_S^2), \tag{10.2.35}$$

where $\tau_S = (2f(0))^{-1}$.

In Section 6.2 we defined the ARE between two estimators to be the reciprocal of their asymptotic variances. For the sample median and mean, this is the same ratio as that based on sample size determinations of their respective tests given earlier in expression (10.2.27).

10.2.3   Confidence Interval for the Median

Suppose the random sample $X_1, X_2, \ldots, X_n$ follows the location model (10.2.1). In this subsection, we develop a confidence interval for the median θ of X_i. Assuming that θ is the true median, the random variable $S(\theta)$, (10.2.9), has a binomial $b(n, 1/2)$ distribution. For $0 < \alpha < 1$, select c_1 so that $P_\theta[S(\theta) \le c_1] = \alpha/2$. Hence we have

$$1 - \alpha = P_\theta[c_1 < S(\theta) < n - c_1]. \tag{10.2.36}$$

Recall in our derivation for the t-confidence interval for the mean in Chapter 3, we began with such a statement and then "inverted" the pivot random variable $t = \sqrt{n}(\overline{X} - \mu)/S$ (S in this expression is the sample standard deviation) to obtain an equivalent inequality with μ isolated in the middle. In this case, the function $S(\theta)$ does not have an inverse, but it is a decreasing step function of θ and the inversion can still be performed. As depicted in Figure 10.2.2, $c_1 < S(\theta) < n - c_1$ if and only if $Y_{c_1+1} \le \theta < Y_{n-c_1}$, where $Y_1 < Y_2 < \cdots < Y_n$ are the order statistics of the sample $X_1, X_2, \ldots, X_n$. Therefore, the interval $[Y_{c_1+1}, Y_{n-c_1})$ is a $(1 - \alpha)100\%$ confidence interval for the median θ. Because the order statistics are continuous random variables, the interval (Y_{c_1+1}, Y_{n-c_1}) is an equivalent confidence interval.

If n is large, then there is a large sample approximation to c_1. We know from the Central Limit Theorem that $S(\theta)$ is approximately normal with mean $n/2$ and variance $n/4$. Then, using the continuity correction, we obtain the approximation

$$c_1 \approx \frac{n}{2} - \frac{z_{\alpha/2}\sqrt{n}}{2} - \frac{1}{2}, \qquad (10.2.37)$$

where $\Phi(-z_{\alpha/2}) = \alpha/2$; see Exercise 10.2.6. In practice, we use the closest integer to c_1.

Example 10.2.5 (Example 10.2.1, Continued). There are 20 data points in the Shoshoni basket data. The sample median of the width to the length is $0.5(0.628 + 0.654) = 0.641$. Because $0.021 = P_{H_0}(S(0.618) \leq 5)$, a 95.8% confidence interval for θ is the interval $(y_6, y_{15}) = (0.606, 0.672)$, which includes 0.618, the ratio of the width to the length, which characterizes the golden rectangle. ∎

EXERCISES

10.2.1. Sketch Figure 10.2.2 for the Shoshoni basket data found in Example 10.2.1. Show the values of the test statistic, the point estimate, and the 95.8% confidence interval of Example 10.2.5 on the sketch.

10.2.2. Show that the test given by (10.2.6) has asymptotically level α; that is, show that under H_0,

$$\frac{S(\theta_0) - (n/2)}{\sqrt{n}/2} \xrightarrow{D} Z,$$

where Z has a $N(0,1)$ distribution.

10.2.3. Let θ denote the median of a random variable X. Consider tseting

$$H_0 : \theta = 0 \text{ versus } H_1 : \theta > 0 .$$

Suppose we have a sample of size $n = 25$.

(a) Let $S(0)$ denote the sign test statistic. Determine the level of the test: reject H_0 if $S(0) \geq 16$.

(b) Determine the power of the test in part (a) if X has $N(0.5, 1)$ distribution.

(c) Assuming X has finite mean $\mu = \theta$, consider the asymptotic test of rejecting H_0 if $\overline{X}/(\sigma/\sqrt{n}) \geq k$. Assuming that $\sigma = 1$, determine k so the asymptotic test has the same level as the test in part (a). Then determine the power of this test for the situation in part (b).

10.2.4. Recall the definition of a scale functional given in Exercise 10.1.4. Show that the parameter τ_S defined in Theorem 10.2.2 is a scale functional.

10.2.5. Show that the sample mean solves Equation (10.2.32).

10.2.6. Derive the approximation (10.2.37).

10.2.7. Show that the power function of the sign test is nonincreasing for the hypotheses

$$H_0 : \theta = \theta_0 \text{ versus } H_1 : \theta < \theta_0. \qquad (10.2.38)$$

10.2.8. Let $X_1, X_2, \ldots, X_n$ be a random sample which follows the location model (10.2.1). In this exercise we want to compare the sign tests and t-test of the hypotheses (10.2.2); so we assume the random errors ε_i are symmetrically distributed about 0. Let $\sigma^2 = \text{Var}(\varepsilon_i)$. Hence the mean and the median are the same for this location model. Assume, also, that $\theta_0 = 0$. Consider the large sample version of the t-test, which rejects H_0 in favor of H_1 if $\overline{X}/(\sigma/\sqrt{n}) > z_\alpha$.

 (a) Obtain the power function, $\gamma_t(\theta)$, of the large sample version of the t-test.

 (b) Show that $\gamma_t(\theta)$ is nondecreasing in θ.

 (c) Show that $\gamma_t(\theta_n) \to 1 - \Phi(z_\alpha - \sigma\theta^*)$, under the sequence of local alternatives (10.2.13).

 (d) Based on part (c), obtain the sample size determination for the t-test to detect θ^* with approximate power γ^*.

 (e) Derive the $\text{ARE}(S, t)$ given in (10.2.27).

10.3 Signed-Rank Wilcoxon

Let $X_1, X_2, \ldots, X_n$ be a random sample that follows Model (10.2.1). Inference for θ based on the sign test is simple and requires few assumptions about the underlying distribution of X_i. On the other hand, sign procedures have the low efficiency of 0.64 relative to procedures based on the t-test given an underlying normal distribution. In this section, we discuss a nonparametric procedure that does attain high efficiency relative to the t-test. We make the additional assumption that the pdf $f(x)$ of ε_i in Model (10.2.1) is symmetric; i.e., $f(x) = f(-x)$, for all x such that $-\infty < x < \infty$. Hence X_i is symmetrically distributed about θ. By Theorem 10.1.1, all location parameters are identical.

First, consider the one-sided hypotheses

$$H_0 : \theta = 0 \text{ versus } H_1 : \theta > 0. \qquad (10.3.1)$$

There is no loss of generality in assuming that the null hypothesis is $H_0 : \theta = 0$, for if it were $H_0 : \theta = \theta_0$, we would consider the sample $X_1 - \theta_0, \ldots, X_n - \theta_0$. Under a symmetric pdf, observations X_i which are the same distance from 0 are equilikely and hence should receive the same weight. A test statistic which does this is the **signed-rank Wilcoxon** given by

$$T = \sum_{i=1}^{n} \text{sgn}(X_i) R|X_i|, \qquad (10.3.2)$$

where $R|X_i|$ denotes the rank of X_i among $|X_1|, \ldots, |X_n|$, where the rankings are from low to high. Intuitively, under the null hypothesis, we expect half of the X_is to be positive and half to be negative. Further, the ranks are uniformly distributed on the integers $\{1, 2, \ldots, n\}$. Hence values of T around 0 are indicative of H_0. On the other hand, if H_1 is true, then we expect more than half of the X_is to be positive and further, the positive observations are more likely to receive the higher ranks. Thus an appropriate decision rule is

$$\text{Reject } H_0 \text{ in favor of } H_1 \text{ if } T \geq c, \qquad (10.3.3)$$

where c is determined by the level α of the test.

Given α, we need the null distribution of T to determine the critical point c. The set of integers $\{-n(n+1)/2, -[n(n+1)/2]+2, \ldots, n(n+1)/2\}$ form the support of T. Also, from Section 10.2, we know that the signs are iid with support $\{-1, 1\}$ and pmf

$$p(-1) = p(1) = \frac{1}{2}. \qquad (10.3.4)$$

A key result is the following lemma:

Lemma 10.3.1. *Under H_0 and symmetry about 0 for the pdf, the random variables $|X_1|, \ldots, |X_n|$ are independent of the random variables $sgn(X_1), \ldots, sgn(X_n)$.*

Proof: Because $X_1, \ldots, X_n$ is a random sample from the cdf $F(x)$, it suffices to show that $P[|X_i| \leq x, \text{sgn}(X_i) = 1] = P[|X_i| \leq x]P[\text{sgn}(X_i) = 1]$. But due to H_0 and the symmetry of $f(x)$, this follows from the following string of equalities

$$P[|X_i| \leq x, \text{sgn}(X_i) = 1] = P[0 < X_i \leq x] = F(x) - \frac{1}{2}$$

$$= [2F(x) - 1]\frac{1}{2} = P[|X_i| \leq x]P[\text{sgn}(X_i) = 1]. \blacksquare$$

Based on this lemma, the ranks of the $|X_i|$s are independent of the signs of the X_is. Note that the ranks are a permutation of the integers $1, 2, \ldots, n$. By the lemma this independence is true for any permutation. In particular, suppose we use the permutation that orders the absolute values. For example, suppose the observations are $-6.1, 4.3, 7.2, 8.0, -2.1$. Then the permutation $5, 2, 1, 3, 4$ orders the absolute values; that is, the fifth observation is the smallest in absolute value, the second observation is the next smallest, etc. This permutation is called the **anti-ranks**, which we denote generally by by $i_1, i_2, \ldots, i_n$. Using the anti-ranks, we can write T as

$$T = \sum_{j=1}^{n} j \, \text{sgn}(X_{i_j}), \qquad (10.3.5)$$

where, by Lemma 10.3.1, $\text{sgn}(X_{i_j})$ are iid with support $\{-1, 1\}$ and pmf (10.3.4).

Based on this observation, for s such that $-\infty < s < \infty$, the mgf of T is

$$
\begin{aligned}
E[\exp\{sT\}] &= E\left[\exp\left\{\sum_{j=1}^{n} sj\,\mathrm{sgn}(X_{i_j})\right\}\right] \\
&= \prod_{j=1}^{n} E[\exp\{sj\,\mathrm{sgn}(X_{i_j})\}] \\
&= \prod_{j=1}^{n}\left(\frac{1}{2}e^{-sj} + \frac{1}{2}e^{sj}\right) \\
&= \frac{1}{2^n}\prod_{j=1}^{n}\left(e^{-sj} + e^{sj}\right).
\end{aligned}
\tag{10.3.6}
$$

Because the mgf does not depend on the underlying symmetric pdf $f(x)$, the test statistic T is distribution free under H_0. Although the pmf of T cannot be obtained in closed form, this mgf can be used to generate the pmf for a specified n; see Exercise 10.3.1.

Because the $\mathrm{sgn}(X_{i_j})$s are mutually independent with mean zero, it follows that $E_{H_0}[T] = 0$. Further, because the variance of $\mathrm{sgn}(X_{i_j})$ is 1, we have

$$
\mathrm{Var}_{H_0}(T) = \sum_{j=1}^{n}\mathrm{Var}_{H_0}(j\,\mathrm{sgn}(X_{i_j})) = \sum_{j=1}^{n} j^2 = n(n+1)(2n+1)/6.
$$

We summarize these results in the following theorem:

Theorem 10.3.1. *Assume that Model (10.2.1) is true for the random sample $X_1,\ldots,X_n$. Assume also that the pdf $f(x)$ is symmetric about 0. Then under H_0,*

$$
T \text{ is distribution free with a symmetric pmf} \tag{10.3.7}
$$
$$
E_{H_0}[T] = 0 \tag{10.3.8}
$$
$$
Var_{H_0}(T) = \frac{n(n+1)(2n+1)}{6} \tag{10.3.9}
$$
$$
\frac{T}{\sqrt{Var_{H_0}(T)}} \text{ has an asymptotically } N(0,1) \text{ distribution.} \tag{10.3.10}
$$

Proof: The first part of (10.3.7) and the expressions (10.3.8) and (10.3.9) were derived above. The asymptotic distribution of T certainly is plausible and can be found in more advanced books. To obtain the second part of (10.3.7), we need to show that the distribution of T is symmetric about 0. But by the mgf of Y, (10.3.6), we have

$$
E[\exp\{s(-T)\}] = E[\exp\{(-s)T\}] = E[\exp\{sT\}].
$$

Hence T and $-T$ have the same distribution, so T is symmetrically distributed about 0. ∎

Critical values for the decision rule (10.3.3) can be obtained from the exact distribution of T. Tables of the exact distribution can be found in applied nonparametric books such as Hollander and Wolfe (1999). A discussion on the computation of the exact distribution by using the language R is given in the next paragraph. But note that the support of T is much denser than that of the sign test, so the normal approximation is good even for a sample size of 10.

There is another formulation of T which is convenient. Let T^+ denote the sum of the ranks of the positive X_is. Then, because the sum of all ranks is $n(n+1)/2$, we have

$$
\begin{aligned}
T &= \sum_{i=1}^{n} \mathrm{sgn}(X_i) R|X_i| = \sum_{X_i>0} R|X_i| - \sum_{X_i<0} R|X_i| \\
&= 2 \sum_{X_i>0} R|X_i| - \frac{n(n+1)}{2} \\
&= 2T^+ - \frac{n(n+1)}{2}.
\end{aligned}
\tag{10.3.11}
$$

Hence T^+ is a linear function of T and thus is an equivalent formulation of the signed-rank test statistic T. For the record, we note the null mean and variance of T^+:

$$
E_{H_0}(T^+) = \frac{n(n+1)}{4} \quad \text{and} \quad \mathrm{Var}_{H_0}(T^+) = \frac{n(n+1)(2n+1)}{24} .
\tag{10.3.12}
$$

If the reader has the computer language R at hand, then the function `psignrank` evaluates the cdf of T^+. For example, for sample size n, the probability $P(T^+ \le t)$ is computed by the command `psignrank(t,n)`.

Let $X_i > 0$ and consider all X_j such that $-X_i < X_j < X_i$. Thus all the averages $(X_i + X_j)/2$, under these restrictions, are positive, including $(X_i + X_i)/2$. From the restriction, though, the number of these positive averages is simply the $R|X_i|$. Doing this for all $X_i > 0$, we obtain

$$
T^+ = \#_{i \le j}\{(X_j + X_i)/2 > 0\}.
\tag{10.3.13}
$$

The pairwise averages $(X_j + X_i)/2$ are often called the *Walsh averages*. Hence the signed-rank Wilcoxon can be obtained by counting the number of positive Walsh averages.

Example 10.3.1 (*Zea mays* Data of Darwin). Reconsider the data set discussed in Example 4.5.1. Recall that W_i is the difference in heights of the cross-fertilized plant minus the self-fertilized plant in pot i, for $i = 1, \ldots, 15$. Let θ be the location parameter and consider the one-sided hypotheses

$$
H_0 : \theta = 0 \quad \text{versus} \quad H_1 : \theta > 0.
\tag{10.3.14}
$$

Table 10.3.1 displays the data and the signed ranks.

Adding up the ranks of the positive items in column 5 of Table 10.3.1, we obtain $T^+ = 96$. Using the exact distribution, the R command is `1-psignrank(95,15))`,

Table 10.3.1: Signed Ranks for Darwin Data, Example 10.3.1

Pot	Cross-Fertilized	Self-Fertilized	Difference	Signed-Rank
1	23.500	17.375	6.125	11
2	12.000	20.375	−8.375	−14
3	21.000	20.000	1.000	2
4	22.000	20.000	2.000	4
5	19.125	18.375	0.750	1
6	21.550	18.625	2.925	5
7	22.125	18.625	3.500	7
8	20.375	15.250	5.125	9
9	18.250	16.500	1.750	3
10	21.625	18.000	3.625	8
11	23.250	16.250	7.000	12
12	21.000	18.000	3.000	6
13	22.125	12.750	9.375	15
14	23.000	15.500	7.500	13
15	12.000	18.000	−6.000	−10

we obtain the p-value, $\widehat{p} = P_{H_0}(T^+ \geq 96) = 0.021$. For comparison, the asymptotic p-value, using the continuity correction is

$$P_{H_0}(T^+ \geq 96) - P_{H_0}(T^+ \geq 95.5) \approx P\left(Z > \frac{95.5 - 60}{\sqrt{15 \cdot 16 \cdot 31/24}}\right)$$
$$= P(Z \geq 2.016) = 0.022,$$

which is quite close to the exact value of 0.021. ∎

Based on the identity (10.3.13), we obtain a useful process. Let

$$T^+(\theta) = \#_{i \leq j}\{[(X_j - \theta) + (X_i - \theta)]/2 > 0\} = \#_{i \leq j}\{(X_j + X_i)/2 > \theta\}. \quad (10.3.15)$$

The process associated with $T^+(\theta)$ is much like the sign process, (10.2.9). Let $W_1 < W_2 < \cdots < W_{n(n+1)/2}$ denote the $n(n+1)/2$ ordered Walsh averages. Then a graph of $T^+(\theta)$ would appear as in Figure 10.2.2, except the ordered Walsh averages would be on the horizontal axis and the largest value on the vertical would be $n(n+1)/2$. Hence the function $T^+(\theta)$ is a decreasing step function of θ, which steps down one unit at each Walsh average. This observation greatly simplifies the discussion on the properties of the signed-rank Wilcoxon.

Let c_α denote the critical value of a level α test of the hypotheses (10.3.1) based on the signed-rank test statistic T^+; i.e., $\alpha = P_{H_0}(T^+ \geq c_\alpha)$. Let $\gamma_{SW}(\theta) = P_\theta(T^+ \geq c_\alpha)$, for $\theta \geq \theta_0$, denote the power function of the test. The translation property, Lemma 10.2.1, holds for the signed-rank Wilcoxon. Hence, as in Theorem 10.2.1, the power function is a nondecreasing function of θ. In particular, the signed-rank Wilcoxon test is an unbiased test for the one-sided hypotheses (10.3.1).

10.3.1   Asymptotic Relative Efficiency

We investigate the efficiency of the signed-rank Wilcoxon by first determining its efficacy. Without loss of generality, we can assume that $\theta_0 = 0$. Consider the same sequence of local alternatives discussed in the last section; i.e.,

$$H_0 : \ \theta = 0 \text{ versus } H_{1n} : \ \theta_n = \frac{\delta}{\sqrt{n}}, \tag{10.3.16}$$

where $\delta > 0$. Contemplate the modified statistic, which is the average of $T^+(\theta)$,

$$\overline{T}^+(\theta) = \frac{2}{n(n+1)} T^+(\theta). \tag{10.3.17}$$

Then, by (10.3.12),

$$E_0[\overline{T}^+(0)] = \frac{2}{n(n+1)} \frac{n(n+1)}{4} = \frac{1}{2} \text{ and } \sigma^2_{\overline{T}^+}(0) = \text{Var}_0[\overline{T}^+(0)] = \frac{2n+1}{6n(n+1)}. \tag{10.3.18}$$

Let $a_n = 2/n(n+1)$. Note that we can decompose $\overline{T}^+(\theta_n)$ into two parts as

$$\overline{T}^+(\theta_n) = a_n S(\theta_n) + a_n \sum_{i<j} I(X_i + X_j > 2\theta_n) = a_n S(\theta_n) + a_n T^*(\theta_n), \tag{10.3.19}$$

where $S(\theta)$ is the sign process (10.2.9) and

$$T^*(\theta_n) = \sum_{i<j} I(X_i + X_j > 2\theta_n). \tag{10.3.20}$$

To obtain the efficacy, we require the mean

$$\mu_{\overline{T}^+}(\theta_n) = E_{\theta_n}[\overline{T}^+(0)] = E_0[\overline{T}^+(-\theta_n)]. \tag{10.3.21}$$

But by (10.2.14), $a_n E_0(S(-\theta_n)) = a_n n(2^{-1} - F(-\theta_n)) \to 0$. Hence we need only be concerned with the second term in (10.3.19). But note that the Walsh averages in $T^*(\theta)$ are identically distributed. Thus

$$a_n E_0(T^*(-\theta_n)) = a_n \binom{n}{2} P_0(X_1 + X_2 > -2\theta_n). \tag{10.3.22}$$

This latter probability can be expressed as follows:

$$
\begin{aligned}
P_0(X_1 + X_2 > -2\theta_n) &= E_0[P_0(X_1 > -2\theta_n - X_2 | X_2)] = E_0[1 - F(-2\theta_n - X_2)] \\
&= \int_{-\infty}^{\infty} [1 - F(-2\theta_n - x)] f(x) \, dx \\
&= \int_{-\infty}^{\infty} F(2\theta_n + x) f(x) \, dx \\
&\approx \int_{-\infty}^{\infty} [F(x) + 2\theta_n f(x)] f(x) \, dx \\
&= \frac{1}{2} + 2\theta_n \int_{-\infty}^{\infty} f^2(x) \, dx, \tag{10.3.23}
\end{aligned}
$$

where we have used the facts that X_1 and X_2 are iid and symmetrically distributed about 0, and the mean value theorem. Hence

$$\mu_{\overline{T}^+}(\theta_n) \approx a_n \binom{n}{2} \left(\frac{1}{2} + 2\theta_n \int_{-\infty}^{\infty} f^2(x)\, dx \right). \tag{10.3.24}$$

Putting (10.3.18) and (10.3.24) together, we have the efficacy

$$c_{T^+} = \lim_{n\to\infty} \frac{\mu'_{\overline{T}^+}(0)}{\sqrt{n}\sigma_{\overline{T}^+}(0)} = \sqrt{12} \int_{-\infty}^{\infty} f^2(x)\, dx. \tag{10.3.25}$$

In a more advanced text, this development can be made into a rigorous argument for the following asymptotic power lemma.

Theorem 10.3.2 (Asymptotic Power Lemma). *Consider the sequence of hypotheses (10.3.16). The limit of the power function of the large sample, size α, signed-rank Wilcoxon test is given by*

$$\lim_{n\to\infty} \gamma_{SR}(\theta_n) = 1 - \Phi(z_\alpha - \delta\tau_W^{-1}), \tag{10.3.26}$$

where $\tau_W = 1/[\sqrt{12} \int_{-\infty}^{\infty} f^2(x)\, dx]$ is the reciprocal of the efficacy c_{T^+} and $\Phi(z)$ is the cdf of a standard normal random variable.

As shown in Exercise 10.3.7, the parameter τ_W is a scale functional.

The arguments used in the determination of the sample size in Section 10.2 for the sign test were based on the asymptotic power lemma; hence, these arguments follow almost verbatim for the signed-rank Wilcoxon. In particular, the sample size needed so that a level α signed-rank Wilcoxon test of the hypotheses (10.3.1) can detect the alternative $\theta = \theta_0 + \theta^*$ with approximate probability γ^* is

$$n_W = \left(\frac{(z_\alpha - z_{\gamma^*})\tau_W}{\theta^*} \right)^2. \tag{10.3.27}$$

Using (10.2.26), the ARE between the signed-rank Wilcoxon test and the t-test based on the sample mean is

$$\text{ARE}(T, t) = \frac{n_t}{n_T} = \frac{\sigma^2}{\tau_W^2}. \tag{10.3.28}$$

We now derive some AREs between the Wilcoxon and the t-test. As noted above, the parameter τ_W is a scale functional and, hence, varies directly with scale transformations of the form aX, for $a > 0$. Likewise, the standard deviation σ is also a scale functional. Therefore, because the AREs are ratios of scale functionals, they are scale invariant. Hence, for derivations of AREs, we can select a pdf with a convenient choice of scale. For example, if we are considering an ARE at the normal distribution, we can work with the $N(0, 1)$ pdf.

Table 10.3.2: AREs Among the sign, the Signed-Rank Wilcoxon, and the t-Tests for Contaminated Normals with $\sigma_c = 3$ and Proportion of Contamination ϵ

ϵ	0.00	0.01	0.02	0.03	0.05	0.10	0.15	0.25
ARE(W, t)	0.955	1.009	1.060	1.108	1.196	1.373	1.497	1.616
ARE(S, t)	0.637	0.678	0.719	0.758	0.833	0.998	1.134	1.326
ARE(W, S)	1.500	1.487	1.474	1.461	1.436	1.376	1.319	1.218

Example 10.3.2 (ARE(W, t) at the normal distribution). If $f(x)$ is a $N(0, 1)$ pdf, then

$$
\tau_W^{-1} = \sqrt{12} \int_{-\infty}^{\infty} \left(\frac{1}{\sqrt{2\pi}} \exp\{-x^2/2\} \right)^2 dx
$$

$$
= \frac{\sqrt{12}}{\sqrt{2}\sqrt{2\pi}} \int_{-\infty}^{\infty} \frac{1}{\sqrt{2\pi}(1/\sqrt{2})} \exp\{-2^{-1}(x/(1/\sqrt{2}))^2\} \, dx = \sqrt{\frac{3}{\pi}}
$$

Hence $\tau_W^2 = \pi/3$. Since $\sigma = 1$, we have

$$
\text{ARE}(W, t) = \frac{\sigma^2}{\tau_W^2} = \frac{3}{\pi} = 0.955. \tag{10.3.29}
$$

As discussed above, this ARE holds for all normal distributions. Hence, at the normal distribution, the Wilcoxon signed-rank test is 95.5% efficient as the t-test. The Wilcoxon is called a **highly efficient** procedure. ∎

Example 10.3.3 (ARE(W, t) at a Family of Contaminated Normals). For this example, suppose that $f(x)$ is the pdf of a contaminated normal distribution. For convenience, we use the standardized pdf given in expression (10.2.30) with $b = 1$. Recall that for this distribution, $(1 - \epsilon)$ proportion of the time the sample is drawn from a $N(0, 1)$ distribution, while ϵ proportion of the time the sample is drawn from a $N(0, \sigma_c^2)$ distribution. Recall that the variance is $\sigma^2 = 1 + \epsilon(\sigma_c^2 - 1)$. Note that the formula for the pdf $f(x)$ is given in expression (3.4.14). In Exercise 10.3.2 it is shown that

$$
\int_{-\infty}^{\infty} f^2(x) \, dx = \frac{(1 - \epsilon)^2}{2\sqrt{\pi}} + \frac{\epsilon^2}{6\sqrt{\pi}} + \frac{\epsilon(1 - \epsilon)}{2\sqrt{\pi}}. \tag{10.3.30}
$$

Based on this, an expression for the ARE can be obtained; see Exercise 10.3.2. We used this expression to determine the AREs between the Wilcoxon and the t-tests for the situations with $\sigma_c = 3$ and ϵ varying from 0.00–0.25, displaying them in Table 10.3.2. For convenience, we have also displayed the AREs between the sign test and these two tests.

Note that the signed-rank Wilcoxon is more efficient than the t-test even at 1% contamination and increases to 150% efficiency for 15% contamination. ∎

10.3.2 Estimating Equations Based on Signed-Rank Wilcoxon

For the sign procedure, the estimation of θ was based on minimizing the L_1 norm. The estimator associated with the signed-rank test minimizes another norm, which is discussed in Exercises 10.3.4 and 10.3.5. Recall that we also show that the location estimator based on the sign test could be obtained by inverting the test. Considering this for the Wilcoxon, the estimator $\widehat{\theta}_W$ solves

$$T^+(\widehat{\theta}_W) = \frac{n(n+1)}{4}. \tag{10.3.31}$$

Using the description of the function $T^+(\theta)$ after its definition, (10.3.15), it is easily seen that $\widehat{\theta}_W = \text{median}\{(X_i + X_j)/2\}$; i.e., the median of the Walsh averages. This is often called the Hodges–Lehmann estimator because of several seminal articles by Hodges and Lehmann on the properties of this estimator; see Hodges and Lehmann (1963).

Several computer packages obtain the Hodges–Lehmann estimate. For example, the minitab (1991) command `wint` returns it.

Once again, we can use practically the same argument that we used for the sign process to obtain the asymptotic distribution of the Hodges–Lehmann estimator. We summarize the result in the next theorem.

Theorem 10.3.3. *Consider a random sample $X_1, X_2, X_3, \ldots, X_n$ which follows Model (10.2.1). Suppose that $f(x)$ is symmetric about 0. Then*

$$\sqrt{n}(\widehat{\theta}_W - \theta) \to N(0, \tau_W^2), \tag{10.3.32}$$

where $\tau_W = \left(\sqrt{12} \int_{-\infty}^{\infty} f^2(x)\, dx\right)^{-1}$.

Using this theorem, the AREs based on asymptotic variances for the signed-rank Wilcoxon are the same as do those defined above.

10.3.3 Confidence Interval for the Median

Because of the similarity between the processes $S(\theta)$ and $T^+(\theta)$, confidence intervals for θ based on the signed-rank Wilcoxon follow the same way as do those based on $S(\theta)$. For a given level α, let c_{W1}, an integer, denote the critical point of the signed-rank Wilcoxon distribution such that $P_\theta[T^+(\theta) \leq c_{W1}] = \alpha/2$. As in Section 10.2.3, we then have that

$$\begin{aligned} 1 - \alpha &= P_\theta[c_{W1} < T^+(\theta) < n - c_{W1}] \\ &= P_\theta[W_{c_{W1}+1} \leq \theta < W_{m-c_{W1}}], \end{aligned} \tag{10.3.33}$$

where $m = n(n+1)/2$ denotes the number of Walsh averages. Therefore, the interval $[W_{c_{W1}+1}, W_{m-c_{W1}})$ is a $(1-\alpha)100\%$ confidence interval for θ.

We can use the asymptotic null distribution of T^+, (10.3.10), to obtain the following approximation to c_{W1}. As shown in Exercise 10.3.3,

$$c_{W1} \approx \frac{n(n+1)}{4} - z_{\alpha/2}\sqrt{\frac{n(n+1)(2n+1)}{24}} - \frac{1}{2}, \tag{10.3.34}$$

where $\Phi(-z_{\alpha/2}) = \alpha/2$. In practice, we use the closest integer to c_{W1}.

Remark 10.3.1 (Computation). Several statistical computing packages compute the signed-rank Wilcoxon analysis. For example, the minitab (1991) commands `wint` and `wtest` compute the Hodges–Lehmann estimate, the distribution free confidence interval, and the Wilcoxon signed-rank test. The R function `wilcox.test` also computes the signed-rank analysis. For example, if x is the vector of observations, then the command `wilcox.test(x,mu=1,conf.int=T,conf.level=.90)` returns the Hodges–Lehmann estimate, a 90% confidence interval, and the test of $H_0 : \theta = 1$ versus $H_1 : \theta \neq 1$. See also Chapter 1 of Hettmansperger and Mc-Kean (2011) for R functions which comnpute the signed-rank Wilcoxon one-sample analysis. ∎

Example 10.3.4 (*Zea mays* Data of Darwin, Continued). Reconsider the data set discussed in Example 10.3.1, where we used the signed-rank Wilcoxon to test the hypotheses that the effect θ was 0. We now obtain the estimate of θ and a 95% confidence interval for it based on the signed-rank Wilcoxon. Recall that $n = 15$; hence, there are 120 Walsh averages. Using a computer package, we sorted these Walsh averages. The point estimate of the effect is the median of these averages which is 3.14. Hence we estimate that cross-fertilized *Zea mays* grow 3.14 inches taller than self-fertilized *Zea mays*. The approximate cutoff point for the confidence interval given by expression (10.3.34) is $c_{W1} = 25$. Hence a 95% confidence interval for θ is $[W_{26}, W_{95}) = [0.500, 5.250)$; that is, we are 95% confident that the true effect is between 0.500 to 5.250 inches. ∎

EXERCISES

10.3.1. (a) For $n = 3$, expand the mgf (10.3.6) to show that the distribution of the signed-rank Wilcoxon is given by

j	-6	-4	-2	0	2	4	6
$P(T = j)$	$\frac{1}{8}$	$\frac{1}{8}$	$\frac{1}{8}$	$\frac{2}{8}$	$\frac{1}{8}$	$\frac{1}{8}$	$\frac{1}{8}$

(b) Obtain the distribution of the signed-rank Wilcoxon for $n = 4$.

10.3.2. Assume that $f(x)$ has the contaminated normal pdf given in expression (3.4.14). Derive expression (10.3.30) and use it to obtain $\mathrm{ARE}(W, t)$ for this pdf.

10.3.3. Use the asymptotic null distribution of T^+, (10.3.10), to obtain the approximation (10.3.34) to c_{W1}.

10.3.4. For a vector $\mathbf{v} \in R^n$, define the function

$$\|\mathbf{v}\| = \sum_{i=1}^{n} R(|v_i|)|v_i|. \qquad (10.3.35)$$

Show that this function is a norm on R^n; that is, it satisfies the properties

1. $\|\mathbf{v}\| \geq 0$ and $\|\mathbf{v}\| = 0$ if and only if $\mathbf{v} = \mathbf{0}$.

2. $\|a\mathbf{v}\| = |a|\|\mathbf{v}\|$, for all a such that $-\infty < a < \infty$.

3. $\|\mathbf{u} + \mathbf{v}\| \leq \|\mathbf{u}\| + \|\mathbf{v}\|$, for all $\mathbf{u}, \mathbf{v} \in R^n$.

For the triangle inequality, use the anti-rank version, that is,

$$\|\mathbf{v}\| = \sum_{j=1}^{n} j|v_{i_j}|. \qquad (10.3.36)$$

Then use the following fact: If we have two sets of n numbers, for example, $\{t_1, t_2, \ldots, t_n\}$ and $\{s_1, s_2, \ldots, s_n\}$, then the largest sum of pairwise products, one from each set, is given by $\sum_{j=1}^{n} t_{i_j} s_{k_j}$, where $\{i_j\}$ and $\{k_j\}$ are the anti-ranks for the t_i and s_i, respectively, i.e., $t_{i_1} \leq t_{i_2} \leq \cdots \leq t_{i_n}$ and $s_{k_1} \leq s_{k_2} \leq \cdots \leq s_{k_n}$.

10.3.5. Consider the norm given in Exercise 10.3.4. For a location model, define the estimate of θ to be

$$\widehat{\theta} = \text{Argmin}_\theta \|X_i - \theta\|. \qquad (10.3.37)$$

Show that $\widehat{\theta}$ is the Hodges–Lehmann estimate, i.e., satisfies (10.4.25).
Hint: Use the anti-rank version (10.3.36) of the norm when differentiating with respect to θ.

10.3.6. Prove that a pdf (or pmf) $f(x)$ is symmetric about 0 if and only if its mgf is symmetric about 0, provided the mgf exists.

10.3.7. In Exercise 10.1.4, we defined the term scale functional. Show that the parameter τ_W, (10.3.26), is a scale functional.

10.4 Mann–Whitney–Wilcoxon Procedure

Suppose $X_1, X_2, \ldots, X_{n_1}$ is a random sample from a distribution with a continuous cdf $F(x)$ and pdf $f(x)$ and $Y_1, Y_2, \ldots, Y_{n_2}$ is a random sample from a distribution with a continuous cdf $G(x)$ and pdf $g(x)$. For this situation there is a natural null hypothesis given by $H_0 : F(x) = G(x)$ for all x; i.e., the samples are from the same distribution. What about alternative hypotheses besides the general alternative not H_0? An interesting alternative is that X is **stochastically larger** than Y, which is defined by $G(x) \geq F(x)$, for all x, with strict inequality for at least one x. This alternative hypothesis is discussed in the exercises.

For the most part in this section, however, we consider the location model. In this case, $G(x) = F(x - \Delta)$ for some value of Δ. Hence the null hypothesis becomes $H_0 : \Delta = 0$. The parameter Δ is often called the **shift** between the distributions and, in this case, the distribution of Y is the same as the distribution of $X + \Delta$; that is,

$$P(Y \leq y) = P(X + \Delta \leq y) = F(y - \Delta). \qquad (10.4.1)$$

If $\Delta > 0$, then Y is stochastically larger than X; see Exercise 10.4.5.

In the shift case, the parameter Δ is independent of what location functional is used. To see this, suppose we select an arbitrary location functional for X, say, $T(F_X)$. Then we can write X_i as

$$X_i = T(F) + \varepsilon_i,$$

where $\varepsilon_1, \ldots, \varepsilon_{n_1}$ are iid with $T(F_\varepsilon) = 0$. By (10.4.1) it follows that

$$Y_j = T(F_X) + \Delta + \varepsilon_j, \quad j = 1, 2, \ldots, n_2.$$

Hence $T(F_Y) = T(F_X) + \Delta$. Therefore, $\Delta = T(F_Y) - T(F_X)$ for any location functional; i.e., Δ is the same no matter what functional is chosen to model location.

Assume then that the shift model, (10.4.1), holds for the two samples. Alternatives of interest are the usual one- and two-sided alternatives. For convenience we pick on the one-sided hypotheses given by

$$H_0 : \ \Delta = 0 \text{ versus } H_1 : \ \Delta > 0 . \tag{10.4.2}$$

The exercises consider the other hypotheses. Under H_0, the distributions of X and Y are the same, and we can combine the samples to have one large sample of $n = n_1 + n_2$ observations. Suppose we rank the combined samples from 1 to n and consider the statistic

$$W = \sum_{j=1}^{n_2} R(Y_j), \tag{10.4.3}$$

where $R(Y_j)$ denotes the rank of Y_j in the combined sample of n items. This statistic is often called the **Mann–Whitney–Wilcoxon** (MWW) statistic. Under H_0 the ranks are uniformly distributed between the X_is and the Y_js; however, under $H_1 : \ \Delta > 0$, the Y_js should get most of the large ranks. Hence an intuitive rejection rule is given by

$$\text{Reject } H_0 \text{ in favor of } H_1 \text{ if } W \geq c. \tag{10.4.4}$$

We now discuss the null distribution of W, which enables us to select c for the decision rule based on a specified level α. Under H_0, the ranks of the Y_js are equilikely to be any subset of size n_2 from a set of n elements. Recall that there are $\binom{n}{n_2}$ such subsets; therefore, if $\{r_1, \ldots, r_{n_2}\}$ is a subset of size n_2 from $\{1, \ldots, n\}$, then

$$P[R(Y_1) = r_1, \ldots, R(Y_{n_2}) = r_{n_2}] = \binom{n}{n_2}^{-1}. \tag{10.4.5}$$

This implies that the statistic W is distribution free under H_0. Although the null distribution of W cannot be obtained in closed form, there are recursive algorithms which obtain this distribution; see Chapter 2 of the text by Hettmansperger and McKean (2011). In the same way, the distribution of a single rank $R(Y_j)$ is uniformly distributed on the integers $\{1, \ldots, n\}$, under H_0. Hence we immediately have

$$E_{H_0}(W) = \sum_{j=1}^{n_2} E_{H_0}(R(Y_j)) = \sum_{j=1}^{n_2} \sum_{i=1}^{n} i \frac{1}{n} = \sum_{j=1}^{n_2} \frac{n(n+1)}{2n} = \frac{n_2(n+1)}{2}.$$

The variance is displayed below (10.4.8) and a derivation of a more general case is given in Section 10.5. It also can be shown that W is asymptotically normal. We summarize these items in the theorem below.

Theorem 10.4.1. *Suppose $X_1, X_2, \ldots, X_{n_1}$ is a random sample from a distribution with a continuous cdf $F(x)$ and $Y_1, Y_2, \ldots, Y_{n_2}$ is a random sample from a distribution with a continuous cdf $G(x)$. Suppose $H_0 : F(x) = G(x)$, for all x. If H_0 is true, then*

$$W \text{ is distribution free with a symmetric pmf} \tag{10.4.6}$$

$$E_{H_0}[W] = \frac{n_2(n+1)}{2} \tag{10.4.7}$$

$$Var_{H_0}(W) = \frac{n_1 n_2(n+1)}{12} \tag{10.4.8}$$

$$\frac{W - n_2(n+1)/2}{\sqrt{Var_{H_0}(W)}} \text{ has an asymptotically } N(0,1) \text{ distribution.} \tag{10.4.9}$$

The only item of the theorem not discussed above is the symmetry of the null distribution, which we show later. First, consider this example:

Example 10.4.1 (Water Wheel Data Set). In an experiment discussed in Abebe et al. (2001), mice were placed in a wheel that is partially submerged in water. If they keep the wheel moving, they avoid the water. The response is the number of wheel revolutions per minute. Group 1 is a placebo group, while Group 2 consists of mice that are under the influence of a drug. The data are

Group 1 X	2.3	0.3	5.2	3.1	1.1	0.9	2.0	0.7	1.4	0.3
Group 2 Y	0.8	2.8	4.0	2.4	1.2	0.0	6.2	1.5	28.8	0.7

Comparison dotplots of the data (asked for in Exercise 10.4.6) show that the two data sets are similar except for the large outlier in the treatment group. A two-sided hypothesis seems appropriate in this case. Notice that a few of the data points in the data set have the same value (are tied). This happens in real data sets. We follow the usual practice and use the average of the ranks involved to break ties. For example, the observations $x_2 = x_{10} = 0.3$ are tied and the ranks involved for the combined data are 2 and 3. Hence we use 2.5 for the ranks of each of these observations. Continuing in this way, the Wilcoxon test statistic is $w = \sum_{j=1}^{10} R(y_j) = 116.50$. The null mean and variance of W are 105 and 175, respectively. The asymptotic test statistic is $z = (116.5 - 105)/\sqrt{175} = 0.869$ with p-value $2(1 - \Phi(0.869)) = 0.38$ (see below for a discussion on exact p-values). Hence H_0 would not be rejected. The test confirms the comparison dotplots of the data. The t-test based on the difference in means is discussed in Exercise 10.4.6. ∎

We next want to derive some properties of the test statistic and then use these properties to discuss point estimation and confidence intervals for Δ. As in the last section, another way of writing W proves helpful in these regards. Without loss of generality, assume that the Y_js are in order. Recall that the distributions of X_i and Y_j are continuous; hence, we treat the observations as distinct. Thus $R(Y_j) = \#_i\{X_i < Y_j\} + \#_i\{Y_i \leq Y_j\}$. This leads to

$$
\begin{aligned}
W = \sum_{j=1}^{n_2} R(Y_j) &= \sum_{j=1}^{n_2} \#_i\{X_i < Y_j\} + \sum_{j=1}^{n_2} \#_i\{Y_i \leq Y_j\} \\
&= \#_{i,j}\{Y_j > X_i\} + \frac{n_2(n_2+1)}{2}. \qquad (10.4.10)
\end{aligned}
$$

Let $U = \#_{i,j}\{Y_j > X_i\}$; then we have $W = U + n_2(n_2+1)/2$. Hence an equivalent test for the hypotheses (10.4.2) is to reject H_0 if $U \geq c_2$. It follows immediately from Theorem 10.4.1 that, under H_0, U is distribution free with mean $n_1 n_2/2$ and variance (10.4.8) and that it has an asymptotic normal distribution. The symmetry of the null distribution of either U or W can now be easily obtained. Under H_0, both X_i and Y_j have the same distribution, so the distributions of U and $U' = \#_{i,j}\{X_i > Y_j\}$ must be the same. Furthermore, $U + U' = n_1 n_2$. This leads to

$$
\begin{aligned}
P_{H_0}\left(U - \frac{n_1 n_2}{2} = u\right) &= P_{H_0}\left(n_1 n_2 - U' - \frac{n_1 n_2}{2} = u\right) \\
&= P_{H_0}\left(U' - \frac{n_1 n_2}{2} = -u\right) \\
&= P_{H_0}\left(U - \frac{n_1 n_2}{2} = -u\right),
\end{aligned}
$$

which yields the desired symmetry result in Theorem 10.4.1.

Tables for the distribution of U can be found in the literature; see, for instance, Hollander and Wolfe (1999). Many computer packages also return its p-values and critical values. If the reader has access to R, the command `pwilcox(u,n1,n2)` computes $P(U \leq u)$, where `n1` and `n2` denote the sample sizes.

Note that if $G(x) = F(x - \Delta)$, then $Y_j - \Delta$ has the same distribution as X_i. So the process of interest here is

$$
U(\Delta) = \#_{i,j}\{(Y_j - \Delta) > X_i\} = \#_{i,j}\{Y_j - X_i > \Delta)\}. \qquad (10.4.11)
$$

Hence $U(\Delta)$ is counting the number of differences $Y_j - X_i$ which exceed Δ. Let $D_1 < D_2 < \cdots < D_{n_1 n_2}$ denote the $n_1 n_2$ ordered differences of $Y_j - X_i$. Then the graph of $U(\Delta)$ is the same as that in Figure 10.2.2, except the D_is are on the horizontal axis and the n on the vertical axis is replaced by $n_1 n_2$; that is, $U(\Delta)$ is a decreasing step function of Δ which steps down one unit at each difference D_i, with the maximum value of $n_1 n_2$.

We can then proceed as in the last two sections to obtain properties of inference based on the Wilcoxon. Let the integer c_α denote the critical value of a level α test of the hypotheses (10.2.2) based on the statistic U; i.e., $\alpha = P_{H_0}(U \geq c_\alpha)$. Let $\gamma_U(\Delta) = P_\Delta(U \geq c_\alpha)$, for $\Delta \geq 0$, denote the power function of the test. The translation property, Lemma 10.2.1, holds for the process $U(\Delta)$. Hence, as in Theorem 10.2.1, the power function is a nondecreasing function of Δ. In particular, the Wilcoxon test is an unbiased test for the one-sided hypotheses (10.4.2).

10.4.1   Asymptotic Relative Efficiency

The asymptotic relative efficiency (ARE) of the Wilcoxon follows along similar lines as for the sign test statistic in Section 10.2.1. Here, consider the sequence of local alternatives given by

$$H_0 : \Delta = 0 \text{ versus } H_{1n} : \Delta_n = \tfrac{\delta}{\sqrt{n}}, \qquad (10.4.12)$$

where $\delta > 0$. We also assume that

$$\tfrac{n_1}{n} \to \lambda_1, \ \tfrac{n_2}{n} \to \lambda_2, \ \text{ where } \lambda_1 + \lambda_2 = 1. \qquad (10.4.13)$$

This assumption implies that $n_1/n_2 \to \lambda_1/\lambda_2$; i.e, the sample sizes maintain the same ratio asymptotically.

To determine the efficacy of the MWW, consider the average

$$\overline{U}(\Delta) = \frac{1}{n_1 n_2} U(\Delta). \qquad (10.4.14)$$

It follows immediately that

$$\mu_U(0) = E_0(\overline{U}(0)) = \tfrac{1}{2} \quad \text{and} \quad \overline{\sigma}_U^2(0) = \tfrac{n+1}{12 n_1 n_2}. \qquad (10.4.15)$$

Because the pairs (X_i, Y_j) are iid we have

$$\mu_U(\Delta_n) = E_{\Delta_n}(\overline{U}(0)) = E_0(\overline{U}(-\Delta_n)) = P_0(Y - X > -\Delta_n). \qquad (10.4.16)$$

The independence of X and Y and the fact $\int_{-\infty}^{\infty} F(x)f(x)\,dx = 1/2$ gives

$$
\begin{aligned}
P_0(Y - X > -\Delta_n) &= E_0(P_0[Y > X - \Delta_n | X]) \\
&= E_0(1 - F(X - \Delta_n)) \\
&= 1 - \int_{-\infty}^{\infty} F(x - \Delta_n)f(x)\,dx \\
&= \frac{1}{2} + \int_{-\infty}^{\infty} (F(x) - F(x - \Delta_n))f(x)\,dx \\
&\approx \frac{1}{2} + \Delta_n \int_{-\infty}^{\infty} f^2(x)\,dx, \qquad (10.4.17)
\end{aligned}
$$

where we have applied the mean value theorem to obtain the last line. Putting together (10.4.15) and (10.4.17), we have the efficacy

$$c_U = \lim_{n \to \infty} \frac{\mu_{\overline{U}}'(0)}{\sqrt{n}\,\sigma_{\overline{U}}(0)} = \sqrt{12}\sqrt{\lambda_1 \lambda_2} \int_{-\infty}^{\infty} f^2(x)\,dx. \qquad (10.4.18)$$

This derivation can be made rigorous, leading to the following theorem:

Theorem 10.4.2 (Asymptotic Power Lemma). *Consider the sequence of hypotheses (10.4.12). The limit of the power function of the size α Mann–Whitney–Wilcoxon test is given by*

$$\lim_{n \to \infty} \gamma_U(\Delta_n) = 1 - \Phi\left(z_\alpha - \sqrt{\lambda_1 \lambda_2}\,\delta \tau_W^{-1}\right), \qquad (10.4.19)$$

where $\tau_W = 1/\sqrt{12} \int_{-\infty}^{\infty} f^2(x)\, dx$ is the reciprocal of the efficacy c_U and $\Phi(z)$ is the cdf of a standard normal random variable.

As in the last two sections, we can use this theorem to establish a relative measure of efficiency by considering sample size determination. Consider the hypotheses (10.4.2). Suppose we want to determine the sample size $n = n_1 + n_2$ for a level α MWW test to detect the alternative Δ^* with approximate power γ^*. By Theorem 10.4.2, we have the equation

$$\gamma^* = \gamma_U(\sqrt{n}\Delta^*/\sqrt{n}) \approx 1 - \Phi(z_\alpha - \sqrt{\lambda_1\lambda_2}\sqrt{n}\Delta^*\tau_W^{-1}). \tag{10.4.20}$$

This leads to the equation

$$z_{\gamma^*} = z_\alpha - \sqrt{\lambda_1\lambda_2}\,\delta\tau_W^{-1}, \tag{10.4.21}$$

where $\Phi(z_{\gamma^*}) = 1 - \gamma^*$. Solving for n, we obtain

$$n_U \approx \left(\frac{(z_\alpha - z_{\gamma^*})\tau_W}{\Delta^*\sqrt{\lambda_1\lambda_2}}\right)^2. \tag{10.4.22}$$

To use this in applications, the sample size proportions $\lambda_1 = n_1/n$ and $\lambda_2 = n_2/n$ must be given. As Exercise 10.4.1 points out, the most powerful two-sample designs have sample size proportions of $1/2$, i.e., equal sample sizes.

To use this to obtain the asymptotic relative efficiency between the MWW and the two-sample pooled t-test, Exercise 10.4.2 shows that the sample size needed for the two-sample t-tests to attain approximate power γ^* to detect Δ^* is given by

$$n_{\mathrm{LS}} \approx \left(\frac{(z_\alpha - z_{\gamma^*})\sigma}{\Delta^*\sqrt{\lambda_1\lambda_2}}\right)^2, \tag{10.4.23}$$

where σ is the variance of e_i. Hence, as in the last section, the asymptotic relative efficiency between the Wilcoxon test (MWW) and the t-test is the ratio of the sample sizes (10.4.22) and (10.4.23), which is

$$\mathrm{ARE}(\mathrm{MWW}, \mathrm{LS}) = \frac{\sigma^2}{\tau_W^2}. \tag{10.4.24}$$

Note that this is the same ARE as derived in the last section between the signed-rank Wilcoxon and the t-test. If $f(x)$ is a normal pdf, then the MWW has efficiency 95.5% relative to the pooled t-test. Thus the MWW tests lose little efficiency at the normal. On the other hand, it is much more efficient than the pooled t-test at the family of contaminated normals (with $\epsilon > 0$), as in Example 10.3.3.

10.4.2 Estimating Equations Based on the Mann–Whitney–Wilcoxon

As with the signed-rank Wilcoxon procedure in the last section, we invert the test statistic to obtain an estimate of Δ. As discussed in the next section, this estimate can be defined in terms of minimizing a norm. The estimator $\widehat{\theta}_W$ solves the estimating equations

$$U(\Delta) = E_{H_0}(U) = \frac{n_1 n_2}{2}. \qquad (10.4.25)$$

Recalling the description of the process $U(\Delta)$ described above, it is clear that the Hodges–Lehmann estimator is given by

$$\widehat{\Delta}_U = \operatorname{med}_{i,j}\{Y_j - X_i\}. \qquad (10.4.26)$$

The asymptotic distribution of the estimate follows in the same way as in the last section based on the process $U(\Delta)$ and the asymptotic power lemma, Theorem 10.4.2. We avoid sketching the proof and simply state the result as a theorem:

Theorem 10.4.3. *Assume that the random variables $X_1, X_2, \ldots, X_{n_1}$ are iid with pdf $f(x)$ and that the random variables $Y_1, Y_2, \ldots, Y_{n_2}$ are iid with pdf $f(x - \Delta)$. Then*

$$\widehat{\Delta}_U \text{ has an approximate } N\left(\Delta, \tau_W^2\left(\frac{1}{n_1} + \frac{1}{n_2}\right)\right) \text{ distribution,} \qquad (10.4.27)$$

where $\tau_W = (\sqrt{12}\int_{-\infty}^{\infty} f^2(x)\,dx)^{-1}$.

As Exercise 10.4.3 shows, provided the $\operatorname{Var}(\varepsilon_i) = \sigma^2 < \infty$, the LS estimate $\overline{Y} - \overline{X}$ of Δ has the following approximate distribution:

$$\overline{Y} - \overline{X} \text{ has an approximate } N\left(\Delta, \sigma^2\left(\frac{1}{n_1} + \frac{1}{n_2}\right)\right) \text{ distribution.} \qquad (10.4.28)$$

Note that the ratio of the asymptotic variances of $\widehat{\Delta}_U$ is given by the ratio (10.4.24). Hence the ARE of the tests agrees with the ARE of the corresponding estimates.

10.4.3 Confidence Interval for the Shift Parameter Δ

The confidence interval for Δ corresponding to the MWW estimate is derived the same way as the Hodges–Lehmann estimate in the last section. For a given level α, let the integer c denote the critical point of the MWW distribution such that $P_\Delta[U(\Delta) \le c] = \alpha/2$. As in Section 10.2.3, we then have

$$\begin{aligned} 1 - \alpha &= P_\Delta[c < U(\Delta) < n_1 n_2 - c] \\ &= P_\Delta[D_{c+1} \le \Delta < D_{n_1 n_2 - c}], \qquad (10.4.29) \end{aligned}$$

where $D_1 < D_2 < \cdots < D_{n_1 n_2}$ denote the order differences $Y_j - X_i$. Therefore, the interval $[D_{c+1}, D_{n_1 n_2 - c})$ is a $(1 - \alpha)100\%$ confidence interval for Δ. Using the null asymptotic distribution of the MWW test statistic U, we have the following approximation for c:

$$c \approx \frac{n_1 n_2}{2} - z_{\alpha/2}\sqrt{\frac{n_1 n_2 (n+1)}{12}} - \frac{1}{2}, \qquad (10.4.30)$$

where $\Phi(-z_{\alpha/2}) = \alpha/2$; see Exercise 10.4.4. In practice, we use the closest integer to c.

Example 10.4.2 (Example 10.4.1, Continued). Returning to Example 10.4.1, the MWW estimate of Δ is $\widehat{\Delta} = 1.15$. The asymptotic rule for the selection of the differences which enter a 95% confidence interval gives the value for $c \approx 24$. Hence the confidence interval is (D_{25}, D_{76}), which for this data set has the value $(-0.7, 2.6)$. Hence, in agreement with the test statistic, the confidence interval covers the null hypothesis of $\Delta = 0$. ∎

Remark 10.4.1 (Computation). Several statistical computing packages compute the Mann–Whitney–Wilcoxon analysis. For example, the minitab (1991) command `mann` computes the Hodges–Lehmann estimate, the distribution free confidence interval, and the Mann–Whitney–Wilcoxon test. The R function `wilcox.test` also computes this analysis. For example, if `x` and `y` are the vectors of observations, then the command `wilcox.test(x,y,conf.int=T,conf.level=.90)` returns the Hodges–Lehmann estimate, a 90% confidence interval, and the test of $H_0 : \Delta = 0$ versus $H_1 : \Delta \neq 0$. See also Hettmansperger and McKean (2011) for R functions which produce the Mann–Whitney–Wilcoxon two-sample analysis ∎

EXERCISES

10.4.1. By considering the asymptotic power lemma, Theorem 10.4.2, show that the equal sample size situation $n_1 = n_2$ is the most powerful design among designs with $n_1 + n_2 = n$, n fixed, when level and alternatives are also fixed.
Hint: Show that this problem is equivalent to maximizing the function

$$g(n_1) = \frac{n_1(n - n_1)}{n^2},$$

and then obtain the result.

10.4.2. Consider the asymptotic version of the t-test for the hypotheses (10.4.2) which is discussed in Example 4.6.2.

  (a) Using the setup of Theorem 10.4.2, derive the corresponding asymptotic power lemma for this test.

  (b) Use your result in part (a) to obtain expression (10.4.23).

10.4.3. Use the Central Limit Theorem to show that expression (10.4.28) is true.

10.4.4. For the cutoff index c of the confidence interval (10.4.29) for Δ, derive the approximation given in expression (10.4.30).

10.4.5. Let X be a continuous random variable with cdf $F(x)$. Suppose $Y = X + \Delta$, where $\Delta > 0$. Show that Y is stochastically larger than X.

10.4.6. Consider the data given in Example 10.4.1.

  (a) Obtain comparison dotplots of the data.

(b) Show that the difference in sample means is 3.11, which is much larger than the MWW estimate of shift. What accounts for this discrepancy?

(c) Show that the 95% confidence interval for Δ using t is given by $(-2.7, 8.92)$. Why is this interval so much larger than the corresponding MWW interval?

(d) Show that the value of the t-test statistic, discussed in Example 4.6.2, for this data set is 1.12 with p-value 0.28. Although, as with the MWW results, this p-value would be considered insignificant, it seems lower than warranted [consider, for example, the comparison dotplots of part (a)]. Why?

10.5 General Rank Scores

Suppose we are interested in estimating the center of a symmetric distribution using an estimator which corresponds to a distribution-free procedure. Presently our choice would be either the sign test or the signed-rank Wilcoxon test. If the sample is drawn from a normal distribution, then of the two we would choose the signed-rank Wilcoxon because it is much more efficient than the sign test at the normal distribution. But the Wilcoxon is not fully efficient. This raises the question: Is there is a distribution-free procedure which is fully efficient at the normal distribution, i.e., has efficiency of 100% relative to the t-test at the normal? More generally, suppose we specify a distribution. Is there a distribution-free procedure which has 100% efficiency relative to the mle at that distribution? In general, the answer to both of these questions is yes. In this section, we explore these questions for the two-sample location problem since this problem generalizes immediately to the regression problem of Section 10.7. A similar theory can be developed for the one-sample problem; see Chapter 1 of Hettmansperger and McKean (2011).

As in the last section, let $X_1, X_2, \ldots, X_{n_1}$ be a random sample from the continuous distribution with cdf and pdf $F(x)$ and $f(x)$, respectively. Let $Y_1, Y_2, \ldots, Y_{n_2}$ be a random sample from the continuous distribution with cdf and pdf, respectively, $F(x - \Delta)$ and $f(x - \Delta)$, where Δ is the shift in location. Let $n = n_1 + n_2$ denote the combined sample sizes. Consider the hypotheses

$$H_0 : \Delta = 0 \text{ versus } H_1 : \Delta > 0. \tag{10.5.1}$$

We first define a general class of rank scores. Let $\varphi(u)$ be a nondecreasing function defined on the interval $(0, 1)$, such that $\int_0^1 \varphi^2(u) \, du < \infty$. We call $\varphi(u)$ a **score** function. Without loss of generality, we standardize this function so that $\int_0^1 \varphi(u) \, du = 0$ and $\int_0^1 \varphi^2(u) \, du = 1$; see Exercise 10.5.1. Next, define the scores $a_\varphi(i) = \varphi[i/(n+1)]$, for $i = 1, \ldots, n$. Then $a_\varphi(1) \leq a_\varphi(2) \leq \cdots \leq a_\varphi(n)$ and assume that $\sum_{i=1}^n a(i) = 0$, (this essentially follows from $\int \varphi(u) \, du = 0$, see Exercise 10.5.12). Consider the test statistic

$$W_\varphi = \sum_{j=1}^{n_2} a_\varphi(R(Y_j)), \tag{10.5.2}$$

where $R(Y_j)$ denotes the rank of Y_j in the combined sample of n observations. Since the scores are nondecreasing, a natural rejection rule is given by

$$\text{Reject } H_0 \text{ in favor of } H_1 \text{ if } W_\varphi \geq c. \qquad (10.5.3)$$

Note that if we use the linear score function $\varphi(u) = \sqrt{12}(u - (1/2))$, then

$$W_\varphi = \sum_{j=1}^{n_2} \sqrt{12}\left(\frac{R(Y_j)}{n+1} - \frac{1}{2}\right) = \frac{\sqrt{12}}{n+1}\sum_{j=1}^{n_2}\left(R(Y_j) - \frac{n+1}{2}\right)$$

$$= \frac{\sqrt{12}}{n+1}W - \frac{\sqrt{12}n_2}{2}, \qquad (10.5.4)$$

where W is the MWW test statistic, (10.4.3). Hence the special case of a linear score function results in the MWW test statistic.

To complete the decision rule (10.5.2), we need the null distribution of the test statistic W_φ. But many of its properties follow along the same lines as that of the MWW test. First, W_φ is distribution free because, under the null hypothesis, every subset of ranks for the Y_js is equilikely. In general, the distribution of W_φ cannot be obtained in closed form, but it can be generated recursively similarly to the distribution of the MWW test statistic. Next, to obtain the null mean of W_φ, use the fact that $R(Y_j)$ is uniform on the integers $1, 2, \ldots, n$. Because $\sum_{i=1}^n a_\varphi(i) = 0$, we then have

$$E_{H_0}(W_\varphi) = \sum_{j=1}^{n_2} E_{H_0}(a_\varphi(R(Y_j))) = \sum_{j=1}^{n_2}\sum_{i=1}^n a_\varphi(i)\frac{1}{n} = 0. \qquad (10.5.5)$$

To determine the null variance, first define the quantity s_a^2 by the equation

$$E_{H_0}(a_\varphi^2(R(Y_j))) = \sum_{i=1}^n a_\varphi^2(i)\frac{1}{n} = \frac{1}{n}\sum_{i=1}^n a_\varphi^2(i) = \frac{1}{n}s_a^2. \qquad (10.5.6)$$

As Exercise 10.5.4 shows, $s_a^2/n \approx 1$. Since $E_{H_0}(W_\varphi) = 0$, we have

$$\text{Var}_{H_0}(W_\varphi) = E_{H_0}(W_\varphi^2) = \sum_{j=1}^{n_2}\sum_{j'=1}^{n_2} E_{H_0}[a_\varphi(R(Y_j))a_\varphi(R(Y_{j'}))]$$

$$= \sum_{j=1}^{n_2} E_{H_0}[a_\varphi^2(R(Y_j))] + \sum_{j \neq j'}\sum E_{H_0}[a_\varphi(R(Y_j))a_\varphi(R(Y_{j'}))]$$

$$= \frac{n_2}{n}s_a^2 - \frac{n_2(n_2-1)}{n(n-1)}s_a^2 \qquad (10.5.7)$$

$$= \frac{n_1 n_2}{n(n-1)}s_a^2; \qquad (10.5.8)$$

see Exercise 10.5.2 for the derivation of the second term in expression (10.5.7). In more advanced books, it is shown that W_φ is asymptotically normal under H_0. Hence the corresponding asymptotic decision rule of level α is

$$\text{Reject } H_0 \text{ in favor of } H_1 \text{ if } z = \frac{W_\varphi}{\sqrt{\text{Var}_{H_0}(W_\varphi)}} \geq z_\alpha. \qquad (10.5.9)$$

To answer the questions posed in the first paragraph of this section, the efficacy of the test statistic W_φ is needed. To proceed along the lines of the last section, define the process

$$W_\varphi(\Delta) = \sum_{j=1}^{n_2} a_\varphi(R(Y_j - \Delta)), \qquad (10.5.10)$$

where $R(Y_j - \Delta)$ denotes the rank of $Y_j - \Delta$ among $X_1, \ldots, X_{n_1}, Y_1 - \Delta, \ldots, Y_{n_2} - \Delta$. In the last section, the process for the MWW statistic was also written in terms of counts of the differences $Y_j - X_i$. We are not as fortunate here, but as the next theorem shows, this general process is a simple decreasing step function of Δ.

Theorem 10.5.1. *The process $W_\varphi(\Delta)$ is a decreasing step function of Δ which steps down at each difference $Y_j - X_i$, $i = 1, \ldots, n_1$ and $j = 1, \ldots, n_2$. Its maximum and minimum values are $\sum_{j=n_1+1}^{n} a_\varphi(j) \geq 0$ and $\sum_{j=1}^{n_2} a_\varphi(j) \leq 0$, respectively.*

Proof: Suppose $\Delta_1 < \Delta_2$ and $W_\varphi(\Delta_1) \neq W_\varphi(\Delta_2)$. Hence the assignment of the ranks among the X_i and $Y_j - \Delta$ must differ at Δ_1 and Δ_2; that is, then there must be a j and an i such that $Y_j - \Delta_2 < X_i$ and $Y_j - \Delta_1 > X_i$. This implies that $\Delta_1 < Y_j - X_i < \Delta_2$. Thus $W_\varphi(\Delta)$ changes values at the differences $Y_j - X_i$. To show it is decreasing, suppose $\Delta_1 < Y_j - X_i < \Delta_2$ and there are no other differences between Δ_1 and Δ_2. Then $Y_j - \Delta_1$ and X_i must have adjacent ranks; otherwise, there would be more than one difference between Δ_1 and Δ_2. Since $Y_j - \Delta_1 > X_i$ and $Y_j - \Delta_2 < X_i$, we have

$$R(Y_j - \Delta_1) = R(X_i) + 1 \quad \text{and} \quad R(Y_j - \Delta_2) = R(X_i) - 1.$$

Also, in the expression for $W_\varphi(\Delta)$, only the rank of the Y_j term has changed in the interval $[\Delta_1, \Delta_2]$. Therefore, since the scores are nondecreasing,

$$
\begin{aligned}
W_\varphi(\Delta_1) - W_\varphi(\Delta_2) &= \sum_{k \neq j} a_\varphi(R(Y_k - \Delta_1)) + a_\varphi(R(Y_j - \Delta_1)) \\
&\quad - \left[\sum_{k \neq j} a_\varphi(R(Y_k - \Delta_2)) + a_\varphi(R(Y_j - \Delta_2)) \right] \\
&= a_\varphi(R(X_i) + 1)) - a_\varphi(R(X_i) - 1)) \geq 0.
\end{aligned}
$$

Because $W_\varphi(\Delta)$ is a decreasing step function and steps only at the differences $Y_j - X_i$, its maximum value occurs when $\Delta < Y_j - X_i$, for all i, j, i.e., when $X_i < Y_j - \Delta$, for all i, j. Hence, in this case, the variables $Y_j - \Delta$ must get all the high ranks, so

$$\max_\Delta W_\varphi(\Delta) = \sum_{j=n_1+1}^{n} a_\varphi(j).$$

Note that this maximum value must be nonnegative. For suppose it was strictly negative, then at least one $a_\varphi(j) < 0$ for $j = n_1 + 1, \ldots, n$. Because the scores are nondecreasing, $a_\varphi(i) < 0$ for all $i = 1, \ldots, n_1$. This leads to the contradiction

$$0 > \sum_{j=n_1+1}^{n} a_\varphi(j) \geq \sum_{j=n_1+1}^{n} a_\varphi(j) + \sum_{j=1}^{n_1} a_\varphi(j) = 0.$$

The results for the minimum value are obtained in the same way; see Exercise 10.5.6. ∎

As Exercise 10.5.7 shows, the translation property, Lemma 10.2.1, holds for the process $W_\varphi(\Delta)$. Using this result and the last theorem, we can show that the power function of the test statistic W_φ for the hypotheses (10.5.1) is nondecreasing. Hence the test is unbiased.

10.5.1   Efficacy

We next sketch the derivation of the efficacy of the test based on W_φ. Our arguments can be made rigorous; see advanced texts. Consider the statistic given by the average

$$\overline{W}_\varphi(0) = \frac{1}{n} W_\varphi(0). \tag{10.5.11}$$

Based on (10.5.5) and (10.5.8), we have

$$\mu_\varphi(0) = E_0(\overline{W}_\varphi(0)) = 0 \quad \text{and} \quad \sigma_\varphi^2 = \mathrm{Var}_0(\overline{W}_\varphi(0)) = \frac{n_1 n_2}{n(n-1)} n^{-2} s_a^2. \tag{10.5.12}$$

Notice from Exercise 10.5.4 that the variance of $\overline{W}_\varphi(0)$ is of the order $O(n^{-2})$. We have

$$\mu_\varphi(\Delta) = E_\Delta[\overline{W}_\varphi(0)] = E_0[\overline{W}_\varphi(-\Delta)] = \frac{1}{n} \sum_{j=1}^{n_2} E_0[a_\varphi(R(Y_j + \Delta))]. \tag{10.5.13}$$

Suppose that $\widehat{F}_{n_1}$ and $\widehat{F}_{n_2}$ are the empirical cdfs of the random samples $X_1, \ldots, X_{n_1}$ and $Y_1, \ldots, Y_{n_2}$, respectively. The relationship between the ranks and empirical cdfs follows as

$$\begin{aligned} R(Y_j + \Delta) &= \#_k\{Y_k + \Delta \leq Y_j + \Delta\} + \#_i\{X_i \leq Y_j + \Delta\} \\ &= \#_k\{Y_k \leq Y_j\} + \#_i\{X_i \leq Y_j + \Delta\} \\ &= n_2 \widehat{F}_{n_2}(Y_j) + n_1 \widehat{F}_{n_1}(Y_j + \Delta). \end{aligned} \tag{10.5.14}$$

Substituting this last expression into expression (10.5.13), we get

$$\begin{aligned} \mu_\varphi(\Delta) &= \frac{1}{n} \sum_{j=1}^{n_2} E_0 \left\{ \varphi \left[\frac{n_2}{n+1} \widehat{F}_{n_2}(Y_j) + \frac{n_1}{n+1} \widehat{F}_{n_1}(Y_j + \Delta) \right] \right\} \tag{10.5.15} \\ &\to \lambda_2 E_0 \left\{ \varphi \left[\lambda_2 F(Y) + \lambda_1 F(Y + \Delta) \right] \right\} \tag{10.5.16} \\ &= \lambda_2 \int_{-\infty}^{\infty} \varphi \left[\lambda_2 F(Y) + \lambda_1 F(Y + \Delta) \right] f(y) \, dy. \tag{10.5.17} \end{aligned}$$

The limit in expression (10.5.16) is actually a double limit, which follows from $\widehat{F}_{n_i}(x) \to F(x)$, $i = 1, 2$, under H_0, and the observation that upon substituting F for the empirical cdfs in expression (10.5.15), the sum contains identically distributed random variables and, thus, the same expectation. These approximations can be made rigorous. It follows immediately that

$$\frac{d}{d\Delta}\mu_\varphi(\Delta) = \lambda_2 \int_{-\infty}^{\infty} \varphi'\left[\lambda_2 F(Y) + \lambda_1 F(Y + \Delta)\right] \lambda_1 f(y + \Delta) f(y)\, dy.$$

Hence

$$\mu_\varphi'(0) = \lambda_1 \lambda_2 \int_{-\infty}^{\infty} \varphi'[F(y)] f^2(y)\, dy. \qquad (10.5.18)$$

From (10.5.12),

$$\sqrt{n}\sigma_\varphi = \sqrt{n}\sqrt{\frac{n_1 n_2}{n(n-1)}}\frac{1}{\sqrt{n}}\sqrt{\frac{1}{n}s_a^2} \to \sqrt{\lambda_1 \lambda_2}. \qquad (10.5.19)$$

Based on (10.5.18) and (10.5.19), the efficacy of W_φ is given by

$$c_\varphi = \lim_{n\to\infty}\frac{\mu_\varphi'(0)}{\sqrt{n}\sigma_\varphi} = \sqrt{\lambda_1 \lambda_2} \int_{-\infty}^{\infty} \varphi'[F(y)] f^2(y)\, dy. \qquad (10.5.20)$$

Using the efficacy, the asymptotic power can be derived for the test statistic W_φ. Consider the sequence of local alternatives given by (10.4.12) and the level α asymptotic test based on W_φ. Denote the power function of the test by $\gamma_\varphi(\Delta_n)$. Then it can be shown that

$$\lim_{n\to\infty}\gamma_\varphi(\Delta_n) = 1 - \Phi(z_\alpha - c_\varphi\delta), \qquad (10.5.21)$$

where $\Phi(z)$ is the cdf of a standard normal random variable. Sample size determination based on the test statistic W_φ proceeds as in the last few sections; see Exercise 10.5.8.

10.5.2   Estimating Equations Based on General Scores

Suppose we are using the scores $a_\varphi(i) = \varphi(i/(n+1))$ discussed in Section 10.5.1. Recall that the mean of the test statistic W_φ is 0. Hence the corresponding estimator of Δ solves the estimating equations

$$W_\varphi(\widehat{\Delta}) \approx 0. \qquad (10.5.22)$$

By Theorem 10.5.1, $W_\varphi(\widehat{\Delta})$ is a decreasing step function of Δ. Furthermore, the maximum value is positive and the minimum value is negative (only degenerate cases would result in one or both of these as 0); hence, the solution to equation (10.5.22) exists. Because $W_\varphi(\widehat{\Delta})$ is a step function, it may not be unique. When it is not unique, though, as with Wilcoxon and median procedures, there is an interval of solutions, so the midpoint of the interval can be chosen. This is an easy equation to solve numerically because simple iterative techniques such as the bisection method or the method of false position can be used; see the discussion on page 210 of Hettmansperger and McKean (2011). The asymptotic distribution of the estimator can be derived using the asymptotic power lemma and is given by

$$\widehat{\Delta}_\varphi \text{ has an approximate } N\left(\Delta, \tau_\varphi^2\left(\tfrac{1}{n_1} + \tfrac{1}{n_2}\right)\right) \text{ distribution,} \qquad (10.5.23)$$

where

$$\tau_\varphi = \left[\int_{-\infty}^{\infty} \varphi'[F(y)] f^2(y)\, dy\right]^{-1}. \qquad (10.5.24)$$

Hence the efficacy can be expressed as $c_\varphi = \sqrt{\lambda_1 \lambda_2} \tau_\varphi^{-1}$. As Exercise 10.5.9 shows, the parameter τ_φ is a scale parameter. Since the efficacy is $c_\varphi = \sqrt{\lambda_1 \lambda_2} \tau_\varphi^{-1}$, the efficacy varies inversely with scale. This observation proves helpful in the next subsection.

10.5.3 Optimization: Best Estimates

We can now answer the questions posed in the first paragraph. For a given pdf $f(x)$, we show that in general we can select a score function which maximizes the power of the test and which minimizes the asymptotic variance of the estimator. Under certain conditions we show that estimators based on this optimal score function have the same efficiency as maximum likelihood estimators (mles); i.e., they obtain the Rao–Cramér Lower Bound.

As above, let $X_1, \ldots, X_{n_1}$ be a random sample from the continuous cdf $F(x)$ with pdf $f(x)$. Let $Y_1, \ldots, Y_{n_2}$ be a random sample from the continuous cdf $F(x - \Delta)$ with pdf $f(x - \Delta)$. The problem is to choose φ to maximize the efficacy c_φ given in expression (10.5.20). Note that maximizing the efficacy is equivalent to minimizing the asymptotic variance of the corresponding estimator of Δ.

For a general score function $\varphi(u)$, consider its efficacy given by expression (10.5.20). Without loss of generality, the relative sample sizes in this expression can be ignored, so we consider $c_\varphi^* = (\sqrt{\lambda_1 \lambda_2})^{-1} c_\varphi$. If we make the change of variables $u = F(y)$ and then integrate by parts, we get

$$
\begin{aligned}
c_\varphi^* &= \int_{-\infty}^{\infty} \varphi'[F(y)] f^2(y)\, dy \\
&= \int_0^1 \varphi'(u) f(F^{-1}(u))\, du \\
&= \int_0^1 \varphi(u) \left[-\frac{f'(F^{-1}(u))}{f(F^{-1}(u))}\right] du. \qquad (10.5.25)
\end{aligned}
$$

Recall that the score function $\int \varphi^2(u)\, du = 1$. Thus we can state the problem as

$$
\begin{aligned}
\max_\varphi c_\varphi^{*2} &= \max_\varphi \left\{\int_0^1 \varphi(u)\left[-\frac{f'(F^{-1}(u))}{f(F^{-1}(u))}\right] du\right\}^2 \\
&= \left\{\max_\varphi \frac{\left\{\int_0^1 \varphi(u)\left[-\frac{f'(F^{-1}(u))}{f(F^{-1}(u))}\right] du\right\}^2}{\int_0^1 \varphi^2(u)\, du \int_0^1 \left[\frac{f'(F^{-1}(u))}{f(F^{-1}(u))}\right]^2 du}\right\} \int_0^1 \left[\frac{f'(F^{-1}(u))}{f(F^{-1}(u))}\right]^2 du.
\end{aligned}
$$

The quantity that we are maximizing in the braces of this last expression, however, is the square of a correlation coefficient, which achieves its maximum value 1. Therefore, by choosing the score function $\varphi(u) = \varphi_f(u)$, where

$$\varphi_f(u) = -\kappa \frac{f'(F^{-1}(u))}{f(F^{-1}(u))}, \qquad (10.5.26)$$

and κ is a constant chosen so that $\int \varphi_f^2(u)\, du = 1$, then the correlation coefficient is 1 and the maximum value is

$$I(f) = \int_0^1 \left[\frac{f'(F^{-1}(u))}{f(F^{-1}(u))} \right]^2 du, \qquad (10.5.27)$$

which is Fisher information for the location model. We call the score function given by (10.5.26) the **optimal score function**.

In terms of estimation, if $\widehat{\Delta}$ is the corresponding estimator, then, according to (10.5.24), it has the asymptotic variance

$$\tau_\varphi^2 = \left[\frac{1}{I(f)} \right] \left(\frac{1}{n_1} + \frac{1}{n_2} \right). \qquad (10.5.28)$$

Thus the estimator $\widehat{\Delta}$ achieves asymptotically the Rao–Cramér lower bound; that is, $\widehat{\Delta}$ is an asymptotically efficient estimator of Δ. In terms of asymptotic relative efficiency, the ARE between the estimator $\widehat{\Delta}$ and the mle of Δ is 1. Thus we have answered the second question of the first paragraph of this section.

Now we look at some examples. The initial example assumes that the distribution of ε_i is normal, which answers the leading question at the beginning of this section. First, though, note an invariance which simplifies matters. Suppose Z is a scale and location transformation of a random variable X; i.e., $Z = a(X - b)$, where $a > 0$ and $-\infty < b < \infty$. Because the efficacy varies indirectly with scale, we have $c_{f_Z}^2 = a^{-2} c_{f_X}^2$. Furthermore, as Exercise 10.5.9 shows, the efficacy is invariant to location and, also, $I(f_Z) = a^{-2} I(f_X)$. Hence the quantity maximized above is invariant to changes in location and scale. In particular, in the derivation of optimal scores, only the form of the density is important.

Example 10.5.1 (Normal Scores). Suppose the error random variable ε_i has a normal distribution. Based on the discussion in the last paragraph, we can take the pdf of a $N(0,1)$ distribution as the form of the density. So consider $f_Z(z) = \phi(z) = (2\pi)^{-1/2} \exp\{-2^{-1}z^2\}$. Then $-\phi'(z) = z\phi(z)$. Let $\Phi(z)$ denote the cdf of Z. Hence the optimal score function is

$$\varphi_N(u) = -\kappa \frac{\phi'(\Phi^{-1}(u))}{\phi(\Phi^{-1}(u))} = \Phi^{-1}(u); \qquad (10.5.29)$$

see Exercise 10.5.5, which shows that $\kappa = 1$ as well as that $\int \varphi_N(u)\, du = 0$. The corresponding scores, $a_N(i) = \Phi^{-1}(i/(n+1))$, are often called the **normal scores**. Denote the process by

$$W_N(\Delta) = \sum_{j=1}^{n_2} \Phi^{-1}[R(Y_j - \Delta)/(n+1)]. \qquad (10.5.30)$$

The associated test statistic for the hypotheses (10.5.1) is the statistic $W_N = W_N(0)$. The estimator of Δ solves the estimating equations

$$W_N(\widehat{\Delta}_N) \approx 0. \tag{10.5.31}$$

Although the estimate cannot be obtained in closed form, this equation is relatively easy to solve numerically. From the above discussion, $\text{ARE}(\widehat{\Delta}_N, \overline{Y} - \overline{X}) = 1$ at the normal distribution. Hence normal score procedures are fully efficient at the normal distribution. Actually, a much more powerful result can be obtained for symmetric distributions. It can be shown that $\text{ARE}(\widehat{\Delta}_N, \overline{Y} - \overline{X}) \geq 1$ at all symmetric distributions. ∎

Example 10.5.2 (Wilcoxon Scores). Suppose the random errors, ε_i, $i = 1, 2, \ldots, n$, have a logistic distribution with pdf $f_Z(z) = \exp\{-z\}/(1 + \exp\{-z\})^2$. Then the corresponding cdf is $F_Z(z) = (1 + \exp\{-z\})^{-1}$. As Exercise 10.5.11 shows,

$$-\frac{f'_Z(z)}{f_Z(z)} = F_Z(z)(1 - \exp\{-z\}) \quad \text{and} \quad F_Z^{-1}(u) = \log\frac{u}{1-u}. \tag{10.5.32}$$

Upon standardization, this leads to the optimal score function,

$$\varphi_W(u) = \sqrt{12}(u - (1/2)), \tag{10.5.33}$$

that is, the Wilcoxon scores. The properties of the inference based on Wilcoxon scores are discussed in Section 10.4. Let $\widehat{\Delta}_W = \text{med}\{Y_j - X_i\}$ denote the corresponding estimate. Recall that $\text{ARE}(\widehat{\Delta}_W, \overline{Y} - \overline{X}) = 0.955$ at the normal. Hodges and Lehmann (1956) showed that $\text{ARE}(\widehat{\Delta}_W, \overline{Y} - \overline{X}) \geq 0.864$ over all symmetric distributions. ∎

Example 10.5.3. As a numerical illustration, we consider some generated normal observations. The first sample, labeled X, was generated from a $N(48, 10^2)$ distribution, while the second sample, Y, was generated from a $N(58, 10^2)$ distribution. There are 15 observations in each sample. The data are displayed in Table 10.5.1, and along with the data, the ranks and the normal scores are exhibited. We consider tests of the two-sided hypotheses $H_0 : \Delta = 0$ versus $H_1 : \Delta \neq 0$ for the Wilcoxon, normal scores, and Student t procedures.

As the following comparison dotplots show, the second sample observations appear to be larger than those from the first sample.

Table 10.5.1: Data for Example 10.5.3

Sample 1 (X)			Sample 2 (Y)		
Data	Ranks	Normal Scores	Data	Ranks	Normal Scores
51.9	15	−0.04044	59.2	24	0.75273
56.9	23	0.64932	49.1	14	−0.12159
45.2	11	−0.37229	54.4	19	0.28689
52.3	16	0.04044	47.0	13	−0.20354
59.5	26	0.98917	55.9	21	0.46049
41.4	4	−1.13098	34.9	3	−1.30015
46.4	12	−0.28689	62.2	28	1.30015
45.1	10	−0.46049	41.6	6	−0.86489
53.9	17	0.12159	59.3	25	0.86489
42.9	7	−0.75273	32.7	1	−1.84860
41.5	5	−0.98917	72.1	29	1.51793
55.2	20	0.37229	43.8	8	−0.64932
32.9	2	−1.51793	56.8	22	0.55244
54.0	18	0.20354	76.7	30	1.84860
45.0	9	−0.55244	60.3	27	1.13098

The test statistics along with their standardized versions, p-values, and corresponding estimates of the shift parameter Δ are

Method	Test Statistic	Standardized	p-Value	Estimate of Δ
Student t	$\overline{Y} - \overline{X} = 5.46$	1.47	0.16	5.46
Wilcoxon	$W = 270$	1.53	0.12	5.20
Normal scores	$W_N = 3.73$	1.48	0.14	5.15

Notice that the standardized tests statistics and their corresponding p-values are quite similar and all would result in the same decision regarding the hypotheses. As shown in the table, the corresponding point estimates of Δ are also alike. The estimates were obtained using the package cited ahead in Remark 10.5.1.

We changed x_5 to be an outlier with value 95.5 and then reran the analyses. The t-analysis was the most affected, for on the changed data, $t = 0.63$ with a p-value of 0.53. In contrast, the Wilcoxon analysis was the least affected ($z = 1.37$ and $p = 0.17$). The normal scores analysis was more affected by the outlier than the Wilcoxon analysis with $z = 1.14$ and $p = 0.25$. ∎

Example 10.5.4 (Sign Scores). For our final example, suppose that the random errors $\varepsilon_1, \varepsilon_2, \ldots, \varepsilon_n$ have a Laplace distribution. Consider the convenient form $f_Z(z) = 2^{-1} \exp\{-|z|\}$. Then $f'_Z(z) = -2^{-1} \mathrm{sgn}(z) \exp\{-|z|\}$ and, hence, $-f'_Z(F_Z^{-1}(u))/f_Z(F_Z^{-1}(u)) = \mathrm{sgn}(z)$. But $F_Z^{-1}(u) > 0$ if and only if $u > 1/2$. The optimal score function is

$$\varphi_S(u) = \text{sgn}\left(u - \frac{1}{2}\right), \tag{10.5.34}$$

which is easily shown to be standardized. The corresponding process is

$$W_S(\Delta) = \sum_{j=1}^{n_2} \text{sgn}\left[R(Y_j - \Delta) - \frac{n+1}{2}\right]. \tag{10.5.35}$$

Because of the signs, this test statistic can be written in a simpler form, which is often called **Mood's** test; see Exercise 10.5.13.

We can also obtain the associated estimator in closed form. The estimator solves the equation

$$\sum_{j=1}^{n_2} \text{sgn}\left[R(Y_j - \Delta) - \frac{n+1}{2}\right] = 0. \tag{10.5.36}$$

For this equation, we rank the variables

$$\{X_1, \ldots, X_{n_1}, Y_1 - \Delta, \ldots, Y_{n_2} - \Delta\}.$$

Because ranks, though, are invariant to a constant shift, we obtain the same ranks if we rank the variables

$$X_1 - \text{med}\{X_i\}, \ldots, X_{n_1} - \text{med}\{X_i\}, Y_1 - \Delta - \text{med}\{X_i\}, \ldots, Y_{n_2} - \Delta - \text{med}\{X_i\}.$$

Therefore, the solution to equation (10.5.36) is easily seen to be

$$\widehat{\Delta}_S = \text{med}\{Y_j\} - \text{med}\{X_i\}. \quad \blacksquare \tag{10.5.37}$$

Other examples are given in the exercises.

Remark 10.5.1 (Computation). Computation of the analyses for general score functions can be performed by the R functions discussed in Chapter 2 of Hettmansperger and McKean (2011). In particular, the normal scores analysis of Example 10.5.3 can be computed by using the command `twosampr2(x,y,score=phinscr)`, where x and y are the vectors containing the X and Y observations, respectively. $\blacksquare$

EXERCISES

10.5.1. In this section, as discussed above expression (10.5.2), the scores $a_\varphi(i)$ are generated by the standardized score function $\varphi(u)$; that is, $\int_0^1 \varphi(u)\,du = 0$ and $\int_0^1 \varphi^2(u)\,du = 1$. Suppose that $\psi(u)$ is a square-integrable function defined on the interval $(0,1)$. Consider the score function defined by

$$\varphi(u) = \frac{\psi(u) - \overline{\psi}}{\int_0^1 [\psi(v) - \overline{\psi}]^2\,dv},$$

where $\overline{\psi} = \int_0^1 \psi(v)\,dv$. Show that $\varphi(u)$ is a standardized score function.

10.5.2. Complete the derivation of the null variance of the test statistic W_φ by showing the second term in expression (10.5.7) is true.
Hint: Use the fact that under H_0, for $j \neq j'$, the pair $(a_\varphi(R(Y_j)), a_\varphi(R(Y_{j'})))$ is uniformly distributed on the pairs of integers (i, i'), $i, i' = 1, 2, \ldots, n$, $i \neq i'$.

10.5.3. For the Wilcoxon score function $\varphi(u) = \sqrt{12}[u - (1/2)]$, obtain the value of s_a. Then show that the $V_{H_0}(W_\varphi)$ given in expression (10.5.8) is the same (except for standardization) as the variance of the MWW statistic of Section 10.4.

10.5.4. Recall that the scores have been standardized so that $\int_{-\infty}^{\infty} \varphi^2(u)\, du = 1$. Use this and a Riemann sum to show that $n^{-1}s_a^2 \to 1$, where s_a^2 is defined in expression (10.5.6).

10.5.5. Show that the normal scores, (10.5.29), derived in Example 10.5.1 are standardized; that is, $\int_0^1 \varphi_N(u)\, du = 0$ and $\int_0^1 \varphi_N^2(u)\, du = 1$.

10.5.6. In Theorem 10.5.1, show that the minimum value of $W_\varphi(\Delta)$ is given by $\sum_{j=1}^{n_2} a_\varphi(j)$ and that it is nonpositive.

10.5.7. Show that $E_\Delta[W_\varphi(0)] = E_0[W_\varphi(-\Delta)]$.

10.5.8. Consider the hypotheses (10.4.2). Suppose we select the score function $\varphi(u)$ and the corresponding test based on W_φ. Suppose we want to determine the sample size $n = n_1 + n_2$ for this test of significance level α to detect the alternative Δ^* with approximate power γ^*. Assuming that the sample sizes n_1 and n_2 are the same, show that

$$ n \approx \left(\frac{(z_\alpha - z_{\gamma^*}) 2\tau_\varphi}{\Delta^*} \right)^2. \tag{10.5.38} $$

10.5.9. In the context of this section, show the following invariances:

(a) Show that the parameter τ_φ, (10.5.24), is a scale functional as defined in Exercise 10.1.4.

(b) Show that part (a) implies that the efficacy, (10.5.20), is invariant to the location and varies indirectly with scale.

(c) Suppose Z is a scale and location transformation of a random variable X; i.e., $Z = a(X - b)$, where $a > 0$ and $-\infty < b < \infty$. Show that $I(f_Z) = a^{-2}I(f_X)$.

10.5.10. Consider the scale parameter τ_φ, (10.5.24), when normal scores are used; i.e., $\varphi(u) = \Phi^{-1}(u)$. Suppose we are sampling from a $N(\mu, \sigma^2)$ distribution. Show that $\tau_\varphi = \sigma$.

10.5.11. In the context of Example 10.5.2, obtain the results in expression (10.5.32).

10.5.12. Let the scores $a(i)$ be generated by $a_\varphi(i) = \varphi[i/(n+1)]$, for $i = 1, \ldots, n$, where $\int_0^1 \varphi(u)\, du = 0$ and $\int_0^1 \varphi^2(u)\, du = 1$. Using Riemann sums, with subintervals of equal length, of the integrals $\int_0^1 \varphi(u)\, du$ and $\int_0^1 \varphi^2(u)\, du$, show that $\sum_{i=1}^{n} a(i) \approx 0$ and $\sum_{i=1}^{n} a^2(i) \approx n$.

10.5.13. Consider the sign scores test procedure discussed in Example 10.5.4.

(a) Show that $W_S = 2W_S^* - n_2$, where $W_S^* = \#_j \left\{ R(Y_j) > \frac{n+1}{2} \right\}$. Hence W_S^* is an equivalent test statistic. Find the null mean and variance of W_S.

(b) Show that $W_S^* = \#_j \{ Y_j > \theta^* \}$, where θ^* is the combined sample median.

(c) Suppose n is even. Letting $W_{XS}^* = \#_i \{ X_i > \theta^* \}$, show that we can table W_S^* in the following 2×2 contingency table with all margins fixed:

	Y	X	
No. items $> \theta^*$	W_S^*	W_{XS}^*	$\frac{n}{2}$
No. items $< \theta^*$	$n_2 - W_S^*$	$n_1 - W_{XS}^*$	$\frac{n}{2}$
	n_2	n_1	n

Show that the usual χ^2 goodness-of-fit is the same as Z_S^2, where Z_S is the standardized z-test based on W_S. This is often called **Mood's median test**; see Example 10.5.4..

10.5.14. Recall the data discussed in Example 10.5.3.

(a) Obtain the contingency table described in Exercise 10.5.13.

(b) Obtain the χ^2 goodness-of-fit test statistic associated with the table and use it to test at level 0.05 the hypotheses $H_0 : \Delta = 0$ versus $H_1 : \Delta \neq 0$.

(c) Obtain the point estimate of Δ given in expression (10.5.37).

10.5.15. Optimal signed-rank based methods also exist for the one-sample problem. In this exercise, we briefly discuss these methods. Let $X_1, X_2, \ldots, X_n$ follow the location model

$$X_i = \theta + e_i, \tag{10.5.39}$$

where $e_1, e_2, \ldots, e_n$ are iid with pdf $f(x)$, which is symmetric about 0; i.e., $f(-x) = f(x)$.

(a) Show that under symmetry the optimal two-sample score function (10.5.26) satisfies

$$\varphi_f(1 - u) = -\varphi_f(u), \quad 0 < u < 1; \tag{10.5.40}$$

that is, $\varphi_f(u)$ is an odd function about $\frac{1}{2}$. Show that a function satisfying (10.5.40) is 0 at $u = \frac{1}{2}$.

(b) For a two-sample score function $\varphi(u)$ which is odd about $\frac{1}{2}$, define the function $\varphi^+(u) = \varphi[(u+1)/2]$, i.e., the top half of $\varphi(u)$. Note that the domain of $\varphi^+(u)$ is the interval $(0, 1)$. Show that $\varphi^+(u) \geq 0$, provided $\varphi(u)$ is nondecreasing.

(c) Assume for the remainder of the problem that $\varphi^+(u)$ is nonnegative and nondecreasing on the interval $(0, 1)$. Define the scores $a^+(i) = \varphi^+[i/(n+1)]$, $i = 1, 2, \ldots, n$, and the corresponding statistic

$$W_{\varphi^+} = \sum_{i=1}^{n} \text{sgn}(X_i) a^+(R|X_i|). \tag{10.5.41}$$

Show that W_{φ^+} reduces to a linear function of the signed-rank test statistic (10.3.2) if $\varphi(u) = 2u - 1$.

(d) Show that W_{φ^+} reduces to a linear function of the sign test statistic (10.2.3) if $\varphi(u) = \text{sgn}(2u - 1)$.

Note: Suppose Model (10.5.39) is true and we take $\varphi(u) = \varphi_f(u)$, where $\varphi_f(u)$ is given by (10.5.26). If we choose $\varphi^+(u) = \varphi[(u+1)/2]$ to generate the signed-rank scores, then it can be shown that the corresponding test statistic W_{φ^+} is optimal, among all signed-rank tests.

(e) Consider the hypotheses

$$H_0 : \theta = 0 \text{ versus } H_1 : \theta > 0.$$

Our decision rule for the statistic W_{φ^+} is to reject H_0 in favor of H_1 if $W_{\varphi^+} > k$, for some k. Write W_{φ^+} in terms of the anti-ranks, (10.3.5). Show that W_{φ^+} is distribution-free under H_0.

(f) Determine the mean and variance of W_{φ^+} under H_0.

(g) Assuming that, when properly standardized, the null distribution is asymptotically normal, determine the asymptotic test.

10.6   Adaptive Procedures

In the last section, we presented fully efficient rank-based procedures for testing and estimation. As with mle methods, though, the underlying form of the distribution must be known in order to select the optimal rank score function. In practice, often the underlying distribution is not known. In this case, we could select a score function, such as the Wilcoxon, which is fairly efficient for moderate- to heavy-tailed error distributions. Or if the distribution of the errors is thought to be quite close to a normal distribution, then the normal scores would be a proper choice. Suppose we use a technique which bases the score selection on the data. These techniques are called **adaptive** procedures. Such a procedure could attempt to estimate the score function; see, for example, Naranjo and McKean (1997). However, large data sets are often needed for these. There are other adaptive procedures which attempt to select a score from a finite class of scores based on some criteria. In this section, we look at an adaptive testing procedure for testing which retains the distribution-free property.

Frequently, an investigator is tempted to evaluate several test statistics associated with a single hypothesis and then use the one statistic that best supports his or her position, usually rejection. Obviously, this type of procedure changes the actual significance level of the test from the nominal α that is used. However, there is a way in which the investigator can first look at the data and then select a test statistic without changing this significance level. For illustration, suppose there are three possible test statistics, W_1, W_2, and W_3, of the hypothesis H_0 with respective critical regions C_1, C_2, and C_3 such that $P(W_i \in C_i; H_0) = \alpha$, $i = 1, 2, 3$. Moreover, suppose that a statistic Q, based upon the same data, selects one and only one of the statistics W_1, W_2, W_3, and that W is then used to test H_0. For example, we choose to use the test statistic W_i if $Q \in D_i$, $i = 1, 2, 3$, where the events defined by D_1, D_2, and D_3 are mutually exclusive and exhaustive. Now if Q and each W_i are independent when H_0 is true, then the probability of rejection, using the entire procedure (selecting and testing), is, under H_0,

$$P_{H_0}(Q \in D_1, W_1 \in C_1) + P_{H_0}(Q \in D_2, W_2 \in C_2) + P_{H_0}(Q \in D_3, W_3 \in C_3)$$
$$= P_{H_0}(Q \in D_1)P_{H_0}(W_1 \in C_1) + P_{H_0}(Q \in D_2)P_{H_0}(W_2 \in C_2)$$
$$+ P_{H_0}(Q \in D_3)P_{H_0}(W_3 \in C_3)$$
$$= \alpha[P_{H_0}(Q \in D_1) + P_{H_0}(Q \in D_2) + P_{H_0}(Q \in D_3)] = \alpha.$$

That is, the procedure of selecting W_i using an independent statistic Q and then constructing a test of significance level α with the statistic W_i has overall significance level α.

Of course, the important element in this procedure is the ability to be able to find a selector Q that is independent of each test statistic W. This can frequently be done by using the fact that complete sufficient statistics for the parameters, given by H_0, are independent of every statistic whose distribution is free of those parameters. For illustration, if independent random samples of sizes n_1 and n_2 arise from two normal distributions with respective means μ_1 and μ_2 and common variance σ^2, then the complete sufficient statistics $\overline{X}, \overline{Y}$, and

$$V = \sum_1^{n_1}(X_i - \overline{X})^2 + \sum_1^{n_2}(Y_i - \overline{Y})^2$$

for μ_1, μ_2, and σ^2 are independent of every statistic whose distribution is free of μ_1, μ_2, and σ^2, such as the statistics

$$\frac{\sum_1^{n_1}(X_i - \overline{X})^2}{\sum_1^{n_2}(Y_i - \overline{Y})^2}, \quad \frac{\sum_1^{n_1}|X_i - \text{median}(X_i)|}{\sum_1^{n_2}|Y_i - \text{median}(Y_i)|}, \quad \frac{\text{range}(X_1, X_2, \ldots, X_{n_1})}{\text{range}(Y_1, Y_2, \ldots, Y_{n_2})}.$$

Thus, in general, we would hope to be able to find a selector Q that is a function of the complete sufficient statistics for the parameters, under H_0, so that it is independent of the test statistic.

It is particularly interesting to note that it is relatively easy to use this technique in *nonparametric* methods by using the independence result based upon complete sufficient statistics for *parameters*. For the situations here, we must find complete sufficient statistics for a cdf, F, of the continuous type. In Chapter 7, it is shown that the order statistics $Y_1 < Y_2 < \cdots < Y_n$ of a random sample of size n from a distribution of the continuous type with pdf $F'(x) = f(x)$ are sufficient statistics for the "parameter" f (or F). Moreover, if the family of distributions contains all probability density functions of the continuous type, the family of joint probability density functions of $Y_1, Y_2, \ldots, Y_n$ is also complete. That is, the order statistics $Y_1, Y_2, \ldots, Y_n$ are complete sufficient statistics for the parameters f (or F).

Accordingly, our selector Q is based upon those complete sufficient statistics, the order statistics under H_0. This allows us to independently choose a distribution-free test appropriate for this type of underlying distribution, and thus increase the power of our test.

A statistical test that maintains the significance level close to a desired significance level α for a wide variety of underlying distributions with good (not necessarily the best for any one type of distribution) power for all these distributions is described as being *robust*. As an illustration, the pooled t-test (Student's t) used to test the equality of the means of two normal distributions is quite robust *provided* that the underlying distributions are rather close to normal ones with common variance. However, if the class of distributions includes those that are not too close to normal ones, such as contaminated normal distributions, the test based upon t is *not* robust; the significance level is not maintained and the power of the t-test can be quite low for heavy-tailed distributions. As a matter of fact, the test based on the Mann–Whitney–Wilcoxon statistic (Section 10.4) is a much more robust test than that based upon t if the class of distributions includes those with heavy tails.

In the following example, we illustrate a robust, adaptive, distribution free procedure in the setting of the two-sample problem.

Example 10.6.1. Let $X_1, X_2, \ldots, X_{n_1}$ be a random sample from a continuous-type distribution with cdf $F(x)$ and let $Y_1, Y_2, \ldots, Y_{n_2}$ be a random sample from a distribution with cdf $F(x - \Delta)$. Let $n = n_1 + n_2$ denote the combined sample size. We test

$$H_0 : \Delta = 0 \text{ versus } H_1 : \Delta > 0,$$

by using one of four distribution-free statistics, one being the Wilcoxon and the other three being modifications of the Wilcoxon. In particular, the test statistics are

$$W_i = \sum_{j=1}^{n_2} a_i[R(Y_j)], \quad i = 1, 2, 3, 4, \tag{10.6.1}$$

where

$$a_i(j) = \varphi_i[j/(n + 1)],$$

and the four functions are displayed in Figure 10.6.1. The score function $\varphi_1(u)$ is the Wilcoxon. The score function $\varphi_2(u)$ is the sign score function. The score function $\varphi_3(u)$ is good for short-tailed distributions, and $\varphi_4(u)$ is good for long, right-skewed distributions with shift alternatives.

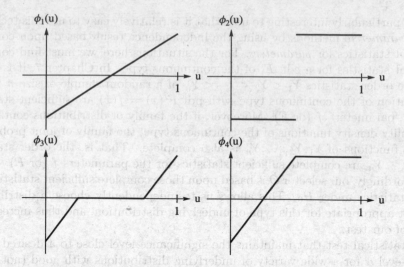

Figure 10.6.1: Plots of the score functions $\varphi_1(u)$, $\varphi_2(u)$, $\varphi_3(u)$, and $\varphi_4(u)$.

We combine the two samples into one denoting the order statistics of the combined sample by $V_1 < V_2 < \cdots < V_n$. These are complete sufficient statistics for $F(x)$ under the null hypothesis. For $i = 1, \ldots, 4$, the test statistic W_i is distribution free under H_0 and, in particular, the distribution of W_i does not depend on $F(x)$. Therefore, each W_i is independent of $V_1, V_2, \ldots, V_n$. We use a pair of selector statistics (Q_1, Q_2), which are functions of $V_1, V_2, \ldots, V_n$, and hence are also independent of each W_i. The first is

$$Q_1 = \frac{\overline{U}_{.05} - \overline{M}_{.5}}{\overline{M}_{.5} - \overline{L}_{.05}}, \tag{10.6.2}$$

where $\overline{U}_{.05}$, $\overline{M}_{.5}$, and $\overline{L}_{.05}$ are the averages of the largest 5% of the Vs, the middle 50% of the Vs, and the smallest 5% of the Vs, respectively. If Q_1 is large (say 2 or more), then the right tail of the distribution seems longer than the left tail; that is, there is an indication that the distribution is skewed to the right. On the other hand, if $Q_1 < \frac{1}{2}$, the sample indicates that the distribution may be skewed to the left. The second selector statistic is

$$Q_2 = \frac{\overline{U}_{.05} - \overline{L}_{.05}}{\overline{U}_{.5} - \overline{L}_{.5}}. \tag{10.6.3}$$

Large values of Q_2 indicate that the distribution is heavy-tailed, while small values indicate that the distribution is light-tailed. Rules are needed for score selection, and here we make use of the benchmarks proposed in an article by Hogg et al. (1975). These rules are tabulated below, along with their benchmarks:

Benchmark	Distribution Indicated	Score Selected
$Q_2 > 7$	Heavy-tailed symmetric	φ_2
$Q_1 > 2$ and $Q_2 < 7$	Right-skewed	φ_4
$Q_1 \leq 2$ and $Q_2 \leq 2$	Light-tailed symmetric	φ_3
Elsewhere	Moderate heavy-tailed	φ_1

Hogg et al. (1975) performed a Monte Carlo power study of this adaptive procedure over a number of distributions with different kurtosis and skewness coefficients. In the study, both the adaptive procedure and the Wilcoxon test maintain their α level over the distributions, but the Student t does not. Moreover, the Wilcoxon test has better power than the t-test, as the distribution deviates much from the normal (kurtosis = 3 and skewness = 0), but the adaptive procedure is much better than the Wilcoxon for the short-tailed distributions, the very heavy-tailed distributions, and the highly skewed distributions which were considered in the study. ∎

The adaptive distribution-free procedure that we have discussed is for testing. Suppose we have a location model and were interested in estimating the shift in locations Δ. For example, if the true F is a normal cdf, then a good choice for the estimator of Δ would be the estimator based on the normal scores procedure discussed in Example 10.5.1. The estimators, though, are not distribution free and, hence, the above reasoning does not hold. Also, the combined sample observations $X_1, \ldots, X_{n_1}, Y_1, \ldots, Y_{n_2}$ are not identically distributed. There are adaptive procedures based on residuals $X_1, \ldots, X_{n_1}, Y_1 - \widehat{\Delta}, \ldots, Y_{n_2} - \widehat{\Delta}$, where $\widehat{\Delta}$ is an initial estimator of Δ; see page 237 of Hettmansperger and McKean (2011) for discussion.

EXERCISES

10.6.1. In Exercises 10.6.2 and 10.6.3, the student is asked to apply the adaptive procedure described in Example 10.6.1 to real data sets. The hypotheses of interest are

$$H_0 : \; \Delta = 0 \text{ versus } H_1 : \; \Delta > 0,$$

where $\Delta = \mu_Y - \mu_X$. The four distribution free test statistics are

$$W_i = \sum_{j=1}^{n_2} a_i[R(Y_j)], \quad i = 1, 2, 3, 4, \tag{10.6.4}$$

where

$$a_i(j) = \varphi_i[j/(n+1)],$$

and the score functions are given by

$$
\begin{aligned}
\varphi_1(u) &= 2u - 1, \quad 0 < u < 1 \\
\varphi_2(u) &= \operatorname{sgn}(2u - 1), \quad 0 < u < 1 \\
\varphi_3(u) &= \begin{cases} 4u - 1 & 0 < u \leq \frac{1}{4} \\ 0 & \frac{1}{4} < u \leq \frac{3}{4} \\ 4u - 3 & \frac{3}{4} < u < 1 \end{cases} \\
\varphi_4(u) &= \begin{cases} 4u - (3/2) & 0 < u \leq \frac{1}{2} \\ 1/2 & \frac{1}{2} < u < 1. \end{cases}
\end{aligned}
$$

Note that we have adjusted the fourth score $\varphi_4(u)$ in Figure 10.6.1 so that it integrates to 0 over the interval $(0, 1)$.

The theory of Section 10.5 states that, under H_0, the distribution of W_i is asymptotically normal with mean 0 and variance

$$\mathrm{Var}_{H_0}(W_i) = \frac{n_1 n_2}{n-1} \left[\frac{1}{n} \sum_{j=1}^{n} a_i^2(j) \right].$$

Note, however, that the scores have not been standardized, so their squares integrate to 1 over the interval $(0, 1)$. Hence, do not replace the term in brackets by 1. If $n_1 = n_2 = 15$, find $\mathrm{Var}_{H_0}(W_i)$, for $i = 1, \ldots, 4$.

10.6.2. Consider the data in Example 10.5.3 and the hypotheses

$$H_0 : \Delta = 0 \text{ versus } H_1 : \Delta > 0,$$

where $\Delta = \mu_Y - \mu_X$. Apply the adaptive procedure described in Example 10.6.1 with the tests defined in Exercise 10.6.1 to test these hypotheses. Obtain the p-value of the test.

10.6.3. Use the adaptive procedure of Exercise 10.6.1 on the data of Example 10.4.1.

10.6.4. Let $F(x)$ be a distribution function of a distribution of the continuous type which is symmetric about its median θ. We wish to test $H_0 : \theta = 0$ against $H_1 : \theta > 0$. Use the fact that the $2n$ values, X_i and $-X_i$, $i = 1, 2, \ldots, n$, after ordering, are complete sufficient statistics for F, provided that H_0 is true.

  (a) As in Exercise 10.5.15, determine the one-sample signed-rank test statistics corresponding to the two-sample score functions $\varphi_1(u)$, $\varphi_2(u)$, and $\varphi_3(u)$ defined in the last exercise. Use the asymptotic test statistics. Note that these score functions are odd about $\frac{1}{2}$; hence, their top halves serve as score functions for signed-rank statistics.

  (b) We are assuming symmetric distributions in this problem; hence, we use only Q_2 as our score selector. If $Q_2 \geq 7$, then select $\varphi_2(u)$; if $2 < Q_2 < 7$, then select $\varphi_1(u)$; and finally, if $Q_2 \leq 2$, then select $\varphi_3(u)$. Construct this adaptive distribution-free test.

  (c) Use your adaptive procedure on Darwin's *Zea mays* data; see Example 10.3.1. Obtain the p-value.

10.7 Simple Linear Model

In this section, we consider the simple linear model and briefly develop the rank-based procedures for it.

Suppose the responses $Y_1, Y_2, \ldots, Y_n$ follow the model

$$Y_i = \alpha + \beta(x_i - \overline{x}) + \varepsilon_i, \quad i = 1, 2, \ldots, n, \tag{10.7.1}$$

where $\varepsilon_1, \varepsilon_2, \ldots, \varepsilon_n$ are iid with continuous cdf $F(x)$ and pdf $f(x)$. In this model, the variables $x_1, x_2, \ldots, x_n$ are considered fixed. The parameter β is the slope parameter, which is the expected change in Y (provided expectations exist) when x increases by one unit. A natural null hypothesis is

$$H_0 : \ \beta = 0 \text{ versus } H_1 : \ \beta \neq 0. \tag{10.7.2}$$

Under H_0, the distribution of Y is free of x.

In Chapter 3 of Hettmansperger and McKean (2011), rank-based procedures for linear models are presented from a geometric point of view; see also Exercises 10.9.11–10.9.12 of Section 10.9. Here, it is easier to present a development which parallels the preceding sections. Hence we introduce a rank test of H_0 and then invert the test to estimate β. Before doing this, though, we present an example which shows that the two-sample location problem of Section 10.4 is a regression problem.

Example 10.7.1. As in Section 10.4, let $X_1, X_2, \ldots, X_{n_1}$ be a random sample from a distribution with a continuous cdf $F(x - \alpha)$, where α is a location parameter. Let $Y_1, Y_2, \ldots, Y_{n_2}$ be a random sample with cdf $F(x - \alpha - \Delta)$. Hence Δ is the shift between the cdfs of X_i and Y_j. Redefine the observations as $Z_i = X_i$, for $i = 1, \ldots, n_1$, and $Z_{n_1+i} = Y_i$, for $i = n_1 + 1, \ldots, n$, where $n = n_1 + n_2$. Let c_i be 0 or 1 depending on whether $1 \leq i \leq n_1$ or $n_1 + 1 \leq i \leq n$. Then we can write the two sample location models as

$$Z_i = \alpha + \Delta c_i + \varepsilon_i, \tag{10.7.3}$$

where $\varepsilon_1, \varepsilon_2, \ldots, \varepsilon_n$ are iid with cdf $F(x)$. Hence the shift in locations is the slope parameter from this viewpoint. ∎

Suppose the regression model (10.7.1) holds and, further, that H_0 is true. Then we would expect that Y_i and $x_i - \overline{x}$ are not related and, in particular, that they are uncorrelated. Hence one could consider $\sum_{i=1}^{n}(x_i - \overline{x})Y_i$ as a test statistic. As Exercise 9.6.8 of Chapter 9 shows, if we additionally assume that the random errors ε_i are normally distributed, this test statistic, properly standardized, is the likelihood ratio test statistic. Reasoning in the same way, for a specified score function we would expect that $a_\varphi(R(Y_i))$ and $x_i - \overline{x}$ are uncorrelated, under H_0. Therefore, consider the test statistic

$$T_\varphi = \sum_{i=1}^{n}(x_i - \overline{x})a_\varphi(R(Y_i)), \tag{10.7.4}$$

where $R(Y_i)$ denotes the rank of Y_i among $Y_1, \ldots, Y_n$ and $a_\varphi(i) = \varphi(i/(n+1))$ for a nondecreasing score function $\varphi(u)$ which is standardized, so that $\int \varphi(u)\,du = 0$ and $\int \varphi^2(u)\,du = 1$. Values of T_φ close to 0 indicate H_0 is true.

Assume H_0 is true. Then $Y_1, \ldots, Y_n$ are iid random variables. Hence any permutation of the integers $\{1, 2, \ldots, n\}$ is equilikely to be the ranks of $Y_1, \ldots, Y_n$. So the distribution of T_φ is free of $F(x)$. Note that the distribution does not depend on $x_1, x_2, \ldots, x_n$. Thus, tables of the distribution are not available, although with high-speed computing, this distribution can be generated. Because $R(Y_i)$ is uniformly distributed on the integers $\{1, 2, \ldots, n\}$, it is easy to show that the null expectation of T_φ is zero. The null variance follows that of W_φ of Section 10.5, so we have left the details for Exercise 10.7.3. To summarize, the null moments are given by

$$E_{H_0}(T_\varphi) = 0 \quad \text{and} \quad \text{Var}_{H_0}(T_\varphi) = \frac{1}{n-1} s_a^2 \sum_{i=1}^{n} (x_i - \overline{x})^2, \qquad (10.7.5)$$

where s_a^2 is the mean sum of the squares of the scores (10.5.6). Also, it can be shown that the test statistic is asymptotically normal. Therefore, an asymptotic level α decision rule for the hypotheses (10.7.2) with the two-sided alternative is given by

$$\text{Reject } H_0 \text{ in favor of } H_1 \text{ if } |z| = \left| \frac{T_\varphi}{\sqrt{\text{Var}_{H_0}(T_\varphi)}} \right| \geq z_{\alpha/2}. \qquad (10.7.6)$$

The associated process is given by

$$T_\varphi(\beta) = \sum_{i=1}^{n} (x_i - \overline{x}) a_\varphi(R(Y_i - x_i\beta)). \qquad (10.7.7)$$

Hence the corresponding estimate of β is given by $\widetilde{\beta}_\varphi$, which solves the estimating equations

$$T_\varphi(\widehat{\beta}_\varphi) \approx 0. \qquad (10.7.8)$$

Similar to Theorem 10.5.1, it can be shown that $T_\varphi(\beta)$ is a decreasing step function of β which steps down at each sample slope $(Y_j - Y_i)/(x_j - x_i)$, for $i \neq j$. Thus the estimate exists. It cannot be obtained in closed form, but simple iterative techniques can be used to find the solution. In the regression problem, though, prediction of Y is often of interest, which also requires an estimate of α. Notice that such an estimate can be obtained as a location estimate based on residuals. This is discussed in some detail in Section 3.5.2 of Hettmansperger and McKean (2011). For our purposes, we consider the median of the residuals; that is, we estimate α as

$$\widehat{\alpha} = \text{med}\{Y_i - \widehat{\beta}_\varphi(x_i - \overline{x})\}. \qquad (10.7.9)$$

Remark 10.7.1. The Wilcoxon estimates of slope and intercept are computed by several packages. The minitab command `rregr` obtains the Wilcoxon fit. Terpstra and McKean (2005) have written a collection of R functions, `ww`, which obtains this fit. The package of R routines, Rfit, also computes this fit; see Kloke and McKean (2011). This package was used for the computations in the following example. ∎

Example 10.7.2 (Telephone Data). Consider the regression data discussed in Exercise 9.6.2. Recall that the responses (y) for this data set are the numbers of telephone calls (tens of millions) made in Belgium for the years 1950–1973, while time in years serves as the predictor variable (x). The data are plotted in Figure 10.7.1. For this example, we used Wilcoxon scores to fit Model (10.7.1). This resulted in the estimates $\widehat{\beta}_W = 0.145$ and $\widehat{\alpha} = -7.15$. The Wilcoxon fitted value $\widehat{Y}_{\varphi,i} = -7.15 + 0.145x_i$ is plotted in Figure 10.7.1. The least squares fit $\widehat{Y}_{\text{LS},i} = -26.0 + 0.504x_i$, found in Exercise 9.6.2, is also plotted. Note that the Wilcoxon fit is much less sensitive to the outliers than the least squares fit.

The outliers in this data set were recording errors; see page 25 of Rousseeuw and Leroy (1987) for more discussion. ∎

Figure 10.7.1: Plot of telephone data, Example 10.7.2, overlaid with Wilcoxon and LS fits.

Similar to Lemma 10.2.1, a translation property holds for the process $T(\beta)$ given by

$$E_\beta[T(0)] = E_0[T(-\beta)]; \qquad (10.7.10)$$

see Exercise 10.7.1. Further, as Exercise 10.7.4 shows, this property implies that the power curve for the one-sided tests of $H_0: \ \beta = 0$ are monotone, assuring the unbiasedness of the tests based on T_φ.

We can now derive the efficacy of the process. Let $\mu_T(\beta) = E_\beta[T(0)]$ and $\sigma_T^2(0) = \text{Var}_0[T(0)]$. Expression (10.7.5) gives the result for $\sigma_T^2(0)$. Recall that for the mean $\mu_T(\beta)$, we need its derivative at 0. We freely use the relationship between rankings and the empirical cdf and then approximate this empirical cdf with the true cdf. Hence

$$
\begin{aligned}
\mu_T(\beta) = E_\beta[T(0)] \;&=\; E_0[T(-\beta)] = \sum_{i=1}^n (x_i - \overline{x}) E_0[a_\varphi(R(Y_i + x_i\beta))] \\
&=\; \sum_{i=1}^n (x_i - \overline{x}) E_0\left[\varphi\left(\frac{n\widehat{F}_n(Y_i + x_i\beta)}{n+1}\right)\right] \\
&\approx\; \sum_{i=1}^n (x_i - \overline{x}) E_0[\varphi(F(Y_i + x_i\beta))] \\
&=\; \sum_{i=1}^n (x_i - \overline{x}) \int_{-\infty}^{\infty} \varphi(F(y + x_i\beta)) f(y)\, dy. \qquad (10.7.11)
\end{aligned}
$$

Differentiating this last expression, we have

$$
\mu_T'(\beta) = \sum_{i=1}^n (x_i - \overline{x}) x_i \int_{-\infty}^{\infty} \varphi'(F(y + x_i\beta)) f(y + x_i\beta) f(y)\, dy,
$$

which yields

$$
\mu_T'(0) = \sum_{i=1}^n (x_i - \overline{x})^2 \int_{-\infty}^{\infty} \varphi'(F(y)) f^2(y)\, dy. \qquad (10.7.12)
$$

We need one assumption on the $x_1, x_2, \ldots, x_n$; namely, $n^{-1}\sum_{i=1}^n (x_i - \overline{x})^2 \to \sigma_x^2$, where $0 < \sigma_x^2 < \infty$. Recall that $(n-1)^{-1}s_a^2 \to 1$. Therefore, the efficacy of the process $T(\beta)$ is given by

$$
\begin{aligned}
c_T \;&=\; \lim_{n\to\infty} \frac{\mu_T'(0)}{\sqrt{n}\sigma_T(0)} = \lim_{n\to\infty} \frac{\sum_{i=1}^n (x_i - \overline{x})^2 \int_{-\infty}^{\infty} \varphi'(F(y)) f^2(y)\, dy}{\sqrt{n}\sqrt{(n-1)^{-1}s_a^2}\sqrt{\sum_{i=1}^n (x_i - \overline{x})^2}} \\
&=\; \sigma_x \int_{-\infty}^{\infty} \varphi'(F(y)) f^2(y)\, dy. \qquad (10.7.13)
\end{aligned}
$$

Using this, an asymptotic power lemma can be derived for the test based on T_φ; see expression (10.7.17) of Exercise 10.7.5. Based on this, it can be shown that the asymptotic distribution of the estimator $\widehat{\beta}_\varphi$ is given by

$$
\widehat{\beta}_\varphi \text{ has an approximate } N\left(\beta, \tau_\varphi^2 / \sum_{i=1}^n (x_i - \overline{x})^2\right) \text{ distribution,} \qquad (10.7.14)
$$

where the scale parameter τ_φ is $\tau_\varphi = (\int_{-\infty}^{\infty} \varphi'(F(y)) f^2(y)\, dy)^{-1}$.

Remark 10.7.2. The least squares (LS) estimates for Model (10.7.1) were discussed in Section 9.6 in the case that the random errors $\varepsilon_1, \varepsilon_2, \ldots, \varepsilon_n$ are iid with a $N(0, \sigma^2)$ distribution. In general, for Model (10.7.1), the asymptotic distribution of the LS estimator of β, say $\widehat{\beta}_{LS}$, is:

$$
\widehat{\beta}_{LS} \text{ has an approximate } N\left(\beta, \sigma^2 / \sum_{i=1}^n (x_i - \overline{x})^2\right) \text{ distribution,} \qquad (10.7.15)
$$

where σ^2 is the variance of ε_i. Based on (10.7.14) and (10.7.15), it follows that the ARE between the rank-based and LS estimators is given by

$$\text{ARE}(\widehat{\beta}_\varphi, \widehat{\beta}_{\text{LS}}) = \frac{\sigma^2}{\tau_\varphi^2}. \tag{10.7.16}$$

Hence, if Wilcoxon scores are used, this ARE is the same as the ARE between the Wilcoxon and t-procedures in the one- and two-sample location models. ∎

EXERCISES

10.7.1. Establish expression (10.7.10). To do this, note first that the expression is the same as

$$E_\beta \left[\sum_{i=1}^n (x_i - \overline{x}) a_\varphi(R(Y_i)) \right] = E_0 \left[\sum_{i=1}^n (x_i - \overline{x}) a_\varphi(R(Y_i + x_i \beta)) \right].$$

Show that the cdfs of Y_i (under β) and $Y_i + (x_i - \overline{x})\beta$ (under 0) are the same.

10.7.2. Suppose we have a two-sample model given by (10.7.3). Assuming Wilcoxon scores, show that the test statistic (10.7.4) is equivalent to the Wilcoxon test statistic found in expression (10.4.3).

10.7.3. Show that the null variance of the test statistic T_φ is the value given in (10.7.5).

10.7.4. Show that the translation property (10.7.10) implies that the power curve for either one-sided test based on the test statistic T_φ of $H_0 : \beta = 0$ is monotone.

10.7.5. Consider the sequence of local alternatives given by the hypotheses

$$H_0 : \beta = 0 \text{ versus } H_{1n} : \beta = \beta_n = \frac{\beta_1}{\sqrt{n}},$$

where $\beta_1 > 0$. Let $\gamma(\beta)$ be the power function discussed in Exercise 10.7.4 for an asymptotic level α test based on the test statistic T_φ. Using the mean value theorem to approximate $\mu_T(\beta_n)$, sketch a proof of the limit

$$\lim_{n \to \infty} \gamma(\beta_n) = 1 - \Phi(z_\alpha - c_T \beta_1). \tag{10.7.17}$$

10.8 Measures of Association

In the last section, we discussed the simple linear regression model in which the random variables, Ys, were the responses or dependent variables, while the xs were the independent variables and were thought of as fixed. Regression models occur in several ways. In an experimental design, the values of the independent variables are prespecified and the responses are observed. Bioassays (dose–response experiments) are examples. The doses are fixed and the responses are observed. If the experimental design is performed in a controlled environment (for example, all other variables are controlled), it may be possible to establish cause and effect between x and Y. On the other hand, in observational studies both the xs and Ys are observed. In the regression setting, we are still interested in predicting Y in terms of x, but usually cause and effect between x and Y are precluded in such studies (other variables besides x may be changing).

In this section, we focus on observational studies but are interested in the strength of the association between Y and x. So both X and Y are treated as random variables in this section and the underlying distribution of interest is the bivariate distribution of the pair (X, Y). We assume that this bivariate distribution is continuous with cdf $F(x, y)$ and pdf $f(x, y)$.

Hence, let (X, Y) be a pair of random variables. A natural null model (baseline model) is that there is no relationship between X and Y; that is, the null hypothesis is given by $H_0 : X$ and Y are independent. Alternatives, though, depend on which measure of association is of interest. For example, if we are interested in the correlation between X and Y, we use the correlation coefficient ρ (Section 9.7) as our measure of the association. A two-sided alternative in this case is $H_1 : \rho \neq 0$. Recall that independence between X and Y implies that $\rho = 0$, but that the converse is not true. However, the contrapositive is true; that is, $\rho \neq 0$ implies that X and Y are dependent. So, in rejecting H_0, we conclude that X and Y are dependent. Furthermore, the size of ρ indicates the strength of the correlation between X and Y.

10.8.1   Kendall's τ

The first measure of association that we consider in this section is a measure of the *monotonicity* between X and Y. Monotonicity is an easily understood association between X and Y. Let (X_1, Y_1) and (X_2, Y_2) be independent pairs with the same bivariate distribution (discrete or continuous). We say these pairs are **concordant** if $\mathrm{sgn}\{(X_1 - X_2)(Y_1 - Y_2)\} = 1$ and are **discordant** if $\mathrm{sgn}\{(X_1 - X_2)(Y_1 - Y_2)\} = -1$. The variables X and Y have an increasing relationship if the pairs tend to be concordant and a decreasing relationship if the pairs tend to be discordant. A measure of this is given by **Kendall's τ**,

$$\tau = P[\mathrm{sgn}\{(X_1 - X_2)(Y_1 - Y_2)\} = 1] - P[\mathrm{sgn}\{(X_1 - X_2)(Y_1 - Y_2)\} = -1]. \quad (10.8.1)$$

As Exercise 10.8.1 shows, $-1 \leq \tau \leq 1$. Positive values of τ indicate increasing monotonicity, negative values indicate decreasing monotonicity, and $\tau = 0$ reflects neither. Furthermore, as the following theorem shows, if X and Y are independent, then $\tau = 0$.

Theorem 10.8.1. *Let (X_1, Y_1) and (X_2, Y_2) be independent pairs of observations of (X, Y), which has a continuous bivariate distribution. If X and Y are independent, then $\tau = 0$.*

Proof: Let (X_1, Y_1) and (X_2, Y_2) be independent pairs of observations with the same continuous bivariate distribution as (X, Y). Because the cdf is continuous, the sign function is either -1 or 1. By independence, we have

$$
\begin{aligned}
P[\operatorname{sgn}(X_1 - X_2)(Y_1 - Y_2) = 1] &= P[\{X_1 > X_2\} \cap \{Y_1 > Y_2\}] \\
&\quad + P[\{X_1 < X_2\} \cap \{Y_1 < Y_2\}] \\
&= P[X_1 > X_2]P[Y_1 > Y_2] \\
&\quad + P[X_1 < X_2]P[Y_1 < Y_2] \\
&= \left(\frac{1}{2}\right)^2 + \left(\frac{1}{2}\right)^2 = \frac{1}{2}.
\end{aligned}
$$

Likewise, $P[\operatorname{sgn}(X_1 - X_2)(Y_1 - Y_2) = -1] = \frac{1}{2}$; hence, $\tau = 0$. ∎

Relative to Kendall's τ as the measure of association, the two-sided hypotheses of interest here are

$$
H_0 : \tau = 0 \text{ versus } H_1 : \tau \neq 0. \tag{10.8.2}
$$

As Exercise 10.8.1 shows, the converse of Theorem 10.8.1 is false. However, the contrapositive is true; i.e., $\tau \neq 0$ implies that X and Y are dependent. As with the correlation coefficient, in rejecting H_0, we conclude that X and Y are dependent.

Kendall's τ has a simple unbiased estimator. Let $(X_1, Y_1), (X_2, Y_2), \ldots, (X_n, Y_n)$ be a random sample of the cdf $F(x, y)$. Define the statistic

$$
K = \binom{n}{2}^{-1} \sum_{i<j} \operatorname{sgn}\{(X_i - X_j)(Y_i - Y_j)\}. \tag{10.8.3}
$$

Note that for all $i \neq j$, the pairs (X_i, Y_i) and (X_j, Y_j) are identically distributed. Thus $E(K) = \binom{n}{2}^{-1} \binom{n}{2} E[\operatorname{sgn}\{(X_1 - X_2)(Y_1 - Y_2)\}] = \tau$.

In order to use K as a test statistic of the hypotheses (10.8.2), we need its distribution under the null hypothesis. Under H_0, $\tau = 0$, so the $E_{H_0}(K) = 0$. The null variance of K is given by expression (10.8.6); see, for instance, page 205 of Hettmansperger (1984). If all pairs $(X_i, Y_i), (X_j, Y_j)$ of the sample are concordant then $K = 1$, indicating a strictly increasing monotone relationship. On the other hand, if all pairs are discordant then $K = -1$. Thus the range of K is contained in the interval $[-1, 1]$. Also, the summands in expression (10.8.3) are either ± 1. From the proof of Theorem 10.8.1, the probability that a summand is 1 is $1/2$, which does not depend on the underlying distribution. Hence the statistic K is distribution-free under H_0. The null distribution of K is symmetric about 0. This is easily seen from the fact that for each concordant pair there is an obvious discordant pair (just reverse an inequality on the Ys) and the fact that concordant and discordant pairs are equilikely under H_0. For tables of the null distribution of K, see Hollander and Wolfe (1999). Also, it can be shown that K is asymptotically normal under H_0. We summarize these results, without proof, in a theorem.

Theorem 10.8.2. *Let $(X_1, Y_1), (X_2, Y_2), \ldots, (X_n, Y_n)$ be a random sample on the bivariate random vector (X, Y) with continuous cdf $F(x, y)$. Under the null hypothesis of independence between X and Y, i.e., $F(x, y) = F_X(x)F_Y(y)$, for all (x, y)*

in the support of (X, Y), *the test statistic* K *satisfies the following properties:*

$$K \text{ is distribution free with a symmetric pmf} \tag{10.8.4}$$

$$E_{H_0}[K] = 0 \tag{10.8.5}$$

$$Var_{H_0}(K) = \frac{2}{9}\frac{2n+5}{n(n-1)} \tag{10.8.6}$$

$$\frac{K}{\sqrt{Var_{H_0}(K)}} \text{ has an asymptotic } N(0,1) \text{ distribution.} \tag{10.8.7}$$

Based on the asymptotic test, a large sample level α test for the hypotheses (10.8.2) is to reject H_0 if $Z_K > z_{\alpha/2}$, where

$$Z_K = \frac{K}{\sqrt{2(2n+5)/9n(n-1)}}. \tag{10.8.8}$$

Most statistical computing packages compute Kendall's τ. For instance, the R command `cor.test(x,y,method=c("kendall"))` obtains K and the test discussed above when x and y are the vectors of the X and Y observations, respectively. We illustrate this test in the next example.

Example 10.8.1 (Olympic Race Times). Table 10.8.1 displays the winning times for two races in the Olympics beginning with the 1896 Olympics through the 1980 Olympics. The data were taken from Hettmansperger (1984). The times in seconds are for the 1500 m and the marathon. The entries in the table for the marathon race are the actual times minus 2 hours. In Exercise 10.8.2 the reader is asked to create a scatterplot of the times for the two races. The plot shows a strongly increasing monotone trend with one obvious outlier (1968 Olympics). An easy calculation shows that $K = 0.695$. The corresponding asymptotic test statistic is $Z_K = 6.27$, with p-value about 0.000, which shows strong evidence to reject the hypothesis of the independence of the times of the races. ∎

10.8.2 Spearman's Rho

As above, assume that $(X_1, Y_1), (X_2, Y_2), \ldots, (X_n, Y_n)$ is a random sample from a bivariate continuous cdf $F(x, y)$. The population correlation coefficient ρ is a measure of linearity between X and Y. The usual estimate is the sample correlation coefficient given by

$$r = \frac{\sum_{i=1}^{n}(X_i - \overline{X})(Y_i - \overline{Y})}{\sqrt{\sum_{i=1}^{n}(X_i - \overline{X})^2}\sqrt{\sum_{i=1}^{n}(Y_i - \overline{Y})^2}}. \tag{10.8.9}$$

A simple rank analog is to replace X_i by $R(X_i)$, where $R(X_i)$ denotes the rank of X_i among $X_1, \ldots, X_n$, and likewise Y_i by $R(Y_i)$, where $R(Y_i)$ denotes the rank of Y_i among $Y_1, \ldots, Y_n$. Upon making this substitution, the denominator of the above ratio is a constant. This results in the statistic

$$r_S = \frac{\sum_{i=1}^{n}(R(X_i) - \frac{n+1}{2})(R(Y_i) - \frac{n+1}{2})}{n(n^2-1)/12}, \tag{10.8.10}$$

Table 10.8.1: Data for Example 10.8.1

Year	1500 m	Marathon*	Year	1500 m	Marathon*
1896	373.2	3530	1936	227.8	1759
1900	246.0	3585	1948	229.8	2092
1904	245.4	5333	1952	225.2	1383
1906	252.0	3084	1956	221.2	1500
1908	243.4	3318	1960	215.6	916
1912	236.8	2215	1964	218.1	731
1920	241.8	1956	1968	214.9	1226
1924	233.6	2483	1972	216.3	740
1928	233.2	1977	1976	219.2	595
1932	231.2	1896	1980	218.4	663

* Actual marathon times are 2 hours + entry.

which is called **Spearman's rho**. The statistic r_S is a correlation coefficient, so the inequality $-1 \leq r_S \leq 1$ is true. Further, as the following theorem shows, independence implies that the mean of r_S is 0.

Theorem 10.8.3. *Suppose* $(X_1, Y_1), (X_2, Y_2), \ldots, (X_n, Y_n)$ *is a sample on* (X, Y), *where* (X, Y) *has the continuous cdf* $F(x, y)$. *If* X *and* Y *are independent, then* $E(r_S) = 0$.

Proof: Under independence, X_i and Y_j are independent for all i and j; hence, in particular, $R(X_i)$ is independent of $R(Y_i)$. Furthermore, $R(X_i)$ is uniformly distributed on the integers $\{1, 2, \ldots, n\}$. Therefore, $E(R(X_i)) = (n+1)/2$, which leads to the result. ∎

Thus the measure of association r_S can be used to test the null hypothesis of independence similar to Kendall's K. Under independence, because the X_is are a random sample, the random vector $(R(X_1), \ldots, R(X_n))$ is equilikely to assume any permutation of the integers $\{1, 2, \ldots, n\}$ and, likewise, the vector of the ranks of the Y_is. Furthermore, under independence, the random vector $[R(X_1), \ldots, R(X_n), R(Y_1), \ldots, R(Y_n)]$ is equilikely to assume any of the $(n!)^2$ vectors $(i_1, i_2, \ldots, i_n, j_1, j_2, \ldots, j_n)$, where $(i_1, i_2, \ldots, i_n)$ and $(j_1, j_2, \ldots, j_n)$ are permutations of the integers $\{1, 2, \ldots, n\}$. Hence, under independence, the statistic r_S is distribution-free. The distribution is discrete and tables of it can be found, for instance, in Hollander and Wolfe (1999). Similar to Kendall's statistic K, the distribution is symmetric about zero and it has an asymptotic normal distribution with asymptotic variance $1/(n-1)$; see Exercise 10.8.6 for a proof of the null variance of r_s. A large sample level α test is to reject independence between X and Y if $|z_S| > z_{\alpha/2}$, where $z_S = \sqrt{n-1}r_s$. We record these results in a theorem, without proof.

Theorem 10.8.4. *Let* $(X_1, Y_1), (X_2, Y_2), \ldots, (X_n, Y_n)$ *be a random sample on the bivariate random vector* (X, Y) *with continuous cdf* $F(x, y)$. *Under the null hypoth-*

esis of independence between X and Y, i.e., $F(x,y) = F_X(x)F_Y(y)$, for all (x,y) in the support of (X,Y), the test statistic r_S satisfies the following properties:

$$r_S \text{ is distribution-free, symmetrically distributed about } 0 \quad (10.8.11)$$

$$E_{H_0}[r_S] = 0 \quad (10.8.12)$$

$$Var_{H_0}(r_S) = \frac{1}{n-1} \quad (10.8.13)$$

$$\frac{r_S}{\sqrt{Var_{H_0}(r_S)}} \text{ is asymptotically } N(0,1). \quad (10.8.14)$$

The statistic r_S is easy to compute in practice. Simply replace the Xs and Ys by their ranks and use any routine which returns a correlation coefficient. For the data in Example 10.8.1, we used the minitab package to rank the data with the command `rank` first and then used the command `corr` to obtain the correlation coefficient. With R, r_s and the test described above are computed by the command `cor.test(x,y,method=c("spearman"))`, where x and y are the vectors of the X and Y observations, respectively.

Example 10.8.2 (Example 10.8.1, Continued). For the data in Example 10.8.1, the value of r_s is 0.905. Therefore, the value of the asymptotic test statistic is $Z_S = 0.905\sqrt{19} = 3.94$. The p-value for a two-sided test is 0.00008; hence, there is strong evidence to reject H_0. ∎

If the samples have a strictly increasing monotone relationship, then it is easy to see that $r_S = 1$; while if they have a strictly decreasing monotone relationship, then $r_S = -1$. Like Kendall's K statistic, r_S is an estimate of a population parameter, but, except for when X and Y are independent, it is a more complicated expression than τ. It can be shown (see Kendall, 1962) that

$$E(r_S) = \frac{3}{n+1}[\tau + (n-2)(2\gamma - 1)], \quad (10.8.15)$$

where $\gamma = P[(X_2 - X_1)(Y_2 - Y_1) > 0]$. For large n, $E(r_S) \approx 6(\gamma - 1/2)$, which is a harder parameter to interpret than the measure of concordance τ.

Spearman's rho is based on Wilcoxon scores; hence, it can easily be extended to other rank score functions. Some of these measures are discussed in the exercises.

EXERCISES

10.8.1. Show that Kendall's τ satisfies the inequality $-1 \leq \tau \leq 1$.

10.8.2. Consider Example 10.8.1. Let Y = winning times of the 1500 m race for a particular year and let X = winning times of the marathon for that year. Obtain a scatterplot of Y versus X, and determine the outlying point.

10.8.3. Consider the last exercise as a regression problem. Suppose we are interested in predicting the 1500 m winning time based on the marathon winning time. Assume a simple linear model and obtain the least squares and Wilcoxon (Section 10.7) fits of the data. Overlay the fits on the scatterplot obtained in Exercise 10.8.2. Comment on the fits. What does the slope parameter mean in this problem?

10.8.4. With regards to Exercise 10.8.3, a more interesting predicting problem is the prediction of winning time of either race based on year.

(a) Make a scatterplot of the winning 1500 m race time versus year. Assume a simple linear model (does the assumption make sense?) and obtain the least squares and Wilcoxon (Section 10.7) fits of the data. Overlay the fits on the scatterplot. Comment on the fits. What does the slope parameter mean in this problem? Predict the winning time for 1984. How close was your prediction to the true winning time?

(b) Same as part (a), except use the winning time of the marathon for that year.

10.8.5. Spearman's rho is a rank correlation coefficient based on Wilcoxon scores. In this exercise we consider a rank correlation coefficient based on a general score function. Let $(X_1, Y_1), (X_2, Y_2), \ldots, (X_n, Y_n)$ be a random sample from a bivariate continuous cdf $F(x, y)$. Let $a(i) = \varphi(i/(n+1))$, where $\sum_{i=1}^{n} a(i) = 0$. In particular, $\bar{a} = 0$. As in expression (10.5.6), let $s_a^2 = \sum_{i=1}^{n} a^2(i)$. Consider the rank correlation coefficient,

$$r_a = \frac{1}{s_a^2} \sum_{i=1}^{n} a(R(X_i))a(R(Y_i)). \tag{10.8.16}$$

(a) Show that r_a is a correlation coefficient on the items

$$\{(a[R(X_1)], a[R(Y_1)]), (a[R(X_2)], a[R(Y_2)]), \ldots, (a[R(X_n)], a[R(Y_n)])\}.$$

(b) For the score function $\varphi(u) = \sqrt{12}(u - (1/2))$, show that $r_a = r_S$, Spearman's rho.

(c) Obtain r_a for the sign score function $\varphi(u) = \text{sgn}(u - (1/2))$. Call this rank correlation coefficient r_{qc}. (The subscript qc is obvious from Exercise 10.8.7.)

10.8.6. Consider the general score rank correlation coefficient r_a defined in Exercise 10.8.5. Consider the null hypothesis $H_0 : X$ and Y are independent.

(a) Show that $E_{H_0}(r_a) = 0$.

(b) Based on part (a) and H_0, as a first step in obtaining the variance under H_0, show that the following expression is true:

$$\text{Var}_{H_0}(r_a) = \frac{1}{s_a^4} \sum_{i=1}^{n} \sum_{j=1}^{n} E_{H_0}[a(R(X_i))a(R(X_j))]E_{H_0}[a(R(Y_i))a(R(Y_j))].$$

(c) To determine the expectation in the last expression, consider the two cases $i = j$ and $i \neq j$. Then using uniformity of the distribution of the ranks, show that

$$\text{Var}_{H_0}(r_a) = \frac{1}{s_a^4} \frac{1}{n-1} s_a^4 = \frac{1}{n-1}. \tag{10.8.17}$$

10.8.7. Consider the rank correlation coefficient given by r_{qc} in part (c) of Exercise 10.8.5. Let Q_{2X} and Q_{2Y} denote the medians of the samples $X_1, \ldots, X_n$ and $Y_1, \ldots, Y_n$, respectively. Now consider the four quadrants:

$$
\begin{aligned}
I &= \{(x,y) : x > Q_{2X}, y > Q_{2Y}\} \\
II &= \{(x,y) : x < Q_{2X}, y > Q_{2Y}\} \\
III &= \{(x,y) : x < Q_{2X}, y < Q_{2Y}\} \\
IV &= \{(x,y) : x > Q_{2X}, y < Q_{2Y}\}.
\end{aligned}
$$

Show essentially that

$$
r_{qc} = \frac{1}{n}\{\#(X_i, Y_i) \in I + \#(X_i, Y_i) \in III - \#(X_i, Y_i) \in II - \#(X_i, Y_i) \in IV\}.
$$

$$(10.8.18)$$

Hence, r_{qc} is referred to as the *quadrant count* correlation coefficient.

10.8.8. Set up the asymptotic test of independence using r_{qc} of the last exercise. Then use it to test for independence between the 1500 m race times and the marathon race times of the data in Example 10.8.1.

10.8.9. Obtain the rank correlation coefficient when normal scores are used; that is, the scores are $a(i) = \Phi^{-1}(i/(n+1))$, $i = 1, \ldots, n$. Call it r_N. Set up the asymptotic test of independence using r_N of the last exercise. Then use it to test for independence between the 1500 m race times and the marathon race times of the data in Example 10.8.1.

10.8.10. Suppose that the hypothesis H_0 concerns the independence of two random variables X and Y. That is, we wish to test $H_0 : F(x, y) = F_1(x)F_2(y)$, where F, F_1, and F_2 are the respective joint and marginal distribution functions of the continuous type, against all alternatives. Let $(X_1, Y_1), (X_2, Y_2), \ldots, (X_n, Y_n)$ be a random sample from the joint distribution. Under H_0, the order statistics of $X_1, X_2, \ldots, X_n$ and the order statistics of $Y_1, Y_2, \ldots, Y_n$ are, respectively, complete sufficient statistics for F_1 and F_2. Use r_S, r_{qc}, and r_N to create an adaptive distribution-free test of H_0.

Remark 10.8.1. It is interesting to note that in an adaptive procedure it would be possible to use different score functions for the Xs and Ys. That is, the order statistics of the X values might suggest one score function and those of the Ys another score function. Under the null hypothesis of independence, the resulting procedure would produce an α level test. ∎

10.9   Robust Concepts

In this section, we introduce some of the concepts in **robust** estimation. We introduce these concepts for the location model discussed in Sections 10.1–10.3 of this chapter and then apply them to the simple linear regression model of Section 10.7. In a review article, McKean (2004), presents three introductory lectures on robust concepts.

10.9.1   Location Model

In a few words, we say an estimator is **robust** if it is not sensitive to outliers in the data. In this section, we make this more precise for the location model. Suppose then that $X_1, X_2, \ldots, X_n$ is a random sample which follows the location model as given in Definition 10.1.2; i.e.,

$$X_i = \theta + \varepsilon_i, \quad i = 1, 2, \ldots, n, \tag{10.9.1}$$

where θ is a location parameter (functional) and ε_i has cdf $F(t)$ and pdf $f(t)$. Let $F_X(t)$ and $f_X(t)$ denote the cdf and pdf of X, respectively. Then $F_X(t) = F(t - \theta)$ and $f_X(t) = f(t - \theta)$.

To illustrate the robust concepts, we use the location estimators discussed in Sections 10.1–10.3: the sample mean, the sample median, and the Hodges–Lehmann estimator. It is convenient to define these estimators in terms of their estimating equations. The **estimating equation** of the sample mean is given by

$$\sum_{i=1}^{n} (X_i - \theta) = 0; \tag{10.9.2}$$

i.e., the solution to this equation is $\widehat{\theta} = \overline{X}$. The estimating equation for the sample median is given in expression (10.2.34), which, for convenience, we repeat:

$$\sum_{i=1}^{n} \operatorname{sgn}(X_i - \theta) = 0. \tag{10.9.3}$$

Recall from Section 10.2 that the sample median minimizes the L_1-norm. So in this section, we denote it as $\widehat{\theta}_{L_1} = \operatorname{med} X_i$. Finally, the estimating equation for the Hodges–Lehmann estimator is given by expression (10.4.25). For this section, we denote the solution to this equation by

$$\widehat{\theta}_{\mathrm{HL}} = \operatorname{med}_{i \le j} \left\{ \frac{X_i + X_j}{2} \right\}. \tag{10.9.4}$$

Suppose, in general, then that we have a random sample $X_1, X_2, \ldots, X_n$, which follows the location model (10.9.1) with location parameter θ. Let $\widehat{\theta}$ be an estimator of θ. Hopefully, $\widehat{\theta}$ is not unduly influenced by an outlier in the sample, that is, a point that is at a distance from the other points in the sample. For a realization of the sample, this sensitivity to outliers is easy to measure. We simply add an outlier to the data set and observe the change in the estimator.

More formally, let $\mathbf{x}_n = (x_1, x_2, \ldots, x_n)$ be a realization of the sample, let x be the additional point, and denote the augmented sample by $\mathbf{x}'_{n+1} = (\mathbf{x}'_n, x)$. Then a simple measure is the rate of change in the estimate due to x relative to the mass of x, $(1/(n+1))$; i.e.,

$$S(x; \widehat{\theta}) = \frac{\widehat{\theta}(\mathbf{x}_{n+1}) - \widehat{\theta}(\mathbf{x}_n)}{1/(n+1)}. \tag{10.9.5}$$

This is called the **sensitivity curve** of the estimate $\widehat{\theta}$.

As examples, consider the sample mean and median. For the sample mean, it is easy to see that

$$S(x; \overline{X}) = \frac{\overline{x}_{n+1} - \overline{x}_n}{1/(n+1)} = x - \overline{x}_n. \tag{10.9.6}$$

Hence the relative change in the sample mean is a linear function of x. Thus, if x is large, then the change in sample mean is also large. Actually, the change is unbounded in x. Thus the sample mean is quite sensitive to the size of the outlier. In contrast, consider the sample median in which the sample size n is odd. In this case, the sample median is $\widehat{\theta}_{L_1,n} = x_{(r)}$, where $r = (n+1)/2$. When the additional point x is added, the sample size becomes even and the sample median $\widehat{\theta}_{L_1,n+1}$ is the average of the middle two order statistics. If x varies between these two order statistics, then there is some change between the $\widehat{\theta}_{L_1,n}$ and $\widehat{\theta}_{L_1,n+1}$. But once x moves beyond these middle two order statistics, there is no change. Hence $S(x; \widehat{\theta}_{L_1,n})$ is a bounded function of x. Therefore, $\widehat{\theta}_{L_1,n}$ is much less sensitive to an outlier than the sample mean.

Because the Hodges–Lehmann estimator $\widehat{\theta}_{\mathrm{HL}}$, (10.9.4), is also a median, its sensitivity curve is also bounded. Exercise 10.9.2 provides a numerical illustration of these sensitivity curves.

Influence Functions

One problem with the sensitivity curve is its dependence on the sample. In earlier chapters, we compared estimators in terms of their variances which are functions of the underlying distribution. This is the type of comparison we want to make here.

Recall that the location model (10.9.1) is the model of interest, where $F_X(t) = F(t - \theta)$ is the cdf of X and $F(t)$ is the cdf of ε. As discussed in Section 10.1, the parameter θ is a function of the cdf $F_X(x)$. It is convenient, then, to use functional notation $\theta = T(F_X)$, as in Section 10.1. For example, if θ is the mean, then $T(F_X)$ is defined as

$$T(F_X) = \int_{-\infty}^{\infty} x \, dF_X(x) = \int_{-\infty}^{\infty} x f_X(x) \, dx, \tag{10.9.7}$$

while if θ is the median, then $T(F_X)$ is defined as

$$T(F_X) = F_X^{-1}\left(\frac{1}{2}\right). \tag{10.9.8}$$

It was shown in Section 10.1 that for a location functional, $T(F_X) = T(F) + \theta$.

Estimating equations (EE) such as those defined in expressions (10.9.2) and (10.9.3) are often quite intuitive, for example, based on likelihood equations or methods such as least squares. On the other hand, functionals are more of an abstract concept. But often the estimating equations naturally lead to the functionals. We outline this next for the mean and median functionals.

Let F_n be the empirical distribution function of the realized sample $x_1, x_2, \ldots, x_n$. That is, F_n is the cdf of the distribution which puts mass n^{-1} on each x_i; see (10.1.1). Note that we can write the estimating equation (10.9.2), which defines the sample mean as

$$\sum_{i=1}^{n}(x_i - \theta)\frac{1}{n} = 0. \tag{10.9.9}$$

This is an expectation using the empirical distribution. Since $F_n \to F_X$ in probability, it would seem that this expectation converges to

$$\int_{-\infty}^{\infty} [x - T(F_X)]f_X(x)\,dx = 0. \tag{10.9.10}$$

The solution to the above equation is, of course, $T(F_X) = E(X)$.

Likewise, we can write the estimating equation (EE), (10.9.3), which defines the sample median, as

$$\sum_{i=1}^{n}\operatorname{sgn}(X_i - \theta)\frac{1}{n} = 0. \tag{10.9.11}$$

The corresponding equation for the functional $\theta = T(F_X)$ is the solution of the equation

$$\int_{-\infty}^{\infty}\operatorname{sgn}[y - T(F_X)]f_X(y)\,dy = 0. \tag{10.9.12}$$

Note that this can be written as

$$0 = -\int_{-\infty}^{T(F_X)} f_X(y)\,dy + \int_{T(F_X)}^{\infty} f_X(y)\,dy = -F_X[T(F_X)] + 1 - F_X[T(F_X)].$$

Hence $F_X[T(F_X)] = 1/2$ or $T(F_X) = F_X^{-1}(1/2)$. Thus $T(F_X)$ is the median of the distribution of X.

Now we want to consider how a given functional $T(F_X)$ changes relative to some perturbation. The analog of adding an outlier to $F(t)$ is to consider a **point-mass contamination** of the cdf $F_X(t)$ at a point x. That is, for $\epsilon > 0$, let

$$F_{x,\epsilon}(t) = (1 - \epsilon)F_X(t) + \epsilon\Delta_x(t), \tag{10.9.13}$$

where $\Delta_x(t)$ is the cdf with all its mass at x; i.e.,

$$\Delta_x(t) = \begin{cases} 0 & t < x \\ 1 & t \geq x. \end{cases} \tag{10.9.14}$$

The cdf $F_{x,\epsilon}(t)$ is a mixture of two distributions. When sampling from it, $(1-\epsilon)100\%$ of the time an observation is drawn from $F_X(t)$, while $\epsilon100\%$ of the time x (an outlier) is drawn. So x has the flavor of the outlier in the sensitivity curve. As Exercise 10.9.4 shows, $F_{x,\epsilon}(t)$ is in an ϵ neighborhood of $F_X(t)$; that is, for all x, $|F_{x,\epsilon}(t) - F_X(t)| \leq \epsilon$. Hence the functional at $F_{x,\epsilon}(t)$ should also be close to $T(F_X)$. The concept for functionals, corresponding to the sensitivity curve, is the function

$$\mathrm{IF}(x;\widehat{\theta}) = \lim_{\epsilon \to 0} \frac{T(F_{x,\epsilon}) - T(F_X)}{\epsilon}, \tag{10.9.15}$$

provided the limit exists. The function $\mathrm{IF}(x; \widehat{\theta})$ is called the **influence function** of
the estimator $\widehat{\theta}$ at x. As the notation suggests, it can be thought of as a derivative
of the functional $T(F_{x\epsilon})$ with respect to ϵ evaluated at 0, and we often determine
it this way. Note that for ϵ small,

$$T(F_{x,\epsilon}) \approx T(F_X) + \epsilon\,\mathrm{IF}(x; \widehat{\theta});$$

hence, the change of the functional due to point-mass contamination is approximately directly proportional to the influence function. We want estimators, whose
influence functions are not sensitive to outliers. Further, as mentioned above, for
any x, $F_{x,\epsilon}(t)$ is close to $F_X(t)$. Hence, at least, the influence function should be a
bounded function of x.

Definition 10.9.1. *The estimator $\widehat{\theta}$ is said to be* **robust** *if $|IF(x; \widehat{\theta})|$ is bounded
for all x.*

Hampel (1974) proposed the influence function and discussed its important properties, a few of which we list below. First, however, we determine the influence
functions of the sample mean and median.

For the sample mean, recall Section 3.4.1 on mixture distributions. The function
$F_{x,\epsilon}(t)$ is the cdf of the random variable $U = I_{1-\epsilon}X + [1 - I_{1-\epsilon}]W$, where X, $I_{1-\epsilon}$,
and W are independent random variables, X has cdf $F_X(t)$, W has cdf $\Delta_x(t)$, and
$I_{1-\epsilon}$ is $b(1, 1 - \epsilon)$. Hence

$$E(U) = (1 - \epsilon)E(X) + \epsilon E(W) = (1 - \epsilon)E(X) + \epsilon x.$$

Denote the mean functional by $T_\mu(F_X) = E(X)$. In terms of $T_\mu(F)$, we have just
shown that

$$T_\mu(F_{x,\epsilon}) = (1 - \epsilon)T_\mu(F_X) + \epsilon x.$$

Therefore,

$$\frac{\partial T_\mu(F_{x,\epsilon})}{\partial \epsilon} = -T_\mu(F) + x.$$

Hence the influence function of the sample mean is

$$\mathrm{IF}(y; \overline{X}) = x - \mu, \qquad (10.9.16)$$

where $\mu = E(X)$. The influence function of the sample mean is linear in x and,
hence, is an unbounded function of x. Therefore, the sample mean is not a robust
estimator. Another way to derive the influence function is to differentiate implicitly
equation (10.9.10) when this equation is defined for $F_{x,\epsilon}(t)$; see Exercise 10.9.6.

Example 10.9.1 (Influence Function of the Sample Median). In this example, we
derive the influence function of the sample median, $\widehat{\theta}_{L_1}$. In this case, the functional
is $T_\theta(F) = F^{-1}(1/2)$, i.e., the median of F. To determine the influence function, we
first need to determine the functional at the contaminated cdf $F_{x,\epsilon}(t)$, i.e., determine
$F_{x,\epsilon}^{-1}(1/2)$. As shown in Exercise 10.9.8, the inverse of the cdf $F_{x,\epsilon}(t)$ is given by

$$F_{x,\epsilon}^{-1}(u) = \begin{cases} F^{-1}\left(\dfrac{u}{1-\epsilon}\right) & u < F(x) \\[2mm] F^{-1}\left(\dfrac{u-\epsilon}{1-\epsilon}\right) & u \geq F(x), \end{cases} \qquad (10.9.17)$$

for $0 < u < 1$. Hence, letting $u = 1/2$, we get

$$T_\theta(F_{x,\epsilon}) = F_{x,\epsilon}^{-1}(1/2) = \begin{cases} F_X^{-1}\left(\frac{1/2}{1-\epsilon}\right) & F_X^{-1}\left(\frac{1}{2}\right) < x \\ F_X^{-1}\left(\frac{(1/2)-\epsilon}{1-\epsilon}\right) & F_X^{-1}\left(\frac{1}{2}\right) > x. \end{cases} \tag{10.9.18}$$

Based on (10.9.18) the partial derivative of $F_{x,\epsilon}^{-1}(1/2)$ with respect to ϵ is seen to be

$$\frac{\partial T_\theta(F_{x,\epsilon})}{\partial \epsilon} = \begin{cases} \frac{(1/2)(1-\epsilon)^{-2}}{f_X\left[F_X^{-1}((1/2)/(1-\epsilon))\right]} & F_X^{-1}\left(\frac{1}{2}\right) < x \\ \frac{(-1/2)(1-\epsilon)^{-2}}{f_X\left[F_X^{-1}(\{(1/2)-\epsilon\}/\{1-\epsilon\})\right]} & F_X^{-1}\left(\frac{1}{2}\right) > x. \end{cases} \tag{10.9.19}$$

Evaluating this partial derivative at $\epsilon = 0$, we arrive at the influence function of the median:

$$\text{IF}(x; \widehat{\theta}_{L_1}) = \begin{cases} \frac{1}{2f_X(\theta)} & \theta < x \\ \frac{-1}{2f_X(\theta)} & \theta > x \end{cases} = \frac{\text{sgn}(x - \theta)}{2f(\theta)}, \tag{10.9.20}$$

where θ is the median of F_X. Because this influence function is bounded, the sample median is a robust estimator. ∎

As derived on p. 46 of Hettmansperger and McKean (2011), the influence function of the Hodges–Lehmann estimator, $\widehat{\theta}_{\text{HL}}$, at the point x is given by:

$$\text{IF}(x; \widehat{\theta}_{\text{HL}}) = \frac{F_X(x) - 1/2}{\int_{-\infty}^{\infty} f_X^2(t)dt}. \tag{10.9.21}$$

Since a cdf is bounded, the Hodges–Lehmann estimator is robust.

We now list three useful properties of the influence function of an estimator. Note that for the sample mean, $E[\text{IF}(X; \overline{X})] = E[X] - \mu = 0$. This is true in general. Let $\text{IF}(x) = \text{IF}(x; \widehat{\theta})$ denote the influence function of the estimator $\widehat{\theta}$ with functional $\theta = T(F_X)$. Then

$$E[\text{IF}(X)] = 0, \tag{10.9.22}$$

provided expectations exist; see Huber (1981) for a discussion. Hence, for the second property, we have

$$\text{Var}[\text{IF}(X)] = E[\text{IF}^2(X)], \tag{10.9.23}$$

provided the squared expectation exists. A third property of the influence function is the asymptotic result

$$\sqrt{n}[\widehat{\theta} - \theta] = \frac{1}{\sqrt{n}} \sum_{i=1}^{n} \text{IF}(X_i) + o_p(1). \tag{10.9.24}$$

Assume that the variance (10.9.23) exists, then because $\text{IF}(X_1), \ldots, \text{IF}(X_n)$ are iid with finite variance, the simple Central Limit Theorem and (10.9.24) imply that

$$\sqrt{n}[\widehat{\theta} - \theta] \xrightarrow{D} N(0, E[\text{IF}^2(X)]). \tag{10.9.25}$$

Thus we can obtain the asymptotic distribution of the estimator from its influence function. Under general conditions, expression (10.9.24) holds, but often the verification of the conditions is difficult and the asymptotic distribution can be obtained more easily in another way; see Huber (1981) for a discussion. In this chapter, though, we use (10.9.24) to obtain asymptotic distributions of estimators. Suppose (10.9.24) holds for the estimators $\widehat{\theta}_1$ and $\widehat{\theta}_2$, which are both estimators of the same functional, say, θ. Then, letting IF_i denote the influence function of $\widehat{\theta}_i$, $i = 1, 2$, we can express the asymptotic relative efficiency between the two estimators as

$$\mathrm{ARE}(\widehat{\theta}_1, \widehat{\theta}_2) = \frac{E[\mathrm{IF}_2^2(X)]}{E[\mathrm{IF}_1^2(X)]}. \tag{10.9.26}$$

As an example, we consider the sample median.

Example 10.9.2 (Asymptotic Distribution of the Sample Median). The influence function for the sample median $\widehat{\theta}_{L_1}$ is given by (10.9.20). Since $E[\mathrm{sgn}^2(X - \theta)] = 1$, by expression (10.9.25) the asymptotic distribution of the sample median is

$$\sqrt{n}[\widehat{\theta} - \theta] \xrightarrow{D} N\left(0, [2f_X(\theta)]^{-2}\right),$$

where θ is the median of the pdf $f_X(t)$. This agrees with the result given in Section 10.2. ∎

Breakdown Point of an Estimator

The influence function of an estimator measures the sensitivity of an estimator to a single outlier, sometimes called the *local sensitivity* of the estimator. We next discuss a measure of *global sensitivity* of an estimator. That is, what proportion of outliers can an estimator tolerate without completely breaking down?

To be precise, let $\mathbf{x}' = (x_1, x_2, \ldots, x_n)$ be a realization of a sample. Suppose we corrupt m points of this sample by replacing $x_1, \ldots, x_m$ by $x_1^*, \ldots, x_m^*$, where these points are large outliers. Let $\mathbf{x}_m = (x_1^*, \ldots, x_m^*, x_{m+1}, \ldots, x_n)$ denote the corrupted sample. Define the bias of the estimator upon corrupting m data points to be

$$\mathrm{bias}(m, \mathbf{x}_n, \widehat{\theta}) = \sup |\widehat{\theta}(\mathbf{x}_m) - \widehat{\theta}(\mathbf{x}_n)|, \tag{10.9.27}$$

where the sup is taken over all possible corrupted samples $\mathbf{x}_m$. If this bias is infinite, we say that the estimator has **broken down**. The smallest proportion of corruption an estimator can tolerate until its breakdown is called its *finite sample breakdown point*. More precisely, if

$$\epsilon_n^* = \min_m \{m/n : \mathrm{bias}(m, \mathbf{x}_n, \widehat{\theta}) = \infty\}, \tag{10.9.28}$$

then ϵ_n^* is called the **finite sample breakdown point** of $\widehat{\theta}$. If the limit

$$\epsilon_n^* \to \epsilon^* \tag{10.9.29}$$

exists, we call ϵ^* the **breakdown point** of $\widehat{\theta}$.

To determine the breakdown point of the sample mean, suppose we corrupt one data point, say, without loss of generality, the first data point. The corrupted sample is then $\mathbf{x}' = (x_1^*, x_2, \ldots, x_n)$. Denote the sample mean of the corrupted sample by $\overline{x}^*$. Then it is easy to see that

$$\overline{x}^* - \overline{x} = \frac{1}{n}(x_1^* - x_1).$$

Hence $\text{bias}(1, \mathbf{x}_n, \overline{x})$ is a linear function of x_1^* and can be made as large (in absolute value) as desired by taking x_1^* large (in absolute value). Therefore, the finite sample breakdown of the sample mean is $1/n$. Because this goes to 0 as $n \to \infty$, the breakdown point of the sample mean is 0.

Example 10.9.3 (Breakdown Value of the Sample Median). Next consider the sample median. Let $\mathbf{x}_n = (x_1, x_2, \ldots, x_n)$ be a realization of a random sample. If the sample size is $n = 2k$, then it is easy to see that in a corrupted sample $\mathbf{x}_n$ when $x_{(k)}$ tends to $-\infty$, the median also tends to $-\infty$. Hence the breakdown value of the sample median is k/n, which tends to 0.5. By a similar argument, when the sample size is $n = 2k + 1$, the breakdown value is $(k+1)/n$ and it also tends to 0.5 as the sample size increases. Hence we say that the sample median is a 50% breakdown estimate. For a location model, 50% breakdown is the highest possible breakdown point for an estimate. Thus the median achieves the highest possible breakdown point. ∎

In Exercise 10.9.10, the reader is asked to show that the Hodges–Lehmann estimate has the breakdown point of 0.29.

10.9.2 Linear Model

In Sections 9.6 and 10.7, respectively, we presented the least squares (LS) procedure and a rank-based (Wilcoxon) procedure for fitting simple linear models. In this section, we briefly compare these procedures in terms of their robustness properties.

Recall that the simple linear model is given by

$$Y_i = \alpha + \beta x_{ci} + \varepsilon_i, \quad i = 1, 2, \ldots, n, \tag{10.9.30}$$

where $\varepsilon_1, \varepsilon_2, \ldots, \varepsilon_n$ are continuous random variable which are iid. In this model, we have centered the regression variables; that is, $x_{ci} = x_i - \overline{x}$, where $x_1, x_2, \ldots, x_n$ are considered fixed. The parameter of interest in this section is the slope parameter β, the expected change (provided expectations exist) when the regression variable increases by one unit. The centering of the xs allows us to consider the slope parameter by itself. The results we present are invariant to the intercept parameter α. Estimates of α are discussed in Section 10.9.2. With this in mind, define the random variable e_i to be $\varepsilon_i + \alpha$. Then we can write the model as

$$Y_i = \beta x_{ci} + e_i, \quad i = 1, 2, \ldots, n, \tag{10.9.31}$$

where $e_1, e_2, \ldots, e_n$ are iid with continuous cdf $F(x)$ and pdf $f(x)$. We often refer to the support of Y as the Y-space. Likewise, we refer to the range of X as the X-space. The X-space is often referred to as the **factor space**.

Least Squares and Wilcoxon Procedures

The first procedure is *least squares* (LS). The estimating equation for β is given by expression (9.6.3) of Chapter 9. Using the fact that $\sum_i x_{ci} = 0$, this equation can be reexpressed as

$$\sum_{i=1}^{n}(Y_i - x_{ci}\beta)x_{ci} = 0. \qquad (10.9.32)$$

This is the estimating equation (EE) for the LS estimator of β, which we use in this section. It is often called the **normal equation**. It is easy to see that the LS estimator is

$$\widehat{\beta}_{LS} = \frac{\sum_{i=1}^{n} x_{ci}Y_i}{\sum_{i=1}^{n} x_{ci}^2}, \qquad (10.9.33)$$

which agrees with expression (9.6) of Chapter 9. The geometry of the LS estimator is discussed in Remark 9.6.1.

For our second procedure, we consider the estimate of slope discussed in Section 10.7. This is a rank-based estimate based on an arbitrary score function. In this section, we restrict our discussion to the linear (Wilcoxon) scores; i.e., the score function is given by $\varphi_W(u) = \sqrt{12}[u - (1/2)]$, where the subscript W denotes the Wilcoxon score function. The estimating equation of the rank-based estimator of β is given by expression (10.7.8), which for the Wilcoxon score function is

$$\sum_{i=1}^{n} a_W(R(Y_i - x_{ci}\beta))x_{ci} = 0, \qquad (10.9.34)$$

where $a_W(i) = \varphi_W[i/(n+1)]$. This equation is the analog of the LS normal equation. See Exercise 10.9.12 for a geometric interpretation.

Influence Functions

To determine the robustness properties of these procedures, first consider a probability model corresponding to Model (10.9.31), in which X, in addition to Y, is a random variable. Assume that the random vector (X, Y) has joint cdf and pdf, $H(x, y)$ and $h(x, y)$, respectively, and satisfies

$$Y = \beta X + e, \qquad (10.9.35)$$

where the random variable e has cdf and pdf $F(t)$ and $f(t)$, respectively, and e and X are independent. Since we have centered the xs, we also assume that $E(X) = 0$. As Exercise 10.9.13 shows,

$$P(Y \leq t | X = x) = F(t - \beta x), \qquad (10.9.36)$$

and, hence, Y and X are independent if and only if $\beta = 0$.

The functional for the LS estimator easily follows from the LS normal equation (10.9.32). Let H_n denote the empirical cdf of the pairs $(x_1, y_1), (x_2, y_2), \ldots, (x_n, y_n)$;

that is, H_n is the cdf corresponding to the discrete distribution, which puts probability (mass) of $1/n$ on each point (x_i, y_i). Then the LS estimating equation, (10.9.32), can be expressed as an expectation with respect to this distribution as

$$\sum_{i=1}^{n} (y_i - x_{ci}\beta) x_{ci} \frac{1}{n} = 0. \tag{10.9.37}$$

For the probability model, (10.9.35), it follows that the functional $T_{\mathrm{LS}}(H)$ corresponding to the LS estimate is the solution to the equation

$$\int_{-\infty}^{\infty} \int_{-\infty}^{\infty} [y - T_{\mathrm{LS}}(H)x] x h(x, y)\, dx dy = 0. \tag{10.9.38}$$

To obtain the functional corresponding to the Wilcoxon estimate, recall the association between the ranks and the empirical cdf; see (10.5.14). For Wilcoxon scores, we have

$$a_W(R(Y_i - x_{ci}\beta)) = \varphi_W \left[\frac{n}{n+1} F_n(Y_i - x_{ci}\beta) \right]. \tag{10.9.39}$$

Based on the Wilcoxon estimating equations, (10.9.34), and expression (10.9.39), the functional $T_W(H)$ corresponding to the Wilcoxon estimate satisfies the equation

$$\int_{-\infty}^{\infty} \int_{-\infty}^{\infty} \varphi_W \{F[y - T_W(H)x]\} x h(x, y)\, dx dy = 0. \tag{10.9.40}$$

We next derive the influence functions of the LS and Wilcoxon estimators of β. In regression models, we are concerned about the influence of outliers in both the $Y-$ and $X-$spaces. Consider then a point-mass distribution with all its mass at the point (x_0, y_0), and let $\Delta_{(x_0, y_0)}(x, y)$ denote the corresponding cdf. Let ϵ denote the probability of sampling from this contaminating distribution, where $0 < \epsilon < 1$. Hence, consider the contaminated distribution with cdf

$$H_\epsilon(x, y) = (1 - \epsilon) H(x, y) + \epsilon \Delta_{(x_0, y_0)}(x, y). \tag{10.9.41}$$

Because the differential is a linear operator, we have

$$dH_\epsilon(x, y) = (1 - \epsilon) dH(x, y) + \epsilon d\Delta_{(x_0, y_0)}(x, y), \tag{10.9.42}$$

where $dH(x, y) = h(x, y)\, dx dy$; that is, d corresponds to the second mixed partial $\partial^2/\partial x\, \partial y$.

By (10.9.38), the LS functional T_ϵ at the cdf $H_\epsilon(x, y)$ satisfies the equation

$$0 = (1 - \epsilon) \int_{-\infty}^{\infty} \int_{-\infty}^{\infty} x(y - xT_\epsilon) h(x, y)\, dx dy + \epsilon \int_{-\infty}^{\infty} \int_{-\infty}^{\infty} x(y - xT_\epsilon)\, d\Delta_{(x_0, y_0)}(x, y). \tag{10.9.43}$$

To find the partial derivative of T_ϵ with respect to ϵ, we simply implicitly differentiate expression (10.9.43) with respect to ϵ, which yields

$$
\begin{aligned}
0 = \ & -\int_{-\infty}^{\infty}\int_{-\infty}^{\infty} x(y - T_\epsilon x)h(x,y)\,dxdy \\
& + (1-\epsilon)\int_{-\infty}^{\infty}\int_{-\infty}^{\infty} x(-x)\frac{\partial T_\epsilon}{\partial \epsilon}h(x,y)\,dxdy \\
& + \int_{-\infty}^{\infty}\int_{-\infty}^{\infty} x(y - xT_\epsilon)\,d\Delta_{(x_0,y_0)}(x,y) + \epsilon B,
\end{aligned}
\tag{10.9.44}
$$

where the expression for B is not needed since we are evaluating this partial at $\epsilon = 0$. Notice that at $\epsilon = 0$, $y - T_\epsilon x = y - Tx = y - \beta x$. Hence, at $\epsilon = 0$, the first expression on the right side of (10.9.44) is 0, while the second expression becomes $-E(X^2)(\partial T/\partial \epsilon)$, where the partial is evaluated at 0. Finally, the third expression is the expected value of the point-mass distribution $\Delta_{(x_0,y_0)}$, which is, of course, $x_0(y_0 - \beta x_0)$. Therefore, solving for the partial $\partial T_\epsilon/\partial \epsilon$ and evaluating at $\epsilon = 0$, we see that the influence function of the LS estimator is given by

$$
\mathrm{IF}(x_0, y_0; \widehat{\beta}_{\mathrm{LS}}) = \frac{(y_0 - \beta x_0)x_0}{E(X^2)}.
\tag{10.9.45}
$$

Note that the influence function is unbounded in both the $Y-$ and $X-$spaces. Hence the LS estimator is unduly sensitive to outliers in both spaces. It is not robust.

Based on expression (10.9.40), the Wilcoxon functional at the contaminated distribution satisfies the equation

$$
\begin{aligned}
0 = \ & (1-\epsilon)\int_{-\infty}^{\infty}\int_{-\infty}^{\infty} x\varphi_W[F(y - xT_\epsilon)]h(x,y)\,dxdy \\
& + \epsilon\int_{-\infty}^{\infty}\int_{-\infty}^{\infty} x\varphi_W[F(y - xT_\epsilon)]\,d\Delta_{(x_0,y_0)}(x,y)
\end{aligned}
\tag{10.9.46}
$$

[technically, the cdf F should be replaced by the actual cdf of the residual, but the result is the same; see page 477 of Hettmansperger and McKean (2011)]. Proceeding to implicitly differentiate this expression with respect to ϵ, we obtain

$$
\begin{aligned}
0 = \ & -\int_{-\infty}^{\infty}\int_{-\infty}^{\infty} x\varphi_W[F(y - xT_\epsilon)]h(x,y)\,dxdy \\
& + (1-\epsilon)\int_{-\infty}^{\infty}\int_{-\infty}^{\infty} x\varphi_W'[F(y - T_\epsilon x)]f(y - T_\epsilon x)(-x)\frac{\partial T_\epsilon}{\partial \epsilon}h(x,y)\,dxdy \\
& + \int_{-\infty}^{\infty}\int_{-\infty}^{\infty} x\varphi_W[F(y - xT_\epsilon)]\,d\Delta_{(x_0,y_0)}(x,y) + \epsilon B,
\end{aligned}
\tag{10.9.47}
$$

where the expression for B is not needed since we are evaluating this partial at $\epsilon = 0$. When $\epsilon = 0$, then $Y - TX = e$ and the random variables e and X are independent. Hence, upon setting $\epsilon = 0$, expression (10.9.47) simplifies to

$$
0 = -E[\varphi_W'(F(e))f(e)]E(X^2)\left.\frac{\partial T_\epsilon}{\partial \epsilon}\right|_{\epsilon=0} + \varphi_W[F(y_0 - x_0\beta)]x_0.
\tag{10.9.48}
$$

Since $\varphi'(u) = \sqrt{12}$, we finally obtain, as the influence function of the Wilcoxon estimator,

$$\text{IF}(x_0, y_0; \widehat{\beta}_W) = \frac{\tau \varphi_W[F(y_0 - \beta x_0)]x_0}{E(X^2)}, \quad (10.9.49)$$

where $\tau = 1/[\sqrt{12} \int f^2(e)\, de]$. Note that the influence function is bounded in the Y–space, but it is unbounded in the X–space. Thus, unlike the LS estimator, the Wilcoxon estimator is robust against outliers in the Y–space, but like the LS estimator, it is sensitive to outliers in the X–space. Weighted versions of the Wilcoxon estimator, though, have bounded influence in both the Y– and X–spaces; see the discussion of the HBR estimator in Chapter 3 of Hettmansperger and McKean (2011). Exercises 10.9.18 and 10.9.19 asks for derivations, respectively, of the asymptotic distributions of the LS and Wilcoxon estimators, using their influence functions.

Breakdown Points

Breakdown for the regression model is based on the corruption of the sample in Model (10.9.31), that is, the sample $(x_{c1}, Y_1), \ldots, (x_{cn}, Y_n)$. Based on the influence functions for both the LS and Wilcoxon estimators, it is clear that corrupting one x_i breaks down both estimators. This is shown in Exercise 10.9.14. Hence the breakdown point of each estimator is 0. The HBR estimator (weighted version of the Wilcoxon estimator cited above), has bounded influence in both spaces and can achieve 50% breakdown; see Chang et al. (1999) and Hettmansperger and McKean (2011).

Intercept

In practice, the linear model usually contains an intercept parameter; that is, the model is given by (10.9.30) with intercept parameter α. Notice that α is a location parameter of the random variables $Y_i - \beta x_{ci}$. This suggests an estimate of location on the residuals $Y_i - \widehat{\beta} x_{ci}$. For LS, we take the sample mean of the residuals; i.e.,

$$\widehat{\alpha}_{LS} = n^{-1} \sum_{i=1}^{n} (Y_i - \widehat{\beta}_{LS} x_{ci}) = \overline{Y}, \quad (10.9.50)$$

because the x_{ci}s are centered. For the Wilcoxon fit, several choices seem appropriate. We use the median of the Wilcoxon residuals. That is, let

$$\widehat{\alpha}_W = \text{med}_{1 \le i \le n}\{Y_i - \widehat{\beta}_W x_{ci}\}. \quad (10.9.51)$$

Remark 10.9.1 (Computation). There are resources available to compute the Wilcoxon estimates. The minitab computer package has the command `rregr`, which computes both the Wilcoxon and LS fits. Terpstra and McKean (2005) developed a collection of R routines which return the Wilcoxon fit. Their algorithm is based on the identity established in Exercise 10.9.15. More recently, Kloke and McKean (2011) developed an R library, `Rfit`, which can be used to obtain the simple Wilcoxon regression fit. ∎

EXERCISES

10.9.1. Consider the location model as defined in expression (10.9.1). Let

$$\widehat{\theta} = \text{Argmin}_\theta \|\mathbf{X} - \theta \mathbf{1}\|_{\text{LS}}^2,$$

where $\| \cdot \|_{\text{LS}}^2$ is the square of the Euclidean norm. Show that $\widehat{\theta} = \overline{x}$.

10.9.2. Obtain the sensitivity curves for the sample mean, the sample median and the Hodges–Lehmann estimator for the following data set. Evaluate the curves at the values -300 to 300 in increments of 10 and graph the curves on the same plot. Compare the sensitivity curves.

$$\begin{array}{cccccccc}
-9 & 58 & 12 & -1 & -37 & 0 & 11 & 21 \\
18 & -24 & -4 & -53 & -9 & 9 & 8 &
\end{array}$$

10.9.3. Consider the influence function for the Hodges–Lehmann estimator given in expression (10.9.21). Show for it that property (10.9.22) is true. Next, evaluate expression (10.9.23) and, hence, obtain the asymptotic distribution of the estimator as given in expression (10.9.25). Does it agree with the result derived in Section 10.3?

10.9.4. Let $F_{x,\epsilon}(t)$ be the point-mass contaminated cdf given in expression (10.9.13). Show that

$$|F_{x,\epsilon}(t) - F_X(t)| \le \epsilon,$$

for all t.

10.9.5. Suppose X is a random variable with mean 0 and variance σ^2. Recall that the function $F_{x,\epsilon}(t)$ is the cdf of the random variable $U = I_{1-\epsilon}X + [1 - I_{1-\epsilon}]W$, where X, $I_{1-\epsilon}$, and W are independent random variables, X has cdf $F_X(t)$, W has cdf $\Delta_x(t)$, and $I_{1-\epsilon}$ has a binomial$(1, 1 - \epsilon)$ distribution. Define the functional $\text{Var}(F_X) = \text{Var}(X) = \sigma^2$. Note that the functional at the contaminated cdf $F_{x,\epsilon}(t)$ has the variance of the random variable $U = I_{1-\epsilon}X + [1 - I_{1-\epsilon}]W$. To derive the influence function of the variance, perform the following steps:

(a) Show that $E(U) = \epsilon x$.

(b) Show that $\text{Var}(U) = (1 - \epsilon)\sigma^2 + \epsilon x^2 - \epsilon^2 x^2$.

(c) Obtain the partial derivative of the right side of this last equation with respect to ϵ. This is the influence function.

Hint: Because $I_{1-\epsilon}$ is a Bernoulli random variable, $I_{1-\epsilon}^2 = I_{1-\epsilon}$. Why?

10.9.6. Often influence functions are derived by differentiating implicitly the defining equation for the functional at the contaminated cdf $F_{x,\epsilon}(t)$, (10.9.13). Consider the mean functional with the defining equation (10.9.10). Using the linearity of the differential, first show that the defining equation at the cdf $F_{x,\epsilon}(t)$ can be expressed as

$$0 = \int_{-\infty}^{\infty} [t - T(F_{x,\epsilon})] dF_{x,\epsilon}(t) = (1-\epsilon) \int_{-\infty}^{\infty} [t - T(F_{x,\epsilon})] f_X(t) \, dt$$

$$+ \epsilon \int_{-\infty}^{\infty} [t - T(F_{x,\epsilon})] \, d\Delta(t). \quad (10.9.52)$$

Recall that we want $\partial T(F_{x,\epsilon})/\partial \epsilon$. Obtain this by implicitly differentiating the above equation with respect to ϵ.

10.9.7. In Exercise 10.9.5, the influence function of the variance functional was derived directly. Assuming that the mean of X is 0, note that the variance functional, $V(F_X)$, also solves the equation

$$0 = \int_{-\infty}^{\infty} [t^2 - V(F_X)] f_X(t) \, dt.$$

(a) Determine the natural estimator of the variance by writing the defining equation at the empirical cdf $F_n(t)$, for $X_1 - \overline{X}, \ldots, X_n - \overline{X}$ iid with cdf $F_X(t)$, and solving for $V(F_n)$.

(b) As in Exercise 10.9.6, write the defining equation for the variance functional at the contaminated cdf $F_{x,\epsilon}(t)$.

(c) Then derive the influence function by implicit differentiation of the defining equation in part (b).

10.9.8. Show that the inverse of the cdf $F_{x,\epsilon}(t)$ given in expression (10.9.17) is correct.

10.9.9. Let $\mathrm{IF}(x)$ be the influence function of the sample median given by (10.9.20). Determine $E[\mathrm{IF}(X)]$ and $\mathrm{Var}[\mathrm{IF}(X)]$.

10.9.10. Let $x_1, x_2, \ldots, x_n$ be a realization of a random sample. Consider the Hodges–Lehmann estimate of location given in expression (10.9.4). Show that the breakdown point of this estimate is 0.29.
Hint: Suppose we corrupt m data points. We need to determine the value of m which results in corruption of one half of the Walsh averages. Show that the corruption of m data points leads to

$$p(m) = m + \binom{m}{2} + m(n-m)$$

corrupted Walsh averages. Hence the finite sample breakdown point is the "correct" solution of the quadratic equation $p(m) = n(n+1)/4$.

10.9.11. For any $n \times 1$ vector $\mathbf{v}$, define the function $\|\mathbf{v}\|_W$ by

$$\|\mathbf{v}\|_W = \sum_{i=1}^{n} a_W(R(v_i)) v_i, \quad (10.9.53)$$

where $R(v_i)$ denotes the rank of v_i among $v_1, \ldots, v_n$ and the Wilcoxon scores are given by $a_W(i) = \varphi_W[i/(n+1)]$ for $\varphi_W(u) = \sqrt{12}[u - (1/2)]$. By using the correspondence between order statistics and ranks, show that

$$\|\mathbf{v}\|_W = \sum_{i=1}^{n} a(i)v_{(i)}, \qquad (10.9.54)$$

where $v_{(1)} \leq \cdots \leq v_{(n)}$ are the ordered values of $v_1, \ldots, v_n$. Then, by establishing the following properties, show that the function (10.9.53) is a **pseudo-norm** on R^n.

(a) $\|\mathbf{v}\|_W \geq 0$ and $\|\mathbf{v}\|_W = 0$ if and only if $v_1 = v_2 = \cdots = v_n$.

   Hint: First, because the scores $a(i)$ sum to 0, show that

$$\sum_{i=1}^{n} a(i)v_{(i)} = \sum_{i<j} a(i)[v_{(i)} - v_{(j)}] + \sum_{i>j} a(i)[v_{(i)} - v_{(j)}],$$

   where j is the largest integer in the set $\{1, 2, \ldots, n\}$ such that $a(j) < 0$.

(b) $\|c\mathbf{v}\|_W = |c|\|\mathbf{v}\|_W,$ for all $c \in R$.

(c) $\|\mathbf{v} + \mathbf{w}\|_W \leq \|\mathbf{v}\|_W + \|\mathbf{w}\|_W,$ for all $\mathbf{v}, \mathbf{w} \in R^n$.

   Hint: Determine the permutations, say, i_k and j_k of the integers $\{1, 2, \ldots, n\}$, which maximize $\sum_{k=1}^{n} c_{i_k} d_{j_k}$ for the two sets of numbers $\{c_1, \ldots, c_n\}$ and $\{d_1, \ldots, d_n\}$.

10.9.12. Remark 9.6.1 discusses the geometry of the LS estimate of β. There is an analogous geometry for the Wilcoxon estimate. Using the norm $\|\cdot\|_W$ defined in expression (10.9.53) of the last exercise, let

$$\widehat{\beta}^* = \text{Argmin} \|\mathbf{Y} - \mathbf{X}_c\beta\|_W,$$

where $\mathbf{Y}' = (Y_1, \ldots, Y_n)$ and $\mathbf{X}_c' = (x_{c1}, \ldots, x_{cn})$. Thus $\widehat{\beta}^*$ minimizes the distance between $\mathbf{Y}$ and the space spanned by the vector $\mathbf{X}_c$.

(a) Using expression (10.9.54), show that $\widehat{\beta}^*$ satisfies the Wilcoxon estimating equation (10.9.34). That is, $\widehat{\beta}^* = \widehat{\beta}_W$.

(b) Let $\widehat{\mathbf{Y}}_W = \mathbf{X}_c\widehat{\beta}_W$ and $\mathbf{Y} - \widehat{\mathbf{Y}}_W$ denote the Wilcoxon vectors of fitted values and residuals, respectively. Sketch a figure analogous to the LS Figure 9.6.2, but with these vectors on it. Note that your figure may not contain a right angle.

(c) For the Wilcoxon regression procedure, determine a vector (not $\mathbf{0}$) that is orthogonal to $\widehat{\mathbf{Y}}_W$.

10.9.13. For Model (10.9.35), show that equation (10.9.36) holds. Then show that Y and X are independent if and only if $\beta = 0$. Hence independence is based on the value of a parameter. This is a case where normality is not necessary to have this independence property.

10.9.14. Consider the telephone data discussed in Example 10.7.2. It is easily seen in Figure 10.7.1 that there are seven outliers in the Y-space. Based on the estimates discussed in this example, the Wilcoxon estimate of slope is robust to these outliers, while the LS estimate is highly sensitive to them.

   (a) For this data set, change the last value of x from 73 to 173. Notice the drastic change in the LS fit.

   (b) Obtain the Wilcoxon estimate for the changed data in part (a). Notice that it has a drastic change also. To obtain the Wilcoxon fit, see Remark 10.9.1 on computation.

   (c) Using the Wilcoxon estimates of Example 10.7.2, change the the value of Y at $x = 173$ to the predicted value of Y based on the Wilcoxon estimates of Example 10.7.2. Note that this point is a "good" point at the outlying x; that is, it fits the model. Now determine the Wilcoxon and LS estimates. Comment on them.

10.9.15. For the pseudo-norm $\|\mathbf{v}\|_W$ defined in expression (10.9.53), establish the identity

$$\|\mathbf{v}\|_W = \frac{\sqrt{3}}{2(n+1)} \sum_{i=1}^{n} \sum_{j=1}^{n} |v_i - v_j|, \qquad (10.9.55)$$

for all $\mathbf{v} \in R^n$. Thus we have shown that

$$\widehat{\beta}_W = \text{Argmin} \sum_{i=1}^{n} \sum_{j=1}^{n} |(y_i - y_j) - \beta(x_{ci} - x_{cj})|. \qquad (10.9.56)$$

Note that the formulation of $\widehat{\beta}_W$ given in expression (10.9.56) allows an easy way to compute the Wilcoxon estimate of slope by using an L_1 (least absolute deviations) routine. Terpstra and McKean (2005) used this identity, (10.9.55), to develop R functions for the computation of the Wilcoxon fit.

10.9.16. Suppose the random variable e has cdf $F(t)$. Let $\varphi(u) = \sqrt{12}[u - (1/2)]$, $0 < u < 1$, denote the Wilcoxon score function.

   (a) Show that the random variable $\varphi[F(e_i)]$ has mean 0 and variance 1.

   (b) Investigate the mean and variance of $\varphi[F(e_i)]$ for any score function $\varphi(u)$ which satisfies $\int_0^1 \varphi(u)\, du = 0$ and $\int_0^1 \varphi^2(u)\, du = 1$.

10.9.17. In the derivation of the influence function, we assumed that x was random. For inference, though, we consider the case that x is given. In this case, the variance of X, $E(X^2)$, which is found in the influence function, is replaced by its estimate, namely, $n^{-1} \sum_{i=1}^{n} x_{ci}^2$. With this in mind, use the influence function of the LS estimator of β to derive the asymptotic distribution of the LS estimator; see the discussion around expression (10.9.24). Show that it agrees with the exact distribution of the LS estimator given in expression (9.6.6) under the assumption that the errors have a normal distribution.

10.9.18. As in the last problem, use the influence function of the Wilcoxon estimator of β to derive the asymptotic distribution of the Wilcoxon estimator. For Wilcoxon scores, show that it agrees with expression (10.7.14).

10.9.19. Use the results of the last two exercises to find the asymptotic relative efficiency (ARE) between the Wilcoxon and LS estimators of β.

Chapter 11

Bayesian Statistics

11.1   Subjective Probability

Subjective probability is the foundation of Bayesian methods, so in this section we offer a discussion of it. Suppose a person has assigned $P(C) = \frac{2}{5}$ to some event C. Then the *odds* against C would be

$$O(C) = \frac{1 - P(C)}{P(C)} = \frac{1 - \frac{2}{5}}{\frac{2}{5}} = \frac{3}{2}.$$

Moreover, if that person is willing to bet, he or she is willing to accept either side of the bet: (1) Win three units if C occurs and lose two if it does not occur, or (2) win two units if C does not occur and lose three if it does. If that is not the case, then that person should review his or her subjective probability of event C.

This is really much like two children dividing a candy bar as equally as possible: One divides it and the other gets to choose which of the two parts seems more desirable, that is, larger. Accordingly, the child dividing the candy bar tries extremely hard to cut it as equally as possible. Clearly, this is exactly what the person selecting the subjective probability does, as he or she must be willing to take either side of the bet with the odds established.

Let us now say the reader is willing to accept the subjective probability $P(C)$ as the fair price for event C, given that you win one unit if case C occurs [that is, your profit is $1 - P(C)$, as you have already paid $P(C)$] and, of course, you lose $P(C)$ if it does not occur. Then, it turns out, all rules (definitions and theorems) on probability found in Chapter 1 follow for subjective probabilities. We do not give proofs of them all; we give proofs of two of them, and some of the others are left as exercises. These proofs were given to us in a personal communication from George Woodworth of the University of Iowa.

Theorem 11.1.1. *If C_1 and C_2 are mutually exclusive, then*

$$P(C_1 \cup C_2) = P(C_1) + P(C_2).$$

Proof: Suppose a person thinks a fair price for C_1 is $p_1 = P(C_1)$ and that for C_2 is $p_2 = P(C_2)$. However, that person believes the fair price for $C_1 \cup C_2$ is p_3, which differs from $p_1 + p_2$. Say, $p_3 < p_1 + p_2$ and let the difference be $d = (p_1 + p_2) - p_3$. A gambler offers this person the price $p_3 + \frac{d}{4}$ for $C_1 \cup C_2$. That person takes the offer because it is better than p_3. The gambler sells C_1 at a discount price of $p_1 - \frac{d}{4}$ and sells C_2 at a discount price of $p_2 - \frac{d}{4}$ to that person. Being a rational person, with those given prices of p_1, p_2, and p_3, all three of these deals seem very satisfactory. However, that person received $p_3 + \frac{d}{4}$ and paid $p_1 + p_2 - \frac{d}{2}$. Thus, before any bets are paid off, that person has

$$p_3 + \frac{d}{4} - \left(p_1 + p_2 - \frac{d}{2} \right) = p_3 - p_1 - p_2 + \frac{3d}{4} = -\frac{d}{4}.$$

That is, the person is down $\frac{d}{4}$ before any bets are settled.

- Suppose C_1 happens: The gambler has $C_1 \cup C_2$ and the person has C_1, so they exchange units and the person is still down $\frac{d}{4}$. The same thing occurs if C_2 happens.

- Suppose neither C_1 or C_2 happens; then the gambler and that person receive zero, and the person is still down $\frac{d}{4}$.

- Of course, C_1 and C_2 cannot occur together since they are mutually exclusive.

Thus we see that it is bad for that person to assign

$$p_3 = P(C_1 \cup C_2) < p_1 + p_2 = P(C_1) + P(C_2),$$

because the gambler can put that person in a position to lose $(p_1 + p_2 - p_3)/4$ no matter what happens. This is sometimes referred to as a **Dutch book**.

The argument when $p_3 > p_1 + p_2$ is similar and can also lead to a Dutch book; it is left as an exercise. Thus p_3 must equal $p_1 + p_2$ to avoid a Dutch book; that is, $P(C_1 \cup C_2) = P(C_1) + P(C_2)$. ∎

Let us prove another one.

Theorem 11.1.2. *If $C_1 \subset C_2$, then $P(C_1) \leq P(C_2)$.*

Proof: Say the person believes the fair prices are such that $p_1 = P(C_1) > p_2 = P(C_2)$. Then if $d = p_1 - p_2$, the gambler sells C_1 to that person for $p_1 - \frac{d}{4}$ and buys C_2 from that person for $p_2 + \frac{d}{4}$. If the person truly believes $p_1 > p_2$, both of these are good deals. Yet before any bets are settled, that person has

$$p_2 + \frac{d}{4} - \left(p_1 - \frac{d}{4} \right) = p_2 - p_1 + \frac{d}{2} = -d + \frac{d}{2} = -\frac{d}{2};$$

that is, that person is down $\frac{d}{2}$.

- If C_1 is true, then C_2 is true, and both receive one unit from each other and that person is still down $\frac{d}{2}$.

- If C_2 happens, but C_1 does not, then the gambler receives one unit from that person and the latter is down $1 + \frac{d}{2}$.

- If neither C_1 nor C_2 happens, neither the gambler nor the person receives anything and the person is still down $\frac{d}{2}$.

The person loses no matter what happens; that is, we have a Dutch book when $p_1 > p_2$. So $p_1 > p_2$ is unfavorable, and thus it must be that the fair prices are $p_1 \leq p_2$. ∎

In the exercises, we give hints how to show that

$P(\mathcal{C}) = 1$ (Exercise 11.1.3)

$P(C^c) = 1 - P(C)$ (Exercise 11.1.4)

If $C_1 \subset C_2$ and $C_2 \subset C_1$ (that is, $C_1 \equiv C_2$), then $P(C_1) = P(C_2)$ (Exercise 11.1.5)

If C_1, C_2, and C_3 are mutually exclusive, then $P(C_1 \cup C_2 \cup C_3) = P(C_1) + P(C_2) + P(C_3)$ (Exercise 11.1.6)

$P(C_1 \cup C_2) = P(C_1) + P(C_2) - P(C_1 \cap C_2)$ (Exercise 11.1.7).

The Bayesian continues to consider subjective conditional probabilities, such as $P(C_1|C_2)$, which is the fair price of C_1 only if C_2 is true. If C_2 is not true, the bet is off. Of course, $P(C_1|C_2)$ could differ from $P(C_1)$. To illustrate, say C_2 is the event that "it will rain today" and C_1 is the event that "a certain person who will be outside on that day will catch a cold." Most of us would probably assign the fair prices so that

$$P(C_1) < P(C_1|C_2).$$

Consequently, a person has a better chance of getting a cold on a rainy day.

The Bayesian can go on to argue that

$$P(C_1 \cap C_2) = P(C_2)P(C_1|C_2),$$

recalling that the bet $P(C_1|C_2)$ is called off if C_2 does not happen by creating a Dutch book situation. However, we do not consider that argument here, and simply state that all the rules of subjective probabilities are the same as those of Chapter 1 using this subjective approach to probability.

EXERCISES

11.1.1. The following amounts are bets on horses A, B, C, D, and E to win.

Horse	Amount
A	$600,000
B	$200,000
C	$100,000
D	$75,000
E	$25,000
Total	$1,000,000

Suppose the track wants to take 20% off the top, namely, $200,000. Determine the payoff for winning with a $2 bet on each of the five horses. (In this exercise, we do not concern ourselves with "place" and "show.")

Hint: Figure out what would be a fair payoff so that the track does not take any money (that is, the track's take is zero), and then compute 80% of those payoffs.

11.1.2. In the proof of Theorem 11.1.1, we considered the case in which $p_3 < p_1 + p_2$. Now, say the person believes that $p_3 > p_1 + p_2$ and create a Dutch book for him.

Hint: Let $d = p_3 - (p_1 + p_2)$. The gambler buys from the person C_1 at a premium price of $p_1 + (d/4)$ and C_2 for $p_2 + (d/4)$. Then the gambler sells $C_1 \cup C_2$ to that person at a discount of $p_3 - (d/4)$. All those are good deals for that person who believes that p_1, p_2, p_3 are correct with $p_3 > p_1 + p_2$. Show that the person has a Dutch book.

11.1.3. Show that $P(\mathcal{C}) = 1$.

Hint: Suppose a person thinks $P(\mathcal{C}) = p \neq 1$. Consider two cases: $p > 1$ and $p < 1$. In the first case, say $d = p - 1$, and the gambler sells the person $\mathcal{C}$ at a discount price of $1 + (d/2)$. Of course, Ω happens and the gambler pays the person one unit, but he is down $1 + (d/2) - 1 = d/2$; therefore, he has a Dutch book. Proceed with the other case.

11.1.4. Show that $P(C^c) = 1 - P(C)$.

Hint: $C^c \cup C = \mathcal{C}$ and use result (11.1.1) and Exercise 11.1.3.

11.1.5. Show that if $C_1 \subset C_2$ and $C_2 \subset C_1$ (that is, $C_1 \equiv C_2$), then $P(C_1) = P(C_2)$.
Hint: Use result (11.1.2) twice.

11.1.6. Show that if C_1, C_2, and C_3 are mutually exclusive, then $P(C_1 \cup C_2 \cup C_3) = P(C_1) + P(C_2) + P(C_3)$.
Hint: Write $C_1 \cup C_2 \cup C_3 = C_1 \cup (C_2 \cup C_3)$ and use result (11.1.1) twice.

11.1.7. Show that $P(C_1 \cup C_2) = P(C_1) + P(C_2) - P(C_1 \cap C_2)$.
Hint: $C_1 \cup C_2 \equiv C_1 \cup (C_1^c \cap C_2)$ and $C_2 \equiv (C_1 \cap C_2) \cup (C_1^c \cap C_2)$. Use result (11.1.1) twice and a little algebra.

11.2   Bayesian Procedures

To understand the Bayesian inference, let us review Bayes Theorem, (1.4.1), in a situation in which we are trying to determine something about a parameter of a distribution. Suppose we have a Poisson distribution with parameter $\theta > 0$, and we know that the parameter is equal to either $\theta = 2$ or $\theta = 3$. In Bayesian inference, the parameter is treated as a random variable Θ. Suppose, for this example, we assign subjective **prior** probabilities of $P(\Theta = 2) = \frac{1}{3}$ and $P(\Theta = 3) = \frac{2}{3}$ to the two possible values. These subjective probabilities are based upon past experiences, and it might be unrealistic that Θ can only take one of two values, instead of a continuous $\theta > 0$ (we address this immediately after this introductory illustration). Now suppose a random sample of size $n = 2$ results in the observations $x_1 = 2$,

$x_2 = 4$. Given these data, what are the **posterior** probabilities of $\Theta = 2$ and $\Theta = 3$? By Bayes Theorem, we have

$$P(\Theta = 2|X_1 = 2, X_2 = 4) = \frac{P(\Theta = 2 \text{ and } X_1 = 2, X_2 = 4)}{P(X_1 = 2, X_2 = 4)}$$

$$= \frac{\left(\frac{1}{3}\right)\frac{e^{-2}2^2}{2!}\frac{e^{-2}2^4}{4!}}{\left(\frac{1}{3}\right)\frac{e^{-2}2^2}{2!}\frac{e^{-2}2^4}{4!} + \left(\frac{2}{3}\right)\frac{e^{-3}3^2}{2!}\frac{e^{-3}3^4}{4!}}$$

$$= 0.245.$$

Similarly,

$$P(\Theta = 3|X_1 = 2, X_2 = 4) = 1 - 0.245 = 0.755.$$

That is, with the observations $x_1 = 2, x_2 = 4$, the posterior probability of $\Theta = 2$ was smaller than the prior probability of $\Theta = 2$. Similarly, the posterior probability of $\Theta = 3$ was greater than the corresponding prior. That is, the observations $x_1 = 2, x_2 = 4$ seemed to favor $\Theta = 3$ more than $\Theta = 2$; and that seems to agree with our intuition as $\bar{x} = 3$. Now let us address in general a more realistic situation in which we place a prior pdf $h(\theta)$ on a support which is a continuum.

11.2.1 Prior and Posterior Distributions

We now describe the Bayesian approach to the problem of estimation. This approach takes into account any prior knowledge of the experiment that the statistician has and it is one application of a principle of statistical inference that may be called **Bayesian statistics**. Consider a random variable X that has a distribution of probability that depends upon the symbol θ, where θ is an element of a well-defined set Ω. For example, if the symbol θ is the mean of a normal distribution, Ω may be the real line. We have previously looked upon θ as being a parameter, albeit an unknown parameter. Let us now introduce a random variable Θ that has a distribution of probability over the set Ω; and just as we look upon x as a possible value of the random variable X, we now look upon θ as a possible value of the random variable Θ. Thus, the distribution of X depends upon θ, an experimental value of the random variable Θ. We denote the pdf of Θ by $h(\theta)$ and we take $h(\theta) = 0$ when θ is not an element of Ω. The pdf $h(\theta)$ is called the **prior** pdf of Θ. Moreover, we now denote the pdf of X by $f(x|\theta)$ since we think of it as a conditional pdf of X, given $\Theta = \theta$. For clarity in this chapter, we use the following summary of this model:

$$\begin{aligned} X|\theta &\sim f(x|\theta) \\ \Theta &\sim h(\theta). \end{aligned} \tag{11.2.1}$$

Suppose that $X_1, X_2, \ldots, X_n$ is a random sample from the conditional distribution of X given $\Theta = \theta$ with pdf $f(x|\theta)$. Vector notation is convenient in this chapter. Let $\mathbf{X}' = (X_1, X_2, \ldots, X_n)$ and $\mathbf{x}' = (x_1, x_2, \ldots, x_n)$. Thus we can write the joint conditional pdf of $\mathbf{X}$, given $\Theta = \theta$, as

$$L(\mathbf{x}|\theta) = f(x_1|\theta)f(x_2|\theta) \cdots f(x_n|\theta). \tag{11.2.2}$$

Thus the joint pdf of **X** and Θ is

$$g(\mathbf{x}, \theta) = L(\mathbf{x} \mid \theta)h(\theta). \tag{11.2.3}$$

If Θ is a random variable of the continuous type, the joint marginal pdf of **X** is given by

$$g_1(\mathbf{x}) = \int_{-\infty}^{\infty} g(\mathbf{x}, \theta) \, d\theta. \tag{11.2.4}$$

If Θ is a random variable of the discrete type, integration would be replaced by summation. In either case, the conditional pdf of Θ, given the sample **X**, is

$$k(\theta|\mathbf{x}) = \frac{g(\mathbf{x}, \theta)}{g_1(\mathbf{x})} = \frac{L(\mathbf{x} \mid \theta)h(\theta)}{g_1(\mathbf{x})}. \tag{11.2.5}$$

The distribution defined by this conditional pdf is called the **posterior distribution** and (11.2.5) is called the **posterior pdf**. The prior distribution reflects the subjective belief of Θ before the sample is drawn, while the posterior distribution is the conditional distribution of Θ after the sample is drawn. Further discussion on these distributions follows an illustrative example.

Example 11.2.1. Consider the model

$$X_i|\theta \quad \sim \quad \text{iid Poisson}(\theta)$$
$$\Theta \quad \sim \quad \Gamma(\alpha, \beta), \alpha \text{ and } \beta \text{ are known.}$$

Hence the random sample is drawn from a Poisson distribution with mean θ and the prior distribution is a $\Gamma(\alpha, \beta)$ distribution. Let $\mathbf{X}' = (X_1, X_2, \ldots, X_n)$. Thus, in this case, the joint conditional pdf of **X**, given $\Theta = \theta$, (11.2.2), is

$$L(\mathbf{x} \mid \theta) = \frac{\theta^{x_1} e^{-\theta}}{x_1!} \cdots \frac{\theta^{x_n} e^{-\theta}}{x_n!}, \quad x_i = 0, 1, 2, \ldots, i = 1, 2, \ldots, n,$$

and the prior pdf is

$$h(\theta) = \frac{\theta^{\alpha-1} e^{-\theta/\beta}}{\Gamma(\alpha)\beta^{\alpha}}, \quad 0 < \theta < \infty.$$

Hence the joint mixed continuous-discrete pdf is given by

$$g(\mathbf{x}, \theta) = L(\mathbf{x} \mid \theta)h(\theta) = \left[\frac{\theta^{x_1} e^{-\theta}}{x_1!} \cdots \frac{\theta^{x_n} e^{-\theta}}{x_n!} \right] \left[\frac{\theta^{\alpha-1} e^{-\theta/\beta}}{\Gamma(\alpha)\beta^{\alpha}} \right],$$

provided that $x_i = 0, 1, 2, 3, \ldots$, $i = 1, 2, \ldots, n$, and $0 < \theta < \infty$, and is equal to zero elsewhere. Then the marginal distribution of the sample, (11.2.4), is

$$g_1(\mathbf{x}) = \int_0^{\infty} \frac{\theta^{\sum x_i + \alpha - 1} e^{-(n+1/\beta)\theta}}{x_1! \cdots x_n! \Gamma(\alpha)\beta^{\alpha}} \, d\theta = \frac{\Gamma\left(\sum_1^n x_i + \alpha\right)}{x_1! \cdots x_n! \Gamma(\alpha)\beta^{\alpha}(n+1/\beta)^{\sum x_i + \alpha}}. \tag{11.2.6}$$

Finally, the posterior pdf of Θ, given $\mathbf{X} = \mathbf{x}$, (11.2.5), is

$$k(\theta|\mathbf{x}) = \frac{L(\mathbf{x}\,|\,\theta)h(\theta)}{g_1(\mathbf{x})} = \frac{\theta^{\sum x_i + \alpha - 1}e^{-\theta/[\beta/(n\beta+1)]}}{\Gamma\left(\sum x_i + \alpha\right)[\beta/(n\beta+1)]^{\sum x_i + \alpha}}, \tag{11.2.7}$$

provided that $0 < \theta < \infty$, and is equal to zero elsewhere. This conditional pdf is of the gamma type, with parameters $\alpha^* = \sum_{i=1}^{n} x_i + \alpha$ and $\beta^* = \beta/(n\beta + 1)$. Notice that the posterior pdf reflects both prior information (α, β) and sample information $(\sum_{i=1}^{n} x_i)$. ∎

In Example 11.2.1, notice that it is not really necessary to determine the marginal pdf $g_1(\mathbf{x})$ to find the posterior pdf $k(\theta|\mathbf{x})$. If we divide $L(\mathbf{x}\,|\,\theta)h(\theta)$ by $g_1(\mathbf{x})$, we must get the product of a factor that depends upon $\mathbf{x}$ but does *not* depend upon θ, say $c(\mathbf{x})$, and

$$\theta^{\sum x_i + \alpha - 1}e^{-\theta/[\beta/(n\beta+1)]}.$$

That is,

$$k(\theta|\mathbf{x}) = c(\mathbf{x})\theta^{\sum x_i + \alpha - 1}e^{-\theta/[\beta/(n\beta+1)]},$$

provided that $0 < \theta < \infty$ and $x_i = 0, 1, 2, \ldots$, $i = 1, 2, \ldots, n$. However, $c(\mathbf{x})$ must be that "constant" needed to make $k(\theta|\mathbf{x})$ a pdf, namely,

$$c(\mathbf{x}) = \frac{1}{\Gamma\left(\sum x_i + \alpha\right)[\beta/(n\beta+1)]^{\sum x_i + \alpha}}.$$

Accordingly, we frequently write that $k(\theta|\mathbf{x})$ is proportional to $L(\mathbf{x}\,|\,\theta)h(\theta)$; that is, the posterior pdf can be written as

$$k(\theta|\mathbf{x}) \propto L(\mathbf{x}\,|\,\theta)h(\theta). \tag{11.2.8}$$

Note that in the right-hand member of this expression, all factors involving constants and $\mathbf{x}$ alone (not θ) can be dropped. For illustration, in solving the problem presented in Example 11.2.1, we simply write

$$k(\theta|\mathbf{x}) \propto \theta^{\sum x_i}e^{-n\theta}\theta^{\alpha-1}e^{-\theta/\beta}$$

or, equivalently,

$$k(\theta|\mathbf{x}) \propto \theta^{\sum x_i + \alpha - 1}e^{-\theta/[\beta/(n\beta+1)]},$$

$0 < \theta < \infty$, and is equal to zero elsewhere. Clearly, $k(\theta|\mathbf{x})$ must be a gamma pdf with parameters $\alpha^* = \sum x_i + \alpha$ and $\beta^* = \beta/(n\beta + 1)$.

There is another observation that can be made at this point. Suppose that there exists a sufficient statistic $Y = u(\mathbf{X})$ for the parameter so that

$$L(\mathbf{x}\,|\,\theta) = g[u(\mathbf{x})|\theta]H(\mathbf{x}),$$

where now $g(y|\theta)$ is the pdf of Y, given $\Theta = \theta$. Then we note that

$$k(\theta|\mathbf{x}) \propto g[u(\mathbf{x})|\theta]h(\theta)$$

because the factor $H(\mathbf{x})$ that does not depend upon θ can be dropped. Thus, if a sufficient statistic Y for the parameter exists, we can begin with the pdf of Y if we wish and write

$$k(\theta|y) \propto g(y|\theta)h(\theta), \qquad (11.2.9)$$

where now $k(\theta|y)$ is the conditional pdf of Θ given the sufficient statistic $Y = y$. In the case of a sufficient statistic Y, we also use $g_1(y)$ to denote the marginal pdf of Y; that is, in the continuous case,

$$g_1(y) = \int_{-\infty}^{\infty} g(y|\theta)h(\theta)\,d\theta.$$

11.2.2   Bayesian Point Estimation

Suppose we want a point estimator of θ. From the Bayesian viewpoint, this really amounts to selecting a decision function δ, so that $\delta(\mathbf{x})$ is a predicted value of θ (an experimental value of the random variable Θ) when both the computed value $\mathbf{x}$ and the conditional pdf $k(\theta|\mathbf{x})$ are known. Now, in general, how would we predict an experimental value of any random variable, say W, if we want our prediction to be "reasonably close" to the value to be observed? Many statisticians would predict the mean, $E(W)$, of the distribution of W; others would predict a median (perhaps unique) of the distribution of W; and some would have other predictions. However, it seems desirable that the choice of the decision function should depend upon a loss function $\mathcal{L}[\theta, \delta(\mathbf{x})]$. One way in which this dependence upon the loss function can be reflected is to select the decision function δ in such a way that the conditional expectation of the loss is a minimum. A **Bayes estimate** is a decision function δ that minimizes

$$E\{\mathcal{L}[\Theta, \delta(\mathbf{x})]|\mathbf{X} = \mathbf{x}\} = \int_{-\infty}^{\infty} \mathcal{L}[\theta, \delta(\mathbf{x})]k(\theta|\mathbf{x})\,d\theta$$

if Θ is a random variable of the continuous type. That is,

$$\delta(\mathbf{x}) = \mathrm{Argmin} \int_{-\infty}^{\infty} \mathcal{L}[\theta, \delta(\mathbf{x})]k(\theta|\mathbf{x})\,d\theta. \qquad (11.2.10)$$

The associated random variable $\delta(\mathbf{X})$ is called a **Bayes estimator** of θ. The usual modification of the right-hand member of this equation is made for random variables of the discrete type. If the loss function is given by $\mathcal{L}[\theta, \delta(\mathbf{x})] = [\theta - \delta(\mathbf{x})]^2$, then the Bayes estimate is $\delta(\mathbf{x}) = E(\Theta|\mathbf{x})$, the mean of the conditional distribution of Θ, given $\mathbf{X} = \mathbf{x}$. This follows from the fact that $E[(W - b)^2]$, if it exists, is a minimum when $b = E(W)$. If the loss function is given by $\mathcal{L}[\theta, \delta(\mathbf{x})] = |\theta - \delta(\mathbf{x})|$, then a median of the conditional distribution of Θ, given $\mathbf{X} = \mathbf{x}$, is the Bayes solution. This follows from the fact that $E(|W - b|)$, if it exists, is a minimum when b is equal to any median of the distribution of W.

It is easy to generalize this to estimate a specified function of θ, say, $l(\theta)$. For the loss function $\mathcal{L}[\theta, \delta(\mathbf{x})]$, a **Bayes estimate** of $l(\theta)$ is a decision function δ that minimizes

$$E\{\mathcal{L}[l(\Theta), \delta(\mathbf{x})]|\mathbf{X} = \mathbf{x}\} = \int_{-\infty}^{\infty} \mathcal{L}[l(\theta), \delta(\mathbf{x})]k(\theta|\mathbf{x})\,d\theta.$$

The random variable $\delta(\mathbf{X})$ is called a **Bayes estimator** of $l(\theta)$.

The conditional expectation of the loss, given $\mathbf{X} = \mathbf{x}$, defines a random variable that is a function of the sample $\mathbf{X}$. The expected value of that function of $\mathbf{X}$, in the notation of this section, is given by

$$\int_{-\infty}^{\infty} \left\{ \int_{-\infty}^{\infty} \mathcal{L}[\theta, \delta(\mathbf{x})] k(\theta|\mathbf{x})\, d\theta \right\} g_1(\mathbf{x})\, d\mathbf{x} = \int_{-\infty}^{\infty} \left\{ \int_{-\infty}^{\infty} \mathcal{L}[\theta, \delta(\mathbf{x})] L(\mathbf{x}|\theta)\, d\mathbf{x} \right\} h(\theta) d\theta,$$

in the continuous case. The integral within the braces in the latter expression is, for every given $\theta \in \Theta$, the **risk function** $R(\theta, \delta)$; accordingly, the latter expression is the mean value of the risk, or the expected risk. Because a Bayes estimate $\delta(\mathbf{x})$ minimizes

$$\int_{-\infty}^{\infty} \mathcal{L}[\theta, \delta(\mathbf{x})] k(\theta|\mathbf{x})\, d\theta$$

for every $\mathbf{x}$ for which $g(\mathbf{x}) > 0$, it is evident that a Bayes estimate $\delta(\mathbf{x})$ minimizes this mean value of the risk. We now give two illustrative examples.

Example 11.2.2. Consider the model

$$X_i|\theta \ \sim \ \text{iid binomial, } b(1, \theta)$$
$$\Theta \ \sim \ \text{beta}(\alpha, \beta), \ \alpha \text{ and } \beta \text{ are known;}$$

that is, the prior pdf is

$$h(\theta) = \begin{cases} \frac{\Gamma(\alpha+\beta)}{\Gamma(\alpha)\Gamma(\beta)} \theta^{\alpha-1}(1-\theta)^{\beta-1} & 0 < \theta < 1 \\ 0 & \text{elsewhere.,} \end{cases}$$

where α and β are assigned positive constants. We seek a decision function δ that is a Bayes solution. The sufficient statistic is $Y = \sum_1^n X_i$, which has a $b(n, \theta)$ distribution. Thus the conditional pdf of Y given $\Theta = \theta$ is

$$g(y|\theta) = \begin{cases} \binom{n}{y} \theta^y (1-\theta)^{n-y} & y = 0, 1, \ldots, n \\ 0 & \text{elsewhere.} \end{cases}$$

Thus, by (11.2.9), the conditional pdf of Θ, given $Y = y$ at points of positive probability density, is

$$k(\theta|y) \propto \theta^y (1-\theta)^{n-y} \theta^{\alpha-1}(1-\theta)^{\beta-1}, \quad 0 < \theta < 1.$$

That is,

$$k(\theta|y) = \frac{\Gamma(n+\alpha+\beta)}{\Gamma(\alpha+y)\Gamma(n+\beta-y)} \theta^{\alpha+y-1}(1-\theta)^{\beta+n-y-1}, \quad 0 < \theta < 1,$$

and $y = 0, 1, \ldots, n$. Hence the posterior pdf is a beta density function with parameters $(\alpha+y, \beta+n-y)$. We take the squared-error loss, i.e., $\mathcal{L}[\theta, \delta(y)] = [\theta - \delta(y)]^2$, as the loss function. Then, the Bayesian point estimate of θ is the mean of this beta pdf, which is

$$\delta(y) = \frac{\alpha+y}{\alpha+\beta+n}.$$

It is very instructive to note that this Bayes estimator can be written as

$$\delta(y) = \left(\frac{n}{\alpha + \beta + n}\right) \frac{y}{n} + \left(\frac{\alpha + \beta}{\alpha + \beta + n}\right) \frac{\alpha}{\alpha + \beta},$$

which is a weighted average of the maximum likelihood estimate y/n of θ and the mean $\alpha/(\alpha + \beta)$ of the prior pdf of the parameter. Moreover, the respective weights are $n/(\alpha + \beta + n)$ and $(\alpha + \beta)/(\alpha + \beta + n)$. Note that for large n, the Bayes estimate is close to the maximum likelihood estimate of θ and that, furthermore, $\delta(Y)$ is a consistent estimator of θ. Thus we see that α and β should be selected so that not only is $\alpha/(\alpha + \beta)$ the desired prior mean, but the sum $\alpha + \beta$ indicates the worth of the prior opinion relative to a sample of size n. That is, if we want our prior opinion to have as much weight as a sample size of 20, we would take $\alpha + \beta = 20$. So if our prior mean is $\frac{3}{4}$, we have that α and β are selected so that $\alpha = 15$ and $\beta = 5$. ∎

Example 11.2.3. For this example, we have the normal model,

$$\begin{aligned} X_i|\theta &\sim \text{ iid } N(\theta, \sigma^2), \text{ where } \sigma^2 \text{ is known} \\ \Theta &\sim N(\theta_0, \sigma_0^2), \text{ where } \theta_0 \text{ and } \sigma_0^2 \text{ are known.} \end{aligned}$$

Then $Y = \overline{X}$ is a sufficient statistic. Hence an equivalent formulation of the model is

$$\begin{aligned} Y|\theta &\sim N(\theta, \sigma^2/n), \text{ where } \sigma^2 \text{ is known} \\ \Theta &\sim N(\theta_0, \sigma_0^2), \text{ where } \theta_0 \text{ and } \sigma_0^2 \text{ are known.} \end{aligned}$$

Then for the posterior pdf, we have

$$k(\theta|y) \propto \frac{1}{\sqrt{2\pi}\sigma/\sqrt{n}} \frac{1}{\sqrt{2\pi}\sigma_0} \exp\left[-\frac{(y-\theta)^2}{2(\sigma^2/n)} - \frac{(\theta - \theta_0)^2}{2\sigma_0^2} \right].$$

If we eliminate all constant factors (including factors involving only y), we have

$$k(\theta|y) \propto \exp\left[-\frac{[\sigma_0^2 + (\sigma^2/n)]\theta^2 - 2[y\sigma_0^2 + \theta_0(\sigma^2/n)]\theta}{2(\sigma^2/n)\sigma_0^2} \right].$$

This can be simplified by completing the square to read (after eliminating factors not involving θ)

$$k(\theta|y) \propto \exp\left[-\frac{\left(\theta - \frac{y\sigma_0^2 + \theta_0(\sigma^2/n)}{\sigma_0^2 + (\sigma^2/n)}\right)^2}{\frac{2(\sigma^2/n)\sigma_0^2}{[\sigma_0^2 + (\sigma^2/n)]}} \right].$$

That is, the posterior pdf of the parameter is obviously normal with mean

$$\frac{y\sigma_0^2 + \theta_0(\sigma^2/n)}{\sigma_0^2 + (\sigma^2/n)} = \left(\frac{\sigma_0^2}{\sigma_0^2 + (\sigma^2/n)}\right) y + \left(\frac{\sigma^2/n}{\sigma_0^2 + (\sigma^2/n)}\right) \theta_0 \qquad (11.2.11)$$

and variance $(\sigma^2/n)\sigma_0^2/[\sigma_0^2 + (\sigma^2/n)]$. If the squared-error loss function is used, this posterior mean is the Bayes estimator. Again, note that it is a weighted average of the maximum likelihood estimate $y = \bar{x}$ and the prior mean θ_0. As in the last example, for large n, the Bayes estimator is close to the maximum likelihood estimator and $\delta(Y)$ is a consistent estimator of θ. Thus the Bayesian procedures permit the decision maker to enter his or her prior opinions into the solution in a very formal way such that the influences of these prior notions are less and less as n increases. ■

In Bayesian statistics, all the information is contained in the posterior pdf $k(\theta|y)$. In Examples 11.2.2 and 11.2.3, we found Bayesian point estimates using the squared-error loss function. It should be noted that if $\mathcal{L}[\delta(y), \theta] = |\delta(y) - \theta|$, the absolute value of the error, then the Bayes solution would be the median of the posterior distribution of the parameter, which is given by $k(\theta|y)$. Hence the Bayes estimator changes, *as it should*, with different loss functions.

11.2.3   Bayesian Interval Estimation

If an interval estimate of θ is desired, we can find two functions $u(\mathbf{x})$ and $v(\mathbf{x})$ so that the conditional probability

$$P[u(\mathbf{x}) < \Theta < v(\mathbf{x})|\mathbf{X} = \mathbf{x}] = \int_{u(\mathbf{x})}^{v(\mathbf{x})} k(\theta|\mathbf{x}) \, d\theta$$

is large, for example, 0.95. Then the interval $u(\mathbf{x})$ to $v(\mathbf{x})$ is an interval estimate of θ in the sense that the conditional probability of Θ belonging to that interval is equal to 0.95. These intervals are often called **credible** or **probability intervals**, so as not to confuse them with confidence intervals.

Example 11.2.4. As an illustration, consider Example 11.2.3, where $X_1, X_2, \ldots, X_n$ is a random sample from a $N(\theta, \sigma^2)$ distribution, where σ^2 is known, and the prior distribution is a normal $N(\theta_0, \sigma_0^2)$ distribution. The statistic $Y = \overline{X}$ is sufficient. Recall that the posterior pdf of Θ given $Y = y$ was normal with mean and variance given near expression (11.2.11). Hence a credible interval is found by taking the mean of the posterior distribution and adding and subtracting 1.96 of its standard deviation; that is, the interval

$$\frac{y\sigma_0^2 + \theta_0(\sigma^2/n)}{\sigma_0^2 + (\sigma^2/n)} \pm 1.96\sqrt{\frac{(\sigma^2/n)\sigma_0^2}{\sigma_0^2 + (\sigma^2/n)}}$$

forms a credible interval of probability 0.95 for θ. ■

Example 11.2.5. Recall Example 11.2.1, where $\mathbf{X}' = (X_1, X_2, \ldots, X_n)$ is a random sample from a Poisson distribution with mean θ and a $\Gamma(\alpha, \beta)$ prior, with α and β known, is considered. As given by expression (11.2.7), the posterior pdf is a $\Gamma(y + \alpha, \beta/(n\beta + 1))$ pdf, where $y = \sum_{i=1}^{n} x_i$. Hence, if we use the squared-error loss function, the Bayes point estimate of θ is the mean of the posterior

$$\delta(y) = \frac{\beta(y + \alpha)}{n\beta + 1} = \frac{n\beta}{n\beta + 1}\frac{y}{n} + \frac{\alpha\beta}{n\beta + 1}.$$

As with the other Bayes estimates we have discussed in this section, for large n this estimate is close to the maximum likelihood estimate and the statistic $\delta(Y)$ is a consistent estimate of θ. To obtain a credible interval, note that the posterior distribution of $\frac{2(n\beta+1)}{\beta}\Theta$ is $\chi^2(2(\sum_{i=1}^{n} x_i + \alpha))$. Based on this, the following interval is a $(1-\alpha)100\%$ credible interval for θ:

$$\left(\frac{\beta}{2(n\beta+1)}\chi^2_{1-(\alpha/2)}\left[2\left(\sum_{i=1}^{n} x_i + \alpha\right)\right]\right), \frac{\beta}{2(n\beta+1)}\chi^2_{\alpha/2}\left[2\left(\sum_{i=1}^{n} x_i + \alpha\right)\right]\right),$$
$$(11.2.12)$$

where $\chi^2_{1-(\alpha/2)}(2(\sum_{i=1}^{n} x_i + \alpha))$ and $\chi^2_{\alpha/2}(2(\sum_{i=1}^{n} x_i + \alpha))$ are the lower and upper χ^2 quantiles for a χ^2 distribution with $2(\sum_{i=1}^{n} x_i + \alpha)$ degrees of freedom. ∎

11.2.4 Bayesian Testing Procedures

As above, let X be a random variable with pdf (pmf) $f(x|\theta)$, $\theta \in \Omega$. Suppose we are interested in testing the hypotheses

$$H_0 : \theta \in \omega_0 \text{ versus } H_1 : \theta \in \omega_1,$$

where $\omega_0 \cup \omega_1 = \Omega$ and $\omega_0 \cap \omega_1 = \phi$. A simple Bayesian procedure to test these hypotheses proceeds as follows. Let $h(\theta)$ denote the prior distribution of the prior random variable Θ; let $\mathbf{X}' = (X_1, X_2, \dots, X_n)$ denote a random sample on X; and denote the posterior pdf or pmf by $k(\theta|\mathbf{x})$. We use the posterior distribution to compute the following conditional probabilities:

$$P(\Theta \in \omega_0|\mathbf{x}) \text{ and } P(\Theta \in \omega_1|\mathbf{x}).$$

In the Bayesian framework, these conditional probabilities represent the truth of H_0 and H_1, respectively. A simple rule is to

$$\text{Accept } H_0 \text{ if } P(\Theta \in \omega_0|\mathbf{x}) \geq P(\Theta \in \omega_1|\mathbf{x});$$

otherwise, accept H_1; that is, accept the hypothesis which has the greater conditional probability. Note that the condition $\omega_0 \cap \omega_1 = \phi$ is required, but $\omega_0 \cup \omega_1 = \Omega$ is not necessary. More than two hypotheses may be tested at the same time, in which case a simple rule would be to accept the hypothesis with the greater conditional probability. We finish this subsection with a numerical example.

Example 11.2.6. Referring again to Example 11.2.1, where $\mathbf{X}' = (X_1, X_2, \dots, X_n)$ is a random sample from a Poisson distribution with mean θ, suppose we are interested in testing

$$H_0 : \theta \leq 10 \text{ versus } H_1 : \theta > 10. \qquad (11.2.13)$$

Suppose we think θ is about 12, but we are not quite sure. Hence we choose the $\Gamma(10, 1.2)$ pdf as our prior, which is shown in the left panel of Figure 11.2.1. The mean of the prior is 12, but as the plot shows, there is some variability (the variance of the prior distribution is 14.4). The data for the problem are

$$\begin{array}{cccccccccc} 11 & 7 & 11 & 6 & 5 & 9 & 14 & 10 & 9 & 5 \\ 8 & 10 & 8 & 10 & 12 & 9 & 3 & 12 & 14 & 4 \end{array}$$

(these are the values of a random sample of size $n = 20$ taken from a Poisson distribution with mean 8; of course, in practice we would not know the mean is 8). The value of the sufficient statistic is $y = \sum_{i=1}^{20} x_i = 177$. Hence, from Example 11.2.1, the posterior distribution is a $\Gamma(177 + 10, 1.2/[20(1.2) + 1]) = \Gamma(187, 0.048)$ distribution, which is shown in the right panel of Figure 11.2.1. Note that the data have moved the mean to the left of 12 to $187(0.048) = 8.976$, which is the Bayes estimate (under squared-error loss) of θ. Using a statistical computing package (we used the `pgamma` command in R), we compute the posterior probability of H_0 as

$$P[\Theta \le 10|y = 177] = P[\Gamma(187, 0.048) \le 10] = 0.9368.$$

Thus $P[\Theta > 10|y = 177] = 1 - 0.9368 = 0.0632$; consequently, our rule would accept H_0.

Figure 11.2.1: Prior (left panel) and posterior (right panel) pdfs of Example 11.2.6

The 95% credible interval, (11.2.12), is (7.77, 10.31), which also contains 10; see Exercise 11.2.7 for details. ∎

11.2.5 Bayesian Sequential Procedures

Finally, we should observe what a Bayesian would do if additional data were collected beyond $x_1, x_2, \ldots, x_n$. In such a situation, the posterior distribution found with the observations $x_1, x_2, \ldots, x_n$ becomes the new prior distribution, additional observations give a new posterior distribution, and inferences would be made from that second posterior. Of course, this can continue with even more observations.

That is, the second posterior becomes the new prior, and the next set of observations yields the next posterior from which the inferences can be made. Clearly, this gives Bayesians an excellent way of handling sequential analysis. They can continue taking data, always updating the previous posterior, which has become a new prior distribution. Everything a Bayesian needs for inferences is in that final posterior distribution obtained by this sequential procedure.

EXERCISES

11.2.1. Let Y have a binomial distribution in which $n = 20$ and $p = \theta$. The prior probabilities on θ are $P(\theta = 0.3) = 2/3$ and $P(\theta = 0.5) = 1/3$. If $y = 9$, what are the posterior probabilities for $\theta = 0.3$ and $\theta = 0.5$?

11.2.2. Let $X_1, X_2, \ldots, X_n$ be a random sample from a distribution that is $b(1, \theta)$. Let the prior of Θ be a beta one with parameters α and β. Show that the posterior pdf $k(\theta | x_1, x_2, \ldots, x_n)$ is exactly the same as $k(\theta | y)$ given in Example 11.2.2.

11.2.3. Let $X_1, X_2, \ldots, X_n$ denote a random sample from a distribution that is $N(\theta, \sigma^2)$, where $-\infty < \theta < \infty$ and σ^2 is a given positive number. Let $Y = \overline{X}$ denote the mean of the random sample. Take the loss function to be $\mathcal{L}[\theta, \delta(y)] = |\theta - \delta(y)|$. If θ is an observed value of the random variable Θ that is $N(\mu, \tau^2)$, where $\tau^2 > 0$ and μ are known numbers, find the Bayes solution $\delta(y)$ for a point estimate θ.

11.2.4. Let $X_1, X_2, \ldots, X_n$ denote a random sample from a Poisson distribution with mean θ, $0 < \theta < \infty$. Let $Y = \sum_1^n X_i$. Use the loss function $\mathcal{L}[\theta, \delta(y)] = [\theta - \delta(y)]^2$. Let θ be an observed value of the random variable Θ. If Θ has the prior pdf $h(\theta) = \theta^{\alpha-1} e^{-\theta/\beta} / \Gamma(\alpha)\beta^\alpha$, for $0 < \theta < \infty$, zero elsewhere, where $\alpha > 0$, $\beta > 0$ are known numbers, find the Bayes solution $\delta(y)$ for a point estimate for θ.

11.2.5. Let Y_n be the nth order statistic of a random sample of size n from a distribution with pdf $f(x|\theta) = 1/\theta$, $0 < x < \theta$, zero elsewhere. Take the loss function to be $\mathcal{L}[\theta, \delta(y)] = [\theta - \delta(y_n)]^2$. Let θ be an observed value of the random variable Θ, which has the prior pdf $h(\theta) = \beta\alpha^\beta / \theta^{\beta+1}$, $\alpha < \theta < \infty$, zero elsewhere, with $\alpha > 0$, $\beta > 0$. Find the Bayes solution $\delta(y_n)$ for a point estimate of θ.

11.2.6. Let Y_1 and Y_2 be statistics that have a trinomial distribution with parameters n, θ_1, and θ_2. Here θ_1 and θ_2 are observed values of the random variables Θ_1 and Θ_2, which have a Dirichlet distribution with known parameters α_1, α_2, and α_3; see expression (3.3.6). Show that the conditional distribution of Θ_1 and Θ_2 is Dirichlet and determine the conditional means $E(\Theta_1 | y_1, y_2)$ and $E(\Theta_2 | y_1, y_2)$.

11.2.7. For Example 11.2.6, obtain the 95% credible interval for θ. Next obtain the value of the mle for θ and the 95% confidence interval for θ discussed in Chapter 6.

11.2.8. In Example 11.2.2, let $n = 30$, $\alpha = 10$, and $\beta = 5$, so that $\delta(y) = (10+y)/45$ is the Bayes estimate of θ.

(a) If Y has a binomial distribution $b(30, \theta)$, compute the risk $E\{[\theta - \delta(Y)]^2\}$.

(b) Find values of θ for which the risk of part (a) is less than $\theta(1-\theta)/30$, the risk associated with the maximum likelihood estimator Y/n of θ.

11.2.9. Let Y_4 be the largest order statistic of a sample of size $n = 4$ from a distribution with uniform pdf $f(x;\theta) = 1/\theta$, $0 < x < \theta$, zero elsewhere. If the prior pdf of the parameter $g(\theta) = 2/\theta^3$, $1 < \theta < \infty$, zero elsewhere, find the Bayesian estimator $\delta(Y_4)$ of θ, based upon the sufficient statistic Y_4, using the loss function $|\delta(y_4) - \theta|$.

11.2.10. Refer to Example 11.2.3; suppose we select $\sigma_0^2 = d\sigma^2$, where σ^2 was known in that example. What value do we assign to d so that the variance of posterior is two thirds the variance of $Y = \overline{X}$, namely, σ^2/n?

11.3 More Bayesian Terminology and Ideas

Suppose $\mathbf{X}' = (X_1, X_2, \ldots, X_n)$ represents a random sample with likelihood $L(\mathbf{x}|\theta)$ and we assume a prior pdf $h(\theta)$. The joint marginal pdf of $\mathbf{X}$ is given by

$$g_1(\mathbf{x}) = \int_{-\infty}^{\infty} L(\mathbf{x}|\theta)h(\theta)d\theta.$$

This is often called the pdf of the **predictive distribution** of $\mathbf{X}$ because it provides the best description of the probabilities about $\mathbf{X}$ given the likelihood and the prior. An illustration of this is provided in expression (11.2.6) of Example 11.2.1. Again note that this predictive distribution is highly dependent on the probability models for X and Θ.

In this section, we consider two classes of prior distributions. The first class is the class of conjugate priors defined by:

Definition 11.3.1. *A class of prior pdfs for the family of distributions with pdfs* $f(x|\theta)$, $\theta \in \Omega$, *is said to define a* **conjugate family of distributions** *if the posterior pdf of the parameter is in the same family of distributions as the prior.*

As an illustration, consider Example 11.2.5, where the pmf of X_i given θ was Poisson with mean θ. In this example, we selected a gamma prior and the resulting posterior distribution was of the gamma family also. Hence the gamma pdf forms a conjugate class of priors for this Poisson model. This was true also for Example 11.2.2 where the conjugate family was beta and the model was a binomial, and for Example 11.2.3, where both the model and the prior were normal.

To motivate our second class of priors, consider the binomial model, $b(1, \theta)$, presented in Example 11.2.2. Thomas Bayes (1763) took as a prior the beta distribution with $\alpha = \beta = 1$, namely $h(\theta) = 1, 0 < \theta < 1$, zero elsewhere, because he argued that he did not have much prior knowledge about θ. However, we note that this leads to the estimate of

$$\left(\frac{n}{n+2}\right)\left(\frac{y}{n}\right) + \left(\frac{2}{n+2}\right)\left(\frac{1}{2}\right).$$

We often call this a **shrinkage** estimate because the estimate y/n is pulled a little toward the prior mean of $1/2$, although Bayes tried to avoid having the prior influence the inference.

Haldane (1948) did note, however, that if a prior beta pdf exists with $\alpha = \beta = 0$, then the shrinkage estimate would reduce to the mle y/n. Of course, a beta pdf with $\alpha = \beta = 0$ is not a pdf at all, for it would be such that

$$h(\theta) \propto \frac{1}{\theta(1-\theta)}, \quad 0 < \theta < 1,$$

zero elsewhere, and

$$\int_0^1 \frac{c}{\theta(1-\theta)} d\theta$$

does not exist. However, such priors are used if, when combined with the likelihood, we obtain a posterior pdf which is a proper pdf. By **proper**, we mean that it integrates to a positive constant. In this example, we obtain the posterior pdf of

$$f(\theta|y) \propto \theta^{y-1}(1-\theta)^{n-y-1},$$

which is proper provided $y > 0$ and $n - y > 0$. Of course, the posterior mean is y/n.

Definition 11.3.2. *Let $\mathbf{X}' = (X_1, X_2, \ldots, X_n)$ be a random sample from the distribution with pdf $f(x|\theta)$. A prior $h(\theta) \geq 0$ for this family is said to be **improper** if it is not a pdf, but the function $k(\theta|\mathbf{x}) \propto L(\mathbf{x}|\theta)h(\theta)$ can be made proper.*

A **noninformative prior** is a prior which treats all values of θ the same, that is, uniformly. Continuous noninformative priors are often improper. As an example, suppose we have a normal distribution $N(\theta_1, \theta_2)$ in which both θ_1 and $\theta_2 > 0$ are unknown. A noninformative prior for θ_1 is $h_1(\theta_1) = 1$, $-\infty < \theta_1 < \infty$. Clearly, this is not a pdf. An improper prior for θ_2 is $h_2(\theta_2) = c_2/\theta_2$, $0 < \theta_2 < \infty$, zero elsewhere. Note that $\log \theta_2$ is uniformly distributed between $-\infty < \log \theta_2 < \infty$. Hence, in this way, it is a noninformative prior. In addition, assume the parameters are independent. Then the joint prior, which is improper, is

$$h_1(\theta_1)h_2(\theta_2) \propto 1/\theta_2, \quad -\infty < \theta_1 < \infty, 0 < \theta_2 < \infty. \tag{11.3.1}$$

Using this prior, we present the Bayes solution for θ_1 in the next example.

Example 11.3.1. Let $X_1, X_2, \ldots, X_n$ be a random sample from a $N(\theta_1, \theta_2)$ distribution. Recall that $\overline{X}$ and $S^2 = (n-1)^{-1} \sum_{i=1}^n (X_i - \overline{X})^2$ are sufficient statistics. Suppose we use the improper prior given by (11.3.1). Then the posterior distribution is given by

$$k_{12}(\theta_1, \theta_2|\overline{x}, s^2) \propto \left(\frac{1}{\theta_2}\right) \left(\frac{1}{\sqrt{2\pi\theta_2}}\right)^n \exp\left[-\frac{1}{2}\left\{(n-1)s^2 + n(\overline{x} - \theta_1)^2\right\}/\theta_2\right]$$

$$\propto \left(\frac{1}{\theta_2}\right)^{\frac{n}{2}+1} \exp\left[-\frac{1}{2}\left\{(n-1)s^2 + n(\overline{x} - \theta_1)^2\right\}/\theta_2\right].$$

To get the conditional pdf of θ_1, given $\overline{x}$ and s^2, we integrate out θ_2

$$k_1(\theta_1|\overline{x}, s^2) = \int_0^\infty k_{12}(\theta_1, \theta_2|\overline{x}, s^2)d\theta_2.$$

To carry this out, let us change variables $z = 1/\theta_2$ and $\theta_2 = 1/z$, with Jacobian $-1/z^2$. Thus

$$k_1(\theta_1|\overline{x}, s^2) \propto \int_0^\infty \frac{z^{\frac{n}{2}+1}}{z^2} \exp\left[-\left\{\frac{(n-1)s^2 + n(\overline{x}-\theta_1)^2}{2}\right\}z\right]dz.$$

Referring to a gamma distribution with $\alpha = n/2$ and $\beta = 2/\{(n-1)s^2+n(\overline{x}-\theta_1)^2\}$, this result is proportional to

$$k_1(\theta_1|\overline{x}, s^2) \propto \{(n-1)s^2 + n(\overline{x}-\theta_1)^2\}^{-n/2}.$$

Let us change variables to get more familiar results; namely, let

$$t = \frac{\theta_1 - \overline{x}}{s/\sqrt{n}} \quad \text{and} \quad \theta_1 = \overline{x} + ts/\sqrt{n},$$

with Jacobian $s/\sqrt{n}$. This conditional pdf of t, given $\overline{x}$ and s^2, is then

$$k(t|\overline{x}, s^2) \propto \{(n-1)s^2 + (st)^2\}^{-n/2}$$

$$\propto \frac{1}{[1 + t^2/(n-1)]^{[(n-1)+1]/2}}.$$

That is, the conditional pdf of $t = (\theta_1 - \overline{x})/(s/n)$, given $\overline{x}$ and s^2, is a Student t with $n-1$ degrees of freedom. Since the mean of this pdf is 0 (assuming that $n > 2$), it follows that the Bayes estimator of θ_1, under squared-error loss, is $\overline{X}$, which is also the mle.

Of course, from $k_1(\theta_1|\overline{x}, s^2)$ or $k(t|\overline{x}, s^2)$, we can find a credible interval for θ_1. One way of doing this is to select the *highest density region* (HDR) of the pdf θ_1 or that of t. The former is symmetric and unimodal about θ_1 and the latter about zero, but the latter's critical values are tabulated; so we use the HDR of that t-distribution. Thus, if we want an interval having probability $1 - \alpha$, we take

$$-t_{\alpha/2} < \frac{\theta_1 - \overline{x}}{s/\sqrt{n}} < t_{\alpha/2}$$

or, equivalently,

$$\overline{x} - t_{\alpha/2}s/\sqrt{n} < \theta_1 < \overline{x} + t_{\alpha/2}s/\sqrt{n}.$$

This interval is the same as the confidence interval for θ_1; see Example 4.2.1. Hence, in this case, the improper prior (11.3.1) leads to the same inference as the traditional analysis. ∎

Example 11.3.2. Usually in a Bayesian analysis, noninformative priors are not used if prior information exists. Let us consider the same situation as in Example

11.3.1, where the model was a $N(\theta_1, \theta_2)$ distribution. Suppose now we consider the **precision** $\theta_3 = 1/\theta_2$ instead of variance θ_2. The likelihood becomes

$$\left(\frac{\theta_3}{2\pi}\right)^{n/2} \exp\left[-\frac{1}{2}\left\{(n-1)s^2 + n(\bar{x} - \theta_1)^2\right\}\theta_3\right],$$

so that it is clear that a conjugate prior for θ_3 is $\Gamma(\alpha, \beta)$. Further, given θ_3, a reasonable prior on θ_1 is $N(\theta_0, \frac{1}{n_0\theta_3})$, where n_0 is selected in some way to reflect how many observations the prior is worth. Thus the joint prior of θ_1 and θ_3 is

$$h(\theta_1, \theta_3) \propto \theta_3^{\alpha-1} e^{-\theta_3/\beta} (n_0\theta_3)^{1/2} e^{-(\theta_1-\theta_0)^2\theta_3 n_0/2}.$$

If this is multiplied by the likelihood function, we obtain the posterior joint pdf of θ_1 and θ_3, namely,

$$k(\theta_1, \theta_3|\bar{x}, s^2) \propto \theta_3^{\alpha+\frac{n}{2}+\frac{1}{2}-1} \exp\left[-\frac{1}{2}Q(\theta_1)\theta_3\right],$$

where

$$Q(\theta_1) = \frac{2}{\beta} + n_0(\theta_1 - \theta_0)^2 + [(n-1)s^2 + n(\bar{x} - \theta_1)^2]$$

$$= (n_0 + n)\left[\left(\theta_1 - \frac{n_0\theta_0 + n\bar{x}}{n_0 + n}\right)^2\right] + D,$$

with

$$D = \frac{2}{\beta} + (n-1)s^2 + (n_0^{-1} + n^{-1})^{-1}(\theta_0 - \bar{x})^2.$$

If we integrate out θ_3, we obtain

$$k_1(\theta_1|\bar{x}, s^2) \propto \int_0^\infty k(\theta_1, \theta_3|\bar{x}, s^2) d\theta_3$$

$$\propto \frac{1}{[Q(\theta_1)]^{[2\alpha+n+1]/2}}.$$

To get this in a more familiar form, change variables by letting

$$t = \frac{\theta_1 - \frac{n_0\theta_0 + n\bar{x}}{n_0 + n}}{\sqrt{D/[(n_0 + n)(2\alpha + n)]}},$$

with Jacobian $\sqrt{D/[(n_0 + n)(2\alpha + n)]}$. Thus

$$k_2(t|\bar{x}, s^2) \propto \frac{1}{\left[1 + \frac{t^2}{2\alpha+n}\right]^{(2\alpha+n+1)/2}},$$

which is a Student t distribution with $2\alpha+n$ degrees of freedom. The Bayes estimate (under squared-error loss) in this case is

$$\frac{n_0\theta_0 + n\bar{x}}{n_0 + n}.$$

It is interesting to note that if we define "new" sample characteristics as

$$n_k = n_0 + n$$

$$\overline{x}_k = \frac{n_0\theta_0 + n\overline{x}}{n_0 + n}$$

$$s_k^2 = \frac{D}{2\alpha + n},$$

then

$$t = \frac{\theta_1 - \overline{x}_k}{s_k/\sqrt{n_k}}$$

has a t-distribution with $2\alpha + n$ degrees of freedom. Of course, using these degrees of freedom, we can find $t_{\gamma/2}$ so that

$$\overline{x}_k \pm t_{\gamma/2}\frac{s_k}{\sqrt{n_k}}$$

is an HDR credible interval estimate for θ_1 with probability $1-\gamma$. Naturally, it falls upon the Bayesian to assign appropriate values to α, β, n_0, and θ_0. Small values of α and n_0 with a large value of β would create a prior, so that this interval estimate would differ very little from the usual one. ∎

Finally, it should be noted that when dealing with symmetric, unimodal posterior distributions, it was extremely easy to find the HDR interval estimate. If, however, that posterior distribution is not symmetric, it is more difficult and often the Bayesian would find the interval that has equal probabilities on each tail.

EXERCISES

11.3.1. Let X_1, X_2 be a random sample from a Cauchy distribution with pdf

$$f(x; \theta_1, \theta_2) = \left(\frac{1}{\pi}\right)\frac{\theta_2}{\theta_2^2 + (x - \theta_1)^2}, \quad -\infty < x < \infty,$$

where $-\infty < \theta_1 < \infty$, $0 < \theta_2$. Use the noninformative prior $h(\theta_1, \theta_2) \propto 1$.

(a) Find the posterior pdf of θ_1, θ_2, other than the constant of proportionality.

(b) Evaluate this posterior pdf if $x_1 = 1, x_2 = 4$ for $\theta_1 = 1, 2, 3, 4$ and $\theta_2 = 0.5, 1.0, 1.5, 2.0$.

(c) From the 16 values in part (b), where does the maximum of the posterior pdf seem to be?

(d) Do you know a computer program that can find the point (θ_1, θ_2) of maximum?

11.3.2. Let $X_1, X_2, \ldots, X_{10}$ be a random sample of size $n = 10$ from a gamma distribution with $\alpha = 3$ and $\beta = 1/\theta$. Suppose we believe that θ has a gamma distribution with $\alpha = 10$ and $\beta = 2$.

(a) Find the posterior distribution of θ.

(b) If the observed $\bar{x} = 18.2$, what is the Bayes point estimate associated with square-error loss function?

(c) What is the Bayes point estimate using the mode of the posterior distribution?

(d) Comment on an HDR interval estimate for θ. Would it be easier to find one having equal tail probabilities?

Hint: Can the posterior distribution be related to a chi-square distribution?

11.3.3. Suppose for the situation of Example 11.3.2, θ_1 has the prior distribution $N(75, 1/(5\theta_3))$ and θ_3 has the prior distribution $\Gamma(\alpha = 4, \beta = 0.5)$. Suppose the observed sample of size $n = 50$ resulted in $\bar{x} = 77.02$ and $s^2 = 8.2$.

(a) Find the Bayes point estimate of the mean θ_1.

(b) Determine an HDR interval estimate with $1 - \gamma = 0.90$.

11.3.4. Let $f(x|\theta)$, $\theta \in \Omega$, be a pdf with Fisher information, (6.2.4), $I(\theta)$. Consider the Bayes model

$$X|\theta \;\sim\; f(x|\theta), \;\; \theta \in \Omega$$
$$\Theta \;\sim\; h(\theta) \propto \sqrt{I(\theta)}. \tag{11.3.2}$$

(a) Suppose we are interested in a parameter $\tau = u(\theta)$. Use the chain rule to prove that

$$\sqrt{I(\tau)} = \sqrt{I(\theta)} \left| \frac{\partial \theta}{\partial \tau} \right|. \tag{11.3.3}$$

(b) Show that for the Bayes model (11.3.2), the prior pdf for τ is proportional to $\sqrt{I(\tau)}$.

The class of priors given by expression (11.3.2) is often called the class of **Jeffreys' priors**; see Jeffreys (1961). This exercise shows that Jeffreys' priors exhibit an invariance in that the prior of a parameter τ, which is a function of θ, is also proportional to the square root of the information for τ.

11.3.5. Consider the Bayes model

$$X_i|\theta, i = 1, 2, \ldots, n \;\sim\; \text{iid with distribution } \Gamma(1, \theta), \; \theta > 0$$
$$\Theta \;\sim\; h(\theta) \propto \frac{1}{\theta}.$$

(a) Show that $h(\theta)$ is in the class of Jeffreys' priors.

(b) Show that the posterior pdf is

$$h(\theta|y) \propto \left(\frac{1}{\theta} \right)^{n+2-1} e^{-y/\theta},$$

where $y = \sum_{i=1}^{n} x_i$.

(c) Show that if $\tau = \theta^{-1}$, then the posterior $k(\tau|y)$ is the pdf of a $\Gamma(n, 1/y)$ distribution.

(d) Determine the posterior pdf of $2y\tau$. Use it to obtain a $(1-\alpha)100\%$ credible interval for θ.

(e) Use the posterior pdf in part (d) to determine a Bayesian test for the hypotheses $H_0 : \theta \geq \theta_0$ versus $H_1 : \theta < \theta_0$, where θ_0 is specified.

11.3.6. Consider the Bayes model

$$X_i|\theta, i = 1, 2, \ldots, n \quad \sim \quad \text{iid with distribution Poisson } (\theta), \; \theta > 0$$
$$\Theta \quad \sim \quad h(\theta) \propto \theta^{-1/2}.$$

(a) Show that $h(\theta)$ is in the class of Jeffreys' priors.

(b) Show that the posterior pdf of $2n\theta$ is the pdf of a $\chi^2(2y+1)$ distribution, where $y = \sum_{i=1}^{n} x_i$.

(c) Use the posterior pdf of part (b) to obtain a $(1-\alpha)100\%$ credible interval for θ.

(d) Use the posterior pdf in part (d) to determine a Bayesian test for the hypotheses $H_0 : \theta \geq \theta_0$ versus $H_1 : \theta < \theta_0$, where θ_0 is specified.

11.3.7. Consider the Bayes model

$$X_i|\theta, i = 1, 2, \ldots, n \sim \text{iid with distribution } b(1, \theta), \; 0 < \theta < 1.$$

(a) Obtain the Jeffreys' prior for this model.

(b) Assume squared-error loss and obtain the Bayes estimate of θ.

11.3.8. Consider the Bayes model

$$X_i|\theta, i = 1, 2, \ldots, n \quad \sim \quad \text{iid with distribution } b(1, \theta), 0 < \theta < 1$$
$$\Theta \quad \sim \quad h(\theta) = 1.$$

(a) Obtain the posterior pdf.

(b) Assume squared-error loss and obtain the Bayes estimate of θ.

11.3.9. Let $\mathbf{X}_1, \mathbf{X}_2, \ldots, \mathbf{X}_n$ be a random sample from a multivariate normal normal distribution with mean vector $\boldsymbol{\mu} = (\mu_1, \mu_2, \ldots, \mu_k)'$ and known positive definite covariance matrix $\boldsymbol{\Sigma}$. Let $\overline{\mathbf{X}}$ be the mean vector of the random sample. Suppose that $\boldsymbol{\mu}$ has a prior multivariate normal distribution with mean $\boldsymbol{\mu}_0$ and positive definite covariance matrix $\boldsymbol{\Sigma}_0$. Find the posterior distribution of $\boldsymbol{\mu}$, given $\overline{\mathbf{X}} = \overline{\mathbf{x}}$. Then find the Bayes estimate $E(\boldsymbol{\mu} \,|\, \overline{\mathbf{X}} = \overline{\mathbf{x}})$.

11.4   Gibbs Sampler

From the preceding sections, it is clear that integration techniques play a significant role in Bayesian inference. Hence, we now touch on some of the Monte Carlo techniques used for integration in Bayesian inference.

The Monte Carlo techniques discussed in Chapter 5 can often be used to obtain Bayesian estimates. For example, suppose a random sample is drawn from a $N(\theta, \sigma^2)$, where σ^2 is known. Then $Y = \overline{X}$ is a sufficient statistic. Consider the Bayes model

$$
\begin{aligned}
Y|\theta &\sim N(\theta, \sigma^2/n) \\
\Theta &\sim h(\theta) \propto b^{-1} \exp\{-(\theta-a)/b\}/(1 + \exp\{-[(\theta-a)/b]\})^2, \quad -\infty < \theta < \infty, \\
&\quad a \text{ and } b > 0 \text{ are known}, \quad\quad\quad\quad\quad\quad\quad\quad\quad\quad\quad (11.4.1)
\end{aligned}
$$

i.e., the prior is a logistic distribution. Thus the posterior pdf is

$$
k(\theta|y) = \frac{\frac{1}{\sqrt{2\pi}\sigma/\sqrt{n}} \exp\left\{-\frac{1}{2}\frac{(y-\theta)^2}{\sigma^2/n}\right\} b^{-1} e^{-(\theta-a)/b}/(1 + e^{-[(\theta-a)/b]})^2}{\int_{-\infty}^{\infty} \frac{1}{\sqrt{2\pi}\sigma/\sqrt{n}} \exp\left\{-\frac{1}{2}\frac{(y-\theta)^2}{\sigma^2/n}\right\} b^{-1} e^{-(\theta-a)/b}/(1 + e^{-[(\theta-a)/b]})^2 \, d\theta}.
$$

Assuming squared-error loss, the Bayes estimate is the mean of this posterior distribution. Its computation involves two integrals, which cannot be obtained in closed form. We can, however, think of the integration in the following way. Consider the likelihood $f(y|\theta)$ as a function of θ; that is, consider the function

$$
w(\theta) = f(y|\theta) = \frac{1}{\sqrt{2\pi}\sigma/\sqrt{n}} \exp\left\{-\frac{1}{2}\frac{(y-\theta)^2}{\sigma^2/n}\right\}.
$$

We can then write the Bayes estimate as

$$
\begin{aligned}
\delta(y) &= \frac{\int_{-\infty}^{\infty} \theta w(\theta) b^{-1} e^{-(\theta-a)/b}/(1 + e^{-[(\theta-a)/b]})^2 \, d\theta}{\int_{-\infty}^{\infty} w(\theta) b^{-1} e^{-(\theta-a)/b}/(1 + e^{-[(\theta-a)/b]})^2 \, d\theta} \\
&= \frac{E[\Theta w(\Theta)]}{E[w(\Theta)]}, \quad\quad\quad\quad\quad\quad\quad\quad\quad\quad\quad\quad (11.4.2)
\end{aligned}
$$

where the expectation is taken with Θ having the logistic prior distribution.

The estimation can be carried out by simple Monte Carlo. Independently, generate $\Theta_1, \Theta_2, \ldots, \Theta_m$ from the logistic distribution with pdf as in (11.4.1). This generation is easily computed because the inverse of the logistic cdf is given by $a + b\log\{u/(1-u)\}$, for $0 < u < 1$. Then form the random variable,

$$
T_m = \frac{m^{-1}\sum_{i=1}^{m} \Theta_i w(\Theta_i)}{m^{-1}\sum_{i=1}^{m} w(\Theta_i)}. \quad\quad\quad\quad\quad\quad\quad\quad\quad\quad (11.4.3)
$$

By the Weak Law of Large Numbers (Theorem 5.1.1) and Slutsky's Theorem (Theorem 5.2.4), $T_m \to \delta(y)$, in probability. The value of m can be quite large. Thus simple Monte Carlo techniques enable us to compute this Bayes estimate. Note that we can bootstrap this sample to obtain a confidence interval for $E[\Theta w(\Theta)]/E[w(\Theta)]$; see Exercise 11.4.2.

Besides simple Monte Carlo methods, there are other more complicated Monte Carlo procedures which are useful in Bayesian inference. For motivation, consider the case in which we want to generate an observation which has pdf $f_X(x)$, but this generation is somewhat difficult. Suppose, however, that it is easy to generate both Y, with pdf $f_Y(y)$, and an observation from the conditional pdf $f_{X|Y}(x|y)$. As the following theorem shows, if we do these sequentially, then we can easily generate from $f_X(x)$.

Theorem 11.4.1. *Suppose we generate random variables by the following algorithm:*

> *1.   Generate $Y \sim f_Y(y)$,*
>
> *2.   Generate $X \sim f_{X|Y}(x|Y)$.*

Then X has pdf $f_X(x)$.

Proof: To avoid confusion, let T be the random variable generated by the algorithm. We need to show that T has pdf $f_X(x)$. Probabilities of events concerning T are conditional on Y and are taken with respect to the cdf $F_{X|Y}$. Recall that probabilities can always be written as expectations of indicator functions and, hence, for events concerning T, are conditional expectations. In particular, for any $t \in R$,

$$
\begin{aligned}
P[T \le t] &= E[F_{X|Y}(t)] \\
&= \int_{-\infty}^{\infty} \left[\int_{-\infty}^{t} f_{X|Y}(x|y)\, dx \right] f_Y(y)\, dy \\
&= \int_{-\infty}^{t} \left[\int_{-\infty}^{\infty} f_{X|Y}(x|y) f_Y(y)\, dy \right] dx \\
&= \int_{-\infty}^{t} \left[\int_{-\infty}^{\infty} f_{X,Y}(x,y)\, dy \right] dx \\
&= \int_{-\infty}^{t} f_X(x)\, dx.
\end{aligned}
$$

Hence the random variable generated by the algorithm has pdf $f_X(x)$, as was to be shown. ∎

In the situation of this theorem, suppose we want to determine $E[W(X)]$, for some function $W(x)$, where $E[W^2(X)] < \infty$. Using the algorithm of the theorem, generate independently the sequence $(Y_1, X_1), (Y_2, X_2), \ldots, (Y_m, X_m)$, for a specified value of m, where Y_i is drawn from the pdf $f_Y(y)$ and X_i is generated from the pdf $f_{X|Y}(x|Y)$. Then by the Weak Law of Large Numbers,

$$
\overline{W} = \frac{1}{m} \sum_{i=1}^{m} W(X_i) \xrightarrow{P} \int_{-\infty}^{\infty} W(x) f_X(x)\, dx = E[W(X)].
$$

Furthermore, by the Central Limit Theorem, $\sqrt{m}(\overline{W} - E[W(X)])$ converges in distribution to a $N(0, \sigma_W^2)$ distribution, where $\sigma_W^2 = \text{Var}(W(X))$. If $w_1, w_2, \ldots, w_m$ is a realization of such a random sample, then an approximate $(1 - \alpha)100\%$ (large sample) confidence interval for $E[W(X)]$ is

$$\overline{w} \pm z_{\alpha/2} \frac{s_W}{\sqrt{m}}, \tag{11.4.4}$$

where $s_W^2 = (m - 1)^{-1} \sum_{i=1}^{m} (w_i - \overline{w})^2$.

To set ideas, we present the following simple example.

Example 11.4.1. Suppose the random variable X has pdf

$$f_X(x) = \begin{cases} 2e^{-x}(1 - e^{-x}) & 0 < x < \infty \\ 0 & \text{elsewhere.} \end{cases} \tag{11.4.5}$$

Suppose Y and $X|Y$ have the respective pdfs

$$f_Y(y) = \begin{cases} 2e^{-2y} & 0 < x < \infty \\ 0 & \text{elsewhere} \end{cases} \tag{11.4.6}$$

$$f_{X|Y}(x|y) = \begin{cases} e^{-(x-y)} & y < x < \infty \\ 0 & \text{elsewhere.} \end{cases} \tag{11.4.7}$$

Suppose we generate random variables by the following algorithm:

       1. Generate $Y \sim f_Y(y)$ as in expression (11.4.6).
       2. Generate $X \sim f_{X|Y}(x|Y)$ as in expression (11.4.7).

Then, by Theorem 11.4.1, X has the pdf (11.4.5). Furthermore, it is easy to generate from the pdfs (11.4.6) and (11.4.7) because the inverses of the respective cdfs are given by $F_Y^{-1}(u) = -2^{-1} \log(1 - u)$ and $F_{X|Y}^{-1}(u) = -\log(1 - u) + Y$.

As a numerical illustration, the R function `condsim1`, found in Appendix B, uses this algorithm to generate observations from the pdf (11.4.5). Using this function, we performed $m = 10,000$ simulations of the algorithm. The sample mean and standard deviation were $\overline{x} = 1.495$ and $s = 1.112$. Hence a 95% confidence interval for $E(X)$ is $(1.473, 1.517)$, which traps the true value $E(X) = 1.5$; see Exercise 11.4.4. ∎

For the last example, Exercise 11.4.3 establishes the joint distribution of (X, Y) and shows that the marginal pdf of X is given by (11.4.5). Furthermore, as shown in this exercise, it is easy to generate from the distribution of X directly. In Bayesian inference, though, we are often dealing with conditional pdfs, and theorems such as Theorem 11.4.1 are quite useful.

The main purpose of presenting this algorithm is to motivate another algorithm, called the **Gibbs Sampler**, which is useful in Bayes methodology. We describe it in terms of two random variables. Suppose (X, Y) has pdf $f(x, y)$. Our goal is to generate two streams of iid random variables, one on X and the other on Y. The Gibbs sampler algorithm is:

Algorithm 11.4.1 (Gibbs Sampler). *Let m be a positive integer, and let X_0, an initial value, be given. Then for $i = 1, 2, 3, \ldots, m$,*

       1.   *Generate $Y_i | X_{i-1} \sim f(y|x)$.*

       2.   *Generate $X_i | Y_i \sim f(x|y)$.*

Note that before entering the ith step of the algorithm, we have generated X_{i-1}. Let x_{i-1} denote the observed value of X_{i-1}. Then, using this value, generate sequentially the new Y_i from the pdf $f(y|x_{i-1})$ and then draw (the new) X_i from the pdf $f(x|y_i)$, where y_i is the observed value of Y_i. In advanced texts, it is shown that

$$Y_i \xrightarrow{D} Y \sim f_Y(y)$$
$$X_i \xrightarrow{D} X \sim f_X(x), \tag{11.4.8}$$

as $i \to \infty$, and

$$\frac{1}{m} \sum_{i=1}^{m} W(X_i) \xrightarrow{P} E[W(X)], \text{ as } m \to \infty. \tag{11.4.9}$$

Note that the Gibbs sampler is similar but not quite the same as the algorithm given by Theorem 11.4.1. Consider the sequence of generated pairs

$$(X_1, Y_1), (X_2, Y_2), \ldots, (X_k, Y_k), (X_{k+1}, Y_{k+1}).$$

Note that to compute (X_{k+1}, Y_{k+1}), we need only the pair (X_k, Y_k) and none of the previous pairs from 1 to $k-1$. That is, given the present state of the sequence, the future of the sequence is independent of the past. In stochastic processes such a sequence is called a **Markov chain**. Under general conditions, the distribution of Markov chains stabilizes (reaches an equilibrium or steady-state distribution) as the length of the chain increases. For the Gibbs sampler, the equilibrium distributions are the limiting distributions in the expression (11.4.8) as $i \to \infty$. How large should i be? In practice, usually the chain is allowed to run to some large value i before recording the observations. Furthermore, several recordings are run with this value of i and the resulting empirical distributions of the generated random observations are examined for their similarity. Also, the starting value for X_0 is needed; see Casella and George (1992) for a discussion. The theory behind the convergences given in the expression (11.4.8) is beyond the scope of this text. There are many excellent references on this theory. A discussion from an elementary level can be found in Casella and George (1992). An informative overview can be found in Chapter 7 of Robert and Casella (1999); see also Lehmann and Casella (1998). We next provide a simple example.

Example 11.4.2. Suppose (X, Y) has the mixed discrete-continuous pdf given by

$$f(x, y) = \begin{cases} \frac{1}{\Gamma(\alpha)} \frac{1}{x!} y^{\alpha+x-1} e^{-2y} & y > 0; \ x = 0, 1, 2, \ldots \\ 0 & \text{elsewhere,} \end{cases} \tag{11.4.10}$$

for $\alpha > 0$. Exercise 11.4.5 shows that this is a pdf and obtains the marginal pdfs. The conditional pdfs, however, are given by

$$f(y|x) \propto y^{\alpha+x-1}e^{-2y} \tag{11.4.11}$$

and

$$f(x|y) \propto e^{-y}\frac{y^x}{x!}. \tag{11.4.12}$$

Hence the conditional densities are $\Gamma(\alpha+x,1/2)$ and Poisson (y), respectively. Thus the Gibbs sampler algorithm is, for $i = 1, 2, \ldots, m$,

1. Generate $Y_i|X_{i-1} \sim \Gamma(\alpha + X_{i-1}, 1/2)$.
2. Generate $X_i|Y_i \sim \text{Poisson}(Y_i)$.

In particular, for large m and $n > m$,

$$\overline{Y} = (n-m)^{-1}\sum_{i=m+1}^{n} Y_i \xrightarrow{P} E(Y) \tag{11.4.13}$$

$$\overline{X} = (n-m)^{-1}\sum_{i=m+1}^{n} X_i \xrightarrow{P} E(X). \tag{11.4.14}$$

In this case, it can be shown (see Exercise 11.4.5) that both expectations are equal to α. The R routine `gibbser2.s` found in Appendix B computes this Gibbs sampler. Using this routine, the authors obtained the following results upon setting $\alpha = 10$, $m = 3000$, and $n = 6000$:

Parameter	Estimate	Sample Estimate	Sample Variance	Approximate 95% Confidence Interval
$E(Y) = \alpha = 10$	$\overline{y}$	10.027	10.775	$(9.910, 10.145)$
$E(X) = \alpha = 10$	$\overline{x}$	10.061	21.191	$(9.896, 10.225)$

where the estimates $\overline{y}$ and $\overline{x}$ are the observed values of the estimators in expressions (11.4.13) and (11.4.14), respectively. The confidence intervals for α are the large sample confidence intervals for means discussed in Example 4.2.2, using the sample variances found in the fourth column of the above table. Note that both confidence intervals trapped $\alpha = 10$. ∎

EXERCISES

11.4.1. Suppose Y has a $\Gamma(1,1)$ distribution while X given Y has the conditional pdf

$$f(x|y) = \begin{cases} e^{-(x-y)} & 0 < y < x < \infty \\ 0 & \text{elsewhere.} \end{cases}$$

Note that both the pdf of Y and the conditional pdf are easy to simulate.

(a) Set up the algorithm of Theorem 11.4.1 to generate a stream of iid observations with pdf $f_X(x)$.

(b) State how to estimate $E(X)$.

(c) If computational facilities are available, write a computer program to estimate $E(X)$ using your algorithm found in part (a).

(d) Using your program, obtain a stream of 2000 simulations. Compute your estimate of $E(X)$ and find an approximate 95% confidence interval.

(e) Show that X has a $\Gamma(2,1)$ distribution. Did your confidence interval trap the true value 2?

11.4.2. Carefully write down the algorithm to obtain a bootstrap percentile confidence interval for $E[\Theta w(\Theta)]/E[w(\Theta)]$, using the sample $\Theta_1, \Theta_2, \ldots, \Theta_m$ and the estimator given in expression (11.4.3). If computation facilities are at hand, obtain code for this bootstrap.

11.4.3. Consider Example 11.4.1.

(a) Show that $E(X) = 1.5$.

(b) Obtain the inverse of the cdf of X and use it to show how to generate X directly.

11.4.4. If computation facilities are at hand, obtain another 10,000 simulations similar to those discussed at the end of Example 11.4.1. Use your simulations to obtain a confidence interval for $E(X)$.

11.4.5. Consider Example 11.4.2.

(a) Show that the function given in expression (11.4.10) is a joint, mixed discrete-continuous pdf.

(b) Show that the random variable Y has a $\Gamma(\alpha, 1)$ distribution.

(c) Show that the random variable X has a negative binomial distribution with pmf

$$p(x) = \begin{cases} \frac{(\alpha+x-1)!}{x!(\alpha-1)!}2^{-(\alpha+x)} & x = 0, 1, 2, \ldots \\ 0 & \text{elsewhere.} \end{cases}$$

(d) Show that $E(X) = \alpha$.

11.4.6. If computation facilities are available, write a program (or use `gibbser2.s` of Appendix B) for the Gibbs sampler discussed in Example 11.4.2. Run your program for $\alpha = 10$, $m = 3000$, and $n = 6000$. Compare your results with those of the authors tabled in the example.

11.4.7. Consider the following mixed discrete-continuous pdf for a random vector (X, Y), (discussed in Casella and George, 1992):

$$f(x, y) \propto \begin{cases} \binom{n}{x} y^{x+\alpha-1}(1-y)^{n-x+\beta-1} & x = 0, 1, \ldots, n, \ 0 < y < 1 \\ 0 & \text{elsewhere,} \end{cases}$$

for $\alpha > 0$ and $\beta > 0$.

(a) Show that this function is indeed a joint, mixed discrete-continuous pdf by finding the proper constant of proportionality.

(b) Determine the conditional pdfs $f(x|y)$ and $f(y|x)$.

(c) Write the Gibbs sampler algorithm to generate random samples on X and Y.

(d) Determine the marginal distributions of X and Y.

11.4.8. If computation facilities are available, write a program for the Gibbs sampler of Exercise 11.4.7. Run your program for $\alpha = 10$, $\beta = 4$, $m = 3000$, and $n = 6000$. Obtain estimates (and confidence intervals) of $E(X)$ and $E(Y)$ and compare them with the true parameters.

11.5   Modern Bayesian Methods

The prior pdf has an important influence in Bayesian inference. We need only consider the different Bayes estimators for the normal model based on different priors, as shown in Examples 11.2.3 and 11.3.1. One way of having more control over the prior is to model the prior in terms of another random variable. This is called the **hierarchical Bayes** model, and it is of the form

$$\begin{aligned} X|\theta &\sim f(x|\theta) \\ \Theta|\gamma &\sim h(\theta|\gamma) \\ \Gamma &\sim \psi(\gamma). \end{aligned} \tag{11.5.1}$$

With this model we can exert control over the prior $h(\theta|\gamma)$ by modifying the pdf of the random variable Γ. A second methodology, **empirical Bayes**, obtains an estimate of γ and plugs it into the posterior pdf. We offer the reader a brief introduction of these procedures in this section. There are several good books on Bayesian methods. In particular, Chapter 4 of Lehmann and Casella (1998) discusses these procedures in some detail.

Consider first the hierarchical Bayes model given by (11.5.1). The parameter γ can be thought of a nuisance parameter. It is often called a **hyperparameter**. As with regular Bayes, the inference focuses on the parameter θ; hence, the posterior pdf of interest remains the conditional pdf $k(\theta|\mathbf{x})$.

These discussions often involve several pdfs; hence, we frequently use g as a generic pdf. It will always be clear from its arguments what distribution it represents. Keep in mind that the conditional pdf $f(\mathbf{x}|\theta)$ does not depend on γ; hence,

$$
\begin{aligned}
g(\theta, \gamma | \mathbf{x}) &= \frac{g(\mathbf{x}, \theta, \gamma)}{g(\mathbf{x})} \\
&= \frac{g(\mathbf{x}|\theta, \gamma) g(\theta, \gamma)}{g(\mathbf{x})} \\
&= \frac{f(\mathbf{x}|\theta) h(\theta|\gamma) \psi(\gamma)}{g(\mathbf{x})}.
\end{aligned}
$$

Therefore, the posterior pdf is given by

$$
k(\theta|\mathbf{x}) = \frac{\int_{-\infty}^{\infty} f(\mathbf{x}|\theta) h(\theta|\gamma) \psi(\gamma)\, d\gamma}{\int_{-\infty}^{\infty} \int_{-\infty}^{\infty} f(\mathbf{x}|\theta) h(\theta|\gamma) \psi(\gamma)\, d\gamma d\theta}. \tag{11.5.2}
$$

Furthermore, assuming squared-error loss, the Bayes estimate of $W(\theta)$ is

$$
\delta_W(\mathbf{x}) = \frac{\int_{-\infty}^{\infty} \int_{-\infty}^{\infty} W(\theta) f(\mathbf{x}|\theta) h(\theta|\gamma) \psi(\gamma)\, d\gamma d\theta}{\int_{-\infty}^{\infty} \int_{-\infty}^{\infty} f(\mathbf{x}|\theta) h(\theta|\gamma) \psi(\gamma)\, d\gamma d\theta}. \tag{11.5.3}
$$

Recall that we defined the Gibbs sampler in Section 11.4. Here we describe it to obtain the Bayes estimate of $W(\theta)$. For $i = 1, 2, \ldots, m$, where m is specified, the ith step of the algorithm is

$$
\begin{aligned}
\Theta_i | \mathbf{x}, \gamma_{i-1} &\sim g(\theta|\mathbf{x}, \gamma_{i-1}) \\
\Gamma_i | \mathbf{x}, \theta_i &\sim g(\gamma|\mathbf{x}, \theta_i).
\end{aligned}
$$

Recall from our discussion in Section 11.4 that

$$
\begin{aligned}
\Theta_i &\xrightarrow{D} k(\theta|\mathbf{x}) \\
\Gamma_i &\xrightarrow{D} g(\gamma|\mathbf{x}),
\end{aligned}
$$

as $i \to \infty$. Furthermore, the arithmetic average

$$
\frac{1}{m} \sum_{i=1}^{m} W(\Theta_i) \xrightarrow{P} E[W(\Theta)|\mathbf{x}] = \delta_W(\mathbf{x}) \text{ as } m \to \infty. \tag{11.5.4}
$$

In practice, to obtain the Bayes estimate of $W(\theta)$ by the Gibbs sampler, we generate by Monte Carlo the stream of values $(\theta_1, \gamma_1), (\theta_2, \gamma_2) \ldots$. Then choosing large values of m and $n^* > m$, our estimate of $W(\theta)$ is the average,

$$
\frac{1}{n^* - m} \sum_{i=m+1}^{n^*} W(\theta_i). \tag{11.5.5}
$$

Because of the Monte Carlo generation these procedures are often called **MCMC**, for **Markov Chain Monte Carlo** procedures. We next provide two examples.

Example 11.5.1. Reconsider the conjugate family of normal distributions discussed in Example 11.2.3, with $\theta_0 = 0$. Here we use the model

$$
\begin{aligned}
\overline{X}|\Theta &\sim N\left(\theta, \frac{\sigma^2}{n}\right), \ \sigma^2 \text{ is known} \\
\Theta|\tau^2 &\sim N(0, \tau^2) \\
\frac{1}{\tau^2} &\sim \Gamma(a, b), \ a \text{ and } b \text{ are known.}
\end{aligned}
\tag{11.5.6}
$$

To set up the Gibbs sampler for this hierarchical Bayes model, we need the conditional pdfs $g(\theta|\overline{x}, \tau^2)$ and $g(\tau^2|\overline{x}, \theta)$. For the first, we have

$$
g(\theta|\overline{x}, \tau^2) \propto f(\overline{x}|\theta) h(\theta|\tau^2) \psi(\tau^{-2}).
$$

As we have been doing, we can ignore standardizing constants; hence, we need only consider the product $f(\overline{x}|\theta) h(\theta|\tau^2)$. But this is a product of two normal pdfs which we obtained in Example 11.2.3. Based on those results, $g(\theta|\overline{x}, \tau^2)$ is the pdf of a $N(\{\tau^2/[(\sigma^2/n) + \tau^2]\}\overline{x}, (\tau^2\sigma^2)/[\sigma^2 + n\tau^2])$. For the second pdf, by ignoring standardizing constants and simplifying, we obtain

$$
\begin{aligned}
g\left(\frac{1}{\tau^2}\Big|\overline{x}, \theta\right) &\propto f(\overline{x}|\theta) g(\theta|\tau^2) \psi(1/\tau^2) \\
&\propto \frac{1}{\tau} \exp\left\{-\frac{1}{2}\frac{\theta^2}{\tau^2}\right\} \left(\frac{1}{\tau^2}\right)^{a-1} \exp\left\{-\frac{1}{\tau^2}\frac{1}{b}\right\} \\
&\propto \left(\frac{1}{\tau^2}\right)^{a+(1/2)-1} \exp\left\{-\frac{1}{\tau^2}\left[\frac{\theta^2}{2} + \frac{1}{b}\right]\right\},
\end{aligned}
\tag{11.5.7}
$$

which is the pdf of a $\Gamma\{a + (1/2), [(\theta^2/2) + (1/b)]^{-1}\}$ distribution. Thus the Gibbs sampler for this model is given by: for $i = 1, 2, \ldots, m$,

$$
\begin{aligned}
\Theta_i|\overline{x}, \tau_{i-1}^2 &\sim N\left(\frac{\tau_{i-1}^2}{(\sigma^2/n) + \tau_{i-1}^2}\overline{x}, \frac{\tau_{i-1}^2\sigma^2}{\sigma^2 + n\tau_{i-1}^2}\right) \\
\frac{1}{\tau_i^2}\Big|\overline{x}, \Theta_i &\sim \Gamma\left(a + \frac{1}{2}, \left(\frac{\theta_i^2}{2} + \frac{1}{b}\right)^{-1}\right).
\end{aligned}
\tag{11.5.8}
$$

As discussed above, for a specified values of large m and $n^* > m$, we collect the chain's values $((\Theta_m, \tau_m), (\Theta_{m+1}, \tau_{m+1}), \ldots, (\Theta_{n^*}, \tau_{n^*}))$ and then obtain the Bayes estimate of θ (assuming squared-error loss):

$$
\widehat{\theta} = \frac{1}{n^* - m} \sum_{i=m+1}^{n^*} \Theta_i.
\tag{11.5.9}
$$

The conditional distribution of Θ given $\overline{x}$ and τ_{i-1}, though, suggests the second estimate given by

$$
\widehat{\theta}^* = \frac{1}{n^* - m} \sum_{i=m+1}^{n^*} \frac{\tau_i^2}{\tau_i^2 + (\sigma^2/n)}\overline{x}. \quad \blacksquare
\tag{11.5.10}
$$

Example 11.5.2. Lehmann and Casella (1998, p. 257) presented the following hierarchical Bayes model:

$$
\begin{aligned}
X|\lambda &\sim \text{Poisson}(\lambda) \\
\Lambda|b &\sim \Gamma(1,b) \\
B &\sim g(b) = \tau^{-1}b^{-2}\exp\{-1/b\tau\}, \quad b > 0, \tau > 0.
\end{aligned}
$$

For the Gibbs sampler, we need the two conditional pdfs, $g(\lambda|x,b)$ and $g(b|x,\lambda)$. The joint pdf is

$$
g(x,\lambda,b) = f(x|\lambda)h(\lambda|b)\psi(b). \tag{11.5.11}
$$

Based on the pdfs of the model, (11.5.11), for the first conditional pdf we have

$$
\begin{aligned}
g(\lambda|x,b) &\propto e^{-\lambda}\frac{\lambda^x}{x!}\frac{1}{b}e^{-\lambda/b} \\
&\propto \lambda^{x+1-1}e^{-\lambda[1+(1/b)]}, \tag{11.5.12}
\end{aligned}
$$

which is the pdf of a $\Gamma(x+1, b/[b+1])$ distribution.

For the second conditional pdf, we have

$$
\begin{aligned}
g(b|x,\lambda) &\propto \frac{1}{b}e^{-\lambda/b}\tau^{-1}b^{-2}e^{-1/(b\tau)} \\
&\propto b^{-3}\exp\left\{-\frac{1}{b}\left[\frac{1}{\tau}+\lambda\right]\right\}.
\end{aligned}
$$

In this last expression, making the change of variable $y = 1/b$ which has the Jacobian $db/dy = -y^{-2}$, we obtain

$$
\begin{aligned}
g(y|x,\lambda) &\propto y^3\exp\left\{-y\left[\frac{1}{\tau}+\lambda\right]\right\}y^{-2} \\
&\propto y^{2-1}\exp\left\{-y\left[\frac{1+\lambda\tau}{\tau}\right]\right\},
\end{aligned}
$$

which is easily seen to be the pdf of the $\Gamma(2, \tau/[\lambda\tau+1])$ distribution. Therefore, the Gibbs sampler is, for $i = 1, 2, \ldots, m$, where m is specified,

$$
\begin{aligned}
\Lambda_i|x, b_{i-1} &\sim \Gamma(x+1, b_{i-1}/[1+b_{i-1}]) \\
B_i = Y_i^{-1}, \text{ where } Y_i|x, \lambda_i &\sim \Gamma(2, \tau/[\lambda_i\tau+1]). \quad \blacksquare
\end{aligned}
$$

As a numerical illustration of the last example, suppose we set $\tau = 0.05$ and observe $x = 6$. The R program `hierarch1.s` in Appendix B performs the Gibbs sampler given in the example. It requires specification of the value of i at which the Gibbs sample commences and the length of the chain beyond this point. We set these values at $m = 1000$ and $n^* = 4000$, respectively, i.e., the length of the chain used in the estimate is 3000. To see the effect that varying τ has on the Bayes estimator, we performed five Gibbs samplers, with these results:

τ	0.040	0.045	0.050	0.055	0.060
$\widehat{\delta}$	6.600	6.490	6.530	6.500	6.440

There is some variation. As discussed in Lehmann and Casella (1998), in general, there is less effect on the Bayes estimator due to variability of the hyperparameter than in regular Bayes due to the variance of the prior.

11.5.1   Empirical Bayes

The empirical Bayes model consists of the first two lines of the hierarchical Bayes model; i.e.,

$$
\begin{aligned}
\mathbf{X}|\theta &\sim f(\mathbf{x}|\theta) \\
\Theta|\gamma &\sim h(\theta|\gamma).
\end{aligned}
$$

Instead of attempting to model the parameter γ with a pdf as in hierarchical Bayes, empirical Bayes methodology estimates γ based on the data as follows. Recall that

$$
\begin{aligned}
g(\mathbf{x},\theta|\gamma) &= \frac{g(\mathbf{x},\theta,\gamma)}{\psi(\gamma)} \\
&= \frac{f(\mathbf{x}|\theta)h(\theta|\gamma)\psi(\gamma)}{\psi(\gamma)} \\
&= f(\mathbf{x}|\theta)h(\theta|\gamma).
\end{aligned}
$$

Consider, then, the likelihood function

$$
m(\mathbf{x}|\gamma) = \int_{-\infty}^{\infty} f(\mathbf{x}|\theta)h(\theta|\gamma)\,d\theta. \tag{11.5.13}
$$

Using the pdf $m(\mathbf{x}|\gamma)$, we obtain an estimate $\widehat{\gamma} = \widehat{\gamma}(\mathbf{x})$, usually by the method of maximum likelihood. For inference on the parameter θ, the empirical Bayes procedure uses the posterior pdf $k(\theta|\mathbf{x},\widehat{\gamma})$.

We illustrate the empirical Bayes procedure with the following example.

Example 11.5.3. Consider the same situation discussed in Example 11.5.2, except assume that we have a random sample on X; i.e., consider the model

$$
\begin{aligned}
X_i|\lambda,\ i=1,2,\ldots,n &\sim \text{iid Poisson}(\lambda) \\
\Lambda|b &\sim \Gamma(1,b).
\end{aligned}
$$

Let $\mathbf{X} = (X_1, X_2, \ldots, X_n)'$. Hence

$$
g(\mathbf{x}|\lambda) = \frac{\lambda^{n\overline{x}}}{x_1!\cdots x_n!}e^{-n\lambda},
$$

where $\overline{x} = n^{-1}\sum_{i=1}^{n} x_i$. Thus the pdf we need to maximize is

$$
\begin{aligned}
m(\mathbf{x}|b) &= \int_0^{\infty} g(\mathbf{x}|\lambda)h(\lambda|b)\,d\lambda \\
&= \int_0^{\infty} \frac{1}{x_1!\cdots x_n!}\lambda^{n\overline{x}+1-1}e^{-n\lambda}\frac{1}{b}e^{-\lambda/b}\,d\lambda \\
&= \frac{\Gamma(n\overline{x}+1)[b/(nb+1)]^{n\overline{x}+1}}{x_1!\cdots x_n!b}.
\end{aligned}
$$

Taking the partial derivative of $\log m(\mathbf{x}|b)$ with respect to b, we obtain

$$\frac{\partial \log m(\mathbf{x}|b)}{\partial b} = -\frac{1}{b} + (n\overline{x} + 1)\frac{1}{b(bn+1)}.$$

Setting this equal to 0 and solving for b, we obtain the solution

$$\widehat{b} = \overline{x}. \tag{11.5.14}$$

To obtain the empirical Bayes estimate of λ, we need to compute the posterior pdf with $\widehat{b}$ substituted for b. The posterior pdf is

$$k(\lambda|\mathbf{x},\widehat{b}) \quad \propto \quad g(\mathbf{x}|\lambda)h(\lambda|\widehat{b})$$
$$\propto \quad \lambda^{n\overline{x}+1-1}e^{-\lambda[n+(1/\widehat{b})]}, \tag{11.5.15}$$

which is the pdf of a $\Gamma(n\overline{x} + 1, \widehat{b}/[n\widehat{b} + 1])$ distribution. Therefore, the empirical Bayes estimator under squared-error loss is the mean of this distribution; i.e.,

$$\widehat{\lambda} = [n\overline{x} + 1]\frac{\widehat{b}}{n\widehat{b} + 1} = \overline{x}, \tag{11.5.16}$$

since $\widehat{b} = \overline{x}$. Thus, for the above prior, the empirical Bayes estimate agrees with the mle. ∎

We can use our solution of this last example to obtain the empirical Bayes estimate for Example 11.5.2 also, for in this earlier example, the sample size is 1. Thus the empirical Bayes estimate for λ is x. In particular, for the numerical case given at the end of Example 11.5.2, the empirical Bayes estimate has the value 6.

EXERCISES

11.5.1. Consider the Bayes model

$$X_i|\theta \quad \sim \quad \text{iid } \Gamma\left(1, \frac{1}{\theta}\right)$$
$$\Theta|\beta \quad \sim \quad \Gamma(2, \beta).$$

By performing the following steps, obtain the empirical Bayes estimate of θ.

(a) Obtain the likelihood function

$$m(\mathbf{x}|\beta) = \int_0^\infty f(\mathbf{x}|\theta)h(\theta|\beta)\, d\theta.$$

(b) Obtain the mle $\widehat{\beta}$ of β for the likelihood $m(\mathbf{x}|\beta)$.

(c) Show that the posterior distribution of Θ given $\mathbf{x}$ and $\widehat{\beta}$ is a gamma distribution.

(d) Assuming squared-error loss, obtain the empirical Bayes estimator.

11.5.2. Consider the hierarchical Bayes model

$$\begin{array}{rcl}
Y & \sim & b(n,p), \ 0 < p < 1 \\
p|\theta & \sim & h(p|\theta) = \theta p^{\theta - 1}, \ \theta > 0 \\
\theta & \sim & \Gamma(1,a), \ a > 0 \text{ is specified.}
\end{array} \qquad (11.5.17)$$

(a) Assuming squared-error loss, write the Bayes estimate of p as in expression (11.5.3). Integrate relative to θ first. Show that both the numerator and denominator are expectations of a beta distribution with parameters $y + 1$ and $n - y + 1$.

(b) Recall the discussion around expression (11.4.2). Write an explicit Monte Carlo algorithm to obtain the Bayes estimate in part (a).

11.5.3. Reconsider the hierarchical Bayes model (11.5.17) of Exercise 11.5.2.

(a) Show that the conditional pdf $g(p|y, \theta)$ is the pdf of a beta distribution with parameters $y + \theta$ and $n - y + 1$.

(b) Show that the conditional pdf $g(\theta|y, p)$ is the pdf of a gamma distribution with parameters 2 and $\left[\frac{1}{a} - \log p\right]^{-1}$.

(c) Using parts (a) and (b) and assuming squared-error loss, write the Gibbs sampler algorithm to obtain the Bayes estimator of p.

11.5.4. For the hierarchical Bayes model of Exercise 11.5.2, set $n = 50$ and $a = 2$. Now, draw a θ at random from a $\Gamma(1, 2)$ distribution and label it θ^*. Next, draw a p at random from the distribution with pdf $\theta^* p^{\theta^* - 1}$ and label it p^*. Finally, draw a y at random from a $b(n, p^*)$ distribution.

(a) Setting m at 3000, obtain an estimate of θ^* using your Monte Carlo algorithm of Exercise 11.5.2.

(b) Setting m at 3000 and n^* at 6000, obtain an estimate of θ^* using your Gibbs sampler algorithm of Exercise 11.5.3. Let $p_{3001}, p_{3002}, \ldots, p_{6000}$ denote the stream of values drawn. Recall that these values are (asymptotically) simulated values from the posterior pdf $g(p|y)$. Use this stream of values to obtain a 95% credible interval.

11.5.5. Write the Bayes model of Exercise 11.5.2 as

$$\begin{array}{rcl}
Y & \sim & b(n,p), \ 0 < p < 1 \\
p|\theta & \sim & h(p|\theta) = \theta p^{\theta - 1}, \ \theta > 0.
\end{array}$$

Set up the estimating equations for the mle of $g(y|\theta)$, i.e., the first step to obtain the empirical Bayes estimator of p. Simplify as much as possible.

11.5.6. Example 11.5.1 dealt with a hierarchical Bayes model for a conjugate family of normal distributions. Express that model as

$$\overline{X}|\Theta \;\sim\; N\left(\theta, \frac{\sigma^2}{n}\right),\; \sigma^2 \text{ is known}$$
$$\Theta|\tau^2 \;\sim\; N(0, \tau^2).$$

Obtain the empirical Bayes estimator of θ.

Appendix A

Mathematical Comments

A.1 Regularity Conditions

These are the regularity conditions referred to in Sections 6.4 and 6.5 of the text. A discussion of these conditions can be found in Chapter 6 of Lehmann and Casella (1998).

Let X have pdf $f(x; \boldsymbol{\theta})$, where $\boldsymbol{\theta} \in \Omega \subset R^p$. For these assumptions, X can be either a scalar random variable or a random vector in R^k. As in Section 6.4, let $\mathbf{I}(\boldsymbol{\theta}) = [I_{jk}]$ denote the $p \times p$ information matrix given by expression (6.4.4). Also, we will denote the true parameter $\boldsymbol{\theta}$ by $\boldsymbol{\theta}_0$.

Assumptions A.1.1. *Additional regularity conditions for Sections 6.4 and 6.5.*

(R6): *There exists an open subset $\Omega_0 \subset \Omega$ such that $\boldsymbol{\theta}_0 \in \Omega_0$ and all third partial derivatives of $f(x; \boldsymbol{\theta})$ exist for all $\boldsymbol{\theta} \in \Omega_0$.*

(R7) *The following equations are true (essentially, we can interchange expectation and differentiation):*

$$E_{\boldsymbol{\theta}}\left[\frac{\partial}{\partial \theta_j} \log f(x; \boldsymbol{\theta})\right] = 0, \quad for\ j = 1, \ldots, p$$

$$I_{jk}(\boldsymbol{\theta}) = E_{\boldsymbol{\theta}}\left[-\frac{\partial^2}{\partial \theta_j \partial \theta_k} \log f(x; \boldsymbol{\theta})\right], \quad for\ j, k = 1, \ldots, p.$$

(R8) *For all $\boldsymbol{\theta} \in \Omega_0$, $\mathbf{I}(\boldsymbol{\theta})$ is positive definite.*

(R9) *There exist functions $M_{jkl}(x)$ such that*

$$\left|\frac{\partial^3}{\partial \theta_j \partial \theta_k \theta_l} \log f(x; \boldsymbol{\theta})\right| \leq M_{jkl}(x), \quad for\ all\ \boldsymbol{\theta} \in \Omega_0,$$

and

$$E_{\boldsymbol{\theta}_0}[M_{jkl}] < \infty, \quad for\ all\ j, k, l \in 1, \ldots, p. \quad \blacksquare$$

A.2   Sequences

Let $\{a_n\}$ be a sequence of real numbers. Recall from calculus that $a_n \to a$ $(\lim_{n\to\infty} a_n = a)$ if and only if

for every $\epsilon > 0$, there exists an N_0 such that $n \geq N_0 \implies |a_n - a| < \epsilon$.   (A.2.1)

Let A be a set of real numbers which is bounded from above; that is, there exists an $M \in R$ such that $x \leq M$ for all $x \in A$. Recall that a is the **supremum** of A if a is the least of all upper bounds of A. From calculus, we know that the supremum of a set bounded from above exists. Furthermore, we know that a is the supremum of A if and only if, for all $\epsilon > 0$, there exists an $x \in A$ such that $a - \epsilon < x \leq a$. Similarly, we can define the **infimum** of A.

We need three additional facts from calculus. The first is the Sandwich Theorem.

Theorem A.2.1 (Sandwich Theorem). *Suppose for sequences $\{a_n\}$, $\{b_n\}$, and $\{c_n\}$ that $c_n \leq a_n \leq b_n$, for all n, and that $\lim_{n\to\infty} b_n = \lim_{n\to\infty} c_n = a$. Then $\lim_{n\to\infty} a_n = a$.*

Proof: Let $\epsilon > 0$ be given. Because both $\{b_n\}$ and $\{c_n\}$ converge, we can choose N_0 so large that $|c_n - a| < \epsilon$ and $|b_n - a| < \epsilon$, for $n \geq N_0$. Because $c_n \leq a_n \leq b_n$, it is easy to see that

$$|a_n - a| \leq \max\{|c_n - a|, |b_n - a|\},$$

for all n. Hence, if $n \geq N_0$, then $|a_n - a| < \epsilon$. ∎

The second fact concerns subsequences. Recall that $\{a_{n_k}\}$ is a subsequence of $\{a_n\}$ if the sequence $n_1 \leq n_2 \leq \cdots$ is an infinite subset of the positive integers. Note that $n_k \geq k$.

Theorem A.2.2. *The sequence $\{a_n\}$ converges to a if and only if every subsequence $\{a_{n_k}\}$ converges to a.*

Proof: Suppose the sequence $\{a_n\}$ converges to a. Let $\{a_{n_k}\}$ be any subsequence. Let $\epsilon > 0$ be given. Then there exists an N_0 such that $|a_n - a| < \epsilon$, for $n \geq N_0$. For the subsequence, take k' to be the first index of the subsequence beyond N_0. Because for all k, $n_k \geq k$, we have that $n_k \geq n_{k'} \geq k' \geq N_0$, which implies that $|a_{n_k} - a| < \epsilon$. Thus, $\{a_{n_k}\}$ converges to a. The converse is immediate because a sequence is also a subsequence of itself. ∎

Finally, the third theorem concerns monotonic sequences.

Theorem A.2.3. *Let $\{a_n\}$ be a nondecreasing sequence of real numbers; i.e., for all n, $a_n \leq a_{n+1}$. Suppose $\{a_n\}$ is bounded from above; i.e., for some $M \in R$, $a_n \leq M$ for all n. Then the limit of a_n exists.*

Proof: Let a be the supremum of $\{a_n\}$. Let $\epsilon > 0$ be given. Then there exists an N_0 such that $a - \epsilon < a_{N_0} \leq a$. Because the sequence is nondecreasing, this implies that $a - \epsilon < a_n \leq a$, for all $n \geq N_0$. Hence, by definition, $a_n \to a$. ∎

Let $\{a_n\}$ be a sequence of real numbers and define the two subsequences

$$b_n = \sup\{a_n, a_{n+1}, \ldots\}, \quad n = 1, 2, 3 \ldots \quad \text{(A.2.2)}$$

$$c_n = \inf\{a_n, a_{n+1}, \ldots\}, \quad n = 1, 2, 3 \ldots. \quad \text{(A.2.3)}$$

It is obvious that $\{b_n\}$ is a nonincreasing sequence. Hence, if $\{a_n\}$ is bounded from below, then the limit of b_n exists. In this case, we call the limit of $\{b_n\}$ the **limit supremum** (limsup) of the sequence $\{a_n\}$ and write it as

$$\overline{\lim_{n\to\infty}} a_n = \lim_{n\to\infty} b_n. \quad \text{(A.2.4)}$$

Note that if $\{a_n\}$ is not bounded from below, then $\overline{\lim}_{n\to\infty} a_n = -\infty$. Also, if $\{a_n\}$ is not bounded from above, we define $\overline{\lim}_{n\to\infty} a_n = \infty$. Hence, the $\overline{\lim}$ of any sequence always exists. Also, from the definition of the subsequence $\{b_n\}$, we have

$$a_n \leq b_n, \quad n = 1, 2, 3, \ldots. \quad \text{(A.2.5)}$$

On the other hand, $\{c_n\}$ is a nondecreasing sequence. Hence, if $\{a_n\}$ is bounded from above, then the limit of c_n exists. We call the limit of $\{c_n\}$ the **limit infimum** (liminf) of the sequence $\{a_n\}$ and write it as

$$\underline{\lim_{n\to\infty}} a_n = \lim_{n\to\infty} c_n. \quad \text{(A.2.6)}$$

Note that if $\{a_n\}$ is not bounded from above, then $\underline{\lim}_{n\to\infty} a_n = \infty$. Also, if $\{a_n\}$ is not bounded from below, $\underline{\lim}_{n\to\infty} a_n = -\infty$. Hence, the $\underline{\lim}$ of any sequence always exists. Also, from the definition of the subsequences $\{c_n\}$ and $\{b_n\}$, we have

$$c_n \leq a_n \leq b_n, \quad n = 1, 2, 3, \ldots. \quad \text{(A.2.7)}$$

Also, because $c_n \leq b_n$ for all n, we have

$$\underline{\lim_{n\to\infty}} a_n \leq \overline{\lim_{n\to\infty}} a_n. \quad \blacksquare \quad \text{(A.2.8)}$$

Example A.2.1. Here are two examples. More are given in the exercises.

1. Suppose $a_n = -n$ for all $n = 1, 2, \ldots.$ Then $b_n = \sup\{-n, -n-1, \ldots\} = -n \to -\infty$ and $c_n = \inf\{-n, -n-1, \ldots\} = -\infty \to -\infty$. So, $\underline{\lim}_{n\to\infty} a_n = \overline{\lim}_{n\to\infty} a_n = -\infty$.

2. Suppose $\{a_n\}$ is defined by

$$a_n = \begin{cases} 1 + \frac{1}{n} & \text{if } n \text{ is even} \\ 2 + \frac{1}{n} & \text{if } n \text{ is odd}. \end{cases}$$

Then $\{b_n\}$ is the sequence $\{3, 2+(1/3), 2+(1/3), 2+(1/5), 2+(1/5), \ldots\}$, which converges to 2, while $\{c_n\} \equiv 1$, which converges to 1. Thus, $\underline{\lim}_{n\to\infty} a_n = 1$ and $\overline{\lim}_{n\to\infty} a_n = 2$. $\blacksquare$

It is useful that the $\underline{\lim}_{n\to\infty}$ and $\overline{\lim}_{n\to\infty}$ of every sequence exists. Also, the sandwich effects of expressions (A.2.7) and (A.2.8) lead to the following theorem.

Theorem A.2.4. *Let $\{a_n\}$ be a sequence of real numbers. Then the limit of $\{a_n\}$ exists if and only if $\underline{\lim}_{n\to\infty} a_n = \overline{\lim}_{n\to\infty} a_n$, in which case, $\lim_{n\to\infty} a_n = \underline{\lim}_{n\to\infty} a_n = \overline{\lim}_{n\to\infty} a_n$.*

Proof: Suppose first that $\lim_{n\to\infty} a_n = a$. Because the sequences $\{c_n\}$ and $\{b_n\}$ are subsequences of $\{a_n\}$, Theorem A.2.2 implies that they converge to a also. Conversely, if $\underline{\lim}_{n\to\infty} a_n = \overline{\lim}_{n\to\infty} a_n$, then expression (A.2.7) and the Sandwich Theorem, A.2.1, imply the result. ∎

Based on this last theorem, we have two interesting applications which are frequently used in statistics and probability. Let $\{p_n\}$ be a sequence of probabilities and let $b_n = \sup\{p_n, p_{n+1}, \ldots\}$ and $c_n = \inf\{p_n, p_{n+1}, \ldots\}$. For the first application, suppose we can show that $\overline{\lim}_{n\to\infty} p_n = 0$. Then, because $0 \leq p_n \leq b_n$, the Sandwich Theorem implies that $\lim_{n\to\infty} p_n = 0$. For the second application, suppose we can show that $\underline{\lim}_{n\to\infty} p_n = 1$. Then, because $c_n \leq p_n \leq 1$, the Sandwich Theorem implies that $\lim_{n\to\infty} p_n = 1$.

We list some other properties in a theorem and ask the reader to provide the proofs in Exercise A.2.2:

Theorem A.2.5. *Let $\{a_n\}$ and $\{d_n\}$ be sequences of real numbers. Then*

$$\overline{\lim_{n\to\infty}} (a_n + d_n) \leq \overline{\lim_{n\to\infty}} a_n + \overline{\lim_{n\to\infty}} d_n \qquad (A.2.9)$$

$$\overline{\lim_{n\to\infty}} a_n = -\underline{\lim_{n\to\infty}} (-a_n). \qquad (A.2.10)$$

EXERCISES

A.2.1. Calculate the $\underline{\lim}$ and $\overline{\lim}$ of each of the following sequences:

(a) For $n = 1, 2, \ldots$, $a_n = (-1)^n \left(2 - \frac{4}{2^n}\right)$.

(b) For $n = 1, 2, \ldots$, $a_n = n^{\cos(\pi n/2)}$.

(c) For $n = 1, 2, \ldots$, $a_n = \frac{1}{n} + \cos \frac{\pi n}{2} + (-1)^n$.

A.2.2. Prove properties (A.2.9) and (A.2.10).

A.2.3. Let $\{a_n\}$ and $\{d_n\}$ be sequences of real numbers. Show that

$$\underline{\lim_{n\to\infty}} (a_n + d_n) \geq \underline{\lim_{n\to\infty}} a_n + \underline{\lim_{n\to\infty}} d_n.$$

A.2.4. Let $\{a_n\}$ be a sequence of real numbers. Suppose $\{a_{n_k}\}$ is a subsequence of $\{a_n\}$. If $\{a_{n_k}\} \to a_0$ as $k \to \infty$, show that $\underline{\lim}_{n\to\infty} a_n \leq a_0 \leq \overline{\lim}_{n\to\infty} a_n$.

Appendix B

R Functions

Below in alphabetical order are the R and S-PLUS routines referenced in the text.

1. **binomci**. Discussed in Example 4.3.1.

```
binomci = function(s,n,theta1,theta2,value,maxstp=100,eps=.00001){
    y1 = pbinom(s,n,theta1)
    y2 = pbinom(s,n,theta2)
    ic1 = 0
    ic2 = 0
    if(y1 >= value){ic1=1}
    if(y2 <= value){ic2=1}
    if((ic1*ic2) > 0){
        istep = 0
        while(istep < maxstp){
            istep = istep + 1
            theta3 = (theta1 + theta2)/2
            y3 = pbinom(s,n,theta3)
            if(y3 > value){
                theta1 = theta3
                y1 = y3
            } else {
                theta2 = theta3
                y2 = y3
            }
            if(abs(theta1-theta2) < eps){istep = maxstp}
        }
        list(solution=theta3,valatsol = y3)
    } else {
        list(error="Bad Starts")
    }
}
```

2. **binpower**. Discussed in Example 4.5.2.

```
binpower<-function(){
n<-20
k1<-11
k2<-12
p0<-.7
x<-seq(.4,1,.01)
pow1<-pbinom(k1,n,x)
pow2<-pbinom(k2,n,x)
#par(mfrow=c(2,2))
postscript(file="figbino.ps")
plot(x,pow2,xlab="p",ylab="Power",ylim=c(0,1),xlim=c(.35,1),
     type="l",lty=2)
lines(x,pow1,lty=1)
text(.72,.4,"Level 0.23")
text(.54,.4,"Level 0.11")
}
```

3. **boottestonemean**. Bootstrap test for

$$H_0 : \theta = \theta_0 \text{ versus } H_A : \theta > \theta_0 .$$

The test is based on the sample mean but can easily be changed to another test.

```
boottestonemean<-function(x,theta0,b){
#
#   x = sample
#   theta0 is the null value of the mean
#   b is the number of bootstrap resamples
#
#   origtest contains the value of the test statistics
#            for the original sample
#   pvalue is the bootstrap p-value
#   teststatall contains the b bootstrap tests
#
n<-length(x)
v<-mean(x)
z<-x-mean(x)+theta0
counter<-0
teststatall<-rep(0,b)
for(i in 1:b){xstar<-sample(z,n,replace=T)
              vstar<-mean(xstar)
```

```
                    if(vstar >= v){counter<-counter+1}
                    teststatall[i]<-vstar}
        pvalue<-counter/b
        list(origtest=v,pvalue=pvalue,teststatall=teststatall)
        }
```

4. **boottesttwo**. Program which obtains the bootstrap test for two samples as discussed in Exercise 4.9.6. The test statistic is the difference in sample means. To change to another test statistic, simply substitute the appropriate call in place of the call to means.

```
boottesttwo<-function(x,y,b){
#
#   x vector containing first sample.
#   y vector containing first sample.
#   b number of bootstrap replications.
#
#   origtest: value of test statistic on original samples
#   pvalue: bootstrap p-value
#   teststatall: vector of bootstrap test statistics
#
n1<-length(x)
n2<-length(y)
v<-mean(y) - mean(x)
z<-c(x,y)
counter<-0
teststatall<-rep(0,b)
for(i in 1:b){xstar<-sample(z,n1,replace=T)
              ystar<-sample(z,n2,replace=T)
              vstar<-mean(ystar) - mean(xstar)
              if(vstar >= v){counter<-counter+1}
              teststatall[i]<-vstar}
pvalue<-counter/b
list(origtest=v,pvalue=pvalue,teststatall=teststatall)
#list(origtest=v,pvaule=pvalue)
}
```

5. **condsim1**. This algorithm generates observations from the pdf (11.4.5).

```
condsim1<-function(nsims){
collect<-rep(0,nsims)
for(i in 1:nsims)
   {y<--.5*log(1-runif(1))
    collect[i]<--log(1-runif(1))+y
```

```
        }
    collect
    }
```

6. **empalphacn**. Obtains the empirical level of the test discussed in Example
   4.8.6.

```
    empalphacn<-function(nsims){
    #
    #   Obtains the empirical level of the test discussed
    #   in Example 4.8.6.
    #
    #   nsims is the number of simulations
    #
    sigmac<-25
    eps<-.25
    alpha<-.05
    n<-20
    tc<-qt(1-alpha,n-1)
    ic<-0
    for(i in 1:nsims){
        samp<-rcn(n,eps,sigmac)
        ttest<-(sqrt(n)*mean(samp))/var(samp)^.5
        if(ttest > tc){ic<-ic+1}
        }
    empalp<-ic/nsims
    err<-1.96*sqrt((empalp*(1-empalp))/nsims)
    list(empiricalalpha=empalp,error=err)
    }
```

7. **gibbser2**. This R program performs the Gibbs sampler given in Example
   11.4.2.

```
    gibbser2 = function(alpha,m,n){
    x0 = 1
    yc = rep(0,m+n)
    xc = c(x0,rep(0,m-1+n))
    for(i in 2:(m+n)){yc[i] = rgamma(1,alpha+xc[i-1],2)
                      xc[i] = rpois(1,yc[i])}
    y1=yc[1:m]
    y2=yc[(m+1):(m+n)]
    x1=xc[1:m]
    x2=xc[(m+1):(m+n)]
    list(y1 = y1,y2=y2,x1=x1,x2=x2)
    }
```

8. **hieracrh1**. This R program performs the Gibbs sampler given in Example 11.5.2.

```
hieracrh1<-function(nsims,x,tau,kstart){
bold<-1
clambda<-rep(0,(nsims+kstart))
cb<-rep(0,(nsims+kstart))
for(i in 1:(nsims+kstart))
   {clambda[i]<-rgamma(1,shape=(x+1),scale=(bold/(bold+1)))
    newy<-rgamma(1,shape=2,scale=(tau/(clambda[i]*tau+1)))
    cb[i]<-1/newy
    bold<-1/newy}
gibbslambda<-clambda[(kstart+1):(nsims+kstart)]
gibbsb<-cb[(kstart+1):(nsims+kstart)]
list(clambda=clambda,cb=cb,gibbslambda=gibbslambda,gibbsb=gibbsb)
}
```

9. **lslinhypoth**. Returns the F_{LS} test statistic and p-value based on the hypothesis matrix am, where the response is in y, and the full model design matrix is in x.

```
lslinhypoth<-function(x,y,am){
n<-length(x[,1])
p<-length(x[1,])
q<-length(am[,1])
beta<-lsfit(x,y)$coef
sig<-sum((lsfit(x,y)$resid)^2)/(n-p)
mid<-am%*%solve(t(x)%*%x)%*%t(am)
top<-t(am%*%beta)%*%solve(mid)%*%am%*%beta/q
fls<-top/sig
pvalue<-1-pf(fls,q,n-p)
list(fls=fls,pvalue=pvalue)
}
```

10. **mixnormal**. This R/S-Plus function returns one iteration of the EM step for Exercise 6.6.8 of Chapter 6. The initial estimate for the step is the input vector theta0.

```
mixnormal = function(x,theta0){
part1=(1-theta0[5])*dnorm(x,theta0[1],theta0[3])
```

```
part2=theta0[5]*dnorm(x,theta0[2],theta0[4])
gam = part2/(part1+part2)
denom1 = sum(1 - gam)
denom2 = sum(gam)
mu1 = sum((1-gam)*x)/denom1
sig1 = sqrt(sum((1-gam)*((x-mu1)^2))/denom1)
mu2 = sum(gam*x)/denom2
sig2 = sqrt(sum(gam*((x-mu2)^2))/denom2)
p = mean(gam)
mixnormal = c(mu1,mu2,sig1,sig2,p)
mixnormal
}
```

11. **mlelogistic**. Obtains the maximum likelihood estimate for the situation discussed in Example 6.2.7.

```
mlelogistic = function(x,theta0=mean(x),numstp=100,eps=.0001){
n = length(x)
numfin = numstp
small = 1.0*10^(-8)
ic = 0
istop = 0
while(istop == 0){
    ic = ic + 1
    expx = exp(-(x - theta0))
    lprime = n-2*sum(expx/(1+expx))
    ldprime = -2*sum(expx/(1+expx)^2)
    theta1 = theta0 - (lprime/ldprime)
    check = abs(theta0-theta1)/abs(theta0 + small)
    if(check < eps){istop=1}
    theta0 = theta1
}
list(theta1=theta1,check=check,realnumstps=ic)
}
```

12. **piest**. Obtains the estimate of pi and its standard error for the simulation discussed in Example 4.8.1.

```
piest<-function(n){
#
#  Obtains the estimate of pi and its standard
#  error for the simulation discussed in Example 4.8.1
#
#  n is the number of simulations
#
```

```
    u1<-runif(n)
    u2<-runif(n)
    cnt<-rep(0,n)
    chk<-u1^2 + u2^2 - 1
    cnt[chk < 0]<-1
    est<-mean(cnt)
    se<-4*sqrt(est*(1-est)/n)
    est<-4*est
    list(estimate=est,standard=se)
    }
```

13. **piest2**. Obtains the estimate of pi and its standard error for the simulation discussed in Example 4.8.4.

```
    piest2<-function(n){
    #
    #  Obtains the estimate of pi and its standard
    #  error for the simulation discussed in Example 4.8.4
    #
    #  n is the number of simulations
    #
    samp<-4*sqrt(1-runif(n)^2)
    est<-mean(samp)
    se<-sqrt(var(samp)/n)
    list(est=est,se=se)
    }
```

14. **percentciboot**. Program which obtains a percentile confidence interval for the mean. To change this to a parameter other than the mean, simply substitute the appropriate function at both calls to the mean.

```
    percentciboot<-function(x,b,alpha){
    # x is a vector containing the original sample.
    # b is the desired number of bootstraps.
    # alpha: (1 - alpha) is the confidence coefficient.
    #
    # theta is the point estimate.
    # lower is the lower end of the percentile confidence interval.
    # upper is the upper end of the percentile confidence interval.
    # thetastar is the vector of bootstrapped theta^*s.
    #
    theta<-mean(x)
    thetastar<-rep(0,b)
    n<-length(x)
```

```
for(i in 1:b){xstar<-sample(x,n,replace=T)
              thetastar[i]<-mean(xstar)
              }
thetastar<-sort(thetastar)
pick<-round((alpha/2)*(b+1))
lower<-thetastar[pick]
upper<-thetastar[b-pick+1]
list(theta=theta,lower=lower,upper=upper,thetastar=thetastar)
#list(theta=theta,lower=lower,upper=upper)
}
```

15. **poisrand**. Discussed in Example 4.8.2.

```
poisrand = function(n,lambda){
#
#   n is the number of simulations
#   lambda is the mean of the Poisson distribution.
#
    poisrand = rep(0,n)
    for(i in 1:n){
        xt = 0
        t = 0
        while(t < 1){
           x = xt
           y = -(1/lambda)*log(1-runif(1))
           t = t + y
           xt = xt + 1
        }
        poisrand[i] = x
    }
    poisrand
}
```

16. **poissonci**. Discussed in Example 4.3.2.

```
poissonci = function(s,n,theta1,theta2,value,maxstp=100,eps=.00001){
    y1 = ppois(s,n*theta1)
    y2 = ppois(s,n*theta2)
    ic1 = 0
    ic2 = 0
    if(y1 >= value){ic1=1}
    if(y2 <= value){ic2=1}
    if((ic1*ic2) > 0){
        istep = 0
```

```
            while(istep < maxstp){
                istep = istep + 1
                theta3 = (theta1 + theta2)/2
                y3 = ppois(s,n*theta3)
                if(y3 > value){
                        theta1 = theta3
                        y1 = y3
                } else {
                        theta2 = theta3
                        y2 = y3
                }
                if(abs(theta1-theta2) < eps){istep = maxstp}
            }
            list(solution=theta3,valatsol = y3)
        } else {
            list(error="Bad Starts")
        }
    }
```

17. **qqplotc4s2** Obtains the (R version) of Figure 4.4.1.

```
qqplotc4s2<-function(){
data<-matrix(scan("c4s2.dat"),ncol=1,byrow=T)
vec<-data[,1]
n<-length(vec)
ps<-(1:n)/(n+1)
normalqs<-qnorm(ps)
y<-sort(vec)
#postscript("try.ps",horizontal=T)
par(mfrow=c(2,2))
boxplot(y,ylab="x")
title(main="Panel A")
plot(normalqs,y,xlab="Normal quantiles",ylab="Sample quantiles")
title(main="Panel B",xlab="Normal quantiles",ylab="Sample quantiles")
plot(qlaplace(ps),y,xlab="Laplace quantiles",ylab="Sample quantiles")
title(main="Panel C")
plot(qexp(ps),y,xlab="Exponential quantiles",ylab="Sample quantiles")
title(main="Panel D")
}

qlaplace<-function(ps){
low<-ps[ps < .5]
high<-ps[ps >= .5]
lowq<-log(2*low)
highq<--log(2*(1-high))
```

```
      qlaplace<-c(lowq,highq)
      }
```

18. **rcn**. Returns a random sample of size n drawn from a contaminated normal distribution with percent contamination ϵ and standard deviation ratio σ_c.

```
      rcn<-function(n,eps,sigmac){
      #
      #  returns a random sample of size n drawn from
      #  a contaminated normal distribution with percent
      #  contamination eps and variance ratio sigmac
      #
      ind<-rbinom(n,1,eps)
      x<-rnorm(n)
      rcn<-x*(1-ind)+sigmac*x*ind
      rcn
      }
```

19. **rscn**. Returns a random sample of size n drawn from a skewed contaminated normal distribution with percent contamination ϵ, standard deviation ratio σ_c, and mean μ_c.

```
      rscn = function(n,eps,sd,mu){
      #
      #  returns a random sample of size n drawn from
      #  a skewed contaminated normal distribution with percent
      #  contamination eps, variance ratio sd, and mean mu.
      #
        x1 = rnorm(n)
        x2 = rnorm(n,mu,sd)
        b1 = rbinom(n,1,eps)
        rscn = x1*(1-b1) + b1*x2
        rscn
      }
```

Appendix C

Tables of Distributions

In this appendix, tables for the following distributions are presented:

Table I Cumulative distribution functions for selected Poisson distributions.

Table II Selected quantiles for chi-square distributions.

Table III Cumulative distribution function for the standard normal random variable.

Table IV Selected quantiles for t-distributions.

Table V Selected quantiles for F-distributions.

These tables were generated using the R software. Most statistical computing packages have functions which obtain probabilities and quantiles for these distributions as well as many other distributions. Furthermore, many hand calculators have such functions.

Table I
Poisson Distribution

The following table presents selected Poisson distributions. The probabilities tabled
are

$$P(X \leq x) = \sum_{w=0}^{x} e^{-m} \frac{m^w}{w!},$$

for the values of m selected.

x	\multicolumn{10}{c}{$m = E(X)$}
	0.100	0.200	0.300	0.400	0.500	0.600	0.700	0.800	0.900	1.000
0	0.905	0.819	0.741	0.670	0.607	0.549	0.497	0.449	0.407	0.368
1	0.995	0.982	0.963	0.938	0.910	0.878	0.844	0.809	0.772	0.736
2	1.000	0.999	0.996	0.992	0.986	0.977	0.966	0.953	0.937	0.920
3	1.000	1.000	1.000	0.999	0.998	0.997	0.994	0.991	0.987	0.981
4	1.000	1.000	1.000	1.000	1.000	1.000	0.999	0.999	0.998	0.996
5	1.000	1.000	1.000	1.000	1.000	1.000	1.000	1.000	1.000	0.999
6	1.000	1.000	1.000	1.000	1.000	1.000	1.000	1.000	1.000	1.000
x	1.100	1.200	1.300	1.400	1.500	1.600	1.700	1.800	1.900	2.000
0	0.333	0.301	0.273	0.247	0.223	0.202	0.183	0.165	0.150	0.135
1	0.699	0.663	0.627	0.592	0.558	0.525	0.493	0.463	0.434	0.406
2	0.900	0.879	0.857	0.833	0.809	0.783	0.757	0.731	0.704	0.677
3	0.974	0.966	0.957	0.946	0.934	0.921	0.907	0.891	0.875	0.857
4	0.995	0.992	0.989	0.986	0.981	0.976	0.970	0.964	0.956	0.947
5	0.999	0.998	0.998	0.997	0.996	0.994	0.992	0.990	0.987	0.983
6	1.000	1.000	1.000	0.999	0.999	0.999	0.998	0.997	0.997	0.995
7	1.000	1.000	1.000	1.000	1.000	1.000	1.000	0.999	0.999	0.999
8	1.000	1.000	1.000	1.000	1.000	1.000	1.000	1.000	1.000	1.000
x	2.200	2.400	2.600	2.800	3.000	3.200	3.400	3.600	3.800	4.000
0	0.111	0.091	0.074	0.061	0.050	0.041	0.033	0.027	0.022	0.018
1	0.355	0.308	0.267	0.231	0.199	0.171	0.147	0.126	0.107	0.092
2	0.623	0.570	0.518	0.469	0.423	0.380	0.340	0.303	0.269	0.238
3	0.819	0.779	0.736	0.692	0.647	0.603	0.558	0.515	0.473	0.433
4	0.928	0.904	0.877	0.848	0.815	0.781	0.744	0.706	0.668	0.629
5	0.975	0.964	0.951	0.935	0.916	0.895	0.871	0.844	0.816	0.785
6	0.993	0.988	0.983	0.976	0.966	0.955	0.942	0.927	0.909	0.889
7	0.998	0.997	0.995	0.992	0.988	0.983	0.977	0.969	0.960	0.949
8	1.000	0.999	0.999	0.998	0.996	0.994	0.992	0.988	0.984	0.979
9	1.000	1.000	1.000	0.999	0.999	0.998	0.997	0.996	0.994	0.992
10	1.000	1.000	1.000	1.000	1.000	1.000	0.999	0.999	0.998	0.997
11	1.000	1.000	1.000	1.000	1.000	1.000	1.000	1.000	0.999	0.999
12	1.000	1.000	1.000	1.000	1.000	1.000	1.000	1.000	1.000	1.000

					$m = E(X)$					
x	4.200	4.400	4.600	4.800	5.000	5.200	5.400	5.600	5.800	6.000
0	0.015	0.012	0.010	0.008	0.007	0.006	0.005	0.004	0.003	0.002
1	0.078	0.066	0.056	0.048	0.040	0.034	0.029	0.024	0.021	0.017
2	0.210	0.185	0.163	0.143	0.125	0.109	0.095	0.082	0.072	0.062
3	0.395	0.359	0.326	0.294	0.265	0.238	0.213	0.191	0.170	0.151
4	0.590	0.551	0.513	0.476	0.440	0.406	0.373	0.342	0.313	0.285
5	0.753	0.720	0.686	0.651	0.616	0.581	0.546	0.512	0.478	0.446
6	0.867	0.844	0.818	0.791	0.762	0.732	0.702	0.670	0.638	0.606
7	0.936	0.921	0.905	0.887	0.867	0.845	0.822	0.797	0.771	0.744
8	0.972	0.964	0.955	0.944	0.932	0.918	0.903	0.886	0.867	0.847
9	0.989	0.985	0.980	0.975	0.968	0.960	0.951	0.941	0.929	0.916
10	0.996	0.994	0.992	0.990	0.986	0.982	0.977	0.972	0.965	0.957
11	0.999	0.998	0.997	0.996	0.995	0.993	0.990	0.988	0.984	0.980
12	1.000	0.999	0.999	0.999	0.998	0.997	0.996	0.995	0.993	0.991
13	1.000	1.000	1.000	1.000	0.999	0.999	0.999	0.998	0.997	0.996
14	1.000	1.000	1.000	1.000	1.000	1.000	1.000	0.999	0.999	0.999
15	1.000	1.000	1.000	1.000	1.000	1.000	1.000	1.000	1.000	0.999
16	1.000	1.000	1.000	1.000	1.000	1.000	1.000	1.000	1.000	1.000

x	6.500	7.000	7.500	8.000	8.500	9.000	9.500	10.000	10.500	11.000
0	0.002	0.001	0.001	0.000	0.000	0.000	0.000	0.000	0.000	0.000
1	0.011	0.007	0.005	0.003	0.002	0.001	0.001	0.000	0.000	0.000
2	0.043	0.030	0.020	0.014	0.009	0.006	0.004	0.003	0.002	0.001
3	0.112	0.082	0.059	0.042	0.030	0.021	0.015	0.010	0.007	0.005
4	0.224	0.173	0.132	0.100	0.074	0.055	0.040	0.029	0.021	0.015
5	0.369	0.301	0.241	0.191	0.150	0.116	0.089	0.067	0.050	0.038
6	0.527	0.450	0.378	0.313	0.256	0.207	0.165	0.130	0.102	0.079
7	0.673	0.599	0.525	0.453	0.386	0.324	0.269	0.220	0.179	0.143
8	0.792	0.729	0.662	0.593	0.523	0.456	0.392	0.333	0.279	0.232
9	0.877	0.830	0.776	0.717	0.653	0.587	0.522	0.458	0.397	0.341
10	0.933	0.901	0.862	0.816	0.763	0.706	0.645	0.583	0.521	0.460
11	0.966	0.947	0.921	0.888	0.849	0.803	0.752	0.697	0.639	0.579
12	0.984	0.973	0.957	0.936	0.909	0.876	0.836	0.792	0.742	0.689
13	0.993	0.987	0.978	0.966	0.949	0.926	0.898	0.864	0.825	0.781
14	0.997	0.994	0.990	0.983	0.973	0.959	0.940	0.917	0.888	0.854
15	0.999	0.998	0.995	0.992	0.986	0.978	0.967	0.951	0.932	0.907
16	1.000	0.999	0.998	0.996	0.993	0.989	0.982	0.973	0.960	0.944
17	1.000	1.000	0.999	0.998	0.997	0.995	0.991	0.986	0.978	0.968
18	1.000	1.000	1.000	0.999	0.999	0.998	0.996	0.993	0.988	0.982
19	1.000	1.000	1.000	1.000	0.999	0.999	0.998	0.997	0.994	0.991
20	1.000	1.000	1.000	1.000	1.000	1.000	0.999	0.998	0.997	0.995
21	1.000	1.000	1.000	1.000	1.000	1.000	1.000	0.999	0.999	0.998
22	1.000	1.000	1.000	1.000	1.000	1.000	1.000	1.000	0.999	0.999
23	1.000	1.000	1.000	1.000	1.000	1.000	1.000	1.000	1.000	1.000

Table II
Chi-Square Distribution

The following table presents selected quantiles of chi-square distribution, i.e., the values x such that

$$P(X \leq x) = \int_0^x \frac{1}{\Gamma(r/2)2^{r/2}} w^{r/2-1} e^{-w/2} \, dw,$$

for selected degrees of freedom r.

r	$P(X \leq x)$							
	0.010	0.025	0.050	0.100	0.900	0.950	0.975	0.990
1	0.000	0.001	0.004	0.016	2.706	3.841	5.024	6.635
2	0.020	0.051	0.103	0.211	4.605	5.991	7.378	9.210
3	0.115	0.216	0.352	0.584	6.251	7.815	9.348	11.345
4	0.297	0.484	0.711	1.064	7.779	9.488	11.143	13.277
5	0.554	0.831	1.145	1.610	9.236	11.070	12.833	15.086
6	0.872	1.237	1.635	2.204	10.645	12.592	14.449	16.812
7	1.239	1.690	2.167	2.833	12.017	14.067	16.013	18.475
8	1.646	2.180	2.733	3.490	13.362	15.507	17.535	20.090
9	2.088	2.700	3.325	4.168	14.684	16.919	19.023	21.666
10	2.558	3.247	3.940	4.865	15.987	18.307	20.483	23.209
11	3.053	3.816	4.575	5.578	17.275	19.675	21.920	24.725
12	3.571	4.404	5.226	6.304	18.549	21.026	23.337	26.217
13	4.107	5.009	5.892	7.042	19.812	22.362	24.736	27.688
14	4.660	5.629	6.571	7.790	21.064	23.685	26.119	29.141
15	5.229	6.262	7.261	8.547	22.307	24.996	27.488	30.578
16	5.812	6.908	7.962	9.312	23.542	26.296	28.845	32.000
17	6.408	7.564	8.672	10.085	24.769	27.587	30.191	33.409
18	7.015	8.231	9.390	10.865	25.989	28.869	31.526	34.805
19	7.633	8.907	10.117	11.651	27.204	30.144	32.852	36.191
20	8.260	9.591	10.851	12.443	28.412	31.410	34.170	37.566
21	8.897	10.283	11.591	13.240	29.615	32.671	35.479	38.932
22	9.542	10.982	12.338	14.041	30.813	33.924	36.781	40.289
23	10.196	11.689	13.091	14.848	32.007	35.172	38.076	41.638
24	10.856	12.401	13.848	15.659	33.196	36.415	39.364	42.980
25	11.524	13.120	14.611	16.473	34.382	37.652	40.646	44.314
26	12.198	13.844	15.379	17.292	35.563	38.885	41.923	45.642
27	12.879	14.573	16.151	18.114	36.741	40.113	43.195	46.963
28	13.565	15.308	16.928	18.939	37.916	41.337	44.461	48.278
29	14.256	16.047	17.708	19.768	39.087	42.557	45.722	49.588
30	14.953	16.791	18.493	20.599	40.256	43.773	46.979	50.892

Table III
Normal Distribution

The following table presents the standard normal distribution. The probabilities tabled are

$$P(Z \le z) = \Phi(z) = \int_{-\infty}^{z} \frac{1}{\sqrt{2\pi}} e^{-w^2/2}\, dw.$$

Note that only the probabilities for $z \ge 0$ are tabled. To obtain the probabilities for $z < 0$, use the identity $\Phi(-z) = 1 - \Phi(z)$. At the bottom of the table, some useful quantiles of the standard normal distribution are displayed.

z	0.00	0.01	0.02	0.03	0.04	0.05	0.06	0.07	0.08	0.09
0.0	.5000	.5040	.5080	.5120	.5160	.5199	.5239	.5279	.5319	.5359
0.1	.5398	.5438	.5478	.5517	.5557	.5596	.5636	.5675	.5714	.5753
0.2	.5793	.5832	.5871	.5910	.5948	.5987	.6026	.6064	.6103	.6141
0.3	.6179	.6217	.6255	.6293	.6331	.6368	.6406	.6443	.6480	.6517
0.4	.6554	.6591	.6628	.6664	.6700	.6736	.6772	.6808	.6844	.6879
0.5	.6915	.6950	.6985	.7019	.7054	.7088	.7123	.7157	.7190	.7224
0.6	.7257	.7291	.7324	.7357	.7389	.7422	.7454	.7486	.7517	.7549
0.7	.7580	.7611	.7642	.7673	.7704	.7734	.7764	.7794	.7823	.7852
0.8	.7881	.7910	.7939	.7967	.7995	.8023	.8051	.8078	.8106	.8133
0.9	.8159	.8186	.8212	.8238	.8264	.8289	.8315	.8340	.8365	.8389
1.0	.8413	.8438	.8461	.8485	.8508	.8531	.8554	.8577	.8599	.8621
1.1	.8643	.8665	.8686	.8708	.8729	.8749	.8770	.8790	.8810	.8830
1.2	.8849	8869	.8888	.8907	.8925	.8944	.8962	.8980	.8997	.9015
1.3	.9032	.9049	.9066	.9082	.9099	.9115	.9131	.9147	.9162	.9177
1.4	.9192	.9207	.9222	.9236	.9251	.9265	.9279	.9292	.9306	.9319
1.5	.9332	.9345	.9357	.9370	.9382	.9394	.9406	.9418	.9429	.9441
1.6	.9452	.9463	.9474	.9484	.9495	.9505	.9515	.9525	.9535	.9545
1.7	.9554	.9564	.9573	.9582	.9591	.9599	9608	.9616	.0625	.9633
1.8	.9641	.9649	.9656	.9664	.9671	.9678	.9686	.9693	.9699	.9706
1.9	.9713	.9719	.9726	.9732	.9738	.9744	.9750	.9756	.9761	.9767
2.0	.9772	.9778	.9783	.9788	.9793	.9798	.9803	.9808	.9812	.9817
2.1	.9821	.9826	.9830	.9834	.9838	.9842	.9846	.9850	.9854	.9857
2.2	.9861	.9864	.9868	.9871	.9875	.9878	.9881	.9884	.9887	.9890
2.3	.9893	.9896	.9898	.9901	.9904	.9906	.9909	.9911	.9913	.9916
2.4	.9918	.9920	.9922	.9925	.9927	.9929	.9931	.9932	.9934	.9936
2.5	.9938	.9940	.9941	.9943	.9945	.9946	.9948	.9949	.9951	.9952
2.6	.9953	.9955	.9956	.9957	.9959	.9960	.9961	.9962	.9963	.9964
2.7	.9965	.9966	.9967	.9968	.9969	.9970	.9971	.9972	.9973	.9974
2.8	.9974	.9975	.9976	.9977	.9977	.9978	.9979	.9979	.9980	.9981
2.9	.9981	.9982	.9982	.9983	.9984	.9984	.9985	.9985	.9986	.9986
3.0	.9987	.9987	.9987	.9988	.9988	.9989	.9989	.9989	.9990	.9990
3.1	.9990	.9991	.9991	.9991	.9992	.9992	.9992	.9992	.9993	.9993
3.2	.9993	.9993	.9994	.9994	.9994	.9994	.9994	.9995	.9995	.9995
3.3	.9995	.9995	.9995	.9996	.9996	.9996	.9996	.9996	.9996	.9997
3.4	.9997	.9997	.9997	.9997	.9997	.9997	.9997	.9997	.9997	.9998
3.5	.9998	.9998	.9998	.9998	.9998	.9998	.9998	.9998	.9998	.9998

α	0.400	0.300	0.200	0.100	0.050	0.025	0.020	0.010	0.005	0.001
z_α	0.253	0.524	0.842	1.282	1.645	1.960	2.054	2.326	2.576	3.090
$z_{\alpha/2}$	0.842	1.036	1.282	1.645	1.960	2.241	2.326	2.576	2.807	3.291

Table IV
t-Distribution

The following table presents selected quantiles of the t-distribution, i.e., the values t such that

$$P(T \le t) = \int_{-\infty}^{t} \frac{\Gamma[(r+1)/2]}{\sqrt{\pi r}\,\Gamma(r/2)(1 + w^2/r)^{(r+1)/2}} \, dw,$$

for selected degrees of freedom r. The last row gives the standard normal quantiles.

r	\multicolumn{6}{c}{$P(T \le t)$}					
	0.900	0.950	0.975	0.990	0.995	0.999
1	3.078	6.314	12.706	31.821	63.657	318.309
2	1.886	2.920	4.303	6.965	9.925	22.327
3	1.638	2.353	3.182	4.541	5.841	10.215
4	1.533	2.132	2.776	3.747	4.604	7.173
5	1.476	2.015	2.571	3.365	4.032	5.893
6	1.440	1.943	2.447	3.143	3.707	5.208
7	1.415	1.895	2.365	2.998	3.499	4.785
8	1.397	1.860	2.306	2.896	3.355	4.501
9	1.383	1.833	2.262	2.821	3.250	4.297
10	1.372	1.812	2.228	2.764	3.169	4.144
11	1.363	1.796	2.201	2.718	3.106	4.025
12	1.356	1.782	2.179	2.681	3.055	3.930
13	1.350	1.771	2.160	2.650	3.012	3.852
14	1.345	1.761	2.145	2.624	2.977	3.787
15	1.341	1.753	2.131	2.602	2.947	3.733
16	1.337	1.746	2.120	2.583	2.921	3.686
17	1.333	1.740	2.110	2.567	2.898	3.646
18	1.330	1.734	2.101	2.552	2.878	3.610
19	1.328	1.729	2.093	2.539	2.861	3.579
20	1.325	1.725	2.086	2.528	2.845	3.552
21	1.323	1.721	2.080	2.518	2.831	3.527
22	1.321	1.717	2.074	2.508	2.819	3.505
23	1.319	1.714	2.069	2.500	2.807	3.485
24	1.318	1.711	2.064	2.492	2.797	3.467
25	1.316	1.708	2.060	2.485	2.787	3.450
26	1.315	1.706	2.056	2.479	2.779	3.435
27	1.314	1.703	2.052	2.473	2.771	3.421
28	1.313	1.701	2.048	2.467	2.763	3.408
29	1.311	1.699	2.045	2.462	2.756	3.396
30	1.310	1.697	2.042	2.457	2.750	3.385
∞	1.282	1.645	1.960	2.326	2.576	3.090

Table V
F-Distribution
Upper 0.05 Critical Points

The following table presents selected 0.95 and 0.99 quantiles of the F-distribution, i.e., for $\alpha = 0.05, 0.01$, the values $F_\alpha(r_1, r_2)$ such that

$$\alpha = P(X \geq F_\alpha(r_1, r_2)) = \int_{F_\alpha(r_1,r_2)}^{\infty} \frac{\Gamma[(r_1 + r_2)/2](r_1/r_2)^{r_1/2} w^{r_1/2-1}}{\Gamma(r_1/2)\Gamma(r_2/2)(1 + r_1 w/r_2)^{(r_1+r_2)/2}} \, dw,$$

where r_1 and r_2 are the numerator and denominator degrees of freedom, respectively.

	$F_{0.05}(r_1, r_2)$								
	r_1								
r_2	1	2	3	4	5	6	7	8	9
1	161.45	199.50	215.71	224.58	230.16	233.99	236.77	238.88	240.54
2	18.51	19.00	19.16	19.25	19.30	19.33	19.35	19.37	19.38
3	10.13	9.55	9.28	9.12	9.01	8.94	8.89	8.85	8.81
4	7.71	6.94	6.59	6.39	6.26	6.16	6.09	6.04	6.00
5	6.61	5.79	5.41	5.19	5.05	4.95	4.88	4.82	4.77
6	5.99	5.14	4.76	4.53	4.39	4.28	4.21	4.15	4.10
7	5.59	4.74	4.35	4.12	3.97	3.87	3.79	3.73	3.68
8	5.32	4.46	4.07	3.84	3.69	3.58	3.50	3.44	3.39
9	5.12	4.26	3.86	3.63	3.48	3.37	3.29	3.23	3.18
10	4.96	4.10	3.71	3.48	3.33	3.22	3.14	3.07	3.02
11	4.84	3.98	3.59	3.36	3.20	3.09	3.01	2.95	2.90
12	4.75	3.89	3.49	3.26	3.11	3.00	2.91	2.85	2.80
13	4.67	3.81	3.41	3.18	3.03	2.92	2.83	2.77	2.71
14	4.60	3.74	3.34	3.11	2.96	2.85	2.76	2.70	2.65
15	4.54	3.68	3.29	3.06	2.90	2.79	2.71	2.64	2.59
16	4.49	3.63	3.24	3.01	2.85	2.74	2.66	2.59	2.54
17	4.45	3.59	3.20	2.96	2.81	2.70	2.61	2.55	2.49
18	4.41	3.55	3.16	2.93	2.77	2.66	2.58	2.51	2.46
19	4.38	3.52	3.13	2.90	2.74	2.63	2.54	2.48	2.42
20	4.35	3.49	3.10	2.87	2.71	2.60	2.51	2.45	2.39
21	4.32	3.47	3.07	2.84	2.68	2.57	2.49	2.42	2.37
22	4.30	3.44	3.05	2.82	2.66	2.55	2.46	2.40	2.34
23	4.28	3.42	3.03	2.80	2.64	2.53	2.44	2.37	2.32
24	4.26	3.40	3.01	2.78	2.62	2.51	2.42	2.36	2.30
25	4.24	3.39	2.99	2.76	2.60	2.49	2.40	2.34	2.28
26	4.23	3.37	2.98	2.74	2.59	2.47	2.39	2.32	2.27
27	4.21	3.35	2.96	2.73	2.57	2.46	2.37	2.31	2.25
28	4.20	3.34	2.95	2.71	2.56	2.45	2.36	2.29	2.24
29	4.18	3.33	2.93	2.70	2.55	2.43	2.35	2.28	2.22
30	4.17	3.32	2.92	2.69	2.53	2.42	2.33	2.27	2.21
40	4.08	3.23	2.84	2.61	2.45	2.34	2.25	2.18	2.12
60	4.00	3.15	2.76	2.53	2.37	2.25	2.17	2.10	2.04
120	3.92	3.07	2.68	2.45	2.29	2.18	2.09	2.02	1.96
∞	3.84	3.00	2.60	2.37	2.21	2.10	2.01	1.94	1.88

Table V
F-Distribution, Continued
Upper 0.05 Critical Points

					$F_{0.05}(r_1, r_2)$				
					r_1				
r_2	10	15	20	25	30	40	60	120	∞
1	241.88	245.95	248.01	249.26	250.10	251.14	252.20	253.25	254.31
2	19.40	19.43	19.45	19.46	19.46	19.47	19.48	19.49	19.50
3	8.79	8.70	8.66	8.63	8.62	8.59	8.57	8.55	8.53
4	5.96	5.86	5.80	5.77	5.75	5.72	5.69	5.66	5.63
5	4.74	4.62	4.56	4.52	4.50	4.46	4.43	4.40	4.36
6	4.06	3.94	3.87	3.83	3.81	3.77	3.74	3.70	3.67
7	3.64	3.51	3.44	3.40	3.38	3.34	3.30	3.27	3.23
8	3.35	3.22	3.15	3.11	3.08	3.04	3.01	2.97	2.93
9	3.14	3.01	2.94	2.89	2.86	2.83	2.79	2.75	2.71
10	2.98	2.85	2.77	2.73	2.70	2.66	2.62	2.58	2.54
11	2.85	2.72	2.65	2.60	2.57	2.53	2.49	2.45	2.40
12	2.75	2.62	2.54	2.50	2.47	2.43	2.38	2.34	2.30
13	2.67	2.53	2.46	2.41	2.38	2.34	2.30	2.25	2.21
14	2.60	2.46	2.39	2.34	2.31	2.27	2.22	2.18	2.13
15	2.54	2.40	2.33	2.28	2.25	2.20	2.16	2.11	2.07
16	2.49	2.35	2.28	2.23	2.19	2.15	2.11	2.06	2.01
17	2.45	2.31	2.23	2.18	2.15	2.10	2.06	2.01	1.96
18	2.41	2.27	2.19	2.14	2.11	2.06	2.02	1.97	1.92
19	2.38	2.23	2.16	2.11	2.07	2.03	1.98	1.93	1.88
20	2.35	2.20	2.12	2.07	2.04	1.99	1.95	1.90	1.84
21	2.32	2.18	2.10	2.05	2.01	1.96	1.92	1.87	1.81
22	2.30	2.15	2.07	2.02	1.98	1.94	1.89	1.84	1.78
23	2.27	2.13	2.05	2.00	1.96	1.91	1.86	1.81	1.76
24	2.25	2.11	2.03	1.97	1.94	1.89	1.84	1.79	1.73
25	2.24	2.09	2.01	1.96	1.92	1.87	1.82	1.77	1.71
26	2.22	2.07	1.99	1.94	1.90	1.85	1.80	1.75	1.69
27	2.20	2.06	1.97	1.92	1.88	1.84	1.79	1.73	1.67
28	2.19	2.04	1.96	1.91	1.87	1.82	1.77	1.71	1.65
29	2.18	2.03	1.94	1.89	1.85	1.81	1.75	1.70	1.64
30	2.16	2.01	1.93	1.88	1.84	1.79	1.74	1.68	1.62
40	2.08	1.92	1.84	1.78	1.74	1.69	1.64	1.58	1.51
60	1.99	1.84	1.75	1.69	1.65	1.59	1.53	1.47	1.39
120	1.91	1.75	1.66	1.60	1.55	1.50	1.43	1.35	1.25
∞	1.83	1.67	1.57	1.51	1.46	1.39	1.32	1.22	1.00

Table V
F-Distribution, Continued
Upper 0.01 Critical Points

r_2	$F_{0.01}(r_1, r_2)$								
	r_1								
	1	2	3	4	5	6	7	8	9
1	4052.2	4999.5	5403.4	5624.6	5763.7	5859.0	5928.4	5981.1	6022.5
2	98.50	99.00	99.17	99.25	99.30	99.33	99.36	99.37	99.39
3	34.12	30.82	29.46	28.71	28.24	27.91	27.67	27.49	27.35
4	21.20	18.00	16.69	15.98	15.52	15.21	14.98	14.80	14.66
5	16.26	13.27	12.06	11.39	10.97	10.67	10.46	10.29	10.16
6	13.75	10.92	9.78	9.15	8.75	8.47	8.26	8.10	7.98
7	12.25	9.55	8.45	7.85	7.46	7.19	6.99	6.84	6.72
8	11.26	8.65	7.59	7.01	6.63	6.37	6.18	6.03	5.91
9	10.56	8.02	6.99	6.42	6.06	5.80	5.61	5.47	5.35
10	10.04	7.56	6.55	5.99	5.64	5.39	5.20	5.06	4.94
11	9.65	7.21	6.22	5.67	5.32	5.07	4.89	4.74	4.63
12	9.33	6.93	5.95	5.41	5.06	4.82	4.64	4.50	4.39
13	9.07	6.70	5.74	5.21	4.86	4.62	4.44	4.30	4.19
14	8.86	6.51	5.56	5.04	4.69	4.46	4.28	4.14	4.03
15	8.68	6.36	5.42	4.89	4.56	4.32	4.14	4.00	3.89
16	8.53	6.23	5.29	4.77	4.44	4.20	4.03	3.89	3.78
17	8.40	6.11	5.18	4.67	4.34	4.10	3.93	3.79	3.68
18	8.29	6.01	5.09	4.58	4.25	4.01	3.84	3.71	3.60
19	8.18	5.93	5.01	4.50	4.17	3.94	3.77	3.63	3.52
20	8.10	5.85	4.94	4.43	4.10	3.87	3.70	3.56	3.46
21	8.02	5.78	4.87	4.37	4.04	3.81	3.64	3.51	3.40
22	7.95	5.72	4.82	4.31	3.99	3.76	3.59	3.45	3.35
23	7.88	5.66	4.76	4.26	3.94	3.71	3.54	3.41	3.30
24	7.82	5.61	4.72	4.22	3.90	3.67	3.50	3.36	3.26
25	7.77	5.57	4.68	4.18	3.85	3.63	3.46	3.32	3.22
26	7.72	5.53	4.64	4.14	3.82	3.59	3.42	3.29	3.18
27	7.68	5.49	4.60	4.11	3.78	3.56	3.39	3.26	3.15
28	7.64	5.45	4.57	4.07	3.75	3.53	3.36	3.23	3.12
29	7.60	5.42	4.54	4.04	3.73	3.50	3.33	3.20	3.09
30	7.56	5.39	4.51	4.02	3.70	3.47	3.30	3.17	3.07
40	7.31	5.18	4.31	3.83	3.51	3.29	3.12	2.99	2.89
60	7.08	4.98	4.13	3.65	3.34	3.12	2.95	2.82	2.72
120	6.85	4.79	3.95	3.48	3.17	2.96	2.79	2.66	2.56
∞	6.63	4.61	3.78	3.32	3.02	2.80	2.64	2.51	2.41

Table V
F-Distribution, Continued
Upper 0.01 Critical Points

					$F_{0.01}(r_1, r_2)$				
					r_1				
r_2	10	15	20	25	30	40	60	120	∞
1	6055.9	6157.3	6208.7	6239.8	6260.7	6286.8	6313.0	6339.4	6365.9
2	99.40	99.43	99.45	99.46	99.47	99.47	99.48	99.49	99.50
3	27.23	26.87	26.69	26.58	26.50	26.41	26.32	26.22	26.13
4	14.55	14.20	14.02	13.91	13.84	13.75	13.65	13.56	13.46
5	10.05	9.72	9.55	9.45	9.38	9.29	9.20	9.11	9.02
6	7.87	7.56	7.40	7.30	7.23	7.14	7.06	6.97	6.88
7	6.62	6.31	6.16	6.06	5.99	5.91	5.82	5.74	5.65
8	5.81	5.52	5.36	5.26	5.20	5.12	5.03	4.95	4.86
9	5.26	4.96	4.81	4.71	4.65	4.57	4.48	4.40	4.31
10	4.85	4.56	4.41	4.31	4.25	4.17	4.08	4.00	3.91
11	4.54	4.25	4.10	4.01	3.94	3.86	3.78	3.69	3.60
12	4.30	4.01	3.86	3.76	3.70	3.62	3.54	3.45	3.36
13	4.10	3.82	3.66	3.57	3.51	3.43	3.34	3.25	3.17
14	3.94	3.66	3.51	3.41	3.35	3.27	3.18	3.09	3.00
15	3.80	3.52	3.37	3.28	3.21	3.13	3.05	2.96	2.87
16	3.69	3.41	3.26	3.16	3.10	3.02	2.93	2.84	2.75
17	3.59	3.31	3.16	3.07	3.00	2.92	2.83	2.75	2.65
18	3.51	3.23	3.08	2.98	2.92	2.84	2.75	2.66	2.57
19	3.43	3.15	3.00	2.91	2.84	2.76	2.67	2.58	2.49
20	3.37	3.09	2.94	2.84	2.78	2.69	2.61	2.52	2.42
21	3.31	3.03	2.88	2.79	2.72	2.64	2.55	2.46	2.36
22	3.26	2.98	2.83	2.73	2.67	2.58	2.50	2.40	2.31
23	3.21	2.93	2.78	2.69	2.62	2.54	2.45	2.35	2.26
24	3.17	2.89	2.74	2.64	2.58	2.49	2.40	2.31	2.21
25	3.13	2.85	2.70	2.60	2.54	2.45	2.36	2.27	2.17
26	3.09	2.81	2.66	2.57	2.50	2.42	2.33	2.23	2.13
27	3.06	2.78	2.63	2.54	2.47	2.38	2.29	2.20	2.10
28	3.03	2.75	2.60	2.51	2.44	2.35	2.26	2.17	2.06
29	3.00	2.73	2.57	2.48	2.41	2.33	2.23	2.14	2.03
30	2.98	2.70	2.55	2.45	2.39	2.30	2.21	2.11	2.01
40	2.80	2.52	2.37	2.27	2.20	2.11	2.02	1.92	1.80
60	2.63	2.35	2.20	2.10	2.03	1.94	1.84	1.73	1.60
120	2.47	2.19	2.03	1.93	1.86	1.76	1.66	1.53	1.38
∞	2.32	2.04	1.88	1.77	1.70	1.59	1.47	1.32	1.00

Appendix D

Lists of Common Distributions

In this appendix, we provide a short list of common distributions. For each distribution, we note the expression where the pmf or pdf is defined in the text, the formula for the pmf or pdf, its mean and variance, and its mgf. The first list contains common discrete distributions, and the second list contains common continuous distributions.

List of Common Discrete Distributions

Bernouli
$0 < p < 1$

(3.1.1)
$p(x) = p^x(1-p)^{1-x}, \quad x = 0, 1$
$\mu = p, \quad \sigma^2 = p(1-p)$
$m(t) = [(1-p) + pe^t], \quad -\infty < t < \infty$

Binomial
$0 < p < 1$
$n = 1, 2, \ldots$

(3.1.2)
$p(x) = \binom{n}{x} p^x(1-p)^{n-x}, \quad x = 0, 1, 2, \ldots, n$

$\mu = np, \quad \sigma^2 = np(1-p)$
$m(t) = [(1-p) + pe^t]^n, \quad -\infty < t < \infty$

Geometric
$0 < p < 1$

(3.1.5)
$p(x) = p(1-p)^x, \quad x = 0, 1, 2, \ldots$
$\mu = \frac{p}{q}, \quad \sigma^2 = \frac{1-p}{p^2}$
$m(t) = p[1 - (1-p)e^t]^{-1}, \quad t < -\log(1-p)$

Hypergeometric (N, D, n)
$n = 1, 2, \ldots, \min\{N, D\}$

(3.1.7)
$p(x) = \frac{\binom{N-D}{n-x}\binom{D}{x}}{\binom{N}{n}}, \quad x = 0, 1, 2, \ldots, n$
$\mu = n\frac{D}{N}, \quad \sigma^2 = n\frac{D}{N}\frac{N-D}{N}\frac{N-n}{N-1}$
The above pmf is the probability of obtaining x Ds in a sample of size n, without replacement.

Negative Binomial
$0 < p < 1$
$r = 1, 2, \ldots$

(3.1.4)
$p(x) = \binom{x+r-1}{r-1} p^r(1-p)^x, \quad x = 0, 1, 2, \ldots$

$\mu = \frac{rp}{q}, \quad \sigma^2 = \frac{r(1-p)}{p^2}$
$m(t) = p^r[1 - (1-p)e^t]^{-r}, \quad t < -\log(1-p)$

Poisson
$m > 0$

(3.2.1)
$p(x) = e^{-m}\frac{m^x}{x!}, \quad x = 0, 1, 2, \ldots$
$\mu = m, \quad \sigma^2 = m$
$m(t) = \exp\{m(e^t - 1)\}, \quad -\infty < t < \infty$

List of Common Continuous Distributions

beta

$\alpha > 0$

$\beta > 0$

(3.3.5)

$f(x) = \frac{\Gamma(\alpha+\beta)}{\Gamma(\alpha)\Gamma(\beta)} x^{\alpha-1}(1-x)^{\beta-1}, \quad 0 < x < 1$

$\mu = \frac{\alpha}{\alpha+\beta}, \quad \sigma^2 = \frac{\alpha\beta}{(\alpha+\beta+1)(\alpha+\beta)^2}$

$m(t) = 1 + \sum_{i=1}^{\infty} \left(\prod_{j=0}^{k-1} \frac{\alpha+j}{\alpha+\beta+j} \right) \frac{t^i}{i!}, \quad -\infty < t < \infty$

Cauchy

(1.9.1)

$f(x) = \frac{1}{\pi} \frac{1}{x^2+1}, \quad -\infty < x < \infty$

Neither the mean nor the variance exists.

The mgf does not exist.

Chi-squared, $\chi^2(r)$

$r > 0$

(3.3.3)

$f(x) = \frac{1}{\Gamma(r/2)2^{r/2}} x^{(r/2)-1} e^{-x/2}, \quad x > 0$

$\mu = r, \quad \sigma^2 = 2r$

$m(t) = (1 - 2t)^{-r/2}, \quad t < \frac{1}{2}$

$\chi^2(r) \Leftrightarrow \Gamma(r/2, 2)$

r is called the degrees of freedom.

Exponential

$\lambda > 0$

(3.3.2)

$f(x) = \lambda e^{-\lambda x}, \quad x > 0$

$\mu = \frac{1}{\lambda}, \quad \sigma^2 = \frac{1}{\lambda^2}$

$m(t) = [1 - (t/\lambda)]^{-1}, \quad t < \lambda$

Exponential$(\lambda) \Leftrightarrow \Gamma(1, 1/\lambda)$

$F, F(r_1, r_2)$

$r_1 > 0$

$r_2 > 0 > 0$

(3.6.6)

$f(x) = \frac{\Gamma[(r_1+r_2)/2](r_1/r_2)^{r_1/2}}{\Gamma(r_1/2)\Gamma(r_2/2)} \frac{(x)^{r_1/2-1}}{(1+r_1 x/r_2)^{(r_1+r_2)/2}}, \quad x > 0$

If $r_2 > 2$, $\mu = \frac{r_2}{r_2-2}$. If $r > 4$, $\sigma^2 = 2 \left(\frac{r_2}{r_2-2} \right)^2 \frac{r_1+r_2-2}{r_1(r_2-4)}$.

The mgf does not exist.

r_1 is called the numerator degrees of freedom.

r_2 is called the denominator degrees of freedom.

Gamma, $\Gamma(\alpha, \beta)$

$\alpha > 0$

$\beta > 0$

(3.3.1)

$f(x) = \frac{1}{\Gamma(\alpha)\beta^\alpha} x^{\alpha-1} e^{-x/\beta}, \quad x > 0$

$\mu = \alpha\beta, \quad \sigma^2 = \alpha\beta^2$

$m(t) = (1 - \beta t)^{-\alpha}, \quad t < \frac{1}{\beta}$

Continuous Distributions, Continued

Laplace   (2.2.1)
$-\infty < \theta < \infty$ $f(x) = \frac{1}{2} e^{-|x-\theta|}, \quad -\infty < x < \infty$
                               $\mu = \theta, \quad \sigma^2 = 2$
                               $m(t) = e^{t\theta} \frac{1}{1-t^2}, \quad -1 < t < 1$

Logistic   (6.1.8)
$-\infty < \theta < \infty$ $f(x) = \frac{\exp\{-(x-\theta)\}}{(1+\exp\{-(x-\theta)\})^2}, \quad -\infty < x < \infty$
                               $\mu = \theta, \quad \sigma^2 = \frac{\pi^2}{3}$
                               $m(t) = e^{t\theta} \Gamma(1-t)\Gamma(1+t), \quad -1 < t < 1$

Normal, $N(\mu, \sigma^2)$ (3.4.6)
$-\infty < \mu < \infty$ $f(x) = \frac{1}{\sqrt{2\pi}\sigma} \exp\left\{-\frac{1}{2}\left(\frac{x-\mu}{\sigma}\right)^2\right\}, \quad -\infty < x < \infty$
$\sigma > 0$

                               $\mu = \mu, \quad \sigma^2 = \sigma^2$
                               $m(t) = \exp\{\mu t + (1/2)\sigma^2 t^2\}, \quad -\infty < t < \infty$

$t, t(r)$ (3.6.1)
$r > 0$ $f(x) = \frac{\Gamma[(r+1)/2]}{\sqrt{\pi r}\Gamma(r/2)} \frac{1}{(1+x^2/r)^{(r+1)/2}}, \quad -\infty < x < \infty$
                               If $r > 1$, $\mu = 0$. If $r > 2$, $\sigma^2 = \frac{r}{r-2}$.
                               The mgf does not exist.
                               The parameter r is called the degrees of freedom.

Uniform   (1.7.4)
$-\infty < a < b < \infty$ $f(x) = \frac{1}{b-a}, \quad a < x < b$
                               $\mu = \frac{a+b}{2}, \quad \sigma^2 = \frac{(b-a)^2}{12}$
                               $m(t) = \frac{e^{bt} - e^{at}}{(b-a)t}, \quad -\infty < t < \infty$

Appendix E

References

Abebe, A., Crimin, K., McKean, J. W., Haas, J. V., and Vidmar, T. J. (2001), Rank-based procedures for linear models: applications to pharmaceutical science data, *Drug Information Journal*, **35**, 947–971.

Afifi, A. A. and Azen, S. P. (1972), *Statistical Analysis: A Computer Oriented Approach*, New York: Academic Press.

Arnold, S. F. (1981), *The Theory of Linear Models and Multivariate Analysis*, New York: John Wiley and Sons.

Box, G. E. P. and Muller, M. (1958), A note on the generation of random normal variates, *Annals of Mathematical Statistics*, **29**, 610–611.

Breiman, L. (1968), *Probability*, Reading, MA: Addison-Wesley.

Buck, R. C. (1965), *Advanced Calculus*, New York: McGraw-Hill.

Casella, G. and George, E. I. (1992), Explaining the Gibbs sampler, *American Statistician*, **46**, 167–174.

Chang, W. H., McKean, J. W., Naranjo, J. D., and Sheather, S. J. (1999), High breakdown rank-based regression, *Journal of the American Statistical Association*, **94**, 205–219.

Chung, K. L. (1974), *A Course in Probability Theory*, New York: Academic Press.

Conover, W. J. and Iman, R. L. (1981), Rank transform as a bridge between parametric and nonparametric statistics, *American Statistician*, **35**, 124–133.

Cramér, H. (1946), *Mathematical Methods of Statistics*, Princeton: Princeton University Press.

Curtiss, J. H. (1942), A note on the theory of moment generating functions, *Annals of Mathematical Statistics*, **13**, 430.

D'Agostino, R. B. and Stephens, M. A. (1986), *Goodness-of-Fit Techniques*, New York: Marcel Dekker.

Davison, A. C. and Hinkley, D. V. (1997), *Bootstrap Methods and Their Applications*, Cambridge, UK: Cambridge University Press.

Draper, N. R. and Smith, H. (1966), *Applied Regression Analysis*, New York: John Wiley & Sons.

DuBois, C., Ed. (1960), *Lowie's Selected Papers in Anthropology*, Berkeley: University of California Press.

Efron, B. (1979), Bootstrap methods: Another look at the jackknife, *Annals of Statistics*, **7**, 1–26.

Efron B. and Tibshirani, R. J. (1993), *An Introduction to the Bootstrap*, New York: Chapman and Hall.

Graybill, F. A. (1969), *Introduction to Matrices with Applications in Statistics*, Belmont, CA: Wadsworth.

Graybill, F. A. (1976), *Theory and Application of the Linear Model*, North Scituate, MA: Duxbury.

Hald, A. (1952), *Statistical Theory with Engineering Applications*, New York: John Wiley & Sons.

Haldane, J. B. S. (1948), The precision of observed values of small frequencies, *Biometrika*, **35**, 297–303.

Hampel, F. R. (1974), The influence curve and its role in robust estimation, *Journal of the American Statistical Association*, **69**, 383–393.

Hardy, G. H. (1992), *A Course in Pure Mathematics*, Cambridge, UK: Cambridge University Press.

Hettmansperger, T. P. (1984), *Statistical Inference Based on Ranks*, New York: John Wiley & Sons.

Hettmansperger, T. P. and McKean, J. W. (2011), *Robust Nonparametric Statistical Methods*, 2nd Ed., Boca Raton, FL: CRC Press.

Hewitt, E. and Stromberg, K. (1965), *Real and Abstract Analysis*, New York: Springer-Verlag.

Hodges, J. L., Jr., and Lehmann, E. L. (1961), Comparison of the normal scores and Wilcoxon tests, In: *Proceedings of the Fourth Berkeley Symposium on Mathematical Statistics and Probability*, **1**, 307–317, Berkeley: University of California Press.

Hodges, J. L., Jr., and Lehmann, E. L. (1963), Estimates of location based on rank tests, *Annals of Mathematical Statistics*, **34**, 598–611.

Hogg, R. V. and Craig, A. T. (1958), On the decomposition of certain chi-square variables, *Annals of Mathematical Statistics*, **29**, 608.

Hogg, R. V., Fisher, D. M., and Randles, R. H. (1975), A two-sample adaptive distribution-free test, *Journal of the American Statistical Association*, **70**, 656–661.

Hollander, M. and Wolfe, D. A. (1999), *Nonparametric Statistical Methods*, 2nd Ed., New York: John Wiley & Sons.

Hsu, J. C. (1996), *Multiple Comparisons*, London: Chapman Hall.

Huber, P. J. (1981), *Robust Statistics*, New York: John Wiley & Sons.

Ihaka, R. and Gentleman, R. (1996), R: A language for data analysis and graphics, *Journal of Computational and Graphical Statistics*, **5**, 229–314.

Jeffreys, H. (1961), *The Theory of Probability*, Oxford: Oxford University Press.

Kendall, M. and Stuart, A. (1979), *The Advanced Theory of Statistics*, Vol. 2, New York: Macmillan.

Kendall, M. G. (1962), *Rank Correlation Methods*, 3rd Ed., London: Griffin.

Kennedy, W. J. and Gentle, J. E. (1980), *Statistical Computing*, New York: Marcel Dekker.

Kloke, J. D. and McKean, J. W. (2011), Rfit: R algorithms for rank-based fitting, Submitted.

Lehmann, E. L. (1983), *Theory of Point Estimation*, New York: John Wiley & Sons.

Lehmann, E. L. (1986), *Testing Statistical Hypotheses*, 2nd Ed., London: Chapman & Hall.

Lehmann, E. L. (1999), *Elements of Large Sample Theory*, New York: Springer-Verlag.

Lehmann, E. L. and Casella, G. (1998), *Theory of Point Estimation*, 2nd Ed., New York: Springer-Verlag.

Lehmann, E. L. and Scheffé, H. (1950), Completeness, similar regions, and unbiased estimation, *Sankhya*, **10**, 305–340.

Marsaglia, G. and Bray, T. A. (1964), A convenient method for generating normal variables, *SIAM Review*, **6**, 260–264.

McKean, J. W. (2004), Robust analyses of linear models, *Statistical Science*, **19**, 562–570.

McKean, J. W. and Vidmar, T. J. (1994), A comparison of two rank-based methods for the analysis of linear models, *American Statistician*, **48**, 220–229.

McLachlan, G. J. and Krishnan, T. (1997), *The EM Algorithm and Extensions*, New York: John Wiley & Sons.

Minitab (1991), MINITAB Reference Manual, Valley Forge, PA: Minitab, Inc.

Mosteller, F. and Tukey, J. W. (1977), *Data Reduction and Regression*, Reading, MA: Addison-Wesley.

Naranjo, J. D. and McKean, J. W. (1997), Rank regression with estimated scores, *Statistics and Probability Letters*, **33**, 209–216.

Nelson, W. (1982), *Applied Lifetime Data Analysis*, New York: John Wiley & Sons.

Neter, J., Kutner, M. H., Nachtsheim, C. J., and Wasserman, W. (1996), *Applied Linear Statistical Models*, 4th Ed., Chicago: Irwin.

Parzen, E. (1962), *Stochastic Processes*, San Francisco: Holden-Day.

Randles, R. H. and Wolfe, D. A. (1979), *Introduction to the Theory of Nonparametric Statistics*, New York: John Wiley and Sons.

Rao, C. R. (1973), *Linear Statistical Inference and Its Applications*, 2nd Ed., New York: John Wiley & Sons.

Robert, C. P. and Casella, G. (1999), *Monte Carlo Statistical Methods*, New York: Springer-Verlag.

Rousseeuw, P. J. and Leroy, A. M. (1987), *Robust Regression and Outlier Detection*, New York: John Wiley & Sons.

Scheffé, H. (1959), *The Analysis of Variance*, New York: John Wiley & Sons.

Seber, G. A. F. (1984), *Multivariate Observations*, New York: John Wiley & Sons.

Serfling, R. J. (1980), *Approximation Theorems of Mathematical Statistics*, New York: John Wiley & Sons.

Shirley, E. A. C. (1981), A distribution-free method for analysis of covariance based on rank data, *Applied Statistics*, **30**, 158–162.

S-PLUS (2000), *S-PLUS 6.0 Guide to Statistics*, Vol. 2, Seattle: Data Analysis Division, MathSoft.

Stapleton, J. H. (1995), *Linear Statistical Models*, New York: John Wiley & Sons.

Terpstra, J. T. and McKean, J. W. (2005), Rank-based analyses of linear models using R, *Journal of Statistical Software*, **14**, http://www.jstatsoft.org/.

Tucker, H. G. (1967), *A Graduate Course in Probability*, New York: Academic Press.

Tukey, J. W. (1977), *Exploratory Data Analysis*, Reading, MA: Addison-Wesley.

Venables, W. N. and Ripley, B. D. (2002), *Modern Applied Statistics with S*, 4th Ed., New York: Springer-Verlag.

Appendix F

Answers to Selected Exercises

Chapter 1

1.2.1 (a) $\{0,1,2,3,4\}$, $\{2\}$; (b) $(0,3)$, $\{x : 1 \le x < 2\}$; (c) $\{(x,y) : 1 < x < 2, 1 < y < 2\}$.

1.2.2 (a) $\{x : 0 < x \le 5/8\}$.

1.2.3 $C_1 \cap C_2 = \{mary, mray\}$.

1.2.8 (a) $\{x : 0 < x < 3\}$, (b) $\{(x,y) : 0 < x^2 + y^2 < 4\}$

1.2.9 (a) $\{x : x = 2\}$, (b) ϕ, (c) $\{(x,y) : x = 0, y = 0\}$.

1.2.10 (a) $\frac{80}{81}$, (b) 1.

1.2.11 $\frac{11}{16}, 0, 1$.

1.2.12 $\frac{8}{3}, 0, \frac{\pi}{2}$.

1.2.13 (a) $\frac{1}{2}$, (b) 0, (c) $\frac{2}{9}$.

1.2.14 (a) $\frac{1}{6}$, (b) 0.

1.2.16 10.

1.3.2 $\frac{1}{4}, \frac{1}{13}, \frac{1}{52}, \frac{4}{13}$.

1.3.3 $\frac{31}{32}, \frac{3}{64}, \frac{1}{32}, \frac{63}{64}$.

1.3.4 0.3.

1.3.5 $e^{-4}, 1 - e^{-4}, 1$.

1.3.6 $\frac{1}{2}$.

1.3.10 (a)$\binom{6}{4}/\binom{16}{4}$, (b) $\binom{10}{4}/\binom{16}{4}$.

1.3.11 $1 - \binom{990}{5}/\binom{1000}{5}$.

1.3.13 (b) $1 - \binom{10}{3}/\binom{20}{3}$.

1.3.15 (a) $1 - \binom{48}{5}/\binom{50}{5}$.

1.3.18 $13 \cdot 12\binom{4}{3}\binom{4}{2}/\binom{52}{5}$.

1.3.21 (a) $0 \le \sum_{i=1}^{3} p_i \le 1$, (b) no.

1.4.3 $\frac{9}{47}$.

1.4.4 $2\frac{13}{52}\frac{12}{51}\frac{26}{50}\frac{25}{49}$.

1.4.6 $\frac{111}{143}$.

1.4.8 (a) 0.022, (b) $\frac{5}{11}$.

1.4.9 $\frac{5}{14}$.

1.4.10 $\frac{3}{7}, \frac{4}{7}$.

1.4.12 (c) 0.88.

1.4.14 (a) 0.1764.

1.4.15 $4(0.7)^3(0.3)$.

1.4.16 0.75.

1.4.18 (a) $\frac{6}{11}$.

1.4.20 $\frac{1}{7}$.

1.4.21 (a) $1 - \left(\frac{5}{6}\right)^6$, (b) $1 - e^{-1}$.

1.4.23 $\frac{3}{4}$.

1.4.25 $\frac{43}{64}$.

1.4.26 $\frac{3}{5}$.

1.4.28 $\frac{5 \cdot 4 \cdot 5 \cdot 4 \cdot 3}{10 \cdot 9 \cdot 8 \cdot 7 \cdot 6}$.

1.4.29 $\frac{13}{4}$.

1.4.30 $\frac{2}{3}$.

1.4.31 $0.518, 0.491$.

1.4.32 No.

1.5.1 $\frac{9}{13}, \frac{1}{13}, \frac{1}{13}, \frac{1}{13}, \frac{1}{13}$.

1.5.2 (a) $\frac{1}{2}$, (b) $\frac{1}{21}$.

1.5.3 $\frac{1}{5}, \frac{1}{5}, \frac{1}{5}$.

1.5.5 (a) $\frac{\binom{13}{x}\binom{39}{5-x}}{\binom{52}{5}}, x = 0, 1, 2, 3, 4, 5$,
(b) $\left[\binom{39}{5} + \binom{13}{1}\binom{39}{4}\right] / \binom{52}{5}$.

1.5.7 $\frac{3}{4}$.

1.5.8 (a) $\frac{1}{4}$, (b) 0, (c) $\frac{1}{4}$, (d) 0.

1.6.2 (a) $p_X(x) = \frac{1}{10}, x = 1, 2, \ldots, 10$,
(b) $\frac{4}{10}$.

1.6.3 (a) $\left(\frac{5}{6}\right)^{x-1}\frac{1}{6}$ $x = 1, 2, 3, \ldots$,
(c) $\frac{6}{11}$.

1.6.4 $\frac{6}{36}, x = 0; \frac{12-2x}{36}, x = 1, 2, 3, 4, 5$.

1.6.7 $\frac{1}{3}, y = 3, 5, 7$.

1.6.8 $\left(\frac{1}{2}\right)^{\sqrt[3]{y}}, y = 1, 8, 27, \ldots$.

1.7.1 $F(x) = \frac{\sqrt{x}}{10}, 0 \le x < 100$;
$f(x) = \frac{1}{20\sqrt{x}}, 0 < x < 100$.

1.7.3 $\frac{5}{8}; \frac{7}{8}; \frac{3}{8}$.

1.7.5 $e^{-2} - e^{-3}$.

1.7.6 (a) $\frac{1}{27}, 1$; (b) $\frac{2}{9}, \frac{25}{36}$.

1.7.8 (a)1; (b) $\frac{2}{3}$; (c) 2.

1.7.9 (b) $\sqrt[3]{1/2}$; (c) 0.

1.7.10 $\sqrt[4]{0.2}$.

1.7.12 (a) $1 - (1-x)^3, 0 \le x < 1$;
(b) $1 - \frac{1}{x}, 1 \le x < \infty$.

1.7.13 $xe^{-x}, 0 < x < \infty$; mode is 1.

1.7.14 $\frac{7}{12}$.

1.7.17 $\frac{1}{2}$.

1.7.19 $-\sqrt{2}$.

1.7.20 $\frac{1}{27}, 0 < y < 27$.

1.7.22 $\frac{1}{\pi(1+y^2)}, -\infty < y < \infty$.

1.7.23 cdf $1 - e^{-y}, 0 \le y < \infty$.

1.7.24 pdf $\frac{1}{3\sqrt{y}}, 0 < y < 1$,
$\frac{1}{6\sqrt{y}}, 1 < y < 4$.

1.8.2 $2, 86.4, -160.8$.

1.8.3 $3, 11, 27$.

1.8.4 $\frac{\log 100.5 - \log 50.5}{50}$.

1.8.5 (a) $\frac{3}{4}$; (b) $\frac{1}{4}, \frac{1}{2}$.

1.8.6 $\frac{3}{20}$.

1.8.7 $7.80.

1.8.8 (a) 2; (b) pdf is $\frac{2}{y^3}, 1 < y < \infty$;
(c) 2.

1.8.9 $\frac{7}{3}$.

1.8.11 (a) $\frac{1}{2}$; (c) $\frac{1}{2}$.

1.9.1 (a) $1.5, 0.75$; (b) $0.5, 0.05$;
(c) 2, does not exist.

1.9.2 $\frac{e^t}{2-e^t}, t < \log 2; 2; 2$.

1.9.12 $10; 0; 2; -30$.

1.9.14 (a) $-\frac{2\sqrt{2}}{5}$; (b) 0; (c) $\frac{2\sqrt{2}}{5}$.

1.9.16 $\frac{1}{2p}$; $\frac{3}{2}$; $\frac{5}{2}$; 5; 50.

1.9.18 $\frac{31}{12}$; $\frac{167}{144}$.

1.9.19 $E(X^r) = \frac{(r+2)!}{2}$.

1.9.23 $\frac{5}{8}$; $\frac{37}{192}$.

1.9.26 $(1 - \beta t)^{-1}, \beta, \beta^2$.

1.10.3 0.84.

Chapter 2

2.1.1 $\frac{15}{64}$; 0; $\frac{1}{2}$; $\frac{1}{2}$.

2.1.2 $\frac{1}{4}$.

2.1.6 $ze^{-z}, 0 < z < \infty$.

2.1.7 $-\log z,\ 0 < z < 1$.

2.1.8 $\binom{13}{x}\binom{13}{y}\binom{26}{13-x-y}/\binom{52}{13}$,
x and y nonnegative integers
such that $x + y \le 13$.

2.1.10 $\frac{15}{2}x_1^2(1 - x_1^2), 0 < x_1 < 1$;
$5x_2^4, 0 < x_2 < 1$.

2.1.13 $\frac{2}{3}$; $\frac{1}{2}$; $\frac{2}{3}$; $\frac{1}{2}$; $\frac{4}{9}$; yes; $\frac{11}{3}$.

2.1.14 $\frac{e^{t_1+t_2}}{(2-e^{t_1})(2-e^{t_2})}, t_i < \log 2$.

2.1.15 $(1 - t_2)^{-1}(1 - t_1 - t_2)^{-2}, t_2 < 1$,
$t_1 + t_2 < 1$; no.

2.2.2

	1	2	3	4	6	9
	$\frac{1}{36}$	$\frac{4}{36}$	$\frac{6}{36}$	$\frac{4}{36}$	$\frac{12}{36}$	$\frac{9}{36}$

2.2.3 $e^{-y_1-y_2}, 0 < y_i < \infty$.

2.2.4 $8y_1 y_2^3, 0 < y_i < 1$.

2.2.6 (a) $y_1 e^{-y_1}, 0 < y_1 < \infty$;
(b) $(1 - t_1)^{-2}, t_1 < 1$.

2.3.1 $\frac{3x_1+2}{6x_1+3}$; $\frac{6x_1^2+6x_1+1}{2(6x_1+3)^2}$.

2.3.2 (a) 2, 5;
(b) $10x_1 x_2^2, 0 < x_1 < x_2 < 1$;
(c) $\frac{12}{25}$; (d) $\frac{449}{1536}$.

2.3.3 (a) $\frac{3x_2}{4}$; $\frac{3x_2^2}{80}$;
(b) pdf is $7(4/3)^7 y^6, 0 < y < \frac{3}{4}$;
(c) $E(X) = E(Y) = \frac{21}{32}$;
$\text{Var}(X_1) = \frac{553}{15360} > \text{Var}(Y) = \frac{7}{1024}$.

2.3.8 $x + 1, 0 < x < \infty$.

2.3.9 (a) $\binom{13}{x_1}\binom{13}{x_2}\binom{26}{5-x_1-x_2}/\binom{52}{5}, x_1, x_2$
nonnegative integers, $x_1 + x_2 \le 5$;
(c) $\binom{13}{x_2}\binom{26}{5-x_1-x_2}/\binom{39}{5-x_1}$,
$x_2 \le 5 - x_1$.

2.3.11 (a) $\frac{1}{x_1}, 0 < x_2 < x_1 < 1$;
(b) $1 - \log 2$.

2.3.12 (b) e^{-1}.

2.4.1 (a) 1; (b) -1; (c) 0.

2.4.2 (a) $\frac{7}{\sqrt{804}}$.

2.4.8 $1, 2, 1, 2, 1$.

2.4.9 $\frac{1}{2}$.

2.5.4 $\frac{5}{81}$.

2.5.5 $\frac{7}{8}$.

2.5.6 $2; 2$.

2.5.8 $\frac{2(1-y^3)}{3(1-y^2)}, 0 < y < 1$.

2.5.9 $\frac{1}{2}$.

2.5.12 $\frac{4}{9}$.

2.5.13 $4; 4$.

2.6.1 (g) $\frac{2+3y+3z}{3+6y+6z}$.

2.6.2 (a) $\frac{1}{6}$; 0;
(b) $(1-t_1)^{-1}(1-t_2)^{-1}(1-t_3)^{-1}$; yes.

2.6.3 pdf is $12(1 - y)^{11}, 0 < y < 1$.

2.6.4 pmf is $\frac{y^3-(y-1)^3}{6^3}$.

2.6.6 $\sigma_1(\rho_{12} - \rho_{13}\rho_{23})/\sigma_2(1 - \rho_{23}^2)$;
$\sigma_1(\rho_{13} - \rho_{12}\rho_{23})/\sigma_3(1 - \rho_{23}^2)$.

2.6.9 (a) $\frac{3}{4}$.

2.7.1 joint pdf $y_2 y_3^2 e^{-y_3}, 0 < y_1 < 1,$
$0 < y_2 < 1, 0 < y_3 < \infty.$

2.7.2 $\frac{1}{2\sqrt{y}}, 0 < y < 1.$

2.7.3 $\frac{1}{4\sqrt{y}}, 0 < y < 1; \frac{1}{8\sqrt{y}}, 1 \le y < 9.$

2.7.7 $24 y_2 y_3^2 y_4^3, 0 < y_i < 1.$

2.7.8 (a) $\frac{9}{16}; \frac{6}{16}; \frac{1}{16};$ (b) $\left(\frac{3}{4} + \frac{1}{4}e^t\right)^6.$

2.8.2 $\frac{8}{3}; \frac{2}{9}.$

2.8.3 7.

2.8.5 2.5; 0.25.

2.8.7 -5; 30.6.

2.8.8 $\frac{\sigma_1}{\sqrt{\sigma_1^2 + \sigma_2^2}}.$

2.8.10 0.265.

2.8.12 22.5; 65.25.

2.8.13 $\frac{\mu_2 \sigma_1}{\sqrt{\sigma_1^2 \sigma_2^2 + \mu_1^2 \sigma_2^2 + \mu_2^2 \sigma_1^2}}.$

2.8.15 0.801.

Chapter 3

3.1.1 $\frac{40}{81}.$

3.1.4 $\frac{147}{512}.$

3.1.6 5.

3.1.9 $\frac{3}{16}.$

3.1.11 $\frac{65}{81}.$

3.1.14 $\left(\frac{1}{3}\right)\left(\frac{2}{3}\right)^{x-3}, x = 3, 4, 5, \ldots.$

3.1.15 $\frac{5}{72}.$

3.1.18 $\frac{1}{6}.$

3.1.19 $\frac{24}{625}.$

3.1.21 (a) $\frac{11}{6}$; (b) $\frac{x_1}{2}$; (c) $\frac{11}{6}.$

3.1.22 $\frac{25}{4}.$

3.1.27 (a) 0.0853; (b) 0.2637; (c) 0.0861, 0.2639.

3.2.1 0.09.

3.2.4 $4^x e^{-4}/x!, x = 0, 1, 2 \ldots.$

3.2.5 0.84.

3.2.8 About 6.7.

3.2.10 8.

3.2.11 2.

3.2.13 (a) $e^{-2} \exp\{(1 + e^{t_1})e^{t_2}\}.$

3.3.1 0.05.

3.3.2 0.831; 12.8.

3.3.3 0.90.

3.3.4 $\chi^2(4).$

3.3.6 pdf is $3e^{-3y}, 0 < y < \infty.$

3.3.7 2; 0.95.

3.3.15 $\frac{11}{16}.$

3.3.16 $\chi^2(2).$

3.3.18 $\frac{\alpha}{\alpha+\beta}; \frac{\alpha\beta}{(\alpha+\beta+1)(\alpha+\beta)^2}.$

3.3.19 (a) 20; (b) 1260; (c) 495.

3.3.20 $\frac{10}{243}.$

3.3.24 (a) $(1 - 6t)^{-8}, t < \frac{1}{6}$;
(b) $\Gamma(\alpha = 8, \beta = 6).$

3.4.2 0.067; 0.685.

3.4.3 1.645.

3.4.4 71.4; 189.4.

3.4.8 0.598.

3.4.10 0.774.

3.4.11 $\sqrt{\frac{2}{\pi}}; \frac{\pi-2}{\pi}.$

3.4.12 0.90.

3.4.13 0.477.

3.4.14 0.461.

3.4.15 $N(0, 1).$

3.4.16 0.433.

3.4.18 0; 3.

3.4.23 $N(0, 2)$.

3.4.28 0.24.

3.4.29 0.159.

3.4.30 0.159.

3.4.32 $\chi^2(2)$.

3.5.1 (a) 0.574; (b) 0.735.

3.5.2 (a) 0.264; (b) 0.440; (c) 0.433; (d) 0.643.

3.5.5 $\frac{4}{5}$.

3.5.6 $(38.2, 43.4)$, .

3.5.17 0.05.

3.6.1 0.05.

3.6.2 1.761.

3.6.9 $\frac{1}{4.74}$; 3.33.

Chapter 4

4.1.1 (b) 101.15; (c) 55.5; $\theta \log 2$ (d) 70.11.

4.1.2 (b) 201, 293.9, 17.14, 11.72; (c) 0.269; (d) 0.207

4.1.3 9.5.

4.1.10 (a) 0.04; (c) 0.0328

4.2.1 $(79.21, 83.19)$, 90%.

4.2.6 $(0.143, 0.365)$.

4.2.7 24 or 25.

4.2.8 $(3.7, 5.7)$.

4.2.9 160.

4.2.10 (a) 1.31σ; (b) 1.49σ.

4.2.11 $c = \sqrt{\frac{n-1}{n+1}}$; $k = 1.60$.

4.2.14 $\left(\frac{5\bar{x}}{24}, \frac{5\bar{x}}{16}\right)$.

4.2.16 6765.

4.2.17 $(3.19, 3.61)$.

4.2.18 (b) $(3.625, 29.101)$.

4.2.21 $(-3.32, 1.72)$.

4.2.26 135 or 136.

4.4.5 $1 - (1 - e^{-3})^4$.

4.4.6 (a) $\frac{1}{8}$.

4.4.10 Weibull.

4.4.11 $\frac{5}{16}$.

4.4.12 pdf: $(2z_1)(4z_2^3)(6z_3^5)$, $0 < z_i < 1$.

4.4.13 $\frac{7}{12}$.

4.4.17 (a) $48y_3^5 y_4, 0 < y_3 < y_4 < 1$; (b) $\frac{6y_3^5}{y_4^6}, 0 < y_3 < y_4$; (c) $\frac{6}{7}y_4$.

4.4.18 $\frac{1}{4}$.

4.4.19 $6uv(u + v), 0 < u < v < 1$.

4.4.24 14.

4.4.25 (a) $\frac{15}{16}$; (b) $\frac{675}{1024}$; (c) $(0.8)^4$.

4.4.26 0.824.

4.4.27 8.

4.4.28 (a) 1.13σ; (b) 0.92σ.

4.4.30 $(40, 124)$, 88%.

4.5.3 $1 - \left(\frac{3}{4}\right)^\theta + \theta \left(\frac{3}{4}\right)^\theta \log\left(\frac{3}{4}\right), \theta = 1, 2$.

4.5.4 0.17; 0.78.

4.5.8 $n = 19$ or 20.

4.5.9 $\gamma\left(\frac{1}{2}\right) = 0.062; \gamma\left(\frac{1}{12}\right) = 0.920$.

4.5.10 $n \approx 73; c \approx 42$.

4.5.12 (a) 0.051; (c) 0.256; 0.547; 0.780.

4.5.13 (a) 0.154; (b) 0.154.

4.6.5 (a) Reject; (b) $p -$ value ≈ 0.005.

4.6.6 (a) Do not reject; (b) $p -$ value ≈ 0.056.

4.7.1 $8.37 > 7.81$; reject.

4.7.3 $b \leq 8$ or $b \geq 32$.

4.7.4 $2.44 < 11.3$; do not reject H_0.

4.7.5 $6.40 < 9.49$; do not reject H_0.

4.7.8 $k = 3,$.

4.8.5 $F^{-1}(u) = \log[u/(1-u)],$.

4.8.8 $F^{-1}(u) = \log[-\log(1-u)]$.

4.8.18 (a) $F^{-1}(u) = u^{1/\beta}$;
(b) e.g., dominated by a uniform pdf.

4.9.3 (a) $\beta \log 2$.

4.9.7 Use $s_x = 20.41$; $s_y = 18.59$.

4.9.9 (a) $\overline{y} - \overline{x} = 9.67$;
20 possible permutations;
(c) P_n^n/n^n.

4.9.10 μ_0; $n^{-1} \sum_{i=1}^n (x_i - \overline{x})^2$.

4.10.1 8.

4.10.4 (a) Beta$(n - j + 1, j)$;
(b) Beta$(n - j + i - 1, j - i + 2)$.

4.10.5 $\frac{10!}{1!3!4!} v_1 v_2^3 (1 - v_1 - v_2)^4$,
$0 < v_2, v_1 + v_2 < 1$.

Chapter 5

5.1.7 No; $Y_n - \frac{1}{n}$.

5.2.1 Degenerate at μ.

5.2.2 Gamma$(\alpha = 1, \beta = 1)$.

5.2.3 Gamma$(\alpha = 1, \beta = 1)$.

5.2.4 Gamma$(\alpha = 2, \beta = 1)$.

5.2.7 Degenerate at β.

5.2.9 0.682.

5.2.10 (b) 0.815.

5.2.13 Degenerate at $\mu_2 + \frac{\sigma_2}{\sigma_1}(x - \mu_1)$.

5.2.14 (b) $N(0,1)$.

5.2.16 (b) $N(0,1)$.

5.2.19 $\frac{1}{5}$.

5.3.2 0.954.

5.3.3 0.604.

5.3.4 0.840.

5.3.5 0.728.

5.3.7 0.08.

5.3.9 0.267.

Chapter 6

6.1.1 $\overline{X}/3$.

6.1.2 (a) $-n/\log(\prod_{i=1}^n X_i)$.
(b) $Y_1 = \min\{X_1, \ldots, X_n\}$.

6.1.4 (a) $Y_n = \max\{X_1, \ldots, X_n\}$.
(b) $(2n+1)/(2n)$.
(c) $\sqrt{1/2Y_n}$.

6.1.5 $1 - \exp\{-2/\overline{X}\}$.

6.1.6 $\widehat{p} = \frac{53}{125}$,
$\sum_{x=3}^5 \binom{5}{x} \widehat{p}^x (1 - \widehat{p})^{5-x}$.

6.1.8 $\overline{x} = 2.109$; $\overline{x}^2 e^{-\overline{x}}/2$.

6.1.9 $\max\left\{\frac{1}{2}, \overline{X}\right\}$.

6.2.7 (a) $\frac{4}{\theta^2}$.

6.2.8 (a) $\frac{1}{2\theta^2}$.

6.3.15 (a) $\left(\frac{1}{3\overline{x}}\right)^{n\overline{x}} \left(\frac{2}{3(1-\overline{x})}\right)^{n-n\overline{x}}$.

6.3.16 (a) $n\overline{x} \log(2/\overline{x}) - n(2 - \overline{x})$.

6.3.17 $\left(\frac{\overline{x}/\alpha}{\beta_0}\right)^{n\alpha}$
$\times \exp\left\{-\sum_{i=1}^n x_i \left(\frac{1}{\beta_0} - \frac{\alpha}{\overline{x}}\right)\right\}$.

6.4.1 $\frac{4}{25}, \frac{11}{25}, \frac{7}{25}$.

6.4.2 (a) $\overline{x}, \overline{y}$,
$\frac{1}{n+m}\left[\sum_{i=1}^n (x_i - \overline{x})^2 + \sum_{i=1}^m (y_i - \overline{y})^2\right]$.
(b) $\frac{n\overline{x} + m\overline{y}}{n+m}$,
$\frac{1}{n+m}\left[\sum_{i=1}^n (x_i - \widehat{\theta}_1)^2 + \sum_{i=1}^m (y_i - \widehat{\theta}_1)^2\right]$

6.4.3 $\widehat{\theta}_1 = \min\{X_i\}$, $\frac{1}{n}\sum_{i=1}^n (X_i - \widehat{\theta}_1)$.

6.4.4 $\widehat{\theta}_1 = \min\{X_i\}$,
$n/\log\left[\prod_{i=1}^n X_i/\widehat{\theta}_1^n\right]$.

6.4.5 $(Y_1 + Y_n)/2, (Y_n - Y_1)/2$; no.

6.4.6 (a) $\overline{X} + 1.282\sqrt{\frac{n-1}{n}}S$;

(b) $\Phi\left(\frac{c-\overline{X}}{\sqrt{(n-1)/nS}}\right)$.

6.4.7 If $\frac{y_1}{n_1} \le \frac{y_2}{n_2}$, then $\widehat{p}_1 = \frac{y_1}{n_1}$ and
$\widehat{p}_2 = \frac{y_2}{n_2}$; else, $\widehat{p}_1 = \widehat{p}_2 = \frac{y_1+y_2}{n_1+n_2}$.

6.5.1 $t = 3 > 2.262$; reject H_0.

6.5.4 (b) $c\frac{\sum_{i=1}^n X_i^2}{\sum_{i=1}^m Y_i^2}$.

6.5.5 $c\frac{\overline{X}}{\overline{Y}}$.

6.5.6 $c\frac{[\max\{-X_1,X_{n_1}\}]^{n_1}[\max\{-Y_1,Y_{n_2}\}]^{n_2}}{[\max\{-X_1,-Y_1,X_{n_1},Y_{n_2}\}]^{n_1+n_2}}$,
$\chi^2(2)$.

6.6.8 The R function **mixnormal** found
in Appendix B produced these results
(first row are initial estimates, second row are the estimates after 500
iterations):

μ_1	μ_2	σ_1	σ_2	π
105.00	130.00	15.00	25.00	0.600
98.76	133.96	9.88	21.50	0.704

Chapter 7

7.1.4 $\frac{1}{3}, \frac{2}{3}$.

7.1.5 $\delta_1(y)$.

7.1.6 $b = 0$, does not exist.

7.1.7 does not exist.

7.2.8 $\prod_{i=1}^n [X_i(1-X_i)]$.

7.2.9 (a) $\frac{n!\theta^{-r}}{(n-r)!}e^{-\frac{1}{\theta}[\sum_{i=1}^r y_i+(n-r)y_r]}$.
(b) $r^{-1}[\sum_{i=1}^r y_i + (n-r)y_r]$.

7.3.2 $60y_3^2(y_5 - y_3)/\theta^5$;
$0 < y_3 < y_5 < \theta$;
$6y_5/5; \theta^2/7; \theta^2/35$.

7.3.3 $\frac{1}{\theta^2}e^{-y_1/\theta}, 0 < y_2 < y_1 < \infty$;
$y_1/2; \theta^2/2$.

7.3.5 $n^{-1}\sum_{i=1}^n X_i^2; n^{-1}\sum_{i=1}^n X_i$;
$(n+1)Y_n/n$.

7.3.6 $6\overline{X}$.

7.4.2 (a) X; (b) X

7.4.3 Y/n.

7.4.5 $Y_1 - \frac{1}{n}$.

7.4.7 (a) Yes; (b) yes.

7.4.8 (a) $E(X) = 0$.

7.4.9 (a) $\max\{-Y_1, 0.5Y_n\}$; (b) yes;
(c) yes.

7.5.1 $Y_1 - \sum_{i=1}^n X_i; Y_1/4n$; yes.

7.5.4 $\overline{x}/\alpha$.

7.5.9 $\overline{x}$.

7.5.11 (b) Y_1/n; (c) θ; (d) Y_1/n.

7.6.1 $\overline{X}^2 - \frac{1}{n}$.

7.6.2 $Y^2/(n^2 + 2n)$.

7.6.5 (a) $\left(\frac{n-1}{n}\right)^Y\left(1 + \frac{Y}{n-1}\right)$;
(b) $\left(\frac{n-1}{n}\right)^{n\overline{X}}\left(1 + \frac{n\overline{X}}{n-1}\right)$;
(c) $N\left(\theta, \frac{\theta}{n}\right)$.

7.6.8 $1 - e^{-2/\overline{X}}; 1 - \left(1 - \frac{2/\overline{X}}{n}\right)^{n-1}$.

7.6.9 (b) $\overline{X}$; (c) $\overline{X}$; (d) $1/\overline{X}$.

7.7.3 Yes.

7.7.5 $\frac{\Gamma[(n-1)/2]}{\Gamma[n/2]}\sqrt{\frac{n-1}{2}}S$.

7.7.6 (b) $\frac{Y_1+Y_n}{2}; \frac{(n+1)(Y_n-Y_1)}{2(n-1)}$.

7.7.9 (a) $\frac{1}{n-1}\sum_{h=1}^n (X_{ih} - \overline{X}_i)$
$\times (X_{jh} - \overline{X}_j)$;
(b) $\sum_{i=1}^n a_i\overline{X}_i$.

7.7.10 $\left(\sum_{i=1}^{n} x_i, \sum_{i=1}^{n} \frac{1}{x_i} \right),$.

7.8.3 $Y_1, ; \sum_{i=1}^{n} (Y_i - Y_1)/n, $.

7.9.13 (a) $\Gamma(3n, 1/\theta), ;$ no$, ;$
(c) $(3n - 1)/Y;$
(e) Beta$(3, 3n - 3)$.

Chapter 8

8.1.4 $\sum_{i=1}^{10} x_i^2 \geq 18.3;$ yes; yes.

8.1.5 $\prod_{i=1}^{n} x_i \geq c$.

8.1.6 $3 \sum_{i=1}^{10} x_i^2 + 2 \sum_{i=1}^{10} x_i \geq c$.

8.1.7 About $96; 76.7$.

8.1.8 $\prod_{i=1}^{n} [x_i(1 - x_i)] \geq c$.

8.1.9 About $39; 15$.

8.1.10 $0.08; 0.875$.

8.2.1 $(1 - \theta)^9 (1 + 9\theta)$.

8.2.2 $1 - \frac{15}{16\theta^4}, 1 < \theta$.

8.2.3 $1 - \Phi \left(\frac{3 - 5\theta}{2} \right)$.

8.2.4 About $54; 5.6$.

8.2.7 Reject H_0 if $\bar{x} \geq 77.564$.

8.2.8 About $27;$ reject H_0 if $\bar{x} \leq 24$.

8.2.10 $\Gamma(n, \theta);$
Reject H_0 if $\sum_{i=1}^{n} x_i \geq c$.

8.2.12 (b) $\frac{6}{32}$; (c) $\frac{1}{32}$.
(d) reject if $y = 0;$
if $y = 1$, reject with probability $\frac{1}{5}$.

8.3.1 $|t| = 2.27 > 2.145;$ reject H_0.

8.3.9 Reject H_0 if $|y_3 - \theta_0| \geq c$.

8.3.11 (a) $\prod_{i=1}^{n} (1 - x_i) \geq c$.

8.4.1 $5.84n - 32.42; 5.84n + 41.62$.

8.4.2 $0.04n - 1.66; 0.04n + 1.20$.

8.4.4 $0.025, 29.7, -29.7$.

8.5.5 $(9y - 20x)/30 \leq c \Rightarrow (x, y) \in$ 2nd.

8.5.7 $2w_1^2 + 8w_2^2 \geq c \Rightarrow (w_1, w_2) \in \text{II}$.

Chapter 9

9.2.4 6.39.

9.2.6 $7.875 > 4.26;$ reject H_0.

9.2.7 $10.224 > 4.26;$ reject H_0.

9.3.2 $r + \theta; 2r + 4\theta$.

9.3.3 Mean: $r_2(\theta + r_1)/[r_1(r_2 - 2)]$.

9.3.6 $\chi^2(\sum a_j - b, 0); \chi^2(b - 1, \theta_4);$
$F(b - 1, \sum a_j - b, \theta_4)$.

9.5.5 $7.00; 9.98$.

9.5.7 $4.79; 22.82; 30.73$.

9.5.9 (a) $7.624 > 4.46,$ reject $H_A;$
(b) $15.538 > 3.84,$ reject H_B.

9.5.10 $8; 0; 0; 0; 0; -3; 1; 2; -2;$
$2; -2; 2; 2; -2; 2; -2; 0; 0; 0; 0$.

9.6.1 (a) $6.478 + 4.483x$.

9.6.7 $\widehat{\beta} = \sum_{i=1}^{n} (X_i/nc_i^2),$
$\sum_{i=1}^{n} [(X_i - \widehat{\beta} c_i)^2/nc_i^2]$.

9.6.12 $\widehat{a} = \frac{5}{3}$.

9.7.2 Reject H_0.

9.8.2 $2; \boldsymbol{\mu}' \mathbf{A} \boldsymbol{\mu}; \mu_1 = \mu_2 = 0$.

9.8.3 (b) $\mathbf{A}^2 = \mathbf{A}; \text{tr}(\mathbf{A}) = 2;$
$\boldsymbol{\mu}' \mathbf{A} \boldsymbol{\mu}/8 = 6$.

9.8.4 (a) $\sum \sigma_i^2/n^2$.

9.8.5 (a) $[1 + (n - 1)\rho](\sigma^2/n)$.

9.9.1 Dependent.

9.9.3 $0, 0, 0, 0$.

9.9.4 $\sum_{i=1}^{n} a_{ij} = 0$.

Chapter 10

10.2.3 (a) $0.1148;$ (b) 0.7836.

10.2.8 (a) $P(Z > z_\alpha - (\sigma/\sqrt{n})\theta)$,
where $E(Z) = 0$ and $\text{Var}(Z) = 1$;
(c) Use the Central Limit Theorem;

(d) $\left[\frac{(z_\alpha - z_{\gamma^*})\sigma}{\theta^*}\right]^2$.

10.4.2 $1 - \Phi[z_\alpha - \sqrt{\lambda_1\lambda_2}(\delta/\sigma)]$.

10.5.3 $\frac{n(n-1)}{n+1}$.

10.5.14 (a) $W_S^* = 9; W_{XS}^* = 6$; (b) 1.2;
(c) 9.5.

10.8.3 $\widehat{y}_{\text{LS}} = 205.9 + 0.015x$;
$\widehat{y}_W = 211.0 + 0.010x$.

10.8.4 (a) $\widehat{y}_{\text{LS}} = 265.7 - 0.765(x-1900)$;
$\widehat{y}_W = 246.9 - 0.436(x - 1900)$;
(b) $\widehat{y}_{\text{LS}} = 3501.0 - 38.35(x-1900)$;
$\widehat{y}_W = 3297.0 - 35.52(x - 1900)$.

10.8.8 $r_{qc} = 16/17 = 0.941$
(zeroes were excluded).

10.8.9 $r_N = 0.835; z = 3.734$.

10.9.4 Cases: $t < y$ and $t > y$.

10.9.5 (c) $y^2 - \sigma^2$.

10.9.7 (a)$n^{-1}\sum_{i=1}^n (Y_i^r - \overline{Y^r})^2$;
(c) $y^2 - \sigma^2$.

10.9.9 $0; [4f^2(\theta)]^{-1}$.

10.9.14 $\widehat{y}_{\text{LS}} = 3.14 + .028x$;
$\widehat{y}_W = 0.214 + .020x$.

Chapter 11

11.1.1 $2.67, 8.00, 16.00, 21.33, 64$.

11.2.1 $0.45; 0.55$.

11.2.3 $[y\tau^2 + \mu\sigma^2/n]/(\tau^2 + \sigma^2/n)$.

11.2.4 $\beta(y + \alpha)/(n\beta + 1)$.

11.2.6 $\frac{y_1+\alpha_1}{n+\alpha_1+\alpha_2+\alpha_3}; \frac{y_2+\alpha_2}{n+\alpha_1+\alpha_2+\alpha_3}$.

11.2.8 (a) $\left(\theta - \frac{10+30\theta}{45}\right)^2 +$
$\left(\frac{1}{45}\right)^2 30\theta(1-\theta)$.

11.2.9 $\sqrt[6]{2}, y_4 < 1; \sqrt[6]{2}y_4, 1 \le y_4$.

11.3.1 (a) $\frac{\theta_2^2}{[\theta_2^2+(x_1-\theta_1)^2][\theta_2^2+(x_2-\theta_1)^2]}$.

11.3.3 (a) 76.84; (b) $(76.25, 77.43)$.

11.3.5 (a) $I(\theta) = \theta^{-2}$; (d) $\chi^2(2n)$.

11.3.8 (a) $\text{beta}(n\overline{x} + 1, n + 1 - n\overline{x})$.

11.4.1 (a) Let U_1 and U_2 be iid
uniform(0,1):

    1.   Draw $Y = -\log(1 - U_1)$
    2.   Draw $X = Y - \log(1 - U_2)$.

11.4.3 (b) $F_X^{-1}(u) = -\log(1 - \sqrt{u})$,
$0 < u < 1$.

11.4.7 (b) $f(x|y)$ is a $b(n, y)$ pmf;
$f(y|x)$ is a $\text{beta}(x + \alpha, n - x + \beta)$
pdf.

11.5.1 (b) $\widehat{\beta} = \frac{1}{2\overline{x}}$; (d) $\widehat{\theta} = \frac{1}{\overline{x}}$.

11.5.2 (a) $\delta(y) =$
$\frac{\int_0^1 \left[\frac{a}{1-a\log p}\right]^2 p^y(1-p)^{n-y}\, dp}{\int_0^1 \left[\frac{a}{1-a\log p}\right]^2 p^{y-1}(1-p)^{n-y}\, dp}$.

Index

相关图书

作者：（美）William Mendenhall 等著
ISBN：978-7-111-26437-8
定价：128.00

作者：（美）Ronald E. Walpole 等著
ISBN：978-7-111-27708-8
定价：98.00

作者：(美)George E.P.Box 等著
ISBN：978-7-111-27258-8
定价：65.00

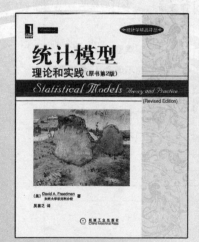

作者：（美）David A. Freedman 著
ISBN：978-7-111-30989-5
定价：45.00

作者：（美）David A. Freedman 著
ISBN：978-7-111-31797-5
定价：38.00

作者：（美）Joseph F. Hair, Jr. 等著
ISBN：978-7-111-34198-7
定价：109.00

教师服务登记表

尊敬的老师：

您好！感谢您购买我们出版的 _____ 教材。

机械工业出版社华章公司为了进一步加强与高校教师的联系与沟通，更好地为高校教师服务，特制此表，请您填妥后发回给我们，我们将定期向您寄送华章公司最新的图书出版信息！感谢合作！

个人资料（请用正楷完整填写）

教师姓名		□先生 □女士	出生年月		职务		职称：□教授 □副教授 □讲师 □助教 □其他	
学校			学院			系别		
联系电话	办公： 宅电： 移动：			联系地址及邮编				
				E-mail				
学历		毕业院校		国外进修及讲学经历				
研究领域								

主讲课程	现用教材名	作者及出版社	共同授课教师	教材满意度
课程： □专 □本 □研 人数： 学期：□春□秋				□满意 □一般 □不满意 □希望更换
课程： □专 □本 □研 人数： 学期：□春□秋				□满意 □一般 □不满意 □希望更换

样书申请			
已出版著作		已出版译作	
是否愿意从事翻译/著作工作 □是 □否	方向		
意见和建议			

填妥后请选择以下任何一种方式将此表返回：（如方便请赐名片）

地　址：北京市西城区百万庄南街1号　华章公司营销中心　　邮编：100037

电　话：(010) 68353079 88378995　传真：(010)68995260

E-mail:hzedu@hzbook.com　marketing@hzbook.com　　图书详情可登录http://www.hzbook.com网站查询